JEPPES

A BOEING COMPANY

# POWERPLANT TECHNICIAN

## TEXTBOOK

ISBN: 978-0-88487-202-3

Cover: 787 Engine Fan Close Up Courtesy of Boeing

Jeppesen
55 Inverness Drive East
Englewood, CO 80112-5498
Web Site: www.jeppesen.com
Email: Captain@jeppesen.com

Printed in the United States of America

10002511-003

# WELCOME TO THE JEPPESEN AVIATION MAINTENANCE TECHNICIAN INTEGRATED TRAINING SYSTEM

Our general, airframe, and powerplant mechanic course materials are fully integrated, providing a complete and systematic training program. Textbooks and test guides are written in a simple to understand format, delivering all the necessary information for you to obtain your aircraft maintenance certificate and ratings. Course materials are organized into the same chapter and section formats to integrate study as you progress through each subject area. FAA Learning Statement Code topics are fully covered and cross-referenced in test guide materials.

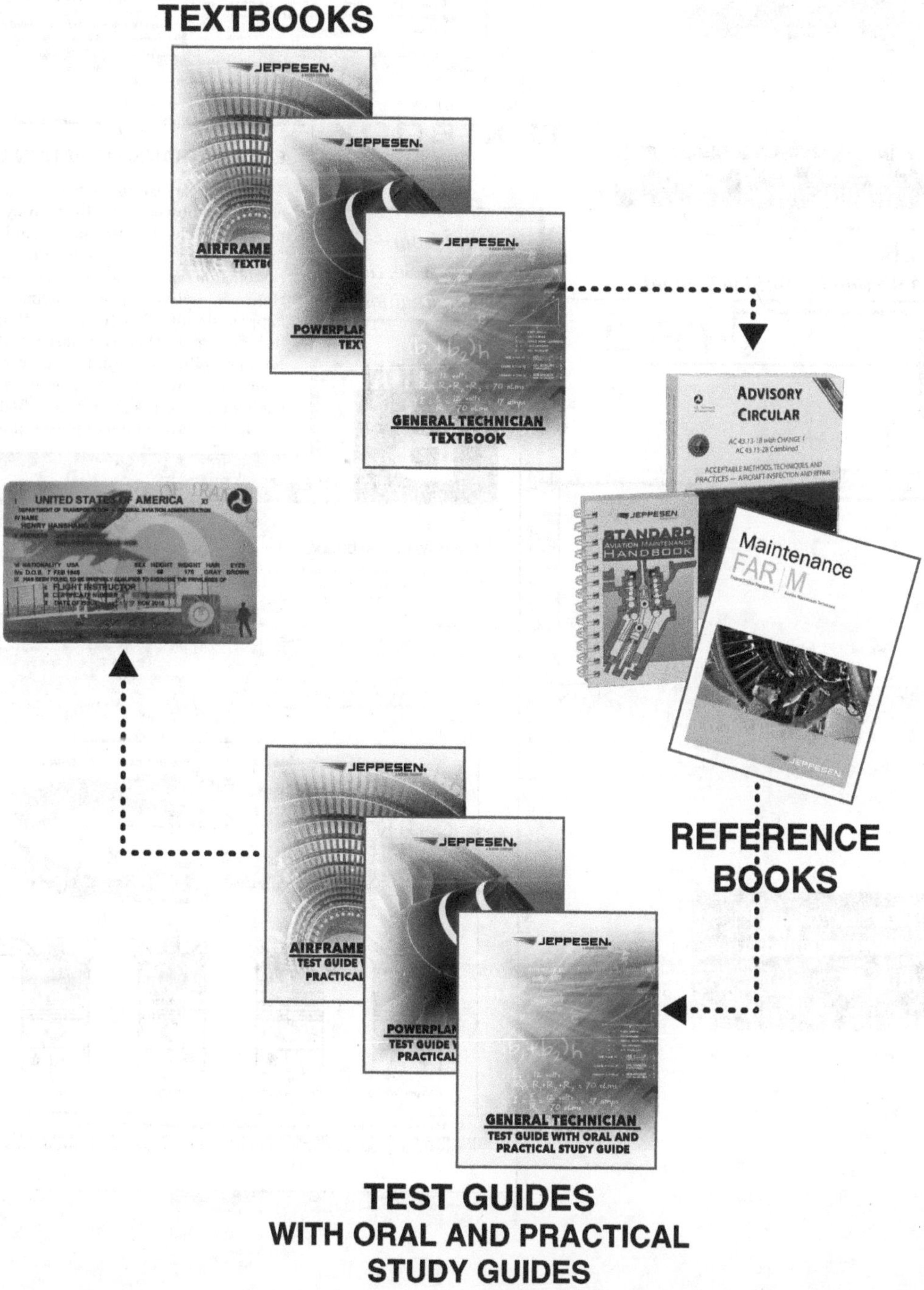

# JEPPESEN INTEGRATED TRAINING SYSTEM

**Test Guides**—presents written test questions, along with the answers, explanations, and references to the applicable *textbook* to provide an integrated learning solution.

**Test Guide questions** are grouped into the same chapter and subsection as the corresponding *textbook* for easy reference.

*Excerpt from Chapter 3 Section B, Turbine Engines*

*Turbine Engines Test Guide* 3-13

**3-58. B02**
The stators in the turbine section of a gas turbine engine

A — increase the velocity of the gas flow.
B — decrease the velocity of the gas flow.
C — increase the pressure of the gas flow.

**3-58. Answer A. JSPT 3-25 (AC 65-12A)**
The fixed stator vanes in the turbine section of [...] bine engine are located ahead of the turbine r[...] turbine stators act as nozzles to increase gas [...] and decrease pressure. Answer (B) is incorrec[...] gas flow velocity increases and answer (C) is [...] because stators cause a decrease in gas pres[...]

**3-59. B03**
The Brayton cycle is known as the constant

A — pressure cycle.
B — temperature cycle.
C — mass cycle.

**3-59. Answer A JSPT 3-38 (AC 65-12A)**
The Brayton cycle describes the combustion process in a turbine engine. This process is also known as the constant pressure cycle because the pressure across the combustion section in a turbine engine remains relatively constant. Answers (B) and (C) are incorrect because temperature and mass flow vary substantially in a turbine engine.

**3-61. B02**
The compressor stators in a gas turbine engine act as diffusers to

A — decrease the velocity of the gas flow.
B — increase the velocity of the gas flow.

A — number of compressor stages.
B — rotor diameter.
C — air inlet velocity.

**3-62. Answer A. JSPT 3-14 (AC 65-12A)**
The primary factor in determining the pressure ratio in an axial-flow compressor is the number of stages within the compressor. Additional factors that affect pressure ratio include overall compressor efficiency and the pressure ratio produced by each stage. Answer (B) is incorrect because changing the rotor diameter affects mass flow, not pressure. Answer (C) is

**Test Guide Reference System**
In this example, you would find the answer to question 3-59 by referring to page 3-38 of the *Jeppesen Powerplant textbook* (JSPT 3-38).

**Workbook**—used to reinforce learning concepts taught in the corresponding *textbook*.

## WORKBOOK

*Excerpt from Chapter 3 Section B, Turbine Engines*

3-4 *Turbine Engines*

**SECTION B**
**OPERATING PRINCIPLES**

1. The operating cycle of events used by turbine engines is known as the ____________-cycle.
2. The Brayton-cycle is known as a constant ____________ (pressure or volume) cycle.
3. A large turbine engine can operate with a thermal efficiency as high as ______ percent.
4. Warm air is ______ (more or less) dense than cool air.
5. As the temperature of the air at the intake of a turbine engine increases, the amount of thrust produced will ____________ (increase or decrease).
6. To counteract the effects of high intake temperatures, some engines use a ____________ thrust augmentation system.
7. Net thrust of a turbine engine will ____________ (increase or decrease) with an increase in altitude.
8. The net effect of airspeed on thrust is that the thrust ______ (will or will not) increase as airspeed increases.
9. The speed at which the ram air pressure rise cancels the pressure drop inside the inlet duct is known as the

**Workbook questions** are grouped into the same chapter and subsection as the corresponding *textbook* for easy reference.

## TEXTBOOK

*Excerpt from Chapter 3 Section B, Turbine Engines*

### ENERGY TRANSFORMATION CYCLE

The energy transformation cycle in a gas turbine engine is known as the **Brayton cycle** or **constant pressure cycle.** The Brayton cycle is similar to the four-stroke cycle in that an intake, compression, combustion, and exhaust event occur in both cycles. However, unlike a piston engine, all four events happen simultaneously and continuously in a gas turbine engine. This gives the gas turbine engine the unique ability to produce power continuously. There is a downside, however, in that a gas turbine engine must burn a great deal of fuel to support the continuous production of power. [Figure 3-67]

3-38

**SECTION B**

**OPERATING PRINCIPLES**

**ENERGY TRANSFORMATION**

Like the piston engine, a gas turbine engine is a form of **heat engine** that converts the chemical energy of fuel into heat energy. Once converted, the heat energy causes an increase in gas pressure that is converted into kinetic energy in the form of a high velocity stream of air. The kinetic energy is then converted into mechanical energy when the expanding gases rotate a series of turbine wheels that drive a compressor and accessories. In the case of turboprop or turboshaft engines, the expanding gases may also drive a second power turbine which drives a propeller or gearbox.

**ENERGY TRANSFORMATION CYCLE**

The energy transformation cycle in a gas turbine engine is known as the **Brayton cycle** or **constant pressure cycle.** The Brayton cycle is similar to the four-stroke cycle in that an intake, compression, combustion, and exhaust event occur in both cycles. However, unlike a piston engine, all four events happen simultaneously and continuously in a gas turbine engine. This gives the gas turbine engine the unique ability to produce power continuously. There is a downside, however, in that a gas turbine engine must burn a great deal of fuel to support the continuous production of power. [Figure 3-67]

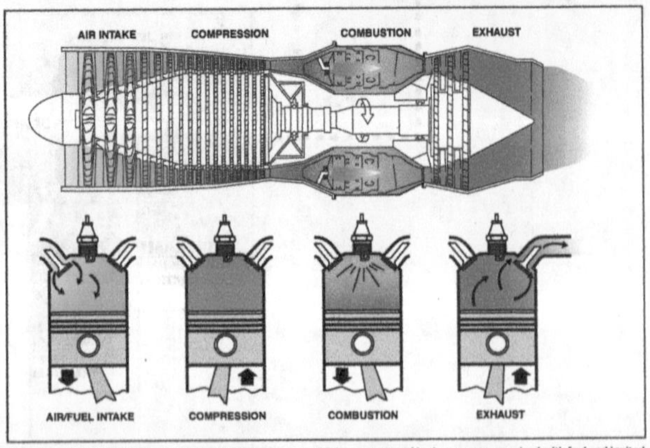


Figure 3-67. In a gas turbine engine, air is taken in through an air inlet, compressed in the compressor, mixed with fuel and ignited in the combustors, then exhausted through the turbines and exhaust nozzle. This allows a gas turbine engine to perform the same functions as a cylinder and piston in a reciprocating engine except that, in a turbine engine, the events happen continuously.

# TEST GUIDE WITH ORAL AND PRACTICAL STUDY GUIDE

*Excerpts from Chapter 3 Section B, Turbine Engines*

*Appendix B Oral Test Questions* B3-1

**Chapter 3 — Turbine Engines**

| Q # | Question and Answer | Page Reference |
|---|---|---|
| 1 | Explain the main difference and advantage of turbofan over turbojet engines.<br>*Answer – A turbofan engine uses a fan to bypass some air around the engine core and to provide thrust. The advantage is that this provides additional thrust without increasing fuel flow.* | JSPT 3-5 |
| 2 | Name the major components in a gas turbine engine.<br>*Answer – Air inlet, compressor section, combustion section, turbine section, exhaust section, gearbox and accessory section.* | JSPT 3-8 |
| 3 | Explain the main difference of the energy transformation cycle in a gas turbine engine compared to a piston engine?<br>*Answer – All four energy events, intake, compression, combustion, and exhaust, occur simultaneously and continuously in a gas turbine engine verses consecutively as in a piston engine.* | JSPT 3-38 |
| 4 | Name the two types of compressors commonly used in turbine engines.<br>*Answer – Axial and centrifugal flow compressors.* | JSPT 3-13 |
| 5 | Name two different methods for attaching turbine engine rotor blades to the rotor disks.<br>*Answer –* | JSPT 3-16 |

**Oral questions** are grouped into the same chapter as the corresponding *textbook.* For easy reference they include the answers, and references to the *textbook* by chapter and page number.

**Oral & Practical Study Guide**—provides an overview of the O&P process, along with sample questions and exercises you will be assigned and required to perform.

B3-4 *Appendix B Practical Test*

**Chapter 3 — Turbine Engines**

| Project # | Project Description | Level |
|---|---|---|
| 1 | ***Project:*** Identify major components of turbine engines.<br>***Given:*** Unlabeled drawings of turbojet or turbofan engines and a list of component nomenclatures.<br>***Performance Standard:*** The applicant will label major components of turbine engines. | 2 |
| 2 | ***Project:*** Identify characteristics of different turbine compressors.<br>***Given:*** Unlabeled drawings of various types of compressors and a list of characteristics.<br>***Performance Standard:*** The applicant will label the drawings of compressors with characteristics. | 2 |
| 3 | ***Project:*** Identify airflow direction and pressure changes in turbojet or turbofan engines.<br>***Given:*** Unlabeled drawings of turbojet or turbofan engines.<br>***Performance Standard:*** The applicant will label, with arrows, the direction of airflow through a turbojet or turbofan engine, and note any change of air pressure between sections. | 2 |

**Practical exercises** are grouped into the same chapter as the corresponding *Textbook.* They include the given or variables for the exercise along with the required performance standard.

Refers back to *Jeppesen training system.*

**Subject matter knowledge codes**—can be used to reference *Jeppesen's training system.*

Using "**B03**" as an example, to find information on the installation of turbine engines, look up the subject "turbine engine installation" in the Jeppesen index and it will refer you to the appropriate chapter and page in the *Powerplant textbook.*

# SUBJECT MATTER KNOWLEDGE CODES

APPENDIX A

## SUBJECT MATTER KNOWLEDGE CODES

### LIST OF REFERENCE MATERIALS AND SUBJECT MATTER KNOWLEDGE CODES

The publications listed in the following pages contain study material you need to be familiar with when preparing for aviation mechanic knowledge tests. All of these publications can be purchased through U.S. Government bookstores, commercial aviation supply houses, or industry organizations. The latest revision of the listed references should be requested. Additional study material is also available through these sources that may be helpful in preparing for aviation mechanic knowledge tests. All publications listed would be excellent for a mechanic to have in a personal reference library.

The following abbreviations are used to identify the reference(s) associated with the subject matter.

### *AVIATION MECHANIC POWERPLANT ABBREVIATIONS AND REFERENCES*

| | |
|---|---|
| ABS | Aircraft Basic Science — Glencoe Division, Macmillan/McGraw-Hill Publication Company |
| AC | Advisory Circular |
| AEE | Aircraft Electricity and Electronics — Glencoe Division, Macmillan/McGraw-Hill Publication Company |
| AMR | Aircraft Maintenance and Repair — Glencoe Division, Macmillan/McGraw-Hill Publication Company |
| JSPT | A & P Technician Powerplant Textbook — Jeppesen Sanderson, Inc. |
| AP | Aircraft Powerplants — Glencoe Division, Macmillan/McGraw-Hill Publication Company |
| CFR | Title 14, Code of Federal Regulations (Part or § [Section]) - GPO |
| PSG | A&P Technician Powerplant Study Guide - Jeppesen Sanderson, Inc. |

**Turbine Engines — AC 65-9A, AC 65-12A, AC 65-15A, CFR Part 33, AP, ACT, JSPT**

| | |
|---|---|
| B01 | Overhaul turbine engine |
| B02 | Inspect, check, service, and repair turbine engines and turbine engine installations |
| B03 | Install, troubleshoot, and remove turbine engines |

# TABLE OF CONTENTS

CHAPTER 1

# RECIPROCATING ENGINES

## INTRODUCTION

The lack of efficient and practical powerplants has limited aircraft development throughout history. For example, in 1483 Leonardo daVinci conceived a flying machine he called the aerial screw. However, without a powerplant, the aerial screw was never developed. In fact, the first patent for a heat engine was taken out in 1791 by John Barber. Unfortunately, Barber's engine was neither efficient nor practical. In 1860, Etienne Lenoir of France built the first practical piston engine. Lenoir's engine, which employed a battery ignition system and used natural gas for fuel, operated industrial machinery such as lathes. The next major breakthrough in piston engine development came in 1876 when Dr. August Otto developed the four-stroke, five-event cycle. The Otto cycle is still used in most modern reciprocating aircraft engines.

# SECTION A

## DESIGN AND CONSTRUCTION

Heat engines convert thermal energy into mechanical energy. A specific volume of air is compressed, and then heated through the combustion of a fuel. In a reciprocating engine, the heated air expands, creating a force that moves a piston and in turn, the piston rod, crankshaft, and propeller or rotor. Reciprocating engines derive their name from the back-and-forth (or reciprocating) movement of their pistons. It is the downward motion of pistons, caused by expanding gases, which generates the mechanical energy needed to accomplish work.

## TYPES OF RECIPROCATING ENGINES

Many types of reciprocating engines have been designed for aircraft since the Wright brothers made aviation history using a four-cylinder in-line engine. Reciprocating engines are commonly classified by cylinder arrangement (radial, in-line, V-type, or opposed) and by fuel type (gasoline or diesel).

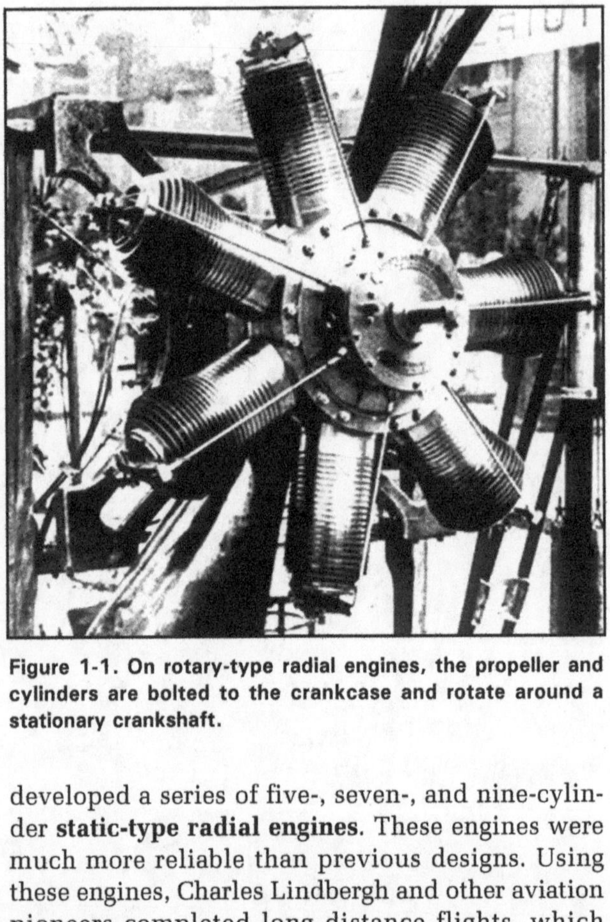

Figure 1-1. On rotary-type radial engines, the propeller and cylinders are bolted to the crankcase and rotate around a stationary crankshaft.

### RADIAL ENGINES

A radial engine consists of a row, or rows of cylinders arranged around a crankcase. The two basic types of radial engines are the rotary-type and the static-type. During World War I, **rotary-type radial engines** were used extensively because of their high power-to-weight ratio. The cylinders of a rotary-type radial engine are mounted radially around a small crankcase and rotate with the propeller, while the crankshaft remains stationary. Some of the more popular rotary-type engines were the Bentley, the Gnome, and the LeRhone. [Figure 1-1]

The large rotating mass of cylinders produced a significant amount of torque, which made aircraft control difficult. This factor, coupled with complications in carburetion, lubrication, and the exhaust system, limited the development of the rotary-type radial engine.

In the late 1920s, the Wright Aeronautical Corporation, in cooperation with the U.S. Navy, developed a series of five-, seven-, and nine-cylinder **static-type radial engines**. These engines were much more reliable than previous designs. Using these engines, Charles Lindbergh and other aviation pioneers completed long distance flights, which demonstrated to the world that the airplane was a practical means of transportation.

The most significant difference between the rotary and the static radial engine is that with the static engine, the crankcase remains stationary and the crankshaft rotates to turn the propeller. Static radial engines have as few as three cylinders and as many as 28. The higher horsepower engines proved most useful. Static radial engines also possessed a high power-to-weight ratio and powered many military and civilian transport aircraft. [Figure 1-2]

**Single-row radial engines** typically have an odd number of cylinders arranged around a crankcase. A typical configuration consists of five to nine evenly spaced cylinders with all pistons connected to a

**Figure 1-2. Radial engines helped revolutionize aviation with their high power and dependability.**

single crankshaft. To increase engine power while maintaining a reasonably-sized frontal area, **multiple-row radial engines** were developed. These engines contain two or more rows of cylinders connected to a single crankshaft. The **double-row radial engine** typically has 14 or 18 cylinders. To improve cooling of a multiple-row radial engine, the rows are staggered to increase the amount of airflow past each cylinder.

The largest, mass-produced, multiple-row radial engine was the Pratt and Whitney R-4360, which consisted of 28 cylinders arranged in four staggered rows of seven cylinders each. The R-4360 developed a maximum 3,400 horsepower, making it the most powerful production radial engine ever used. [Figure 1-3]

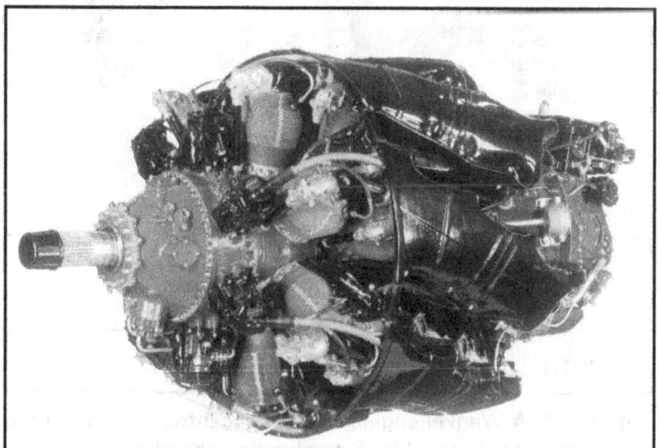

**Figure 1-3. The Pratt and Whitney R-4360 engine was the largest practical radial engine used in aviation. Development and advancement in turbojet and turboprop engines eclipsed the performance of large multiple-row radial engines.**

## IN-LINE ENGINES

In-line reciprocating engines generally have an even number of cylinders aligned in a single row parallel with the crankshaft. The pistons are either upright above or inverted below the crankshaft. This engine can be either liquid-cooled or air-cooled. [Figure 1-4]

Courtesy of Austro Engine GmbH

**Figure 1-4. The Austro Engine company manufactures inline diesel-powered aircraft engines.**

In-line engines have a comparatively small frontal area, which enables them to be enclosed by streamlined nacelles or cowlings. Because of this, in-line engines were popular among early racing aircraft. A benefit of an inverted in-line engine is that the crankshaft is higher off the ground. The higher crankshaft allowed greater propeller ground clearance, permitting the use of shorter landing gear. Historically, in-line engines were used on tail-wheel aircraft; they enabled manufacturers to use shorter main gear, which increased forward visibility while taxiing.

In-line engines have two primary disadvantages. They have relatively low power-to-weight ratios and, because the rearmost cylinders of an air-cooled in-line engine receive relatively little cooling air, in-line engines are typically liquid-cooled or are limited to only four or six cylinders. As a result, most in-line engine designs are confined to low- and medium-horsepower engines used in light aircraft.

In 2003, Thielert Aircraft Engines (now Centurion Aircraft Engines) began delivering new, certified kerosene-powered, in-line reciprocating engines for light aircraft. In 2009, Austro Engine certified a similar engine.

## V-TYPE ENGINES

In-line engines evolved into **V-type engines**. Two rows of cylinders, called banks, are oriented 45, 60, or 90 degrees apart from a single crankshaft. Two banks of cylinders typically produce more horsepower than an in-line engine. Because the cylinder banks share a single crankcase and a single crankshaft, V-type engines have a reasonable power-to-weight ratio with a small frontal area. The pistons can be located either above the crankshaft or below the crankshaft. Most V-type engines had 8 or 12 cylinders. V-type engines can be either liquid- or air-cooled. V-12 engines developed during World War II achieved some of the highest horsepower ratings of any reciprocating engine. Today, V-type engines are typically found on classic military and experimental racing aircraft. [Figure 1-5]

**Figure 1-5. V-type engines provide an excellent combination of weight and power with a small frontal area.**

## OPPOSED-TYPE ENGINES

Opposed-type engines are the most common reciprocating engines currently used on light aircraft. Opposed engines can be designed to produce as little as 36 horsepower or as much as 400 horsepower. Opposed engines always have an even number of cylinders, with each cylinder on one side of a crankcase "opposing" a cylinder on the other side. The majority of opposed engines are air-cooled and horizontally mounted when installed on fixed-wing aircraft, but they can be mounted vertically in helicopters.

Opposed engines have a relatively small, lightweight crankcase that contributes to a high power-to-weight ratio. The compact cylinder arrangement provides a comparatively small frontal area, which enables the engine to be enclosed by streamlined nacelles or cowlings. With opposing cylinders, power impulses tend to cancel each other out, resulting in less vibration than other engine types. [Figure 1-6]

**Figure 1-6. A horizontally opposed engine combines a good power-to-weight ratio with a relatively small frontal area. This style of engine powers most light aircraft in service today.**

## WANKEL ENGINES

Although not a reciprocating engine, the Wankel (or rotary) engine deserves mention as an Otto cycle engine with potential for greater use in powered aircraft. Wankel engines have a good power-to-weight ratio, and their compact design can be enclosed by streamlined nacelles or cowlings. Instead of using a crankshaft, connecting rods, pistons, cylinders, and conventional valve train, the Wankel engine uses an eccentric shaft and triangular rotor turning in an oblong combustion chamber. This reduction in moving parts contributes to increased reliability. Early designs had problems associated with sealing the combustion chamber, which affected efficiency and engine life. [Figure 1-7]

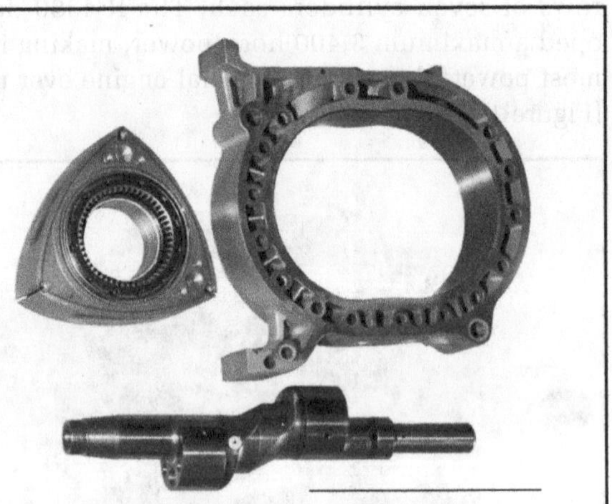

© MISTRAL Engines, www.mistral-engines.com

**Figure 1-7. A Wankel engine uses an eccentric shaft to turn a triangular rotor in an oblong combustion chamber.**

## ENGINE COMPONENTS

As an aviation maintenance technician, you must be familiar with an engine's components in order to understand its operating principles. Furthermore, your understanding of an engine's basic construction enhances your ability to perform routine maintenance operations.

The basic parts of a reciprocating engine include the crankcase, cylinders, pistons, connecting rods, valves, valve-operating mechanism, and crankshaft. The valves, pistons, and spark plugs are located in the cylinder assembly, while the valve operating mechanism, crankshaft, and connecting rods are located in the crankcase. [Figure 1-8]

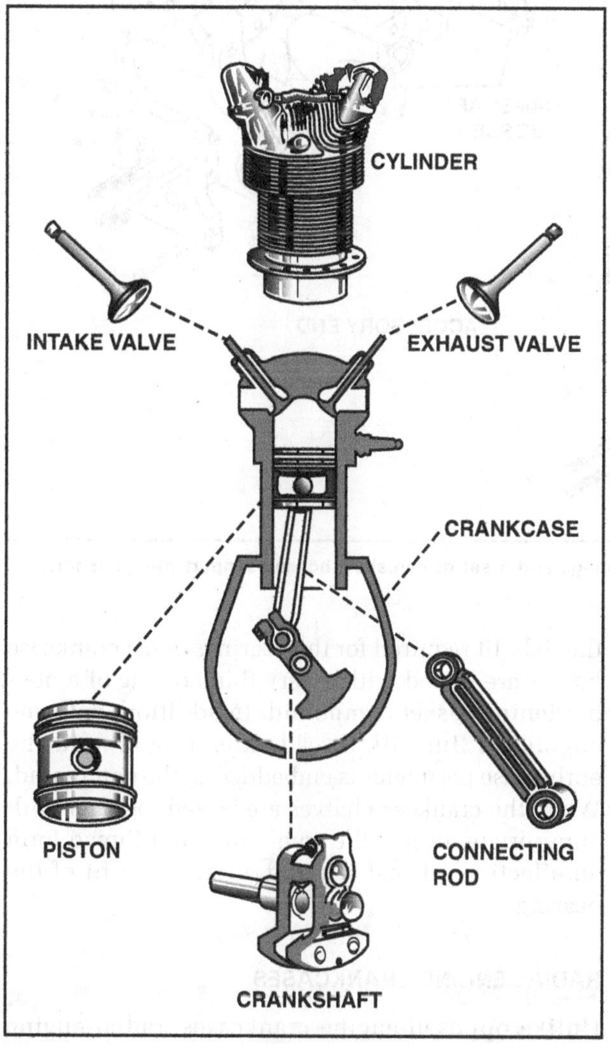


**Figure 1-8. In a basic reciprocating engine, the cylinder forms a chamber where the fuel/air mixture is compressed and burned. The piston compresses the fuel mixture and transmits power to the crankshaft through the connecting rods. The intake valve allows the fuel/air mixture into the cylinder while the exhaust valve lets the exhaust gases out.**

For all of the reciprocating engine types discussed, the horizontally opposed and static-type radial designs represent the majority of reciprocating engines in service today. Because of this, the discussion on engine components centers on these types.

The use of diesel fuel in reciprocating engines designed for aircraft is increasing. For a discussion of components specific to diesel engines, see Chapter 1, Section C.

### CRANKCASE

The crankcase is the core of a reciprocating engine. It contains the engine's internal parts and provides attach points for the cylinders, external accessories, and airframe installation. Additionally, the crankcase provides a tight enclosure for the lubricating oil. Due to great internal and external forces; crankcases must be extremely rigid and strong. A crankcase is subjected to dynamic bending moments that change continuously in direction and magnitude. For example, combustion exerts tremendous forces to the pistons and the propeller exerts unbalanced centrifugal and inertial forces. To remain functional, a crankcase must be capable of absorbing these forces while maintaining its structural integrity.

Today, most crankcases consist of at least two pieces; however, some crankcases are cast as one piece, and some consist of up to five pieces. To provide the necessary strength and rigidity while reducing weight, most aircraft crankcases are made of cast aluminum alloys.

#### OPPOSED ENGINE CRANKCASES

A typical horizontally-opposed engine crankcase consists of two pieces of cast aluminum alloy manufactured in sand castings or permanent molds. Crankcases manufactured by the permanent mold process, or permamold, as it is called by some manufacturers, are denser than those made by sand-casting. Greater density permits molded crankcases to have relatively thinner walls than similar sand-cast crankcases. In addition, molded crankcases tend to better resist cracking due to fatigue. Most opposed crankcases are approximately cylindrical, with smooth areas machined to serve as cylinder pads. A **cylinder pad** is the surface on which a cylinder mounts to the crankcase.

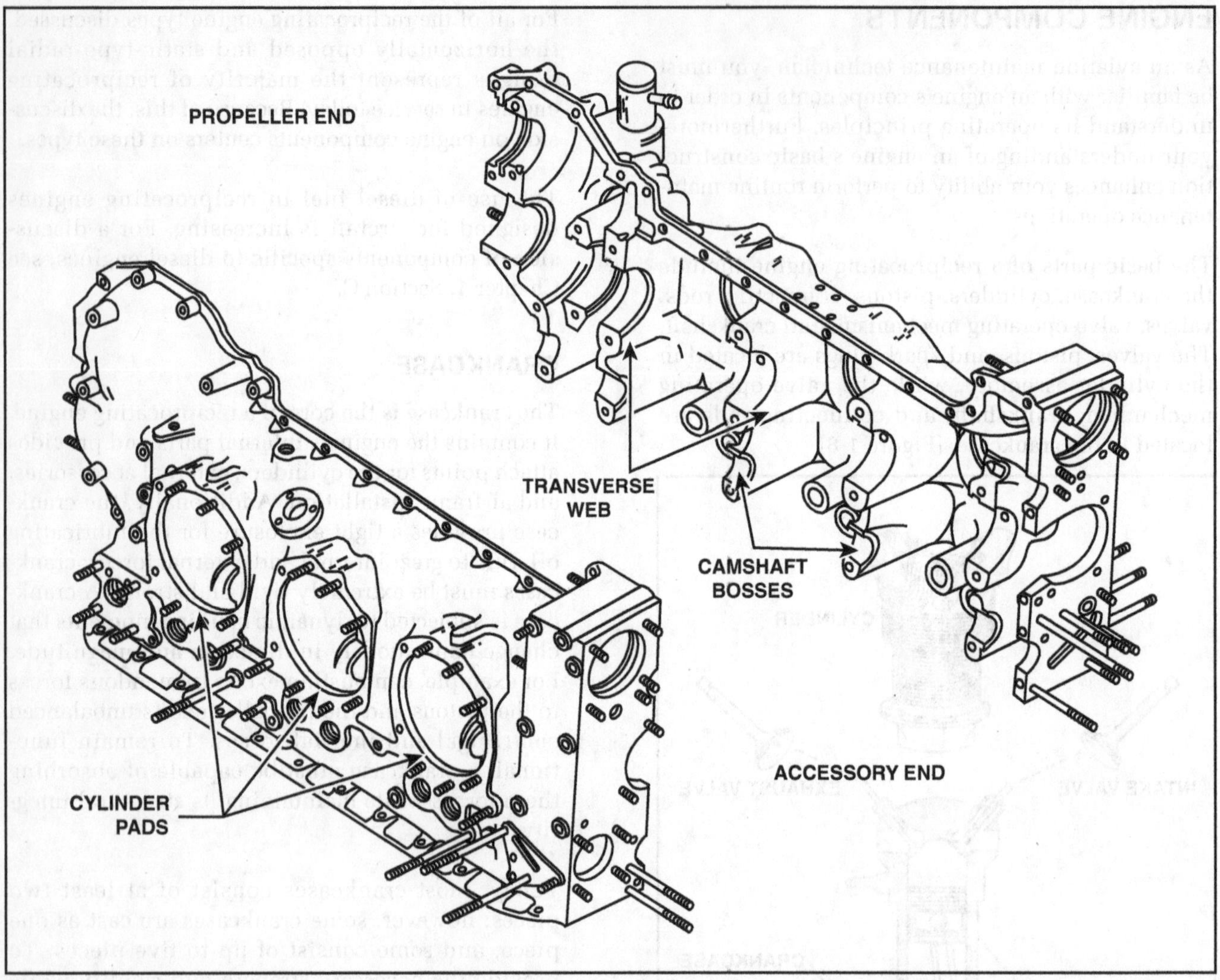


**Figure 1-9. The transverse webs in the crankcase support the main bearings and a set of camshaft bosses support the camshaft.**

For the crankcase to support a crankshaft, a series of transverse webs are cast directly into the crankcase parallel to its longitudinal axis. In addition to supporting the crankshaft, these webs add strength and form an integral part of the structure. [Figure 1-9]

The crankcase is integral to the lubrication system. Passages are drilled into the case halves to deliver oil to the moving parts within the crankcase. Additionally, oil passages are machined into the crankcase to scavenge (collect) oil and return it to the main tank or sump.

Most crankcases split vertically; the halves are aligned and held together with studs, bolts, and nuts. Through-bolts are typically used around the crankshaft bearings and smaller bolts and nuts are used around the case perimeter. Because the crankcase typically contains oil, it must be sealed to prevent leakage. To ensure that the seal does not affect the tight fit required for the bearings, most crankcase halves are sealed with a very thin coating of a non-hardening gasket compound. In addition, on some engines, a fine silk thread extending around the entire case perimeter is embedded in the compound. When the crankcase halves are bolted together with appropriate torque, the compound and thread form an effective oil seal without altering the fit of the bearing.

### RADIAL ENGINE CRANKCASES

Unlike opposed-engine crankcases, radial-engine crankcases are divided by function. The number of sections can be as few as three or as many as seven, depending on the size and type of engine. A typical radial engine crankcase separates into four main sections: nose, power, supercharger, and accessory. [Figure 1-10]

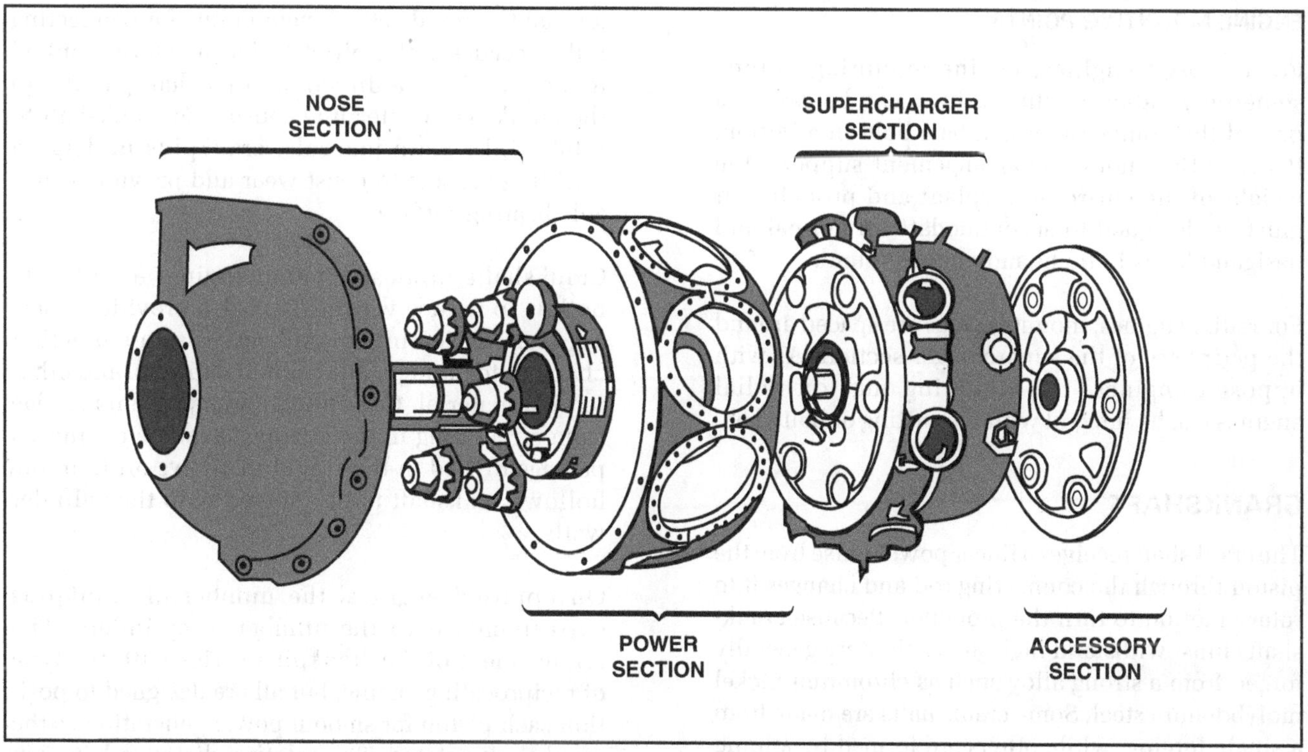


**Figure 1-10. The four sections of a radial engine crankcase are nose, power, supercharger, and accessory.**

The **nose section** is mounted at the front of a radial engine crankcase and bolts directly to the power section. A typical nose section is made of an aluminum alloy that is cast as one piece with a domed or convex shape. This section typically supports and contains a propeller governor drive shaft, the propeller shaft, a cam ring, and, if required, a propeller reduction gear assembly. In addition, the nose section might have mounting points for magnetos or other engine accessories.

The second section of a radial engine crankcase is referred to as the power section and it contains the components that transfer energy from the pistons to the crankshaft. Like an opposed engine crankcase, the power section absorbs stress from the crankshaft assembly and the cylinders. The **power section** can be one, two, or three pieces. A one-piece power section usually consists of a solid piece of aluminum alloy. Multipiece power sections are typically manufactured from aluminum or magnesium and bolted together. The power section contains machined bosses that support the crankshaft bearings and add strength.

Cylinders are attached around the perimeter of the power section to machined cylinder pads. In general, studs are installed into threaded holes in the power section to provide a means of attaching the cylinders. The inner circumference of a cylinder pad is sometimes chamfered or tapered to permit the installation of a large, rubber O-ring around the cylinder skirt. This O-ring seals the joint between the cylinder and the cylinder pads.

The diffuser or **supercharger section** is located directly behind the power section and is typically made of cast aluminum alloy or magnesium. This section houses the supercharger and its related components. A supercharger is an engine device that compresses air for the engine's cylinders, enabling the engine to produce more power. The supercharger section incorporates attach points to secure the engine assembly to the engine mounts.

The **accessory section** is usually cast of aluminum alloy or magnesium. On engines with one piece accessory sections, the casting is machined to provide means for mounting accessories. Two-piece accessory sections consist of an aluminum alloy casting and a separate magnesium cover plate that provides attach points for the accessories. Possible accessories include magnetos, carburetors, pumps, starters, and generators.

The gear train in the accessory section contains both spur- and bevel-type gears to drive various engine components and accessories. Spur-type gears drive heavily loaded accessories or those that would be affected by backlash in the gear train. Bevel-type gears handle lighter loads, but accommodate short drive shafts for various accessories.

### ENGINE MOUNTING POINTS

For opposed engines, engine mounting points, sometimes called mounting lugs, can be cast as a part of the crankcase or can be a bolt-on addition. Because this mounting arrangement supports the weight of the entire powerplant and propeller, it must be designed to accommodate all normal and designed loads in flight and on the ground.

For radial engines, mounting lugs are spaced around the periphery of the supercharger section. As with opposed engines, the mounting lugs on radial engines can be integral with the casting or bolted on.

## CRANKSHAFT

The crankshaft receives a linear power pulse from the piston through the connecting rod and changes it to rotary motion to turn the propeller. Because crankshafts must withstand high stress, they are generally forged from a strong alloy such as chromium-nickel molybdenum steel. Some crankshafts are made from a single forging, while others are formed by joining several components. The number of crankpins varies depending on the type of engine and the number of cylinders. Regardless of the number of throws or the number of pieces used in construction, all crankshafts have the same basic components, including main bearing journals, crankpins, and crank cheeks. [Figure 1-11]

The centerline of a crankshaft runs through the center of the **main bearing journals**. These journals support the crankshaft as it rotates. All crankshafts require at least two main journals to support the crankshaft, absorb the operational loads, and transmit stress from the crankshaft to the crankcase. To minimize wear, most main bearing journals are hardened through a nitriding process.

A crankshaft has one or more **crankpins** (also known as **throws**, **crank throws**, and **connecting-rod bearing journals**) located at specific points along its length. Crankpins are offset from the main bearing journal to provide attachment points for connecting rods. Because of this offset design, any force applied to a crankpin in a direction other than parallel to the crankshaft center line causes the crankshaft to rotate. Like main journals, crankpins undergo a nitriding process to resist wear and provide a suitable bearing surface.

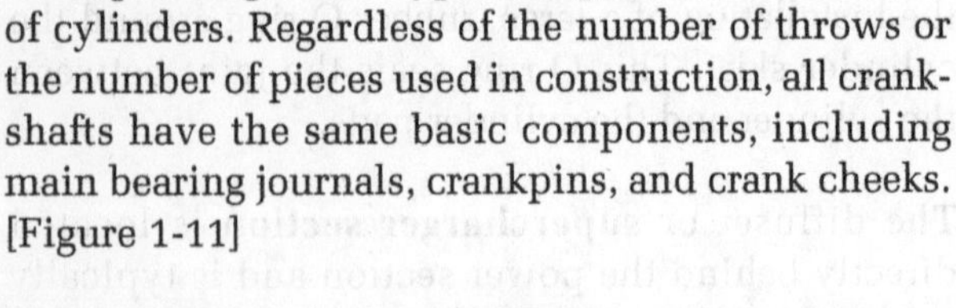


**Figure 1-11. Every crankshaft has main bearing journals, one or more crankpins, and crank cheeks.**

Crankshafts in most aviation engines are usually hollow to reduce weight. This also provides a passage for lubricating oil and serves as a collection chamber for **sludge**, dirt, carbon deposits, and other foreign material. Centrifugal force prevents sludge from circulating in the engine. On some engines, a passage drilled in the crankpin allows oil from the hollow crankshaft to be sprayed onto the cylinder walls.

On opposed engines, the number of crankpins corresponds with the number of cylinders. The arrangement of the crankpins varies with the type of reciprocating engine, but all are designed to position each piston for smooth power generation as the crankshaft rotates. The relative distance between crankpins on a crankshaft is measured in degrees. [Figure 1-12]

Crank cheeks, or crank arms, are required to connect crankpins to each other and to the main journal of the crankshaft. In some designs, the cheeks extend beyond the journal to provide an attach point for counterweights that help balance the crankshaft. Most crank cheeks have drilled passageways to permit oil to flow from the main journal to the crankpin.

### CRANKSHAFT BALANCE

Excessive engine vibration can cause metal structures to fatigue and fail or wear excessively. An unbalanced crankshaft can cause excessive vibration. To help minimize unwanted vibration, crankshafts are balanced statically and dynamically.

A crankshaft is in **static balance** when the weight of the entire assembly is balanced around its axis of rotation. To test a crankshaft for static balance, the outside main journals are placed on two knife-edge balancing blocks. If the crankshaft tends to favor any one rotational position during the test, it is out of static balance.

After a crankshaft is statically balanced, it must also be dynamically balanced. A crankshaft is considered in **dynamic balance** when the centrifugal forces and power pulses are offset with counter-

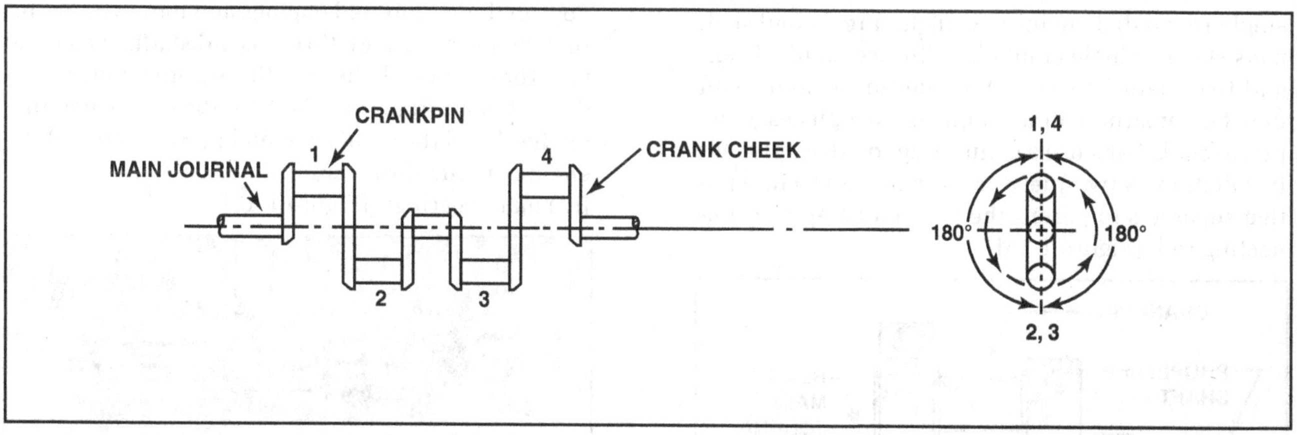


Figure 1-12. On a four cylinder engine, crankpins one and four are 180 degrees apart from crankpins two and three.

weights. (Crankshafts for smaller engines do not always use counterweights.) A **dynamic damper** is a counterweight that is fastened to a crankshaft's crank cheek assembly so that it can move back and forth in a small arc. Some crankshafts use two or more of these assemblies, each attached to a different crank cheek. The construction of the dynamic damper used in one type of engine consists of a movable slotted-steel counterweight attached to a crank cheek by two spool-shaped steel pins that extend through oversized holes in the counterweight and crank cheek. The difference in diameter between the pins and the holes enables the dynamic damper to oscillate. [Figure 1-13]

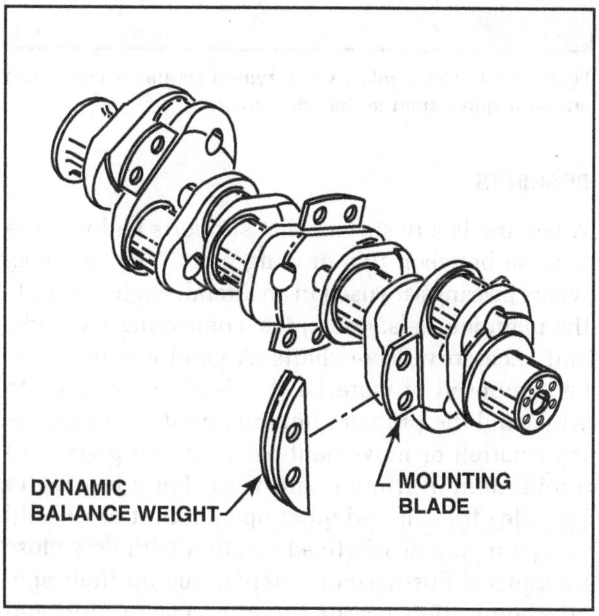


Figure 1-13. Movable counterweights act as dynamic dampers to reduce the centrifugal and impact vibrations in an aircraft engine.

Each time a cylinder fires, force is transmitted to the crankshaft, causing it to flex. This happens hundreds of times every minute. Dynamic dampers oscillate, or swing, with every pulse from a firing cylinder to absorb some of this force. [Figure 1-14]

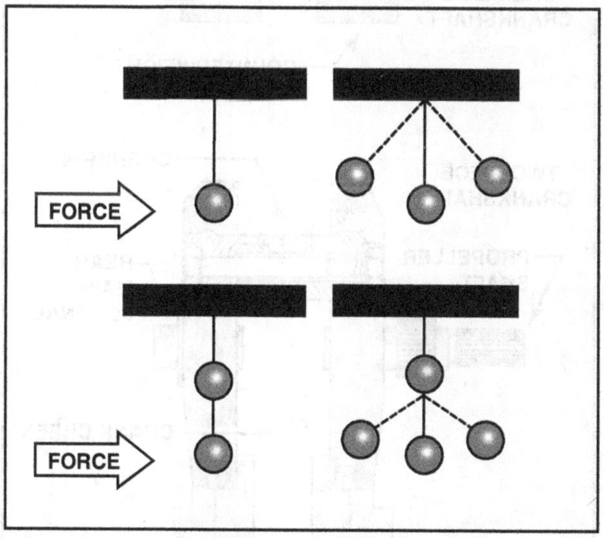


Figure 1-14. Think of the crankshaft as a pendulum that swings at its natural frequency when a force is applied. The greater the force, the greater the distance the pendulum swings. However, if a second pendulum is suspended from the first and a force is applied, the second pendulum begins to oscillate opposite the applied force. This opposite oscillation dampens the oscillation of the first pendulum. You can think of a dynamic damper as a short pendulum hung from a crankshaft that is tuned to the frequency of power impulses.

## CRANKSHAFT TYPES

The type of crankshaft used on a particular engine depends on the number and arrangement of the engine's cylinders. The most common types of crankshafts are **single-throw**, two-throw, four-throw, and six-throw. The simplest crankshaft is the single-throw, or 360–degree crankshaft, used on single-row radial engines. A single-throw crankshaft consists of a single crankpin with two crank cheeks and two main journals. A single-throw crankshaft may be constructed out of one or two pieces. One-piece crankshafts use a connecting rod that splits for installation. A two-piece crankshaft uses a crankpin that separates to permit the use of a one-piece connecting rod. [Figure 1-15]

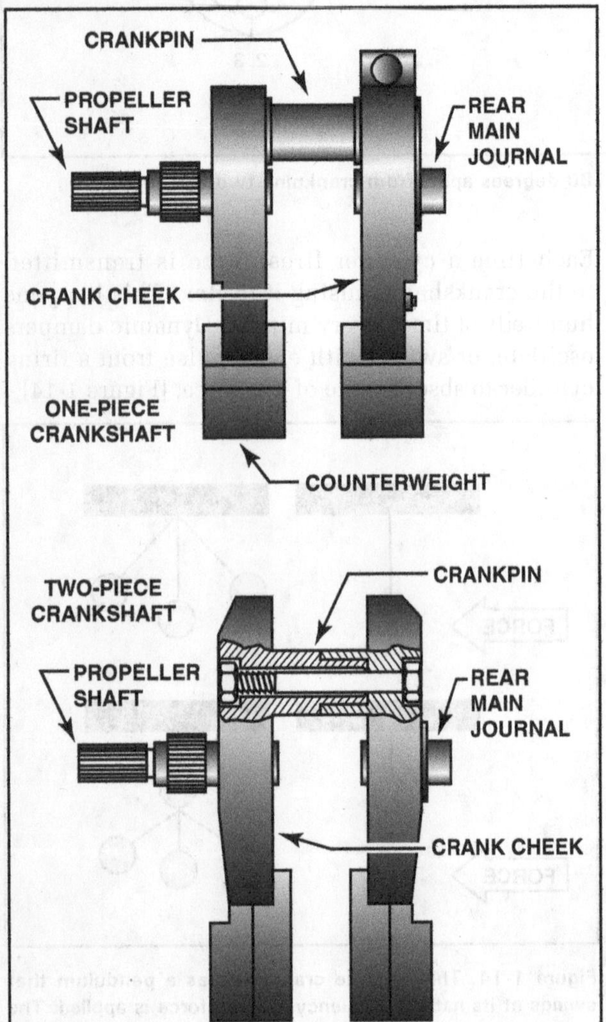


**Figure 1-15. A one-piece, single-throw crankshaft is cast as one solid piece. However, a clamp type, two-piece crankshaft is held together by a bolt that passes through the crankpin.**

Twin-row radial engines require a two-throw crankshaft, one throw for each bank of cylinders. The throws on a **two-throw crankshaft** are typically set 180 degrees apart and can consist of either one or three pieces. Although uncommon, two cylinder opposed engines also use two-throw crankshafts.

Four-cylinder opposed engines and four cylinder in-line engines use **four-throw crankshafts**. On some four-throw crankshafts, two throws are arranged 180 degrees apart from the other two throws. Depending on the size of the crankshaft and power output of the engine, a four-throw crankshaft has either three or five main bearings. [Figure 1-16]

**Figure 1-16. A typical four-throw crankshaft from a four cylinder, opposed engine is machined from one piece of steel.**

Six-cylinder opposed and in-line engines as well as 12-cylinder V-type engines use **six-throw crankshafts**. A typical six-throw crankshaft is forged as one piece and consists of four main bearings and six throws that are 60 degrees apart. [Figure 1-17]

**Figure 1-17. The crankpins in a typical six-throw crankshaft are 60 degrees apart in the firing order.**

## BEARINGS

A bearing is any surface that supports and reduces friction between two moving parts. Typical areas where bearings are used in an aircraft engine include the main journals, crankpins, connecting rod ends, and accessory drive shafts. A good bearing must be composed of material that is strong enough to withstand the pressure imposed on it, while allowing rotation or movement between two parts with a minimum of friction and wear. For a bearing to provide efficient and quiet operation, it must hold two parts in a nearly fixed position with very close tolerances. Furthermore, depending on their specific application, bearings must be able to withstand radial loads, thrust loads, or both.

There are two ways in which bearing surfaces move in relation to each other. One is by the sliding movement of one surface against another, and the second is for one surface to roll over another. Reciprocating

**Figure 1-18. The three most common types of bearings in reciprocating engines are plain, roller, and ball. Plain bearings rely on the sliding movement of one metal against another; both roller and ball bearings use rolling movement.**

engines use bearings that rely on both types of movement. Aircraft reciprocating engines typically use include plain bearings, ball bearings, and roller bearings. [Figure 1-18]

### PLAIN BEARINGS

Plain bearings are generally used as crankshaft main bearings, cam ring and camshaft bearings, connecting rod end bearings, and accessory drive shaft bearings. These bearings are typically subject to radial loads only; however, flange-type plain bearings are often used as axial thrust bearings in opposed reciprocating engines.

Plain bearings are usually made of nonferrous metals such as silver, bronze, Babbitt, tin, or lead. One type of plain bearing consists of thin shells of silver-plated steel; with lead-tin plated over the silver on the inside surface only. Smaller bearings, such as those used to support various accessory drive shafts, are called **bushings**. One type of bushing that is used in aviation is the oil impregnated porous Oilite® bushing. With this type of bushing, the heat produced by friction draws the impregnated oil to the bearing surface to provide lubrication during engine operation.

### BALL BEARINGS

A ball bearing assembly consists of grooved inner and outer races, one or more sets of polished steel balls, and a **bearing retainer**. The balls are held in place and kept evenly spaced by the bearing retainer, and the inner and outer **bearing races** provide a smooth surface for the balls to roll over. However, some races have a deep groove that matches the curvature of the balls to provide more support and enable the bearing to carry high radial loads. Because the balls in a ball bearing assembly provide a small contact area, this type of bearing has the least amount of rolling friction.

Ball bearings are well-suited to withstand thrust loads; because of this, they are used as thrust bearings in large radial and gas turbine engines. In applications in which thrust loads are greater in one direction, a larger race is used on the side of the increased load.

Most ball bearings that you encounter as a technician are used in accessories such as magnetos, alternators, turbochargers, and vacuum pumps. Many of these bearings are prelubricated and sealed to provide trouble-free operation between overhauls. However, if a sealed ball bearing must be serviced, you must use the proper tools to avoid damaging the bearing and its seals.

### ROLLER BEARINGS

Roller bearings are similar in construction to ball bearings except that polished steel rollers are used instead of balls. The rollers provide a greater contact area and a corresponding increase in rolling friction over that of a ball bearing. Roller bearings are available in many styles and sizes, but most aircraft engines either have a straight roller or tapered roller bearing. **Straight roller bearings** are suitable when the bearing is subjected to radial loads only. For example, most high-power aircraft engines use straight roller bearings as crankshaft main bearings. **Tapered roller bearings**, on the other hand, have cone-shaped inner and outer races that enable the bearing to withstand both radial and thrust loads.

## CONNECTING RODS

The connecting rod is the link that transmits the force exerted on the piston to the crankshaft. Most connecting rods are made of a durable steel alloy; however, low-horsepower engines sometimes use aluminum. The weight of a connecting rod corresponds to the amount of inertia it possesses when the rod and piston stop before accelerating in the opposite direction at the end of each stroke. Engine manufacturers strive to make connecting rods as light as possible, to reduce inertial forces, but still maintain their necessary strength. A typical connecting rod is forged with a cross-sectional shape resembling an "H" or "I." There are also a few tubular connecting rods. The **crankpin end** of the connecting rod connects to the crankshaft and the **piston end** connects to the piston. The three major types of connecting rod assemblies are plain, master-and-articulated, and fork-and-blade.

### PLAIN CONNECTING RODS

Plain connecting rods are used in opposed and in-line engines. The piston end of a plain connecting rod is fitted with a bronze bushing to accommodate the piston pin. The bushing is typically pressed into the connecting rod and reamed to a precise dimension to fit the piston pin. The crankpin end is usually fitted with a two-piece bearing, which is held in place by the cap and secured by bolts or by studs and nuts. The bearing inserts are typically steel lined with a nonferrous alloy such as Babbitt, lead, bronze, or copper.

Connecting rods are often matched with pistons for balance and crankpins for fit. If a connecting rod is ever removed, it should be replaced in the same cylinder and relative position. Connecting rods and caps might be stamped to identify the corresponding cylinder and piston assembly. For example, a number "1" indicates the connecting rod and cap belong with the number 1 cylinder and piston assembly. [Figure 1-19]

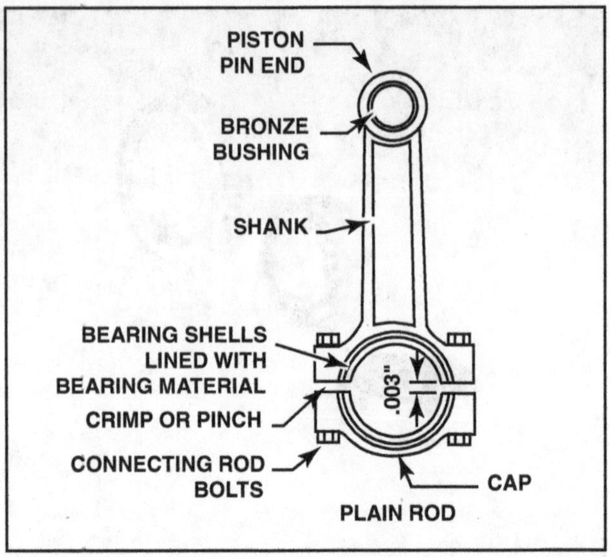


**Figure 1-19. The two piece bearing shell on a typical plain connecting rod fits tightly in the crankpin end of the connecting rod. The bearing is held in place by pins or tangs that fit into slots cut into the cap and connecting rod. The piston end of the connecting rod contains a bushing that is pressed into place.**

### MASTER-AND-ARTICULATED ROD ASSEMBLY

Radial engines use a master-and-articulated rod assembly to connect the pistons to the crankshaft. In this type of assembly, one piston in each row of cylinders is connected to the crankshaft by a **master rod**. The remaining pistons are connected to the master rod with **articulated rods**. For example, a nine-cylinder single-row engine has one master rod and eight articulating rods and a double-row 18-cylinder engine has two master rods and 16 articulating rods.

Master rods are typically manufactured from a steel alloy forging that is machined and heat-treated for maximum strength. Articulated rods are constructed of a forged steel alloy with an I- or H- cross-sectional profile. Bronze bushings are pressed into the bores in each end of the articulated rods.

The master rod serves as the only link between all of the pistons and the crankpin. The piston end of a master rod contains the **piston pin bearing**. The crankpin end of a master rod contains the **crankpin bearing (master rod bearing)**. A typical crankpin bearing must be able to withstand the radial loads placed on the rod assembly. A set of flange holes is machined around the crankpin end of a master rod to provide an attachment point for the articulated rods. A master rod can be one piece or multiple pieces. As a rule, a **one-piece rod** is used with a multiple-piece crankshaft, while a **multiple-piece (or split-type) master rod** is used with a single-piece crankshaft. [Figure 1-20]

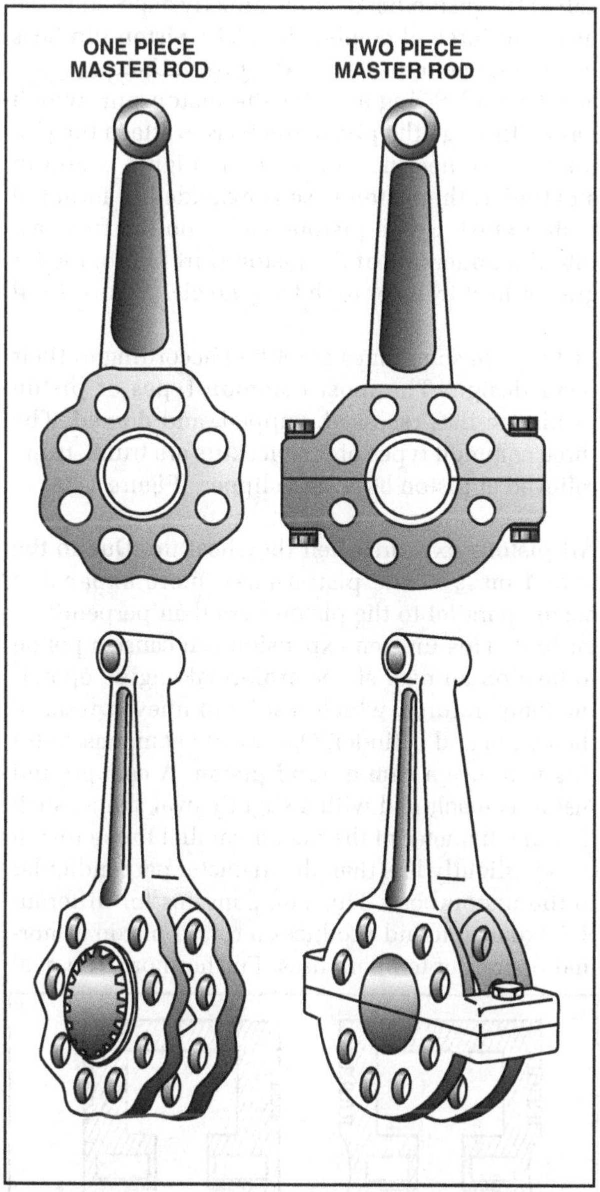


**Figure 1-20. On a single piece master rod, the master-and-articulated rods are assembled and installed on the crankpin before the crankshaft sections are joined together. On a multiple piece master rod, the crankpin end of the master rod and its bearing are split and installed on the crankpin. The bearing cap is then set in place and bolted to the master rod.**

Each articulated rod is hinged to the master rod by a **knuckle pin**. Some knuckle pins are pressed into the master rod so they do not rotate in the flange holes; other **full-floating knuckle pins** have a loose fit that enables them to rotate in both the flange holes and articulated rods. In either type of installation, a lock plate on each side retains the knuckle pins and prevents lateral movement. [Figure 1-21]

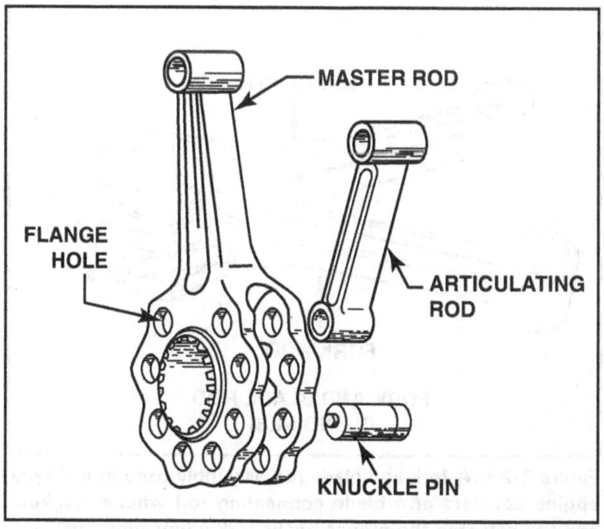


**Figure 1-21. Articulated rods are attached to the master rod by knuckle pins. A knuckle pin lock plate retains the pins.**

As the crankshaft rotates, the crankpin bearing is the only portion of a master rod assembly that travels in a true circle. Because the flange holes on a master rod are arranged around the crankpin, the knuckle pins travel in an elliptical path. [Figure 1-22]

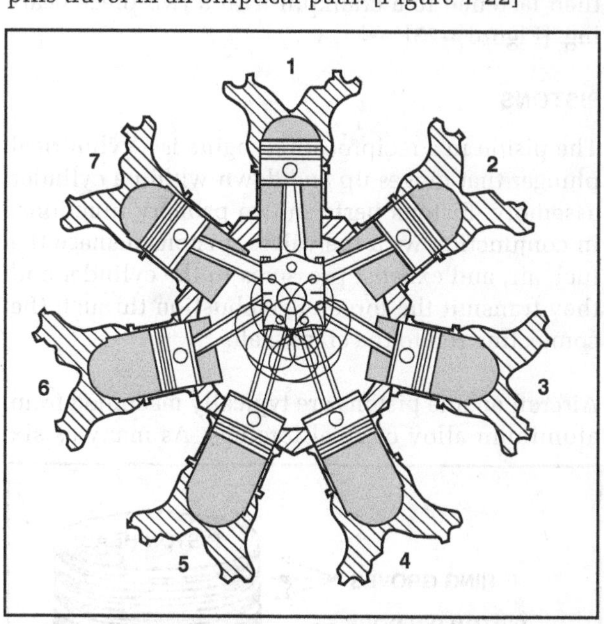


**Figure 1-22. Knuckle pins rotate in different elliptical paths. Each articulated rod has a varying degree of angularity relative to the center of the crank throw.**

Because of the varying angularity, not all pistons move an equal amount in each cylinder for a given number of degrees of crankshaft rotation. To compensate for this, the knuckle pin holes in the master rod flange are positioned at varying distances from the center of the crankpin.

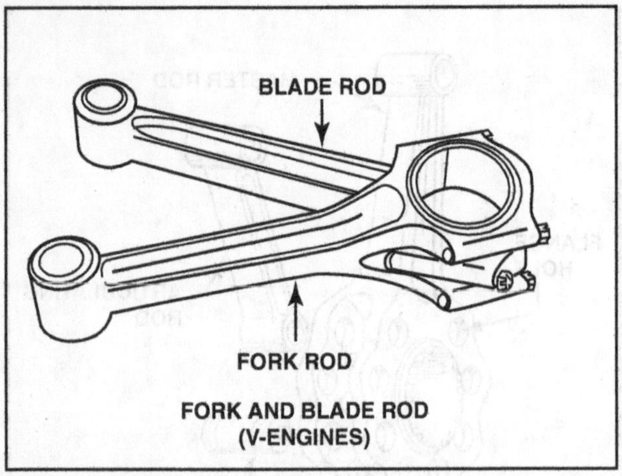


**Figure 1-23. A fork-and-blade rod assembly used in a V-type engine consists of a blade connecting rod whose crankpin end fits between the prongs of the fork connecting rod.**

### FORK-AND-BLADE ROD ASSEMBLY

The fork-and-blade rod assembly used in V-type engines consists of a **fork connecting rod** and a **blade connecting rod**. The forked rod is split at the crankpin end to allow space for the blade rod to fit between the prongs. The fork-and-blade assembly is then fastened to a crankpin with a two-piece bearing. [Figure 1-23]

### PISTONS

The piston in a reciprocating engine is a cylindrical plunger that moves up and down within a cylinder assembly. Pistons perform two primary functions; in conjunction with the valves, pistons manage the fuel, air, and exhaust pressures in the cylinder and they transmit the force of combustion through the connecting rod to the crankshaft.

Aircraft engine pistons are typically machined from aluminum alloy or steel forgings. As many as six ring grooves are then machined into a piston's outside surface to hold a set of piston rings. The portion of the piston between the **ring grooves** is commonly referred to as a **ring land**. The piston's top surface is called the **piston head** and is directly exposed to the heat and force of combustion. The **piston pin boss** is an enlarged area inside the piston that provides additional bearing area for the piston pin, which passes through the **piston pin boss** to attach the piston to a connecting rod. To help align a piston in a cylinder, the piston base is extended to form the **piston skirt**. Some pistons have cooling fins cast into the underside of the piston skirt to provide for greater heat transfer to the engine oil. [Figure 1-24]

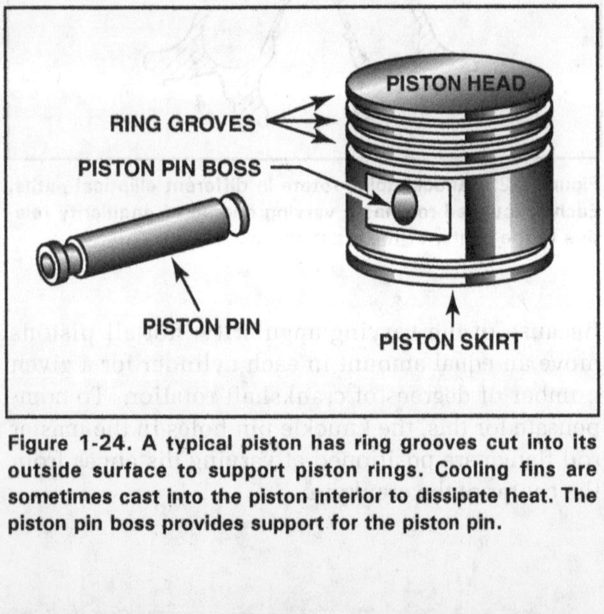


**Figure 1-24. A typical piston has ring grooves cut into its outside surface to support piston rings. Cooling fins are sometimes cast into the piston interior to dissipate heat. The piston pin boss provides support for the piston pin.**

Pistons are sometimes classified according to their head design. The most common types of piston heads are flat, recessed, cupped, and domed. The three common types of piston skirts are trunk, trunk relieved at piston boss, and slipper. [Figure 1-25]

All pistons expand when they heat up. Due to the added mass at the piston boss, more expansion occurs parallel to the piston boss than perpendicular to it. This uneven expansion can cause a piston to take on an oval shape at normal engine operating temperatures, which results in uneven wear of the piston and cylinder. One way to compensate for this is to use a **cam-ground piston**. A cam-ground piston is machined with a slightly oval shape, such that the diameter of the piston parallel to the piston boss is slightly less than the diameter perpendicular to the piston boss. This compensates for differential expansion and produces a round piston at normal operating temperatures. Furthermore, the oval

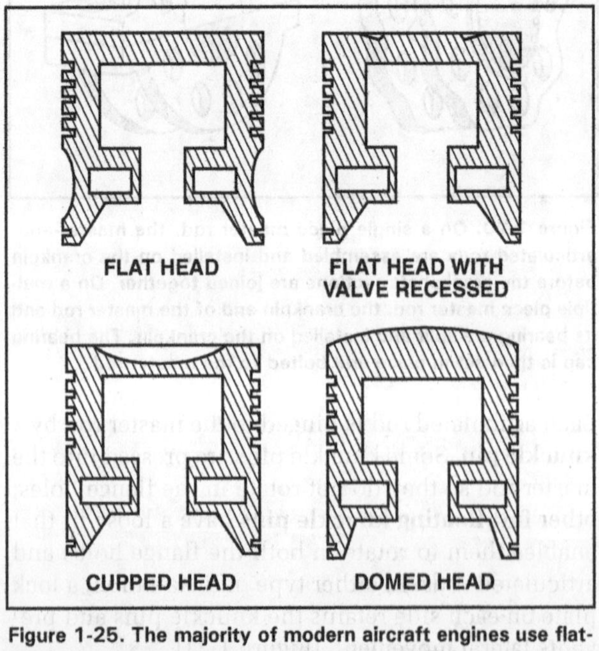


**Figure 1-25. The majority of modern aircraft engines use flat-head pistons; however, other designs are still in service.**

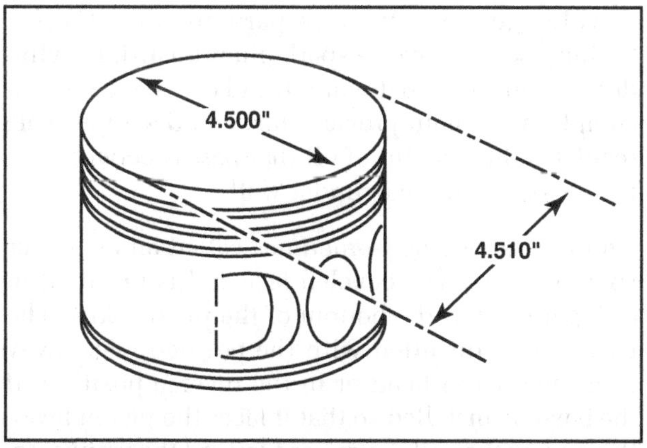


**Figure 1-26. Cam ground pistons compensate for the greater expansion parallel to the piston boss during engine operation. The diameter of a cam ground piston measures several thousandths of an inch larger perpendicular to the piston boss than parallel to the piston boss.**

shape holds the piston centered in the cylinder during engine warm-up and prevents the piston from moving laterally within a cylinder. [Figure 1-26]

## PISTON RINGS

Piston rings perform three functions. They prevent pressure leakage from the combustion chamber, control oil seepage into the combustion chamber, and transfer heat from the piston to the cylinder walls. Piston rings are spring-loaded and press against the cylinder walls; when properly lubricated, they form an effective seal.

Piston rings are usually made of high-grade gray cast iron or chrome-plated, mild steel. The chrome-plated rings can withstand higher temperatures. During manufacture, the ring is machined to the desired cross-section, and then split for installation in a piston ring groove. The point where a piston ring is split is called the piston ring gap. The gap can be a simple butt joint with flat faces, an angle joint with angled faces, or a step joint. [Figure 1-27]

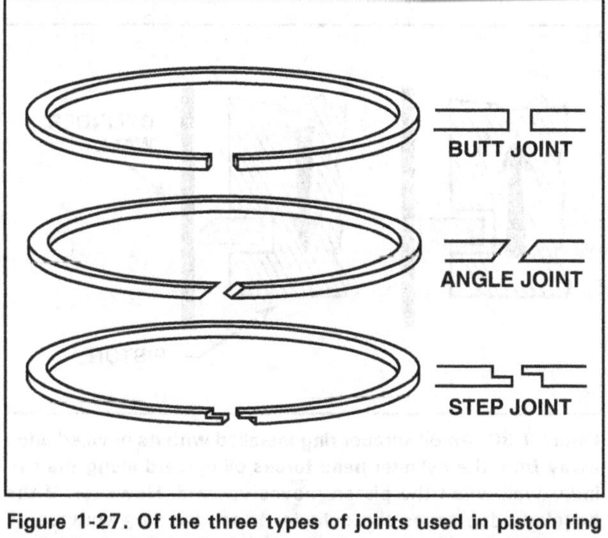


**Figure 1-27. Of the three types of joints used in piston ring gaps, the butt joint is the most common in aircraft engines.**

As an engine reaches operating temperature, piston rings expand. To accommodate expansion, piston rings need a gap. If the gap is too large, the two faces will not come together and provide an adequate seal. If the gap is too small, the ring faces will bind against each other and the cylinder wall resulting in scoring damage to the cylinder wall. Ring gaps must be staggered, or offset to create the best seal, which prevents combustion gases from leaking past the rings into the crankcase. This **blow-by**, as it is often called, results in a loss of power and increased oil consumption.

To form an effective seal, the rings must exert equal pressure around the entire cylinder wall and provide a gas-tight fit against the sides of the ring grooves. New piston rings require some wear-in during engine operation so that the ring contour matches the cylinder wall. A ring that matches its cylinder is considered to be **seated**. The two main types of piston rings used in reciprocating engines are compression rings and oil rings. [Figure 1-28]

The **compression rings**, located in the ring grooves immediately below the piston head, prevent gas from escaping around the piston during engine operation. The number of compression rings used on each piston is determined by the engine manufacturer. Two or three compression rings on each piston is common. The cross section of a compression ring can be rectangular, wedge shaped, or tapered. Because compression rings receive limited lubrication and are closest to the heat of combustion, they are more prone to sticking.

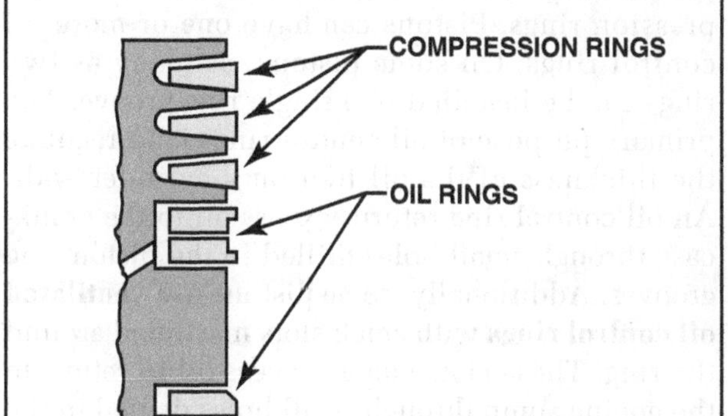


**Figure 1-28. Compression rings are installed in the upper piston ring grooves to help prevent the combustion gases from escaping. Oil rings, on the other hand, are installed near the middle and bottom of a piston to control the amount of oil applied to the cylinder wall.**

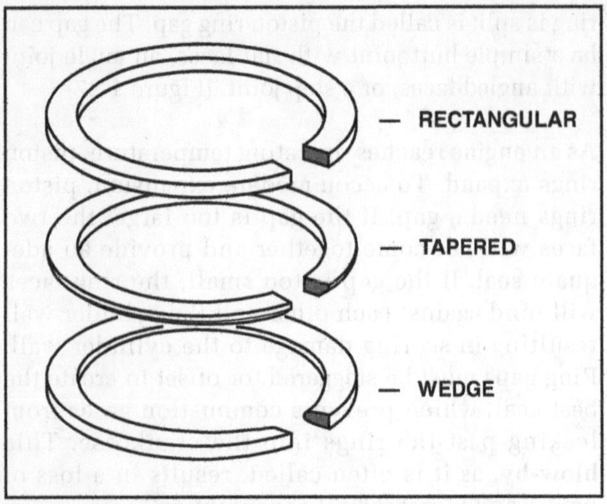


**Figure 1-29. Compression rings can have three different ring cross sections. The tapered face presents the narrowest bearing edge to the cylinder wall to reduce friction and accelerate ring seating.**

A rectangular compression ring fits flat against a cylinder wall with a large contact area to provide a tight seal. The large contact area requires a relatively long time to seat. Tapered rings have a beveled face to reduce contact area, which reduces friction and hastens ring seating. Wedge-shaped rings also have a beveled face to promote rapid ring seating. Because the profile is wedge shaped, the piston ring grooves must also be beveled. Less material is cut away, so piston ring lands and grooves are stronger. The wedge shape also helps prevent a ring from sticking in a groove. [Figure 1-29]

**Oil rings** control the amount of oil applied to the cylinder walls and prevent oil from entering the combustion chamber. The two types of oil rings that are found on most engines are oil control rings and oil scraper rings. **Oil control rings** are placed in the piston ring grooves below the compression rings. Pistons can have one or more oil control rings. On some pistons, as many as two rings can be installed in a single ring groove. The primary purpose of oil control rings is to regulate the thickness of the oil film on a cylinder wall. An oil control ring returns excess oil to the crankcase through small holes drilled in the piston ring grooves. Additionally, some pistons use **ventilated oil control rings** with small slots machined around the ring. These slots enable excess oil to return to the engine sump through small holes drilled in the piston ring groove.

If excessive oil enters the combustion chamber, it will burn and leave a coating of carbon on the combustion chamber walls, piston head, spark plugs, and valves. Carbon buildup on the ring grooves or valve guides can cause parts to stick. Carbon buildup can also cause spark plugs misfiring, cylinder preignition or detonation, and excessive oil consumption. To help prevent this, an **oil scraper ring** regulates the amount of oil that passes between the piston skirt and the cylinder wall.

An oil scraper ring, sometimes called an **oil wiper ring**, usually has a beveled face and is installed in a ring groove at the bottom of the piston skirt. The ring can be installed with the beveled edge away from the piston head or in the reverse position. If the bevel is installed so that it faces the piston head, the ring pushes oil downward toward the crankcase. If the bevel is installed to face away from the piston head, on the upward stroke, the scraper ring retains surplus oil above the ring. On the downward stroke, oil is returned to the crankcase by the oil control rings and piston ring grooves. It is very important that these rings are installed in accordance with the manufacturer's instructions. [Figure 1-30]

## PISTON PINS

A piston pin joins the piston to the connecting rod. Piston pins are tubular, and are machined from a case-hardened, nickel-steel alloy forging. Piston pins are sometimes called **wrist pins** because the motion of the piston and the connecting rod is similar to a human wrist.

Piston pins can be stationary, semifloating, or full-floating. **Stationary piston pins** are secured to the piston by a setscrew that prevents rotation. **Semifloating piston** pins are loosely attached to the connecting rod by clamping around a reduced-diameter section of the pin. **Full-floating piston pins** rotate freely in both the connecting rod and the piston; these pins are used in most modern aircraft engines.

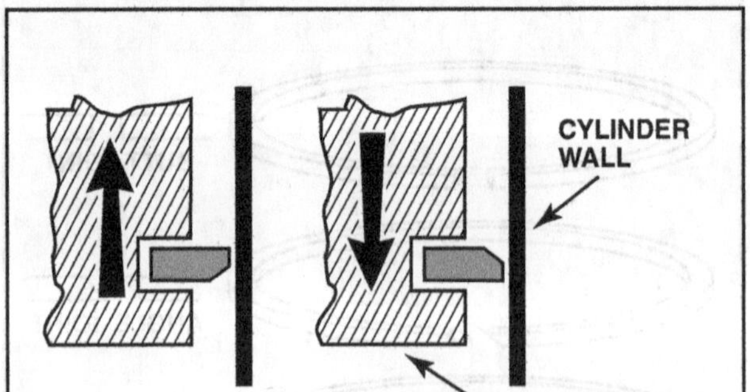


**Figure 1-30. An oil scraper ring installed with its beveled edge away from the cylinder head forces oil upward along the cylinder wall when the piston moves upward. However, if the beveled edge faces the cylinder head, the ring scrapes oil toward the crankcase when the piston moves down.**

A full-floating piston pin must be held in place laterally to prevent it from rubbing and scoring the cylinder walls. Three devices that are used to hold a piston pin in place are circlets, spring rings, and metal plugs. A **circlet** is similar to a snap ring that fits into a groove cut into each end of the piston boss. A **spring ring** also fits into grooves cut into the ends of a piston boss, but it consists of a single circular spring-steel coil. Both circlets and spring rings are used primarily on earlier piston engines. The current practice is to install a plug of relatively soft aluminum called a **piston-pin plug**. These plugs are inserted into the open ends of the piston pins to provide a good bearing surface against the cylinder walls. Due to the plug's soft aluminum construction and cylinder lubrication, the metal-to-metal contact causes no damage to the cylinder walls.

## CYLINDERS

The cylinder is the combustion chamber where the burning and expansion of gases takes place to produce engine power. Furthermore, a cylinder houses the piston and connecting rod assembly along with the valves and spark plugs. When designing and constructing a cylinder, manufacturers must consider several factors. A cylinder must be strong enough to withstand the internal pressures developed during engine operation yet be lightweight to minimize engine weight. Additionally, the materials used in the construction of a cylinder must have good heat-conducting properties for efficient cooling. Finally, a cylinder assembly must be relatively simple and cost-effective to manufacture, inspect, and maintain.

A typical air-cooled engine cylinder consists of a cylinder head, barrel, mounting flange, skirt, cooling fins, and valve assembly. On some of the earliest two- and four-cylinder horizontally opposed engines, the cylinder barrels were cast as part of the crankcase halves. This required the use of removable cylinder heads. However, on almost all modern engines, individual cylinders are cast as a component, separate from the crankcase, and the heads are permanently attached during the manufacturing process. To do this, the cylinder head is expanded through heating and then screwed down onto a chilled cylinder barrel. As the head cools, it contracts, and as the barrel warms, it expands, resulting in a gas-tight joint. [Figure 1-31]

### CYLINDER BARRELS

The material used to construct a cylinder barrel must be as light as possible, yet have the proper characteristics for operating at high temperatures and pressures. Furthermore, a cylinder barrel must possess good bearing characteristics and high tensile strength. The most commonly used material that meets these requirements is a high-strength steel alloy such as chromium-molybdenum steel or nickel chromium-molybdenum steel.

**Figure 1-31. The cylinder assembly, the piston assembly, connecting rods, crankshaft, and crankcase constitute the power section of a reciprocating engine.**

Cylinder barrels are machined from a forged blank, with a **skirt** that projects into the crankcase and a **mounting flange** that is used to attach the cylinder to the crankcase. The lower cylinders on radial engines and all the cylinders on inverted engines typically have extended cylinder skirts. The longer skirt helps keep oil from draining into the combustion chamber and causing hydraulic lock after an engine has been shut down. The exterior of a cylinder barrel consists of several thin **cooling fins** that are machined into the exterior cylinder wall and a set of threads that are cut at the top of the barrel so that it can be screwed into the cylinder head.

The inside of a cylinder, or **cylinder bore**, is usually machined smooth to a uniform, initial dimension, and then honed to a final dimension. However, some cylinder bores are machined with a slight taper, so that the diameter of the top of the barrel is slightly smaller than the diameter at the cylinder skirt. This is called a choke bore cylinder and is designed to compensate for the uneven expansion caused by the higher operating temperatures and larger mass near the cylinder head. With a **choke bore cylinder**, the greater expansion at the top of the cylinder is compensated for by the taper, resulting in a uniform

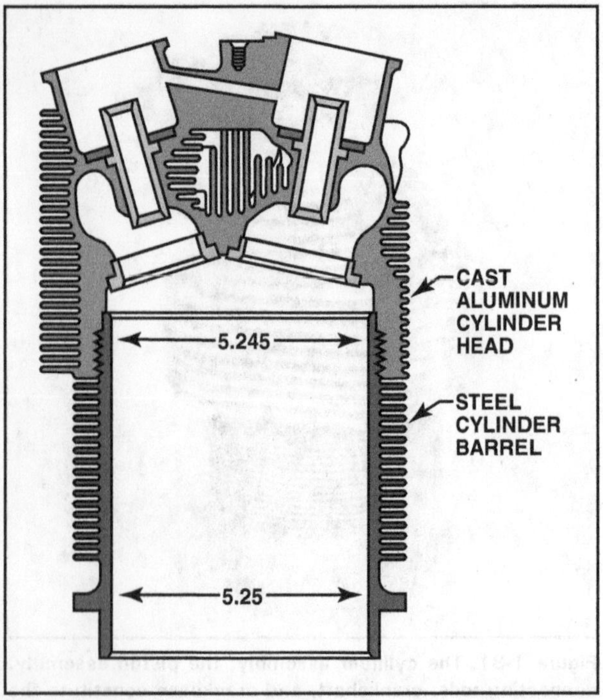


**Figure 1-32. In most reciprocating engines, the greater mass of the cylinder head retains heat and expands, causing the upper portion of the cylinder to expand more than the lower portion. However, with a choke-bored cylinder, the diameter at the top of the cylinder is less than the diameter at the bottom of the cylinder which helps compensate for the uneven expansion.**

cylinder diameter at normal operating temperatures. The amount of choke is usually between .003 and .005 inches. [Figure 1-32]

The inside wall of a cylinder barrel is continuously subjected to the reciprocating motion of the piston rings. Therefore, in an effort to minimize cylinder barrel wear and increase barrel life, most cylinder walls are hardened. The two most common methods used to provide a hard wearing surface are nitriding and chrome plating.

**Nitriding** is a form of case hardening that changes the surface strength of steel by infusing the metal with a hardening agent. During the nitriding process, a cylinder barrel is first ground to the required size and smoothness and then placed in a special furnace filled with ammonia gas. The furnace heats a cylinder barrel to approximately 1,000 degrees Fahrenheit. At this temperature, the ammonia gas breaks down into nitrogen and hydrogen. The steel in the cylinder barrel contains a small percentage of aluminum, which combines with the nitrogen to form a layer of hard, wear-resistant aluminum nitrides. The depth of a nitrided surface depends on the length of time that the cylinder is exposed to the ammonia gas but a typical thickness is approximately 0.020 inch. However, the surface hardness gradually decreases with depth until the hardness is the same as the core metal.

Because nitriding is neither plating nor coating, it changes a cylinder bore by only two to four ten thousandths of an inch. This dimensional change requires a cylinder to be honed to an accurate, micro-smooth finish after the nitriding process is complete. Most manufacturers identify a nitrided cylinder by applying a band of blue paint around the cylinder base, or to certain cooling fins.

A disadvantage of nitrided cylinders is that they do not hold oil for extended periods. This increases a cylinder's susceptibility to corrosion. If an engine with nitrided cylinders is out of service for an extended period, the cylinder walls should be coated with sticky preservative oil.

**Chrome-plating** refers to a method of hardening a cylinder by applying a thin coating of chromium to the inside of the cylinder barrels. Chromium is a hard, natural element with a high melting point, high heat conductivity, and a very low coefficient of friction. The process used to chrome-plate a cylinder is known as **electroplating**.

Chrome-plated cylinders have many advantages over both plain steel and nitrided cylinders. For example, chromed cylinders are less susceptible to rust or corrosion because of chromium's natural corrosion resistance. Therefore, chromed cylinders tend to wear longer. Another benefit of chrome-plating is that after a cylinder wears beyond its usable limits, it can be chrome-plated back to its original size. To identify a cylinder that has been chrome-plated, a band of orange paint is sometimes applied around the cylinder base or to some of the cooling fins.

A problem associated with chrome-plating is that, in its natural state, chromium is so smooth that it does not retain enough oil to lubricate the piston rings. To overcome this, a reverse current is applied to the cylinder after the chromium has been applied. The current causes microscopic surface cracks to open, forming an interconnected network of cracks to retain oil on the cylinder wall. This procedure is often referred to as **chrome channeling**. [Figure 1-33]

Engines with chrome-plated cylinders tend to consume slightly more oil than engines with nitrided or steel cylinders because the plating channels retain more oil than the piston rings can effectively scavenge. Furthermore, chrome-plated cylinders are typ-

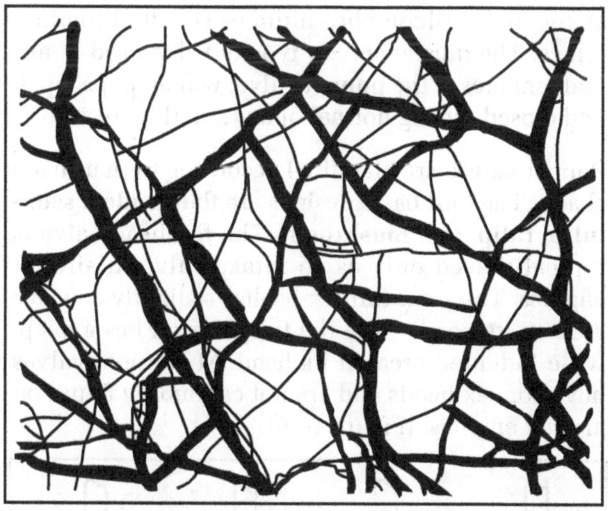

Figure 1-33. Microcracks formed in chrome plating retain oil to aid in cylinder lubrication. This image is an enlarged photomicrograph of the cylinder wall.

ically more difficult to seal, or break in, immediately after an engine is overhauled. This is a result of the oil film on the cylinder wall preventing the necessary wear, or seating, of the piston rings during the break-in period.

In an effort to overcome the disadvantages of chrome-plated and nitrided cylinders, manufacturers have developed some new plating processes. Instead of channeling, one of these processes involves mechanically impregnating silicon carbide particles into a chromed cylinder wall. The silicon carbide provides a somewhat rough finish so it retains lubricating oil, yet is smooth enough to enable effective oil scavenging. Furthermore, the silicon carbide provides a surface finish that is more conducive to piston ring seating during the engine break-in period. This plating process is commonly referred to as either **CermiCrome®** or **Nu-Chrome®** plating. This process has been largely discontinued.

Another plating process, variously called **CermiNil™**, **Nickel+Carbide™**, or **Nikasil®**, uses nickel with silicon carbide particles as the plating material. Although nickel is not as durable as chromium, it provides for an extremely hard finish while the silicon carbide particles increase the hardness of the material and aid in retaining lubricating oil. A unique characteristic of this process is that the silicon carbide particles are infused throughout the plating, not only on the surface. This tends to improve the wear properties of a cylinder while maintaining a smooth surface for effective oil scavenging.

### CYLINDER HEADS

The cylinder head covers the cylinder barrel to form the enclosed chamber for combustion. In addition, cylinder heads contain intake and exhaust valve ports, spark plugs, and valve actuating mechanisms. Cylinder heads also transfer heat away from the cylinder barrels. Air-cooled cylinder heads are generally made of forged or die-cast aluminum alloy because it conducts heat well, is lightweight, and is durable. The inner shape of a cylinder head can be flat, semispherical, or peaked. The semispherical type is most widely used because it is stronger and provides for rapid and thorough scavenging of exhaust gases.

Cooling fins are cast or machined onto the outside of a cylinder head to transfer heat to the surrounding air. However, due to the temperature differences across the cylinder head, it is necessary to provide more cooling-fin area on various sections. For example, because the exhaust valve region is typically the hottest part of the internal surface, that portion of the cylinder head has more fin area. The intake portion of the cylinder head typically has few cooling fins because the fuel/air mixture sufficiently cools this area.

After a cylinder head is cast, spark plug bushings, or inserts, are installed. Typically, each cylinder head has two spark plugs for increased performance and for system redundancy. On older engines, spark plug openings consisting of bronze or steel bushings were shrunk and screwed into the cylinder head. However, most modern engines use stainless steel **Heli-Coil® inserts**. These inserts can be easily replaced if the threads become damaged.

Intake and exhaust ports are machined into each cylinder head to enable the fuel/air mixture to enter the cylinder and the exhaust gases to exit. Gaskets are often used to seal between the cylinder and the intake and exhaust manifolds. A synthetic rubber seal is typically used for attaching the intake manifold. Because of the high temperatures associated with exhaust gases, a metal gasket is typically used for the exhaust manifold. Each manifold is held in place by a nut secured to mounting studs or bolts threaded into the cylinder head. [Figure 1-34]

## VALVES

Engine valves regulate the flow of gases into and out of a cylinder by opening and closing at the appropri-

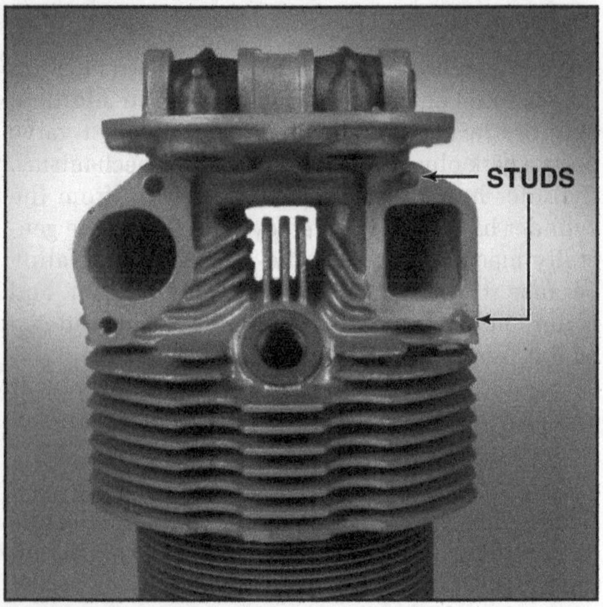


**Figure 1-34. Threaded studs for attaching intake and exhaust manifolds typically remain in the cylinder.**

ate time during the Otto cycle. Each cylinder has at least one **intake valve** and one **exhaust valve**. The intake valve controls the amount of fuel/air mixture that enters through the intake port, and the exhaust valve lets the exhaust gases exit the cylinder through the exhaust port. Some high-powered engines have two intake and two exhaust valves for each cylinder.

The valves used in aircraft engine cylinders are subject to high temperatures, corrosion, and extreme operating stresses. Therefore, valves must be designed and constructed for durability. Intake valves operate at lower temperatures than exhaust valves and are typically made of chrome, nickel, or tungsten steel. Because exhaust valves operate under much higher temperatures, they are usually made of materials with greater heat resistance such as Inconel® silicon-chromium or cobalt-chromium alloys. The most common type of valve used in aircraft engines is the **poppet valve**, which 'pops' open and closed during normal operation. [Figure 1-35]

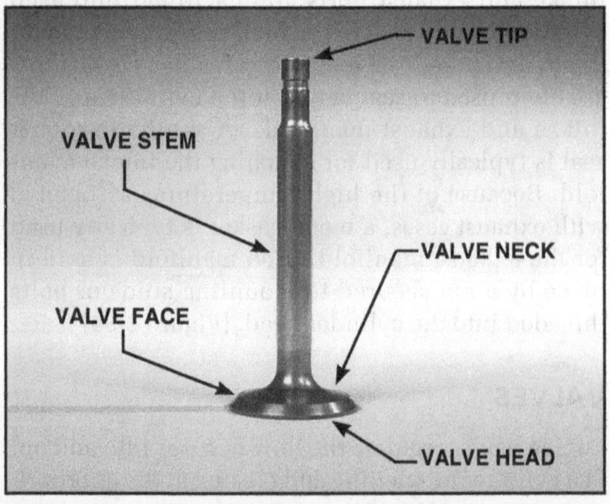


**Figure 1-35. The basic components of a poppet valve include the valve head, valve face, valve neck, valve stem, and valve tip.**

Poppet valves are classified according to their head shape. The four basic designs are **flat-headed, semi-tulip, tulip**, and **mushroom**. The flat-head valve is typically used only as an intake valve in aircraft engines. The semi-tulip valve has a slightly concave area on its head while the tulip design has a deep, wide indented area on its head. Mushroom valves have convex heads and are not commonly found on aircraft engines. [Figure 1-36]

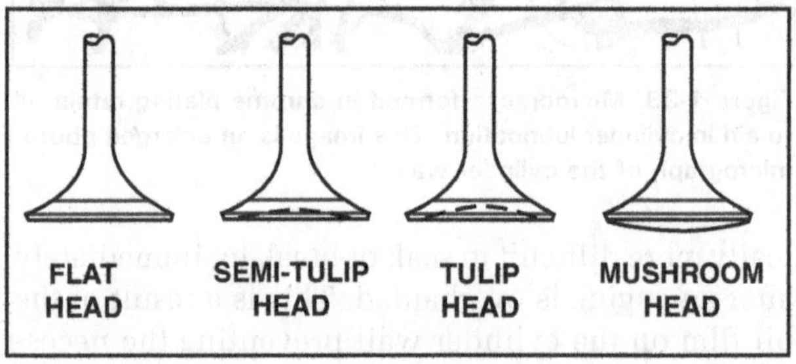


**Figure 1-36. Aircraft engine valves are classified according to their head profile.**

The valve face creates a seal at its respective port. The valve and corresponding seat are typically ground to an angle of between 30 and 60 degrees to form a tight seal. In some engines, the intake valve face is ground to 30 degrees and the exhaust valve is ground to 45 degrees. The engine manufacturer specifies the exact angle to be ground based on airflow, efficiency, and sealing ability. Valve faces are often made more durable by welding **Stellite**®, an alloy of cobalt and chromium, to the valve face. After the Stellite is applied, the face is ground to the correct angle. Stellite resists high temperatures and corrosion and withstands the shock and wear associated with valve operation.

The **valve stem** keeps the valve head properly aligned as it opens and closes. Most valve stems are surface hardened to resist wear. The **tip** of a valve stem is also hardened to withstand both wear and hammering. In some cases, a **rotator cap** is placed over the valve tip to increase service life. A machined groove near the valve stem tip receives a **split key**, or **keeper key**, that keeps the valve-spring retaining washers in place and holds the valve in the cylinder head. [Figure 1-37]

On some radial engines, the valve stems have an additional groove below the split key groove. This second groove is used to hold a safety circlet or spring ring, preventing the valve from falling into the cylinder in the event the valve tip breaks off.

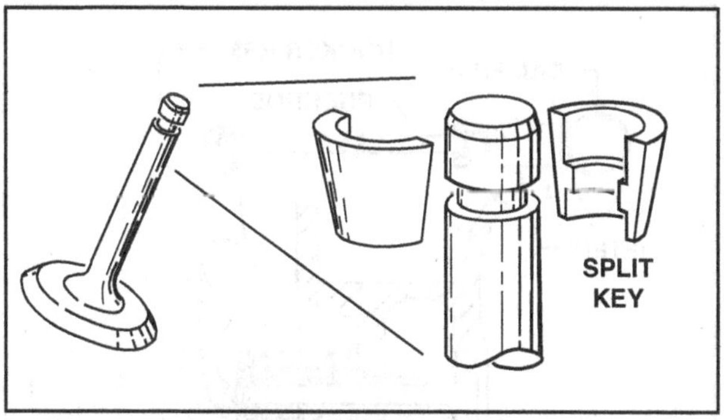


Figure 1-37. The groove near the tip of a valve stem allows a split retainer key to hold spring tension on a valve as well as keep the valve from falling into the cylinder.

To help dissipate heat, some exhaust valve stems are hollowed out and then partially filled with **metallic sodium**. The sodium melts at approximately 208 degrees Fahrenheit. Due to the up and down motion of the valve, the melted sodium circulates and transfers heat from the valve head into the stem where it is dissipated through the cylinder head. In some cases, sodium-filled valves can reduce valve operating temperature by as much as 400 degrees Fahrenheit. [Figure 1-38]

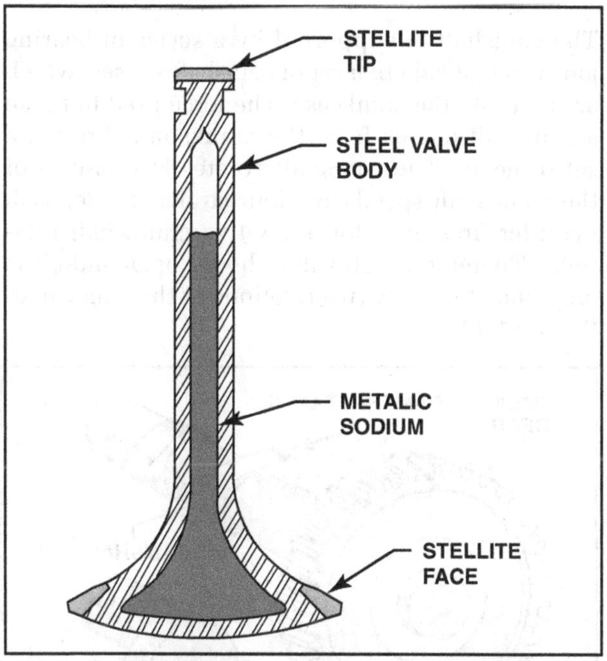


Figure 1-38. Some valves are filled with metallic sodium to reduce their operating temperatures. During operation, the sodium melts and transfers heat to the stem, which conducts it to the cylinder head.

When overhauling an aircraft engine, you must determine whether the old valves are sodium-filled. As a rule, Teledyne Continental engines do not use sodium filled valves, while many Textron-Lycoming engines do. Regardless of the engine, you must follow the manufacturer's recommendations and instructions for handling and installing the valves. Sodium is a dangerous material that burns violently when exposed to air. Because of this, sodium-filled valves should never be cut, broken, or handled in a manner that would expose the sodium to air. In all cases, sodium valves must be disposed of in an appropriate manner.

## VALVE SEATING COMPONENTS

A valve's face must seat firmly against the cylinder head. To accomplish this, several individual components work together, including valve seats, valve guides, valve springs, and valve spring retainers. [Figure 1-39]

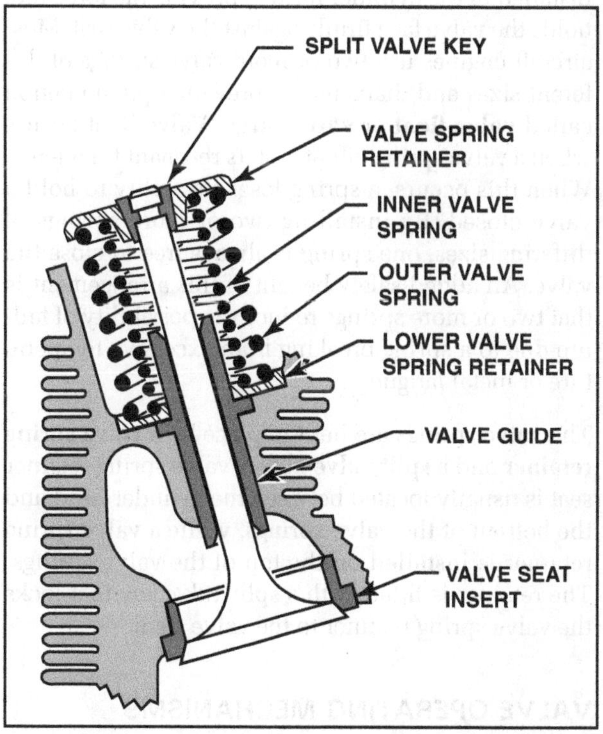


Figure 1-39. The valve seat insert provides a sealing surface for the valve face while the valve guide supports the valve and keeps it aligned with the seat. Valve springs close the valve and are held in place by a valve retainer and a split valve key.

A **valve seat** is a circular ring of hardened metal that provides a uniform sealing surface for the valve face. A typical valve seat is made of either bronze or steel and machined to an oversize fit. To install a valve seat, the cylinder head is heated and the valve seat is chilled and then pressed into the head with a special tool called a mandrel. When the assembly cools, the cylinder head shrinks and firmly retains the valve seat. After it is installed, the valve seat is precisely ground to provide a sealing surface for the valve face. Typically, the valve seat is ground to the same angle as the valve face. However, there are some instances where a valve face may be ground to an angle that is from one-quarter to one full degree shallower than the valve seat. The angular difference produces an interference fit that helps to ensure a more positive seating.

A **valve guide** is a cylindrical sleeve that provides support to the valve stem and keeps the valve face aligned with the valve seat. Valve guides are made from a variety of materials such as steel, tin-bronze, or aluminum-bronze and are installed in the cylinder head with a shrink fit in the same manner as valve seats.

**Valve springs** are helical-coiled springs that are installed in the cylinder head to provide the force that holds the valve face firmly against the valve seat. Most aircraft engines use two or more valve springs of different sizes and diameters to prevent a phenomenon called **valve float** or **valve surge.** Valve float occurs when a valve spring vibrates at its resonant frequency. When this occurs, a spring loses its ability to hold a valve closed. By installing two or more springs of differing sizes, one spring is always free to close the valve. An added safety benefit of this arrangement is that two or more springs reduce the possibility of failure due to a spring breaking from excessive temperature or metal fatigue.

The valve springs are held in place by a **valve spring retainer** and a **split valve key.** A valve spring retainer seat is usually located between the cylinder head and the bottom of the valve springs, while a valve spring retainer is installed on the top of the valve springs. The retainer is fitted with a split valve key that locks the valve spring retainer to the valve stem.

## VALVE OPERATING MECHANISMS

Reciprocating engines require a valve operating mechanism to open each valve at the correct time, hold it open, and then close it. A typical valve operating mechanism includes an internally driven camshaft or cam ring that pushes against a valve lifter. The valve lifter, or tappet, transmits the force from the cam to a push rod, which in turn, actuates a rocker arm to overcome the valve spring tension and open the valve. [Figure 1-40]

### OPPOSED ENGINES

On an opposed engine, valve operation is controlled with a **camshaft.** A typical camshaft consists of a round shaft with a series of **cams,** or **lobes.** These transform the rotational motion of the camshaft to the linear motion needed to actuate a valve. The shape of a cam determines the distance that a valve

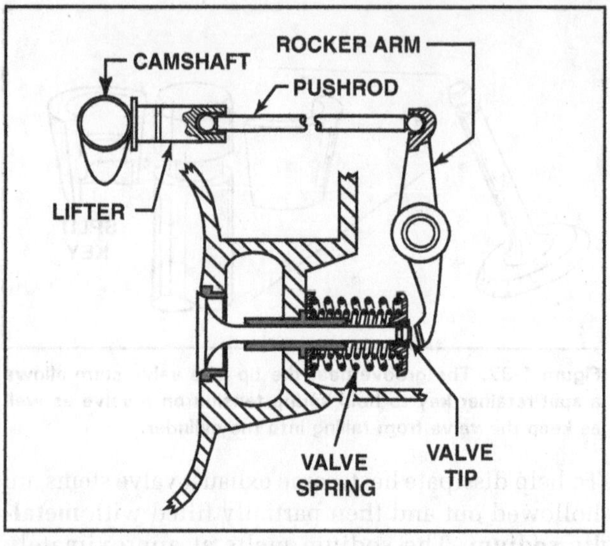


**Figure 1-40. The typical valve operating mechanism includes a camshaft (or cam ring), a tappet (or lifter), a push rod, and a rocker arm.**

is lifted off its seat and the length of time that the valve is open. Because cams are continuously moving across another metal surface, lobes are hardened to resist wear. [Figure 1-41]

The camshaft is supported by a series of bearing journals that ride in a set of camshaft bosses, which are cast into the crankcase. The force used to rotate a camshaft comes from the crankshaft through a set of gears. The camshaft rotates at one-half of the crankshaft speed. In a four-stroke engine, each cylinder fires once for every two crankshaft rotations. Therefore, each valve should open and close only once for every two rotations of the crankshaft. [Figure 1-42]

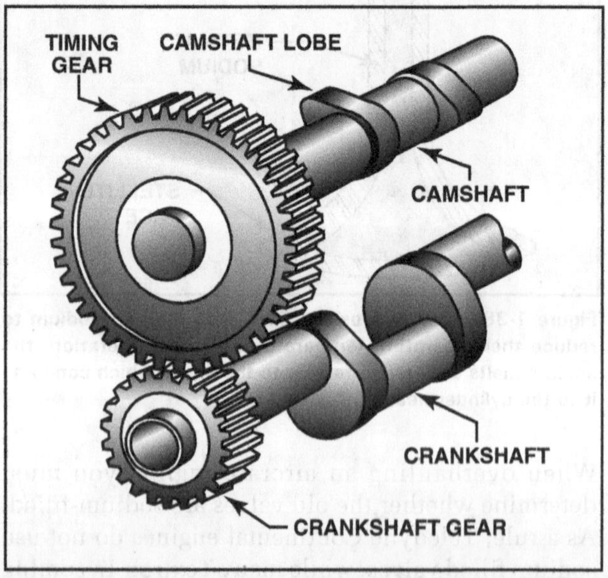


**Figure 1-42. In the typical opposed engine, the camshaft timing gear has twice as many teeth as the crankshaft gear. The camshaft rotates at one-half of the crankshaft's speed.**

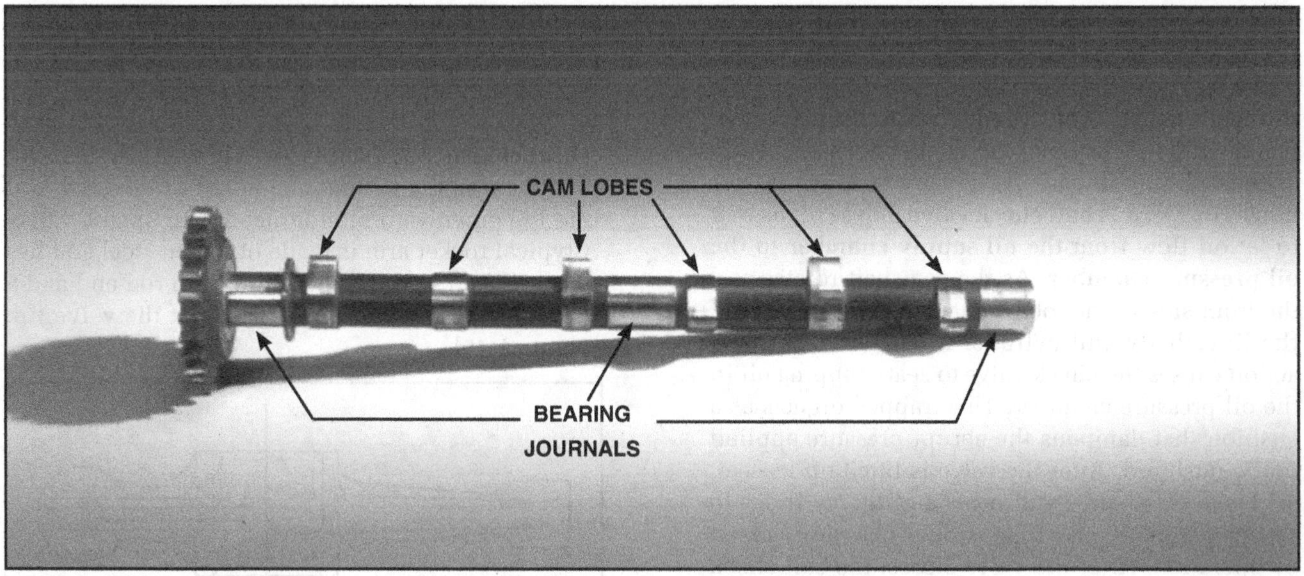


**Figure 1-41. The raised lobe on a camshaft transforms the rotary motion of the camshaft to linear motion.**

As the camshaft rotates, the lobe raises the valve lifter. A **valve lifter**, or **tappet**, transmits the lifting force of the cam to the push rod. Valve lifters in opposed engines can be solid or hydraulic. A **solid lifter** is a solid metal cylinder that directly transfers the lifting force from the camshaft to the push rod. The cam follower face of a solid lifter is flat with a polished surface, while the push rod end contains a spherical cavity that houses the push rod. Holes drilled in the lifter enable oil to flow through the lifter to lubricate the push rod.

Most opposed engines use hydraulic lifters. **Hydraulic lifters** use oil pressure to cushion normal impact and remove play within the valve operating mechanism. A typical hydraulic lifter consists of a cam follower face, a lifter body, a hydraulic plunger and spring, a check valve, and a push rod socket. The entire lifter assembly floats in a machined hole in the crankcase and rests on the camshaft. [Figure 1-43]

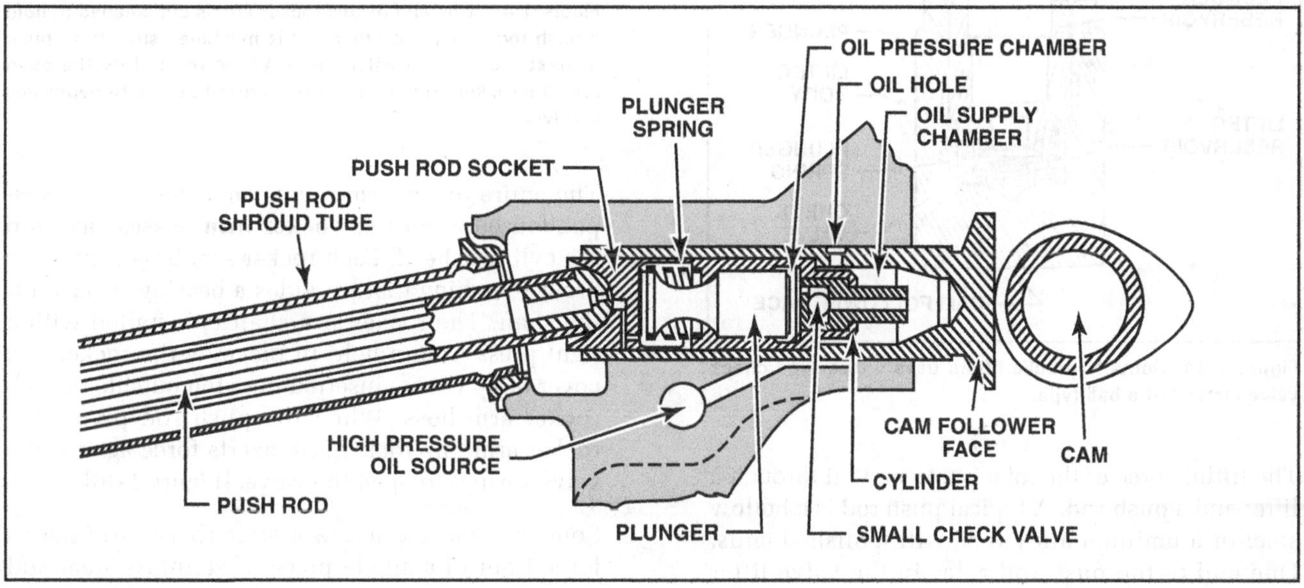


**Figure 1-43. A typical hydraulic lifter consists of a push rod socket, a hydraulic plunger and spring, a check valve, a lifter body, and a cam follower face.**

The **cam follower face** is the smooth, hardened surface of the lifter that contacts the lobe. When the follower face is on the back side of a lobe, the hydraulic **plunger spring** forces the **hydraulic plunger** outward so that the push rod socket presses firmly against the push rod. As the hydraulic plunger moves outward, a **ball check valve** moves off its seat to let oil flow from the **oil supply chamber** to the **oil pressure chamber**. As the camshaft rotates and the front side of the lobe contacts the follower face, the lifter body and cylinder move outward. This action causes the check valve to seat, trapping oil in the oil pressure chamber. This trapped oil acts as a cushion that dampens the abrupt pressure applied to the push rod. After the valve is lifted off its seat, oil leaks between the plunger and the cylinder to compensate for any dimensional changes caused by operation. After the valve closes, the ball check valve is unseated and oil flows from the supply chamber to the pressure chamber in preparation for another cycle. A second type of hydraulic lifter is similar in construction to the lifter just discussed, except that a disk check valve is used instead of a ball check valve. [Figure 1-44]

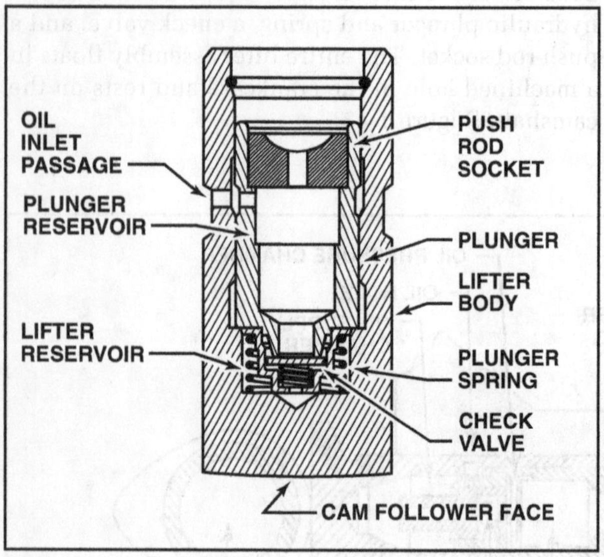


**Figure 1-44. Some hydraulic lifters uses a disk-type check valve instead of a ball-type.**

The lifting force of the lobe is transmitted through a lifter and a **push rod**. A typical push rod is a hollow steel or aluminum-alloy tube with polished ends. One end of the push rod rides in the valve lifter socket while the other end fits into a socket in the rocker arm. Push rods typically have holes drilled in each end to let oil flow from the valve lifter to the valve components in the cylinder head. On most aircraft reciprocating engines, the push rods are enclosed by a thin metal shroud, or tube, that runs from the cylinder head to the crankcase. In many cases, these tubes also provide a return path for the oil that is pumped up to the cylinder head.

A **rocker arm** is a pivoting lever in the cylinder head that changes the lifting movement of the push rod into the downward motion needed to open a valve. A typical rocker arm is made of forged steel and has a cup-shaped socket to hold the push rod end and a polished surface that pushes against the valve tip. [Figure 1-45]

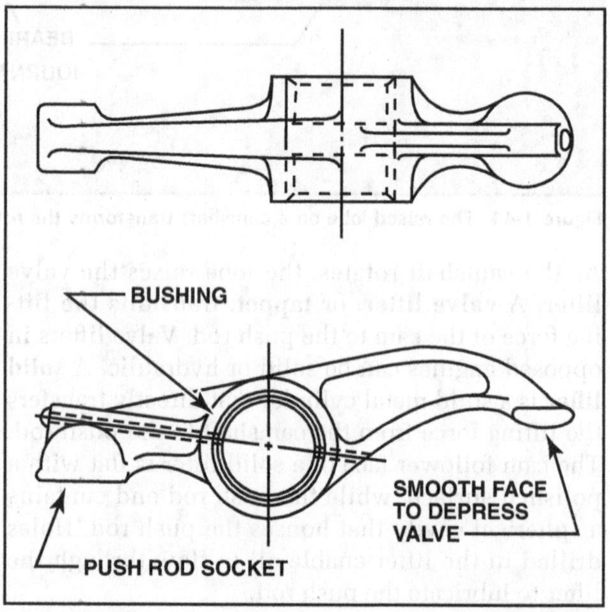


**Figure 1-45. One end of this rocker arm is cup-shaped to hold a push rod, while the other end is machined smooth to push against the tip of a valve stem. When rotated by the push rod, the rocker arm pivots on its center bushing to depresses a valve.**

The entire rocker arm pivots on a shaft that is suspended between two **rocker arm bosses** cast into the cylinder head. Each rocker arm boss contains a bronze bushing that provides a bearing surface for the shaft. The rocker arm shaft is installed with a light press fit and held in place by the rocker-box cover or by covers inserted over the outside of each rocker arm boss. When the push rod pivots the rocker arm, the rocker arm exerts force against the valve springs to open the valve. [Figure 1-46]

Some engines use a newer style rocker arm that is forged out of a single piece of stainless steel and rotates on a pressed-in roller bearing. Additionally, the valve end of the rocker arm is fitted with a roller. This roller helps eliminate side loads when the valve is opened, which helps minimize wear on the valve guide and valve stem.

Figure 1-46. A rocker arm is supported by a shaft suspended between a set of rocker arm bosses.

## RADIAL ENGINES

Radial engines use some of the same components in their valve operating mechanisms as opposed engines, but with some significant differences. For example, in place of a camshaft, a radial engine uses cam rings; the number of rings is the same as the number of cylinder rows. A **cam ring** is a circular piece of steel with a series of raised lobes on its outer edge. A cam ring for a typical seven-cylinder engine has three or four lobes while a cam ring in a nine-cylinder engine has four or five lobes. The lobes in a radial engine differ from those in an opposed engine in that each lobe is constructed with a **cam ramp** on each side of the lobe. This ramp reduces the initial shock of an abruptly rising lobe. The smooth area between the lobes is called the **cam track**. On a single row radial engine a single cam ring with two cam tracks is used. One track operates the intake valve while the second track operates the exhaust valve.

In a single-row radial engine, the cam ring is usually located between the propeller reduction gearing and the front end of the power section. In a twin-row radial engine, a second cam for the valves in the rear row is installed between the rear end of the power section and the supercharger section.

The cam ring is mounted concentrically with the crankshaft and is driven by the crankshaft through a series of gears. However, unlike a traditional camshaft which rotates at half the speed of a crankshaft, the rotational speed of a cam ring varies due to size and gearing. To determine the rotation speed of a given cam ring, you must know the number of lobes on the cam ring, the cam ring's direction of rotation relative to the crankshaft, and the number of cylinders on the engine. The direction of cam ring rotation varies on different engines and depends on whether the cam ring has internal or external drive teeth. Externally driven cam rings turn in the same direction as the crankshaft, while internally driven rings turn opposite from crankshaft rotation. [Figure 1-47]

If a table is not available, determine cam ring speed by using the formula:

$$\text{Cam Ring Speed} = \frac{1}{\text{Number of Lobes} \times 2}$$

| 5 Cylinders | | 7 Cylinders | | 9 Cylinders | | Direction of Rotation |
|---|---|---|---|---|---|---|
| Number of Lobes | Speed | Number of Lobes | Speed | Number of Lobes | Speed | |
| 3 | 1/6 | 4 | 1/8 | 5 | 1/10 | With Crankshaft |
| 2 | 1/4 | 3 | 1/6 | 4 | 1/8 | Opposite Crankshaft |

Figure 1-47. This chart identifies cam ring speed for various radial engine configurations.

In place of a cam follower face, a radial engine uses cam rollers. A **cam roller** consists of a small wheel that rolls along the cam track. When the cam roller rides over a lobe on the cam ring, the roller pushes against a **tappet** that is enclosed in a **tappet guide**. The tappet, in turn, actuates a push rod that performs the same function as an opposed engine push rod. Radial engine rocker arms have adjusting screws and lock screws that enable you to adjust the push rod-to-rocker arm clearance. In addition, many radial engine rocker arms are equipped with rollers on their valve ends to reduce friction, eliminate side loading on the valve stem, and reduce tip deformation. [Figure 1-48]

## VALVE CLEARANCE ADJUSTMENT

**Valve clearance** describes the space between the tip of the valve stem and the rocker arm face. For an engine to run properly, the correct valve clearance must be maintained. During normal engine operating temperatures, the cylinder assemblies expand and force the cylinder head, along with its valve operating components, further away from the crankcase. However, due to their relatively small mass, the push rods expand less. As a result, the clearance between the rocker arm and valve stem increases. If this valve clearance is not controlled, the engine will run poorly, and valve damage might result.

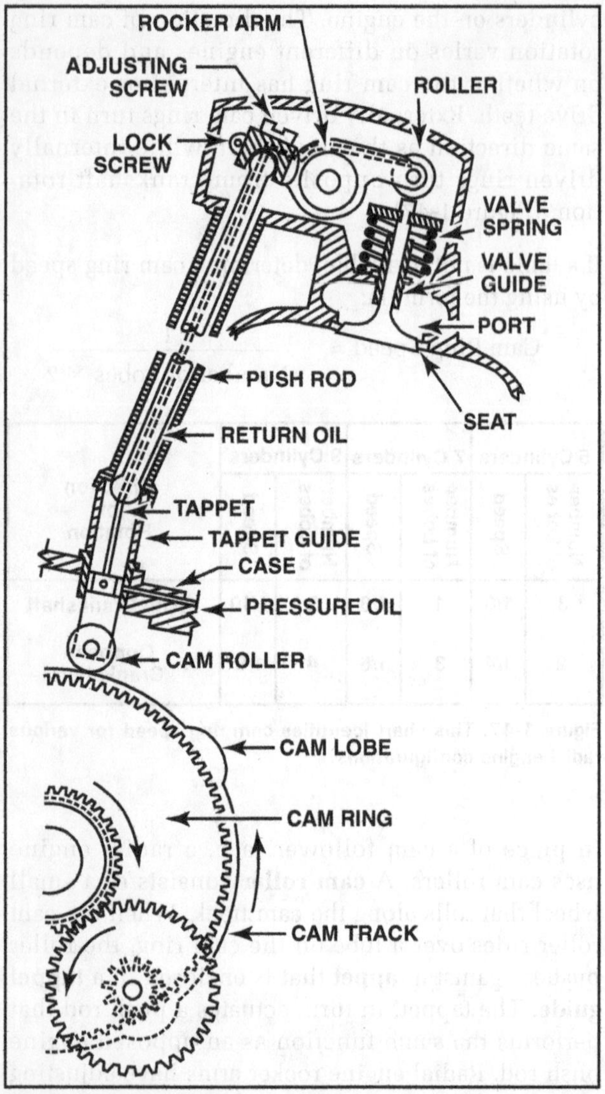


**Figure 1-48. The valve operating mechanism for a radial engine performs the same functions as one on an opposed engine.**

An engine manufacturer's maintenance manual specifies either a cold or hot valve clearance. As its name implies, a **cold clearance** is set when the engine is cold. Due to the expansion properties discussed earlier, this clearance is typically less than the **hot** or **running clearance**, which is set when the engine is hot. Engines that require valve adjustments have adjustment screws and locknuts mounted in their rocker arms at the push rod fitting.

Engines that use hydraulic lifters do not require valve adjustments because they automatically maintain a zero running valve clearance during normal operation. For this reason, hydraulic lifters are often called **zero clearance**, or **zero lash** lifters. However, hydraulic lifters must operate within a specific clearance range when the hydraulic lifter is not filled with oil, or "dry." During cylinder replacement, you must check that the dry-lifter clearance is within specified limits.

To perform a **dry-lifter clearance check**, the lifter body must first have all residual oil removed. The procedure to "bleed down" the lifter varies between engine manufacturers, but usually consists of depressing the check valve to drain all trapped oil. After the oil is drained, check the valve operating mechanism for the proper rocker arm face-to-valve tip clearance using the same procedure employed on engines with solid lifters.

Some large radial engines incorporate a **floating cam ring** that requires a special procedure when adjusting valve clearance. To obtain the correct adjustment, the cam ring must be seated to eliminate cam bearing clearance. This usually involves depressing two valves to seat the cam ring, which then enables you to accurately measure a third valve. This procedure is repeated for each cylinder.

## CYLINDER NUMBERING

You will often need to refer to a specific area on an engine or to a specific cylinder. Therefore, you should be familiar with the manufacturer's particular system of cylinder numbering. Regardless of how an engine is mounted in an aircraft, the propeller shaft end is always referred to as the front of an engine, and the accessory end is always the rear of an engine. Furthermore, when referring to either the right or left side of an engine, always assume you are viewing the engine from the rear, or accessory, end. Similarly, crankshaft rotation is always referenced from the rear of an engine and is specified as either clockwise or counterclockwise.

To identify a specific cylinder, all engine cylinders are numbered. However, opposed engines do not use a standard numbering system. Teledyne Continental Motors and Textron-Lycoming both manufacture four- and six-cylinder horizontally opposed engines, but each company uses a different numbering system. For example, Continental begins its cylinder numbering with the rearward cylinder while Lycoming begins with the forward cylinder. Both companies place the odd numbered cylinders on the right and the even numbered cylinders on the left. [Figure 1-49]

In general, single-row radial engine cylinders are numbered consecutively in a clockwise pattern starting with the top cylinder. The difference with double-row radial engines is that all of the rear cylinders are odd-numbered and front cylinders are

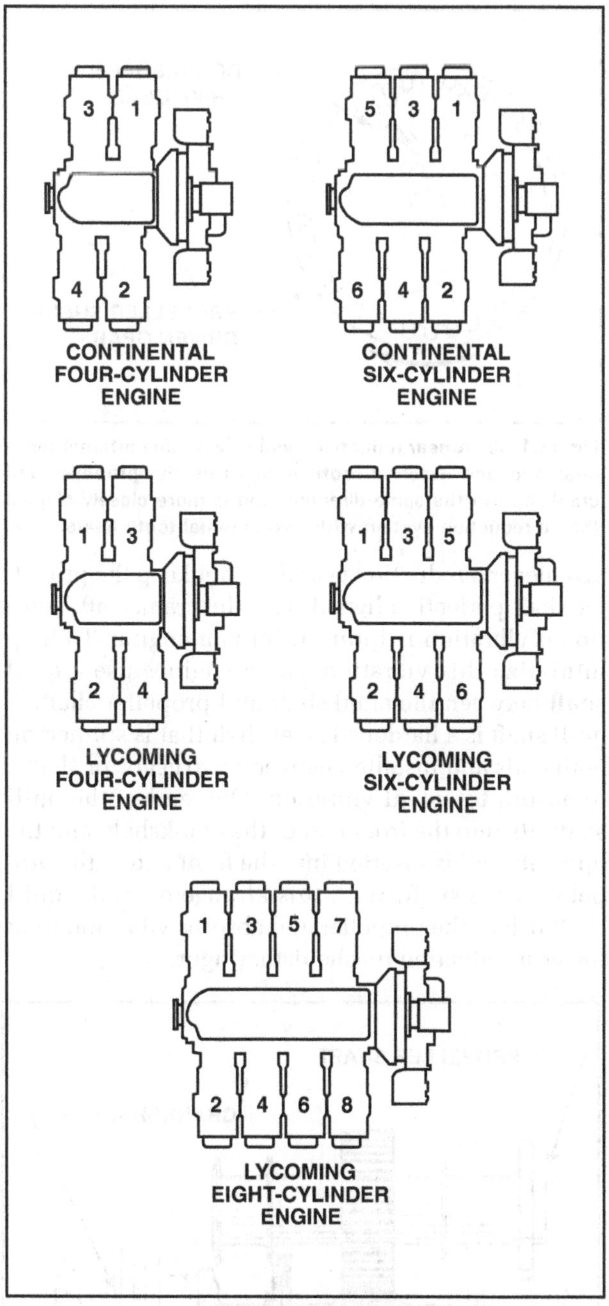


**Figure 1-49. Cylinder numbering varies by manufacturer; always refer to the appropriate service information to determine how the cylinders of a specific engine are numbered.**

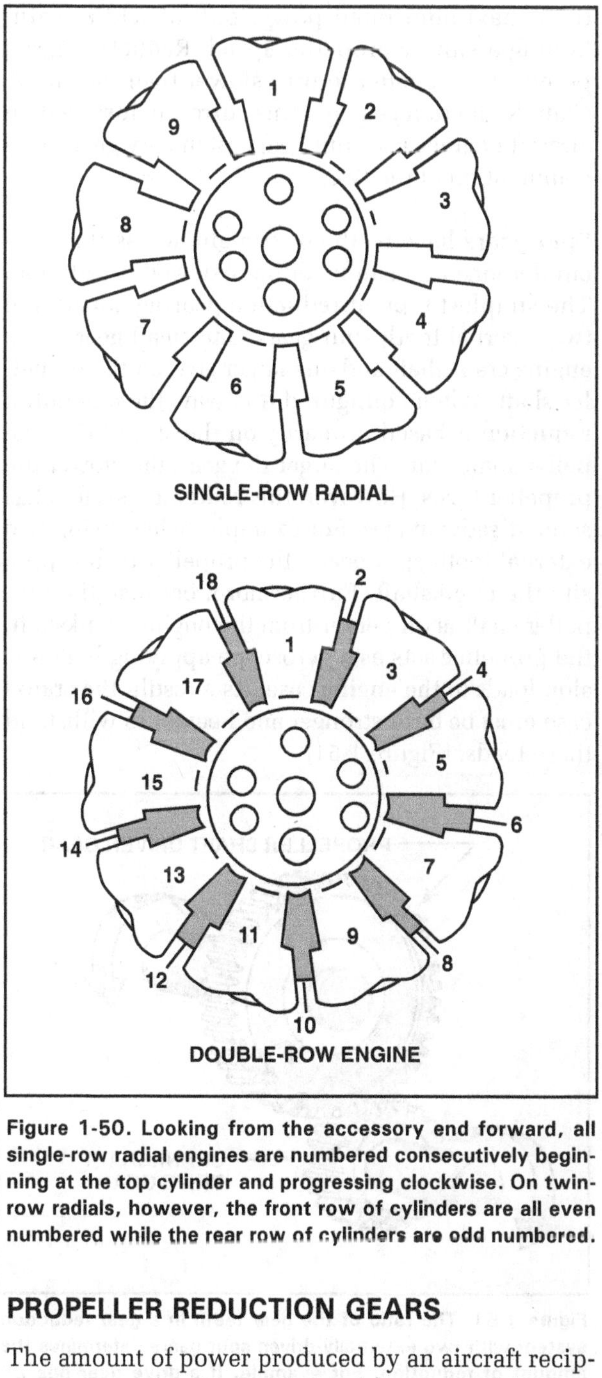


**Figure 1-50. Looking from the accessory end forward, all single-row radial engines are numbered consecutively beginning at the top cylinder and progressing clockwise. On twin-row radials, however, the front row of cylinders are all even numbered while the rear row of cylinders are odd numbered.**

even-numbered. For example, the top cylinder of the rear row is the number one cylinder, while the number two cylinder is the first cylinder in the front row clockwise from the number one cylinder. The number three cylinder is the next cylinder clockwise from the number two cylinder but is in the rear row. Some radial engines designed in eastern European countries reverse this pattern. [Figure 1-50]

## PROPELLER REDUCTION GEARS

The amount of power produced by an aircraft reciprocating engine is determined by several factors, including the amount of pressure exerted on the pistons during each power stroke and the number of power strokes completed in a given time period. As a rule, the faster an engine turns the more power it produces. However, this rule does not apply to propellers. As a propeller blade tip approaches the speed of sound, it cannot efficiently convert the engine's power into thrust. In other words, a propeller needs to be operated at a specific speed to achieve maximum efficiency. Some high-powered engines use a propeller reduction gear system to produce their maximum rated power output while maintaining a slower propeller speed. Reduction gears permit the propeller to turn slower than the crankshaft. Reduction gear systems currently installed on aircraft engines use spur gears, planetary gears, or a combination of the two.

**Spur gears** have teeth cut straight across their circumference and can be either external or internal. The simplest type of reduction gearing consists of two external tooth spur gears, one small gear on an engine crankshaft and one larger gear on the propeller shaft. When configured this way, the amount of reduction is based primarily on the size of the propeller shaft gear. The larger the gear, the slower the propeller turns. However, this reduction system has some disadvantages. For example, when using two external tooth spur gears, the propeller turns opposite the crankshaft. Furthermore, because the propeller shaft is off-center from the engine crankshaft, the propeller acts as a gyroscope applying high torsion loads to the engine case. As a result, the crankcase must be built stronger and heavier to withstand these loads. [Figure 1-51]

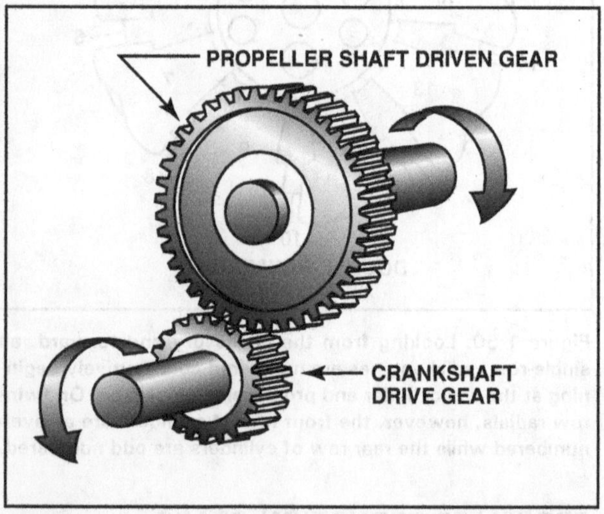


**Figure 1-51. The ratio of the gear teeth in a gear reduction system with two externally-driven spur gears determines the amount of reduction. For example, if a drive gear has 25 teeth and the driven gear has 50 teeth, a ratio of 1:2 exists and the propeller turns at one half the crankshaft speed.**

One way to overcome some of the disadvantages of a simple spur gear arrangement is to use an internal-tooth spur gear on the propeller shaft and an external-tooth spur gear on the crankshaft. In addition to allowing the propeller to turn in the same direction as the engine, this arrangement aligns the propeller shaft more closely with the crankshaft, which eliminates much of the stress placed on the crankcase. [Figure 1-52]

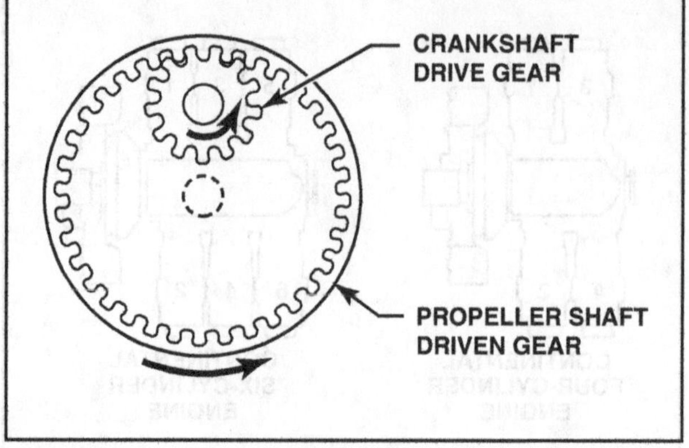


**Figure 1-52. A gear reduction system with one internal-tooth gear and one external-tooth gear turns the propeller and crankshaft in the same direction and is more closely aligned than a reduction system with two external-tooth gears.**

Whenever a reduction gear does not keep the propeller shaft perfectly aligned with the crankshaft, additional vibration is induced into an engine. To help minimize this vibration, some engines use a **quill shaft** between the crankshaft and propeller shaft. A quill shaft is a hardened steel shaft that is splined on both ends and installed between two gears, or shafts, to absorb torsional vibration. One end of the quill shaft fits into the front end of the crankshaft, and the opposite end is inserted into the front end of the propeller drive shaft. With this arrangement, the quill shaft drives the propeller and absorbs vibration from the gear reduction mechanism. [Figure 1-53]

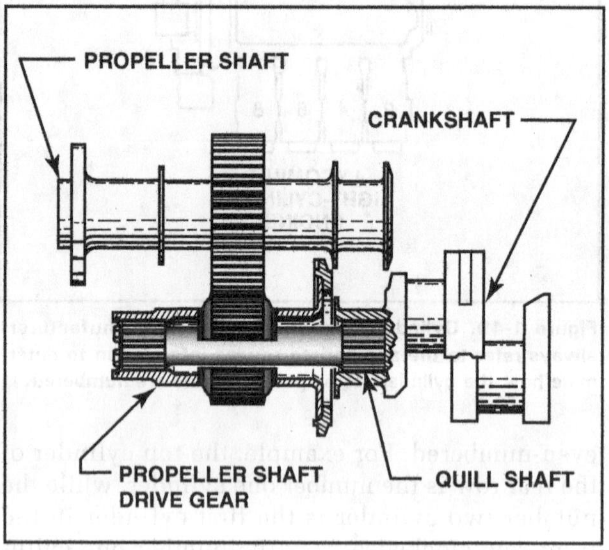


**Figure 1-53. A quill shaft minimizes torsional vibration between a propeller shaft and the crankshaft.**

In a **planetary reduction gear system** the propeller shaft is attached to a housing that contains several small gears called **planetary gears**. The planetary gears rotate between a **sun gear** and a **ring gear** (sometimes called a **bell gear**). The crankshaft drives either the sun gear or the ring gear depending on the individual installation. The planetary gear reduction system keeps the propeller shaft aligned with the crankshaft, transmits power with a minimum of weight and space, and keeps the propeller's direction of rotation the same as the engine. Planetary gears are used on some horizontally opposed engines as well as radial and turboprop engines. [Figure 1-54]

You can determine the reduction rate that a particular gearing arrangement achieves by this formula:

$$\text{Gear Ratio} = \frac{\text{Teeth On Ring Gear} + \text{Teeth On Sun Gear}}{\text{Teeth On Ring Gear}}$$

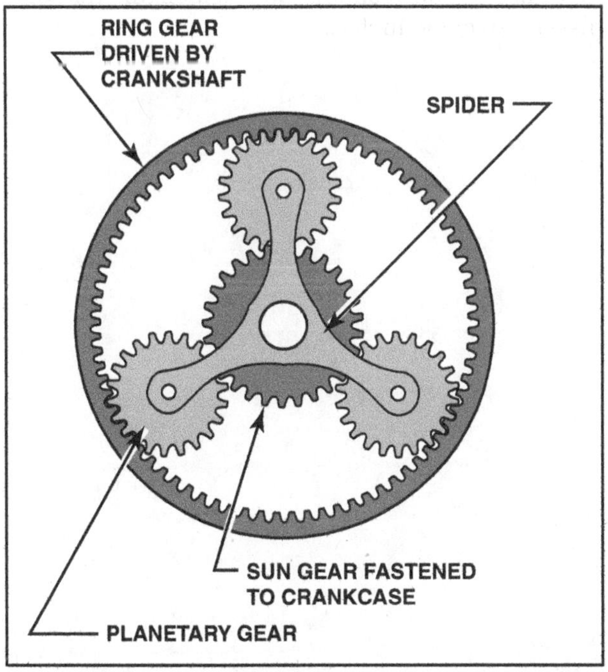


**Figure 1-54. In a planetary gear reduction system, the propeller is attached to the planetary gear spider and the crankshaft turns either the sun gear or the ring gear.**

For example, if there are 72 teeth on the ring gear and 36 teeth on the sun gear, the propeller turns at a ratio of 1.5 to 1. However, reduction ratios are traditionally expressed in whole numbers, so this example is expressed as a 3 to 2 reduction. In other words, the crankshaft must turn three revolutions for every two revolutions of the propeller shaft. Neither the number of teeth on the planetary gears nor the number of planetary gears contributes to the computation for gear reduction.

## PROPELLER SHAFTS

All aircraft reciprocating engines have a propeller shaft. As an aviation technician, you must be familiar with the various types of propeller shafts, including tapered, splined, and flanged shafts.

**Tapered propeller shafts** were used on most of the early, low-powered engines. On a tapered propeller shaft, the shaft diameter tapers toward the end of the shaft. To prevent a propeller hub from rotating on a tapered shaft, one or more key slots are milled into the shaft. In addition, the end of the shaft is threaded to receive a propeller retaining nut. [Figure 1-55]

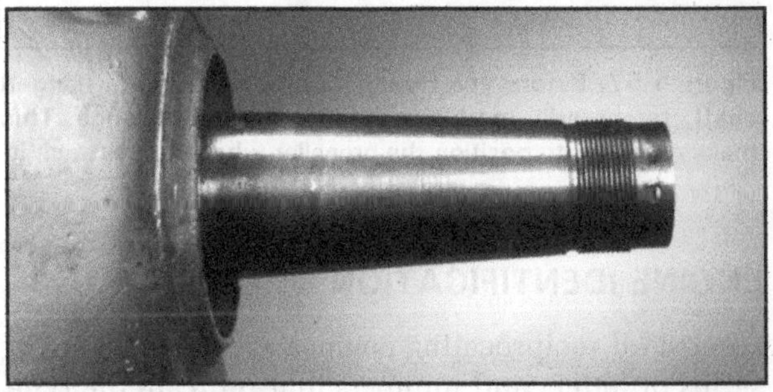

**Figure 1-55. A tapered propeller shaft changes in diameter along its length and uses a metal key to keep a propeller from rotating.**

High-powered engines require a stronger method of attaching propellers. Most high powered radial engines use **splined propeller shafts**. A spline is a rectangular groove that is machined into the propeller shaft. Most splined shafts have a master spline that is approximately twice the size of any other spline. This master spline assures that a propeller is attached to a propeller shaft a specific way so that vibration is kept to a minimum. [Figure 1-56]

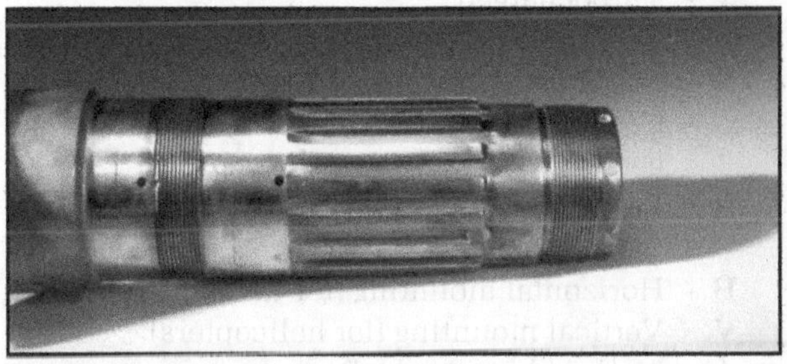

**Figure 1-56. All splined propeller shafts are identified by an SAE number. For example, SAE 50 identifies a splined shaft that meets SAE design specifications for a 50 size shaft. The SAE number does not refer to the number of splines.**

Modern horizontally opposed aircraft engines use a **flanged propeller shaft**. The crankshaft is forged with a flat flange on its end. A propeller is bolted directly to the flange. To provide additional support for the propeller, most flanged propeller shafts incorporate a short shaft forward of the flange and a series of studs around the flange circumference. [Figure 1-57]

**Figure 1-57. Before you remove a propeller from a flanged shaft, temporarily mark the propeller hub and flange. This makes it easier to position the propeller when you reattach it.**

## ENGINE IDENTIFICATION

Almost all reciprocating engines are identified by a series of letters and numbers that indicate the type and size of the engine. For simplicity, most manufacturers use the same identification system. In most cases, an engine identification code consists of a letter or series of letters followed by a number and model designation. The first letters indicate an engine's cylinder arrangement and basic configuration. The following list indicates several of the letters used as well as their meanings:

- O - Horizontally opposed engine
- R - Radial engine
- I - In-line engine
- V - V-type engine
- T - Turbocharged
- I - Fuel injected
- S - Supercharged
- G - Geared nose section (propeller reduction gearing)
- L - Left-hand rotation (for multi-engine installations)
- H - Horizontal mounting (for helicopters)
- V - Vertical mounting (for helicopters)
- A - Modified for aerobatics

The numbers in an engine identification code indicate an engine's piston displacement in cubic inches. For example, an O-320 indicates a horizontally opposed engine with a displacement of 320 cubic inches. Some engine identification codes include a letter designation after the displacement to indicate a model change or modification to a basic engine. Check with the manufacturer's specification sheets to interpret these letters correctly because their meaning differs among manufacturers.

Consider an engine with the following identification code: LIO-360-C. This code designates an engine that has left hand rotation, is fuel-injected and horizontally opposed, displaces 360 cubic inches, and is a C model. Similarly, a GTSIO-520-F engine is an F-model version of a geared, turbo-supercharged, fuel-injected, horizontally opposed engine that displaces 520 cubic inches.

# SUMMARY CHECKLIST

- ✓ Reciprocating engines operate according to the Otto cycle.
- ✓ The most common type of reciprocating engine used for light aircraft has opposed cylinders.
- ✓ The major parts of a reciprocating engine are the crankcase, cylinders, pistons, connecting rods, valves, valve-operating mechanism, and crankshaft.
- ✓ The major sections of a radial engine are nose, power, supercharger, and accessory.
- ✓ The surface finish of cylinder walls is critical for a proper seal between the engine crankcase and cylinder combustion chamber.
- ✓ A valve face and seat are machined for a tight seal.
- ✓ A camshaft controls valve operation in an opposed engine.

# KEY TERMS

rotary-type radial engines
static-type radial engines
single-row radial engines
multiple-row radial engines
double-row radial engines
V-type engines
cylinder pad
nose section
power section
supercharger section
accessory section
main bearing journals
crankpins
throws
crank throws
connecting-rod bearing journals
sludge
counterweight
static balance
dynamic balance
dynamic damper
single-throw crankshaft
two-throw crankshaft
four-throw crankshaft
six-throw crankshaft
bushings
bearing retainer
bearing races
straight roller bearings
tapered roller bearings
crankpin end
piston end
master rod
articulated rods
piston pin bearing
crankpin bearing

master rod bearing
one-piece rod
multiple-piece master rod
split-type master rod
knuckle pin
full-floating knuckle pins
fork connecting rod
blade connecting rod
ring grooves
ring land
piston head
piston pin boss
piston skirt
cam-ground piston
blow-by
seated
compression rings
oil rings
oil control rings
ventilated oil control rings
oil scraper ring
oil wiper ring
wrist pins
stationary piston pins
semifloating piston pins
full-floating piston pins
circlet
spring ring
piston-pin plug
skirt
mounting flange
cooling fins
cylinder bore
choke bore cylinder
nitriding
chrome-plating
electroplating
chrome channeling
CermiCrome
Nu-Chrome
CermiNil
Nickel+Carbide
Nikasil
Heli-Coil inserts
intake valve
exhaust valve
poppet valve
flat-headed head
semi-tulip head
tulip head
mushroom head
Stellite
valve stem
valve tip
rotator cap
split key
keeper key
metallic sodium
valve seat
valve guide
valve springs
valve float
valve surge
valve spring retainer
split valve key
camshaft
cams
lobes
valve lifter
tappet
solid lifter
hydraulic lifters
cam follower face
plunger spring
hydraulic plunger
ball check valve
oil supply chamber
oil pressure chamber
push rod
rocker arm
rocker arm bosses
cam ring
cam ramp
cam track
cam roller
tappet
tappet guide
valve clearance
cold clearance
hot clearance
running clearance
zero clearance
zero lash lifters
dry-lifter clearance check
floating cam ring
spur gears
quill shaft
planetary reduction gear system
planetary gears
sun gear
ring gear
bell gear
tapered propeller shafts
splined propeller shafts
flanged propeller shaft

# QUESTIONS

1 Radial engines have appeared in two forms: the _______-radial and the _______-radial.

2 The _______ _______-type engine has two banks of cylinders directly opposite each other with a crankshaft in the middle.

3. Horizontally opposed engine crankcases are usually cast from ____________ alloy.

4. Many crankcase halves are sealed using a thin coat of non-hardening gasket compound and a _______ _______.

5. The three main parts of a crankshaft are the

   a. ____________________.

   b. ____________________.

   c. ____________________.

6. The outer surface of the crankpins and journals are hardened by ______________.

7. A crankshaft is checked for _______ (static or dynamic) balance by placing it on knife edges and observing any tendency to rotate.

8. To reduce vibration to a minimum during engine operation _____________ _____________ are incorporated on the crankshaft.

9. What are the three types of bearings in general use?

   a. ____________________.

   b. ____________________.

   c. ____________________.

10. The crankshaft usually rotates in _______ bearings.

11. The ______________ _______ is the link which transmits forces between the piston and the crankshaft.

12. The connecting rod attaches to the _______ _______ of the crankshaft.

13. What are the three types of connecting rod assemblies?

   a. ____________________.

   b. ____________________.

   c. ____________________.

14. The ______________-type connecting rod is used on horizontally opposed engines.

15. The ______________ _______ ______________ rod assembly is used in radial engines.

16. The ______________ pins connect the articulating rods to the master rod.

17. Most aircraft pistons are machined from ________________ alloy forgings.

18. Most piston rings are made of high-grade ____________ ____________.

19. The top rings installed on an aircraft piston are called the ______________ rings.

20. The piston ring below the compression rings is called the _______ ____________ ring.

21. The piston ring at the bottom of the piston skirt is called the _______ ____________ ring.

22. The piston pins used in modern aircraft engines are the __________-____________ type.

23. Another name for a piston pin is a ____________ pin.

24. Oil control rings regulate the ____________ of the oil film on the cylinder wall.

25. The cylinder assembly is composed of two major parts:

a. ________________________.

b. ________________________.

26. A ______ bore cylinder is one where the bore is ground so that the diameter at the top portion of the barrel is slightly smaller than the diameter of the main part of the barrel.

27. The two methods commonly used to harden cylinder walls include:

a. ________________________.

b. ________________________.

28. Cylinders which have been chrome plated are identified by ______________ (what color) paint.

29. Cylinders which have been nitrided are identified by ______________ (what color) paint.

30. __________ (Nitrided or Chrome plated) cylinders are very susceptible to rust and must be kept covered with a preservative oil.

31. Cylinder heads of air-cooled engines are generally made of ______________ alloy.

32. Heat is transferred away from the cylinder head through ____________ cast into the head.

33. There is a greater depth and area of cooling fins on the ______________ (exhaust or intake) side of an air-cooled cylinder head.

34. The propeller shaft end of an aircraft engine is always the ______ (front or rear) end, regardless of how it is mounted in the aircraft.

35. When referring to the right or left side of the engine, always assume you are viewing it from the ______ (front or rear).

36. The heads of poppet valves come in four shapes including:

    a. ______________________________.

    b. ______________________________.

    c. ______________________________.

    d. ______________________________.

37. Hollow exhaust valves may be partially filled with ______________ (what material) to aid in their cooling.

38. Valve _______ is the distance that valve is lifted off its seat.

39. Valve ____________ is the length of time that valve is open.

40. The valve mechanism of a horizontally opposed engine is operated by a cam _______.

41. The camshaft on a horizontally opposed engine rotates at _______ the crankshaft speed.

42. The two types of valve lifters used in aircraft engines include:

    a. ______________________________.

    b. ______________________________.

43. The _______ _______ transmit the movement of the cam follower to the rocker arm.

44. One end of the _______ _______ bears against the push rod and the other against the valve stem.

45. The valve mechanism of a radial engine is operated by one or more cam ______________.

46. A four-lobe cam ring on a nine-cylinder radial engine will turn at ____________ the crankshaft speed.

47. Hydraulic valve lifters are also known as ____________ ____________ lifters.

48. The running valve clearance of hydraulic valve lifters is ______________.

49. The direction of rotation between a propeller shaft and the crankshaft in an engine using a planetary gear reduction system is ________________ (the same or opposite).

50. An aircraft engine having a planetary gear system using an 80 tooth bell gear driven by the crankshaft and a fixed 62 tooth sun gear will have a gear reduction of _______:1. This is the same as 16:_______.

51. Three types of attachments for a propeller to an aircraft engine crankshaft are:

    a. ______________________________.

    b. ______________________________.

    c. ______________________________.

52. ______________-type propeller shafts are used on most modern horizontally opposed aircraft engines.

53. Indicate what is meant by each letter or number in the following engine designations.

a. R-985

1. R = ____________________________.

2. 985 = __________________________.

b. O300-D

1. O = ____________________________.

2. 300 = __________________________.

3. D = ____________________________.

c. LTIO-540

1. L = ____________________________.

2. T = ____________________________.

3. I = ____________________________.

4. O = ____________________________.

5. 540 = __________________________.

# SECTION B

## OPERATING PRINCIPLES

### ENERGY TRANSFORMATION

Aircraft engines are **heat engines**—that is, they convert the chemical energy of fuel into heat energy. The heat energy increases gas pressure within a cylinder. The expanding gases force the piston downward, at which point the heat energy is transformed into mechanical energy to rotate the crankshaft. Because the fuel is burned inside the engine, an aircraft engine is referred to as an **internal combustion** engine. When fuel is burned outside an engine to produce mechanical energy, the process is called **external combustion**.

A steam engine is an example of an external combustion engine. Burning fuel heats a boiler to produce steam, which is then channeled through the engine. Depending on the type of engine, the steam either forces pistons to turn a crankshaft or spins a turbine. External combustion engines are relatively inefficient at converting heat into work; however, the relatively low cost of fuel to operate external combustion engines makes them viable for ground-based applications like electrical powerplants.

Internal combustion engines require specific types of fuel. Most engines burn liquefied petroleum gases such as butane or propane, while others use liquid kerosene, gasoline, or alcohol. Most aircraft reciprocating engines require leaded gasoline. In addition to providing chemical energy, liquid fuels also lubricate the upper cylinder components and, when the fuel grade is properly matched to the engine, provide resistance to detonation. For a fuel to be used in a type-certified aircraft, it must be approved by the engine manufacturer and the Federal Aviation Administration.

The process of converting the chemical energy of fuel into mechanical energy is similar in all internal combustion engines. Fuel is measured then vaporized and mixed with an appropriate amount of air to create a combustible mixture. The fuel/air mixture is compressed and ignited within a cylinder. As the mixture burns, it releases energy, causing the noncombustible gases, like nitrogen, to expand. Because nitrogen comprises approximately 78 percent of air, the potential for expansion is substantial. The expanding gas exerts pressure on a piston, driving it downward to rotate the crankshaft, changing the mechanical energy from linear to rotary motion. This cycle can be understood as a series of five events, which occur in this order:

**Intake**—the intake valve opens as the piston travels downward drawing fuel and air into a cylinder. The exhaust valve is closed.

**Compression**—the intake valve closes and the fuel/air mixture is compressed as the piston travels upward.

**Ignition**—the compressed fuel-air mixture is ignited by a spark.

**Power**—burning gases expand, forcing the piston downward, which causes the crankshaft to rotate.

**Exhaust**—the exhaust valve opens and the burned gases are forced out of the cylinder as the piston travels upward. As the piston reaches the top of the cylinder, the exhaust valve closes and the sequence repeats.

### ENERGY TRANSFORMATION CYCLES

One **cycle** represents a complete series of events required to produce mechanical energy. The engine operating cycle repeats continually.

The two operating cycles in general use today are the **four-stroke**, or **Otto cycle** (named after August Otto, who developed it) and the **two-stroke**. The majority of piston engines for aircraft operate on the more efficient four-stroke cycle; however, a few small powerplants use the two-stroke cycle. One stroke is accomplished in 180 degrees of crankshaft rotation where the piston travels between its limits in the cylinder. A **stroke** is the distance the piston travels from its outward limit, referred to as **top dead center (TDC)**, to its inward limit, known as **bottom dead center (BDC)**. [Figure 1-58]

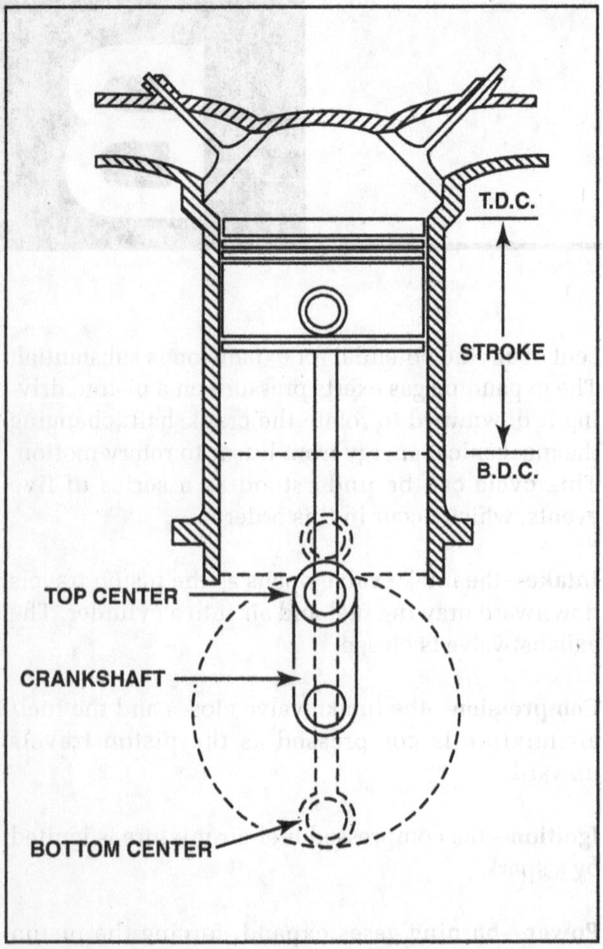


**Figure 1-58. One stroke is equivalent to the distance a piston head travels between bottom dead center and top dead center. In all reciprocating engines, one complete stroke occurs with each 180 degrees of crankshaft rotation.**

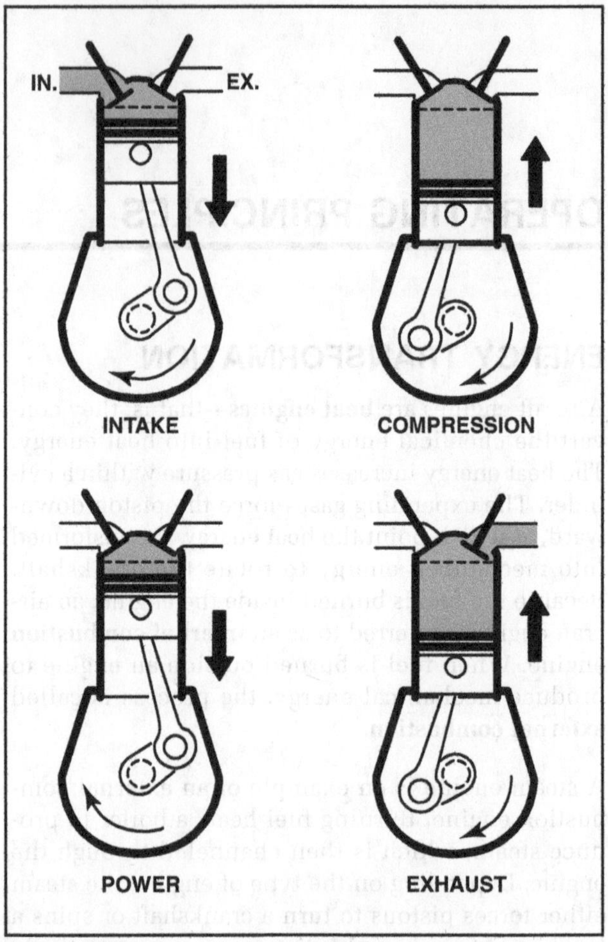


**Figure 1-59. The four strokes that take place in the Otto cycle include intake, compression, power, and exhaust.**

## FOUR-STROKE CYCLE

The four strokes of the Otto cycle are called intake, compression, power, and exhaust. Completing this cycle requires two revolutions of the crankshaft. The four-stroke cycle is sometimes referred to as a constant volume cycle because the burning fuel inside the cylinder increases pressure with almost no change in volume. [Figure 1-59]

The exact timing of ignition and timing of the valves varies considerably between engine types. Timing is always related to crankshaft position, measured in degrees of rotation according to the stroke in which the event occurs. For example, the intake valve of a particular engine might open 15 degrees before TDC during the exhaust stroke. Because a certain amount of travel is required to open a valve fully, the specified timing represents the point at which the valve begins to open rather than the full-open valve position.

### INTAKE STROKE

The intake stroke begins with the piston at TDC and the intake valve open. During this stroke, crankshaft rotation pulls the piston downward, lowering the pressure in the cylinder and drawing in fuel and air. The quantity, or weight, of fuel and air that enters the cylinder is determined by the throttle position. For example, when the throttle is fully open, the greatest amount of fuel and air enters a cylinder and the engine generates its greatest power.

### COMPRESSION STROKE

After the piston reaches BDC on the intake stroke, it reverses direction and begins the compression stroke. Depending on the specific engine, the intake valve typically closes about 50 to 75 degrees past BDC on the compression stroke. The delay in closing the intake valve permits the momentum of incoming gases to charge the cylinder more effectively. After the intake valve closes, the continued upward travel of the piston compresses the fuel/air mixture. As the piston approaches TDC, the mixture is ignited by electric sparks from two spark plugs threaded in the cylinder head. Depending on the specific engine, the sparks typically fire between 20 and 35 degrees before TDC during the compression strike. By igniting the mixture before TDC, complete combustion and maximum pressure are ensured by the time the piston begins the power stroke. Ignition timing for each engine model is set by the manufacturer. For engines equipped with full authority digital engine control (FADEC), ignition timing is computer controlled and optimized in each cylinder for each cycle.

#### POWER STROKE

After the compression stroke, the piston reverses direction and begins the power stroke. The rapidly expanding gases push the piston downward. These gases can exceed 3,000 degrees Fahrenheit while pushing down on a piston with a force greater than 15 tons. As the gases expand, they cool considerably and exit the cylinder at a much lower temperature.

The exhaust valve opens before BDC of the power stroke to assist exhaust gas scavenging. The movement of the piston applies positive pressure to expel the gases out the exhaust port. Proper exhaust gas scavenging is important because any exhaust that remains in a cylinder dilutes the incoming fuel/air charge on the next intake stroke. Additionally, proper exhaust gas scavenging helps control cylinder head temperature.

The ignition and rapid burning of the fuel/air charge in an engine produces a power impulse. The number and timing of impulses affects engine vibration. Generally, engines with more cylinders produce more power impulses and less vibration than those with fewer cylinders.

#### EXHAUST STROKE

After the piston reaches BDC on the power stroke, it reverses direction and begins the exhaust stroke. Exhaust gases are rapidly expelled, causing a drop in pressure. Using the low pressure to speed the flow of fuel and air into the cylinder, the intake valve opens somewhere between 8 and 55 degrees before the piston reaches TDC of the exhaust stroke.

#### VALVE TIMING

Proper valve timing is crucial for efficient engine performance. Valve timing refers to the opening and closing of the intake and exhaust valves as related to the crankshaft position. The number of crankshaft degrees that a valve opens before the piston reaches dead center is called **valve lead**. If a valve does not open at the proper time, the volume of fuel and air taken into the cylinder will be affected, causing the engine to run rough or not at all.

The number of degrees that a valve remains open after the piston passes dead center is called **valve lag**. At the beginning of the compression stroke, the intake valve remains open for a few degrees to ensure the maximum amount of fuel and air enters the combustion chamber.

The number of degrees during which both the intake and exhaust valves are open is called **valve overlap**. This valve overlap permits the fuel/air charge to enter the cylinder early to increase engine efficiency and assist cylinder cooling. Because of valve overlap, the inertia of the exhaust gas draws in fresh fuel/air, which aids in expelling the exhaust. [Figure 1-60]

In this example, notice that the valve lead and lag are greater near BDC than TDC. The exhaust valve leads BDC by 60 degrees and the intake valve lags by 60 degrees. On the other hand, when the piston is near TDC, the intake valve leads top center by 15 degrees while the exhaust valve lags by 10 degrees.

The ratio of the piston's linear distance to the degrees of crankshaft rotation varies depending on position of the crankshaft. For example, when the crankshaft is near TDC or BDC, it moves less per degree of rotation than if it were mid-travel. Additionally, piston velocity is highest at the 90 degree point and lowest at top and bottom dead center positions. The reduction in speed at both TDC and BDC provides a smoother transition when the piston changes its direction of travel. [Figure 1-61]

#### FIRING ORDER

An engine's firing order is the sequence that ignition events occur in the cylinders and is designed to maintain balance and reduce vibration. For example, a four-cylinder Continental model O-200-A has a firing order of 1-3-2-4. The Lycoming model O-320-E3D has the same firing order, but the manufacturers number their engine's cylinders differently. For this reason, always understand the specific information for the engine you are working on from the manufacturer's maintenance instructions. [Figure 1-62]

The firing order in radial engines ensures that power impulses follow the crank throw during rotation. For example, on all single-row radial engines, the

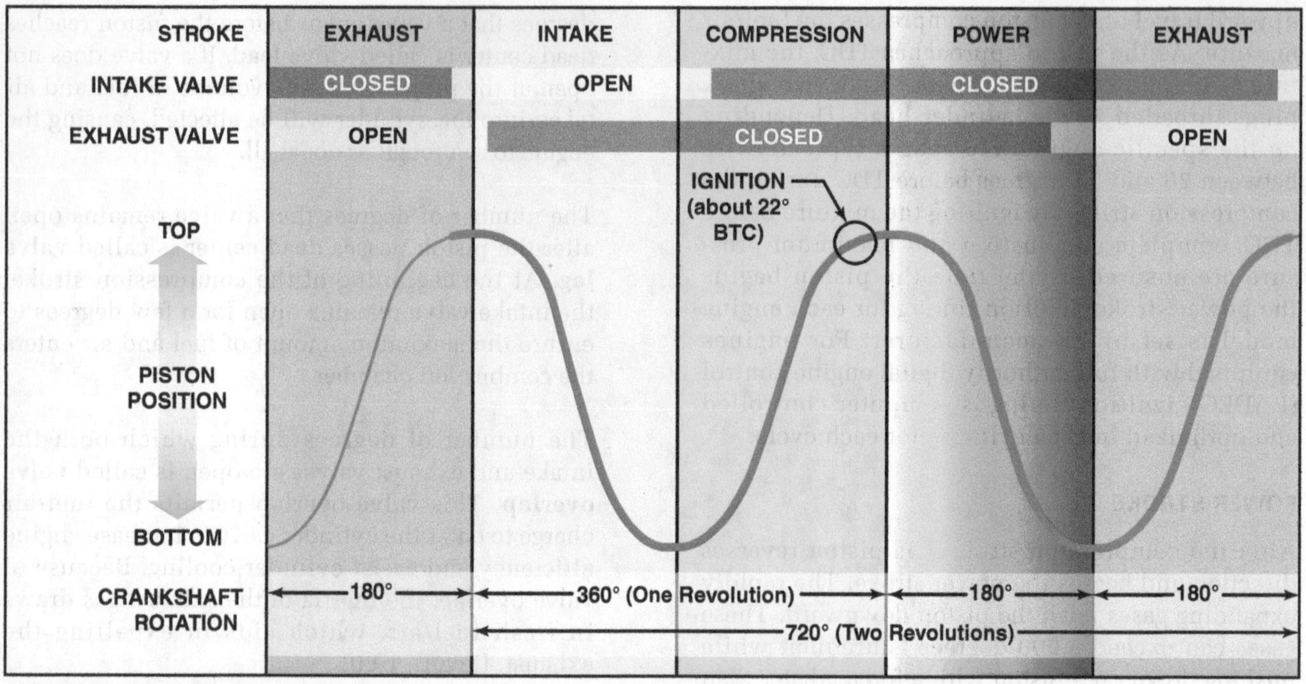


**Figure 1-60. This timing diagram shows piston and valve positions during the four strokes of the Otto cycle. The bold line indicates that the five events (intake, compression, ignition, power, and exhaust) do not perfectly align with the four strokes (intake, compression, power, and exhaust).**

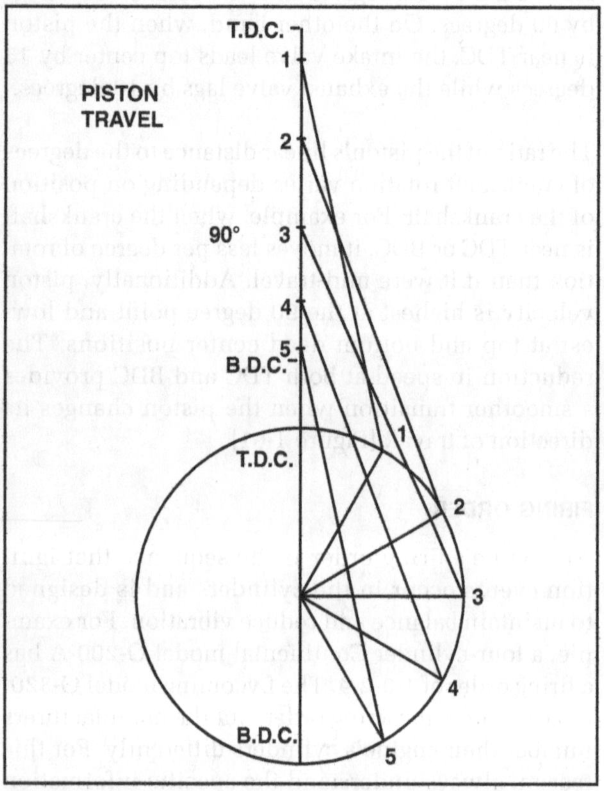


**Figure 1-61. The circle represents crankpin travel, and the vertical line represents piston travel. The piston moves more per degree of travel near top center than near bottom center.**

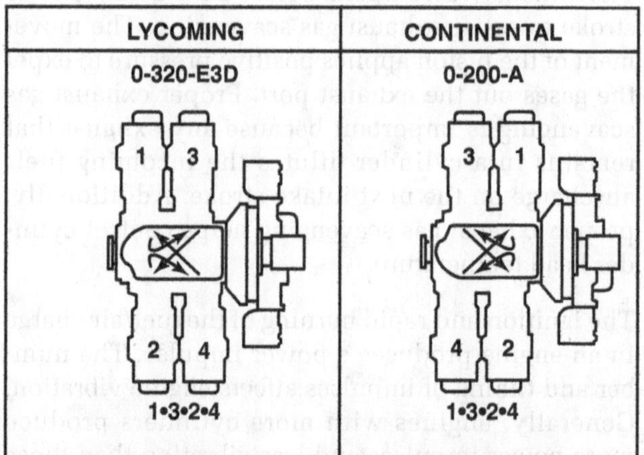


**Figure 1-62 The method of cylinder numbering and firing order varies between engine manufacturers and models.**

odd numbered cylinders fire in succession first, followed by the even cylinders. Therefore, the firing order on a seven cylinder radial engine is 1-3-5-7-2-4-6. The firing order on a nine cylinder radial engine is 1-3-5-7-9-2-4-6-8.

A double-row radial engine may be thought of as two single-row radial engines sharing a common crankshaft. As with a single-row radial, the power impulses occur sequentially in alternate cylinders, but in both rows. To balance the power impulses between the rows, after a cylinder fires in the first row, its opposite cylinder in the second row fires. As an example, consider a 14 cylinder double-row radial engine with two rows of seven cylinders. You should recall from the discussion in the previous section, that on a double-row radial engine, all first row cylinders are even numbered and rear row cylinders are odd numbered. After cylinder 1 fires in the back row, cylinder10 fires in the front row. The power impulses alternate between cylinder rows to establish a firing order of 1-10-5-14-9-4-13-8-3-12-7-2-11-6. [Figure 1-63]

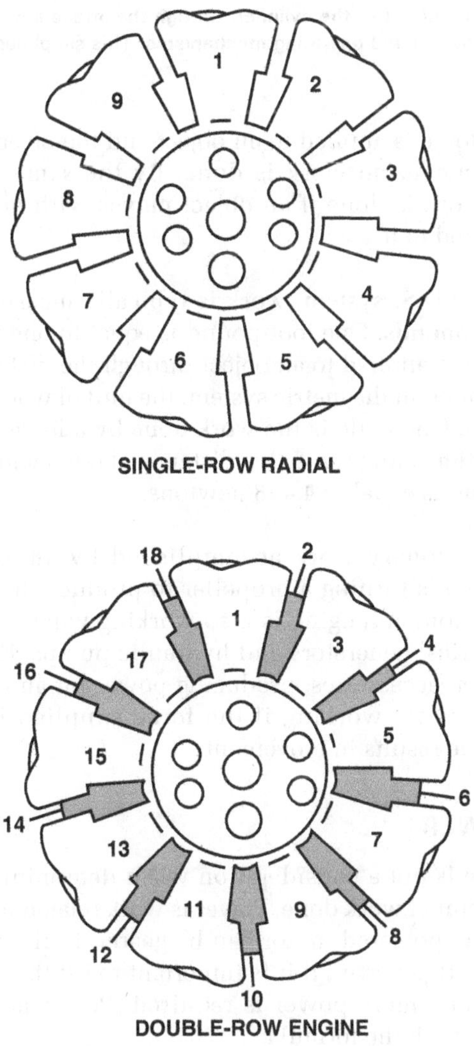


**Figure 1-63. The method of cylinder numbering and firing order varies between engine manufacturers and models.**

## POWER IMPULSES

Power impulses, created during the power stroke, affect the balance and smoothness of an operating engine. The more cylinders, the closer an engine's power impulses occur during each rotation of the crankshaft. The more closely spaced the power impulses, the smoother the engine runs, especially at low speeds.

## TWO-STROKE CYCLE

The two-stroke cycle contains the same five events as the four-stroke cycle. Because the five events occur in two piston strokes instead of four, one cycle is completed in a single rotation of the crankshaft. [Figure 1-64]

In the two-stroke cycle, while the piston moves toward TDC, two events occur. The piston compresses the fuel/air charge in the cylinder and creates an area of low pressure within the crankcase. This low pressure pulls fuel and air into the crankcase through an open valve. A few degrees before TDC, ignition of the fuel/air mixture occurs. The pressure from the expanding gases forces the piston downward. This stroke compresses the fuel/air charge in the crankcase. As the piston approaches BDC, it uncovers the exhaust port, which permits the exhaust to be purged from the cylinder. Almost immediately, the piston uncovers the intake port, which permits the pressurized fuel/air charge in the crankcase to enter the cylinder. The cycle repeats itself as the piston compresses the fuel/air charge in the cylinder and draws a fresh fuel/air charge into the crankcase.

To limit the dilution of the incoming fuel/air mixture with exhaust gases, most two-stroke engines use pistons with baffled heads to deflect the fuel/air charge upward and away from the exiting exhaust gases. Baffled piston heads do not completely eliminate the mixing problem. Because the exhaust and intake events take place almost simultaneously, some of the fuel/air charge becomes diluted by the exhaust gases and some is discharged from the exhaust port before it can be compressed and ignited. This reduces the engine's overall efficiency.

Lubrication of a two-stroke engine is accomplished while the fuel/air mixture circulates in the crankcase. The fuel provides only part of the lubrication. Oil is typically added to the fuel when the fuel tank is filled. This eliminates the need for an oil sump, which reduces the weight of a two-stroke engine.

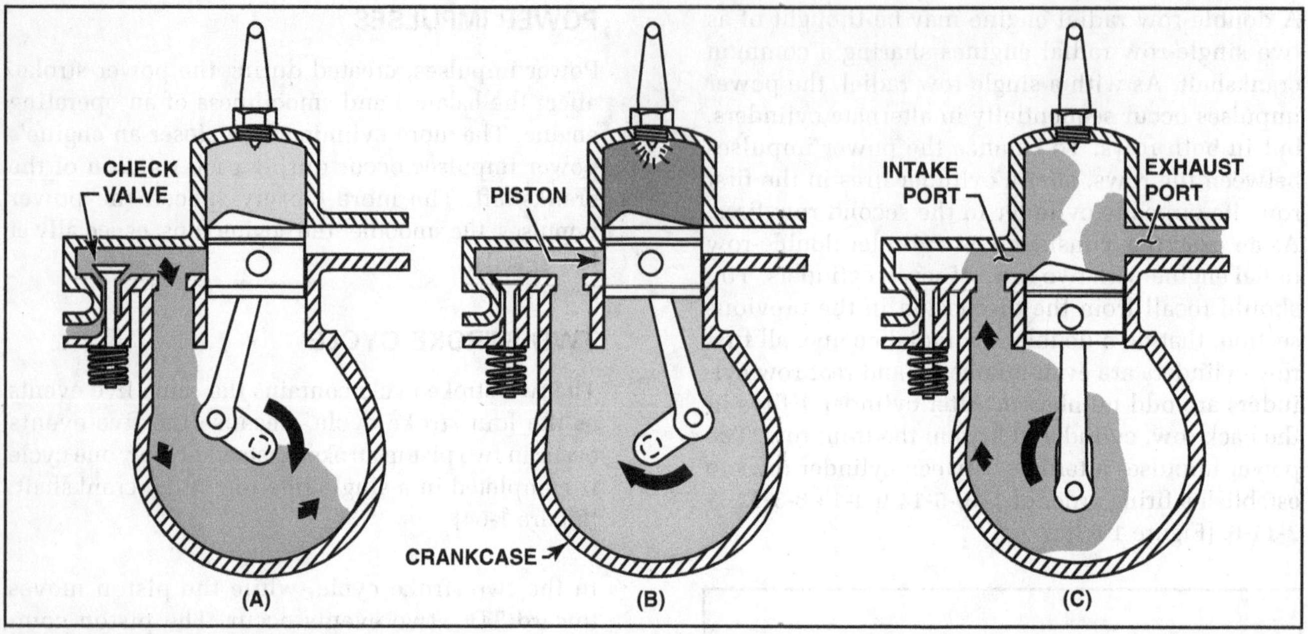


**Figure 1-64. In a two-stroke engine, the piston controls the flow of gases into and out of the cylinder through the intake and exhaust ports. This eliminates the need for either an intake or exhaust valve and their associated operating mechanisms. This simplifies a two-stroke engine's construction and minimizes weight.**

The simplicity and low weight of two-stroke cycle engines make them useful for ultralights and light sport aircraft, but because two-stroke cycle engines are less efficient and more difficult to cool than the four-cycle engine, they are impractical for larger aircraft.

## WORK-POWER CONSIDERATIONS

Aircraft engines are rated according to their ability to perform work and produce power. An engine's design and construction determine its effectiveness at converting the chemical energy of fuel to work and power. The following discussion provides an explanation of work and power as well as a means of calculating both. Additionally, several factors that affect an engine's power output are discussed.

### WORK

IWork is the result of force moving an object. The amount of work accomplished is directly proportional to the force applied and the distance moved. In mathematical terms, work is defined as the product of force multiplied by distance.

Work = Force × Distance

Example:
If an engine weighing 400 pounds is lifted 10 feet, the work accomplished is equal to 4,000 foot-pounds.

Work = 400 pounds × 10 feet
= 4,000 foot-pounds

If a force is applied to an object and the object does not move, no work is done. By the same token, no work is done if an object moves with no force applied to it.

In the U.S. system, work is typically measured in **foot-pounds**. One foot-pound is equal to one pound of force applied to an object through the distance of one foot. In the metric system, the unit of work is the **joule**. One joule is the work done by a force of one **newton** acting through a distance of one meter. One pound is equal to 4.448 newtons.

The primary work accomplished by an aircraft engine is turning a propeller to produce thrust. In addition, an engine is also working when turning electrical generators and hydraulic pumps. Engine-driven accessories, producing power for an aircraft system are working if the force supplied by the engine results in movement.

### POWER

Time is not a consideration when determining the amount of work done. Power is work related to time. A low-powered motor can be geared to lift a large weight; however, if it is important to lift the weight quickly, more power is required. Power is calculated with the formula:

$$\text{Power} = \frac{\text{Force} \times \text{Distance}}{\text{Time}}$$

Power is defined as the time-rate of doing work. In the Imperial system, power is expressed as foot-pounds per second; in the metric system, it is expressed as joules per second.

The power rating of an engine represents how quickly an engine-propeller combination can respond to power demands. The power rating indicates whether an engine can deliver the force needed to produce a specific amount of work in a given time. For example, a large airplane needs more power than a small airplane to take off because more force is needed to accelerate a heavier object the same distance in the same amount of time.

## HORSEPOWER

Another unit of measure for power is horsepower. Horsepower was first used by James Watt to compare the performance of his steam engine with a typical English draft horse. One horsepower is the amount of power required to do 33,000 foot-pounds of work in one minute or 550 foot-pounds of work in one second. The formula for calculating horsepower is:

$$\text{Horsepower} = \frac{\text{Force} \times \text{Distance}}{33{,}000 \times \text{Time}}$$

## INDICATED HORSEPOWER

Indicated horsepower (IHP) represents the total power developed in the cylinders without accounting for friction losses within the engine. To calculate indicated horsepower, you must know the **indicated mean effective pressure (IMEP)** within the cylinders. This can be determined by attaching an indicating device to a cylinder to measure the actual pressure during a complete operating cycle. From this data, average pressure is computed. This average pressure is included in the indicated horsepower calculation with other engine specifications. The formula used to calculate an engine's indicated horsepower rating is:

$$\text{Indicated Horsepower} = \frac{PLANK}{33{,}000}$$

Where:

**P** = the **IMEP** inside the cylinder during a power stroke measured in pounds per square inch.
**L** = the length of the stroke in feet.
**A** = the area of the piston head in square inches.
**N** = the number of power strokes per minute for one cylinder. For a four-stroke engine, this is found by dividing the r.p.m. by two.
**K** = the number of cylinders.

In this formula, the area of the piston times the mean effective pressure [P ¥ A] provides the force acting on the piston in pounds. This force, multiplied by the length of the stroke in feet [(PA) × L], results in the work performed in one power stroke. When the work of one power stroke is multiplied by the number of power strokes per minute [(PLA) × N] the result is the number of foot-pounds per minute of work produced by one cylinder. Multiplying the work of one cylinder by the number of cylinders on the engine [(PLAN) × K] reveals the amount of work performed, in foot-pounds, by the engine. Because horsepower is defined as work done at the rate of 33,000 foot-pounds per minute, divide the total work performed by 33,000 to determine indicated horsepower.

Check your understanding of this formula by calculating the indicated horsepower for a six-cylinder engine with a bore of five inches, a stroke of five inches, turning at 2,750 r.p.m., and with an IMEP of 125 p.s.i. per cylinder.

Where:

P = 125 psi
L = .416 foot
A = $\pi \times 2.5^2$ = 19.63 square inches.
N = 2,750 ÷ 2 = 1,375
K = 6

$$IHP = \frac{PLANK}{33{,}000}$$

$$= \frac{125 \times .416 \times 19.63 \times 1{,}375 \times 6}{33{,}000}$$

$$= \frac{8{,}421{,}270}{33{,}000}$$

$$= 255.19$$

In this problem, the indicated horsepower is approximately 255.

## FRICTION HORSEPOWER

Indicated horsepower is the theoretical power of a frictionless engine. However, such an engine does not exist. All engines require energy to draw a fuel/air charge into the combustion chamber, compress it, and expel exhaust gases. Furthermore, gears, pistons, and accessories create friction that must be overcome. Although friction can be reduced by lubrication, it cannot be eliminated. Therefore, not all of the horsepower developed in an engine goes to driving the propeller. The power necessary to overcome the friction and energy losses is known as **friction horsepower**. This value is determined by driving an engine with a calibrated motor and measuring the power needed to turn the engine at a given speed.

## BRAKE HORSEPOWER

The actual amount of power delivered to turn a propeller is called brake horsepower. Brake horsepower can be determined by subtracting an engine's friction horsepower from its indicated horsepower. In practice, measuring an engine's brake horsepower involves measuring **torque**, or twisting moment. Torque is a measure of load and is properly expressed in pound-feet or Newton-meters.

A number of devices can measure torque, including the dynamometer and torquemeter. Early powerplant design engineers measured brake horsepower using a **Prony brake dynamometer**, which used a hinged collar, or brake, clamped to the propeller shaft. The collar functioned as an adjustable friction brake. An arm of a known length was attached to the hinged collar and applied force to a scale while the propeller shaft rotated. By multiplying the force registered on the scale by the length of the arm, engineers could determine the torque exerted by the rotating shaft.

After the torque is known, the work done per revolution of the propeller shaft is computed using the following equation:

$$\text{Work per revolution} = 2\pi \times \text{Torque}$$

If the work per revolution is multiplied by the r.p.m., the result is work per minute, or power. Because work is expressed in foot-pounds per minute, this quantity is divided by 33,000 to arrive at engine brake horsepower. The formula for calculating brake horsepower is:

$$\text{Brake Horsepower} = \frac{2\pi \times \text{Torque} \times \text{rpm}}{33{,}000}$$

Check your understanding of this formula by calculating the brake horsepower for an engine that develops 600 foot-pounds of torque while turning at 2,700 r.p.m.

$$\text{Brake Horsepower} = \frac{6.28 \times 600 \times 2{,}700}{33{,}000}$$

$$= \frac{10{,}173{,}600}{33{,}000}$$

$$= 308.3$$

If the friction between the brake collar and propeller shaft imposes a load without stopping the engine, brake horsepower can be computed without knowing the amount of friction between the collar and drum. As long as the torque increase is proportional to the r.p.m. decrease, the horsepower delivered at the shaft remains unchanged. [Figure 1-65]

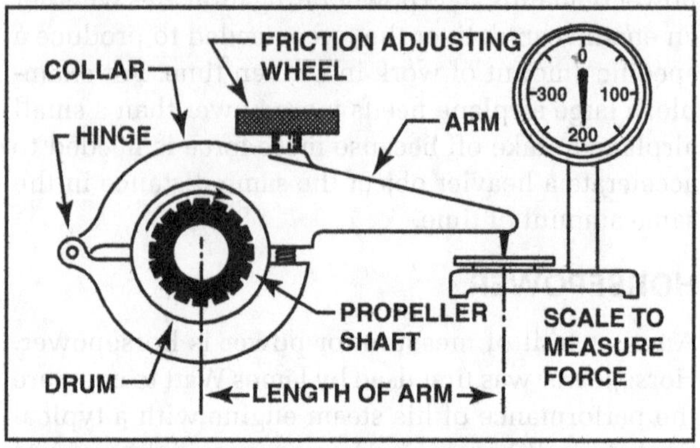


**Figure 1-65.The 3-foot arm of the Prony brake is exerting a force of 200 pounds on the scale. This results in a torque of 600 foot-pounds.**

Today, brake horsepower is most often measured with an **electric or hydraulic dynamometer**. With an electric dynamometer, an engine drives an electrical generator. The output of the generator is used to do work; the amount of work done in a given time is used to calculate the power that the engine produces. [Figure 1-66]

## PISTON DISPLACEMENT

Piston displacement is defined as the volume of air moved by a piston as it changes position from BDC

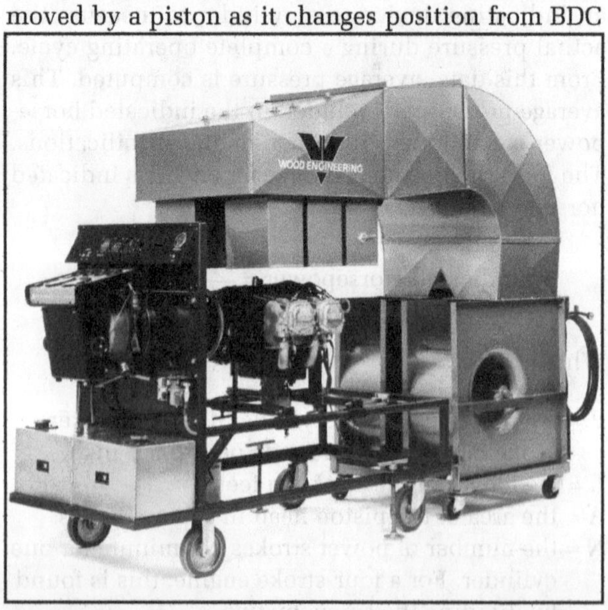


**Figure 1-66. With a dynamometer, the power produced by an engine drives an electrical generator or fluid pump to accurately measure power output.**

to TDC. To determine a piston's displacement, multiply the area of a piston head ($A = \pi r^2$) by the length of its stroke.

Check your understanding of this formula by calculating the area of a piston with a 4 inch diameter.

$$\begin{aligned} \text{Area} &= \pi r^2 \\ &= 3.14 \times 2^2 \\ &= 12.56 \text{ square inches} \end{aligned}$$

After the area of one piston is known, total piston displacement is calculated with the following formula:

$$\text{Total Piston Displacement} = A \times L \times N$$

Where:

A = area of piston head in square inches
L = length of the stroke in inches
N = number of cylinders

Using the example presented earlier, determine the total engine displacement if each of the four cylinders has a six inch stroke.

$$\begin{aligned} \text{Piston Displacement} &= A \times L \times N \\ &= 12.56 \times 6 \times 4 \\ &= 301.44 \text{ cubic inches} \end{aligned}$$

The total engine displacement is 301.44 cubic inches. Since the amount of work done by the expanding gases is determined in part by the piston area and the piston stroke, it should be evident that increasing either the cylinder bore or the piston stroke increases piston displacement.

## ENGINE EFFICIENCY

Energy is the capacity for doing work and cannot be created or destroyed. However, energy can be transformed from potential, or stored energy into kinetic energy. Aircraft reciprocating engines transform the potential, or chemical energy stored in fuel into heat energy during the combustion process. The heat energy is then converted to kinetic energy by mechanical means. Engine design and construction, fuel type, and environmental conditions all play a part in how efficiently an engine converts a fuel's potential energy. To determine how efficient an engine is, several factors must be examined, including an engine's thermal, volumetric, and mechanical efficiency.

### THERMAL EFFICIENCY

Thermal efficiency (TE) is a percentage that refers to the amount of heat energy an engine can convert to useful work compared to the potential of the fuel. You can use an engine's thermal efficiency rating to determine its relative inefficiency compared to similar engines. For example, consider two engines that produce the same amount of horsepower, but consume different amounts of fuel. The engine that uses less fuel converts a greater portion of the available energy into useful work and, therefore, has a higher thermal efficiency. Thermal efficiency is found by the following formula:

$$\text{Thermal Efficiency} = \frac{\text{Horsepower} \times 33{,}000}{F \times BTU \times K}$$

Where:

Horsepower = An engine's brake or indicated horsepower
33,000 = Number of foot-pounds of work per minute in one horsepower
F = Weight of fuel burned per minute
BTU = Heat value of the fuel burned measured in BTUs
K = Constant representing the number of foot-pounds of work each BTU is capable of doing in one second

Thermal efficiency can be calculated using either brake or indicated horsepower. If brake horsepower is used, the result is **brake thermal efficiency (BTE)**, and if indicated horsepower is used, the result is **indicated thermal efficiency (ITE)**.

The constant 33,000 is the number of foot-pounds of work per minute in one horsepower. When horsepower is multiplied by 33,000, the power output of an engine is expressed in foot-pounds per minute.

Most engine performance data related to fuel consumption is expressed in terms of gallons per hour. Therefore, becoming proficient at converting gallons per hour to pounds per minute is an important skill. For example, the weight of 100LL aviation gasoline is six pounds per gallon. If a particular engine burns 12 gallons per hour, you must multiply the gallons consumed per hour by six pounds and divide the product by 60, the number of minutes per hour. The resulting fuel burn is 1.2 pounds per minute ($(12 \times 6) \div 60 = 1.2$).

In the Imperial system of measurement, the relationship between heat and work is the **British Thermal Unit**, or **BTU**. Each pound of 100LL aviation gasoline contains approximately 20,000 BTUs of heat energy. Therefore, 20,000 is typically used in the formula for determining thermal efficiency.

By multiplying the pounds per minute of fuel an engine burns by 20,000, you get the total number of BTUs, or total heat energy produced by a given engine. One BTU is capable of doing 778 foot-pounds of work. Therefore, when you multiply the total number of BTUs by the constant 778, both the top and bottom of the formula produce a product that is in foot-pounds.

Based on this information, the formula used to calculate thermal efficiency can be simplified to read:

$$\text{Thermal efficiency} = \frac{\text{Horsepower} \times 33{,}000}{\text{F} \times 20{,}000 \times 778}$$

or

$$\text{Thermal efficiency} = \frac{\text{Horsepower} \times 33{,}000}{\text{F} \times 15{,}560{,}000}$$

To check your understanding of this formula, determine the brake thermal efficiency of a piston engine that produces 150 brake horsepower while burning 8 gallons of aviation gasoline per hour.

$$\text{BTE} = \frac{150 \times 33{,}000}{(8 \times 6 \div 60) \times 20{,}000 \times 778}$$

$$= \frac{4{,}950{,}000}{.8 \times 20{,}000 \times 778}$$

$$= \frac{4{,}950{,}000}{12{,}448{,}000}$$

$$= .398$$

$$= 39.8 \text{ percent}$$

Most reciprocating engines are between 30 and 40 percent efficient. The remaining heat is lost through the exhaust gases, the cooling system, and the friction within the engine. In fact, of the total heat produced in a reciprocating engine, 30 to 40 percent is used for power output; 15 to 20 percent is lost in cooling; 5 to 10 percent is lost in overcoming friction of moving parts; and 40 to 45 percent is lost through the exhaust.

### VOLUMETRIC EFFICIENCY

Volumetric efficiency (VE) is the percentage that results from dividing the volume of fuel and air an engine takes into its cylinders in one cycle by the total piston displacement. For example, if an engine draws in a volume of fuel and air that is exactly equal to the engine's total piston displacement, volumetric efficiency is 100 percent. Similarly, if an engine whose total piston displacement is 320 cubic inches draws in 288 cubic inches of fuel and air, the volumetric efficiency is 90 percent.

Because the density of air drawn into an engine varies with changes in the atmosphere, the only way to calculate volumetric efficiency is to make corrections for nonstandard temperature and pressure. You might recall from earlier studies that standard temperature is 59°F (15°C) and standard pressure at sea level is 29.92 inches of mercury (1013.2 millibars). Based on this, the formula for determining volumetric efficiency is:

$$\text{VE} = \frac{\text{Vol. of mixture corrected for nonstd. conditions}}{\text{Total piston displacement}}$$

The volumetric efficiency of normally aspirated engines is less than 100 percent. Bends, surface roughness, and obstructions inside the induction system slow the flow of air, which in turn reduces the air pressure within the manifold. However, because turbocharged engines compress the air before it enters the cylinders, these often have volumetric efficiencies greater than 100 percent.

Anything that lowers the density, or volume, of air entering a cylinder decreases volumetric efficiency. Some of the typical factors that affect volumetric efficiency of a nonturbocharged engine include:

**Partial throttle operation**—When the throttle plate is not completely open, the volume of air that flows into the cylinders is restricted.

**Induction friction**—Friction in the induction system slows airflow, causing a decrease in air density in the cylinders. The amount of friction created is directly proportional to the length of the intake pipes and inversely proportional to their cross-sectional area. In other words, long, small diameter intake pipes create the most friction while short, large diameter intake pipes create less friction.

**Induction bends**—Directional changes in the induction system limit airflow and decrease the air density that enters the cylinders.

**Elevated induction air temperatures**—As the temperature of the intake air increases, air density decreases. A lower air density means that less air enters the cylinders.

**Elevated cylinder head temperatures**—As cylinder heads and combustion chambers heat up, air density in the cylinders decreases, which reduces volumetric efficiency.

**Incomplete scavenging**—If the valve overlap in an engine is incorrect, exhaust gases that remain in the combustion chamber displace some of the incoming fuel/air mixture. When this happens, less fuel and air is drawn into the cylinders and a lower volumetric efficiency results.

**Improper valve timing**—If an intake valve does not remain open long enough for a complete charge of fuel and air to enter a cylinder, volumetric efficiency drops.

**Changes in altitude**—As an aircraft climbs, ambient air pressure drops and air density decreases. As an engine draws this "thinner" air into its cylinders, volumetric efficiency drops. This problem can be overcome to a certain degree by turbocharging an engine. Turbocharging an engine raises induction air pressure above ambient pressure, which increases the density of the fuel/air charge entering the cylinders.

### MECHANICAL EFFICIENCY

Mechanical efficiency is a percentage obtained by dividing brake horsepower by indicated horsepower. This represents the percentage of power developed in the cylinders that reaches the propeller. For example, an engine that develops 160 brake horsepower and 180 indicated horsepower has a ratio of 160:180, representing a mechanical efficiency of 89 percent. Because aircraft engines are mechanically efficient, it is not unusual for ninety percent of indicated horsepower to be converted into usable brake horsepower.

The most significant factor that affects mechanical efficiency is internal engine friction. The friction between moving parts in an engine is relatively constant throughout its speed range. Therefore, the mechanical efficiency of an engine is highest when the engine is running at the speed at which maximum brake horsepower is developed.

## FACTORS AFFECTING POWER

According to the general gas law, which combines Boyle's Law and Charles' Law, a definite relationship exists between gas volume, temperature, and pressure. This relationship is the reason why the internal combustion process must be precisely controlled for an engine to produce power efficiently.

### MANIFOLD PRESSURE

At a given engine speed, changes in manifold air pressure (also called or manifold absolute pressure or MAP), affect engine power output. Manifold air pressure readings provide a means of selecting power settings for high performance aircraft. Absolute pressure is measured in inches of mercury (in. Hg.) or pounds per square inch absolute (p.s.i.a.). MAP gauges indicate absolute pressure of the fuel/air mixture at a point just outside of a cylinder intake port.

Excessive pressures and temperatures shorten engine life by overstressing cylinders, pistons, connecting rods, bearings, crankshaft journals, and valves. Continued operation beyond the upper limit of manifold absolute pressure contributes to worn engine parts, decreased power output with lower efficiency, and even engine failure.

### DETONATION AND PREIGNITION

During normal combustion, a fuel/air mixture burns in a controlled and predictable way. The entire process is completed in a fraction of a second; the spark plugs ignite the mixture, which burns away from the plugs until all of the fuel is consumed. By providing two ignition sparks at the same time, the dual spark plug design, common in most aircraft reciprocating engines, promotes complete and even burning of the fuel/air charge. The plugs are arranged opposite one another so that the flame advances, burning the mixture in a wave-like form, toward the center of the cylinder. Normal combustion causes a smooth buildup of temperature and pressure so that maximum force is applied to the piston at exactly the right time in the power stroke. [Figure 1-67]

**Detonation** describes uncontrolled ignition and explosive burning of the fuel/air mixture in a cylinder. Detonation causes high temperatures and pressures,

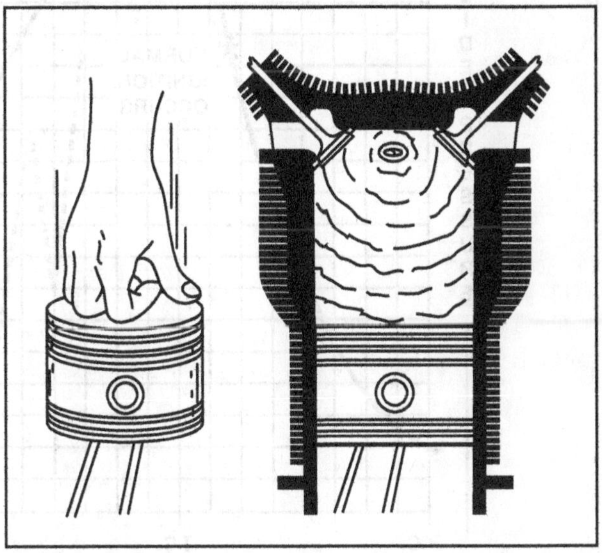

**Figure 1-67. During normal combustion, the fuel/air mixture burns evenly, producing a steady force illustrated by the hand pushing down on the piston.**

which contribute to an engine running rough, overheating, and losing power. When detonation occurs in an engine, damage to or even failure of pistons, cylinders, or valves is possible. The high pressures and temperatures, combined with turbulence, cause a "hammering" action on a cylinder and piston that can burn a hole completely through

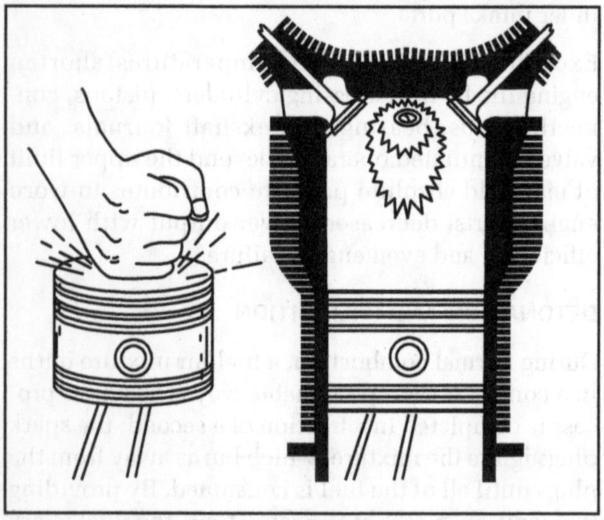

Figure 1-68. When detonation occurs, the fuel/air charge burns in an explosive fashion. The rapid increase in pressure produces a 'hammering' force on the piston.

a cylinder or piston in seconds. Detonation is often detected by hearing a "knock" in the engine. [Figure 1-68]

Conditions that can cause detonation include using a fuel grade lower than recommended and allowing the engine to overheat. Other factors that can contribute to detonation are incorrect ignition timing, high manifold pressure at low speed, an excessively lean fuel/air mixture, and a compression ratio greater than 12:1. [Figure 1-69]

**Preignition** occurs when the fuel/air mixture ignites before the spark plugs fire. This is caused by a hot spot in a cylinder such as a carbon particle, overheated valve edges, silica deposits on a spark plug, or a red-hot spark plug electrode. Hot spots are caused by poor engine cooling, dirty induction air filters, or an engine that has been shut down at a high r.p.m. If an engine continues running after ignition is turned off, preignition is a possible cause.

Preignition and detonation can occur simultaneously, and one can cause the other. Sometimes distinguishing between the two is difficult because both result in engine roughness and high operating temperatures.

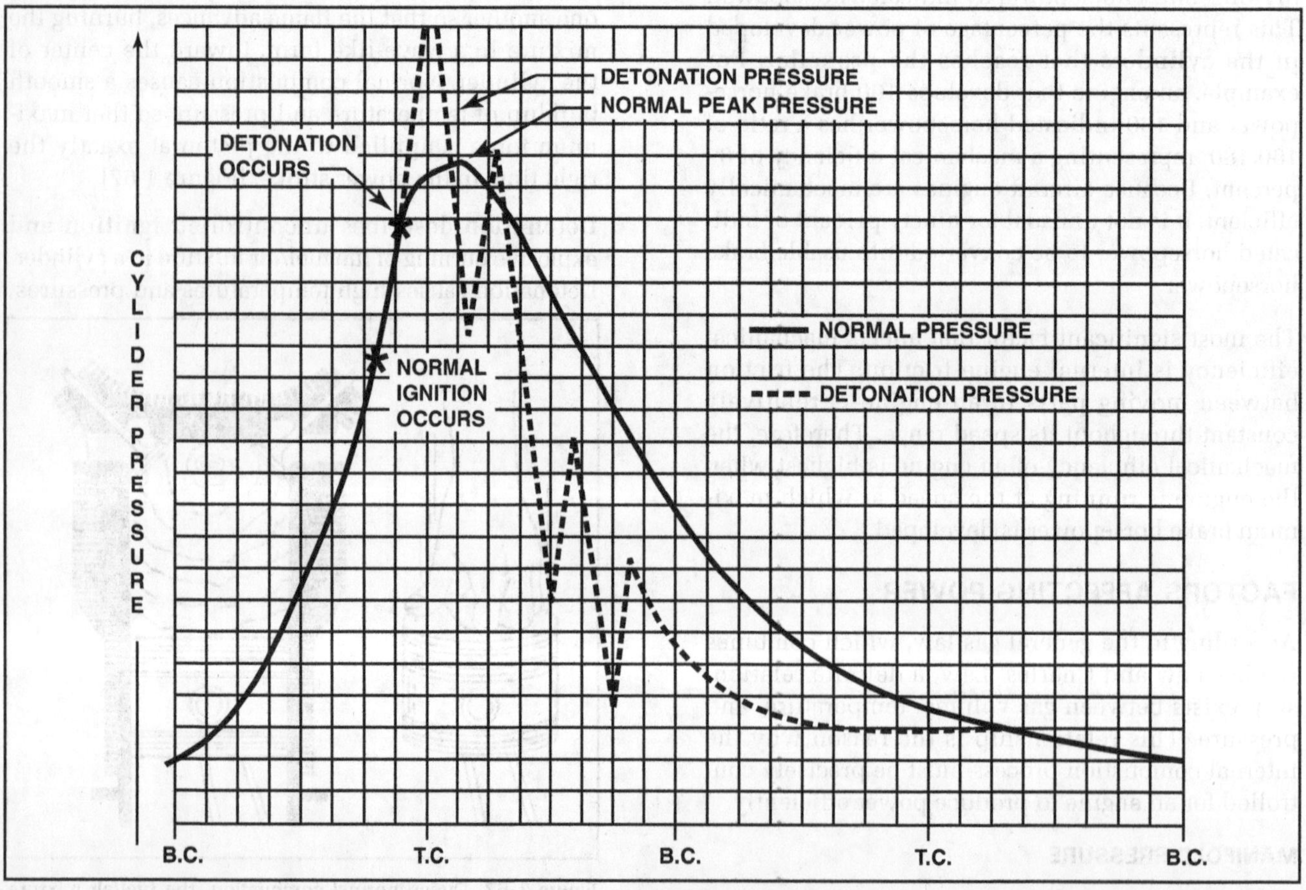


Figure 1-69. This chart illustrates pressure in a cylinder as it passes through its various strokes. When normal combustion occurs, cylinder pressure builds and dissipates evenly. However, when detonation occurs, cylinder pressure fluctuates dramatically.

## COMPRESSION RATIO

Compression of the fuel/air mixture is necessary to receive a reasonable amount of work during the power stroke. The fuel/air charge in the cylinder can be compared to a coil spring in that the more it is compressed, the more work it can accomplish.

The compression ratio is defined as the relationship of cylinder volume with the piston at the bottom of its stroke to the cylinder volume with the piston at the top of its stroke. For example, if there are 140 cubic inches of space in a cylinder when the piston is at BDC and 20 cubic inches of space when the piston is at TDC, the compression ratio is 140:20 or, in its most simple form, 7:1. [Figure 1-70]

To a large extent, an engine's compression ratio determines the amount of heat energy that is converted into useful work. High compression ratios enable the fuel/air mixture to release its energy rapidly and produce maximum pressure inside a cylinder just as the piston begins the power stroke. As a rule, the higher the compression ratio, the greater an engine's power output.

Compression ratios are determined by an engine's design. For example, a long throw crankshaft increases the piston stroke and compression ratio. Similarly, if you mill the mating surface of a cylinder head, you effectively decrease the distance between the cylinder head and piston head, which also increases the compression ratio. A third way to increase a compression ratio is to install domed pistons.

The characteristics of available fuels determine the practical limits of compression ratios selected during engine design. For example, if the compression ratio of an engine is increased beyond a fuel's critical pressure, detonation will occur. As a result, engine manufacturers specify the correct grade of fuel for use. Avoid using lower fuel grades.

If an engine is turbocharged, the amount of turbocharging imposes limits on the engine's compression ratio. Although turbocharging does not change an engine's compression ratio, it does increase manifold pressure as well as each cylinder's mean effective pressure. As you may remember from your study of the gas laws, as the pressure of a gas increases, so does temperature. As a result,

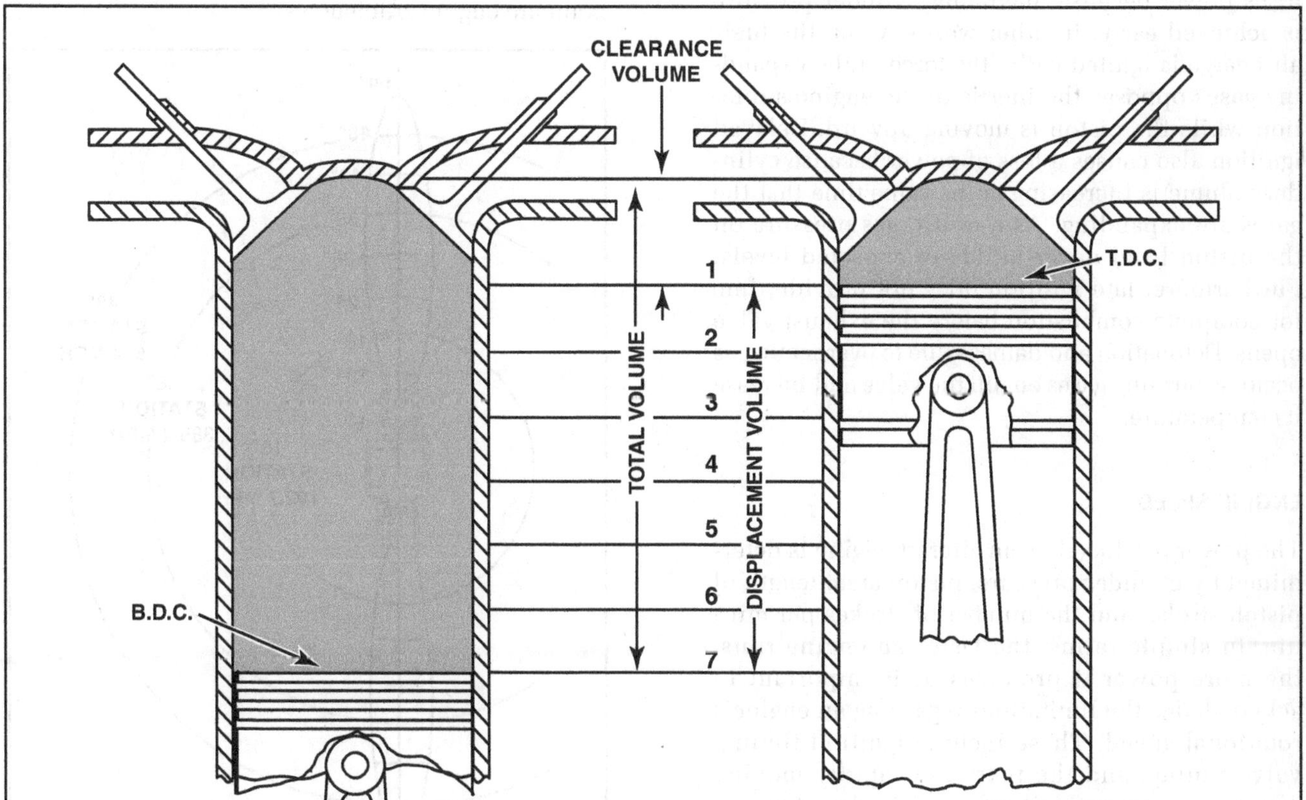


**Figure 1-70. The cylinder compression ratio describes the cylinder volume when the piston is at bottom dead center to the cylinder volume when the piston is at top dead center. In this example, the compression ratio is 7:1.**

turbocharging raises the temperature of the fuel/air mixture in an engine's cylinders, which increases the possibility of detonation. Therefore, compression ratios in turbocharged engines are limited to compensate for the higher temperatures of the fuel/air mixture.

### IGNITION TIMING

In a properly timed ignition event, complete combustion and maximum pressure occur when the piston passes TDC at the beginning of the power stroke. This requires that ignition timing be set to ignite the fuel/air charge shortly before the piston reaches TDC on the compression stroke. For example, most Continental and Lycoming engines ignite the fuel/air charge between 20 and 32 degrees before TDC on the compression stroke.

An automobile engine employs variable timing to change the ignition as operating conditions change. Aircraft engines, on the other hand, use fixed timing. Fixed timing requires a compromise between what is required to provide best performance for takeoff and best performance at cruise.

If the ignition event occurs too early, the engine loses power because maximum cylinder pressure is achieved early. In other words, when the fuel/air charge is ignited early, the force of the expanding gases opposes the inertia of the engine's rotation while the piston is moving upward. Delayed ignition also causes a loss of power because cylinder volume is increasing at the same time that the gases are expanding. As a result, gas pressure on the piston head never builds to expected levels. Furthermore, late ignition does not provide time for complete combustion before the exhaust valve opens. Detonation and damage due to overheating as occur as burning gases engulf the valve and increase its temperature.

### ENGINE SPEED

The power produced by an aircraft engine is determined by cylinder pressure, piston area, length of piston stroke, and the number of strokes per minute. In simple terms, the faster an engine runs, the more power it produces. It is important to acknowledge the limitations regarding an engine's rotational speed. These include ignition timing, valve timing, and the inertia of rapidly moving pistons. For example, if intake and exhaust valves move too quickly, they can "float"—that is, they do not seat properly. In addition, the inertia of pistons reversing their direction of travel thousands of times per minute can overstress crankshaft journals and bearings when engine speed exceeds safe limits.

Another limitation to the maximum rotational speed of an engine is propeller tip speed. To produce thrust efficiently, the tip speed of a propeller blade cannot exceed the speed of sound. Keeping in mind that the further a point is from the propeller hub, the faster it moves through the air, high-powered engines operating at high speed must be fitted with short propeller blades or propeller reduction gearing. Reduction gears enable the propeller to turn at a slower, more efficient speed. [Figure 1-71]

### SPECIFIC FUEL CONSUMPTION

Brake-specific fuel consumption (BSFC) refers to the number of pounds of fuel an engine burns in one hour to produce one horsepower at a given speed. For an engine that burns 12 gallons (72 pounds) per hour and produces 180 brake horsepower, the brake specific fuel consumption is 0.4 pounds (72 pounds ÷ 180 BHP). A BSFC of 0.4 and 0.5 pounds of fuel per horsepower hour is common for modern aircraft reciprocating engines. Although it is not a measure of power, specific fuel consumption can be used to compare engine efficiencies.

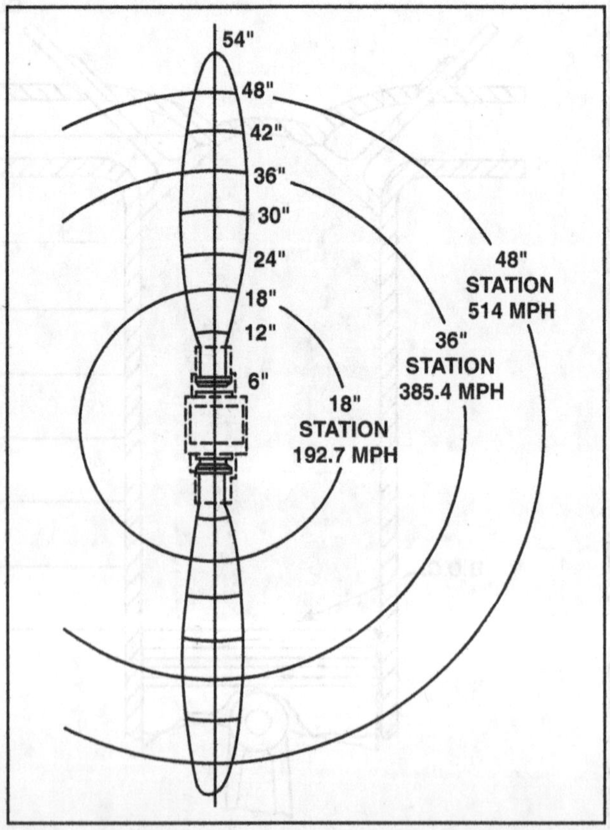


**Figure 1-71. A propeller's speed increases toward the blade tips. When propeller tip speeds exceed the speed of sound, propeller efficiency drops.**

Engine speed alters the specific fuel consumption of an engine. Engine design, volumetric efficiency, and friction losses are factors that affect fuel consumption. For most engines, the best specific fuel consumption occurs at a cruise power setting at approximately 75 percent power. The variability of an engine's specific fuel consumption is often illustrated in a chart in the aircraft flight manual. [Figure 1-72]

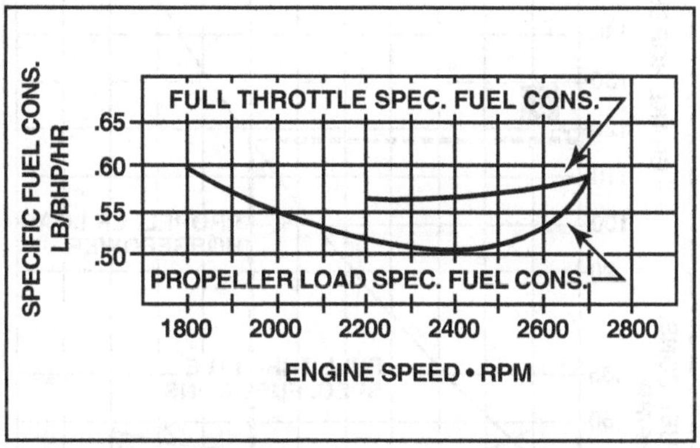


**Figure 1-72. Aircraft engines tend to operate most efficiently around 2,400 r.p.m. Below this speed, an engine does not develop maximum power for the amount of fuel it is using. Above 2,400 r.p.m, friction horsepower increases, causing an overall drop in brake horsepower. A typical engine requires about 0.51 pounds of fuel per hour for each horsepower it produces at 2,400 r.p.m.**

### ALTITUDE

As an aircraft climbs, there is a corresponding decrease in ambient air pressure and density. Whenever an aircraft engine operates at a **density altitude** above sea level, less air is drawn into the engine for combustion, resulting in decreased power output.

Even though the actual, or true, altitude at a location does not change, density altitude changes constantly. For example, on a hot day as the air heats and pressure drops, air becomes less dense, causing the density altitude to increase. Turbocharging an engine is a way to overcome the problems associated with higher density altitudes. Turbochargers compress air, which increases the pressure and density of the fuel/air charge that enters the cylinders.

### FUEL/AIR RATIO

Gasoline and other liquid fuels must be converted from a liquid state to vapor before they will burn. In addition, for complete combustion, the ratio of fuel vapor to oxygen in the air must be correct. For aviation gasoline, a **stoichiometric mixture** is a perfectly balanced fuel/air mixture of 15 parts of air to 1 part of fuel, by weight. Combustible fuel/air ratios range from 8:1 to 18:1.

Mixture controls enable the fuel/air ratio to be adjusted from idle cut-off to full rich conditions. Leaning the mixture raises engine operating temperatures while enriching the mixture provides a cooling effect. Leaning becomes necessary as altitude increases, because air density drops, causing the fuel/air ratio to gradually become richer. **Best power** mixture develops maximum power at a particular engine speed and is typically used during takeoff. **Best economy** mixture provides the best specific fuel consumption and results in an aircraft's maximum range and optimum fuel economy.

## DISTRIBUTION OF POWER

When you compare the amount of potential energy that is available in aviation gasoline to the actual power that is delivered to the propeller shaft, you discover that an aircraft engine is a fairly inefficient machine. For example, a typical six-cylinder engine develops about 200 brake horsepower when burning 14 gallons of fuel per hour. However, the burning fuel releases enough heat energy to produce 667 horsepower. When you examine the distribution of power you learn that 200 of the 667 horsepower is delivered to the propeller while approximately 33 horsepower is used to overcome friction and compress the air in the cylinders. In addition, cooling and exhaust systems lose about 434 horsepower to the air. The power loss continues when power is delivered to the propeller, because to propel an aircraft through the air, the torque produced by an engine must be converted into thrust. A propeller converts only about 90 percent of the torque it receives into thrust, so the actual thrust horsepower delivered by the propeller is only 180 horsepower (from the original 667). [Figure 1-73]

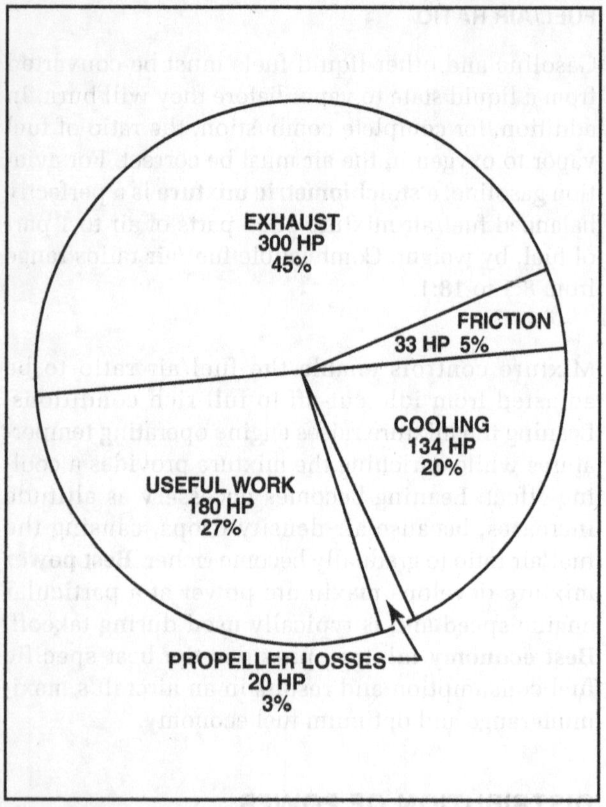


**Figure 1-73. The distribution of power from aviation gasoline consumed by a typical 200 horsepower engine.**

## POWER CURVES

Most engine manufacturers produce a set of power curves for each engine they build. These charts show the power developed for specific r.p.m. as well as indicate the specific fuel consumption at corresponding power settings. [Figure 1-74]

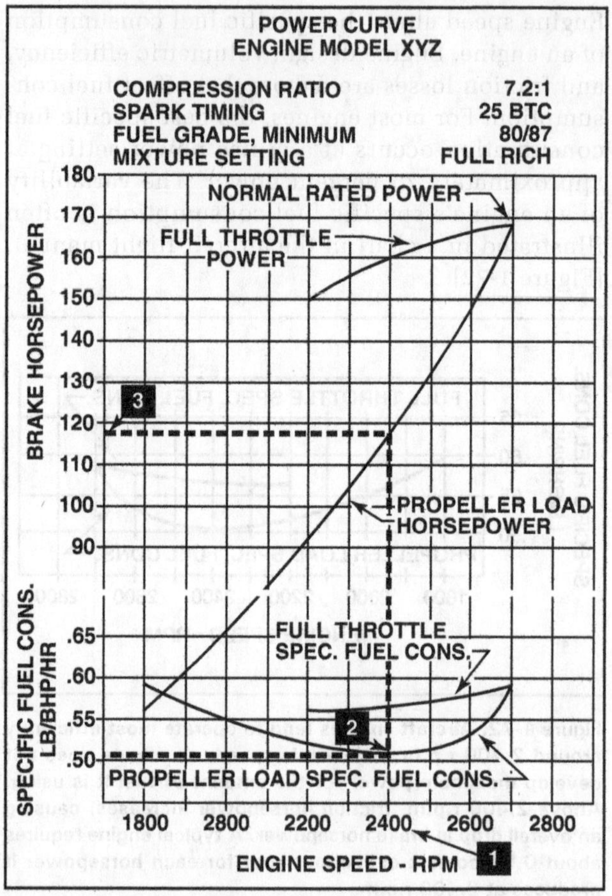


**Figure 1-74. This power curve chart illustrates the typical power curve for a four-cylinder aircraft engine. The upper curve shows the maximum amount of power produced at full throttle. The diagonal power curve represents the amount of horsepower produced with less than full throttle. The two bottom curves represent the specific fuel consumptions for full throttle operations and propeller load conditions. To use this chart, assume you have an engine operating at a cruise power setting of 2,400 r.p.m. (item 1). At this power setting the specific fuel consumption is 0.51 LB/BHP/HR (item 2), and the engine produces 118 brake horsepower (item 3). By multiplying the specific fuel consumption by the brake horsepower, you can determine the engine's fuel consumption of 60.18 pounds per hour (0.51x118 = 60.18).**

# SUMMARY CHECKLIST

✓ A stroke is the distance that a piston travels between its top and bottom positions.

✓ The Otto cycle (or four-stroke cycle) involves five events during four strokes of a piston in a cylinder.

✓ The two-stroke cycle involves five events during two strokes of a piston in a cylinder.

✓ Work is the product of force multiplied by distance.

✓ Power is the quotient of work divided by time.

✓ Horsepower is a standard unit of power that represents 33,000 foot-pounds of work per minute.

✓ Thermal efficiency indicates the percentage of potential energy in a fuel that is converted into kinetic energy.

✓ Volumetric efficiency is the quotient of the total volume of fuel and air drawn into a cylinder divided by the total piston displacement.

✓ Detonation is the uncontrolled ignition and explosive burning of the fuel/air mixture in a cylinder.

✓ Preignition occurs when the fuel/air mixture is ignited before the spark plugs fire.

✓ A stoichiometric fuel/air mixture for a reciprocating engine that burns aviation gasoline is 15 parts air to 1 part fuel by weight.

# KEY TERMS

heat engines
internal combustion
external combustion
intake
compression
ignition
power
exhaust
cycle
four-stroke cycle
Otto cycle
two-stroke cycle
stroke
top dead center
TDC
bottom dead center
BDC
valve lead
valve lag
valve overlap
foot-pounds
joule
newton
indicated mean effective pressure
IMEP
PLANK
friction horsepower
torque
Prony brake dynamometer
electric dynamometer
hydraulic dynamometer
brake thermal efficiency
BTE
indicated thermal efficiency
ITE
British Thermal Unit
BTU
partial throttle operation
induction friction
induction bends
elevated induction air temperatures
incomplete scavenging
improper valve timing
changes in altitude
detonation
preignition
density altitude
stoichiometric mixture
best power mixture
best economy mixture

# QUESTIONS

1. All heat engines convert ______ energy into ______ energy.

2. The two basic types of heat engines are

   a. ______________________.

   b. ______________________.

3. The five events that must take place in an internal combustion engine to convert the chemical energy in fuel into mechanical energy are

   a. ______________________.

   b. ______________________.

   c. ______________________.

   d. ______________________.

   e. ______________________.

4. The Otto-cycle of engine operation is a constant ____________ (volume or pressure) cycle.

5. On which stroke of a four-stroke cycle engine does each of these events begin to occur?

   a. Intake valve opens ____________.

   b. Intake valve closes ____________.

   c. Exhaust valve opens ____________.

   d. Exhaust valve closes ____________.

   e. Ignition occurs ____________.

6. Valve overlap occurs at the end of the ______ stroke and the beginning of the ______ stroke.

7. Identify each cylinder of the engines below by placing the letter used on the drawing next to the proper cylinder number.

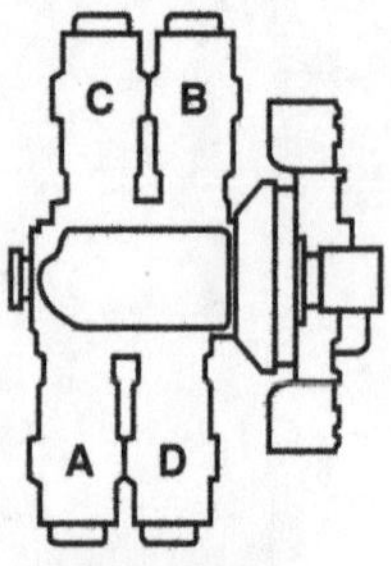


CONTINENTAL FOUR-CYLINDER ENGINE

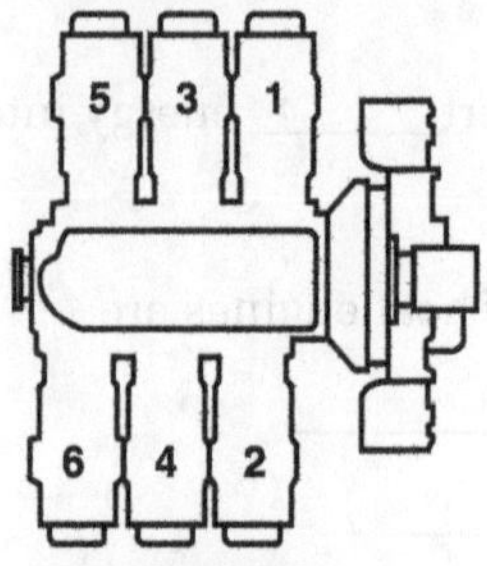


CONTINENTAL SIX-CYLINDER ENGINE

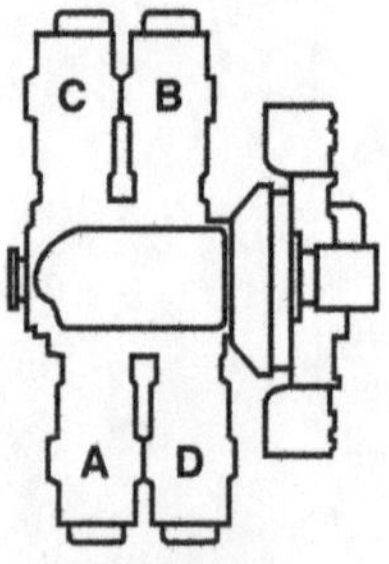


LYCOMING FOUR-CYLINDER ENGINE

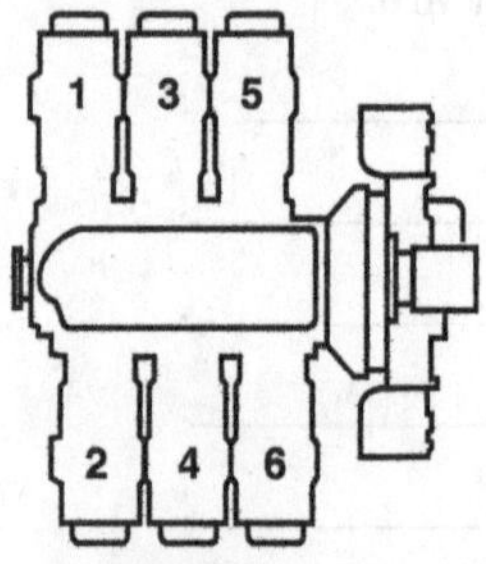


LYCOMING SIX-CYLINDER ENGINE

a. Lycoming engines #1 ____ #2 ____ #3 ____ #4 ____

b. Continental engines #1 ____ #2 ____ #3 ____ #4 ____

8. Write the firing order for each of these engines.

a. Lycoming 4-cylinder horizontally opposed engine ____-____-____-____.

b. Continental 4-cylinder horizontally opposed engine ____-____-____-____.

c. Lycoming 6-cylinder horizontally opposed engine ____-____-____-____-____-____.

d. Continental 6-cylinder horizontally opposed engine ____-____-____-____-____-____.

e. 9-cylinder radial engine ____-____-____-____-____-____-____-____-____.

f. 18-cylinder radial engine ____-____-____-____-____-____-____-____-____-____-____-____-____-____-____-____-____-____.

9. The product of Force × Distance is known as ______________.

10. The rate of doing work is known as ______________.

11. One horsepower is equal to ______ foot-pounds of work done in one minute, or ______ foot-pounds of work done in one second.

12. The horsepower delivered to the propeller shaft of an aircraft engine is called ______ horsepower.

13. The power required to rotate the engine and to compress the air is called ______ horsepower.

14. Brake horsepower + friction horsepower = _______ horsepower.

15. A six-cylinder engine that turns at 2,600 rpm and has a bore of 4.0 inches, a stroke of 4.0 inches, and an IMEP of 120 psi will produce _______ horsepower.

16. A six-cylinder engine with a bore of 4.375 inches and a stroke of 5.125 inches has a piston displacement of _______ cubic inches.

17. A four-cylinder engine with a bore of 4.375 inches and a stroke of 3.875 inches has a piston displacement of _______ cubic inches.

18. The nominal weight of aviation gasoline is _______ pounds per gallon.

19. The nominal heat energy content of one pound of aviation gasoline is _______ Btu.

20. One British Thermal Unit of heat energy will perform _______ foot-pounds of work.

21. The thermal efficiency of an engine that burns 102 gallons of aviation gasoline per hour to produce 1,400 horsepower is _______ percent.

22. A normally aspirated aircraft engine typically_______ (can or cannot) attain a volumetric efficiency of 100%.

23. As the temperature of the air increases, the density _______________ (increases or decreases).

24. The ratio of brake horsepower to indicated horsepower is the _______ efficiency of the engine.

25. _______________ is the spontaneous combustion of the unburned charge ahead of the flame fronts after the ignition of the fuel/air charge in a reciprocating engine.

26. If a cylinder has a volume with the piston at the top of its stroke of 14.5 cubic inches and a piston displacement of 90 cubic inches, its compression ratio is _______:1.

27. If a cylinder has a volume with the piston at the top of its stroke of 23 cubic inches and a piston displacement of 131 cubic inches, its compression ratio is _______:1.

28. ______________ occurs when the fuel/air mixture ignites before the spark jumps across the terminals of the spark plug.

29. A serious loss of power and damage to exhaust valves in an aircraft engine can be caused by _______ (early or late) ignition timing.

30. In order to efficiently produce thrust, the tip speed of a propeller blade must not exceed ______________.

31. The two variables used by a pilot to control the amount of power an engine is producing are engine speed and cylinder pressure, indicated as _______ and ______________ respectively.

32. An engine that developes 180 brake horsepowerwith a brake specific fuel consumption of 0.47 will consume _______ gallons of aviation gasoline per hour.

33. A typical reciprocating aircraft engine converts only about _______% of the heat energy released into useful work.

SECTION

C

## DIESEL ENGINE TECHNOLOGY

For economic and environmental reasons, many oil companies have curtailed or even eliminated the production of 100LL aviation gasoline (avgas). Due in part to low demand, outside the United States 100LL is significantly more expensive where it is available. In the future, a possibility exists that production of 100LL may be eliminated; as a result, engine manufacturers are designing, developing, and producing powerplants that operate on alternative fuels. Some manufacturers redesigned engines to operate on unleaded automotive gasoline or biofuels while others designed new engines that operate on diesel or jet fuel.

Diesel engines are commonly used to power automobiles and generators. In the 1920s and 1930s, diesel engines were used in aircraft, but advancements and improvements in gasoline engines outpaced diesel technology, and its use declined. Advancements in diesel technology for aircraft powerplants have made it a practical and economical alternative. With new construction materials and advanced electronic engine monitoring and control devices, the use of diesel reciprocating engines in aircraft is growing. The FAA has granted Type Certification to a number of new diesel powerplants, most developed by foreign manufacturers.

This section provides a brief overview of the history, theory, and operation of diesel engines. Additional information includes a brief survey of designs presently installed on certified aircraft and a few designs that are under development.

### HISTORY

Rudolph Diesel developed the first prototype diesel engine in 1893. However, during initial testing, a cylinder head separated. Four years subsequent to this initial failure, another engine was developed that proved more reliable. With fairly minor refinement, the diesel engine was found to be ideally suited for use in marine and heavy equipment. Its prime advantage was that it provided the lowest specific fuel consumption of any powerplant available at the time (as low as .26 lb/hp/hr). [Figure 1-75]

Diesel engines were initially used in airplanes and airships in the 1930's. The "Jumo" diesel, for example, delivered full sea level horsepower up to 40,000 feet while developing a brake specific fuel consumption (BSFC) of .356 lb/hp/hr, which equated to developing one horsepower for each 1.5 pounds of engine weight. [Figure 1-76]

**Figure 1-75. Rudolph Diesel invented the engine that bears his name at the end of the 19th Century.**

Figure 1-76. The Jumo 4 was the first diesel engine installed in an aircraft.

## ADVANTAGES OF DIESEL ENGINES IN AIRCRAFT

In the United States, diesel engines are often thought of as being noisy, heavy, or dirty. New technologies and cleaner fuel have addressed all of these concerns. A diesel engine's relatively low speed and high torque is ideal for aircraft use because it can turn a larger diameter propeller at slow, efficient speeds.

Diesel fuels are considered "heavy fuels." Although jet-A, or diesel fuel, weighs more per gallon than gasoline, it produces more BTUs per gallon. Heavy fuels possess a higher flashpoint and cost less to refine. In many countries, aviation gasoline is two or three times more expensive than diesel fuel, making diesel engine operation significantly more economical.

Diesel engines have much lower BSFC than engines using aviation gasoline; this translates into increased range and endurance. A diesel engine consumes around 0.32 to 0.38 pounds of fuel for each horsepower produced in one hour. For example, at full power, a 150 horsepower diesel engine burns 55.5 pounds or 8.3 gallons of fuel per hour (0.37 pounds of fuel x 150 horsepower). At full power, a 150 horsepower Otto cycle engine using avgas consumes around 0.53–0.59 pounds/horsepower/hour, which equates to 88.5 pounds or 14.75 gallons per hour (0.59 pounds of fuel x 150 horsepower).

Diesel engines are inherently more durable and experience less overall engine wear than Otto cycle engines because the lubricating properties of diesel fuel are greater than those of gasoline. Furthermore, because diesel engines do not require ignition systems, reliability is increased and the possibility of electromagnetic interference (EMI) is eliminated.

Modern diesel engines are typically equipped with advanced, full-authority digital engine control systems (FADEC). In most cases, a FADEC system provides a pilot with a single power lever control; propeller pitch control is automatic. This enables the propeller to develop the maximum thrust for a given condition. The simplicity of operating a modern diesel engine reduces pilot workload—an important factor in aviation safety.

## DIESEL COMBUSTION

Unlike an Otto cycle engine, a diesel engine has no throttle, spark plugs, or fuel/air metering device. The air drawn into the cylinder (or pumped into the cylinder with a supercharger, turbocharger, or both) is compressed by the piston. The compression ratio in a diesel engine is between 16 to 22:1, which is significantly higher than the 6.5 to 9.5:1 used in Otto cycle engines. The result of this increased pressure is a corresponding increase in temperature—beyond what is necessary to ignite the fuel. At a specific time before TDC on the compression stroke, fuel is injected into the cylinder. At the point of injection, the fuel is too rich to burn. However, as the fuel vaporizes and mixes with the air, the fuel/air charge combusts from the high temperature and pressure.

Diesel engines operate much leaner than gasoline engines. In an Otto cycle engine, the air to fuel ratio is typically between 12:1 and 20:1 to burn. However, the mixture in a diesel engine is often in the 30:1 to 35:1 range, and can be as high as 80:1 with the engine running at idle.

Because detonation is not a problem with diesel engines, superchargers and turbochargers are frequently used to increase power output with less risk of engine damage compared to gasoline engines. Superchargers use an engine-driven drive mechanism to turn a compressor. Turbochargers use exhaust gases to drive a compressor. (See chapter 5 for more information on turbochargers and superchargers.)

Supercharged and turbocharged diesel engines deliver improved efficiency and power by directing hot induction air through an intercooler to reduce temperature. An intercooler is a heat exchanger, similar in design to a radiator or oil cooler.[Figure 1-77]

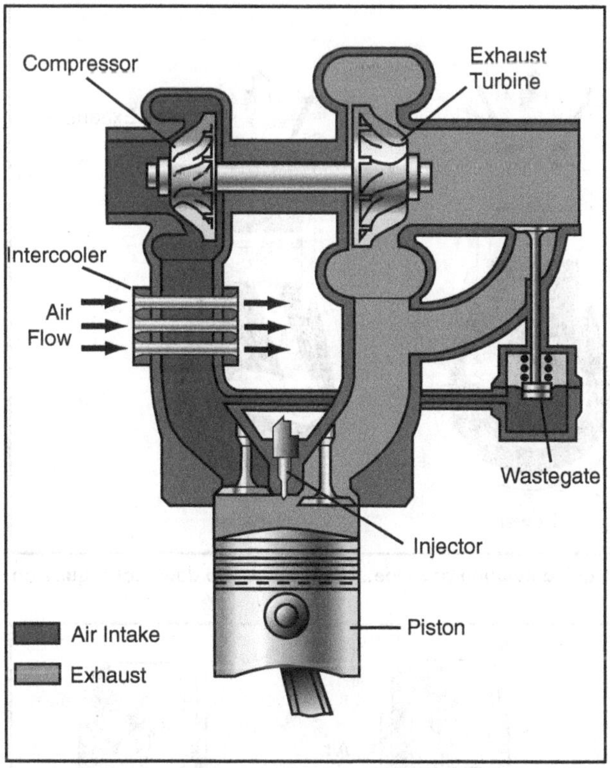


**Figure 1-77. Four stroke diesel engines can be turbocharged and intercooled to increase performance.**

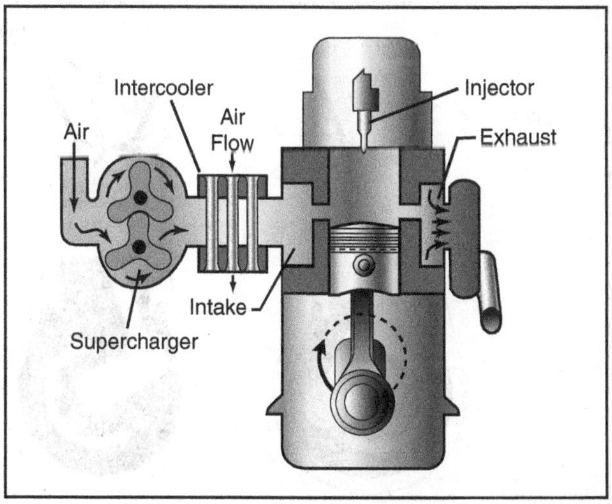


**Figure 1-78. Two stroke diesel engines can be supercharged and intercooled to increase performance.**

## FUEL INJECTION

Without a throttle plate, engine power is controlled by the amount of fuel injected into the cylinders. A fuel pump must deliver the proper amount of fuel, at the appropriate time, and for the proper duration to each cylinder for every cycle.

## DESIGN TYPES

A diesel engine can be designed to use a two- or four-stroke cycle with cylinders arranged in a horizontally opposed, radial, inline, or V configuration. These design types were discussed earlier in this chapter. However, diesel two- and four-stroke designs have some unique characteristics. [Figure 1-78]

Similar to their gasoline counterparts, four-stroke diesel engines are typically more fuel efficient than two-stroke engines. In a two-stroke diesel, when the piston moves down and uncovers the intake and exhaust ports, expanding gases cease applying pressure on the piston. This results in a loss of efficiency compared to a four stroke diesel because the force of the expanding gas is not applied throughout the entire power stroke. Compared to two-stroke gasoline engines, the loss of efficiency with a two-stroke diesel engine is less because of direct injection: that is, no fuel is lost while the exhaust port is open. A further benefit is a reduction in emissions because unburned fuel is not included in the exhaust. [Figures 1-79 and 1-80]

### DIESEL AND OTTO CYCLE ENGINE COMPARISONS

As previously discussed, a major advantage of a diesel engine is its durability. Diesel fuels help lubricate internal engine parts much better than gasoline, so diesels tend to exhibit less wear on valve stems, valve guides, cylinder walls, and piston rings. Diesel engines are usually rated for a longer time between overhaul (TBO) or time between replacement (TBR) than comparable gasoline engines. [Figure 1-81]

Figure 1-81 compares the performance of two gasoline engines with four aircraft diesel engine designs. The chart demonstrates that diesel engines have better fuel efficiency than their gasoline-powered counterparts. The BSFC of the diesels, measured in pounds per horsepower per hour, is 6-19% lower at 75% power. Gasoline engines cannot achieve this measure of fuel economy—the fuel mixture would be too lean, which would result in significantly higher temperatures and reduced safety margins for octane and detonation.

The ratio of horsepower to weight is generally better for diesel engines than for comparable gasoline engines. This disparity will likely increase as expected reductions in the weight of diesel engines are achieved and their power output improves with technical advancements. Diesel engines generally develop more torque at a lower speed than gasoline engines. Keep in mind that propeller efficiency is

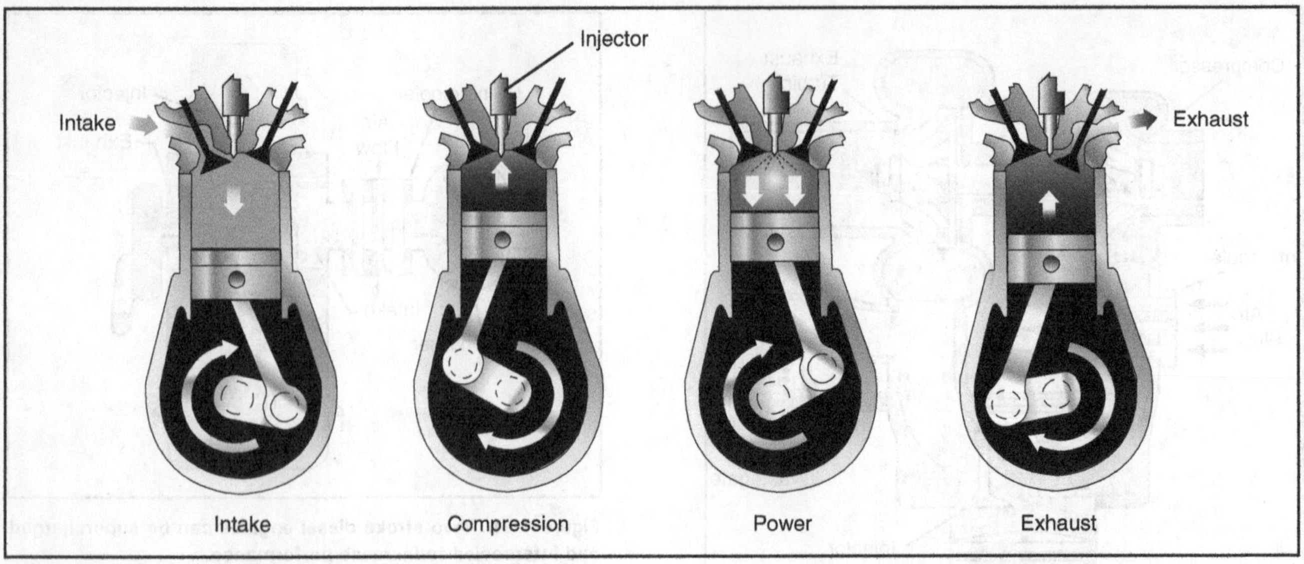


**Figure 1-79. A four stroke diesel engine is similar to an Otto cycle engine using aviation gasoline. The diesel cycle does not require an ignition source; the fuel combusts because of extreme pressure.**

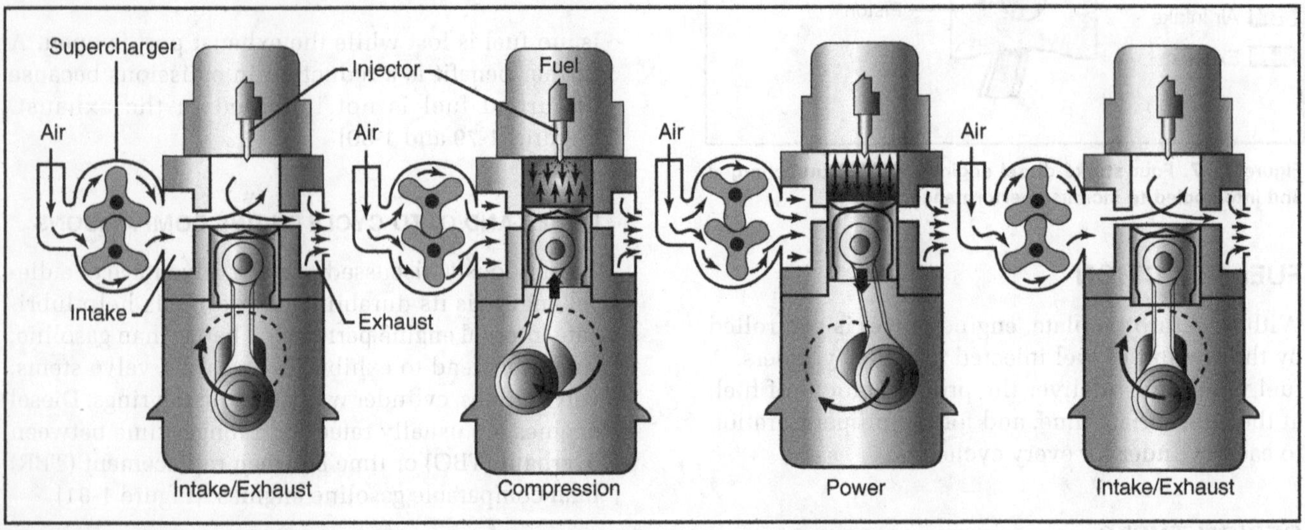


**Figure 1-80. A two stroke diesel engine is simpler than a four stroke, but ultimately less fuel efficient.**

improved at slower speeds, so a larger diameter propeller can operate more efficiently. For example, the diesel-powered Centurion 2.0 is rated at 135 horsepower, but it can replace a gasoline engine rated at 180 horsepower. The thrust produced by the propeller on a Centurion 2.0 is equivalent to the thrust delivered by the typical 180 horsepower gasoline engine.

## AIRCRAFT APPLICATIONS

Several airframe and engine manufacturers are exploring opportunities to install diesel engines on new and existing airframes. Several diesel powerplants are currently certified or in the process of certification for new and retrofit installations.

The Diamond DA-42 is a certified, four-place, twin engine, diesel-powered airplane. Early aircraft used Centurion 2.0 engines. Later models use 170HP Austro AE300 engines. This aircraft cruises at 175 KIAS, burning only 14 U.S. gallons per hour (g.p.h.). At an economy setting, the aircraft cruises at 152 knots and burns 9.8 U.S. g.p.h.

Other aircraft manufacturers, including Cirrus, Cessna, Socata, and Maule, have commented publicly about development programs to incorporate diesel engines on their airframes.

Several companies are developing diesel engines for aircraft. For example, the Société de Motorisations Aéronautiques (SMA) has developed an opposed, air-cooled R305-230 engine, and as of this writ-

| | Lycoming | Lycoming | Delta Hawk | Thielert | Zoche | SMA | Austro |
|---|---|---|---|---|---|---|---|
| Model | IO-540 | O-360 | DH200V | Centurion 1.7 | ZO 02A | SR305-230 | AE 300 |
| Design | Opposed | Opposed | V | Inline | Radial | Opposed | Inline |
| Cycle | 4 Stroke | 4 Stroke | 2 Stroke | 4 Stroke | 2 Stroke | 4 Stroke | 4 Stroke |
| Fuel | Avgas | Avgas | Diesel | Diesel | Diesel | Diesel | Diesel |
| Displacement | 540 in | 360 in | 202 in | 103 in | 325 in | 305 in | 121.5 in |
| Weight | 444 lbs | 270 lbs | 315 lbs | 295 lbs | 271 lbs | 423 lbs | 414 lbs |
| Horsepower | 300 | 180 | 200 | 135 | 300 | 230 | 168 |
| Horsepower/Pound | 0.68 | 0.67 | 0.63 | 0.45 | 1.1 | 0.54 | 0.41 |
| Propeller Speed | 2700 | 2700 | 2700 | 2300 | 2500 | 2200 | 2300 |
| TBO or TBR | 2000 | 2000 | 000 | 2400 | 2000 | 3000 | 1000 |
| Compression Ratio | 8.7:1 | 8.5:1 | 16.5:1 | 18:1 | 17:1 | 15:1 | 19:1 |
| Cruise (75%) Fuel Consumption | 16 gal/hr | 9 gal/hr | 8.5 gal/hr | 5.09 gal/hr | 11.1 gal/hr | 7.6 gal/hr | 5.5 gal/hr |
| Cooling | Air | Air | Liquid | Liquid | Air | Air | Liquid |
| Sea Level HP to: | Sea Level | Sea Level | 16,000-18,000 ft | 6,000 ft | 9,000 ft 24,000 ft expected | 13,000 ft | 11,800 ft |
| Cruise BSFC | 0.426 | 0.400 | 0.375 | 0.337 | 0.346 | 0.345 | 0.325 |

**Figure 1-81. This chart compares the performance of similar reciprocating engines that use either aviation gasoline or diesel fuel**

ing, Deltahawk is currently producing engines for the experimental aircraft market, but is pursuing plans to make engines for type certificated aircraft. Likewise, the German firm Zoche is developing a series of diesel-powered radial engines and intends to pursue certification in the near future.

# SUMMARY CHECKLIST

✓ Although aviation diesel fuels are heavier than aviation gasoline, diesel fuel contains more potential energy per gallon.

✓ Diesel engines have fewer components than similarly configured Otto cycle engines.

✓ The fuel/air mixture for a diesel engine is typically 30 parts air to 1 part fuel by weight; thus a diesel engine uses approximately twice as much air per part of fuel than an aviation gasoline-burning engine.

# RECIPROCATING ENGINE OPERATION, INSTRUMENTS, MAINTENANCE, AND OVERHAUL

CHAPTER 2

## INTRODUCTION

As a powerplant technician, you will be responsible for operating, maintaining, inspecting, and overhauling aircraft engines. Performing these tasks requires the ability to recognize when an engine is performing normally and when its performance has deteriorated. You will need knowledge and skills to effectively troubleshoot engine problems and perform any necessary repair work. Furthermore, you will need special knowledge and skills for performing an engine overhaul. This chapter provides a foundation for operating, maintaining, and overhauling reciprocating engines.

# SECTION A

## ENGINE OPERATION, INSTRUMENTS, AND MAINTENANCE

### OPERATION

As an aviation maintenance technician, you must be thoroughly familiar with the procedures for operating a reciprocating engine from the cockpit. This includes understanding the engine instrumentation, ground run procedures, and safety items associated with starting, running, and stopping an aircraft engine. A good place to begin is with the location and movement of the engine controls. The three primary controls for reciprocating engines are the throttle, propeller, and mixture. The engine controls on most modern aircraft use standardized shapes and colors. [Figure 2-1]

After you become familiar with the engine controls, locate the corresponding and auxiliary engine instruments. In addition, identify and understand all placards and other markings on or near the instruments. Important engine operating information is displayed in the cockpit and must be monitored continuously during an engine run. As an engine operator, you must be skilled in interpreting instrument data to prevent engine damage.

### ENGINE INSTRUMENTATION

You must have a basic understanding of how engine instruments work to successfully operate and troubleshoot an engine. Interpreting instrument markings correctly enables you to determine how an engine is performing. Instrument markings establish limits and operational ranges. Markings also enable you to distinguish between normal operation, time-limited operation, and unauthorized operating conditions. The ranges for engine instrument markings are based on limits found in the engine's Type Certificate Data Sheet. Traditionally, instrument marking codes are green, blue, yellow, and red lines or arcs as well as intermediate blank spaces.

**Green arcs** or lines are the most widely used instrument markings; they usually indicate a safe or normal range of operation. Usually, the high end of a green arc indicates a maximum limit for continuous operation while the low end indicates the minimum limit. Operation in this range typically has no restrictions.

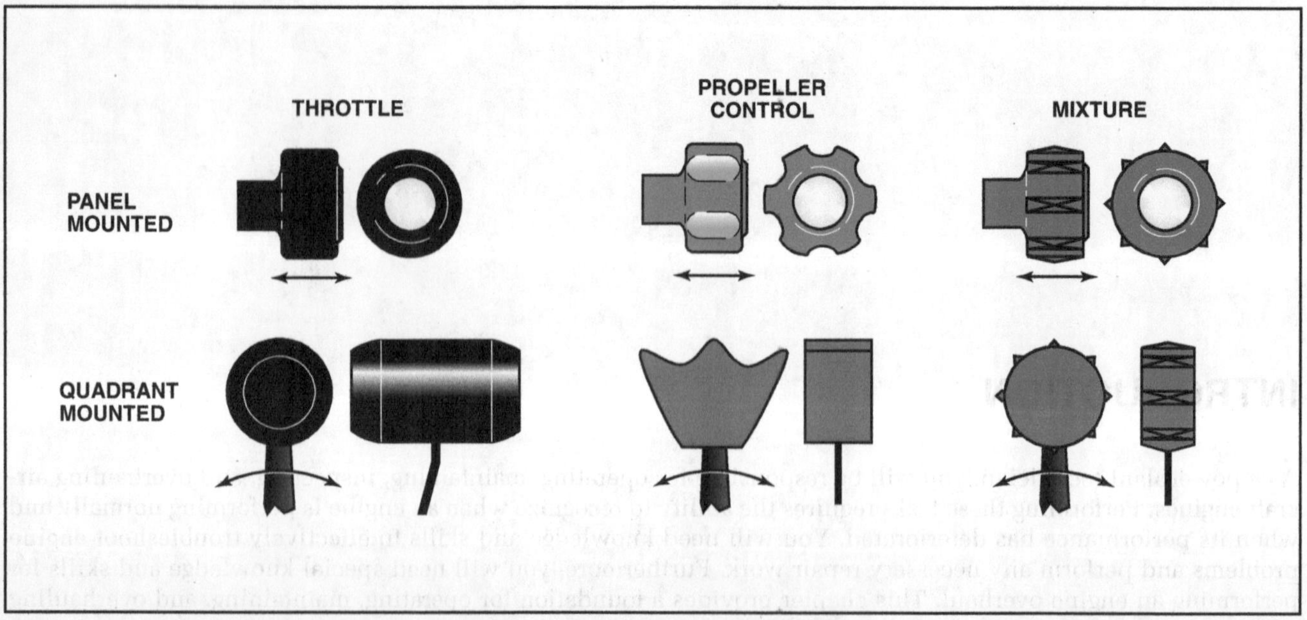


**Figure 2-1. For standardization purposes, the primary engine controls are arranged from left to right beginning with the throttle, propeller control, and mixture. In addition, each lever is color-coded and uniquely shaped.**

A **yellow arc** or line indicates a caution range for limited operation. However, in some cases, a yellow arc might be omitted on instruments if it is too small to be clearly visible. When this is the case, the manufacturer's instructions will specify a caution range. Engine operation in the yellow arc can indicate an impending problem and should be considered a warning to change an operational setting.

A **red line** indicates the edge of a safe operating limit. Operation beyond a red line typically indicates a dangerous operating condition. A **red arc** indicates a restricted operating range where excessive vibration or other stresses could endanger the engine or the airframe.

**Blue arcs** or lines are rare, but can be used to indicate an allowable range of operations under a unique set of circumstances. For example, a blue arc might indicate an acceptable fuel flow when flying above a specific altitude. Blue arcs are used only on certain engine instruments such as the tachometer, fuel flow indicator, manifold pressure gauge, cylinder head temperature gauges, or torque meter.

The colored arcs and lines on engine instruments are typically painted directly on the instrument face. However, some older aircraft instrument markings might be painted on the instrument glass. In these cases, a white line is used as an **index mark** between the instrument glass and the instrument case. Any discontinuity in the white radial line indicates that the instrument glass has moved. Because misalignment between the glass and the case renders the instrument range and limit markings inaccurate and unreliable, you must reposition and secure the glass.

Increasingly, modern aircraft use digital displays to indicate engine performance. Digital displays use the same colors, but might indicate the performance in a variety of ways. [Figure 2-2]

Now that you understand how to interpret the markings on engine instruments, the following paragraphs provide an overview of specific instruments. As each instrument is discussed, keep in mind that the performance limits of individual engine models vary considerably. Therefore, the procedures and operational ranges that are used in this section do not necessarily correspond to any specific engine.

## CARBURETOR AIR TEMPERATURE GAUGE

Carburetor air temperature (CAT) is measured at the carburetor inlet by a temperature sensing bulb in the ram air intake duct. The sensing bulb senses temperature in the carburetor and sends a signal to

**Figure 2-2.** Digital flight displays present engine performance information intuitively and efficiently.

a cockpit instrument calibrated in degrees. The primary purpose of a CAT gauge is to indicate when carburetor ice might form. [Figure 2-3]

**Figure 2-3.** This carburetor air temperature gauge highlights the danger of induction system icing when the temperature is between −15°C to +5°C.

In addition to identifying the conditions in which ice might form, the carburetor air temperature gauge can indicate the onset of detonation. If a CAT gauge has a red line identifying a maximum operating temperature, engine operation above that temperature increases the chance of detonation occurring.

Checking CAT before engine startup and immediately after shutdown provides an indication of fuel temperature in the carburetor body. During startup, this information can be used to identify whether fuel is warm enough to vaporize. For aircraft with pressure-type carburetors, a high CAT after engine shutdown warns of trapped fuel that could expand and produce potentially damaging fuel pressure. Alternately, high CAT temperatures after shutdown can also indicate the onset of **vapor lock**, which results from vaporized fuel bubbles that stop the flow of fuel to an engine. If CAT readings are observed after engine shutdown, the fuel selector valve and throttle should be left open until the engine cools. This relieves fuel pressure by letting some of the expanding fuel return to the tank.

### FUEL PRESSURE GAUGE

Many aircraft have a fuel pressure gauge that displays the pressure of fuel supplied to the carburetor or fuel control unit. Most fuel pressure instruments display fuel pressure in pounds per square inch (p.s.i.) to enable the pilot to determine whether the engine is receiving the appropriate amount of fuel for a given power setting. Pilots can also use the fuel pressure gauge to verify the operation of an auxiliary fuel pump. [Figure 2-4]

**Figure 2-4. The upper fuel pressure gauge is typical for an engine equipped with a float type carburetor (fuel pressure range between 0.5 psi and 8 p.s.i.). The lower fuel pressure is typical for engines equipped with a fuel injection system (fuel pressure between 14 and 45 p.s.i.).**

Fuel pressure can be measured in multiple ways. One type of fuel pressure gauge uses a Bourdon tube. A **Bourdon tube** is a flattened metal tube formed in a circular shape. One end of the tube is open, while the other end is sealed. The open end of the Bourdon tube is connected to the engine fuel system with a capillary tube containing pressurized fuel. As fuel pressure increases, the tube tends to straighten. Through a series of gears, this motion is used to move an indicating needle on the instrument face. [Figure 2-5]

Another type of fuel pressure indicator uses a **pressure capsule**, or **diaphragm**, instead of a Bourdon tube. A diaphragm-type pressure indicator is also connected to the engine fuel system with a capillary tube. As the diaphragm becomes pressurized, it expands, which causes an indicator needle to rotate. [Figure 2-6]

A third type of fuel pressure indicator replaces the diaphragm with a **bellows**. Operation is similar to the diaphragm pressure indicator, but the bellows provides a greater range of motion for greater accuracy. As the fuel pressure increases, the expansion of the bellows inside the instrument case moves the indicator needle. [Figure 2-7]

Another type of fuel pressure indicating system is electric. Aircraft with electric fuel pressure indicat-

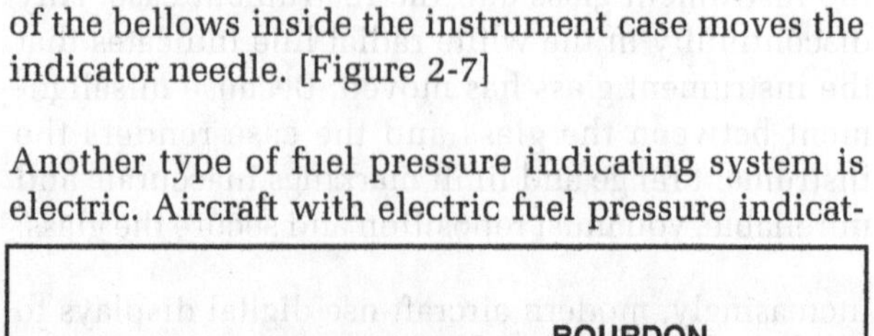


**Figure 2-5. When pressurized fuel enters a Bourdon tube, the tube straightens and causes an indicator needle to move. Because the amount a Bourdon tube straightens is proportional to the pressure applied, they are often used to indicate pressure.**

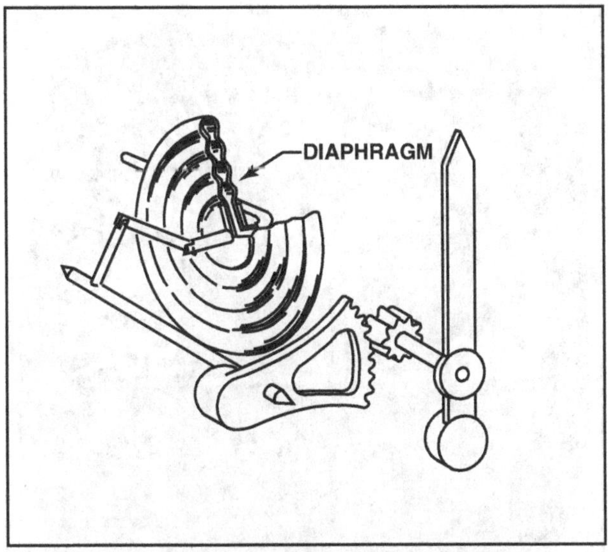


**Figure 2-6. Pressure applied inside a diaphragm causes it to expand, rotating the sector gear. The sector gear moves the pinion gear attached to a pointer on a common shaft.**

ing systems use pressure sensors, or **transducers**, that transmit electrical signals proportional to the fuel pressure to the cockpit. An electric fuel pressure gauge in the cockpit receives the signals and displays fuel pressure information. An advantage of electric fuel pressure indicating systems is that they avoid introducing fuel into the cockpit.

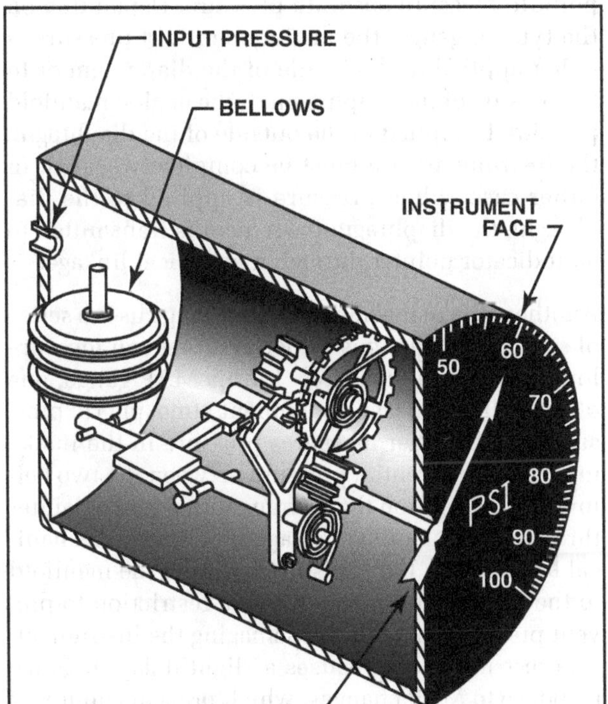


**Figure 2-7. A bellows offers the advantage of a greater range of motion than a Bourdon tube or diaphragm and is sometimes used with aircraft.**

On aircraft with direct fuel injection or continuous-flow fuel injection systems, fuel pressure is typically measured as a pressure drop across the injection nozzles. The pressure drop at the nozzles is proportional to the amount of fuel being supplied to the engine and engine power output. Therefore, the gauges in this type of fuel pressure indication system can also be calibrated in p.s.i. or as a percentage of power.

## FUEL FLOW INDICATOR

A fuel flow indicator measures the rate of fuel that an engine burns, expressed in gallons or pounds per hour. This is the most accurate indicator of engine fuel consumption. When combined with other instrument indications, the amount of fuel that an engine burns can be used to set the engine to obtain maximum power, speed, range, or economy. [Figure 2-8]

On aircraft with a continuous-flow fuel injection system, the fuel flow indicator can measure the pressure drop across the fuel injection nozzles to determine fuel flow. This is possible because fuel pressure in a direct fuel injection system is proportional to fuel flow. With this type of system, a higher fuel flow produces a greater pressure differential across the injectors, and a corresponding increase in fuel flow is indicated in the cockpit. However, if an injector nozzle becomes clogged, the pressure differential across that nozzle increases, which generates a false high-fuel-flow reading.

**Figure 2-8. A typical fuel flow indicator displays the number of gallons (or pounds) per hour an engine consumes. Normal fuel flow indicated by this gauge is between 4.25 and 11.5 g.p.h.**

Another type of fuel flow measurement system measures the volume of fuel flowing to an engine. This type of system is commonly referred to as an **autosyn** system and incorporates a movable vane within the fuel line leading to the engine. As fuel flows through the line, it displaces the vane. A spring force opposes the fuel flow and returns the vane to neutral when no fuel is flowing. The vane movement is electrically transmitted to the flow indicator in the cockpit.

The movement of the vane must be linear to get an accurate flow measurement. To do this, the restriction created by the vane must get larger as the vane increases its rotation. This increase is calibrated into the design of the flowmeter sender unit.

In addition to a fuel flow gauge, some aircraft are equipped with fuel totalizers. A computerized **fuel totalizer** provides a digital readout that indicates the amount of fuel used, fuel remaining, current rate of fuel consumption, and the time remaining for flight at the current power setting. Early totalizers were mechanical counters that responded to electric pulses; however, new systems use electronic counters. Fuel totalizers are usually mounted on the instrument panel and are electrically connected to a flowmeter installed in the fuel line to the engine. When the aircraft is serviced with fuel, the counter is set to the total amount of fuel in all tanks. As the flowmeter senses fuel flow, it sends a signal to a microprocessor, which calculates fuel used and fuel remaining.

## MANIFOLD PRESSURE GAUGE

A manifold absolute pressure (MAP) gauge measures the absolute pressure of the fuel/air mixture within the intake manifold. All aircraft that have a constant-speed propeller to indicate engine power output have a MAP gauge. Pilots use MAP gauge indications to set the engine power at a pressure level that will not damage the engine. Doing so is especially critical for aircraft with turbocharged engines. [Figure 2-9]

When the engine is not running, the MAP gauge displays the local ambient, or atmospheric, pressure. However, after the engine is started, the manifold pressure drops significantly, sometimes to half the existing ambient air pressure. At full power, the manifold pressure in normally aspirated engines will not exceed ambient pressure, but in turbocharged engines manifold pressure can exceed ambient pressure.

**Figure 2-9. A manifold absolute pressure gauge displays absolute air pressure in the engine's intake manifold in inches of mercury. The green arc indicates the normal operating range and the red line indicates maximum allowable manifold pressure.**

A mechanical MAP gauge consists of a sealed diaphragm constructed of two concentrically corrugated thin metal discs that are soldered together to form a chamber. The chamber is evacuated, creating a partial vacuum that can be used as a reference point to measure absolute pressure. Depending on the type of gauge, the engine manifold pressure is either applied to the inside of the diaphragm or to the outside of the diaphragm. If the engine manifold pressure is applied to the outside of the diaphragm, the instrument case must be completely sealed. In either case, when pressure is applied to the diaphragm, the diaphragm movement is transmitted to an indicator pointer through mechanical linkage.

Another type of mechanical MAP gauge uses a series of stacked diaphragms or bellows that can measure low or negative pressures. In this MAP gauge, one of the bellows measures ambient atmospheric pressure and the other measures pressure in the intake manifold. Differential pressure between the two bellows causes motion that is transmitted to the pointer through a mechanical linkage. For either mechanical MAP gauge, the pressure line from the manifold to the instrument must contain a restriction to prevent pressure surges from damaging the instrument. The restriction also causes a slight delay in gauge response to MAP changes, which prevents jumpy or erratic instrument pointer motion. [Figure 2-10]

An analog or digital MAP gauge receives an electric signal from a pressure sensor attached to the manifold.

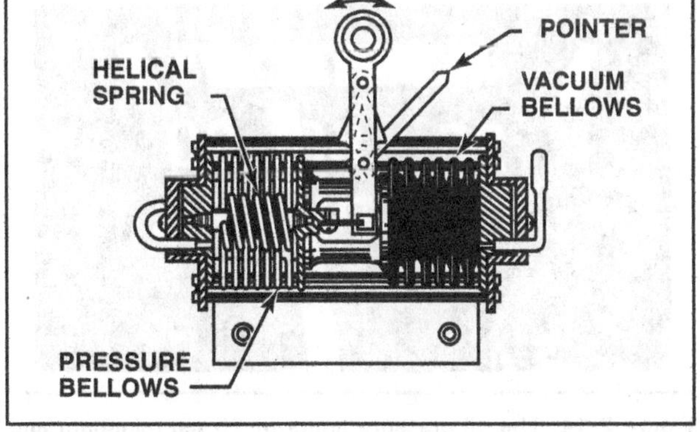


**Figure 2-10. The differential pressure bellows of a manifold pressure gauge measures the difference between intake manifold pressure and a partial vacuum.**

Whenever you run an engine equipped with a MAP gauge, check the gauge for proper operation. For example, before you start the engine, verify that the MAP gauge indicates ambient pressure. After the engine is started, verify that the MAP drops. When engine power is increased, the manifold pressure should increase evenly and in proportion to the engine power output.

## OIL TEMPERATURE GAUGE

The oil temperature gauge enables pilots to monitor the temperature of the oil entering the engine. This is important because oil circulation cools the engine as it lubricates the moving parts. Most oil temperature gauges are calibrated in degrees and sense oil temperature at the engine's oil inlet. [Figure 2-11]

Most oil temperature systems are electrically operated using either a **Wheatstone bridge** circuit or a ratiometer circuit. A Wheatstone bridge circuit consists of three fixed resistors and one variable resistor whose resistance varies with temperature. [Figure 2-12]

Initially, when power is applied to a Wheatstone bridge circuit all four resistances are equal; there is

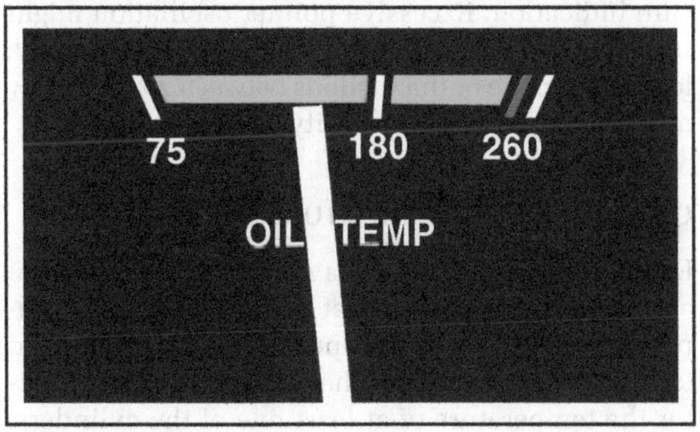


**Figure 2-11. The green arc between 75°F and 245°F on this oil temperature instrument shows the desired oil temperature range for continuous operation. The red line is located at 245°F and indicates the maximum permissible oil temperature.**

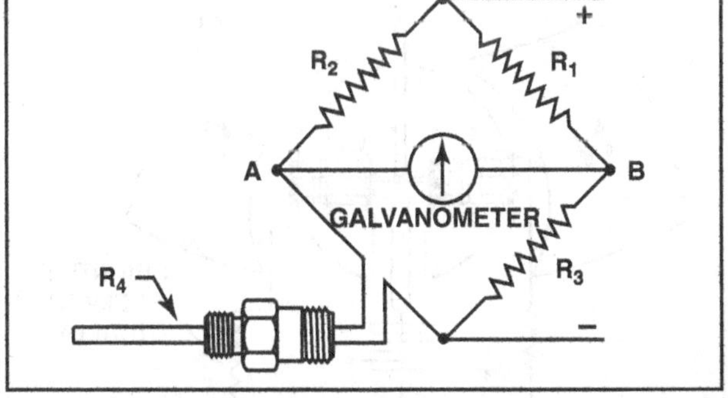


**Figure 2-12. A typical Wheatstone bridge has three fixed resistors and one variable resistor. The temperature probe contains a variable resistor; resistance changes depending on the temperature of the oil flowing past the probe. The bridge in the circuit consists of a galvanometer that is calibrated in degrees to indicate temperature.**

no difference in potential between the bridge junctions. Engine oil heats the probe and the resistance of the variable resistor increases. With more current flowing through the fixed resistor than the variable resistor, a voltage differential exists between the bridge junctions. This causes current to flow through the galvanometer indicator. A greater voltage differential causes increased current flow through the indicator, which causes the instrument needle to deflect. Because indicator current flow is directly proportional to oil temperature, the indicator is calibrated in degrees.

A **ratiometer** circuit measures current ratios and is more reliable than a Wheatstone bridge, especially when the supply voltage varies. Typically, a simple ratiometer circuit consists of two parallel branches powered by the aircraft electrical system. One branch consists of a fixed resistor and coil, and the other branch consists of a variable resistor and coil. The two coils are wound on a rotor that pivots between the poles of a permanent magnet, which causes a meter movement in the gauge. [Figure 2-13]

The permanent magnet is shaped so that the air gap between the magnet and coils is larger at the bottom than at the top. Therefore, the flux density, or magnetic field, is progressively stronger from the bottom of the air gap to the top. Current flow through the coils creates electromagnets that interact with the permanent magnet. The rotor pivots until the magnetic forces are balanced. When the resistance of the temperature probe is equal to the fixed resistor, current flow is equal and the indicator points to the center position. When the probe temperature increases, resistance increases. Decreased current through the temperature-sensing branch causes a current flow imbalance and the pointer indicates the oil temperature.

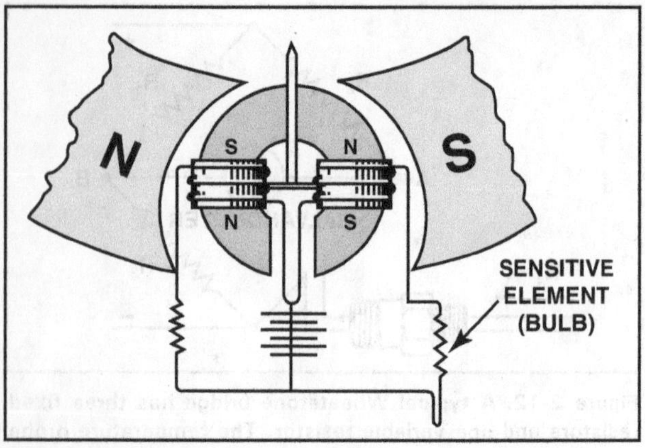


**Figure 2-13. A ratiometer temperature measuring system operates with two circuit branches that balance electromagnetic forces. One branch contains a coil and fixed resistor while the other contains a coil and variable resistor, located in the temperature sensing probe. The coils are wound on a rotor which pivots in the center of a permanent magnet air gap.**

Ratiometer temperature measuring systems are extremely accurate and used when supply voltage might undergo significant variation. Aircraft and engine manufacturers generally prefer ratiometer oil temperature sensing over Wheatstone bridge systems.

Many modern engines use analog or digital gauges that display an electric signal from a temperature sensor attached to an oil cooler.

Some older gauges used **vapor pressure** in a Bourdon tube to measure oil temperature. The Bourdon tube is connected to a liquid-filled temperature-sensing bulb by a capillary tube. The bulb, which is installed in the engine's oil inlet line, is heated by the oil. As the volatile liquid in the sensing bulb is heated, vapor pressure in the capillary and Bourdon tubes increases, which causes the Bourdon tube to straighten. The straightening motion is mechanically translated to the indicator to show temperature.

## OIL PRESSURE GAUGE

Aircraft are equipped with an oil pressure gauge to enable pilots to monitor the engine lubrication system. Oil pressure in most reciprocating engines is typically controlled within a narrow operating range. Inadequate oil pressure can lead to oil starvation in engine bearings. Excessive oil pressure can rupture gaskets and seals. [Figure 2-14]

Modern aircraft generally use analog or digital pressure displays with electrical transmitters. These systems are highly accurate and require little maintenance.

**Figure 2-14. The oil pressure limits of 25 psi minimum and 90 psi maximum on this gauge are representative of a typical small aircraft engine. The normal operating range of 60 to 90 psi ensures enough oil pressure to protect bearing surfaces without rupturing engine seals and gaskets.**

Earlier oil pressure gauges use a Bourdon tube to control the indicator. The gauge is connected to a point downstream from the engine oil pump by a capillary tube. The gauge measures the pressure of the oil delivered to the engine. To protect them from occasional surges, most gauges have a small inlet restriction.

A disadvantage of this type of oil pressure indicator is poor performance in cold weather: the oil in the line between the engine and cockpit gauge might congeal. The congealed oil will cause false readings of either low or no oil pressure. This error can be minimized by filling the oil line with very light oil.

Oil pressure should be monitored regularly, especially during engine start-up. For example, many aircraft manuals instruct you to look for an indication of oil pressure within 30 seconds, or one minute in extremely cold weather. If oil pressure is not indicated in that time, you should shut down the engine. Engine shutdown is precautionary to prevent damage until you are able to determine why there is no pressure indication. Excessive pointer oscillation might indicate that air is trapped in the oil line. Finally, low oil pressure or fluctuations between zero and low might indicate low oil quantity.

## CYLINDER HEAD TEMPERATURE GAUGE

Engine temperature can have a dramatic affect on engine performance. Most reciprocating engine-powered aircraft are equipped with a cylinder head temperature (CHT) gauge that enables pilots to monitor the temperature of at least one of the cylinders. Some gauges display the temperature of each cylinder. For an engine with only one probe, the manufacturer typically installs it on the cylinder expected to have the highest temperature. [Figure 2-15]

**Figure 2-15. A typical cylinder head temperature gauge consists of a relatively large green arc and a single red line. The instrument above has a normal operating range that begins at 200°F and peaks at a red line of 475°F.**

Most cylinder head temperature gauges are galvanometers that display temperature in degrees. Recall that a galvanometer measures the amount of electrical current produced by a thermocouple. A **thermocouple** is a circuit consisting of two wires of dissimilar metal connected at two junctions to form a loop. Any time that a temperature difference exists between the two junctions, a small electrical current is generated. The change in current is directly proportional to the change in temperature. Typical dissimilar metal combinations employed are iron and constantan, or Chromel® and Alumel®. Because a thermocouple generates its own electrical current, CHT gauges normally operate independently from the aircraft power system.

The two junctions of a thermocouple circuit are commonly referred to as the hot and cold junctions. The **hot junction** is installed in the cylinder head in one of two ways. The two dissimilar wires might be joined inside a bayonet probe that is then inserted into a threaded receptacle in a cylinder or the wires might be embedded in a special copper spark plug gasket. The **cold**, or **reference, junction** is typically located in the instrument case.

Thermocouple instrument systems are polarized and extremely sensitive to resistance changes within their electrical circuits. Therefore take special care when replacing or repairing them. First, observe all color-coding and polarity markings: accidentally reversing the wires will cause the meter to move off-scale on the zero side. Second, ensure that all electrical connections are clean and tightened to the correct torque setting.

Thermocouple wiring leads are typically supplied in matched sets, secured together by a common braid. Furthermore, the leads are a specified length, matched to the system, to provide accurate temperature indications. The length of the leads cannot be altered because doing so changes their resistance. In some cases, the wiring leads are permanently attached to a thermocouple, necessitating the replacement of the entire assembly if a wire breaks or becomes damaged.

### EXHAUST GAS TEMPERATURE GAUGE

Another performance monitoring instrument used with reciprocating engines is the exhaust gas temperature (EGT) gauge. An EGT gauge measures the temperature of the exhaust at some point past the exhaust port. Because the fuel/air mixture setting directly affects combustion temperature, pilots can use an EGT gauge to set the mixture for the best power or fuel economy. A typical EGT gauge is calibrated in degrees. [Figure 2-16]

Like the cylinder head temperature gauge, EGT indicating systems also use thermocouples to sense temperature. Thermocouple wiring for an EGT is usually made from Chromel and Alumel. Alumel, enclosed in a green lead, is normally the negative lead; while Chromel, enclosed in white insulation, is the positive lead. The hot junction of an EGT thermocouple is usually mounted somewhere on the exhaust manifold with direct exposure to the exhaust gasses. The cold junction is located in the instrument case.

EGT readings are commonly used to set the fuel/air mixture for best economy and best power settings. For example, leaning the fuel/air mixture to obtain a peak EGT value results in a mixture that delivers the best economy and maximum endurance. However, most engine manufacturers caution

**Figure 2-16. The fuel/air mixture can be set for best fuel efficiency by using an EGT gauge and following the aircraft checklist instructions.**

against continuous operation at or below peak EGT with high power settings. Depending on the manufacturer's instructions, many engines are set to best power by adjusting the mixture to peak EGT, then enriching it to lower the EGT by about 25 degrees Fahrenheit. Some digital EGT monitoring systems can direct a pilot to make specific fuel adjustments for optimal performance.

### ENGINE ANALYZERS

Many reciprocating engine-powered aircraft use some form of analyzer to monitor engine performance. CHT gauges and EGT gauges are used in the simplest systems. From the information provided by an analyzer, a pilot can accurately adjust engine controls to obtain desired engine performance.

It is often difficult to detect small changes in engine instrument indications, yet it is critical for pilots to know whether a system is operating abnormally. Therefore, in addition to an engine analyzer, an aircraft might be equipped with a system of annunciator lights or digitally displayed warnings on a primary flight display (PFD) or multifunction display (MFD) to attract attention when an engine parameter is outside its normal range.

### TACHOMETER

A tachometer displays the revolutions per minute (r.p.m.) of the engine crankshaft. This primary engine instrument, together with the manifold pressure gauge on airplanes with a constant speed propeller, provides a means by which to monitor and set engine performance. Most nondigital tachometer displays are divided in increments of 100 r.p.m. and marked with a red line to indicate the maximum limit. [Figure 2-17]

**Figure 2-17. The tachometer is a primary engine instrument which provides engine r.p.m. indications. A typical tachometer instrument face is calibrated in hundreds of r.p.m. and has both a green arc and red line.**

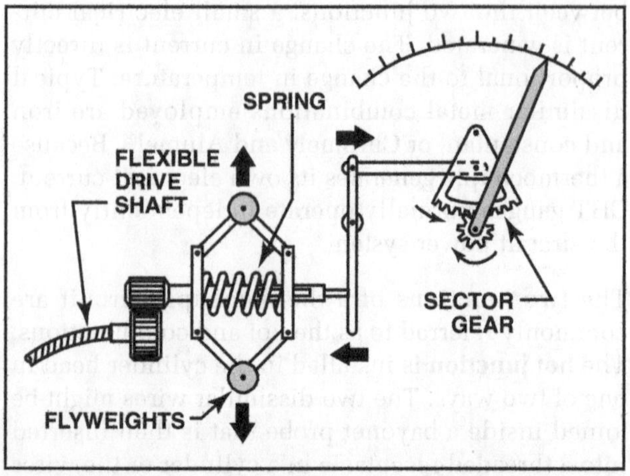

**Figure 2-18. A mechanical tachometer consists of a set of flyweights driven by a flexible shaft attached to the engine. The outward movement of the flyweights is transferred to the pointer and is proportional to the engine's speed.**

The four common types of tachometers are mechanical, magnetic, electric, and electronic. **Mechanical tachometers** were used on early aircraft and consisted of a set of flyweights driven by a flexible drive shaft through a set of gears. A flexible shaft extends from the instrument to a drive gear within the engine. The drive shaft rotates a set of flyweights in the instrument and centrifugal force pulls the flyweights outward. This outward movement is transferred to a pointer through a gear mechanism. [Figure 2-18]

**Magnetic tachometers** also use a flexible drive shaft; however, instead of flyweights, the mechanism for indicating r.p.m. is a cylindrical magnet inside a **drag cup**. As the drive shaft rotates the magnet, electromagnetic forces cause the drag cup to rotate in the same direction as the magnet. The drag cup is attached to a spring that limits rotation. Cup rotation is proportional and calibrated to indicate engine speed. [Figure 2-19]

Use of a flexible drive shaft to operate a tachometer is limited by the distance between the engine and cockpit. Electric tachometers were developed to replace the drive shaft with wires. A typical electric tachometer system consists of a **tachometer generator** mounted on the engine and the indicator with a synchronous motor inside. As the engine rotates, the tachometer generator produces AC voltage with

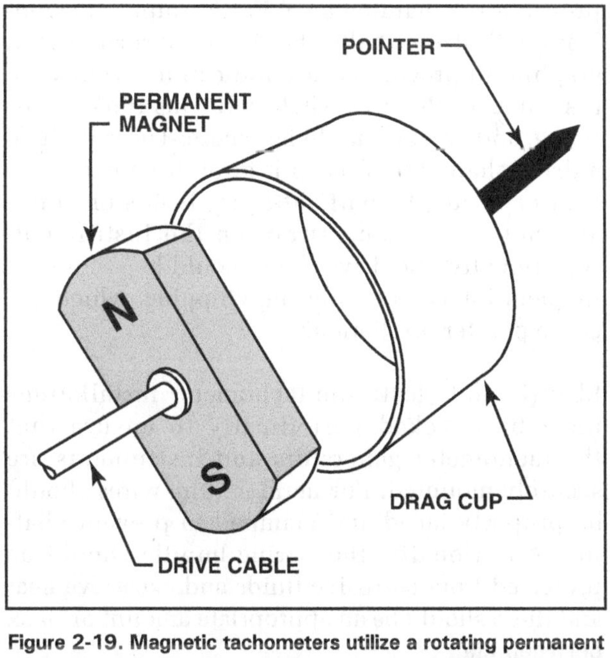


**Figure 2-19. Magnetic tachometers utilize a rotating permanent magnet and drag cup to provide indications. Electromagnetic forces generated by the spinning magnet are balanced by a spring attached to the drag cup.**

a frequency directly proportional to engine speed. The AC voltage powers the synchronous motor in the indicator, causing it to turn at the same speed as the generator. The synchronous motor spins a magnet and drag cup assembly similar to a magnetic tachometer to display r.p.m. [Figure 2-20]

Electronic tachometers indicate engine r.p.m. by counting electric pulses from the engine or the magneto system. A signal can be derived from an engine component, special magneto breaker points, or the rotating magnet in a magneto. The system counts pulses, which are sent digitally to the tachometer display in the cockpit. As engine speed increases, pulse frequency and voltage increase, causing the meter movement to register increasing r.p.m.

A simple electronic tachometer is installed with two electrical connections; one connection to ground and one to the engine or magneto sensor. This type of system depends on timing pulses strong enough to operate the instrument without amplification. A more complex version of the electronic tachometer has an internal solid state amplifier, which requires a third connection for 12-volt power from the aircraft electrical system. The internal amplifier amplifies weak pulses and provides a uniform pulse voltage to the digital counter circuitry.

On multiengine aircraft, the cockpit might have a tachometer for each engine or a single instrument might be used for both engines. If a single tachometer is used, the indicating needle for the right engine is identified by the letter "R" while the indicating needle for the left engine is identified by an "L." [Figure 2-21].

14 CFR Part 27 (Airworthiness standards: Normal category rotorcraft) requires that all helicopters have at least two tachometer systems. One tachometer indicates engine speed, while the second tachometer provides main rotor speed.

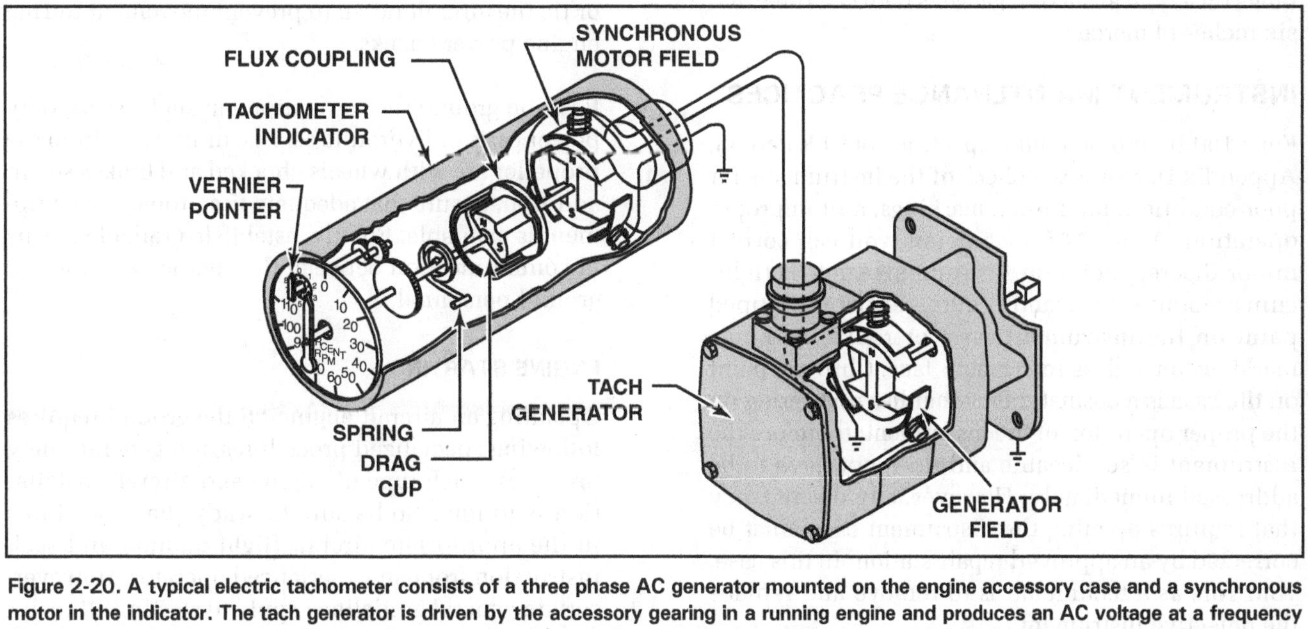


**Figure 2-20. A typical electric tachometer consists of a three phase AC generator mounted on the engine accessory case and a synchronous motor in the indicator. The tach generator is driven by the accessory gearing in a running engine and produces an AC voltage at a frequency directly proportional to engine. The synchronous motor in the indicator is, in turn, driven by the AC voltage from the tach generator at the same speed, or frequency. The motor spins a drag cup assembly to move the Instrument pointer.**

Figure 2-21. Multi-engine aircraft are sometimes equipped with a single tachometer that provides r.p.m. indications for both engines. The needle with an "R" represents the right engine while the needle with an "L" represents the left engine.

## SUCTION GAUGE

The suction gauge is not officially classified as an engine instrument because it does not indicate any engine performance information. However, aviation maintenance technicians refer to the suction gauge to adjust the suction regulator and to verify the operation of the vacuum pump. Most suction gauges are calibrated in inches of mercury and indicate a reduction in pressure from ambient. The normal operating range on a typical suction gauge is between three and six inches of mercury.

## INSTRUMENT MAINTENANCE PRACTICES

For a 100-hour or annual inspection, 14 CFR Part 43, Appendix D, requires a check of the instruments for poor condition, mounting, markings, and improper operation. As an A&P technician, you can correct minor discrepancies on instruments such as tightening mount screws and B nuts, repairing chipped paint on the instrument case, or replacing range markings on a glass instrument face. Chipped paint on the case is a cosmetic flaw that has no bearing on the proper operation of the instrument; therefore the instrument is serviceable and does not have to be addressed immediately. However, any discrepancy that requires opening the instrument case must be corrected by an approved repair station. In this case, your role as a technician is to remove and replace the defective instrument.

Although an A&P license does not permit you to disassemble instruments, you can perform basic preventative maintenance. For example, tachometers with drive shafts should be lubricated with graphite to prevent erratic indications. Hardware that attaches the drive shaft to the instrument, airframe, and engine should be secure. The routing of a drive shaft should keep it away from excessive heat or fluids, be without sharp bends or kinks, and not impose any strain on the instrument. Additionally, the drive shaft should be secured at frequent intervals to prevent whipping, which can cause pointer oscillation.

Electric and electronic tachometer installations must be checked periodically to ensure that the tachometer generators and instruments are securely mounted. Furthermore, the wires should be properly laced and clamped to prevent chafing. Additionally, the wiring bundle should be protected from corrosive fluids and excessive heat and there should be an appropriate amount of slack between clamps.

## GROUND OPERATIONS

Operating an aircraft engine on the ground is a necessary part of an inspection. Because this activity presents a safety hazard to personnel and surrounding equipment, you must take certain precautions. Conduct engine runups in an area specifically designated for that purpose. Ensure that the runup area is level with a clear surface, and position the airplane into the wind and in such a way as to avoid blowing dirt into a hangar or onto other aircraft. For powerful aircraft, you should chock the wheels securely or tie the aircraft down to prevent movement during engine power checks.

Position ground service equipment such as auxiliary power carts or hydraulic service units away from the propeller arc with wheels chocked and brakes set. In addition, ensure that adequate fire protection equipment is available. Finally, establish a reliable means of communication between the engine operator and ground personnel.

### ENGINE STARTING

Operating an aircraft engine on the ground requires following specialized procedures and general safety practices. Each type of engine and aircraft installation is unique, so be sure to study the procedures in the appropriate aircraft flight manual and seek instruction from an experienced operator. However, certain general guidelines apply to starting all reciprocating-engine aircraft. Before every engine start, unmoor the aircraft, check engine fluids, and verify that cockpit engine controls are intact and operational. In addition, carry out the engine runup in a safe area with fire extinguishing equipment and appropriate personnel.

The potential for fire is always present when starting an engine. Because of this, an adequately-sized carbon dioxide fire extinguisher should be available. For large aircraft, where engines are not visible from the cockpit, a fire guard should be stationed with a view of the engines and a means of communicating with the cockpit.

If a carbureted reciprocating engine is over-primed and backfires through the carburetor, the gasoline in the induction system can ignite. If an induction fire occurs, continue cranking the engine to draw the fire into the cylinders. If this fails, signal the fire guard to extinguish the fire.

To start the typical, opposed cylinder, gasoline-powered engine, verify that fuel is available in the tank selected by the fuel selector. Move the mixture control to the full rich position. Most reciprocating engines have a carburetor heat control or alternate air control. Either of these should be in the closed, or full-forward, position. For engines with a constant-speed propeller, move propeller control to full, or forward, position. Move the throttle control lever to a position about one-half inch from the closed position. Leave the avionics switch in the off position, but turn the aircraft master switch on. Prime the engine as specified by aircraft flight manual. Turn the magnetos on and engage the starter (in many aircraft there is a single, keyed switch). After the engine starts, adjust the throttle control for an engine speed of 1000 r.p.m. and check for oil pressure.

If the engine becomes flooded during an attempt to start, place the mixture in the idle cutoff position. Advance the throttle forward to the full open position. Use the starter to turn the engine and clear the cylinders of excess fuel. After this is complete, you can repeat the normal start procedure.

#### ENGINE WARM-UP

Operate the engine at a speed between 800 and 1000 r.p.m. until normal operating temperatures are attained. At lower speeds, leave the mixture control at the recommended setting. Avoid using a lean mixture to hasten engine warm-up. Proper engine warm-up is important, particularly when the condition of the engine is unknown. An improperly adjusted idle mixture, intermittently firing spark plugs, or improperly adjusted valves all have an overlapping effect on engine stability. For airplanes equipped with a constant-speed propeller, set the propeller control to the high r.p.m. (low pitch) position. This is important to avoid engine damage due to inadvertent operation of the engine at high power when the control is set in the low r.p.m. (high pitch) position.

During warm-up, monitor the engine instruments for indicators of normal operation. As noted before, the oil pressure gauge should indicate pressure within 30 seconds after a start. If this does not occur, shut the engine down immediately. In cold weather, it can take up to 60 seconds to see an indication of oil pressure.

For carbureted engines, use carburetor heat as required when icing conditions exist. In some instances, heating carburetor air during warm-up prevents ice formation and ensures smooth operation. However, the warm air provided by the carburetor heat system is unfiltered and should not be used in dusty or dirty environments.

Perform a **magneto safety check** during warm-up to verify that ignition system connections are secure and the system will operate correctly at the higher power settings in later phases of the ground check. This test is accomplished at idle r.p.m. When you switch from both magnetos to either the left or right magneto, a noticeable drop in r.p.m. should occur. A magneto r.p.m. drop indicates that the opposite magneto is properly grounded. When the engine is switched from "both" to "off" the engine will stop generating power if both magnetos are properly grounded. Failure to obtain a drop in r.p.m. in a single magneto position, or failure of the engine to cut out when switched to "off" indicates that one or both ground connections are incomplete.

#### GROUND CHECK

After engine warm-up, a ground check is performed to verify the operation of the powerplant and accessory equipment. Take instrument readings under various conditions for comparison with established normal performance data. Generally, the ground check items are included in a preflight run-up checklist.

During the ground check, point the aircraft into the wind, if possible, to take advantage of the cooling airflow. Use the aircraft manufacturer's approved checklists. The actions included in ground checks typically include:

1. Open the cowl flaps (if equipped).
2. Set the mixture to the full rich position.
3. Verify that the propeller control is in the high r.p.m. (low pitch) position.

4. Set the carburetor heat control in the cold position (or alternate air in closed position).
5. Adjust the throttle to obtain the specified r.p.m. and lean the mixture as required.
6. If the engine is carbureted, apply carburetor heat; you should note a slight drop in engine speed. After the engine speed stabilizes, return the carburetor heat control to the cold position.
7. Move the magneto switch from "both" to "right" and back to "both." Then, switch from "both" to "left" and back to "both." You should observe a slight drop in speed (about 25 to 150 r.p.m.) while operating on the right and left magnetos. The drop on either magneto should be approximately the same (with a typical maximum difference of 50 r.p.m.). Check magneto operation according to the engine manufacturer's instructions and tolerances.
8. If the aircraft is equipped with a constant-speed propeller, pull the throttle control toward the low r.p.m. (high pitch) position until you observe a decrease in engine speed. Check propeller operation according to propeller manufacturer's instructions.
9. Check fuel pressure or fuel flow and oil pressure. All must be within established tolerances.
10. Depending on the equipment in the aircraft, check the performance of the electrical system and the vacuum system with the ammeter and suction gauge.
11. Return the throttle to the idle position.

### OPERATING FLEXIBILITY

During a ground check, you should verify whether an engine runs smoothly across its power range. Operating flexibility is the ability of an engine to perform smoothly and reliably at all speeds from idle to full-power. The engine should idle properly and accelerate smoothly to the engine's maximum speed under normal conditions as well as with carburetor heat or alternate air controls on.

### IGNITION OPERATION

By comparing the engine r.p.m. drop encountered while checking magnetos to a known standard, you can determine whether a magneto is properly timed and whether the ignition leads are properly grounded. You might also discover other discrepancies. For example, an *immediate* drop in r.p.m. occurring when you switch to one magneto can indicate a faulty spark plug or ignition harness. However, a slower than normal drop in r.p.m. is usually caused by incorrect ignition timing. This condition also causes a loss of power, but the power loss does not occur as quickly as that due to a defective spark plug.

An engine that quits firing completely when switched to one magneto indicates a malfunction in that magneto ignition system. Conversely, no drop in engine speed likely indicates a defective ground connection. Another discrepancy is indicated when an excessive difference in r.p.m. exists when switching between the left and right magnetos, which is likely due to a difference in timing between the left and right magnetos.

### POWER CHECK

Most aircraft manufacturers require you to operate the engine at full power during the ground check. The power check measures an engine's performance against the manufacturer's established standard. Any given propeller, operating at a constant air density and specific blade angle, requires the same horsepower to turn at a certain speed.

When you conduct a power check on an engine with either a fixed-pitch propeller or a propeller test club, record the maximum engine speed obtained while the aircraft is stationary and the throttle is fully advanced. Compare the static engine speed with the manufacturer's prescribed limits, taking into account current atmospheric conditions, including air temperature, pressure, and the altitude above mean sea level. A static engine speed below prescribed limits indicates that the engine is not developing full power.

When you conduct a power check on an engine equipped with a constant-speed (or variable pitch) propeller, position the propeller control in the high r.p.m. (low pitch) position and advance the throttle to the manufacturer's target r.p.m. Compare the resulting manifold pressure reading with the manufacturer's prescribed range. If engine performance is weak, functioning cylinders must provide more power to the engine for a given r.p.m. Consequently, the throttle will need to be advanced further, resulting in increased manifold pressure. Therefore, higher than normal manifold pressure for a given r.p.m. often indicates an underperforming cylinder or delayed ignition timing. Conversely, low manifold pressure probably indicates that ignition timing is early. Early ignition timing can cause detonation and a loss of power at high power settings.

#### IDLE SPEED AND MIXTURE

If an engine is operated at idle for extended periods of time with an excessively rich fuel/air mixture, the excess fuel tends to build up and foul the spark plugs. But with a properly adjusted idle mixture setting, the engine can operate at idle for long periods. The correct setting results in minimal spark plug fouling and exhaust smoking.

In addition to adjusting mixture in the cockpit with the mixture control, you should perform a mixture check during the ground check to verify proper adjustment of the carburetor or fuel injection system. To perform this check, move the throttle aft to the closed position and pull the mixture control aft to the "idle cutoff" position. Observe the change in r.p.m. just before the engine stops producing power, and then quickly return the mixture control to the "rich" position. Record the rise in r.p.m.

With a properly adjusted engine, r.p.m. should increase slightly (typically 25 r.p.m.) before dropping off dramatically. If the increase in r.p.m. is less than what the manufacturer requires or if no increase occurs, the idle mixture is too lean. However, if the r.p.m. increases above the published value, the mixture is too rich.

#### ACCELERATION AND DECELERATION

Aircraft engines must accelerate and decelerate rapidly. Therefore, during a ground check you should smoothly move the throttle from idle to full power. The engine should accelerate without hesitation and with no evidence of engine backfiring. Similarly, pull the throttle back from full power to idle. The r.p.m. should decrease evenly, without afterfiring (that is, fuel burning in the exhaust system).

Checking acceleration and deceleration can reveal borderline conditions that are undetectable during other checks. The high cylinder pressures developed during this check create significant strain on both the ignition system and the fuel metering system. Identifying discrepancies at an early stage provides for lower cost repairs and increased operational safety.

#### ENGINE STOPPING

The procedure used to shut down an engine varies slightly from engine to engine based on the fuel system. Therefore, always follow the shutdown instructions provided by the manufacturer. Generally, most engines are stopped by moving the mixture control to the idle cut off position. This procedure ensures that all of the fuel in the cylinders and induction system is burned. After all of the fuel is burned, the chance of an accidental start is significantly reduced. After the engine stops, turn the ignition switch to off and remove the key.

If an engine becomes excessively warm during ground operations, let the engine idle for a short time before you shut it down. Letting the cylinder head and oil temperatures cool helps to prevent unnecessary engine damage from shock cooling.

## ENGINE PERFORMANCE

A reciprocating engine consists of hundreds of parts that must all work properly for an engine to operate efficiently. If a component or system fails completely or in part, engine performance suffers. Therefore, it is critically important that you understand the interrelationships between various engine systems and recognize that a given malfunction might have a root cause that seems unrelated.

#### COMPRESSION

For an engine to produce power, all cylinder openings must be sealed during compression strokes. Three factors are critical to ensure proper compression. First, piston rings must be in good condition to prevent leakage between the piston and cylinder walls. Second, the intake and exhaust valves must close tightly to prevent compression loss through the valve ports. Third, valve timing must be correct when the engine is operating at its normal speed. Remember, any time cylinder compression is low, engine performance suffers.

#### FUEL MIXTURE

For best operation, each cylinder must receive the proper fuel/air mixture. If the fuel/air mixture is too rich or too lean, the brake horsepower will decrease. [Figure 2-22]

When an engine is first started, the mixture is typically placed in the full rich position to promote engine starting. However, an engine cannot produce its rated power for any given throttle setting with a full rich mixture. Therefore, before an aircraft takes off, mixture is leaned to the point that the engine produces its maximum, or best, power. In cruise flight, the mixture is normally leaned further to achieve the best economy. Specific leaning procedures should be in accordance with

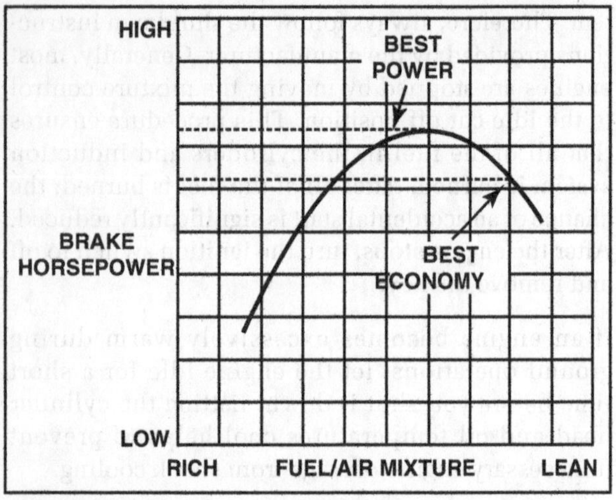


**Figure 2-22. The power an engine develops is determined in part by the fuel/air mixture. As you can see in the graph above, an engine's power output increases to a maximum point as the fuel mixture is leaned. However, beyond this point, the power output falls off as the mixture is further leaned.**

the aircraft flight manual. On some engine fuel systems, an altitude compensating aneroid makes all mixture adjustments, so the mixture control is not always used.

The temperature of combustion in a cylinder corresponds directly to the ratio of the fuel/air mixture. For example, an excessively rich mixture burns cool because excess fuel provides a cooling effect. As the mixture is leaned, the amount of excess fuel available decreases and cylinder temperatures increase. However, if the fuel/air mixture becomes too lean, combustion cannot occur and cylinder temperatures and engine power drop off. [Figure 2-23]

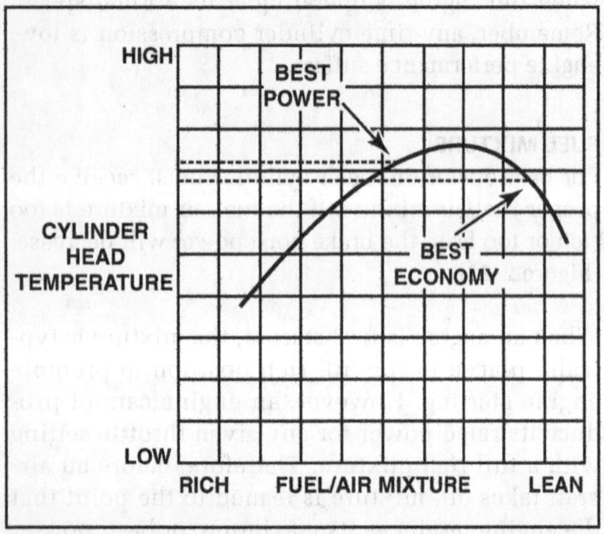


**Figure 2-23. Cylinder head temperature varies with the fuel/air ratio. Notice that excessively rich and excessively lean mixtures produce lower cylinder temperatures.**

### INDUCTION MANIFOLD

An engine's induction manifold distributes air, sometimes mixed with fuel, to the cylinders. On a carbureted engine, liquid fuel is introduced into the airstream; the fuel is vaporized and delivered to the cylinders along with the air. Any nonvaporized fuel clings to the walls of the induction manifold, which affects how much fuel reaches the cylinders. A very rich mixture is often required to start a cold engine. In a cold engine, some of the fuel in the airstream condenses and clings to the walls of the manifold. After the engine warms up and airflow increases through the induction manifold, more fuel is vaporized and less condenses in the manifold.

Any leak in an engine's induction system affects the mixture at the cylinders. When a leak exists, excess air is introduced, causing the mixture to become excessively lean, possibly to the extent where normal combustion cannot occur. This is most pronounced at low r.p.m. settings: because the volume of airflow is low, the additional air from a leak significantly leans the fuel/air mixture.

### IGNITION TIMING

An ignition system consists of two magnetos, an ignition harness, and a set of spark plugs. The magneto is a device that generates electrical energy to ignite the fuel/air mixture. A **magneto** generates high voltage, which is released when breaker points open. A distributor routes the electrical impulses to the cylinders in the specific firing order. For a magneto to operate correctly, it must have correct internal timing. In addition, a magneto must also be correctly timed to the engine. Magneto-to-engine timing is set for the distributor to fire the number one cylinder on the compression stroke at the manufacturer-defined number of degrees before top dead center (TDC).

The **ignition harness** consists of a set of insulated and shielded high-voltage **leads** that transmit the impulses from the magneto distributor to the spark plugs. Each lead terminates at its own spark plug. Although simple, the ignition harness is a critical part of the ignition system. A number of discrepancies can cause a failure. For example, insulation might break down on a wire inside the lead or chafing might permit high-voltage energy to leak through the shielding to ground. Alternately, an open circuit can result from a broken wires or faulty connections.

Any serious defect in an individual lead prevents the high-voltage impulse from reaching the spark plug. When only one spark plug in the cylinder fires, a substantial loss of power occurs, greatly affecting aircraft performance. A bad lead to each spark plug in the same cylinder can prevent the cylinder from generating any power at all.

The most common ignition harness defect, and most difficult to detect, is high-voltage leakage. A special harness tester is used to perform this check. [Figure 2-24]

Spark plugs are simple in construction and operation. Nonetheless, faulty or incorrect spark plugs can contribute to many malfunctions of aircraft engines. Therefore, be sure that you install the approved spark plugs specified for a particular engine. A primary factor used by a manufacturer to select a particular spark plug is its heat range. The **heat range** of a spark plug defines the operating temperature of the firing end of the spark plug.

## MAINTENANCE

Engine reliability is paramount for safe aircraft operations. To maintain reliability, you must perform the appropriate engine inspections and maintenance according to the manufacturer's schedule. Airworthiness standards related to the design, construction, maintenance, and overhaul of aircraft engines are contained in 14 CFR 33, Airworthiness Standards: Aircraft Engines. Appendix A of this part requires that engine manufacturers provide instructions for continued airworthiness for each type of engine they produce. Instructions for continued airworthiness include maintenance manuals, operating instructions, inspection items and intervals,

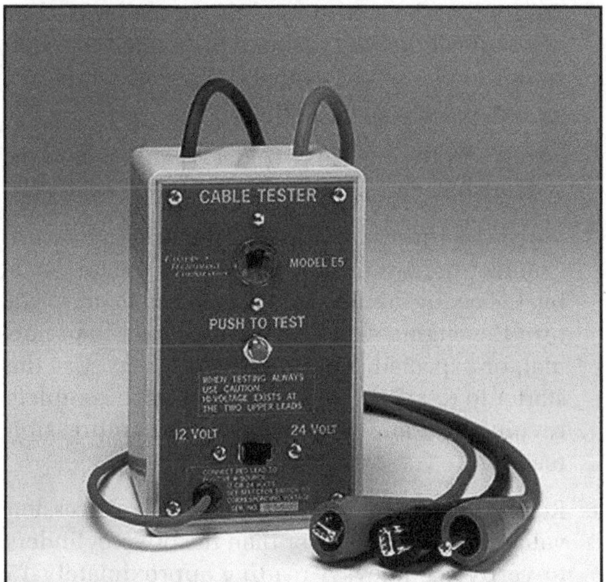


Courtesy of Easter Technology

**Figure 2-24. A high tension ignition cable tester is used to detect defects in ignition leads.**

overhaul procedures, and airworthiness limitations. Engine maintenance tasks and overhaul operations are established by the manufacturer and are scheduled at intervals based on calendar time and accumulated hours of operation.

### COMPRESSION TESTING

A cylinder compression test measures the quality of combustion chamber sealing. A cylinder with good compression provides more power than one with low compression. Leaking valves tend to be the most common cause of cylinder leaks. Improper timing or valve clearance can cause leaks, particles can keep valves from seating, and the valves themselves might have been burned or warped. Sometimes low compression results from excessive wear of piston rings and cylinder walls.

Before performing a compression test, you should run an engine to ensure that the piston rings, cylinder walls, and other parts are near operating temperature and freshly lubricated. If performing a compression check after engine build-up or replacing a cylinder, it is not always possible to operate the engine for this test. In a case like this, spray a small amount of lubricating oil into the cylinder barrels before conducting the test; then rotate the engine several times to lubricate the piston ring seals.

Compression can be measured in two different ways: differential or direct. A **differential pressure** test (also called a cylinder leakage test) measures air leakage in a cylinder. The tester has two gauges: one indicates pressure going into the cylinder and the other indicates how much pressure remains. Using Bernoulli's principle, increased air flow related to cylinder leakage indicates a change of pressure. A theoretical, "perfect cylinder" would not leak, and as such, no pressure drop would occur. [Figure 2-25]

To perform a differential compression test, follow the aircraft manufacturer's instructions. If the propeller is not secured in place, filling a cylinder with compressed air may cause the propeller to rotate. For your own safety, follow all printed and common sense precautions. This procedure should normally be conducted by two technicians. Following are some general guidelines that apply to most differential compression tests:

1. Turn the ignition off and remove the key. Move the throttle control to the closed position. Move the mixture control to the idle cutoff position. Move the fuel selector to the off position.

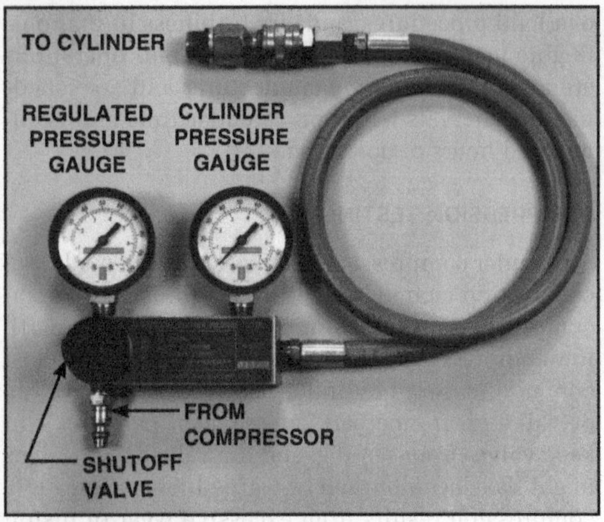

**Figure 2-25. A differential compression tester measures leakage in a cylinder and is a valuable diagnostic tool.**

2. Remove the most accessible spark plug from each cylinder and install a compression tester adapter in the spark plug hole.
3. Turning the propeller by hand, rotate the engine in its normal direction of travel until the piston in the cylinder you are testing reaches TDC on the compression stroke. If you pass TDC, reverse the propeller at least 180 degrees. Then, resume turning the propeller in the normal direction of rotation to eliminate backlash in the valve operating mechanism and to keep the piston rings seated on the lower ring lands.
4. Ensure that the shutoff valve on the compression tester is closed. Connect the compression tester to a compressed air source regulated between 100 and 150 p.s.i. Adjust the regulator of the compression tester for 80 p.s.i.
5. Verify that the shutoff valve on the tester is closed, and then connect the tester to the compression tester adapter in the spark plug hole. Ensure that the propeller path is clear of all people and objects; then support the blade to prevent rotation. Do not let go of the propeller until after pressure is relieved from the cylinder. Open the shutoff valve on the compression tester.
6. With the regulated pressure at 80 p.s.i., read the cylinder pressure gauge. If the cylinder pressure gauge indicates less than the minimum allowed for the engine, rotate the propeller in its normal direction to seat the piston rings in their grooves. Be careful—whenever you move the propeller while air pressure is applied to the piston, ensure that you have tightly secured the propeller. Check the differential pressure of each cylinder and record the readings.

If a cylinder indicates low compression, rotate the engine with the starter or operate the engine to takeoff power before rechecking the low cylinder. While you are checking compression, listen carefully and try to identify any sources of leakage. Assuming a cylinder without cracks, air can leak in three areas: past the intake valve, past the exhaust valve, and past the piston rings. Leakage past the exhaust valve is typically identified by a hissing or whistling at the exhaust stack. Air leaking past the intake valve can usually be heard through the induction system. A hissing sound in the crankcase breather or through the oil filler cap indicates air leaking past the piston rings.

A **direct compression test** measures the actual pressures within a cylinder. While providing an accurate picture of the quality of cylinder compression, this method is less effective for discerning defective components within a cylinder.

Most engine maintenance manuals do not contain instructions for performing a direct compression test. However, follow these general guidelines to perform this procedure:

1. Turn the ignition off and remove the key. Move the throttle control to the closed position. Move the mixture control to the idle cutoff position. Move the fuel selector to the off position.
2. Remove the most accessible spark plug from each cylinder.
3. Ensure that the area around the propeller is clear of people and objects. Rotate the engine with the starter to clear the cylinders of any accumulated oil and loose carbon particles.
4. Install a tester in each cylinder. If only one tester is available, check each cylinder individually.
5. Move the throttle control to the open position. Connect the aircraft to external power for rotating the engine because a weak aircraft battery will turn the engine slowly, showing lower than normal, or expected, compression readings. Use the starter to rotate the engine at least three complete revolutions, and then record the compression readings.
6. Recheck any cylinder that registers a compression value significantly lower than the other cylinders to verify accuracy. A reading approximately 15 p.s.i. lower than the others indicates a cylinder leak that must be repaired. To be sure that the low reading is not the result of faulty test equipment, repeat the compression check with a unit known to be accurate.

## VALVE ADJUSTMENT

As stated before, for an engine to produce maximum rated power, the valves must open and close properly and seal tightly. Valve clearance is a critical factor in making sure that the valves operate properly. For example, when valve clearance is excessive, the valves do not open as wide or remain open as long as they should. This reduces valve duration and the valve overlap period. On the other hand, when valve clearance is less than specified, the period of valve overlap is lengthened.

When valve clearances are wrong, it is unlikely that all clearances are wrong in the same direction. Instead, there is typically too much clearance in some cylinders and too little in others. Naturally, this results in a variation in valve overlap between cylinders. When this happens, it becomes impossible to set the idle fuel mixture for all cylinders, which results in individual cylinders producing various amounts of power. A noticeable effect on mixture distribution between cylinders occurs with a difference in valve clearance as little as 0.005 inch. Variations in valve clearance also effect volumetric efficiency. For example, excessive intake valve clearance results in the valve opening late and closing early. This prevents the cylinder from admitting a full charge of fuel and air. Power is reduced, particularly at high power settings. Improper exhaust valve clearance also affects engine performance, For example, excessive exhaust valve clearance shortens the exhaust event and causes poor scavenging. The late opening can also lead to cylinder overheating because the hot exhaust gases are held in the cylinder beyond the time specified for their release.

Insufficient intake valve clearance has an opposite effect. When an intake valve opens early and closes late, the likely result is backfiring at low speeds. When exhaust valve clearance is insufficient, the early opening shortens the power event and reduces power. The pressure in the cylinder is released before all the useful expansion has worked on the piston. In addition, the late valve closing causes the exhaust valve to remain open for a larger portion of the intake stroke. This may result in a portion of the fuel/air mixture being lost through the exhaust port.

For a valve to seat, the valve must be in good condition, with no significant pressure being exerted against the end of the valve by the rocker arm. If the expansion of engine parts were uniform, the ensuing valve seating would be easy to address. The clearance in a valve actuating system is very small when an engine is cold but increases as the engine operates at normal temperatures. The disparity is caused by differences in the expansion properties of the various metals and the range of temperatures in an operating engine.

Valve clearances change directly with temperature; therefore, in extremely cold temperatures, insufficient clearance can hold a valve open. Thus, cold weather starting might be difficult, if not impossible, because the cylinders are unable to pull the fuel/air mixture into the combustion chamber. Furthermore, if this engine were started, unseated valves would allow some of the fuel/air mixture to leak past the valves on the compression stroke.

Accurate valve adjustment also establishes the intended valve seating velocity. If valve clearances are excessive, the velocity of valve seating will be high, resulting in pounding and stem stretching—conditions that commonly precede valve failure.

The engine manufacturer specifies the valve inspection period for each engine. In addition, you should inspect and adjust the valve mechanism whenever there is a complaint or evidence of rough engine operation, backfiring, loss of compression, or hard starting. In all cases, follow the exact procedure described by the engine manufacturer because unique factors might be involved.

### HYDRAULIC LOCK

Hydraulic lock is a condition that can develop in a radial engine where oil or liquid fuel accumulates, or pools, in the lower cylinders, or lower intake pipes. Because fluids cannot be compressed, attempts to start an engine with hydraulic lock can cause severe damage to the engine. Before attempting to start any radial engine that has not run in the previous 30 minutes, check for hydraulic lock. To do this, make sure the ignition switches are off, then rotate the propeller by hand at least two revolutions in the normal direction. Hydraulic lock is indicated by an abnormal amount of effort required to rotate the propeller.

To eliminate hydraulic lock, remove one of the spark plugs from the lower cylinders and rotate the propeller in the direction of rotation, allowing the piston to expel any liquids. Never attempt to clear hydraulic lock by rotating the propeller in the opposite direction; that would only transfer any liquid from the cylinder to an intake pipe. Doing so increases the possibility of hydraulic lock on a subsequent start. [Figure 2-26]

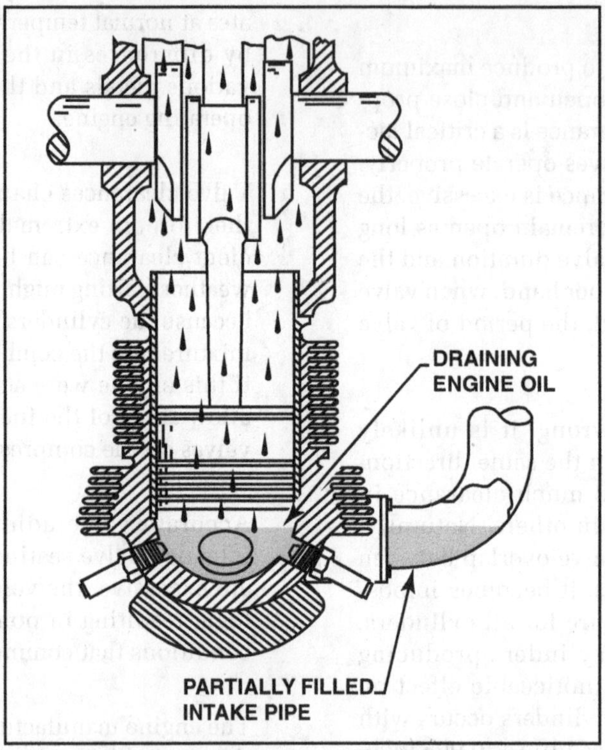


**Figure 2-26. Oil or fuel can seep past the piston rings on the lower cylinders of a radial engine, causing hydraulic lock. The presence of hydraulic lock is identified by an abnormal amount of effort required to rotate the propeller. If a start is attempted under these conditions, severe engine damage can result.**

# SUMMARY CHECKLIST

✓ Engine gauges provide information about the operating condition of an engine.

✓ Many types of sensors and displays are used to deliver engine performance data. These can be electrical, hydraulic, pneumatic, mechanical, digital, or a combination.

✓ Required instrument markings are listed in an aircraft's Type Certificate Data Sheet.

✓ A maintenance technician should perform an aircraft engine operational inspection before and after scheduled maintenance checks and when troubleshooting reported engine discrepancies.

✓ A cylinder compression test is performed to evaluate the quality of the seal in the combustion chamber made by the pistons, piston rings, and cylinder walls as well as the intake and exhaust valves.

✓ A cylinder compression test is most safely performed by two technicians.

# KEY TERMS

green arc
yellow arc
red line
red arc
blue arc
index mark
vapor lock
Bourdon tube
pressure capsule
diaphragm
bellows
transducers
autosyn
fuel totalizer
Wheatstone bridge
ratiometer
vapor pressure
thermocouple
hot junction
cold junction
reference junction
mechanical tachometers
magnetic tachometers
drag cup
tachometer generator
magneto safety check
magneto
ignition harness
leads
heat range
differential pressure test
direct compression test

# QUESTIONS

1. By what three means are cockpit controls identified?

   a. ____________.

   b. ____________.

   c. ____________.

2. What color is used to identify the mixture control? _______.

3. The normal range of operation is indicated by a ______ (what color) arc on most instruments.

4. A yellow arc on an engine instrument indicates a ______ range.

5. If the instrument markings are on the cover glass of an instrument a _______ (what color) index mark is required.

6. Fuel pressure gauges are usually calibrated in what units? _______

7. Manifold pressure gauges measure the ______________ (absolute or gauge) pressure inside the intake manifold.

8. Low oil pressure or fluctuating readings on the oil pressure gauge is often a sign of _______ _______ _____________.

9. Engine oil pressure should be indicated within ______ seconds after start-up of an aircraft engine.

10. Before attempting to start any radial engine that has been shut down for more than 30 minutes you should

11. To eliminate a hydraulic lock, remove one of the ______ _______ from each of the lower cylinders and pull the engine through in the direction of rotation.

12. When starting a reciprocating engine, the carburetor heat control should be in the ______ (hot or cold) position.

13. During a ground check or runup, the aircraft should be headed ______ (into or away from) the wind.

14. When performing a power check on an engine with a variable-pitch propeller, the propeller should be in the ______ (low or high) pitch setting.

15. During an idle mixture check if, when the mixture control is moved to the idle-cutoff position, the engine speed does not increase or drops immediately it indicates that the idle mixture is too ______ (rich or lean).

16. A reciprocating engine is stopped by placing the mixture control in the ____________ (full rich or idle cut-off) position.

17. An air leak at the cylinder end of an intake pipe will result in a ______ (rich or lean) mixture within that cylinder.

18. What are the three main parts of an ignition system?

    a. ____________.

    b. ____________.

    c. ____________.

19. Efficient engine troubleshooting is based on a ____________ (random or systematic) analysis of what is happening.

20. ____________ occurs when the contents of the intake manifold or induction system ignite prior to entering the cylinders.

21. An overly rich mixture that continues to burn in the exhaust system is referred to as ____________.

22. The two basic types of compression tests used on reciprocating engines are

    a. ____________.

    b. ____________.

23. The ____________ compression test checks compression by measuring air leakage in the cylinders.

24. The regulator of the differential compression tester should be adjusted to allow ______ psi of compressed air to enter the cylinder.

25. When performing a differential compression test, the cylinder being tested must be on the ______ stroke with the piston at top dead center.

26. For best results, a differential compression test should be performed after the piston rings and cylinder walls have been freshly ______.

27. Engines equipped with ____________ (solid or hydraulic) lifters must have the valve clearances checked and adjusted periodically.

28. Air leaking past the ______ valve during a differential compression test is indicated by a hissing sound heard at the carburetor inlet.

29. A hissing sound heard at the crankcase breather will indicate air leaking past the ____________.

30. When valve clearance is less than it should be, valve overlap is ____________ (lengthened or shortened).

31. A compression value of approximately _______ psi lower than the other cylinders indicates a cylinder leak that must be repaired.

32. When valve clearance is insufficient, the valve will open _______ (early or late) and close _______ (early or late).

33. Before performing a preflight inspection, always be sure that the _______ (ignition or master) switch is in the "OFF" position.

SECTION B

# ENGINE REMOVAL AND OVERHAUL

## ENGINE REMOVAL

Engine removal involves a series of critical tasks that should be accomplished in an orderly manner to prevent personal injury or aircraft damage. The steps necessary to remove an engine vary for every combination of airframe and engine; however, some general guidelines apply for all. These guidelines are not a substitute for the manufacturer's instructions.

## REASONS FOR REMOVAL

Several circumstances call for an engine to be removed from an aircraft; for example, the engine has reached the manufacturer's published **time between overhaul (TBO)** or performance has degraded significantly. Furthermore, if the engine experiences a sudden stoppage event or if an excessive quantity of metal particles is found in the oil, removal is probably in order. In addition, certain maintenance tasks or repairs can require engine removal. However, before you remove an engine, always consult the applicable manufacturer's instructions to determine if engine removal is necessary.

### ENGINE SERVICE LIMITS

Environmental, operational, and design factors affect engine life. In addition, the frequency and type of preventive maintenance has a direct bearing on the useful life of an engine. As a result, establishing definitive engine overhaul and replacement times is difficult. However, by tracking the service life of several different engines, manufacturers have developed schedules for recommended TBOs.

Aircraft owners operating under 14 CFR Part 91 are not required to comply with a manufacturer's recommended TBO. However, to exceed the recommended times, the FAA requires that an alternate inspection program be approved and complied with. In addition, if an aircraft is operated for hire under 14 CFR 135 as an air taxi, the operator must comply with TBO and the maximum time in service established by the manufacturer.

When a manufacturer delivers a new engine, a permanent record of the engine's operating time is established in the powerplant logbook. Any time that maintenance is performed, a logbook entry should be made referencing the **total time (TT)** the engine has accumulated since it was new. After an engine is overhauled, this record should be continued without interruption. Thereafter, engine operation time should also be referenced **since major overhaul (SMOH)**. Engine inspection and service requirements are based on time since new or major overhaul.

### ATTRITION FACTORS

Sometimes before an engine reaches TBO, signs of severe performance deterioration can lead to engine removal. As engine components wear, symptoms such as increased oil consumption, higher engine operating temperatures or a general loss of power can indicate that an early overhaul might be necessary. Careful monitoring of these conditions over time provides important information for deciding to remove an engine. Several environmental or operational reasons can shorten normal engine life. For example, operating at maximum power settings for prolonged periods of time, frequent starts in extremely cold temperatures, and inadequate preventative maintenance all shorten the useful life of an engine.

### SUDDEN SPEED REDUCTION OR STOPPAGE

A **sudden speed reduction** occurs when the engine is turning and one or more propeller blades strike an object such as a runway light, tool box, hangar, or other aircraft. If this occurs, engine speed drops rapidly until the obstruction is cleared. In this case, the engine continues to operate and its speed typically returns to its previous value. When this occurs, the engine should be shut down immediately to prevent further damage. Inspections of engines that have experienced a sudden speed reduction reveal varying amounts of damage. For example, when the speed reduction occurs at a relatively low speed, the internal damage is typically minor. At low speed, engine power output is also low and the propeller absorbs most of the shock. However, when a sudden speed reduction occurs at high engine speed, more of the impact force is transferred to the engine with a greater likelihood for severe internal damage.

When an engine experiences a sudden reduction in speed, comply with the manufacturer's inspection procedures. At a minimum, you should thoroughly inspect the propeller, engine mounts, crankcase, and, if applicable, the nose section. In addition, remove the engine oil screens or filters to inspect for the presence of metal particles. Then drain the oil into a clean container, straining it through a clean cloth (or filter), and check the cloth and oil for metal particles. The presence of metal particles may indicate the failure of internal engine components and necessitates engine removal and overhaul. However, if metal particles are found with the appearance of fine filings, continue inspection to determine whether the engine can be returned to service.

Remove the propeller to check for misalignment of the crankshaft. On engines that use a propeller gear reduction system, remove the propeller drive shaft. With a dial indicator, rotate the crankshaft and check for misalignment. Engines with flange-type propeller shafts must be checked at the outside edge of the flange; spline-type propeller shafts should be checked at both the front and rear cone seats. The amount of shaft misalignment is referred to as its **runout**. Runout tolerances are published in the manufacturer's maintenance or overhaul manual. If the runout exceeds limits, remove and replace the crankshaft. However, if the crankshaft runout is within the manufacturer's established limits, you can install a serviceable propeller and check propeller track.

If propeller tracking measurements are acceptable, reinstall the oil filter or screen, and service the engine with oil. Start the engine to determine whether it operates smoothly with normal power output. During the ground check, if operation is normal, shut the engine down and repeat the inspection for metal particles in the oil system. The presence of metal indicates internal engine damage and requires further inspection. However, if there are no heavy metal particles in the engine oil, the engine should be scheduled for a flight test. If engine operation is within normal parameters during the flight test, look again for metal in the oil system. If no metal is found, continue the engine in service, but recheck the oil screens for the presence of metal after 10 hours of operation, and again after 20 hours. If you find no indication of internal failure after 20 hours of operation, no further special inspections are necessary.

A **sudden stoppage** is an event in which the engine stops quickly and completely, typically in less than one propeller revolution. The causes of a sudden stoppage are engine seizing or a propeller blade striking an object. Whenever an engine comes to a sudden and abrupt stop, the inertia of the moving parts creates destructively high torque forces that can result in internal gear damage, a bent or broken crankshaft, or damaged crankshaft bearings. When sudden stoppage occurs, manufacturer's instructions usually mandate a complete engine teardown and inspection.

## METAL PARTICLES IN OIL

The presence of excessive metal particles in an engine oil filter or screen or in the oil itself can indicate failure of an internal engine component. In any case, the source of unexpected particles in engine oil must be identified and addressed before the aircraft is released for flight. Be aware that due to the construction of aircraft oil systems, residual metal particles (from a previous engine or component failure) might be present in the oil sludge.

Identify the material particles removed from oil. One way you can determine whether a particle is metal or carbon is to place the material on a flat metal object and strike it with a hammer. (Be sure to wear protective eyewear.) If the particle is carbon, it will disintegrate; however, if it is metal, it will remain intact or change shape. Carbon particles can build up and break loose from the inside of the engine and be mistaken for metal. Check metal particles with a magnet to determine whether the particles are ferrous (containing iron) or nonferrous. Ferrous particles are typically produced by the piston ring wear, whereas nonferrous particles are typically produced by worn journal bearings, such as main and connecting rod bearings.

You can supplement the visual oil inspection with a **spectrometric oil analysis program**, in which you collect an oil sample for laboratory analysis when you drain the engine oil. The laboratory reports the types and quantity of foreign particles found, along with an identification of possible sources. An oil analysis program can detect problems before they become serious and prevent catastrophic engine failure. [Figure 2-27]

## UNSTABLE ENGINE OPERATION

When unstable engine operation persists for a period of time, an engine might be removed for a thorough inspection. Excessive engine vibration, backfiring, afterfiring, cutting out in flight, and reduced power output are all symptoms of potentially serious conditions. Removal might become necessary if previous troubleshooting attempts have been unsuccessful. Duplicating an intermittent malfunction is sometimes easier when the engine is mounted on a test stand with specialized test equipment.

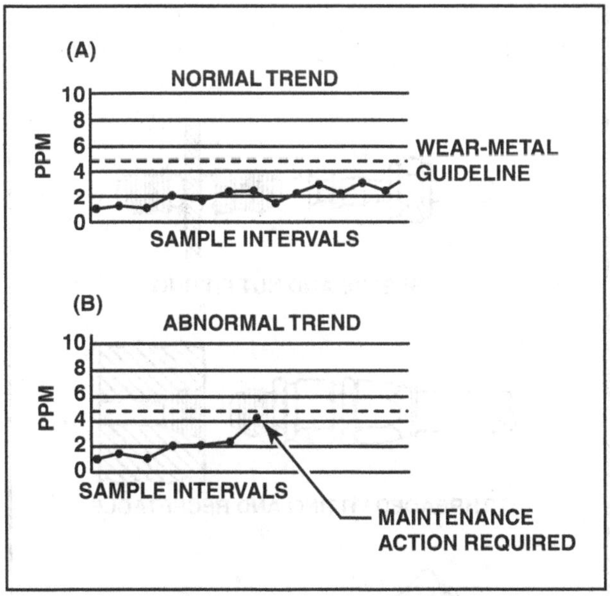


**Figure 2-27. (A) Over time, a normal engine experiences a gradual increase in the amount of metal suspended in its oil. (B) After a baseline is established, a sudden increase in the amount of metal usually indicates an internal engine problem.**

Many operators use **engine condition monitoring** to track the performance of their engine against a baseline, such as that of a new or newly overhauled engine. Coupled with trend analysis techniques, this information can help predict engine (or component) failure and identify necessary preventative or corrective maintenance.

## PREPARATION FOR REMOVAL

When you remove an engine from an aircraft, fluids might leak from the engine, creating a fire hazard. Therefore, engine removal should take place in a well-ventilated area with a fire extinguisher nearby. After the aircraft is positioned in place, chock the main gear wheels to keep it from rolling. If the aircraft has tricycle landing gear, support the tail to prevent the aircraft from tipping back when you remove the engine. In addition, if the aircraft uses gas-charged landing gear shock struts, you might have to deflate them to prevent over-extension after the weight of the engine is removed from the aircraft.

### IGNITION, FUEL, AND BATTERY

Before removing an engine, make sure that the magneto switch is in the OFF position. After you remove the engine cowl, you should remove at least one spark plug from each cylinder. Doing so prevents compression and eliminates the possibility of engine kickback or inadvertent startup when the propeller is turned.

To help prevent fuel leaks and spills, make sure that all fuel shutoff valves are closed. Fuel selector valves are either manually or electrically operated. If an electric solenoid-operated shutoff valve is installed, you might need to apply battery power to close the valve.

Disconnect the battery to reduce the possibility of electrical sparks. If the aircraft will be out of service for more than a few days, take the battery to the battery maintenance area for cleaning, servicing, and charging.

After you remove the cowl, clean it thoroughly and inspect its condition; look for burns, cracks, or elongated fastener holes that require repair. If the cowling needs no repair, move it to a safe place.

### ENGINE OIL

After the magnetos and battery are disarmed, drain the engine oil into a clean container. Use a large metal drip tray under the engine to catch any spills. Remove the drain plug or open the drain valve. In addition, be sure to drain oil from the cooler, return line, and filter. Leave all valves and drains open until the system is completely empty. Reinstall drain plugs, close drain valves, and wipe residual oil from around the drain points. [Figure 2-28]

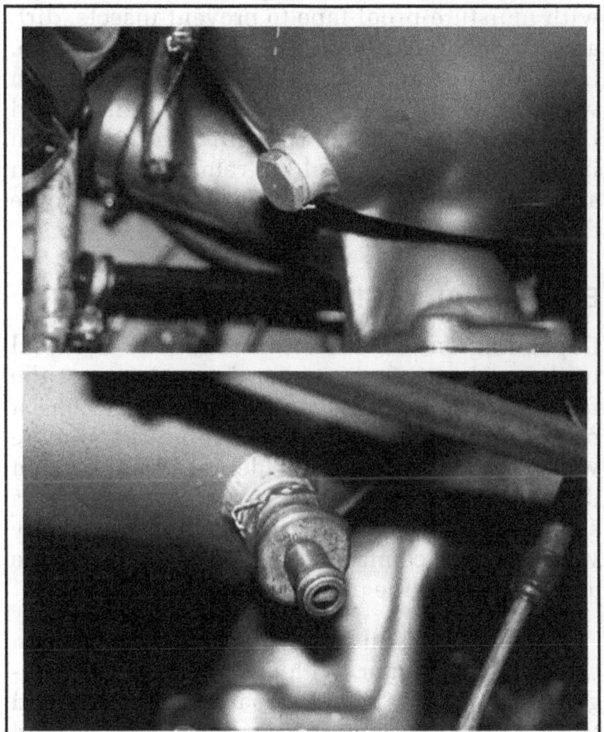

**Figure 2-28. Most of the engine oil in a typical horizontally opposed engine is drained by removing an oil drain plug or opening a drain valve.**

## PROPELLER

After you remove the spark plugs, the propeller can be turned safely and easily. The propeller is often overhauled at the same time as the engine. Typically, one technician can safely remove a fixed-pitch propeller from a light aircraft without additional equipment. However, to remove a larger, constant-speed propeller, you should use a hoist with a propeller sling. In addition, you should seek assistance to prevent damage to the propeller and the surrounding equipment. In every case, follow the manufacturer's instructions for propeller removal.

## FLUID LINES

Disconnect and drain the remaining fluid lines and reservoirs. Fluid lines can be flexible rubber hoses, aluminum-alloy tubing, and stainless steel tubing. For an engine with a float carburetor, after you remove the fuel line, drain the float bow. Most fluid lines that carry high pressure are attached to threaded fittings by a standard B-nut. Low-pressure hoses can also be secured in this manner as well as secured to fittings with hose clamps. Note that quick-disconnect fittings use internal check valves that prevent fluid loss when the line is disconnected. [Figure 2-29]

After you drain a fluid line, plug or cover the ends with moisture-proof tape to prevent insects, dirt, and other foreign matter from entering the line. Label all lines and fittings to minimize confusion when reinstalling them on a new engine. Fluid lines are often replaced at engine overhaul. Even if you intend to discard the removed lines, you should label them as a guide for how to best route the replacements.

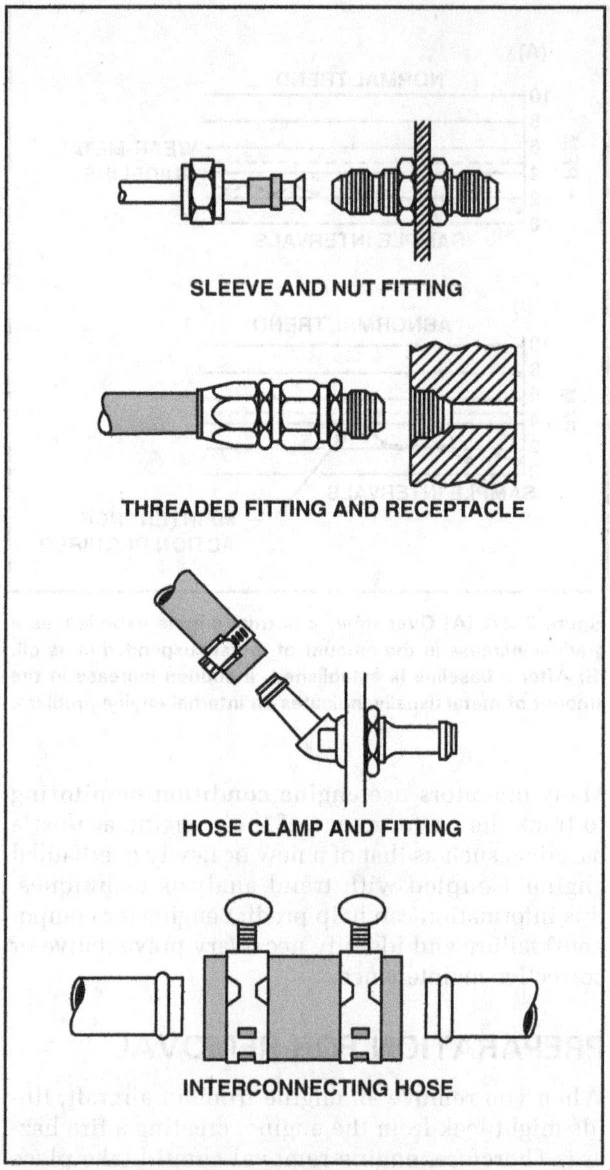


**Figure 2-29. Fluid lines are typically connected to the firewall or an accessory by a B-nut, a threaded fitting and a receptacle, or hose clamps.**

## ELECTRICAL WIRING

Depending on the aircraft installation, electrical leads can be disconnected at the engine or at the firewall. AN and MS connectors typically consist of a plug and receptacle for attaching one or more wires. To help prevent accidental disconnection during aircraft operation, the plug assembly is screwed to the receptacle and secured with safety wire. Open the connection by cutting the safety wire and unscrewing the plug connector.

A terminal strip is another type of wiring connection you might encounter. With this arrangement, a single lead or a group of individual leads is connected to a post on a terminal strip. Except for ground wires, this type of connection is usually enclosed in a junction box. Wire leads are typically terminated with a ring connector that fits over a screw post and is secured with a nut and lock washer. Open the connection by removing the nut and lock washer and lifting the terminal off of the screw post. [Figure 2-30]

In some applications, electrical connections are made with knife-type or wrist-lock connectors. These connectors are normally sealed with a protective sheathing. To open them, remove the sheathing and pivot the terminal connectors to separate.

Protect the exposed ends of connectors with moisture-proof tape when they are disconnected. Also, coil loose cables and secure conduits out of the way to prevent entanglement and damage during engine removal and installation. Label all wires and harnesses to eliminate confusion when making connections after the engine is installed.

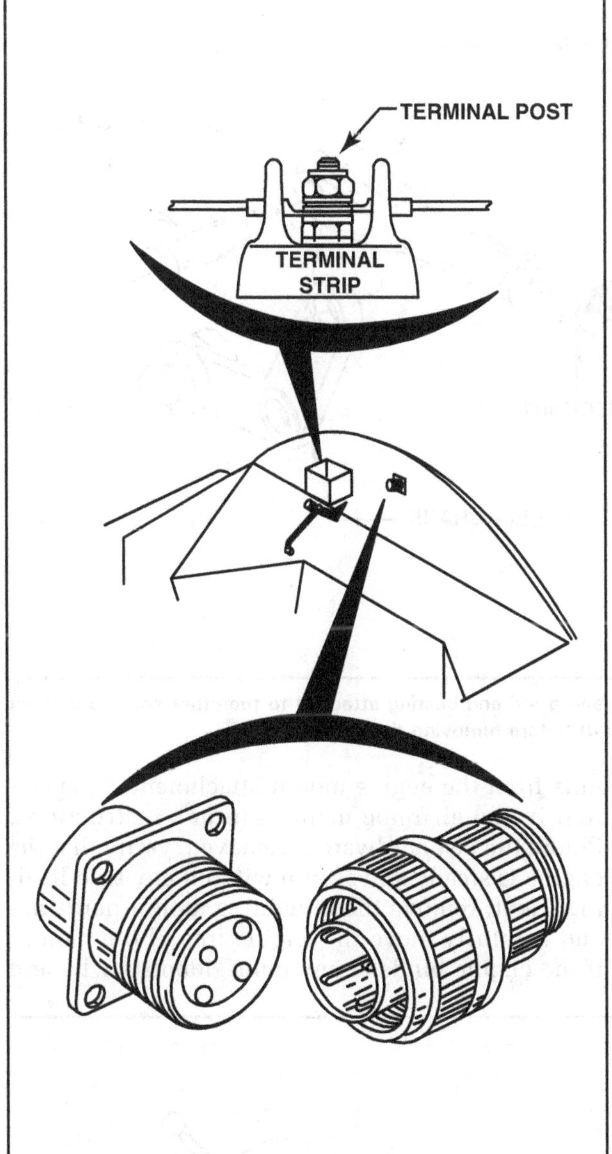


Figure 2-30. Aircraft that use firewall electrical disconnect points use two kinds of electrical connections. One type is a junction box containing terminal strips and terminal posts while the second type consists is a plug-type connector like a cannon plug or Amphenol connector.

## ENGINE CONTROLS

Engine control cables and rods enable the engine to be controlled from within the cockpit. A typical control cable includes its protective housing. In most cases, a cable or rod is threaded at both ends, and includes a clevis on one end and a rod end bearing on the other end. On most aircraft, the rod end bearing is connected to the engine or accessory with a bolt and nut, and secured with a cotter pin. To disconnect, remove the cotter pin, nut, and bolt. Simple cables, such as those used to control carburetor heat, might be attached by clamping action from a screw.

After you disconnect all engine control linkages, inspect the hardware for wear. Cotter pins must be replaced, but if the nuts and bolts remain airworthy, reinstall them in the control rod so they do not get misplaced. Control rods should either be removed completely or tied back to prevent them from damage during engine removal and installation. [Figure 2-31]

Some engine installations use a bellcrank to actuate a control rod; you might need to remove the bellcrank to access the control rod. In such cases, you must also remove the turnbuckle that joins the bellcrank to the actuating cable. Before removing a turnbuckle, mark the depth of engagement of the cable ends. These marks help you to quickly approximate the original position of the controls before final rigging. [Figure 2-32]

## INTAKE AND EXHAUST COMPONENTS

For most aircraft, you must disconnect the air intake and exhaust system components before removing the engine. Because installation of these and other components vary among different engines and aircraft, always follow the manufacturer's instructions for all procedures.

# ENGINE HOISTING

After all airframe connections are free and clear, the engine is ready for hoisting. If an engine is thoroughly prepared, removal is typically a simple task. One decision that remains is whether to remove only the engine or the engine with the mount attached. For a typical overhaul, only the engine is normally removed. However, if you are replacing an engine with a **quick engine change assembly (QECA),** the separation point is usually the firewall. A QECA includes the powerplant with accessories already installed and attached to the engine mount assembly.

Before you loosen and remove the engine attach points, attach a hoist with a sling to support the engine's weight. Aircraft engines have specific points for hoisting. The location of attach points and the sling arrangement varies according to the engine's size and weight. Always follow the engine manufacturer's procedures and use the recommended equipment. For your safety, inspect the sling and hoist before use. Be sure that the hoist is sufficiently rated to lift the engine safely with the hoist arm extended. In most cases, lifting capacity is reduced as the further the hoist arm is extended. [Figure 2-33]

Some engine hoists are fitted with powered drives. Use extra caution with power hoists and seek assis-

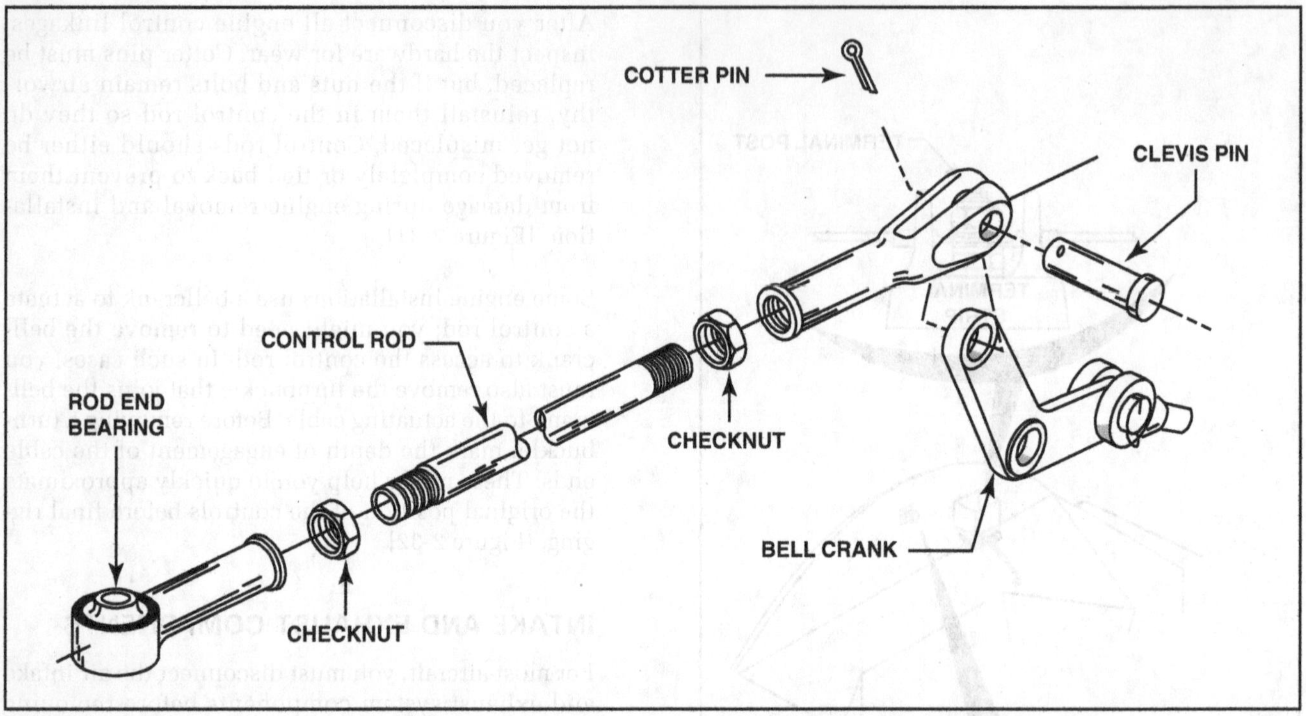


**Figure 2-31. A typical control rod has a clevis pin attached to one end and a rod end bearing attached to the other end. To prevent damaging a control rod, it is best to remove it completely from the aircraft before removing the engine.**

tance from an experienced operator until you are proficient in their use.

Before lifting an engine, verify that the aircraft tail is supported and that wheel chocks are secure. Then raise the engine just enough to remove the engine weight from the mount before removing the nuts from the engine mount attachments as specified in the airframe manufacturer's instructions. Before the last hardware is removed, verify that the engine is steady and secure without any side-loading. Next, remove the remaining mount hardware and carefully move the engine free of the mount; if the engine binds at any point, identify why and

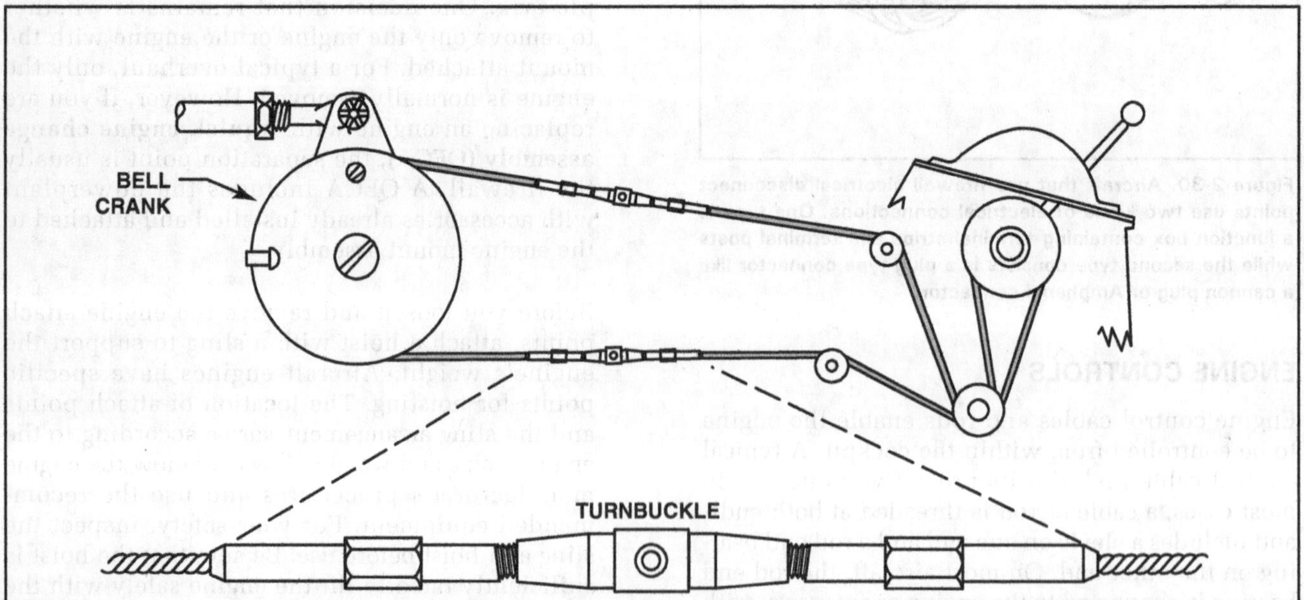


**Figure 2-32. Some control systems consist of a cable and pulley arrangement to actuate engine controls. With this style of system, the cable assembly may have to be separated at a turnbuckle in order to remove the control rod.**

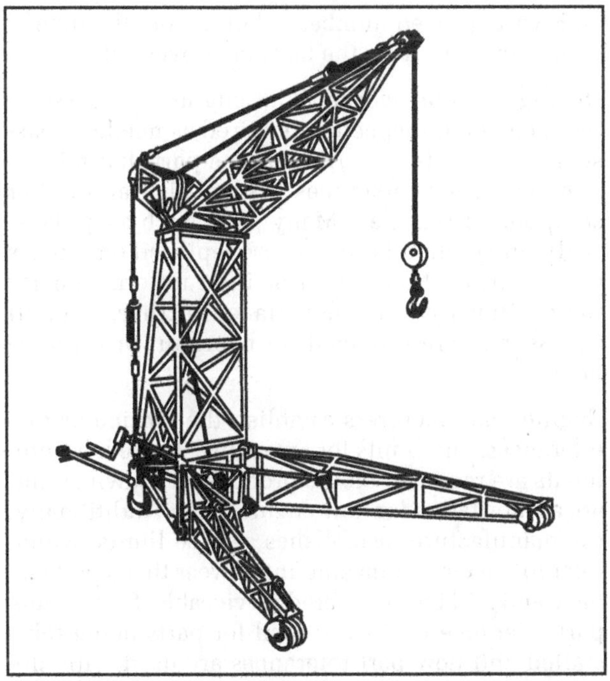

**Figure 2-33. When using a hoist and frame assembly, make sure the hoist can reach the engine with adequate clearance and is rated for the weight of the engine being lifted.**

maneuver the engine as necessary until it moves freely. After the engine is clear of the airframe, lower it to an engine stand and secure it with the appropriate hardware.

## ENGINE COMPARTMENT

Whenever you remove an engine from an aircraft, thoroughly inspect the engine compartment and make any necessary repairs. Examine the nacelle for corrosion, cracks, missing rivets, or other visible defects. Cracks in the cowling or ducts can be stop-drilled or patched if they are within acceptable limits specified in the manufacturer's structural repair manual.

Check the physical condition and operation of engine controls. If there are any control cables and pulleys in the nacelle, inspect them for broken wire strands and pulley binding, flat spots, chipped edges, and excessive play. Inspect the condition of bearings in control rods and verify that the rods are not bent, chafed, or misaligned.

Inspect all exposed electrical wiring for breaks, chafing, deteriorated insulation, or other damage. In addition, examine crimped and soldered terminals for security and cleanliness. Check connector plugs for damage, corrosion, and overall condition. Ensure that electrical bonding straps are firmly attached and in good condition with no fraying or corrosion. Measure the electrical resistance of bonding straps to the airframe and compare with the airframe manufacturer's specifications. Repair and replace identified discrepancies as specified in the manufacturer's specifications and Federal Aviation Regulations.

Examine the condition of hydraulic and pneumatic tubes; they should not be dented, nicked, kinked, or twisted, and the attaching clamps should be secure. Check all air ducts for dents and the condition of the rubber (or fabric) antichafing strips at their joints. Work out any dents and replace antichafing strips if they have pulled loose or no longer form a tight seal.

Inspect hoses for weather checking or cold flow. **Weather checking** is a cracking of the outside covering of hoses that can penetrate the reinforcement webbing. **Cold flow** refers to deep, permanent impressions caused by hose clamps. Both types of damage weaken hoses and can eventually cause leaks. In addition to the hoses, you should inspect the exhaust assembly for security of attachment, cracks, and excessive corrosion.

For engines that use a dry sump oil system, remove the oil tank for thorough cleaning. The oil cooler and temperature regulator are usually removed and sent for overhaul, though sometimes they are returned as an exchange unit with the removed engine.

## ENGINE MOUNTS

You should inspect the engine mount structure before you attach the new or overhauled engine on an aircraft. Check the engine mount for bends, dents, flat spots, or elongated bolt holes. A dye penetrant inspection will help reveal cracks, porous areas, or other defects. Ferrous parts, such as engine mounting bolts, are usually checked by magnetic particle inspection.

Engines are mounted to airframes in several different ways, using a variety of engine mount structures. Most mounts are constructed from formed and riveted sheet metal, forged alloy fittings, welded steel tubing, or a combination of the three. Large horizontally opposed engines are often attached with forged alloy fittings mounted to a riveted aluminum structure. Steel-tube engine mounts are used with large and small horizontally opposed and radial engines. Steel-tube engine mounting structures bolt to the engine firewall.

Most modern reciprocating engine aircraft use **Dynafocal®** engine mounts. On a Dynafocal engine mount, the mounting points are turned inward, pointing towards the engine's center of gravity. This design limits the transmission of engine vibration to the airframe. [Figure 2-34]

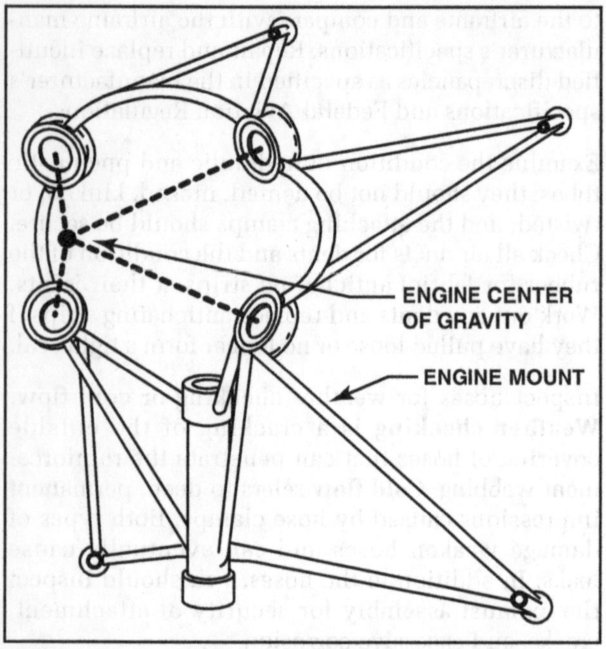


**Figure 2-34. The mounting points on a Dynafocal engine mount are turned inward toward the engine's center of gravity.**

Most engine mount assemblies incorporate vibration-isolating **shock mounts** to dampen engine vibration, but still permit restricted engine movement. Shock mounts are designed so that the weight of the engine is supported on rubber. The shock mounts absorb much of the engine vibration, reducing the amount that is transmitted to the airframe.

# OVERHAUL

When aircraft operators delay or neglect scheduled maintenance, the risk of premature engine or component failure increases. However, a well-maintained engine ordinarily provides reliable operation up to the recommended TBO. Upon reaching TBO, the engine should be overhauled to detect and repair worn or damaged parts. The only reliable way to identify parts worn beyond limits is to disassemble the engine and perform a thorough inspection.

Engine manufacturers provide overhaul instructions with general instructions and specific tolerances to determine airworthiness of each part. Parts that do not meet the manufacturer's specifications must be replaced, though parts that do meet tolerances can be reinstalled in the engine. However, if a part is near its airworthiness limit, you should consider replacement to avoid failure or unacceptable wear before the next scheduled overhaul.

## MAJOR OVERHAUL

A major overhaul entails a complete engine reconditioning. The specific interval between major overhauls is based on manufacturer recommendations or an FAA-approved number of hours from the time of manufacture or from the last major overhaul.

During a major overhaul, an engine is disassembled, cleaned, inspected, repaired as needed, reassembled, and tested. Any engine part that fails to meet specified tolerances is identified and either scrapped or repaired. Many parts such as gaskets, seals, and certain hardware are replaced regardless of condition. Manufacturer instructions specify which items you must replace. Furthermore, all accessories are removed for overhaul or replacement.

Engine manufacturers establish the particular fits, tolerances, and limits for an engine. These measurements are recorded on the production drawings and are authoritative for new engine parts. Additionally, the manufacturer establishes service limits, which refer to the maximum amount of wear that a part can have and still be considered serviceable. Serviceable part tolerance limits are used for parts being reinstalled and new part tolerances are used with any new parts.

Engine total time continues to accumulate after an engine has been overhauled. However, the amount of hours since major overhaul (SMOH) should be added to the engine log. Only new engines and **rebuilt engines** are granted a **zero time** status. 14 CFR Part 43 describes a rebuilt engine as an one that has been disassembled, cleaned, inspected, repaired as necessary, reassembled, and tested to the same tolerances and limits as a new engine. A rebuilt engine can contain either new or used parts that conform to new part tolerances and limits or to approved oversized or undersized dimensions. Only the manufacturer, or an agency approved by the manufacturer, can rebuild an engine and offer zero time. A zero time designation allows the owner or operator to start a new maintenance record with no reference to previous operating history. The maintenance log of a rebuilt aircraft must include the date that the engine was rebuilt, all changes made as required by airworthiness directives, and compliance with manufacturer's service bulletins.

Some advertisements for engine overhauls or exchange programs use the term **remanufactured engine**. It is important to note that this term is not defined by regulations or engine manufacturers, so you should question potential vendors about what the term means.

## TOP OVERHAUL

Compared with a major overhaul, a **top overhaul** is limited to the engine cylinders. During a typical top overhaul, the cylinders, pistons, and valve operating mechanisms are disassembled, cleaned, inspected, reconditioned, and reassembled. The piston rings are replaced and the valve guides and seats are inspected and replaced if necessary. When performing a top overhaul, a minimum amount of engine disassembly is required to gain access to the cylinders. In most cases, this includes removal of the intake manifold, ignition harness, and exhaust collectors. It is usually unnecessary to remove engine accessories such as magnetos, starters, and alternators.

In all cases, the final decision regarding whether to perform a top overhaul or major overhaul is up to the owner or operator. Disagreement exists about the value of a top overhaul. Some repair facilities and engine manufacturers argue that if you are going to remove all of an engine's cylinders, it is relatively inexpensive to overhaul the entire engine. An alternate view, however, is that because most crankcase assemblies are more durable than cylinders and valve trains, a top overhaul often provides the most economical way to improve an engine's performance.

## OVERHAUL PROCEDURES

The specific procedures to overhaul an engine are listed in its maintenance and overhaul manuals. The following discussion is a general overview of the practices and procedures in a major overhaul of a typical horizontally opposed engine.

Using the engine manufacturer's manuals, service bulletins, and other service information is critical for an overhaul. One of your first tasks should be researching airworthiness directives and manufacturer's service bulletins. Additionally, you need to gather the necessary inspection forms and tools for the job.

When an airplane arrives for an engine overhaul, inventory all of the accessories. These include the alternator, vacuum pump, hydraulic pump, and propeller governor. Accessories will be removed and sent to appropriate repair facilities for overhaul. Other components, including intercylinder baffles, carburetor or fuel injection components, magnetos, ignition leads, and the induction system, are considered engine parts and remain with the engine.

### DISASSEMBLY

Before disassembling an engine, install it on a sturdy stand and inspect its general condition. Look for signs of oil leakage, overheating, or impact damage, and make notes of any discrepancies you find. Clean the engine with an appropriate solvent to remove dirt and oil. However, be sure to rinse all of the solvent from the engine.

After the engine is clean, remove the accessories and send them out for overhaul. Remove and set aside the exhaust system, intercylinder baffles, ignition leads, spark plugs, and induction system components. When disassembling the engine, label all removed parts by attaching a tag to each part as you remove it. Place nuts, bolts, and other small parts in suitable containers during disassembly to prevent loss and damage. Discard safety wire, cotter pins, and some other safety devices that are used only once and replace them with new parts. [Figure 2-35]

Use the proper procedures for each task to avoid damaging engine parts or hardware. For example, manufacturers recommend that before removing any cylinder, the associated piston should be placed at top dead center on the compression stroke. Doing so enables you to remove the cylinder without applying any pressure to the valve mechanism and provides support to the piston and connecting rod as you extract the cylinder. If the connecting rod and piston are not properly supported, they can fall and strike the crankcase, which can lead to failure in subsequent operations.

Crankshaft bearings, oil seals, gaskets, and stressed bolts and nuts are typically replaced at overhaul and should be discarded. In every case, consult the applicable manufacturer's maintenance and overhaul manuals and service bulletins for a complete listing of required replacement items. Note any loose or damaged studs or fittings and examine them closely for evidence of more serious wear or damage.

Completely disassemble the engine and lay out the parts on a clean workbench for a preliminary inspec-

**Figure 2-35. After being mounted on an engine stand, an engine is disassembled for a thorough visual inspection and cleaning.**

tion. Before you clean the internal engine parts, perform a visual inspection to look for residual deposits of metallic particles in oil residue and sludge, which might indicate an impending failure. Cleaning the parts before inspection could flush away the particles and make identifying damage more difficult. [Figure 2-36]

## CLEANING

After you disassemble and visually inspect an engine, clean all of the parts. Soak or spray each part with a commercial safety solvent approved by the engine manufacturer. Water-soluble degreasing solutions with soap or caustic compounds are normally not recommended because water-soluble solutions can be corrosive to aluminum and magnesium. Furthermore, residual soap can become trapped in the pores of engine components and cause oil contamination and foaming after the engine is returned to service. [Figure 2-37]

Solvent is not always strong enough to remove hard carbon deposits that can build up on interior engine surfaces. To remove these deposits, follow the manufacturer's recommendations and use an approved decarbonizing solution. For personal safety, exercise caution and follow the manufacturer's recommendations. Always wear protective clothing and eye protection when you are working with these chemicals. Decarbonizing solutions are available in a water-soluble or a hydrocarbon base. Hydrocarbon-based solution is preferable because the water-soluble solutions have the same corrosion-inducing properties as water-soluble degreasers.

Avoid leaving engine parts in a decarbonizing solution longer than the prescribed time periods. Be sure the solution is safe for magnesium parts before

**Figure 2-36. Engine parts are laid out in an orderly fashion on a clean workbench after cleaning to facilitate inspection. Keeping parts arranged in an orderly manner minimizes loss or accidental damage.**

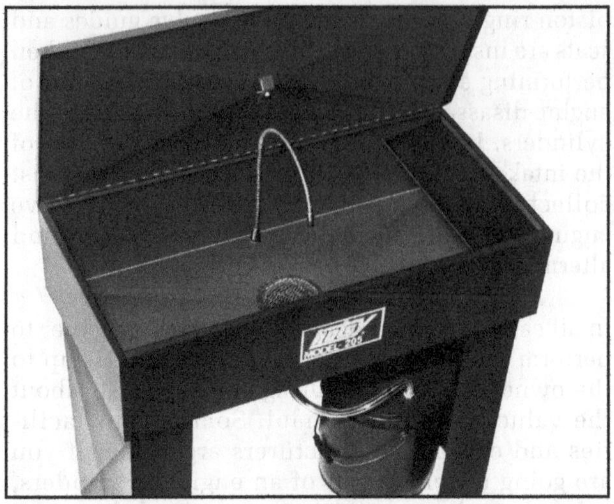

**Figure 2-37. Several manufacturers produce fixtures that circulate an approved solvent for cleaning engine parts. These fixtures limit solvent splashes and provide containment for small parts that could otherwise be misplaced or lost.**

immersing them. Do not mix steel and magnesium parts in the same container because the cleaning solution might cause a chemical reaction between the dissimilar metals and corrode the magnesium. Be especially careful with accessory housings because they often have high magnesium content.

After the parts have soaked the prescribed time, clean them to remove all traces of the decarbonizing solution. You can steam-clean parts or use mineral spirits and a stiff-bristle parts cleaning brush. Except for bearings or polished surfaces, remove any remaining carbon deposits with a scraper or wire brush, or by grit-blasting with plastic pellets or organic media such as rice, baked wheat, or crushed walnut shells. However, before beginning any grit-blasting process, insert rubber or plastic plugs in all drilled oil passages and mask all machined surfaces with a recommended material. Bolts and screws can be screwed into threaded holes to prevent grit from getting into the screw threads; discard this hardware after the part is cleaned. Because valve seats are typically hardened, they can usually be left unprotected during grit-blasting. In fact, you can use grit-blasting to remove the glaze that forms on valve seats, as well as the enamel from cylinder cooling fins that does not come off in a decarbonizing solution. To avoid damage when using a grit blast, use the lowest air pressure practical and blast the part only long enough to remove the carbon.

Always use extra caution when using mechanical means to clean hard carbon deposits; you can cause unintentional damage if you use the tools too aggressively. Pay extra attention when cleaning any part with abrasive tools.

To clean machined or polished bearing surfaces such as journals and crankpins, use crocus cloth moistened with mineral spirits. After all the carbon is removed, polish the surfaces with dry crocus cloth.

Because hollow crankpins in a crankshaft are used as sludge chambers, the plugs must be removed from the crankpin ends for cleaning and visual inspection. If the crankpins are not thoroughly cleaned, sludge loosened during cleaning can clog crankshaft oil passages and cause subsequent bearing failure.

After cleaning, coat steel parts with a film of protective oil to prevent corrosion. If the oil coating must be removed for subsequent inspections, it is imperative to reapply it when the inspections are complete.

## VISUAL INSPECTION

After the engine parts are clean, they must be inspected for damage. The first type of inspection is a thorough visual inspection. Use a magnifying glass, flashlight, and borescope to detect visible surface defects in parts. Following is a list of terms that describe common types of defects:

**Abrasion**—An area of roughened scratches or marks usually caused by foreign matter between moving parts.

**Brinelling**—One or more indentations on bearing races usually caused by high static loads or application of force during installation or removal. Indentations are rounded or spherical due to the impression left by the ball bearings or rollers.

**Burning**—Surface damage caused by excessive heat as a result of improper fit, insufficient lubrication, or over-temperature operation.

**Burnishing**—Polishing of one surface by sliding contact with a smooth, harder surface. Usually no displacement or removal of metal occurs.

**Burr**—A sharp or roughened projection of metal usually resulting from machine processing, drilling, or cutting.

**Chafing**—Wear caused by a rubbing action between two parts under light pressure.

**Chipping**—The breaking away of pieces of material, caused by excessive stress concentrations or careless handling.

**Corrosion**—Loss of metal by a chemical or electrochemical action. Corrosion is generally removed by mechanical means.

**Crack**—A partial separation of material usually caused by vibration, overloading, internal stresses, defective assembly, fatigue, or sudden impact.

**Cut**—Loss of metal, usually to an appreciable depth, caused by a sharp object such as a saw blade, chisel, or screwdriver.

**Dent**—A small, rounded surface depression usually found in sheet metal. Most dents result from impact with another object.

**Erosion**—Loss of surface metal caused by the mechanical action of foreign objects, such as grit or fine sand. The eroded area will be rough and might be lined in the direction in which the foreign material moved relative to the surface.

**Flaking**—The breaking loose of small pieces of metal or coated surfaces caused by defective plating or excessive loading.

**Fretting**—A form of surface corrosion caused by minute movement between two parts clamped together under pressure.

**Galling**—A severe chafing or fretting in which metal is transferred from one part to another.

**Gouging**—A condition where metal is displaced, often a result of a foreign material becoming trapped between moving parts.

**Grooving**—A recess or channel with smooth or rounded edges resulting from misaligned parts.

**Inclusion**—A foreign material contained within a part, often introduced during manufacture by rolling or forging.

**Nick**—A sharp gouge or V-shaped depression, often caused by careless handling of tools or parts.

**Peening**—A series of blunt surface depressions.

**Pitting**—Small hollows of irregular shape in the surface, usually caused by corrosion or minute mechanical chipping of surfaces.

**Scoring**—A series of deep scratches caused by foreign particles between moving parts or careless assembly and disassembly techniques.

**Scratches**—Shallow, thin lines or marks, varying in degree of depth and width, caused by improper handling or the presence of fine foreign particles during operation.

**Scuffing or Pick Up**—A buildup (or rolling of metal) from one area to another, often caused by insufficient lubrication or clearance, or the presence of foreign matter.

**Spalling**—A bearing defect in which chips of the hardened bearing surface are broken out.

**Stain**—A localized change in color that is noticeably different in appearance from the surrounding area.

**Upsetting**—A displacement of material beyond the normal surface contour commonly referred to as a bulge or bump. When a part is upset, there is usually no metal loss.

## CRANKCASE

Forces working in a crankcase produce highly stressed areas that can eventually develop cracks, especially around mating and bearing surfaces, mounting bosses, threaded holes and studs, openings, and structural fillet areas. Although more elaborate methods for crack detection are available, a thorough visual inspection is an efficient way to quickly detect serious damage that requires replacement.

In addition to looking for cracks, inspect all lubrication channels and oil ports to verify that the passages are open and unrestricted. Furthermore, check for loose or bent studs and examine stud and hole threads with a flashlight. Note all discrepancies for repair after the inspection is complete.

## GEARS

The primary purpose of a gear is to transmit force through motion; these parts are continuously stressed and wear should be expected. Visually examine all gears for cracked or chipped teeth and the presence of pitting or excessive wear. Deep pit marks or excessive wear on gear teeth are reasons to reject and replace a gear. Minor scratches and abrasions on a gear's bearing surfaces can be dressed out with a fine crocus cloth; however, deep scoring or scratches are unacceptable.

## BEARINGS

Inspect ball and roller bearings for smoothness and freedom of movement. While you look at the bearing, feel the bearing parts carefully to identify any roughness, flat spots on balls or rollers, and dents or corrosion on the races. Additionally, check for pitting, scoring, and galling on the outside surfaces of races. Pitting on a thrust bearing race that cannot be removed by polishing with crocus cloth requires replacement. Inspect journal bearings for galling, burning, scoring, spalling, misalignment, or an out-of-round condition.

Bearing inserts, such as bushings and plain bearings are usually replaced. However, inspecting them can help you detect wear on their mating surfaces or mounting bosses. Scratching and light scoring of aluminum bearing surfaces in the engine, when within limits of the engine manufacturer's overhaul manual, is usually acceptable However, other defects can require rejection of the part even when it falls within certain tolerance limits.

## CRANKSHAFT

A crankshaft is typically the heaviest, most highly stressed part of an aircraft engine. Because few repairs are approved for crankshafts, the main purpose of a visual inspection is to determine whether the crankshaft is within limits for wear. Inspect the main and crankpin journal bearing surfaces for burning, pitting, scoring, or spalling; pay special attention to the fillets at the edges of journal surfaces. If any pitting cannot be removed by polishing with crocus cloth, you might have to replace the crankshaft. If the crankshaft is equipped with oil transfer tubes, check them for tightness.

## CONNECTING RODS

Inspect connecting rods for small cracks, corrosion, pitting, nicks, or other damage. Look for galling between the bearing insert and rod—this condition is an indication that the engine might have experienced an overspeed condition or an excessively high manifold pressure. If galling does exist or if a connecting rod is twisted or bent, reject and replace the rod.

## PISTONS AND PISTON PINS

Ensure that all carbon buildup is removed from the ring grooves and oil relief holes. Inspect each piston for cracks, scores, and scratches on the outside and inside with a magnifying glass. Another method for detecting cracks is to carefully heat the piston in an oven to open cracks and force out residual oil. Pistons with deep scoring, cracked or broken ring lands, cracked skirts, and badly scored piston pin holes should be rejected. [Figure 2-38]

Examine piston pins for scoring, cracks, and pitting. In addition, check the interior surfaces of piston pins for pitting and corrosion. Because pins are often case hardened, cracks are more likely to be visible inside the pin than on the outside. If any pitting cannot be removed by polishing with crocus cloth, reject the pin and replace it.

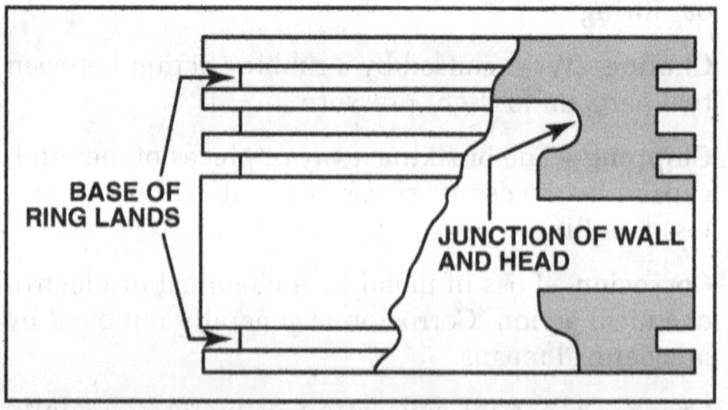


**Figure 2-38. When visually inspecting a piston, look for cracks that form at the base of ring lands and at the junction of the piston head and wall.**

### CYLINDERS

An effective visual inspection of a cylinder for external and internal cracks requires that the cylinder be free of carbon deposits and paint. Cracks near the edge of fins might be repairable, but cracks at the base require rejection and replacement. The amount of fin damage allowed on a given cylinder is established by the manufacturer and based on a percentage of total fin area. Dented or bent fins are best left alone because the attempt to straighten a fin typically results in breaking the fin.

When inspecting the inside of a cylinder barrel, light amounts of pitting, rust, and scoring are not cause for concern. When new rings are installed and begin to wear, this damage is quickly removed. If large amounts of pitting, rust, and scoring are present, hone or regrind the cylinder walls. Inspect valve seat inserts for pitting, burning, scoring, and asymmetrical wear. If any of these exist, reface the seat. Inspect spark plug thread inserts for thread condition and looseness by running a tap of the proper size through the insert. Any damage to threads requires replacement of the insert.

While inspecting the valve guides, look closely to ensure that all carbon was removed during cleaning. Carbon deposits could cover or fill any pitting, which makes detection difficult. If you leave a pitted valve guide in the engine, carbon deposits might again collect in the pits and cause valve sticking when the engine is returned to service.

Check rocker shaft bosses for scoring, cracks, rocker shaft-to-shaft boss clearance, and out-of-round conditions. Scoring occurs when the rocker shaft turns in the bosses because the shaft is too loose in the bosses or because the rocker arm is too tight on the shaft. Uneven wear on the rocker shaft bosses is evidence of sticking valves, which cause the rocker shaft to work up and down.

### CAMSHAFT

Inspect camshaft bearing surfaces and lobes for irregularities such as feathered edges, abrasions, nicks, or upsets. Any surface damage on a lobe can damage a lifter. Reject and replace a camshaft with lobe damage or if spalling, pitting, or surface cracks are present.

### VALVES AND VALVE MECHANISMS

You must disassemble, clean, and visually inspect hydraulic valve lifters during an overhaul. A lifter's plunger and cylinder are matched, so take extra care to avoid mixing parts of one lifter with those of another. Lifters should be free from nicks, scratches, and chips. Verify that a check valve operates properly by pressing the plunger into the cylinder and noting its action when you release it. The plunger should bounce back quickly to indicate satisfactory operation. If the plunger does not rebound as expected, perform a leakage test with test equipment before discarding the lifter as defective.

Verify that the push rods are clean, paying special attention to the oil passage. Ball ends should be smooth, free from nicks and scratches, and must fit tightly in the lifter and rocker arm ball sockets. To check for straightness, roll push rods across a clean, flat surface.

Inspect valve rockers for cracks as well as worn, pitted, or scored tips. As with the push rods, verify that the oil passage is clear. Insufficient lubrication can lead to burnishing and galling of a rocker shaft caused by the bronze rocker bushing and the heat of friction.

A visual inspection of the valves provides valuable information about engine condition. Some engine overhaul manuals require intake and exhaust valve replacement. When valves are permitted to be reused, a detailed inspection is required. Look for evidence of overheating, as well as nicks and scratches in the valve stem, especially near the spring retainer groove. These discrepancies require that the valve be replaced.

Valve springs are also subject to great stress during operation. Inspect springs for cracks, rust, and broken ends. If corrosion or visible wear is present, discard and replace springs.

### THREADED FASTENERS

Inspection criteria for threaded fasteners vary depending on the component, and application. The overhaul manual might specify replacement of certain bolts, nuts, studs, and screws. Carefully examine reusable threaded fasteners for cracks or damaged threads. Cross-threading caused by improper installation, torn threads caused by trapped foreign matter, and flattened threads caused by improper fit are examples of thread damage that warrant replacement. Replace any fasteners that exhibit evidence of damage from overtightening or improper tools. Small defects such as slight nicks or burrs can be dressed out with a small file, fine abrasive cloth, or honing stone.

## STRUCTURAL INSPECTION

After you have visually inspected all engine parts, you must inspect key components with special processes to verify their structural integrity. If you detect a fault during a special inspection, immediately tag the part as unairwothy and obtain a replacement part. Some of the more common structural inspections include magnetic particle, liquid penetrant, eddy current, ultrasonic, and radiography inspection.

## MAGNETIC PARTICLE INSPECTION

The nondestructive inspection method most frequently used for iron parts is magnetic particle inspection. A magnetic particle inspection detects cracks, splits, seams, and voids that form when a metal ruptures. Magnetic particle inspection can also identify manufacturing defects such as cold shuts and inclusions.

With magnetic particle inspection, a part is magnetized and a solution containing iron particles is poured or sprayed over the part. When a part containing a significant amount of iron is subjected to a strong magnetic field, the part becomes magnetized. The magnetized part develops north and south poles, between which is a continuous stream of magnetic flux. If the part contains a defect, the normal lines of flux are disrupted and, when viewed under a black light, defects are visible.

For magnetic particle inspection to indicate a fault, the part must be magnetized so that the lines of flux are perpendicular to the fault. A defect that is perpendicular to the flux creates a large disruption and is relatively easy to detect. However, a flaw that is parallel to the lines of flux creates only a minimal disruption to the magnetic field and is difficult to detect. To thoroughly inspect a part, magnetize it both longitudinally and circularly. The easiest way to recall which damage is visible during an inspection is that visible damage is parallel to current flow.

In longitudinal magnetization, current flows around the part through a coil that encircles it; lines of flux are established through the part. Defects that cross the flux are detected. [Figure 2-39]

With circular magnetization, current flows through the part being inspected; lines of magnetic flux form around the part. Flaws or defects aligned along the length of the part are detected. Current is sent through the part by placing it between the heads of the magnetizing equipment. A tubular part can be magnetized by installing a conductive rod through its center and placing the rod between the heads of the magnetizing equipment. [Figure 2-40]

Large flat objects can be magnetized circularly by passing current through the part using test probes. The magnetic field is oriented perpendicular to the current flowing between the probes. [Figure 2-41]

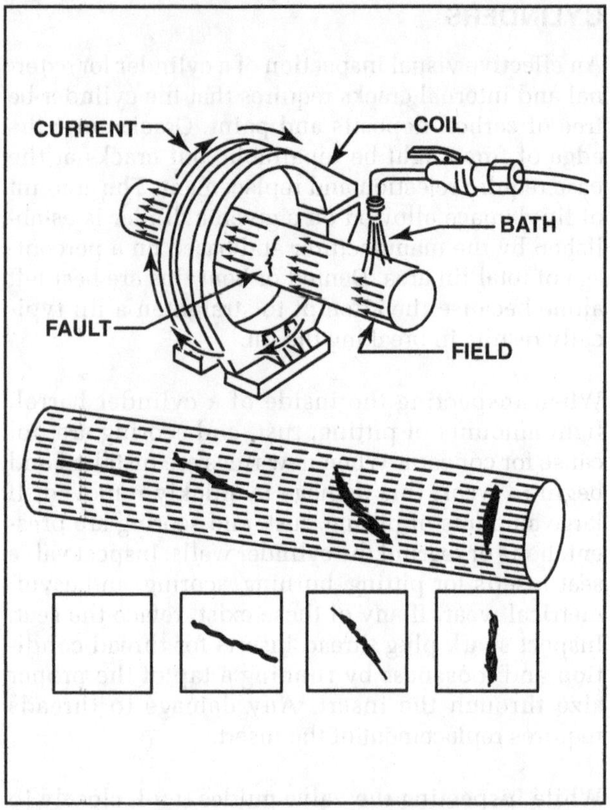


**Figure 2-39. When a part is magnetized in a coil, the lines of flux pass through the material longitudinally. As the flux lines pass through the part, faults that disrupt the flux are detected.**

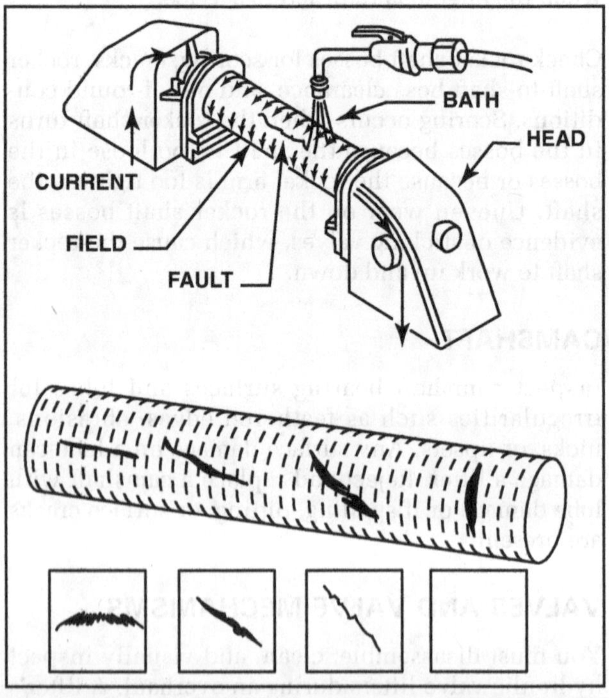


**Figure 2-40. When a part is magnetized between heads, the lines of flux encircle the material. As the flux lines pass through the part, faults that disrupt the flux are detected.**

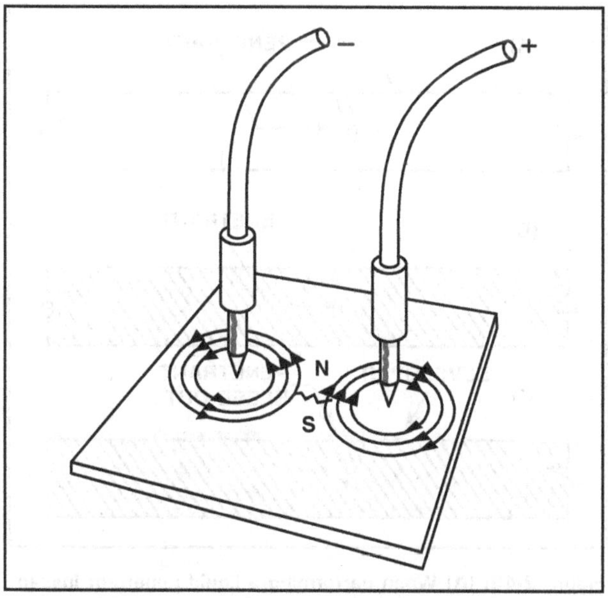


**Figure 2-41. When a part is magnetized between probes, the lines of flux encircle the probes. As the flux lines pass through the part, only faults that are aligned with the flux are detected.**

In general, the testing media for magnetic particle inspection are extremely fine iron oxides that are dyed with a gray, black, red, or fluorescent dye. Iron oxides can be used dry or mixed with kerosene to form a solution. Dry particles require no special preparation and are well-suited for use with portable equipment in the field. The wet method is more common with stationary equipment in a repair or inspection facility. A clean solution is important; when the solution becomes contaminated, the equipment should be cleaned and refilled with clean solution.

Depending on the application, different magnetizing procedures may be used. The strength of the magnetic field is the primary difference between residual magnetization and continuous magnetization. The residual procedure is used only with heat-treated steels. Current is applied to magnetize the part, and then turned off before the test media is applied. For the continuous magnetization procedure, the current is not turned off before the test media is applied. This method is more sensitive, detecting more subsurface discontinuities than residual magnetism. The overhaul manual specifies the type of magnetization to be used on various parts. [Figure 2-42]

Residual magnetism in a part after inspection can be detrimental to aircraft operation. Therefore, before a part is returned to service, it must be thoroughly **degaussed**, or demagnetized. To degauss a part, you must disrupt the magnetic poles and flux. Subject the part to a magnetizing force opposite that of the original force used to magnetize it. Because AC current does not penetrate a surface very deeply, complete demagnetization of some parts requires DC current. The part is placed in a

| PART | METHOD OF MAGNETIZATION | D.C. AMPERES | CRITICAL AREAS | POSSIBLE DEFECTS |
|---|---|---|---|---|
| CRANKSHAFT | CIRCULAR AND LONGITUDINAL | 2500 | JOURNALS, FILLETS, OIL HOLES, THRUST FLANGES, PROP FLANGE | FATIGUE CRACKS, HEAT CRACKS |
| CONNECTING ROD | CIRCULAR AND LONGITUDINAL | 1800 | ALL AREAS | FATIGUE CRACKS |
| CAMSHAFT | CIRCULAR AND LONGITUDINAL | 1500 | LOBES, JOURNALS | HEAT CRACKS |
| PISTON PIN | CIRCULAR AND LONGITUDINAL | 1000 | SHEAR PLANES, ENDS, CENTER | FATIGUE CRACKS |
| ROCKER ARMS | CIRCULAR AND LONGITUDINAL | 800 | PAD, SOCKET UNDER SIDE ARMS AND BOSS | FATIGUE CRACKS |
| GEARS TO 6 INCH DIAMETER | CIRCULAR OR ON CENTER CONDUCTOR | 1000 TO 1500 | TEETH, SPLINES, KEYWAYS | FATIGUE CRACKS |
| GEARS OVER 6 INCH DIAMETER | SHAFT CIRCULAR TEETH BETWEEN HEADS TWO TIMES 90 | 1000 TO 1500 | TEETH, SPLINES | FATIGUE CRACKS |
| SHAFTS | CIRCULAR AND LONGITUDINAL | 1000 TO 1500 | SPLINES, KEYWAYS, CHANGE OF SECTION | FATIGUE CRACKS, HEAT CRACKS |
| THRU BOLTS ROD BOLTS | CIRCULAR AND LONGITUDINAL | 500 | THREADS UNDER HEAD | FATIGUE CRACKS |

**Figure 2-42. A typical magnetic particle inspection schedule provides details on the method of magnetization, required current, critical areas, and possible defects.**

coil and subjected to more current than initially used. Current flows through the coil in one direction, and then is reversed repeatedly as the amount of current is decreased.

Check for residual magnetism with a magnet strength indicator. Parts must be demagnetized to within the limits specified in the overhaul manual before being returned to service. Follow the overhaul manual instructions for the specific magnetic particle inspection required for each component and be sure to check the overhaul manual for warnings or restrictions before proceeding. For example, magnetizing the plunger assembly of a hydraulic valve lifter interferes with the steel check valve's ability to seat properly, making it difficult to demagnetize the assembly sufficiently to prevent further problems.

## LIQUID PENETRANT INSPECTION

Liquid penetrant inspection is a nondestructive inspection method for locating cracks, porosity, or other types of surface defects. Penetrant inspection is usable on all metals, as well as nonporous plastics.

Dye penetrant inspection is based on the principle of **capillary attraction.** Cover the area to be inspected with a low viscosity, low surface tension penetrating liquid. Allow the penetrant to remain on the surface of the part long enough for the penetrant to be drawn into any fault open to the surface. Carefully remove excess penetrant from the surface, and then cover surface with a developer agent. By process of reverse capillary action, the developer draws the penetrant out of cracks or other faults, and forms a visible line in the developer. A fault is normally indicated by a sharp, clear line. Fuzzy or indistinct results indicate that the part might have been insufficiently cleaned before the developer was applied. [Figure 2-43]

Two types of dyes are used in liquid penetrant inspection: fluorescent and colored. An ultraviolet light is used with a fluorescent penetrant to make faults visible. With the colored dye, faults are visible as a colored line on the white developer.

Successfully using liquid penetrant requires that the surface be free of grease, dirt, and oil. Cleanliness ensures that the penetrant enters any cracks or faults. A volatile, petroleum-based solvent is most effective for removing all traces of oil and grease. Because some materials are damaged by solvents, take care to ensure that the cleaner is safe for the particular part. If vapor degreasing is impractical, clean the part by scrubbing with a solvent or a strong detergent solution. Do not use grit-blast, scrapers, or a wire brush to clean parts before inspection with liquid penetrant. These tools can fill in and obscure surface discontinuities and

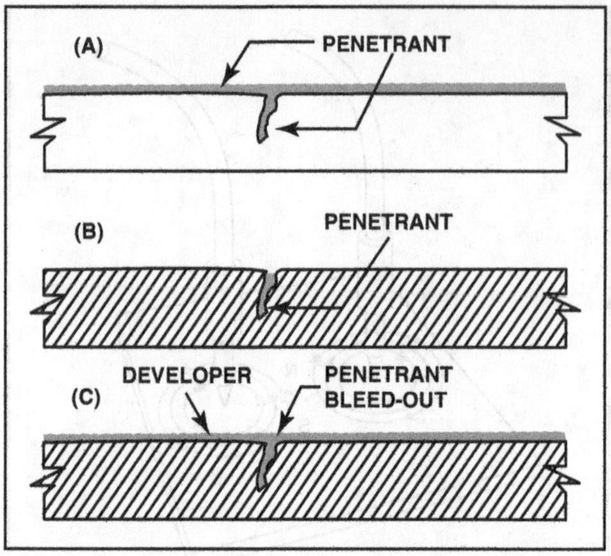


**Figure 2-43. (A) When performing a liquid penetrant inspection, spread penetrant over the surface of the material being examined and allowed sufficient time for capillary action to take place. (B) Wash excess penetrant from the surface; leave any cracks and surface flaws filled. (C) Spray an absorbent developer over the surface to blot out any penetrant. A crack will show up as a bright line against the white developer.**

defects by the process of inclusion. After the part is clean, rinse and dry it thoroughly.

Penetrant can be applied to a part by immersion or by swabbing or brushing the solution onto the part's surface. Some penetrant is available in aerosol cans to spray in small areas for a localized inspection. Whichever application method you use, completely cover the area with the penetrating liquid for the manufacturer's recommended length of time, referred to as **dwell time,** which is determined by the size and shape of the suspected discontinuities. For example, small, thin cracks require a longer dwell time than large wide cracks. If the part is heated, dwell time decreases, but if the part becomes too hot, the penetrant will evaporate.

Depending on the type of penetrant, after the dwell time has elapsed, clean the surface with water, an emulsifying agent, or a solvent. **Water-soluble penetrants** are the easiest to remove. Spray the surface with water at a pressure of 30 to 40 p.s.i., and position the nozzle at a 45-degree angle to the surface to avoid washing the penetrant from cracks or faults.

**Post-emulsifying penetrants** are not water-soluble and must be treated with an emulsifying agent for cleaning. Varying the dwell time of the emulsifier affects the amount of penetrant that a part absorbs. The intent is to remove all of the surface penetrant while leaving the penetrant within a defect.

Other penetrants are removable from the surface only with a towel dampened with solvent. Solvent should not be sprayed onto the surface, and the part should not be immersed in solvent; to do so would remove the penetrant from faults or dilute it to a point that prevents fault indication.

After a part is clean, apply the developer. Three types of developers are used to draw penetrants from faults. Although they function the same way, application methods differ. Apply developer immediately after cleaning the part; if penetrant bleeds out before the developer is applied, you might not be able to identify defects.

A dry developer is a powdery material, such as talcum, that adheres to a part and draws penetrant out of surface faults. To apply it, the part is typically placed in a bin of loose developer. For larger components, dry powder can be applied with a soft brush or blown over the surface with a powder gun. After the powder is on the surface for the recommended time, remove the excess with low-pressure air.

The penetrant used with a dry developer is often treated with a fluorescent or colored dye. Parts using the fluorescent dye must be examined under a black light. Colored dye penetrants do not require use of a black light.

If you are using a wet developer, apply it as soon as the part is cleaned. With wet developer, the white powder is mixed with water and flowed over the surface or the part is immersed in the developer solution. Air-dry the part and inspect it the same way as with dry developer. As described with dry developers, wet developers are used with penetrants treated with fluorescent or colored dyes.

The most commonly used developer is a powder suspended in solvent, applied from a pressure spray can. When dry, spray a thin moist coat of developer on the part. The developer dries rapidly and draws penetrant from a fault. The penetrant stains the developer and, depending on the dye, is visible with natural or black light. [Figure 2-44]

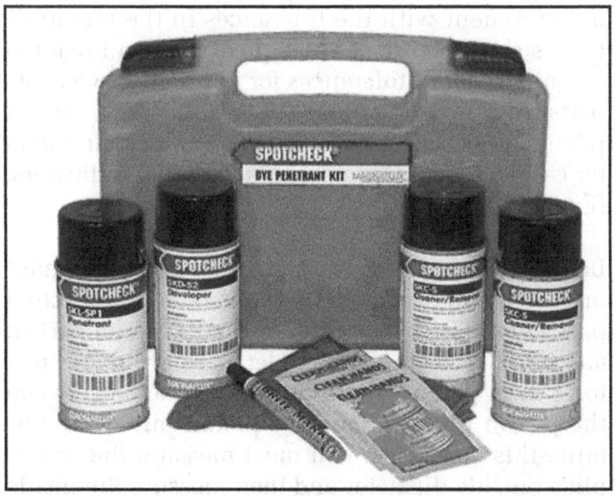


**Figure 2-44. Portable test kits of dye penetrant are available for inspecting localized areas on an aircraft.**

## EDDY CURRENT INSPECTION

Eddy current inspection is a testing method that requires little or no part preparation and can detect surface and subsurface flaws in most metals. Furthermore, it can differentiate among base metals and alloys, as well as a metal's heat treat condition. Eddy current inspection is based on the principle of current acceptance. The test equipment measures the ease with which a material accepts induced current. In addition to the presence of voids or faults, the factors that affect the test are material conductivity, permeability, and mass. Eddy currents flow through electrically conductive material under the influence of an induced electromagnetic field.

## ULTRASONIC INSPECTION

Ultrasonic inspection test equipment sends an amplified signal through a transducer to the material. The transducer causes the test material to vibrate at a given frequency. Upon reaching the back side of the material, the signals bounce back, are received by the transducer, and displayed on the CRT or LCD screen.

## RADIOGRAPHIC INSPECTION

Radiographic inspection photographs the inside of a structure. The test equipment uses high energy from the x-ray and gamma ray bands of the electromagnetic spectrum. The amount of energy these rays contain is related inversely to their wavelength. In other words, the shorter the wavelength, the greater its energy. They have no electrical charge or mass, travel in straight lines at the speed of light, and are able to penetrate matter. The depth of penetration is dependent upon the ray's energy.

Certain characteristics of x-rays and gamma rays make them especially useful for nondestructive inspection. Both types of rays are absorbed by the matter through which they pass; the amount of absorption is proportional to the density of the material. Furthermore, because x-rays and gamma rays ionize certain materials, they can create a permanent record when used to expose photographic film.

## DIMENSIONAL INSPECTION

After you determine that an engine part is structurally sound, you must measure it and compare the measurement with the tolerances in the manufacturer's specifications. The typical overhaul manual contains a list of tolerances for new and serviceable parts. A dimensional inspection requires the use of precision measuring instruments such as micrometer calipers, telescoping gauges, and dial indicators. [Figure 2-45]

In many cases, the values provided in the overhaul manual are clearance dimensions rather than actual part sizes. The limits refer to the fit of one part in another. For example, the tolerances given for "piston pin in piston" represent the clearance between the piston pin boss and the piston pin. To determine this clearance, you must measure the piston pin's outside diameter and then measure the inside diameter of the piston pin boss in the piston. The difference between these two values represents the "piston pin in piston" clearance. The capital "L" in the 0.013L "piston pin in piston" serviceable limit denotes a loose fit, meaning that the inside diameter of the piston pin boss is greater than the outside diameter of the piston pin.

Some parts, such as a bushing in the small end of a connecting rod, call for installation with an **interference** (or **tight) fit** and are indicated by a capital "T" following the dimension numbers. All interference fits require special procedures or equipment to assemble the parts. For example, dimension 0.0025T to 0.0050T means that the bushing must be between two-and-a-half to five thousandths of an inch larger than the hole into which it will be installed.

You must measure all of the parts listed in the table to determine whether their dimensions comply with the part specifications Replace or repair any part that does not fall within the listed tolerances. Parts with an interference fit (such as a bushing in a connecting rod) do not need to be measured unless their condition requires that the bushing be replaced.

## CRANKCASE

The dimensional inspection of a crankcase requires temporary assembly of the case halves. For example, to check main bearing clearances, the main bearing inserts must be installed in the crankcase halves and the case halves must be reassembled and tightened to the specified torque. A telescoping gauge is set to the inside diameter of each main bearing and measured with a caliper. Then the crankshaft journals are measured with the same micrometer. When you know both dimensions, you can determine the fit.

With the crankcase halves assembled, check the camshaft bearing clearances as well. Because the camshaft bearings on many engines are machined into the crankcase, there are no camshaft bearing inserts. To check the camshaft bearing clearances, use the same procedure as crankshaft bearing clearance.

## CRANKSHAFT

A crankshaft has several areas that require dimensional inspection. Main bearing journals are normally measured with a micrometer caliper as part of the process to determine crankshaft journal-to-main bearing clearances in the crankcase. Additionally, rod bearing journals are checked with a micrometer caliper while determining rod bearing journal clearance.

Another crankshaft dimensional inspection is crankshaft runout. To check for runout, a crankshaft is supported on vee-blocks at locations specified in the overhaul manual. A dial indicator is zeroed and placed at points along the crankshaft and the crankshaft is rotated. Total runout is the sum of indications over and under zero on the dial indicator. If the runout exceeds the dimensions given in the manufacturer's table of limits, the crankshaft must be replaced. No attempt should be made to straighten a bent crankshaft or attempt any other repair that might damage the nitrided surface of a bearing journal.

## CONNECTING RODS

Check connecting rods for twist and convergence. To check for twist, insert arbors into each end of a connecting rod. Position the arbors across parallel blocks. Using thickness gauges, measure for any space between the arbors and the parallel blocks. The amount of twist is determined by the thickness of the gauge that can be inserted. [Figure 2-47]

Measure any difference between the large and small arbors on both sides of a connecting rod to determine convergence. Attach a **parallelism gauge** to one end of the large arbor. Adjust the gauge to touch the small arbor. Then, move the parallelism gauge to the other side of the arbor. If the gauge does not fit the same on both sides, determine the convergence (difference) with a thickness gauge. [Figure 2-48]

Any rods that are twisted or bent beyond serviceable limits must be replaced. When replacement is necessary, the weight of the new rod should be matched within one-half ounce of its opposite rod to minimize vibrations.

## PISTONS, RINGS, AND PISTON PINS

Pistons with flat heads should be dimensionally checked with a straightedge and a thickness gauge. The presence of an abnormal depression in the top of a piston might have been caused by detonation.

| DESCRIPTION | SERVICEABLE LIMITS | NEW PARTS | |
|---|---|---|---|
| | | MINIMUM | MAXIMUM |
| First piston ring in cylinder (P/N 635814)........................Gap: | 0.059 | 0.033 | 0.049 |
| First piston ring in cylinder (P/N 639273)........................Gap: | 0.074 | 0.048 | 0.064 |
| Second piston ring in cylinder (P/N 635814)....................Gap: | 0.050 | 0.024 | 0.040 |
| Second piston ring in cylinder (p/N 639273)....................Gap: | 0.069 | 0.043 | 0.059 |
| Third piston ring in cylinder..............................................Gap: | 0.059 | 0.033 | 0.049 |
| Fourth piston ring in cylinder............................................Gap: | 0.050 | 0.024 | 0.040 |
| Fifth piston ring in cylinder...............................................Gap: | 0.059 | 0.033 | 0.049 |
| Piston pin in piston (standard or 0.005" oversize)...Diameter: | 0.013L | 0.0001L | 0.0007L |
| Piston pin in cylinder.......................................End Clearance: | 0.090 | 0.031 | 0.048 |
| Piston pin in connecting rod busing.......................Diameter: | 0.0040L | 0.0022L | 0.0026L |
| Bushing in connecting rod........................................Diameter: | | 0.0025T | 0.0050T |
| Connecting rod bearing on crankpin.......................Diameter: | 0.006L | 0.0009L | 0.0034L |
| Connecting rod on crankpin...........................Side Clearance: | 0.016 | 0.006 | 0.010 |
| Bolt in connecting rod..............................................Diameter: | | 0.0000 | 0.0018L |
| Connecting bearing and bushing twist or convergence per inch of length......................................... : | 0.001 | 0.0000 | 0.0005 |
| CRANKSHAFT | | | |
| Crankshaft in main bearing........................................ Diameter: | 0.005L | 0.0012L | 0.0032L |
| Propeller reduction gear shaft in bearing................ Diameter: | | 0.0012L | 0.0032L |
| Propeller drive shaft in shaft.................................... Diameter: | | 0.0012L | 0.0032L |
| Crankpins..........................................................Out-of-Round: | 0.0015 | 0.0000 | 0.0032L |
| Main journals.....................................................Out-of-Round: | 0.0015 | 0.0000 | 0.0005 |
| Propeller drive shaft.........................................Out-of-Round: | 0.002 | 0.0000 | 0.002 |
| Propeller drive shaft in thrust bearing............End Clearance: | 0.020 | 0.006 | 0.0152 |
| Crankshaft run-out at center main journals (shaft supported at thrust rear journals) full indicator reading..........................................................: | 0.015 | 0.000 | 0.015 |
| Propeller shaft run-out at propeller flange (when supported at front and rear journals) full indicator reading..........................................................: | 0.003 | 0.000 | 0.002 |
| Damper pin bushing in crankcheek extension..........Diameter: | | 0.0015T | 0.003 T |
| Damper pin busing in counterweight.........................Diameter: | | 0.0015T | 0.003 T |
| Damper pin in counterweight...........................End Clearance: | 0.040 | 0.001 | 0.023 |
| Alternator drive gear on reduction gear...................Diameter: | | 0.001T | 0.004 T |
| Crankshaft gear on crankshaft.................................Diameter: | | 0.000 | 0.002 T |
| CANSHAFT | | | |
| Camshaft journals in crankcase...............................Diameter: | 0.005L | 0.001L | 0.003 L |
| Camshaft in crankcase...................................End Clearance: | 0.014 | 0.005 | 0.009 |
| Camshaft run-out at center (shaft supported at end journals) full indicator reading:.........................................................: | 0.003 | 0.000 | 0.001 |
| Camshaft gear on camshaft flange..........................Diameter: | | 0.005T | 0.0015L |
| Governor gear on crankshaft....................................Diameter: | 0.006L | 0.002L | 0.002 L |
| CRANKCASE AND ATTACHED PARTS | | | |
| Thru bolts in crankcase.............................................Diameter: | | 0.005T | 0.0013L |
| Hydraulic lifter in crankcase.....................................Diameter: | 0.0035L | 0.001L | 0.0025L |
| Governor drive shaft in crankcase...........................Diameter: | | 0.0014L | 0.0034L |

**Figure 2-45. When performing a dimensional inspection on engine components, measure each component and compare the dimensions to the limits in the overhaul manual.**

**Figure 2-46. A dimensional inspection of the main journal bearing inserts and camshaft bearings requires assembly of the crankcase halves. Use a telescoping gauge and micrometer to determine the appropriate clearances.**

**Figure 2-47. To check a connecting rod for twist, place parallel blocks under the ends of the arbors and attempt to pass a thickness gauge between each arbor end and the block. A gap means the connecting rod is twisted. The engine overhaul manual specifies the permissible amount of twist.**

If so, the piston should be discarded due to possible stress cracks around the pin bosses and at the junction of the piston head and walls. Measure the outside diameter of a piston with a micrometer at the piston skirt and at each ring land. Record these measurements for later use when checking cylinder bore dimensions to determine piston to cylinder clearance. [Figure 2-49]

In addition to the pistons, the piston rings must be dimensionally checked. For each piston ring, measure the end gap clearance and side clearance. **End gap** is the space between the two ends of a piston ring after it is installed in a cylinder. **Side clearance** is the space between a piston ring and its associated ring land.

Measure end gap by placing a ring into a cylinder barrel and squaring it to the cylinder with a piston.

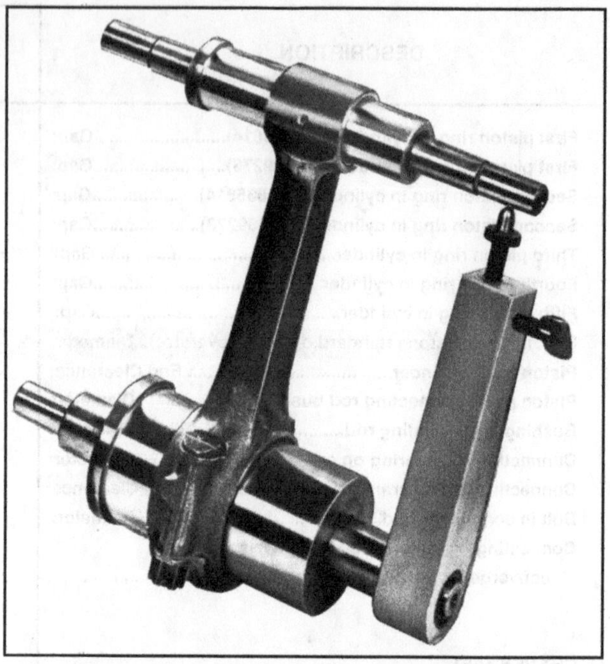

**Figure 2-48. To check a connecting rod for convergence, mount a parallelism gauge to one end of the large arbor and measure the distance between the arbors on both sides. The difference in the measurements is the amount of bend in the rod.**

After the ring is in position, use a thickness gauge to measure the gap between the ends of the ring. If the gap is correct, the ring can be used in that cylinder.

To check a piston ring's side clearance, place each piston ring in its proper groove and measure the clearance between the ring and land with a thickness gauge. If tapered rings are installed, hold a straightedge against the side of the piston. [Figure 2-50]

**Figure 2-49. Use a straightedge and thickness gauge to check the flatness of a piston head. The presence of a depression in the top of a piston head may indicate damage from detonation and could be cause for rejection.**

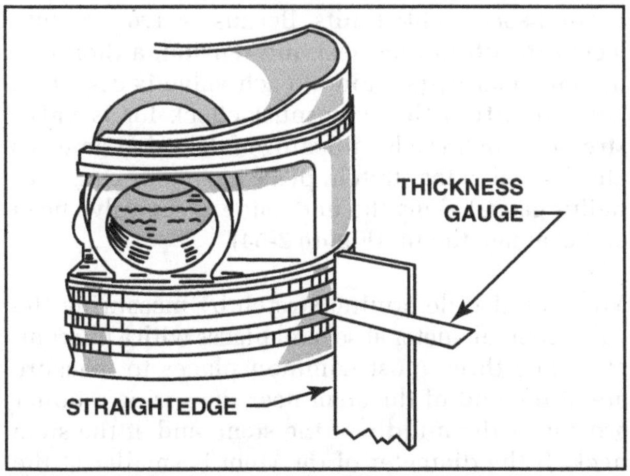


**Figure 2-50. To check side clearance, use a straightedge to hold the piston rings squarely in their grooves and insert a thickness gauge between each ring and ring land.**

Piston pins receive several dimensional checks. As part of determining the clearance between a piston pin and the bore of the piston pin boss, measure the outside diameter of the piston pin. By subtracting the piston pin diameter from the bore dimension, the piston pin-to-bore clearance is obtained.

Check a piston pin for straightness by placing it on vee-blocks and measuring runout with a dial indicator. Some overhaul manuals also require you to check end clearance between the piston pin and the cylinder wall. The length of a piston pin must be measured with a caliper and compared with the cylinder bore dimensions. [Figure 2-51]

## CYLINDERS

To check cylinder barrels for wear, you can use with a cylinder bore gauge, a telescoping gauge and a

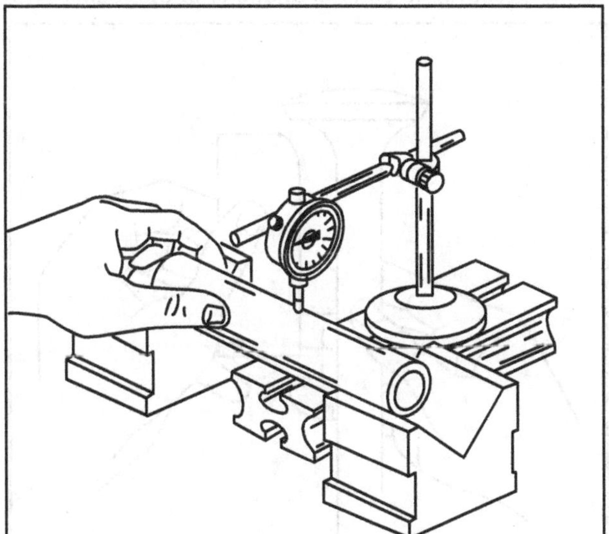

**Figure 2-51. Piston pins are dimensionally inspected for straightness with vee-blocks and a dial indicator. As a pin rotates on the vee-blocks, the dial indicator records runout.**

micrometer, or an inside micrometer. Cylinder barrel measurements enable you to calculate cylinder taper, out-of-roundness, bore diameter wear, and the fit between piston skirt and cylinder. Each measurement in a cylinder barrel should be taken in two positions, 90 degrees apart.

Cylinder taper is the difference between the diameters at the top and at the bottom of a cylinder. The natural wear pattern of a cylinder often results in a larger diameter at the top of a cylinder where the temperature, pressure, and erosive conditions are most intense. Keep in mind that some cylinders are designed with an intentional taper, or choke. In such a case, be careful to distinguish wear from intentional taper. If wear has created a step in the taper, you must exercise care while making measurements to achieve accurate readings. [Figure 2-52]

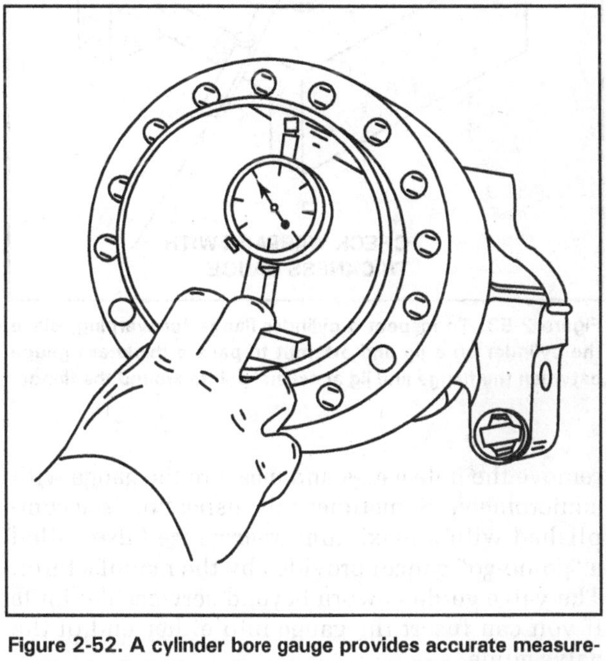

**Figure 2-52. A cylinder bore gauge provides accurate measurements of cylinder bore, taper, and an out-of-round condition.**

When inspecting for an out-of-round condition, measure at the top of the cylinder. Additionally, a measure at the cylinder skirt to detect dents or other damaged caused by careless handling. Also, check a cylinder's flange should for warpage. To carry out this test, place the cylinder on the appropriate fixture and use a thickness gauge to check for gaps between the fixture and flange. [Figure 2-53]

Another dimensional inspection required on a cylinder checks for valve guide wear and excessive clearance. The inside diameter of a valve guide is checked with a small hole gauge and micrometer. To do this, place the small hole gauge inside the valve guide and expand it until it fits snugly. Then

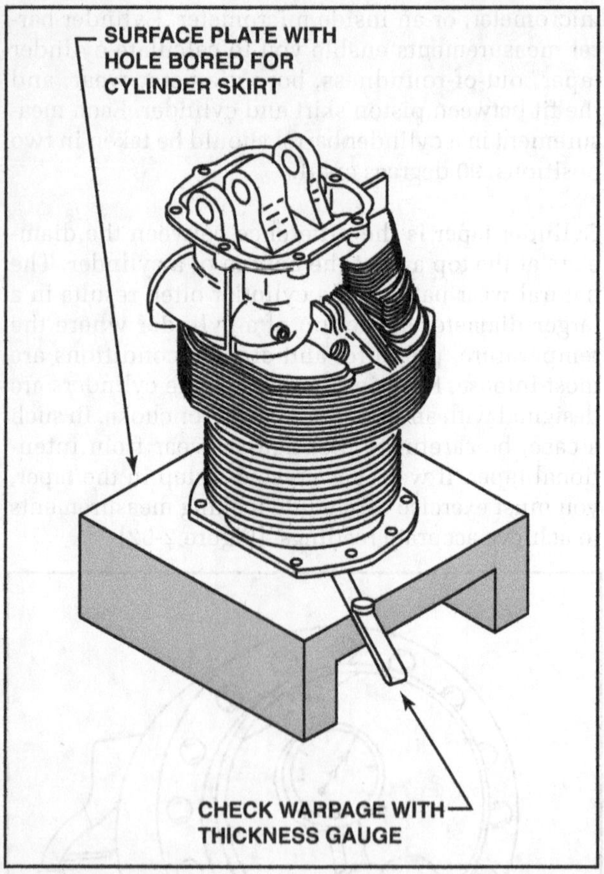


**Figure 2-53. To inspect a cylinder flange for warping, place the cylinder on a jig and attempt to pass a thickness gauge between the flange and jig at several points around the flange.**

remove the hole gauge and measure the gauge with a micrometer. Sometimes this inspection is accomplished with a maximum wear gauge (also called a "go-no-go" gauge) provided by the manufacturer. The valve guide is worn beyond serviceable limits if you can insert the gauge into either end of the valve guide.

## CAMSHAFT

The dimensions of camshaft bearing journals are measured when checking clearances between the camshaft and camshaft bearings in the crankcase. In addition, if an overhaul manual specifies a taper on the lobes, you must make a dimensional check to determine if the taper is within limits.

As with a crankshaft, you check a camshaft for straightness by placing it on vee-blocks and measuring the runout with a dial indicator. If the readings exceed serviceable limits, replace the camshaft.

## VALVES AND VALVE MECHANISMS

Valves, valve springs, rocker arms, and rocker shafts must be measured to detect parts that are worn beyond serviceable limits. Because valves are subjected to substantial heat and tension, a thorough dimensional inspection of each valve is essential. One condition that you must check for is **valve stretch**, which is a lengthening of the valve stem. To check a valve for stretch, place a contour gauge (or radius gauge) along the underside of the valve head and evaluate the fit. [Figure 2-54]

You can also determine stretch by measuring the valve stem diameter at several places with a micrometer. The three most common places to measure are at the end of the stem near the spring retainer groove, at the middle of the stem, and at the stem neck. If the diameter of the stem is smaller at the center (or neck) than it is at either end, the valve has likely stretched.

In addition to stretch, you must also check the runout of the valve face. Secure the valve in the chuck of a valve grinder and measure the runout with a dial indicator. If the runout is within limits, proceed to measuring the valve head thickness (or valve margin). [Figure 2-55]

Check valve springs for compression and wire diameter. To check for compression, use a valve spring tester to compress each spring to a specific height. Compare the force required to compress the spring with the specifications in the overhaul manual. Measure the wire diameter of the spring with a small caliper.

Each rocker arm shaft and bushing must be measured to determine clearance. Measure the inside diameter of each rocker arm shaft bushing with a small telescoping gauge (or hole gauge) and micrometer. Next, measure the outside diameter of the rocker arm

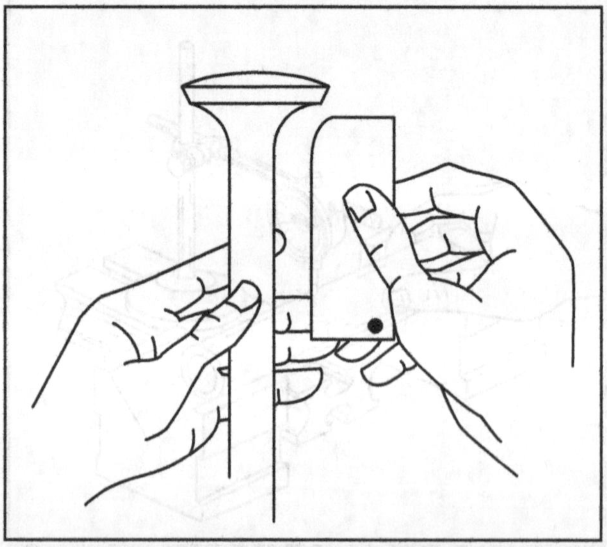

**Figure 2-54. One method for detecting stretched valves is to hold a contour gauge along the underside of each valve head.**

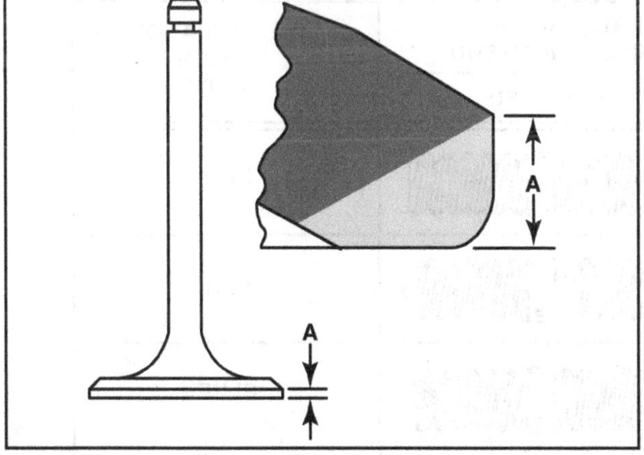


Figure 2-55. In order to reuse a valve, the valve stem must run true with the valve face and the valve margin must be within the manufacturer's specifications.

shaft with a micrometer. The difference between the dimensions is the shaft-to-bushing clearance.

### OIL PUMP HOUSING

It is important to measure the distance between the oil pump mating surface and the oil pump gears. To measure the distance, use a depth micrometer. Retract the spindle of the depth gauge until it is flush with the fixed bar and the micrometer head reads zero. Then lay the bar across the oil pump housing and extend the spindle until it contacts the oil pump gear. Read the micrometer head to determine the distance between the housing and the gear.

## REPAIR

After completing the visual, structural, and dimensional inspections, you can now repair minor discrepancies to engine components. Use a fine oil stone, crocus cloth, or similar abrasive substance to remove burrs, nicks, scratches, scoring, or galling. You can also use swiss pattern files or small edged stones to remove small nicks. Flanged surfaces that are bent, warped, or nicked can be repaired by lapping on a surface plate. Sometimes, defective threads can be repaired with a suitable die or tap; however, avoid tapping a hole too deep and creating an oversized tapped hole. If you remove galling or scratches from the bearing surface of a journal, buff the surface to a high finish with fine crocus cloth before returning to service. After completing repairs, clean parts thoroughly to remove all abrasives; then verify proper fit with mating parts.

### CRANKCASE

Cracks, damaged studs or threads, and excessive bearing clearances are examples of repairable crankcase defects. Cracks can be repaired only by the engine manufacturer or a certified repair station approved for the task. Cracks are repaired with a form of inert gas welding. After the crack is welded, the weld bead is shot-peened to relieve stress and machined to match the rest of the surface. Damage to a bearing cavity can be repaired in a similar manner, with machining following welding.

Camshafts normally rotate in the crankcase without bearing inserts. If camshaft bearings are found to have excessive clearances, the only repair is to line-bore the bearings and install an oversized camshaft.

If bent or loose studs were identified during inspection, they must be removed and replaced. If standard size studs do not fit appropriately, install oversized studs. Oversize studs are identified by a color code and stamped marks to indicate the amount of oversizing. [Figure 2-56]

If internal case threads cannot be repaired with a tap, Heli-Coil® inserts can be used. These inserts provide new threads, which permit standard size studs or hardware to be installed. No decrease in strength occurs with this type of repair.

### CRANKSHAFT

Slight roughness on the surface of a crankshaft's main journals or crankpins can be polished away with fine crocus cloth. Turn the crankshaft in a lathe and loop a strip of crocus cloth around the surface to be polished. If sludge chambers were removed for cleaning, reinstall them at this time.

All major repairs made on a crankshaft must be done by the manufacturer or a certified repair station approved for the task. Possible repairs include grinding out-of-round crankshaft main journals or crankpins to an acceptable undersize. If grinding is performed on a crankshaft, nitriding is required and the appropriate, undersized bearing inserts must be installed in the crankcase.

### CONNECTING RODS

The only repairs permitted on a connecting rod are replacement of the piston pin bushing and crankpin bearing inserts. Due to the interference fit between the connecting rod and piston pin bushing, an arbor press and a special bushing installation drift are required. After the new bushing is pressed into place, reaming is required to obtain the dimensions specified in the overhaul manual. Because the tolerances are very tight, special equipment is generally required to ream connecting rod bushings.

### PISTONS

Pistons are regularly replaced during an overhaul; however, if a piston was only recently installed and is within limits, it may be reused. Repairs to pistons are limited; only the removal of light scoring is allowed. When removing scoring on a piston skirt,

| TYPICAL PART NO. | OVERSIZE ON PITCH DIA. OF COARSE THREAD (INCHES) | OPTIONAL IDENTIFICATION MARKS ON COURSE THREAD END | | IDENTIFICATION COLOR CODE |
|---|---|---|---|---|
| | | STAMPED | MACHINED | |
| XXXXXX | STANDARD | NONE |  | NONE |
| XXXXXXXP003 | .003 |  |  | RED |
| XXXXXXP006 | .006 |  |  | BLUE |
| XXXXXXP009 | .009 |  | 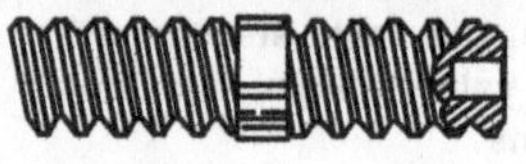 | GREEN |
| XXXXXXP007 | .007 |  | | BLUE |
| XXXXXXP012 | .012 |  | | GREEN |

**Figure 2-56 Oversize studs have color codes and stamped identification marks to show the degree of oversize.**

use nothing more abrasive than crocus cloth. Scoring above a piston's top ring groove may be removed by machining or sanding as long as piston diameter is not reduced below specified minimums.

Whether you reuse pistons or install a new set, it is important to match the weight of individual pistons. The maximum allowable weight difference is listed in the manufacturer's table of limits. New pistons are often purchased in matched sets with weight differences considerably below the manufacturer's maximum.

## VALVES AND VALVE MECHANISMS

If the valve has sufficient material, it can be refaced by grinding. A wet valve grinder is the preferred method of refacing because a mixture of soluble oil and water cools the valve and removes grinding particles while machining.

The operation of valve grinding machines varies depending on the manufacturer. Always take time to familiarize yourself with the equipment you intend to use. The following discussion provides an overview of the steps common to refacing a valve with a grinding machine.

Before grinding a valve, run a diamond dresser across the stone; cut just deep enough to true and clean the stone. Follow the overhaul manual specifications to set the movable head for the correct valve face angle. Valves are usually ground to a standard angle of 30 degrees or 45 degrees. However, sometimes an interference fit from 0.5 degree to 1.5 degrees less than the standard angle might be required. An interference fit provides a positive seal with an extremely narrow contact surface. Because the spring force on the valve is concentrated in a very small area, a tighter seal is provided. [Figure 2-57]

Insert the valve into the chuck with the valve face approximately two inches away from the chuck. If the valve extends beyond this distance, excessive wobbling may occur. Prior to starting the grinder, check the travel of the valve face across the stone. Adjust both the "in" and "out" travel stops so that the valve completely passes the stone on both sides but does not contact the stem. [Figure 2-58]

With the valve positioned in the chuck, start the grinder and direct the flow of grinding fluid over the valve face. Back the workhead table (with the valve fixture) all the way out; then adjust laterally to position the valve directly in front of the stone. Advance the valve toward the stone slowly until it makes contact. The intensity of the grinding sound indicates the size of cut being made by the stone. Slowly draw the valve back and forth across the full width of the stone without increasing the cut. When the grinding sound diminishes (or ceases) the cut is complete. Move the workhead table to the aft stop,

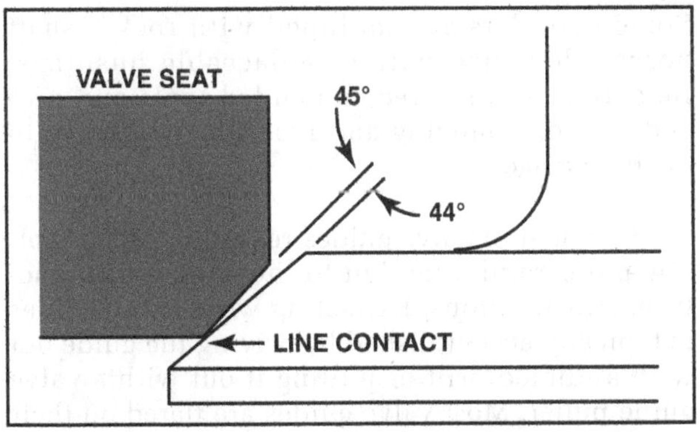


**Figure 2-57. An interference fit provides a positive seal along a fine contact area.**

and then stop the rotation of the valve to inspect the valve face. If another cut is needed, restart valve rotation and slowly move the valve forward to the grinding stone to increase the cut. When grinding valves, you should remove material in only small cuts. Large cuts cause chattering and produce a rough valve surface. Remove the minimum material necessary to clean up wear marks or pits from the valve face.

After grinding, measure the margin to ensure that the valve edge has not been ground too thin. A thin edge is called a feather edge and can overheat and cause preignition. A feather edge is likely to burn away quickly and will result in the need for another overhaul. [Figure 2-59]

If necessary, valve tips can be resurfaced on a valve grinder to remove cupping or wear. Ensure that the side of the grinding stone is true. Position the valve in a clamp to enable you to grind the valve tip on the side of the stone. Turn on the grinder. Press the valve lightly against the stone while moving the tip back and forth across the side without going off the edge. Keep the valve tip cool by covering it with plenty of grinding fluid. [Figure 2-60]

If the valve tip is ground, the bevel on its edge will be partially removed. This bevel prevents the valve guide from being scratched when the valve is installed. To restore the bevel, mount the appropriate fixture at a 45-degree angle to the stone. Hold the valve in the fixture with one hand and turn the valve head with your other hand. Using light pressure, grind all the way around the tip.

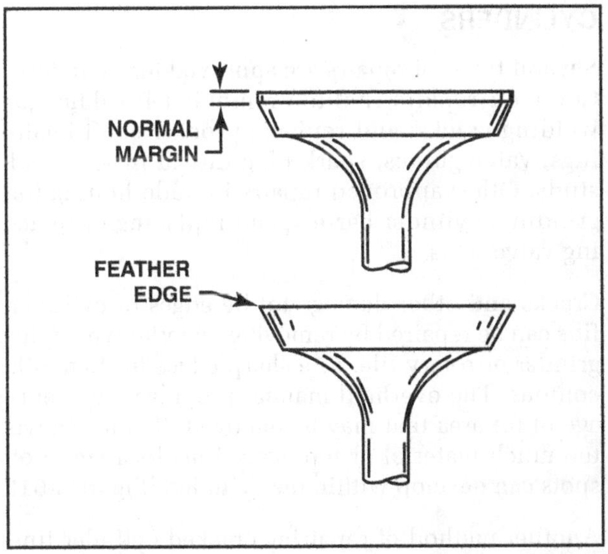


**Figure 2-59. A valve should still have an acceptable margin after grinding. A feather edge is caused by grinding a valve too much.**

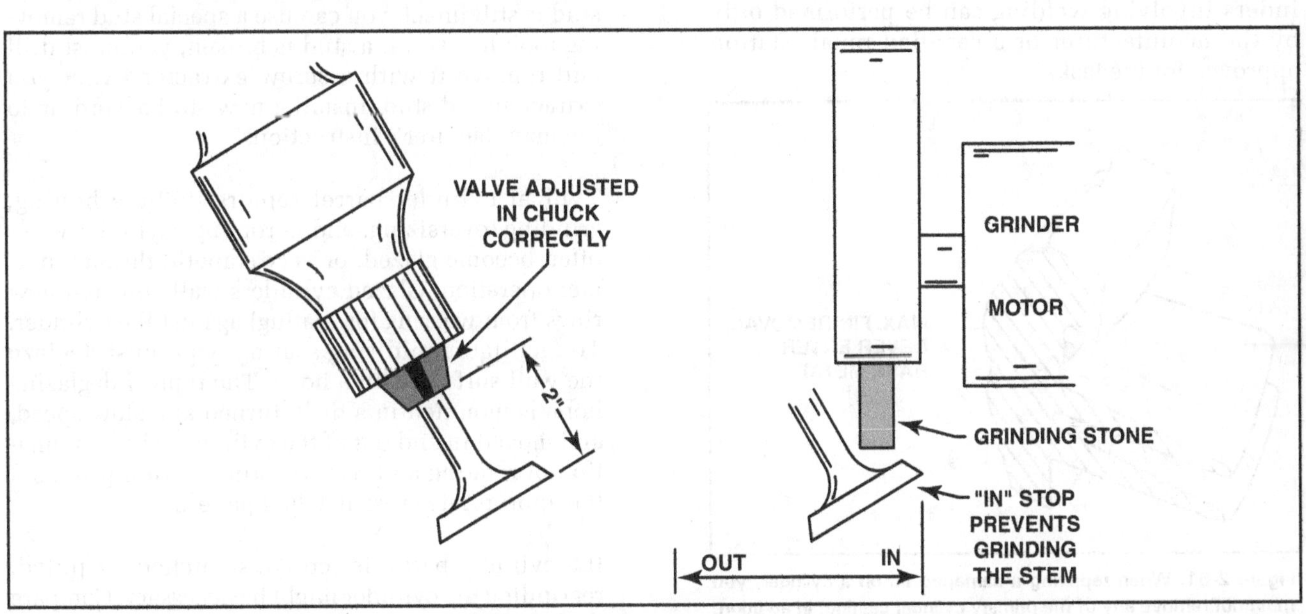


**Figure 2-58. When a valve is secured in the chuck of a valve grinding machine, adjust the "in" and "out" stops so the valve face passes the stone completely on both sides. Be sure that the stem does not contact the grinding stone.**

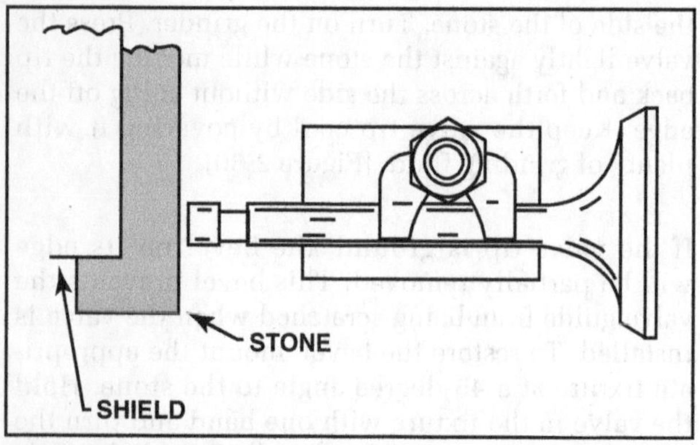


Figure 2-60. To accurately grind a valve tip, the valve must be held securely in place and be aligned perpendicular to the side of the grinding stone.

## CYLINDERS

Several types of repairs are approved for cylinders. Common repairs include removing fin damage; welding cracks; and replacing rocker shaft bushings, valve guides, spark plug thread inserts, and studs. Other approved repairs include honing (or grinding) cylinder barrels, and replacing or refacing valve seats.

Cracks and other damage to the edges of cylinder fins can be repaired by removing material with a die grinder or rotary file. File sharp edges to a smooth contour. The overhaul manual provides a percentage of fin area that may be removed. If you remove too much material or too many fins, localized hot spots can develop within the cylinder. [Figure 2-61]

Another method of repairing cracked cylinder fins involves grinding out the crack and welding. Excess material from the weld is ground (or machined) away to match the original contour. Repairs to cylinders involving welding can be performed only by the manufacturer or a certified repair station approved for the task.

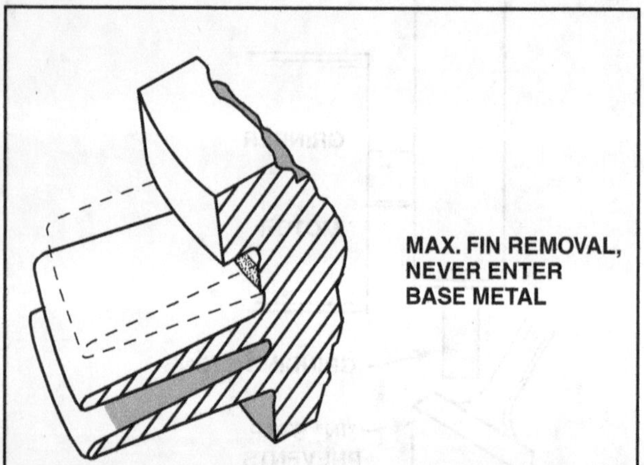


Figure 2-61. When repairing a damaged fin on a cylinder, you must not remove any of the primary cylinder casting. In addition, fin loss near spark plug openings or exhaust ports can cause dangerous local hot spots.

Some cylinders are equipped with rocker shaft bosses that incorporate replaceable bushings. Be sure to use the recommended tools and procedures for removing and inserting a bushing to avoid damage.

Replacement of valve guides requires special tooling and careful attention to the engine manufacturer's instructions. Extracting worn valve guides is typically accomplished by driving the guide out with a piloted drift or pulling it out with a valve guide puller. Most valve guides are flared on their outside end; therefore, they must be driven or pulled from the inside. Guides are installed in the cylinder with an interference fit; removal requires heating the cylinder and freezing the extraction tool to facilitate valve guide removal. Heating the cylinder causes the valve guide hole to expand and the chilled extraction tool causes the guide to contract. The combined effects of these changes are typically sufficient to reduce the interference fit to enable removal.

Valve seat inserts are removed in a manner similar to valve guides, using hot and cold temperatures. Engine manufacturers typically specify special tools for valve seat extraction and installation.

You can replace damaged spark plug thread inserts with Heli-Coil inserts as specified by an engine manufacturer. Use official Heli-Coil tools and follow the overhaul manual instructions carefully to prevent damaging the cylinder.

The studs that secure the exhaust pipe to a cylinder are subject to extreme heat and highly corrosive exhaust gas and must be replaced occasionally. If a stud is still intact, you can use a special stud removing tool; hwever, if a stud is broken, you must drill and remove it with a screw extractor. After you extract an old stud, install a new stud according to the manufacturer's instructions.

Typical cylinder barrel repairs include honing, grinding, oversizing, and chroming. Cylinder walls often become glazed, or very smooth, through normal operation. Glazed cylinders walls prevent new rings from wearing (or seating) against the cylinder. To facilitate rapid ring seating, you must **deglaze** the wall surface with a hone. The typical deglazing hone is mounted in a drill, turned at a slow speed, and moved in and out of the cylinder. The combination of rotating and reciprocating motion produces the appropriate cross-hatched pattern.

If a cylinder barrel is scored, scratched, or pitted, regrinding the cylinder might be necessary. Compare the barrel dimensions to the manufacturer's table of limits to determine whether enough material is present to permit grinding. In some cases, a cylinder can be ground to a standard oversize. Standard oversizes are 0.010, 0.015, and 0.020 inch. Instead of oversizing, another option is to apply chrome plating after grinding to restore the cylinder to its original diameter. Because grinding and chrome plating require specialized equipment, these repairs are normally performed by a certified repair station approved for the task. Note that cylinders with nitrided surfaces may not be ground away.

## REFACING VALVE SEATS

Modern reciprocating engines are equipped with either bronze or steel valve seats. Steel seats are made from a hard, heat-resistant steel alloy and are commonly used for exhaust. Bronze seats are made from an alloy of aluminum bronze or phosphor bronze alloys and used for both intake and exhaust seats.

Valve seats are normally refaced at each overhaul. Additionally, valve seats are ground every time a valve or valve guide is replaced. Grinding stones are used for refacing steel components while cutters (or reamers) are preferred for bronze seats. Grinding stones are often permissible for use with bronze seats if cutters are not available. Because bronze is a fairly soft metal, it loads the grinding stone quickly. This increases the time required for the task because a fair amount of time is consumed by redressing the stone.

Valve seats can be ground either wet or dry. A wet grinder is preferred because the continuous flow of oil and water washes away grinding residue and cools the stone and seat. In addition, wet grinding produces a smoother, more accurate surface than dry grinding. Grinding stones are typically made of silicon carbide or aluminum oxide.

The grinding process employs three grades of stones: rough, finishing, and polishing. A rough stone makes the initial cut to remove pits, scores, and burn marks as well as align the valve seat and guide. Next, a finishing stone removes any grinding marks to produce a smooth finish. When a manufacturer requires a highly polished valve seat, a polishing stone completes the job.

Whenever a grinding stone becomes loaded with metal or grooved; it must be cleaned. You clean (or dress) a stone by installing it on an appropriate fixture and cutting the surface with a diamond dressing tool. A diamond dresser is also used to reduce a stone's diameter. Dress a stone only the minimum amount necessary.

Refacing valves starts by mounting the cylinder firmly in a fixture. Install an expanding pilot into the valve guide. The pilot must be tight to ensure quality; any movement is detrimental to the finished grind. If you are wet-grinding, insert a fluid hose through a spark plug hole. [Figure 2-62]

Grinding requires a steady hand and particular skill. Center the stone on the pilot; off-center grinding results in chattering and a rough grind. The proper stone speed for grinding is between 8,000 and 10,000 r.p.m. The maximum pressure on the stone should not exceed the weight of the grinding equipment. While grinding, remove stone pressure every few seconds to allow coolant to wash away any residue and remain in the desired speed range. Inspect the condition of the valve seat frequently so that only the minimum amount of material is removed to achieve the desired finish.

After grinding a valve seat, verify that the surface is even and true. A special dial indicator is used to measure runout; an acceptable range is typically between 0.0 and 0.002 inch. After you verify that the seat is even and true, check the contact area between the valve face and seat. Evenly spread a transfer compound (often a blue dye, known as Prussian blue), on the valve seat and press the valve against it. Remove the valve and evaluate the transferred dye. Unless valves are ground with an interference fit, the desired contact area is centered, one-third to two-thirds the width of the valve face.

If the valve seat makes contact in the upper or lower third of the valve face, the top and bottom edges of the stone need additional grinding with stones of different cutting angles. This is known as "narrowing the seat." [Figure 2-63]

The angle of a valve seat determines which stones should be used when narrowing a valve seat. For

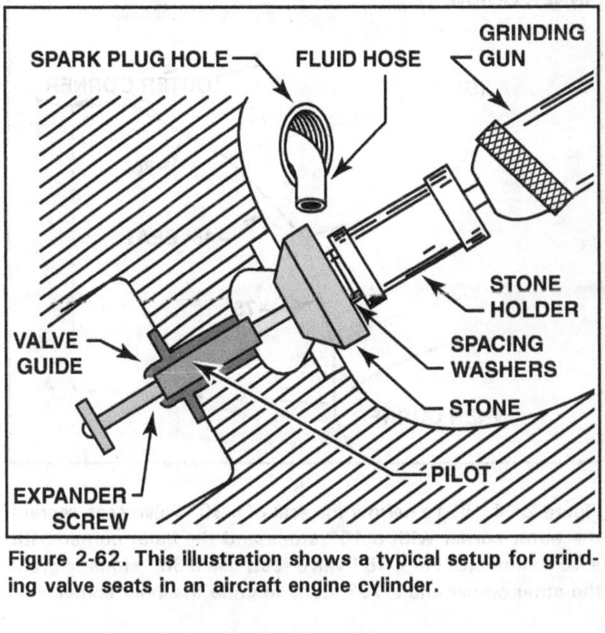


**Figure 2-62. This illustration shows a typical setup for grinding valve seats in an aircraft engine cylinder.**

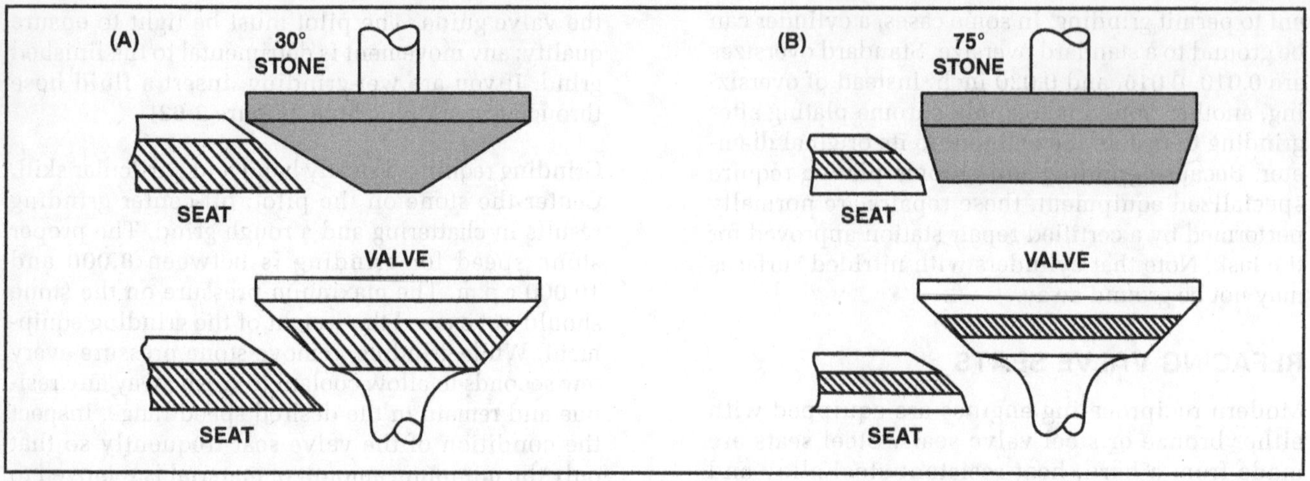


**Figure 2-63. (A) If a valve seat contacts the upper third of the valve face, the seat can be regrouped to a lesser angle. (B) Contact with the bottom third of the valve face requires regrinding a valve seat's inner corner to a greater angle.**

example, with a 30° seat, it is common practice to use a 15° cutting stone on the outer corner and a 45° stone on the inner corner. On the other hand, to narrow the seat of a 45° valve seat, the outer corner is reground to 30° while the inner corner is reground to 75°. [Figure 2-64]

If a valve seat is ground excessively, the valve face will make contact too far up in the cylinder head. This adversely affects valve clearance, spring tension, and valve fit. To check for this condition, insert the valve into the guide and measure the height of the valve stem above the location specified in the overhaul manual.

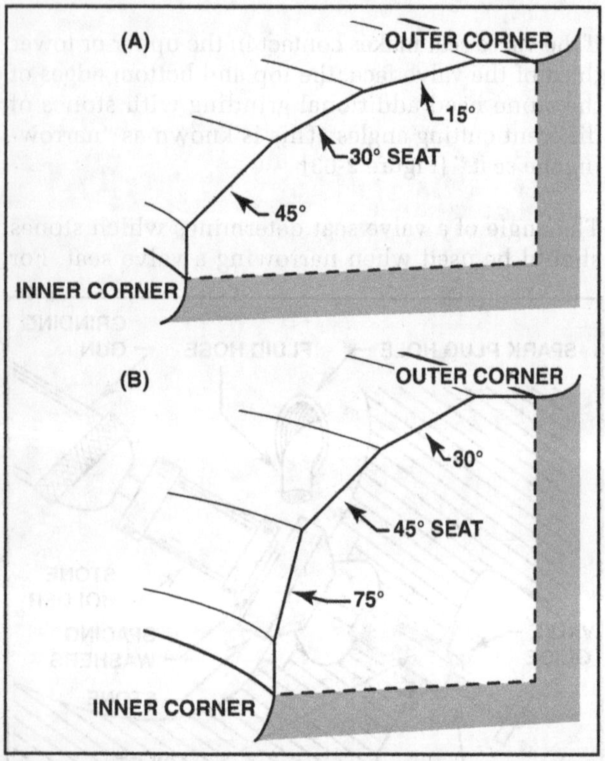


**Figure 2-64. (A) To narrow the seat of a 30° valve seat, regrind the outer corner with a 15° stone and the inner corner with a 45° stone. (B) For a 45° valve seat, use a 30° stone to grind the outer corner and a 75° stone to grind the inner corner.**

After grinding either surface, some manufacturers require lapping a valve to its seat. **Lapping** creates a smooth contact surface. Apply a small amount of lapping compound to the valve face and rotate the valve while it contacts the seat. When the contact area is defined by a smooth, grey finish, remove the lapping compound from the valve face, seat, and adjacent areas. [Figure 2-65]

Check the valve mating surfaces for leaks by installing the valves in the cylinder. With finger pressure on the valve stem, pour kerosene or solvent into the valve port and look for leakage into the combustion chamber. If no leaking occurs, the operation is finished. If kerosene leaks past the valve, continue lapping until the leakage stops.

## REASSEMBLY

After inspecting all of the parts and repairing or replacing components, you are now ready to reassemble the engine. Make sure that all parts are thoroughly cleaned and lubricated appropriately.

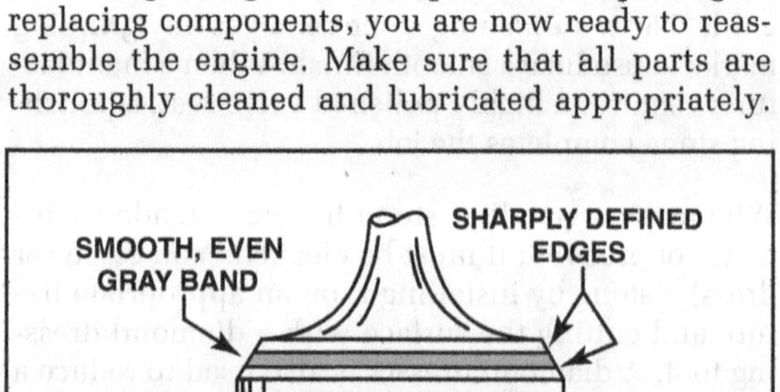


**Figure 2-65. Proper valve lapping produces an extremely smooth surface and a well-defined contact area.**

Be sure to follow the manufacturer's instructions. Following are general assembly procedures that pertain to most reciprocating engines.

## CRANKSHAFT

Typically, a reconditioned crankshaft is fully assembled; however, if it is not, reinstall the counterweights and all sludge chamber components. For a crankshaft with hollow crankpins, carefully reinstall the sludge chamber tubes to avoid covering the ends of the oil passages. Install expansion plugs and secure any gears that attach to the crankshaft. A vertical buildup fixture facilitates installation and lubrication of the connecting rods. When attaching connecting rods to a crankshaft, make sure that the numbers stamped on the rods are correctly oriented. The torque and safety of connecting rod hardware is critical; follow the requirements specified in the overhaul manual.

## CRANKCASE

Set the crankcase halves on a clean, flat work surface and install the main bearing inserts, being careful to ensure that the tangs (or dowels) are properly positioned. Lubricate and install the hydraulic lifters in one of the crankcase halves. Lubricate the camshaft bearing journal surfaces and install the camshaft over the lifters. Lubricate the main bearings and install the crankshaft. Install the front oil seal around the propeller shaft and apply a thin layer of nonhardening gasket compound to the outside mating surface of each half of the crankcase. When recommended by the manufacturer, embed a length of fine silk thread in the gasket compound on one of the crankcase halves.

Lubricate and install the remaining hydraulic lifters in the other crankcase half. Support lifters in place while flipping the crankcase over and carefully lowering it onto the half with the crankshaft and camshaft. Pay special attention to properly seating the front oil seal and observe any special instructions regarding the main bearings. Install new hardware to attach the crankcase halves and torque in the sequence recommended by the manufacturer.

Mount to a vertical buildup fixture to install the gears and accessory case. Be sure to align the timing marks properly. If misaligned, valves will open and close at the wrong time for combustion and the engine will not run.

## CYLINDERS

Before installing valves in a cylinder, lubricate the stems with the specified lubricant. Place the cylinder over a post fixture to support the valves while installing the valve springs and retainers. After the valve assemblies are complete, install a cylinder base seal around the cylinder skirt, and install any intercylinder baffles and fin stabilizers that will not interfere with subsequent assembly.

## PISTONS AND RINGS

You should keep in mind several precautions when installing new rings on a piston. Chrome-plated rings can be used only in plain steel or nitrided cylinders. Cast iron rings can be used only in chrome-plated cylinders. In either case, you use a ring expander to install the rings. This tool reduces the risk of accidentally scratching the piston or breaking a ring. Always install the ring so that the part number faces the top of the piston.

After the rings are installed, lubricate the assembly with the manufacturer's approved lubricant. Stagger the ring gaps and attach the pistons to their corresponding connecting rods with a piston pin. Compress the piston rings with a ring compressor tool and then slide the cylinder over the piston up to the piston pin. Reposition the ring compressor over the lowest oil ring and slide the cylinder over the rest of the piston. You should verify that push rod housings (tubes), oil seals, and push rods are in place and slide the cylinder onto the cylinder pad. Install the cylinder base attaching hardware. After all cylinders are attached to the crankcase, tighten and torque the cylinder attaching hardware in the order specified by the manufacturer. Lubricate and install the rocker arm assemblies.

## FINAL ASSEMBLY

Use a new gasket when installing the oil sump on the crankcase, and tighten the attaching hardware. Install and time the magnetos on their mount pads according to the overhaul manual instructions. Use new seals and gaskets when installing the carburetor or fuel injection system components and the induction system. Install remaining accessories (including the engine-driven pumps and alternator) and baffling.

## BLOCK TESTING

The final step in the overhaul process is to test the engine. At an overhaul facility, the engine is operated in a test cell to seat piston rings, burnish bushings, and collect data to evaluate engine performance. Piston ring seating is accomplished primarily by controlled engine operation in the high speed range. On the other hand, the burnishing of bearings is accomplished at low engine speeds.

Engine performance is evaluated in a test cell during block testing by specialized test equipment and standard engine instruments. Operational test procedures vary with individual engines. The failure of any internal part during an engine run-in requires that the engine be disassembled and repaired. If an engine accessory fails, a new accessory is installed and the test continues. Following successful completion of block test requirements, engines are either installed on an aircraft or treated with a corrosion preventative and placed in storage. [Figure 2-66]

**Figure 2-66. Block testing of an overhauled engine is conducted in a test cell with specialized test equipment and standard engine instruments.**

## LOGBOOK ENTRIES

After an overhaul is complete, you must make the appropriate maintenance entries. In addition to recording the information required by the Federal Aviation Regulations, list all of the new parts you installed. Furthermore, you should document the details from all dimensional and structural inspections, along with evidence of compliance with airworthiness directives and service bulletins. For any major repairs, you must complete form 337 and keep one of the copies in the engine logbook.

# ENGINE INSTALLATION

A repaired, overhauled, or replaced engine must be prepared for installation. Install all of the accessories and baffling. If the engine mount was removed with the engine, reinstall it. If the engine had been preserved for storage, follow the depreservation procedures in the overhaul manual.

If an aircraft owner wants to install a different model of engine than was originally approved, a **Supplemental Type Certificate (STC)** is required for this change. Without an STC, engine replacement is limited to the models listed on the original Type Certificate.

## HOISTING FOR INSTALLATION

When a new or overhauled engine is ready for installation, position the engine stand as close as possible to the aircraft. Attach the sling to the engine and raise the hoist until it is supports the majority of the engine's weight. Now, remove the bolts attaching the engine to the stand and hoist the engine to the desired height.

## MOUNTING THE ENGINE

Before you mount an engine on an aircraft, you should have inspected the integrity of both the engine mount structure and the shock mounts and gathered all of the necessary hardware. You should request assistance from as many people as necessary to safely maneuver the engine into position on the aircraft. To help prevent injuring personnel or damaging the aircraft or the engine, slowly ease the engine into position, ensuring that the engine clears all obstacles. Position the engine to align the engine mounting lugs and mounting points on the engine mount. If the mount is already attached to the engine, align the engine mount with the aircraft structure. Engines are heavy and possess substantial inertia when swinging from a hoist. Therefore, exercise caution to avoid damage to the nacelle framework, ducts, or firewall connections.

After the engine is aligned, insert the mounting bolts and secure with the appropriate hardware, tightening to the manufacturer's recommended torque value. The manufacturer's instructions define the sequence for tightening mounting bolts. While the attaching hardware is being tightened, ensure that the hoist continues to support the engine's weight. Otherwise, the engine's weight on the mounting bolts might prevent you from properly tightening the nuts with the proper torque.

After the mounting hardware is properly torqued and safetied, the engine hoist can be removed. Be sure to connect the bonding straps to provide an electrical path between the engine, the mount, and the airframe. Failure to install these necessary components could result in the electric current from the starter passing through engine controls or metal fuel lines. This condition could start a fire or cause extensive damage to the aircraft.

## CONNECTIONS AND ADJUSTMENTS

After you mount the engine, connect the electrical leads and fluid lines to the engine and accessories. There are no rules governing the order in which you connect accessories. However, you should aim for efficiency and follow any published instructions from the manufacturer.

Engine induction systems vary with nearly every combination of aircraft and engine. All induction systems must be leak-free. Install the induction system components carefully with new gaskets and flexible tubes (when used). Use the proper clamps and hardware and, if required, use air pressure to check the system for leaks. A pressure check typically requires blocking the system on one end and supplying a specific pressure of compressed air at the other. Measure the leakage rate and compare it with the manufacturer's standard to determine if it falls within acceptable limits.

Install a new (or serviceable) air induction filter. Several types of induction filters are available; understand and follow the cleaning and replacement instructions for the approved and appropriate filter in use on the aircraft.

Similarly, the exhaust system must be assembled carefully to prevent exhaust gas leakage. Carefully examine the entire system and repair or replace any damaged components as necessary. During assembly, tighten all clamps and nuts gradually and progressively until you reach the correct torque. During assembly, attaching parts should be tapped with a soft-faced mallet to reduce the chance of binding. With some systems, a ball joint connects a stationary portion of the system to another. A ball joint compensates for slight misalignments and normal engine movement from vibration. Ball joints must be installed with the specified clearance to prevent binding when the hot exhaust gases cause the system to expand.

Hoses used with low pressure systems, such as vacuum and instrument air, are often secured with clamps. Examine clamps before installation and replace any that are distorted or defective. After you install a hose, route it away from engine and airframe parts that could damage it, and be sure that it is adequately supported. Oftentimes, rubber lined **Adel clamps** are installed at specified intervals to provide protection and support for these hoses.

Before tightening the fittings on rigid metal tubing, ensure that the threads are clean and in good condition. When specified in the instructions, apply a thread-sealing compound to the fitting before installation. Exercise care to prevent cross-threading any fittings and to ensure correct torque. Overtightening a fitting increases the likelihood of a leak or failure.

Ensure that all electrical connections are clean and secure. For terminals attached to a threaded terminal post, use a lock washer to prevent the nut from backing off. When knurled connector plugs are used, prevent accidental disconnection with steel safety wire. After routing wires, anchor them to prevent chafing within thc nacelle.

The engine control system is specifically designed for a particular airframe/engine combination. A combination of rigid push-pull rods, flexible push-pull wire encased in a coiled wire sheath, or cables and pulleys is likely. Engine controls must be accurately adjusted to ensure instantaneous response to a control input. Therefore, make all adjustments in accordance with the procedures outlined in the manufacturer's instructions.

For most light aircraft, flexible push-pull cables are used to control the engine throttle, mixture, propeller governor, and carburetor heat or alternate air. A flexible control cable must be adequately supported to operate properly. Support is often provided by a terminal mounting clamp in the cockpit and another near the component on the engine. Between the terminal clamps, intermediate clamps support the cable every three to four feet and on both sides of bends. The radius of a cable bend should be at least six inches. Upon installation or inspection, ensure that the flexible housing extends approximately one inch beyond the terminal clamp to permit angular movement and smooth motion of the control cable through its entire range of motion. An engine component controlled by a flexible control is typically limited to 90 degrees (45 degrees of angular motion to either side of center position. [Figure 2-67]

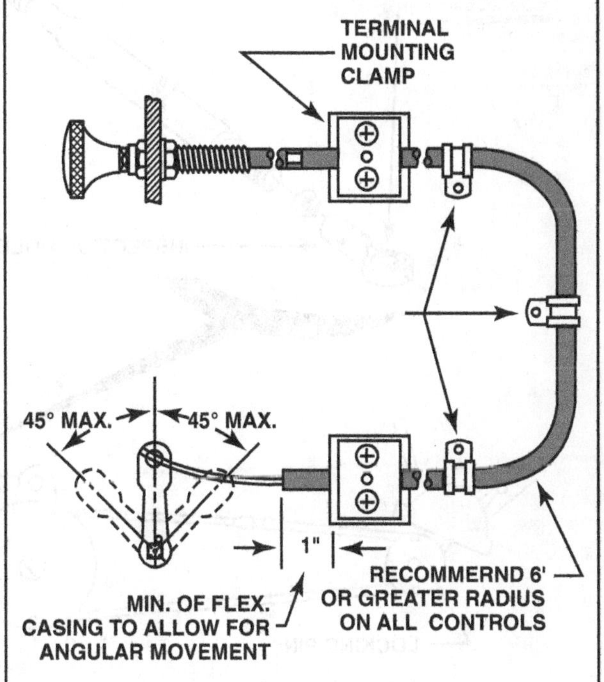


**Figure 2-67. Many small single-engine airplanes use a push-pull wire throttle control encased in a protective sheath.**

Several adjustment steps are required for a throttle control system using cables, pulleys, and a drum. A drum is essentially a pulley with at least one complete loop of cable around its circumference. To aid adjustment, the drum has a hole that accommodates a locking pin to establish a reliable reference point. To adjust a control system, loosen the serrated control arm in the nacelle. Next, back off the stop so that the throttle valve moves to its closed position. Insert a locking pin in the cable drum. Adjust the control rod length as specified and tighten the serrated throttle control arm. Then, loosen the cable turnbuckles enough to permit movement of the control lever so that you can insert the quadrant locking pin. Tighten the turnbuckles and use a tensiometer to verify that the cable tension is set within the manufacturer's specifications. Reset valve stop position, safety the turnbuckles, remove the lockpins from the cable and quadrant drums, and verify proper control operation. [Figure 2-68]

Properly adjusted engine controls must have a degree of **cushion (springback)** at their fully open and closed positions. Simply stated, the stops at the engine component reach their outermost limits before the control levers reach their corresponding stop in the cockpit. The cushion provides assurance that the throttle and mixture valves fully open and close. On multiengine aircraft, the cushion for throttle, mixture, and propeller controls must be equal and the levers must align in any selected power setting. This reduces the likelihood of having to set each control individually while trying to synchronize engine operations.

After installing and adjusting the engine, install the propeller. If the propeller is fixed pitch, lift it into position and attach it to the crankshaft propeller flange. However, if installing a constant-speed propeller, new gaskets and o-rings are required. Lift large propellers with an appropriate sling and hoist. Never attempt to position a propeller without enough assistance or the necessary equipment. Always follow the manufacturer's recommended installation procedure.

## GROUND TEST PREPARATION

With the engine installed on an aircraft or test stand, you are almost ready for the test run. Install properly gapped spark plugs and tighten them to manufacturer torque specifications. Attach the ignition leads to the spark plugs. Fill the engine with oil approved by the manufacturer and recheck the security of all oil and fuel line connections.

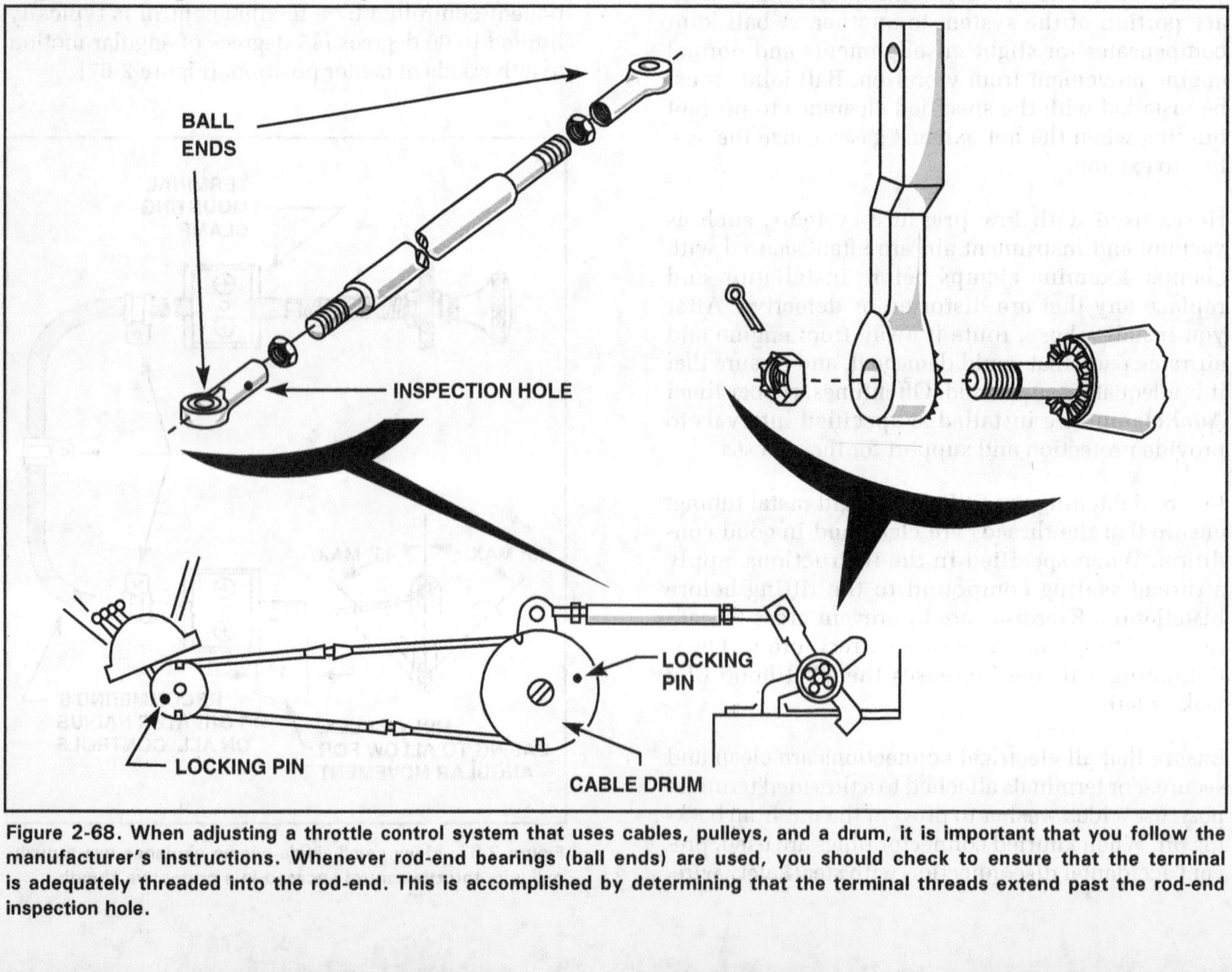


**Figure 2-68. When adjusting a throttle control system that uses cables, pulleys, and a drum, it is important that you follow the manufacturer's instructions. Whenever rod-end bearings (ball ends) are used, you should check to ensure that the terminal is adequately threaded into the rod-end. This is accomplished by determining that the terminal threads extend past the rod-end inspection hole.**

## PREOILING

To prevent engine bearing failure on the initial start, preoil the engine. When an engine has not operated for an extended period of time, engine oil drains away from the internal bearing surfaces. Without adequate oil on the bearings, the initial friction can destroy them. By forcing oil throughout the engine before startup, you prevent unnecessary damage to a new or newly overhauled engine.

One method of preoiling involves removing one spark plug from each cylinder. This allows the crankshaft to be rotated easily with the starter. After this is done, attach a pressure oiler to the engine. Air pressure forces oil through the engine when you use the starter to turn over the engine. Be sure to adhere to the manufacturer's limits for oil pressure. After all of the oil galleys are full, oil will flow out of the return line. At this point, stop cranking the engine and disconnect the preoiler tank. [Figure 2-69]

On a typical dry-sump engine, the preoiler is connected to the inlet of the engine-driven oil pump. Either the oil return line is disconnected or a fitting is removed near the nose of the engine to allow overflow to exit the engine.

For engines with a wet sump, the process is similar except that the preoiler is connected to the oil temperature fitting and a drain line is unnecessary. With the preoiler connected and pumping oil, the engine is turned over with the starter until oil pressure is indicated on the cockpit gauge. After this occurs, discontinue cranking the engine, disconnect the preoiler tank, and check the oil level to make sure that the engine is not overfilled.

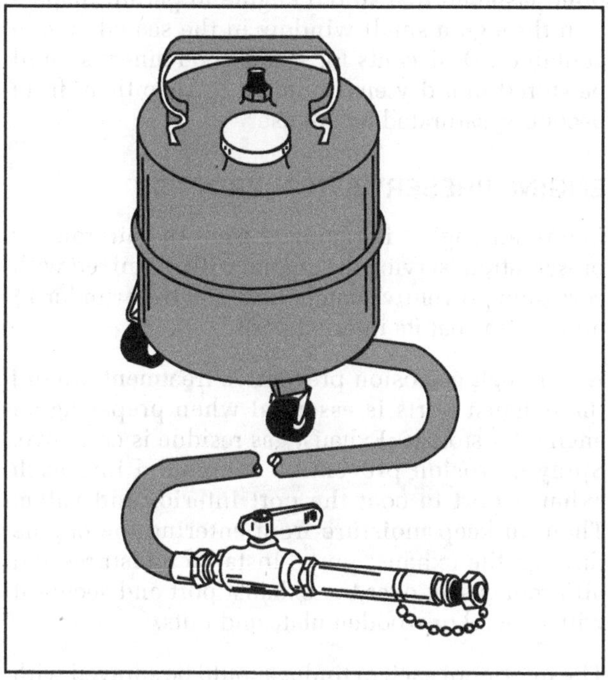

**Figure 2-69. Pre-oiling an engine with a special tank helps prevent bearing failure when an engine is first started after an overhaul or after being idle for a long time.**

The engine can also be preoiled with the engine driven pump. Again, remove one spark plug from each cylinder and service the engine with the appropriate amount of oil. Place the mixture control in the idle-cutoff position; turn the fuel shutoff valve and ignition switch to their off positions; and put the throttle control in its idle position. Then, crank the engine with the starter until the oil pressure gauge indicates oil pressure.

After preoiling the engine, replace the spark plugs and reconnect all oil system lines. Operate the engine within four hours to avoid having to repeat the preoiling procedure.

### FUEL SYSTEM BLEEDING

Before attempting to start a newly installed engine, purge the fuel system to bleed air bubbles from the fuel lines and pumps and to remove any preservative oil from the fuel system. The bleeding procedure varies depending on the aircraft fuel system, so be sure to consult the manufacturer's instructions for specific directions.

### COWL FLAP RIGGING

Engine cowl flaps regulate the passage of cooling air through the engine compartment. Adjust them according to the airframe manufacturer's instructions. When adjustments are complete, operate the system and then recheck to ensure that the system operates according to specified limits. If a cowl flap position indicator is installed, verify that it accurately reports the flap position.

### FINAL PREPARATION STEPS

After all ground test preparations are complete and you are satisfied that the engine can be safely run, verify that the aircraft battery is reinstalled and, if necessary, have a ground power cart plugged into the aircraft. Consult the aircraft checklist to start and runup the engine as necessary.

## POST-RUN CHECKS AND ADJUSTMENTS

After the initial ground run and flight test, perform a thorough visual inspection and make final adjustments. Exercise caution to avoid getting burned by the hot engine. Fuel pressure and oil pressure might require adjustment along with ignition timing, valve clearances, idle speed, and idle mixture. Remove the oil sump plug, screen and oil filter to inspect for the presence of any metal particles. If no unexpected particles are found, clean and reinstall the plug and screen. Install a new engine oil filter.

Visually inspect all lines for leakage and tight connections, and correct any discrepancies. Check hose clamps for tightness and retighten as necessary, especially on new hose. Closely inspect all oil system connections for leaks. Inspect the cylinder hold-down nuts (or cap screws) for security. Check the integrity of all items secured with safety wire.

## ENGINE PRESERVATION

An engine that is going to be put in storage or not operated for more than a month should be preserved and protected to prevent corrosion. Damaging rust and other corrosion can occur unless an engine is regularly operated or otherwise protected. The following discussion describes preservation of an engine removed from an aircraft; however, the materials and methods discussed apply to all types of engine storage.

## CORROSION PREVENTATIVE COMPOUNDS

The primary purpose of engine and engine accessory preservation procedures is to prevent corrosion. Corrosion occurs whenever a metal such as steel, iron, or aluminum combines with oxygen to form an oxide. If a base metal is properly sealed, corrosion cannot occur. Most corrosion-preventive compounds are petroleum-based products that prevent air from reaching the metal's surface by forming a wax-like film over the surface.

Corrosion-preventive compounds are manufactured to different specifications based on specific needs. Light compounds are typically mixed with engine oil for short term preservation and can be sprayed into a cylinder or other components. Short-term corrosion-preventive compounds are intended for use in engines that remain inactive for fewer than 30 days. To attain the correct proportions of lubricating oil and corrosion-preventive compounds, mix the fluids externally, and then add them to the engine. Adding preservative mixture to oil already in an engine is a poor maintenance practice and should be avoided.

A heavy corrosion-preventive compound is used for long-term preservation; it forms a heavy, wax-like barrier over a metal surface. Before applying a heavy compound, heat it to a liquid state. After the compound cools on an engine, the only way to remove it is with a commercial solvent or kerosene spray.

Corrosion preventive compounds are effective moisture barriers, but they eventually break down over time in the presence of high humidity. Also, compounds can eventually dry out because the oil base gradually evaporates. When this happens, the engine needs to be preserved again or corrosion is likely to occur.

## DEHYDRATING AGENTS

Dehydrating agents, often referred to as **desiccants**, are used in engine preservation because they remove moisture from the local atmosphere. Common **silica gel** is an ideal desiccant because it does not dissolve when saturated. Bags of silica gel are placed around and inside the accessible parts of a stored engine. Silica gel is also used in clear plastic plugs, called **dehydrator plugs**, which are screwed into an engine's spark plug holes. The silica gel in the dehydrator plugs is typically treated with **cobalt chloride** to provide a visual indicator of the moisture content inside the preserved engine. Cobalt chloride-treated silica gel appears bright blue in the presence of low relative humidity. As humidity increases, the shade of blue lightens, turning lavender at about 30 percent relative humidity. If the relative humidity exceeds 30 percent, the color changes to various shades of pink, and becomes completely white at 60 percent relative humidity. With relative humidity below 30 percent, corrosion is unlikely to take place. Bright blue dehydrator plugs indicate low moisture content and low risk of internal corrosion.

Cobalt chloride-treated silica gel is also used in special envelopes to indicate humidity. An envelope is often fastened to a stored engine to permit inspection through a small window in the sealed engine container. Desiccants for storage containers should be stored in a dry environment to keep them from becoming saturated before use.

## ENGINE PRESERVATION PROCESS

Before an engine is removed from the aircraft for preservation, service the engine with oil mixed with corrosion preventive compound, and then run for 15 minutes to coat its internal parts.

A thorough corrosion preventive treatment around the exhaust ports is essential when preparing an engine for storage. Exhaust gas residue is corrosive. Spray corrosion preventive compound into each exhaust port to coat the port interior and valve. Then, to keep moisture from entering the engine through the exhaust ports, install a moisture- and oil-proof gasket over the exhaust port and secure it with a metal or wooden plate and nuts.

The interior of each cylinder should be sprayed with a corrosion preventive compound. This prevents moisture and oxygen from reacting with deposits remaining from combustion. Rotate the engine until each piston is at bottom dead center and apply the compound through the spark plug opening. Positioning the piston at bottom dead center lets you coat the entire cylinder interior. After spraying each cylinder with its piston at bottom dead center, spray each cylinder again, but do not rotate the crankshaft. From this point forward, the crankshaft must not be moved or the corrosion preventive seal will be broken. Immediately after the corrosion preventive compound dries, insert a dehydrator plug in each spark plug opening. In addition, the firing end of each ignition lead should be attached to a dehydrator plug. [Figure 2-70]

Seal the intake manifold when storing an engine. If a carburetor is installed on the engine and it is not removed for storage, wire the valve open and install a seal over the inlet. If the carburetor is removed, install a seal at the carburetor mounting pad. In either case, the seal should be moisture- and oil-proof gasket supported by a wood or metal plate and bolted in place. Bags of silica gel should be placed inside the intake manifold. Be sure to make the installation of silica gel bags obvious to reduce the possibility of a technician neglecting to remove them when the engine is removed from storage.

## ENGINE SHIPPING CONTAINERS

Preserved engines should be protected in a shipping container. Engines often come in specially designed metal or wooden containers with mounts to support and protect the engine. Some overhauled engines are sealed in containers pressurized with an inert gas such as nitrogen.

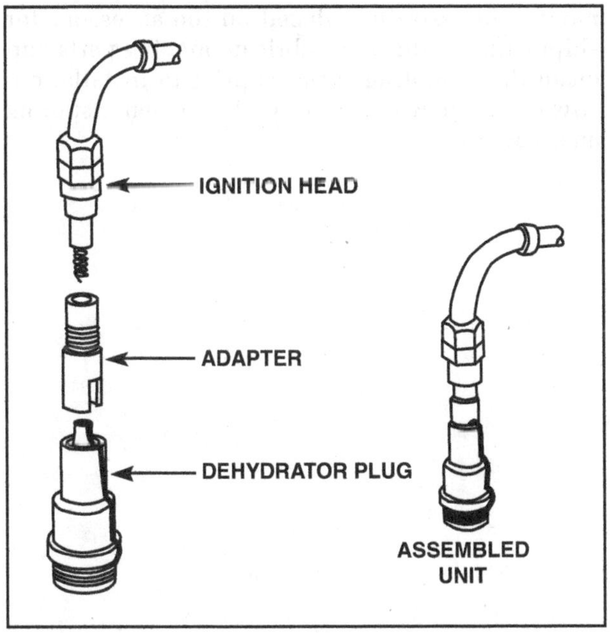


**Figure 2-70. Securing the ignition harness leads to the dehydrator plugs protects them from being damaged as the engine is moved.**

Wooden crates and metal containers are available for horizontal mounting or vertical mounting of the engine. When an engine is stored horizontally in a metal container, special ventilation plugs can be installed. If stored vertically, only the upper spark plug holes in each cylinder receive a ventilation plug while the lower spark plug holes are fitted with nonventilation plugs. Dehydrator plugs with dessicant removed and unserviceable spark plugs work well as nonventilation plugs.

An engine is secured to the container with the same type of hardware used to mount the engine to the aircraft. Some containers also provide a special mounting area for accessories removed from the engine being sent for overhaul.

Before attaching a cover lid on an engine box, spray the engine exterior with a heavy coating of corrosion preventive. At a minimum, be sure to apply corrosion preventive compound to the propeller shaft. Wrap the shaft in a plastic or moisture-proof sleeve. Perform a final inspection to be certain that all openings are sealed, and that only the proper accessories have been included for storage or shipping. If possible, seal the entire engine in a plastic or moisture-proof bag. While lowering the cover into position, be careful to avoid twisting or tearing the protective envelope. Secure the cover and mark the box with the dates of engine removal and preservation along with engine condition. [Figure 2-71]

## INSPECTION OF STORED ENGINES

Most maintenance shops inspect engines in storage according to a schedule. Humidity indicators are normally inspected every 30 days. If an engine is protected with a sealed envelope, the inspection period may be extended to every 90 days. Under

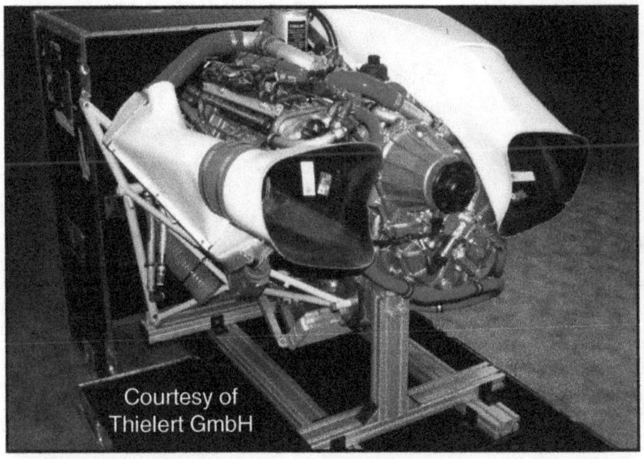


**Figure 2-71. Engines that need repairs or overhaul must be protected during storage and shipment. For this reason, shipping crates or containers tailored to a specific engine model must always be used to transport the engine.**

normal conditions, the humidity indicator inside a metal container is inspected every 180 days.

If more than half of the dehydrator plugs indicate the presence of excessive moisture, respray the cylinder interiors with corrosion preventive compound. An engine in a metal container for which the humidity indicator shows low humidity and air pressure below 1 p.s.i. only needs to be repressurized. If the humidity indicator shows high humidity, the engine should be represerved.

## ENGINE DEPRESERVATION

Preserved engines must undergo depreservation before being returned to service. Depreservation procedures are typically included in the engine manufacturer's overhaul manual or provided by the facility that preserved the engine. Because the procedures vary with the type of engine and the degree of preservation, the following information is only a general overview of these procedures.

For engines in pressurized containers, bleed off the pressure through the container's relief valve. Remove the cover and place aside. Remove any loose accessories; then remove the engine with a hoist and secure it to the aircraft or an engine stand. Remove all covers and desiccant bags from the engine. As each cover is removed, inspect the area for corrosion and foreign objects. If dehydrator plugs indicate water contamination, thoroughly inspect the cylinder walls for corrosion. A cylinder showing evidence of corrosion or other damage should be removed and further inspected.

Remove the oil screens from the engine and wash them in kerosene or an approved solvent to remove preservative accumulations. After cleaning, immerse the screens in clean oil and reinstall them in the engine.

For radial engines, carefully check the interior of the lower cylinders and intake pipes for the presence of excessive corrosion-preventive compound. Excess compound can circulate through the engine and settle at low points, creating a liquid (or hydraulic) lock. Any liquid preservative compounds remaining in the engine should be drained or removed with a hand pump.

After finishing with the inside of the engine, remove the protective covering from the propeller shaft. Lightly coat the propeller shaft with engine oil or the engine manufacturer's recommended lubricant. Clean the engine exterior. Clean the engine with an appropriate solvent that will not leave any residue or affect the operation of the accessories.

## ACCESSORY DEPRESERVATION

Engine performance depends, in part, on the condition of the engine accessories. An error in the installation of an accessory can result in engine malfunction or even irreparable damage. Follow the recommended procedures in the accessory's overhaul manual regarding depreservation and return to service.

Review the records enclosed with an engine to determine how long the accessories have been in storage. Some accessories are life-limited and might be considered unsafe if their storage time exceeds the manufacturer's limits. Inspect all accessories visually for corrosion and for freedom of operation before installation. Remove any plastic plugs and movement restraints placed on the accessory for shipment. In addition, lubricate moving parts and clean the mounting surfaces prior to installation. Always use new o-rings or gaskets when installing an accessory.

# SUMMARY CHECKLIST

✓ An engine is removed for overhaul when it reaches the manufacturer's published time between overhauls (TBO) or when performance has degraded significantly.

✓ Every maintenance entry for an engine must record total time (TT) and, when appropriate, the time since major overhaul (SMOH).

✓ A spectrometric oil analysis program (SOAP) requires regular collection of an oil sample for lab analysis to evaluate internal engine condition.

✓ Magnetic particle inspection is a nondestructive method used to locate cracks and defects in ferrous parts.

✓ The liquid penetrant inspection method is a nondestructive inspection method of locating cracks, porosity, and other types of damage. The penetrant can be colored (often red) or fluorescent.

✓ A dimensional inspection is often used to check the wear or fit of a part.

✓ An overhauled engine should be preoiled before its first start.

✓ Engines in storage must be protected from corrosion with dehydrating agents and a moisture-proof barrier.

# KEY TERMS

time between overhaul
TBO
total time
TT
since major overhaul
SMOH
sudden speed reduction
runout
sudden stoppage
spectrometric oil analysis program
SOAP
engine condition monitoring
quick engine change assembly
QECA
weather checking
cold flow
Dynafocal engine mounts
shock mounts
rebuilt engines
zero time
remanufactured engine
top overhaul
abrasion
brinelling
burning
burnishing
burr
chafing
chipping
corrosion
crack
cut
dent
erosion
flaking
fretting
galling
gouging
grooving
inclusion
nick
peening
scuffing
pick up
pitting
scoring
scratches
spalling
stain
upsetting
degaussed
capillary attraction
dwell time
water-soluble penetrants
post-emulsifying penetrants
interference fit
tight fit
parallelism gauge
end gap
side clearance
valve stretch
deglaze
lapping
Supplemental Type Certificate
STC
Adel clamps
cushion
springback
desiccants
silica gel
dehydrator plugs
cobalt chloride
time between overhaul
TBO

# QUESTIONS

1. The very rapid (in less than one revolution) and complete stoppage of an engine is known as
______________________________.

2. The regular use of ______________ ________ ______________ provides an operator with a record of metals present in the used engine oil.

3. Engine mount bolts that are to be reused are generally checked using ______________ ______________ inspection.

4. With a ______________ engine mount, the mounting points are turned inward so they point toward the engine's center of gravity.

5. The reconditioning of the cylinder, piston, and valve operating mechanism is known as a ______ overhaul.

6. The complete reconditioning of a powerplant is known as a ______ overhaul.

7. ______________ (overhauled or rebuilt) engines are those that have been disassembled, cleaned, inspected, repaired as necessary, reassembled, and tested in accordance with approved standards.

8. ______________ (overhauled or rebuilt) engines are those that have been disassembled, cleaned, inspected, repaired as necessary, reassembled, and tested to the same tolerances and limits as a new item, using either new parts or used parts that conform to new parts tolerances and limits.

9. Hard carbon may be removed by soaking the engine parts in a ______________ solution.

10. Match the following conditions with the term that is used to describe them:

a. _______ A small, round depression in a surface usually caused by the part being struck by another object.

b. _______ A formn of surface corrosion caused by minute movement between two parts clamped together with considerable pressure.

c. _______ A sharp or roughened projection of metal usually resulting from machine processing, drilling, or cutting.

d. _______ A series of deep scratches caused by foreign particles between moving parts.

e. _______________ A severe condition of chafing or fretting in which a transfer of metal from one part to another occurs.

f. _______ The breaking loose of small pieces of metal or coated surfaces which is usually caused by defec tive plating or excessive loading.

g. _______ Presence of foreign or extraneous material wholly within a portion of metal. Such material is introduced during the manufacturing process.

h. _______ Wear caused by the rubbing action between two parts under light pressure.

i. _______ A series of blunt depressions in a surface.

j. _______ Loss of metal by a chemical or electrochemical attack.

1. Burr
2. Chafing
3. Corrosion
4. Dent
5. Flaking
6. Fretting
7. Galling
8. Inclusion
9. Peening
10. Scoring

11. Engine parts manufactured from ferrous metals can be inspected for hidden cracks using _______________ (dye-penetrant or magnetic particle) inspection.

12. Hydraulic valve lifter plungers and cylinders _______ (are or are not) interchangeable with parts from another assembly.

13. Most engine parts should be tested using both _______________ and _______________ magnetization.

14. When using continuous magnetism, the magnetic particle medium is applied _______________ (at the same time or after) as the magnetizing current.

15. All parts which have been checked using magnetic particle inspection must be _______________ (demagnetized or degreased) before being placed into service.

16. Hydraulic valve lifter plunger assemblies _______ (should or should not) be checked using the magnetic particle inspection.

17. All nonferrous engine parts should be inspected using the _______________ (dye-penetrant or magnetic particle) inspection method.

18. Dye-penetrant may be applied by

    a. _______________.

    b. _______________.

    c. _______________.

19. The time that penetrant is allowed to stay on a part is called the _______ time.

20. The two sets of limits that appear in a manufacturer's Table of Limits are

    a. _______________.

    b. _______________.

21. Connecting rods may be checked for _______ (bend or twist) using arbors and a parallelism gauge.

22. What two measurements should be made when installing new piston rings on the piston?

    a. _______________.

    b. _______________.

23. Dimensional inspection of cylinder barrels should include

    a. _______________________________.

    b. _______________________________.

    c. _______________________________.

    d. _______________________________.

    e. _______________________________.

24. All measurements involving cylinder barrels should be taken at a minimum of two positions _______ degrees apart.

25. Crankshafts are checked for straightness by placing them in vee-blocks and using a _______ indicator.

26. A .003 oversize stud will be identified by the prefix P003 after the part number and _______ (what color) paint on the stud.

27. When the valve face is ground between 1 and 1-1/2 degrees flatter than the valve seat it is referred to as an

_________________ fit.

28. Valves which have been ground so there is no margin left are said to have a _______________ edge.

29. Cylinder barrels which are worn beyond limits may be restored by

a. ______________.

b. ______________.

c. ______________.

30. The three grades of stones used in refacing valve seats are

a. ______________.

b. ______________.

c. ______________.

31. The maximum pressure used on a valve seat grinding stone should never be more than that exerted by the weight of the ______________.

32. Valve seating may be checked using ______________ transfer dye.

33. The contact surface of a valve and valve seat should be _______ to _______ the width of the valve face, and in the middle of the face.

34. A 30 degree valve seat may be narrowed using stones ground to an angle of _______ degrees and _______ degrees.

35. Chrome-plated rings may be used with _______ (what material) cylinders.

36. Only _______ _______ (what material) rings can be used with nitrided or chrome-plated cylinders.

37. The end gaps of piston rings should be ______________ (staggered or aligned) on the piston.

38. After an overhaul, an engine should be run-in or _______ tested.

39. What term is used to describe the rigging procedure that ensures the travel of the throttle valve is not limited by the stops on the throttle control quadrant? ______________

40. To prevent failure of the engine bearings during the first start after an overhaul, some form of, _______-______________ is required.

41. One of the steps in preserving an engine is to spray a corrosion preventative compound into each cylinder with the piston at bottom dead center. After the last cylinder is coated with the corrosion preventative compound, the crankshaft ______________ (should or should not) be moved.

42. Cobalt chloride treated _______ gel is used in dehydrator plugs which can be screwed into the spark plug holes of a reciprocating engine.

43. Dehydrator plugs are _______ (what color) when relatively low humidity exists.

# CHAPTER 3

# TURBINE ENGINES

## INTRODUCTION

Efforts to design a working gas turbine engine started at the beginning of the 20$^{th}$ century. By the end of World War II, engineers had succeeded in placing a few turbine engines in combat. The war effort brought about many advances in gas turbine technology, which proved useful for commercial aircraft design. Turbine engines offered several characteristics that reciprocating engines could not match including increased reliability, longer mean times between overhaul, higher airspeeds, ease of operation at high altitudes, and a high power-to-weight ratio Aircraft such as Lockheed's Super Constellation represented the practical limits of piston power technology and required frequent engine maintenance. During the 1950s, a gradual transition began from piston power to gas turbine jets and turboprops. Classic workhorses like the Douglas DC-3 and DC-7 gave way to the Boeing 707 and Douglas DC-8.

# SECTION A

## DESIGN AND CONSTRUCTION

Newton's third law of motion states that for every action there is an equal and opposite reaction. Jet propulsion applies this law by accelerating a quantity of air through an orifice (or nozzle). The acceleration of the air is the action and forward movement is the reaction. In nature, a squid propels itself through the water using a form of jet propulsion. A squid takes sea water into its body and uses its muscles to add energy to the water, then expels the water in the form of a jet. This action produces a reaction that propels the squid forward. [Figure 3-1]

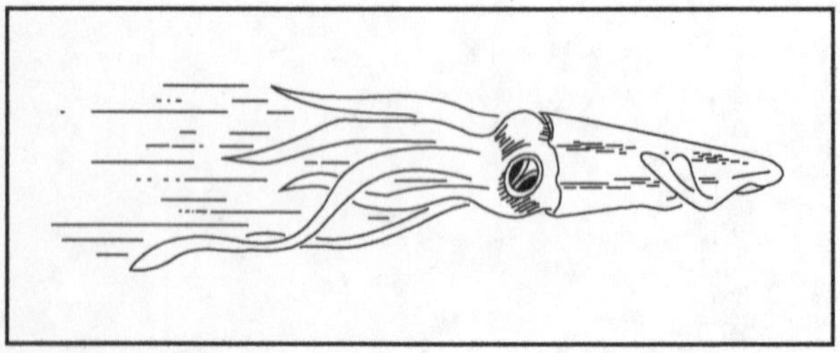

**Figure 3-1. Many technological developments are made by observations of the natural world. A squid propels itself through the water by jet reaction.**

**Figure 3-2. Hero's aeolipile, invented long before Newton postulated his Laws of Motion, proved that power by reaction was possible.**

As early as 250 B.C., a writer and mathematician named Hero devised a toy using this reaction principle. The toy, called the **aeolipile**, consisted of a covered kettle of water that was heated to produce steam. The steam was routed through two vertical tubes into a spherical container. Attached to the spherical container were several discharge tubes arranged radially around the container. As steam filled the container, it would escape through the discharge tubes causing the sphere to rotate. [Figure 3-2]

A modern example of Newton's reaction principle is observed when the end of an inflated balloon is released. As the air in the balloon rushes out the opening, the balloon flies wildly around a room. In spite of the everyday examples, scientific efforts to apply Newton's reaction principle to mechanical designs were largely unsuccessful until the 20th century.

## HISTORY OF JET PROPULSION

The history of mechanical jet propulsion began in 1900, when Dr. Sanford Moss submitted a thesis on gas turbines. Later, Dr. Moss became an engineer for the General Electric Company in England. While there, he applied some of his concepts in the development of the turbo-supercharger. His design used a small turbine wheel, driven by exhaust gases, to turn a supercharger.

Dr. Moss's research influenced the development of what became the first successful turbojet engine. Dr. Frank Whittle of England was granted his first patent for a jet engine in 1930. Eleven years later, the engine completed its first flight in a Gloster model E28/39 aircraft. The engine produced about one thousand pounds of thrust and

Figure 3-3. Dr. Frank Whittle of England patented the first turbojet engine, the Whittle W1, in 1930. Its first flight occurred in a Gloster E28/39 aircraft in 1941.

propelled the aircraft at speeds over 400 miles per hour. [Figure 3-3]

While Whittle was developing the gas turbine engine in England, Hans Von Ohain, a German engineer, designed and built a jet engine that produced 1,100 pounds of thrust. This engine was installed in a Heinkel He-178 aircraft and made a successful flight on August 27, 1939. As a result, it is recognized as the first practical flight of a jet-propelled aircraft. [Figure 3-4]

In the United States, research in the field of jet propulsion lagged. Because of its extensive experience in building electrical generating turbines and turbo-superchargers the General Electric Company received a contract to research and develop a gas turbine engine in 1941. The result was the GE-1A engine, a centrifugal-compressor type engine that

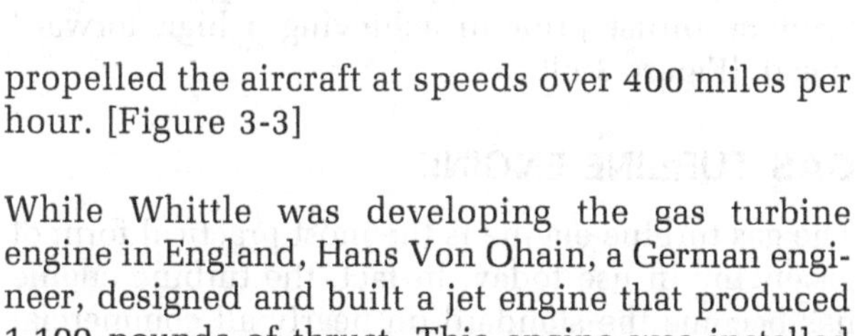

Figure 3-4. German engineer Hans Von Ohain designed and built the turbojet engine that powered the Heinkel He-178 in the world's first jet-powered flight in 1939.

produced approximately 1,650 pounds of thrust. Two of these engines were used to power a Bell XP-59 "Airacomet." The Airacomet flew for the first time in October 1942 and proved the concept of jet-powered flight. However, it was never used in combat due to a limited flight time of 30 minutes. [Figure 3-5]

Figure 3-5. First flown in 1942, the Bell XP-59 was the first American jet-powered aircraft.

## JET PROPULSION TODAY

Today, the majority of commercial aircraft use some form of jet propulsion. Currently, several manufacturers produce entire lines of jet-powered aircraft that cruise in excess of 600 miles per hour and carry up to five hundred passengers or several tons of cargo.

Another step in the progression of commercial and military aviation was the ability to produce an engine that would propel an aircraft faster than the speed of sound. Today, several military aircraft travel at speeds in excess of Mach one. Supersonic aircraft are presently in use in military and research applications. The Concorde, a supersonic commercial aircraft built collaboratively by a British and French consortium, was in service from 1976 through 2003. The Concorde was capable of flying at 2.2 times the speed of sound.

In addition to military and commercial aviation, jet propulsion is widely used in business jets. The use of twin-engine aircraft has grown in part due to the efficiency and reliability of the jet engines.

## TYPES OF JET PROPULSION

Newton's reaction principle has been applied to several propulsive devices used in aviation. All produce thrust in the same manner; they accelerate a mass of gases within the engine. The most common types of propulsive engines are the rocket, the ramjet, the pulsejet, and the gas turbine.

### ROCKET

A rocket is a non-air-breathing engine that carries its own fuel and the oxygen needed for the fuel to burn. The two types of rockets in use are solid-propellant rockets and liquid-propellant rockets. **Solid-propellant rockets** use a solid fuel formed into a specific shape that promotes an optimum burning rate when mixed with an oxidizer. After the fuel is ignited, it produces an extremely high-velocity discharge of gas through a nozzle at the rear of the rocket body. The reaction to the rapid discharge is forward motion of the rocket body. Solid fuel rockets are used primarily to propel some military weapons and occasionally to provide additional thrust for takeoff of heavily loaded aircraft. In the latter case, booster rockets attached to an aircraft structure provide the additional thrust needed for special-condition takeoffs. [Figure 3-6]

The second type of rocket is a **liquid-fuel rocket**, which uses fuel and an oxidizing agent such as liquid oxygen. The two liquids are carried in tanks aboard the rocket. When the liquids are mixed, a violent reaction occurs, which generates a tremendous amount of heat. The resulting high-velocity gas jet behind the rocket provides enough thrust to propel it.

## RAMJET

A ramjet is an **athodyd** (or **aero-thermodynamic-duct**), an air-breathing engine with no moving parts. With no rotating compressor to draw air into the engine, a ramjet must be moving forward at high velocity before it can produce thrust. After air enters the engine, fuel is injected and ignited to provide the heat needed to accelerate the air and produce thrust. Because ramjets must be moving forward to produce thrust, their use is limited. Ramjets are used in some military weapons delivery systems in which the vehicle is accelerated to a high enough velocity for the ramjet to take over power for sustained flight. [Figure 3-7]

## PULSEJET

Pulsejet engines are similar to ramjets except that the air intake duct is equipped with a series of shutter valves that are spring-loaded to the open position. Air drawn through the open valves enters a combustion chamber where it is heated by burning fuel. As the air within the combustion chamber expands, the increased air pressure increases to force the shutter valves closed. After it is enclosed aft of the shutters, the expanding air in the chamber is forced rearward to produce thrust. A pulsejet is typically considered more useful than a ramjet because pulsejets can produce thrust prior to achieving a high forward speed. [Figure 3-8]

Figure 3-6. Rocket assisted takeoff (RATO) devices are small, solid propellant rocket motors attached to an airplane to provide additional takeoff thrust at high-altitude airports or for lifting extremely heavy loads.

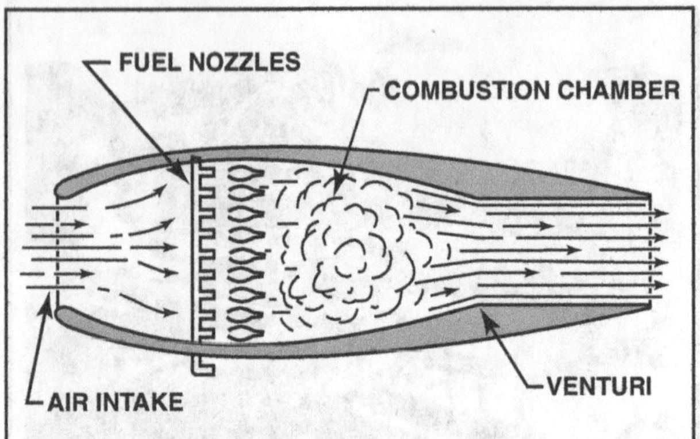


Figure 3-7. As a ramjet moves forward, air enters the intake and proceeds to a combustion chamber where fuel is added and ignited. The heat from the burning fuel accelerates the flow of air through a venturi to produce thrust.

## GAS TURBINE ENGINE

The gas turbine engine is the most practical form of jet engine in use today. In fact, the turbine engine has become the standard on nearly all commercial (transport category), business, and military aircraft. The remainder of this section will focus on the gas turbine engine. The four most common types of gas turbine engines are the turbojet, turbopropeller (turboprop), turboshaft, and turbofan.

### TURBOJET ENGINES

The basic operating principles of a turbojet engine are straightforward. Air enters through an inlet duct and proceeds to the compressor. After the air is compressed, it flows to a combustor section where fuel is added and ignited. The heat generated by the burning fuel causes the compressed air to expand and flow toward the rear of the engine. As the air moves rearward, it passes through a set of turbine wheels connected to the compressor blades. The expanding air spins the turbines, which in turn drive the compressor. After it moves past the turbines, the air exits the engine at a much higher velocity than the incoming air. The difference in velocity between the air entering and the air exiting the engine produces thrust.

One of the most important aspects of turbojet engine operation that you must be familiar with is the

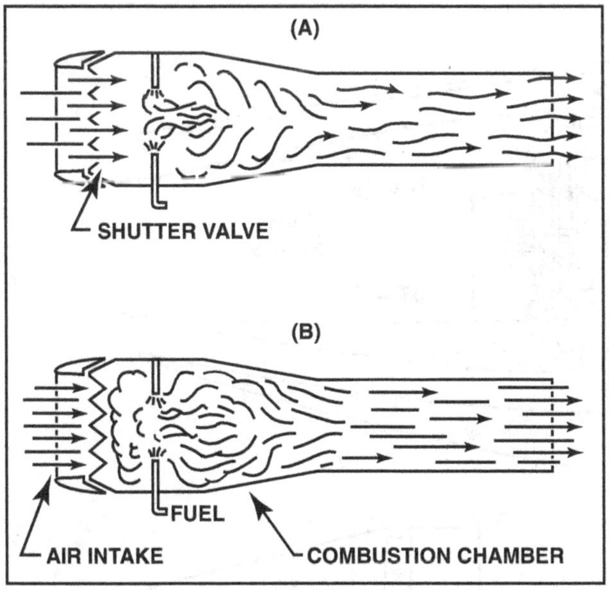


**Figure 3-8. (A) In a pulsejet engine, air is drawn into the combustion chamber and mixed with fuel when the shutter valve is open. (B) As the fuel burns, air pressure within the chamber increases and forces the shutter valves to close. After the shutter closes, the expanding air within the engine accelerates through the exhaust nozzle to produce thrust.**

**engine pressure ratio**, or **EPR**. An engine's EPR is the ratio of the turbine discharge pressure to the engine inlet air pressure. EPR gauge readings are an indication of the amount of thrust being produced for a given power lever setting. Total pressure pickups, or EPR probes, measure the air pressure at two points in the engine; one EPR probe is located at the compressor inlet and a second just aft of the last stage turbine in the exhaust section. EPR readings are often used to verify power settings for takeoff, climb, and cruise. EPR readings are affected by and are dependent on pressure altitude and outside air temperature (OAT).

## TURBOPROPELLER ENGINES

A gas turbine engine that delivers power to a propeller is referred to as a turbopropeller, or turboprop, engine. Turboprop engines are similar in design to turbojet engines except that the power produced by a turboprop engine is delivered to a reduction gear system that spins a propeller. Reduction gearing is necessary because optimum propeller performance is achieved at much slower speeds than the engine operating speed. Turboprop engines are used extensively in business and commuter aircraft because the combination of jet power and propeller efficiency provides good performance characteristics at speeds between 300 and 400 miles per hour. Additionally, most turboprop engines operate with the best specific fuel consumption of any gas turbine engine. [Figure 3-9]

**Figure 3-9. Turboprop powerplants are common on corporate and commuter twin-engine aircraft.**

## TURBOSHAFT ENGINES

A gas turbine engine that delivers power to a shaft that can drive something else is referred to as a turboshaft engine. The biggest difference between a turbojet and turboshaft engine is that on a turboshaft engine, most of the energy produced by the expanding gases is used to drive a turbine rather than produce thrust. Many helicopters use a turboshaft gas turbine engine. In addition, turboshaft engines are widely used as auxiliary power units and, in industrial applications, to drive electrical generators and surface transportation systems. The output of a turboprop or turboshaft engine is measured by **shaft horsepower** rather than thrust.

## TURBOFAN ENGINES

A turbofan engine consists of a multibladed, ducted propeller driven by a gas turbine engine. Turbofans were developed to provide a compromise between the best features of the turbojet and the turboprop. Turbofan engines have turbojet-type cruise speed capability, yet retain some of the short-field takeoff capability of a turboprop. Nearly all present day airliners are powered by turbofan engines for these reasons as well as because turbofans are relatively fuel-efficient.

A turbofan engine can have the fan mounted either in the front or back of the engine. Engines that have the fan mounted in front of the compressor are called **forward-fan engines**, and turbofan engines that have the fan mounted to the turbine section are called **aft-fan engines**. [Figure 3-10]

Inlet air passing through a turbofan engine is usually divided into two separate streams of air. One stream passes through the engine core, and a second stream coaxially bypasses the engine core. From this bypass stream of air, this powerplant is referred to as a bypass engine. To discuss bypass engines, you must be familiar with three terms—thrust ratio, bypass ratio, and fan pressure ratio. A turbofan engine's **thrust ratio** is a comparison of the thrust

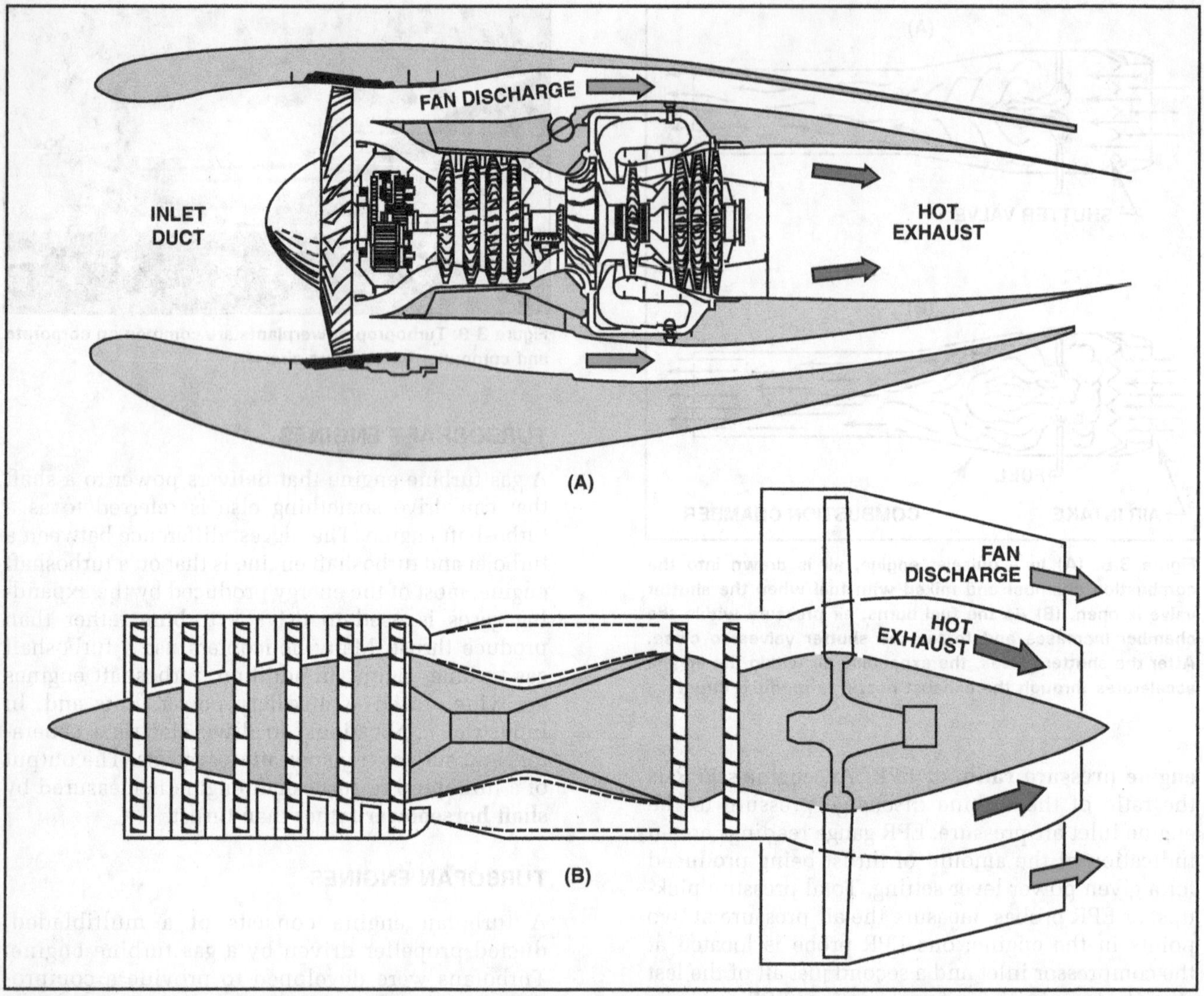


**Figure 3-10. (A) A forward-fan turbofan engine uses a relatively large-diameter, ducted fan that produces thrust and provides intake air to the compressor. (B) An aft-fan turbofan engine has a fan mounted on the aft turbine. This arrangement is rarely used because an aft fan does not contribute to air compression at the inlet.**

produced by the fan to the thrust produced by the engine core exhaust. On the other hand, a turbofan's **bypass ratio** refers to the ratio of incoming air that bypasses the core to the amount of air that passes through the engine core. Turbofans in civil aircraft are generally divided into three classifications based on bypass ratio: low bypass (1:1); medium bypass (2:1 or 3:1); and high bypass (4:1 or greater). Fan diameter determines a fan's bypass ratio and thrust ratio.

Generally, airflow mass in the fan section of a low-bypass engine is the same as airflow mass in the compressor. The fan discharge could be slightly higher or lower depending on the engine model, but bypass ratios are approximately 1:1. In some engines, the bypass air is vented directly overboard through a short fan duct. However, in a **ducted fan**, the bypass air is ducted along the entire length of the engine. Full fan ducts reduce aerodynamic drag and noise emissions. In either case, the end of the duct usually has a converging discharge nozzle that increases velocity and produces reactive thrust. [Figure 3-11]

Medium- or intermediate-bypass engines have airflow bypass ratios ranging from 2:1 to 3:1. These engines have thrust ratios similar to their bypass ratios. The fans used on these engines have a larger diameter than the fans used on low-bypass engines of comparable power.

High bypass turbofan engines have bypass ratios of 4:1 or greater and use the largest diameter fan of any of the bypass engines. High bypass turbines offer higher propulsive efficiencies and better fuel economy than low or medium bypass turbines. Consequently, they are the engines of choice on

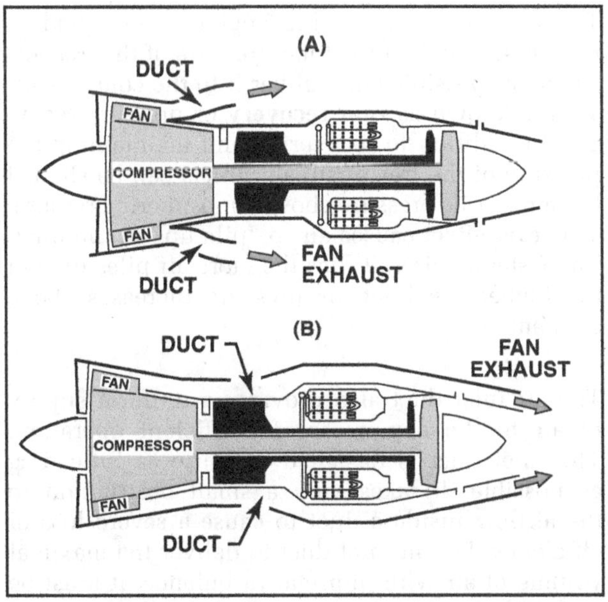


**Figure 3-11. (A) Bypass air is ejected directly overboard in forward-fan engines with a short fan duct. (B) With a ducted fan, bypass air is ducted along the engine's entire length.**

large airliners used for long flights. Some common high-bypass turbofan engines include Pratt and Whitney's JT9D and PW4000, the Rolls-Royce RB-211, and the General Electric CF6. One version of the JT9D has a bypass ratio of 5:1 with 80 percent of the thrust provided by the fan, and only 20 percent by the core engine. [Figure 3-12]

Another term you must be familiar with is **fan pressure ratio,** which is the ratio of air pressure leaving the fan to the air pressure entering the fan. The fan pressure ratio on a typical low bypass fan is approximately 1.5:1, whereas the fan pressure ratio for some high bypass fans can be as high as 7:1. To obtain high fan pressure ratios, most high bypass engines are designed with high aspect ratio blades. **Aspect ratio** is the ratio of a blade's length to its width, or chord. Therefore, a long blade with a narrow chord has a higher aspect ratio than a short blade with a wide chord. Although high aspect ratio fan blades are used most often, low aspect ratio blades are currently coming into wider use. Technological advances in blade construction have overcome the weight problems associated with low aspect ratio blades in the past. Weight savings in low aspect ratio blades have been achieved with hollow titanium blades with inner reinforcements made of composite materials. Another benefit of low aspect ratio blades is their size, which makes them less susceptible to foreign object damage, particularly bird strikes.

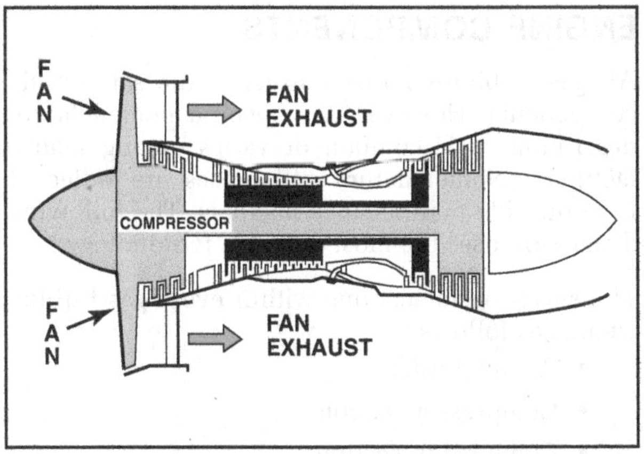


**Figure 3-12. High-bypass turbofan engines use large diameter fans with a bypass ratio of 4:1 or greater.**

## UNDUCTED FAN ENGINES

New engine designs with higher efficiencies than most engines in use are designated as **ultra-high bypass (UHB) propfan** and **unducted fan (UDF) engines**. These new engines use titanium, lightweight stainless steel, and composite materials to improve fuel economy over several high-bypass turbofan engines by more than 15 percent. By incorporating propellers with composite blades between 12 and 15 feet in diameter, engine designers have achieved 30:1 bypass ratios. Composite propeller blades are lighter and provide safe operation at tip speeds higher than conventional blades. [Figure 3-13]

Current research and development indicates that these engines have the potential to produce 10,000 to 15,000 horsepower for an aircraft carrying 150 to 200 passengers at speeds near 0.8 Mach. Another design encases the propfan in a conventional cowl inlet, which can achieve Mach 0.9. These engines are known as **ducted ultra-high bypass engines.**

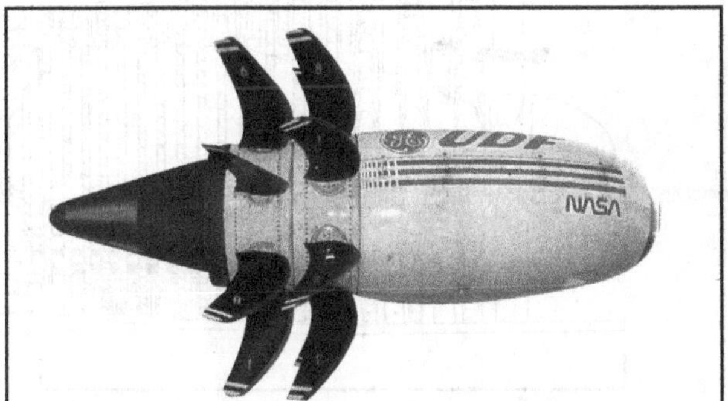


**Figure 3-13. Research in unducted fan engines points to greater fuel efficiency for future transport aircraft.**

## ENGINE COMPONENTS

All gas turbine engines consist of the same basic components. However, the specific nomenclature describing each component varies among manufacturers. Nomenclature differences are reflected in applicable maintenance manuals. The following discussion uses the most common terminology.

The seven basic sections within every gas turbine engine, as follows:

- Air inlet duct
- Compressor section
- Combustion section
- Turbine section
- Exhaust section
- Accessory section
- Auxiliary systems

Auxiliary systems are those systems necessary for starting, lubrication, fuel supply, and auxiliary purposes such as anti-icing, cooling, and pressurization

Additional terms you will likely encounter include hot section and cold section. The **hot section** includes the combustion, turbine, and exhaust sections. The **cold section** includes the air inlet duct and the compressor section. [Figure 3-14]

## AIR INLET DUCT

The air inlet duct on a turbojet engine is normally considered part of the airframe, not the powerplant. However, the function of an air inlet duct and its importance to engine performance make it a necessary part of any discussion on gas turbine engine design and construction.

The air inlet to a turbine engine is designed to recover as much of the total pressure of the free airstream as possible and deliver it to the compressor. This is known as **ram recovery** or pressure recovery. In addition to recovering and maintaining the pressure of the free airstream, inlets can be shaped to increase air pressure above atmospheric pressure. This **ram effect** causes air to "pile up" in the inlet. The faster an aircraft flies the more air piles up and the higher the inlet air pressure increases above ambient.

The air inlet duct also provides a uniform supply of air to the compressor for efficient operation. The inlet duct is designed to cause as little drag as possible. It takes only a small obstruction to the airflow inside a duct to cause a severe loss of efficiency. For an inlet duct to deliver the maximal volume of air with minimal turbulence, it must be maintained as close to its original condition as possible. Any repairs to an inlet duct must retain the duct's smooth aerodynamic shape. To help prevent damage or corrosion to an inlet duct, an inlet cover should be installed any time the engine is not operating. [Figure 3-15]

Many types of air inlet ducts have been designed to accommodate variations in airframe and engine combinations as well as engine-mounting locations. In addition, air inlets are designed differently for operation at different airspeeds. Some of the most common engine inlet duct mounting locations are on the engine itself, in the wing, and on the fuselage. Finally, aircraft speed plays a major part in air inlet ducts design, with special consideration given to subsonic flight, supersonic flight, and engine operation at very slow or no forward speed at all.

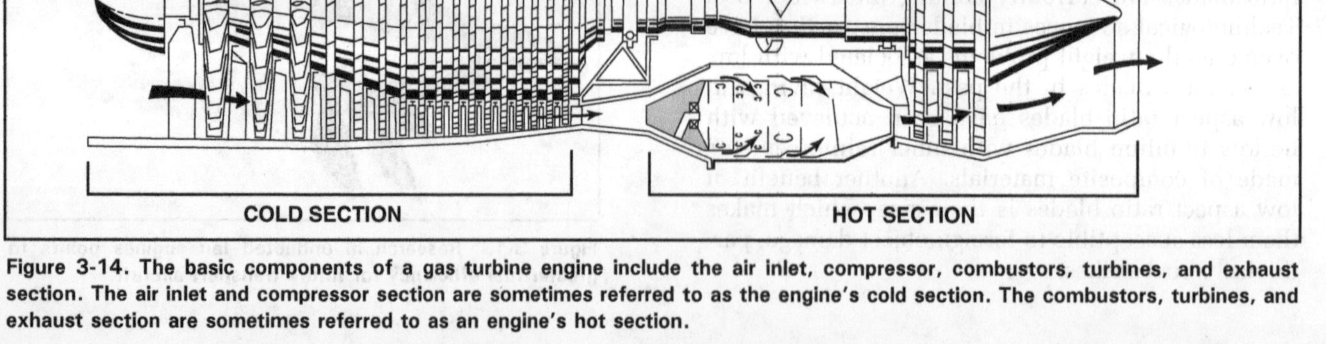


**Figure 3-14. The basic components of a gas turbine engine include the air inlet, compressor, combustors, turbines, and exhaust section. The air inlet and compressor section are sometimes referred to as the engine's cold section. The combustors, turbines, and exhaust section are sometimes referred to as an engine's hot section.**

Figure 3-15. To ensure the operating efficiency of an inlet duct, you must inspect it periodically for foreign object damage and corrosion.

## ENGINE-MOUNTED INLETS

Several large commercial aircraft and large military aircraft use wing-mounted engines. In a few cases, such as the DC-10 and L-1011, a combination of wing mounted and vertical stabilizer mounted engines are used. In these cases, the air inlet duct is located directly in front of the compressor and is mounted to the engine. Integral mounting of the inlet with an engine reduces air inlet length, which increases efficiency. [Figure 3-16]

Figure 3-16. A McDonnell-Douglas DC-10 is designed with wing-mounted engines and an engine in the vertical stabilizer. The air inlet ducts on all of these engines are mounted to the engine and positioned directly in front of the compressor.

In addition to the wing- and vertical stabilizer-mounted engines, some commercial aircraft and a majority of small business jets are fitted with aft fuselage mounted engines. The air inlet ducts on engines mounted in this fashion are identical to air inlet ducts on wing-mounted engines; the duct is relatively short and is mounted directly to the engine. [Figure 3-17]

Figure 3-17. Engines mounted on the aft fuselage accommodate short, efficient air inlet ducts that attach to the front of each engine.

## WING-MOUNTED INLETS

Some aircraft with engines mounted inside the wings feature air inlet ducts in the wing's leading edge. Aircraft such as the Aerospatiale Caravelle, the de Havilland® Comet, and the de Havilland Vampire all use wing-mounted inlets. Typically, wing-mounted inlet ducts are positioned near the wing root area. [Figure 3-18]

## FUSELAGE-MOUNTED INLETS

Engines mounted inside a fuselage typically use air inlet ducts located near the front of the fuselage.

Figure 3-18. The Hawker-Siddeley 801 "Nimrod" uses aerodynamically shaped, wing-mounted air inlet ducts to reduce drag.

For example, many early military aircraft were designed with an air inlet duct in the nose of the fuselage. In addition, some modern supersonic military aircraft have inlet ducts located just under the aircraft nose. Although using an air inlet duct of this type enables the aircraft manufacturer to build a more aerodynamically efficient aircraft, the increased length of the inlet duct introduces some inefficiency. [Figure 3-19]

Some military aircraft use air inlet ducts mounted on the sides of the fuselage. This arrangement works well for both single- and twin-engine aircraft. By mounting an air inlet duct on each side of an aircraft, the duct length can be shortened without adding a significant amount of drag to the aircraft. However, a disadvantage to this arrangement is that some sudden flight maneuvers can cause an imbalance in ram air pressure between the two ducts. An air pressure imbalance acting on a compressor face can result in a slight loss of power. [Figure 3-20]

## SUBSONIC INLETS

A typical subsonic air inlet consists of a fixed geometry duct with a diameter that progressively increases from front to back. This **divergent** shape works like a venturi; as the intake air spreads out, the velocity of the air decreases and the pressure increases. This added pressure contributes significantly to engine efficiency after the aircraft reaches its design cruising speed. At this speed, the compressor reaches its optimum aerodynamic efficiency and produces the most compression at the best fuel economy. It is at this design cruise speed that the inlet, compressor, combustor, turbine, and exhaust duct are designed to match each other as a unit. If any mismatch occurs because of damage, contamination, or ambient conditions, engine performance suffers. For additional information on subsonic air inlet ducts, refer to the discussion on turbine engine induction systems in Section B of Chapter 5.

## SUPERSONIC INLETS

On supersonic aircraft, a typical air inlet duct has either a fixed or variable geometry with a diameter

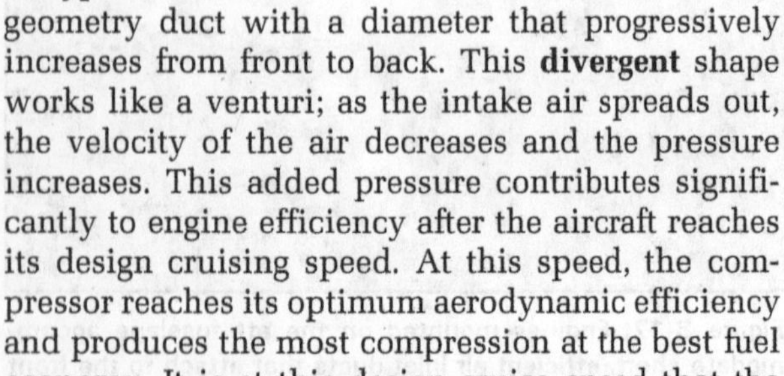

Figure 3-19. The single-entrance inlet duct takes full advantage of ram effect much like engine-mounted air inlet ducts. Although the aircraft is aerodynamically clean, the length of the duct makes it less efficient than engine-mounted types.

Figure 3-20. The short length of divided-entrance inlet ducts is relatively efficient.

that progressively decreases, then increases from front to back. This **convergent-divergent** shape is used to slow the incoming airflow to subsonic speed before it reaches the compressor.

In addition to the convergent-divergent shape, many supersonic inlet ducts employ a movable plug or throat that changes duct geometry according to flight conditions. This variable geometry is necessary so that the duct can accommodate a wide range of flight speeds. For additional information on supersonic air inlet ducts, refer to the discussion on turbine engine induction systems in Section B of Chapter 5.

## BELLMOUTH INLETS

Bellmouth inlet ducts have a convergent profile that is designed for obtaining high aerodynamic efficiency when stationary or in slow flight. Bellmouth inlet ducts are typically used on helicopters, some slow-moving aircraft, and on engines being run in ground test stands. A typical bellmouth inlet duct is short in length and has rounded shoulders that offer little air resistance. However, because their shape produces a great deal of drag in forward flight, bellmouth inlet ducts are typically not used on high-speed aircraft. Because bellmouth inlet ducts are most efficient when stationary, engine manufacturers typically collect engine performance data from engines fitted with a bellmouth inlet duct.

## FOREIGN OBJECT DAMAGE

Prevention of foreign object damage (FOD) is a top priority among turbine engine operators and manufacturers. One of the easiest ways to help prevent foreign object damage is to install an inlet screen over an engine's inlet duct. The use of inlet screens is common on many rotorcraft and turboprop engines as well as on engines installed in test stands. However, inlet screens are seldom used on high mass airflow engines because icing and screen failures can cause serious engine damage. [Figure 3-21]

Figure 3-21. Several makes of helicopters and turboprop aircraft use inlet screens to help prevent foreign object damage.

Additional devices that prevent foreign object damage include sand and ice separators. The basic design of a sand or ice separator consists of an air intake with at least one venturi and a series of sharp bends. The venturi accelerates the flow of incoming air and debris, and the inertia of the debris prevents it from following the bends in the intake. This action enables sand particles and other small debris to be channeled away from the compressor and into a sediment trap. [Figure 3-22]

Another type of separator used on some turboprop aircraft incorporates a movable vane that extends into the inlet airstream, where it creates a more prominent venturi and a sudden turn in the engine inlet. Combustion air can follow the sharp curve, but sand and ice particles cannot. The movable vane is operated by a pilot through a control handle in the cockpit. [Figure 3-23]

Some gas turbine engine inlets tend to form a vortex between the ground and the inlet during ground operations. This vortex can become strong enough to lift water and debris, such as sand, small stones, and small hardware, from the ground and direct it into the engine. To help alleviate this problem, a **vortex dissipater**, sometimes called a **vortex destroyer** or a **blow-away jet**, is installed on some gas turbine engines. A typical vortex dissipater routes high-pressure bleed air to a discharge nozzle located in the lower part of the engine cowl. This discharge nozzle directs a continuous blast of bleed air between the ground and air inlet to prevent a vortex from developing. Most aircraft equipped with a vortex dissipater also have a landing gear switch that arms the dissipater whenever the engine is operating with weight on the main gear. [Figure 3-24]

## COMPRESSOR SECTION

A gas turbine engine takes in a quantity of air, adds energy to it, and then discharges the air to produce thrust. Accordingly, the more air forced into an

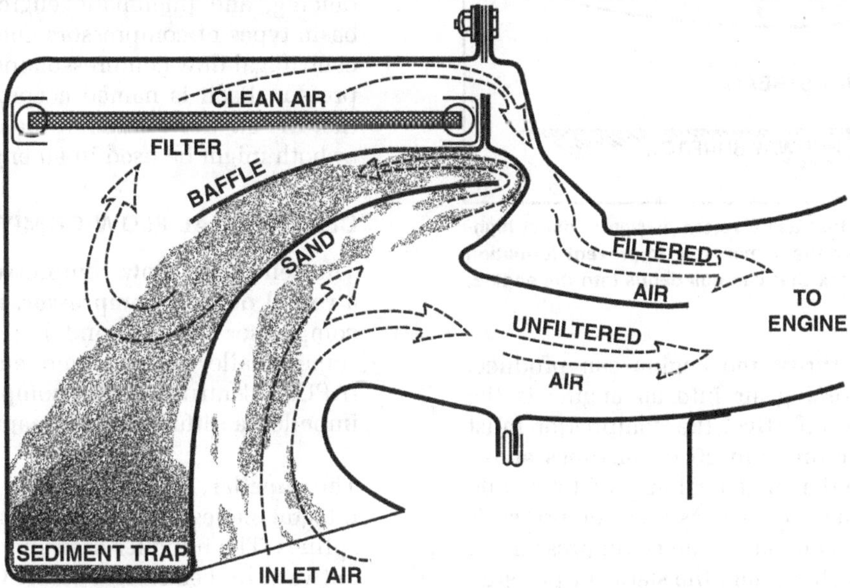


Figure 3-22. Sand and dust separators are typical for a turbine-powered helicopter. The venturi in the air inlet accelerates air and sand, but because the sand has too much inertia, it cannot make the turn leading to the engine.

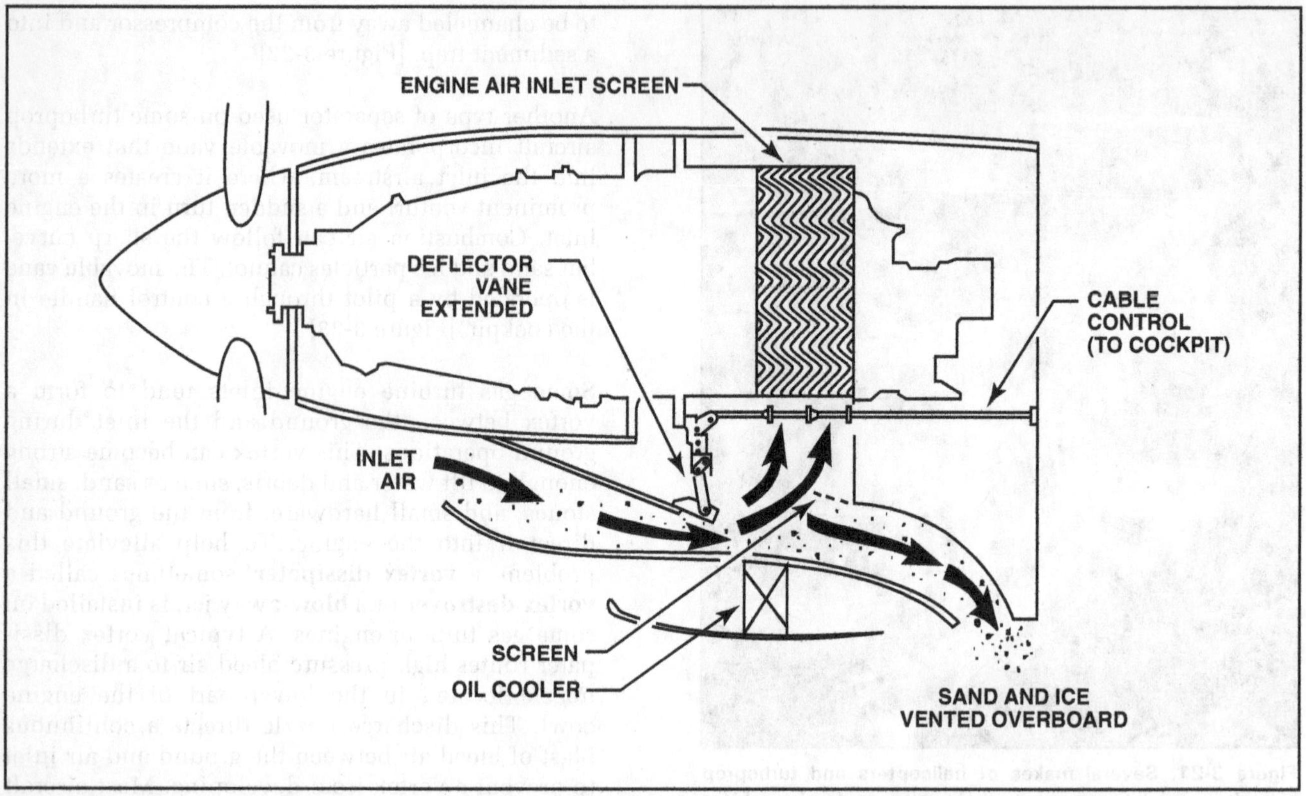


**Figure 3-23. When a pilot actuates a movable-vane sand separator, a small vane extends into the airstream and creates a venturi. The inertia of the sand and ice particles carries them past the air intake and discharges them overboard.**

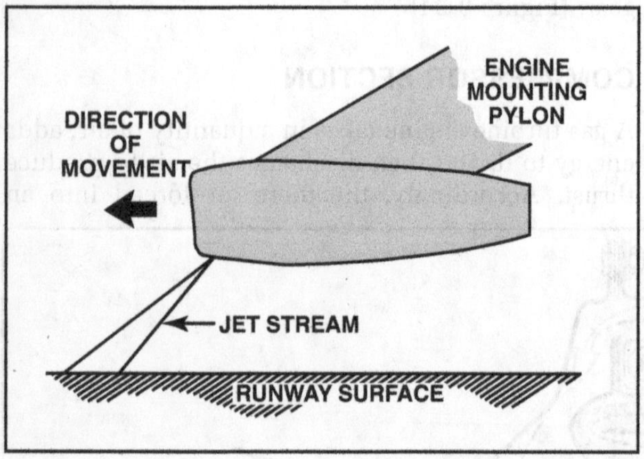


**Figure 3-24. Engines that use a vortex dissipater direct high-pressure bleed air from the compressor to prevent formation of a low-pressure vortex that can pull debris into the engine.**

engine, the more thrust the engine can produce. The component forcing air into an engine is the compressor. To be effective, the compressor must increase intake air pressure 20 to 30 times above ambient and move the air at a velocity of 400 to 500 feet per second. One way to measure a compressor's effectiveness is by comparing the static pressure of the compressor discharge and the static air pressure at the inlet. If the discharge air pressure is 30 times greater than the inlet air pressure, the **compressor pressure ratio** is 30:1.

In addition to supporting combustion and providing the air necessary to produce thrust, the compressor section performs several secondary functions. For example, a compressor supplies bleed air to cool the hot section and heated air for anti-icing. Additionally, compressor bleed air is used for cabin pressurization, air conditioning, fuel system deicing, and pneumatic engine starting. The two basic types of compressors currently in use are the centrifugal flow compressor and the axial flow compressor. Each is named according to the direction that the air flows through the compressor, and one or both might be used in an engine design.

## CENTRIFUGAL FLOW COMPRESSORS

The centrifugal flow compressor, sometimes called a **radial outflow compressor**, is one of the earliest compressor designs, and it is still used today in some smaller engines and auxiliary power units (APUs). Centrifugal flow compressors consist of an impeller, a diffuser, and a manifold. [Figure 3-25]

The **impeller, or rotor**, consists of a forged disk with integral blades coupled to a common power shaft by splines. The impeller draws in air and accelerates it outward by centrifugal force. Centrifugal compressors can have one or two impellers. Compressors having only one impeller are referred to as **single-stage compressors**; those with two impellers are

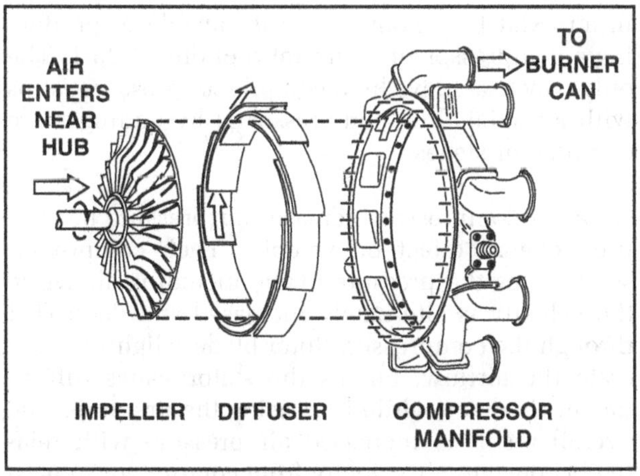


**Figure 3-25. A single-stage centrifugal compressor consists of an impeller, a diffuser, and a compressor manifold.**

referred to as **double-stage compressors.** More than two compressor stages is impractical because the benefits gained by additional stages are negated by energy losses when the airflow slows between impellers. Furthermore, the added weight of each impeller requires more energy from an engine to drive the compressor. [Figure 3-26]

When two impellers are mounted back-to-back, a **double-sided** or **double entry impeller** is created. A single-stage, double-sided impeller permits a higher mass airflow than single-stage, single-sided impellers. Therefore, engines with double-sided impellers typically have a smaller overall diameter. [Figure 3-27]

A drawback of the double-sided impeller is that the ducting necessary to move intake air to both sides of the impeller is complex. Ducting for double-entry compressor engines employs a **plenum chamber.**

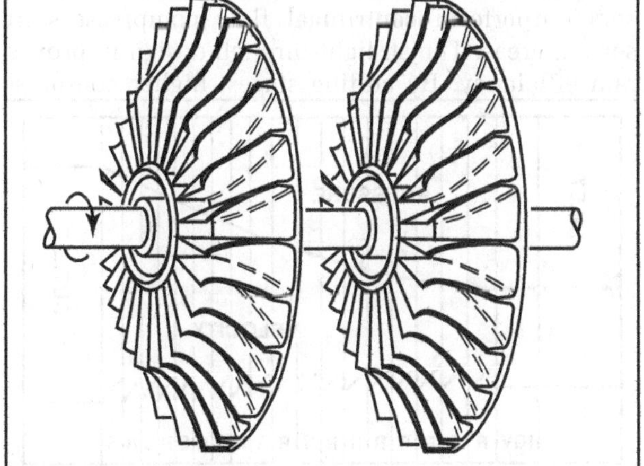

**Figure 3-26. A two-stage impeller produces a higher compressor pressure ratio. Because of efficiency losses, centrifugal compressors rarely exceed two stages.**

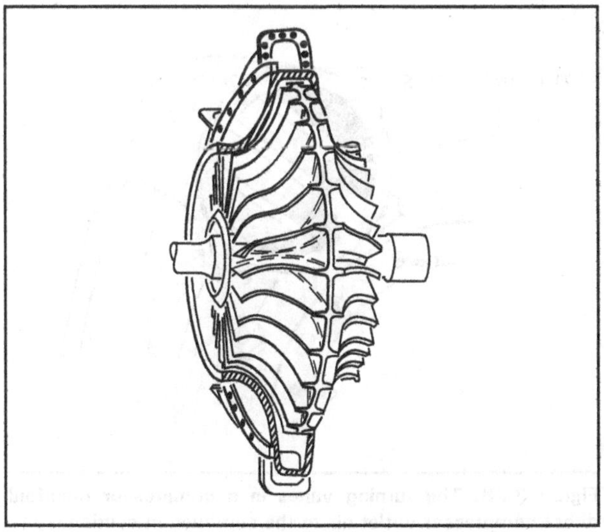

**Figure 3-27. A single-stage, dual-sided impeller enables a small diameter engine to produce a high-mass airflow.**

This chamber is necessary because the air must enter the engine at an angle nearly perpendicular to the engine axis; the air must surround the engine compressor with positive pressure. In addition to the plenum chamber, some double-entry compressors use **auxiliary air-intake doors (blow-in doors).** These blow-in doors admit air into the engine compartment during ground operation when engine air requirements exceed the available incoming airflow. The doors stay closed by spring action when the engine is not operating. During operation, however, the doors open whenever engine compartment pressure drops below atmospheric pressure. During takeoff and flight, the doors remain closed as ram air pressure works with the springs.

After the air moves through the impeller, it is expelled into a divergent duct called a **diffuser.** In the diffuser section, the air becomes dispersed; its velocity is decreased, and its pressure is increased.

The **compressor manifold** distributes the air in a smooth flow to the combustion section. The manifold has an outlet port for each combustion chamber, and the air is evenly divided. A compressor outlet elbow is bolted to each outlet port. Each elbow functions as an air duct, and these units are often referred to as **outlet ducts, outlet elbows,** or **combustion chamber inlet ducts.** The ducts change the direction of the airflow from radial to axial. To improve efficiency, **turning vanes** or **cascade vanes** are sometimes fitted inside the elbows. These vanes reduce air pressure losses by providing a smooth, turning surface. [Figure 3-28]

Advantages of centrifugal flow compressors include simplicity of manufacture, relatively low cost, low

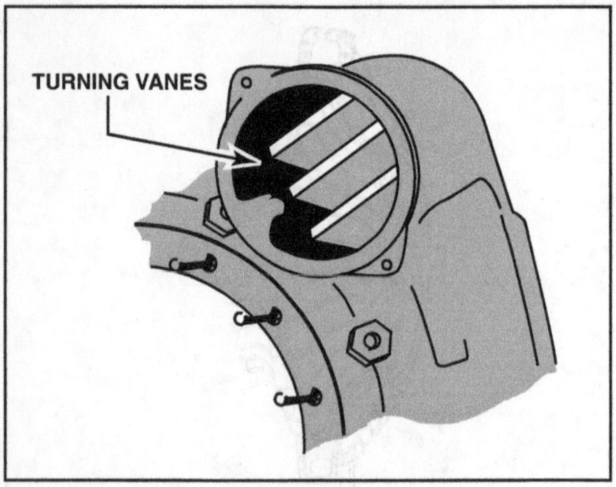


**Figure 3-28. The turning vanes in a compressor manifold direct compressor outlet air to the combustion section.**

weight, low starting power requirements, and good operating efficiency over a wide range of rotational speeds. Additionally, the short length and spoke-like design of a centrifugal flow compressor enable it to accelerate air rapidly and immediately deliver it to the diffuser. Tip speeds of centrifugal compressors can reach Mach 1.3, but pressure within the compressor casing prevents airflow separation and provides an efficient energy transfer into the airflow. Although most centrifugal compressors are limited to two stages, the high-pressure rise per stage enables modern centrifugal compressors to obtain compressor pressure ratios of 15:1.

A typical centrifugal compressor has a few disadvantages that make it unsuitable for use in some engines. For example, the large frontal area required for a given airflow increases aerodynamic drag. In addition, the practical limitations on the number of stages restrict scaling up for larger and more powerful engines.

## AXIAL FLOW COMPRESSORS

An axial flow compressor has two main elements—a rotor and a stator. The **rotor** includes rows of blades fixed on a rotating spindle. The angle and airfoil contour of the blades force air rearward, much like a propeller. The **stator** vanes are arranged in fixed rows between the rows of rotor blades and act as diffusers. At each stage, air velocity decreases and pressure increases. Each consecutive row of rotor blades and stator vanes comprises a **pressure stage**. The number of stages is determined by the amount of air and total pressure rise required in the design of an engine.

Unlike a centrifugal compressor, which is capable of compressor pressure ratios of 15:1, a single stage in an axial flow compressor is capable of producing a compressor pressure ratio of only 1.25:1. The only way to achieve high compressor pressure ratios with an axial flow compressor is by adding more compressor stages.

An axial compressor increases air pressure but has little overall effect on velocity. Each compressor stage raises the pressure of the incoming air while the velocity is alternately increased and decreased through the compressor. Rotor blades slightly accelerate the airflow, but as the stator vanes diffuse the air, it slows while increasing the pressure. The overall result is increased air pressure with relatively constant air velocity from compressor inlet to outlet. [Figure 3-29]

As air passes through an axial flow compressor, the space between the rotor shaft and the stator casing gradually decreases; each stage of blades and vanes is smaller than the preceding stage. This convergence maintains a constant air velocity as air density increases in each stage of compression. [Figure 3-30]

On most axial flow compressors, the case is divided horizontally in halves, which permits technicians to inspect and maintain rotor blades and stator vanes. A compressor case also contains provisions to extract bleed air for a variety of uses.

Disadvantages of axial flow compressors include a relatively high weight and high starting power requirements. Also, the low-pressure rise per stage of 1.25:1 requires many stages to achieve high compressor pressure ratios. Furthermore, axial flow compressors are expensive and difficult to manufacture.

In spite of these drawbacks, axial flow compressors outperform centrifugal flow compressors in several areas. The straight-through design improves ram efficiency. By adding stages, higher compres-

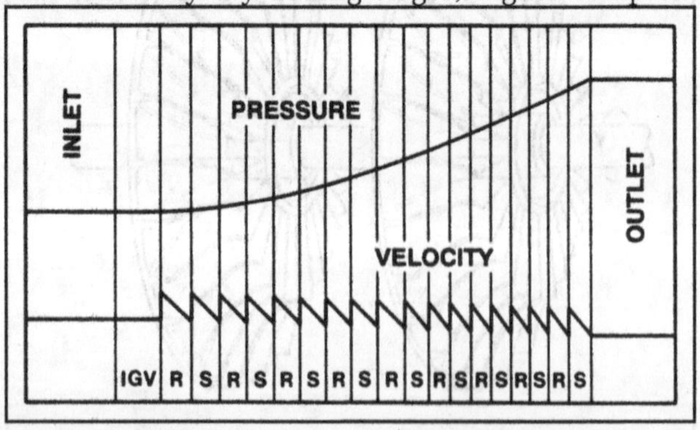


**Figure 3-29. In an axial compressor, airflow velocity remains nearly constant as air pressure increases while air flows through each stage of compression.**

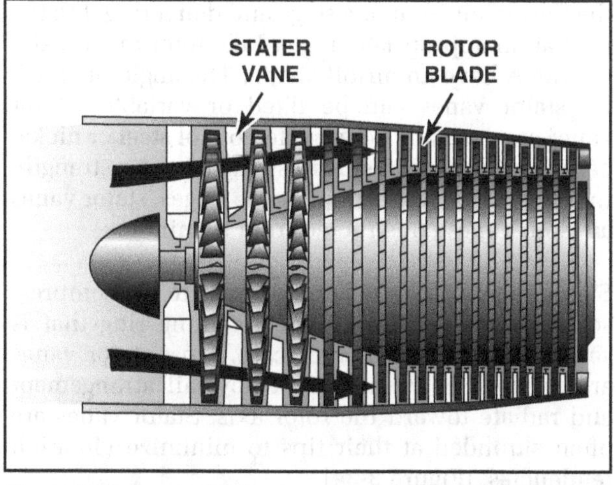


Figure 3-30. In an axial flow compressor, the divergent shape causes the air velocity to remain nearly constant while pressure gradually increases.

sor pressure ratios are possible. Finally, the small frontal area of an axial flow compressor reduces aerodynamic drag.

### Compressor Rotor Blades

The airfoil cross-section of rotor blades used in an axial flow compressor has a varied angle of incidence, or twist. This twist compensates for variations in blade velocity caused by relative distance from the rotational axis—that is, the further a section of blade is from the axis, the faster it travels. [Figure 3-31]

Axial flow compressors typically have from 10 to 18 compression stages. (In a turbofan engine, the fan is considered the first stage rotor). The base, or **root**, of a rotor blade is often designed to fit loosely into the rotor disk to enable easy assembly and to provide vibration dampening. As the compressor rotor rotates, centrifugal force holds the blades in their correct position, and the airstream over each blade provides a shock-absorbing or cushioning effect. Rotor blade roots are designed with a number of different shapes such as a **bulb, fir tree,** or **dovetail.** To prevent them from backing out of their slots, most blades are attached with a pin and a lock tab or locker to secure the coupling. [Figure 3-32]

Some long fan blades are supported by a mid-span **shroud**, which makes them more resistant to the bending forces created by the airstream. These shrouds block some of the airflow and create aerodynamic drag, reducing fan efficiency. In addition, when the mating surfaces on a mid-span shroud become excessively worn, the shrouds can overlap. This is known as shingling and can cause fan vibration and engine damage.

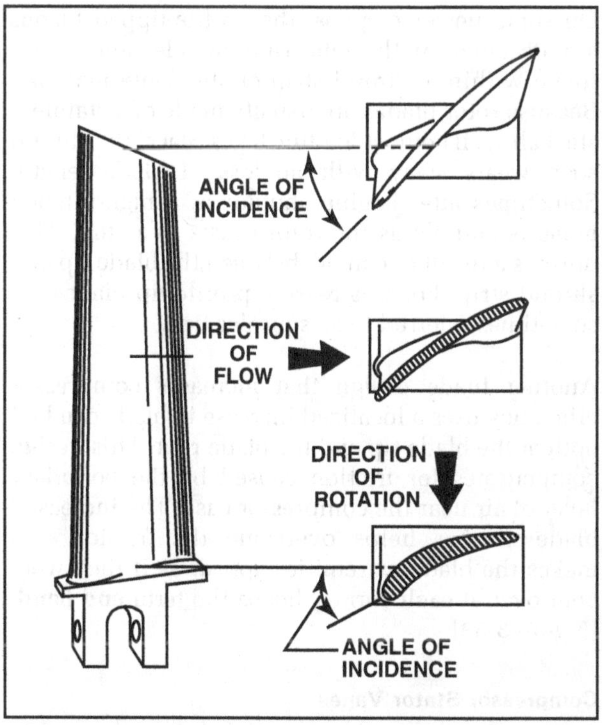


Figure 3-31. Compressor rotor blades are twisted to compensate for blade velocity variations along the length of the blade.

Some blades are cut off square at the tip and are referred to as **flat machine tips**. Other blades have a reduced thickness at the tips and are called **profile tips**. All rotating machinery has a tendency to vibrate, and profiling a compressor blade increases its natural vibration frequency. Increasing the natural frequency of a blade above the frequency of rotation reduces overall vibration. Also, the thin trailing edge of profile tipped blades creates a vortex that increases air velocity and prevents air from spilling back over the blade tips.

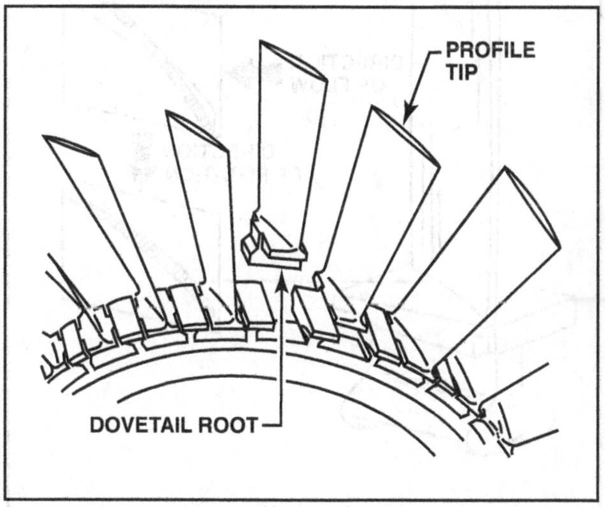


Figure 3-32. A dovetail on the base of this compressor blade fits loosely into a dovetail slot in the compressor wheel. A small locking device such as a pin, key, or plate prevents the blade from backing out.

On some newer engines, the profile-tipped blades are designed with tight running clearances and rotate within a shroud strip of abradable material. Because rotor blades are usually made of a stainless steel alloy, if contact loading takes place, the shroud strip wears away with no loss of blade length. Sometimes after engine shutdown, a high-pitched noise is audible as the rotor coasts to a stop. This noise is a result of contact between the blade tip and shroud strip. For this reason, profile tip blades are sometimes referred to as squealer tips.

Another blade design that increases compressor efficiency uses a localized increase in blade camber, both at the blade tip and the blade root. This design compensates for friction caused by the boundary layer of air near the compressor case. The increased blade camber helps overcome the friction and makes the blade extremities appear as if they were bent over at each corner, hence the term **end bend**. [Figure 3-33]

### Compressor Stator Vanes

Stator vanes are stationary blades located between each row of rotor blades in an axial flow compressor. Stator vanes diffuse air coming off the rotor, which decreases its velocity and increases its pressure. Stators also help prevent swirling by directing the flow of air from one stage and delivering it to the next at an appropriate angle. Like rotor blades, stator vanes have an airfoil shape. The angle of attack for stator vanes can be fixed or variable. Stator vanes are normally constructed out of steel or nickel because the materials possess high fatigue strength. In low-pressure and temperature stages, stator vanes are sometimes constructed from titanium.

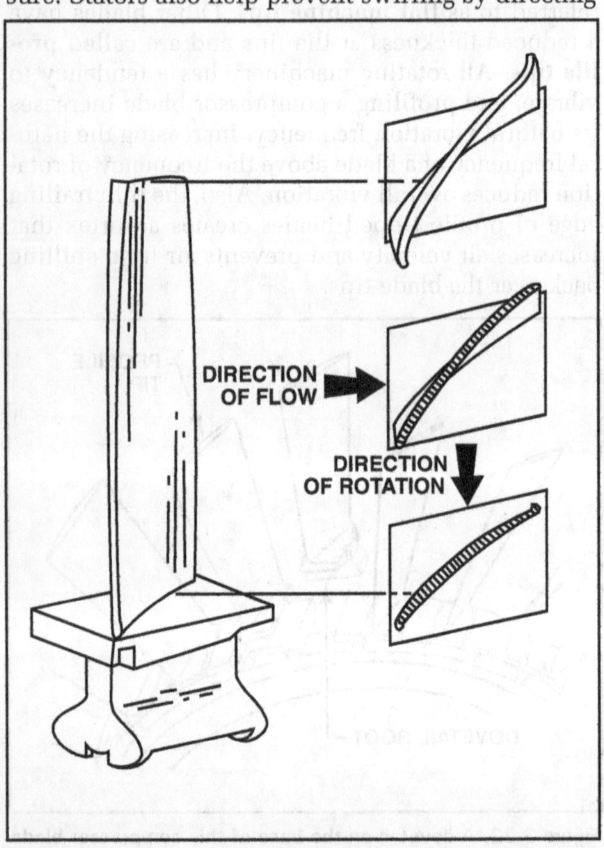


**Figure 3-33. The increased blade camber on some compressor blades is referred to as "end bend." This increase in camber helps prevent airflow stagnation near the tips.**

Stator vanes can be secured directly to the compressor case or to a stator vane retaining ring that is secured to the compressor case. Most stator vanes are attached in rows with a dovetail arrangement and radiate toward the rotor axis. Stator vanes are often shrouded at their tips to minimize vibration tendencies. [Figure 3-34]

Stator vanes positioned in front of the first stage rotor blades are called **inlet guide vanes**. These vanes direct airflow to the first stage rotor blades at the best angle while creating a swirling motion in the direction of engine rotation. This action improves aerodynamics of the compressor by reducing drag on the first stage rotor blades. Some axial compressors with high compressor pressure ratios use variable inlet guide vanes plus several stages of variable stator vanes. Variable inlet guide vanes and stators automatically reposition themselves to maintain proper airflow through the engine under varying operating conditions.

The last set of vanes through which the compressor air passes is the **outlet vane assembly**. These vanes straighten and smooth airflow to the diffuser and prepare the air mass for combustion.

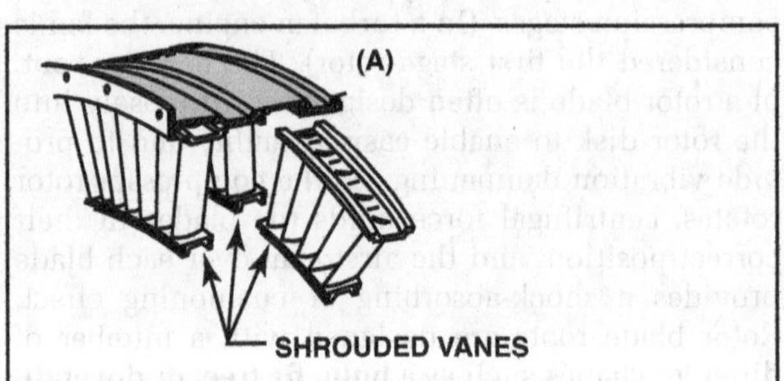


**Figure 3-34. Compressor stator vanes can be attached directly to the compressor case (A) or to a retaining ring that is attached to the case by a retaining screw (B). In addition, stator vanes are sometimes equipped with shrouds to minimize the effects of vibration.**

## MULTIPLE-SPOOL COMPRESSORS

In a basic axial flow compressor, the compressor and turbine are connected by a single shaft and rotate as a single unit. Because there is only one compressor unit, the compressor is commonly referred to as a **single-spool compressor**. Although single-spool compressors are relatively simple and inexpensive to manufacture, they have a few drawbacks. For example, in a long axial compressor, the rear stages operate at a fraction of their capacity, while the forward stages are typically overloaded. Furthermore, the large mass of a single-spool compressor does not respond quickly to abrupt control input changes. [Figure 3-35]

Engine designers devised a way to overcome the limitations of single-spool compressors by splitting the compressor into two or three sections. Each section connects to a portion of the turbine section by coaxial shafts. For example, split-compressor engines with two compressor sections are identified as **dual-spool** or **twin-spool compressors**. The front section of a dual-spool compressor is called the **low-pressure, low-speed**, or **N1 compressor**. This low pressure compressor is typically driven by a two-stage turbine at the rear of the turbine section. The second compressor section of a twin-spool compressor is called the high-pressure, high-speed, or N2 compressor and is typically driven by a single stage high-pressure turbine at the front of the turbine section. The shaft connecting the low-pressure compressor and turbine typically rotates inside the shaft connecting the high-pressure compressor and turbine. On some turbofan engines, the forward fan is attached to the low-pressure compressor and both turn at the same speed. [Figure 3-36]

Because the spools are not physically connected to one another, each seeks its best operating speed. However, for any given power lever setting, the

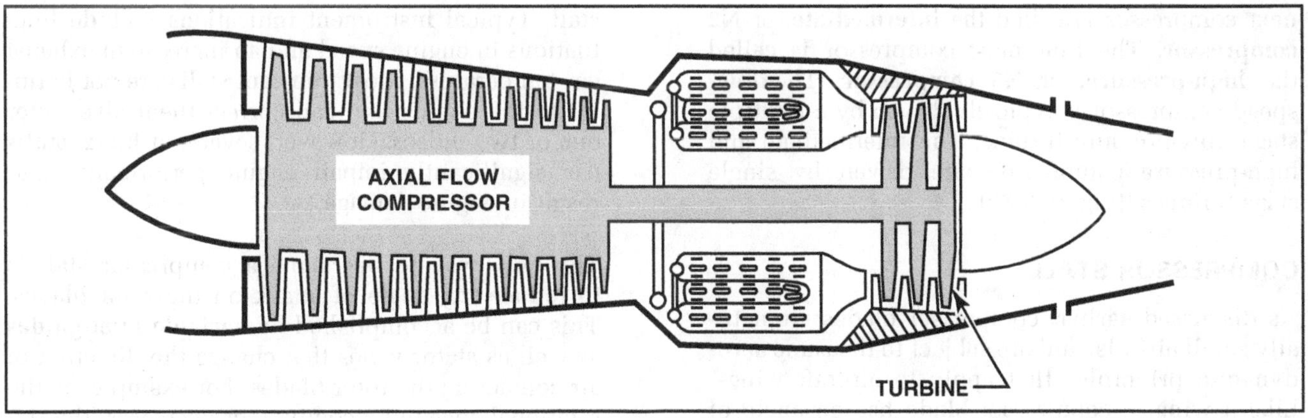


**Figure 3-35. In a single-spool compressor, one compressor unit is connected to the turbine section by a shaft.**

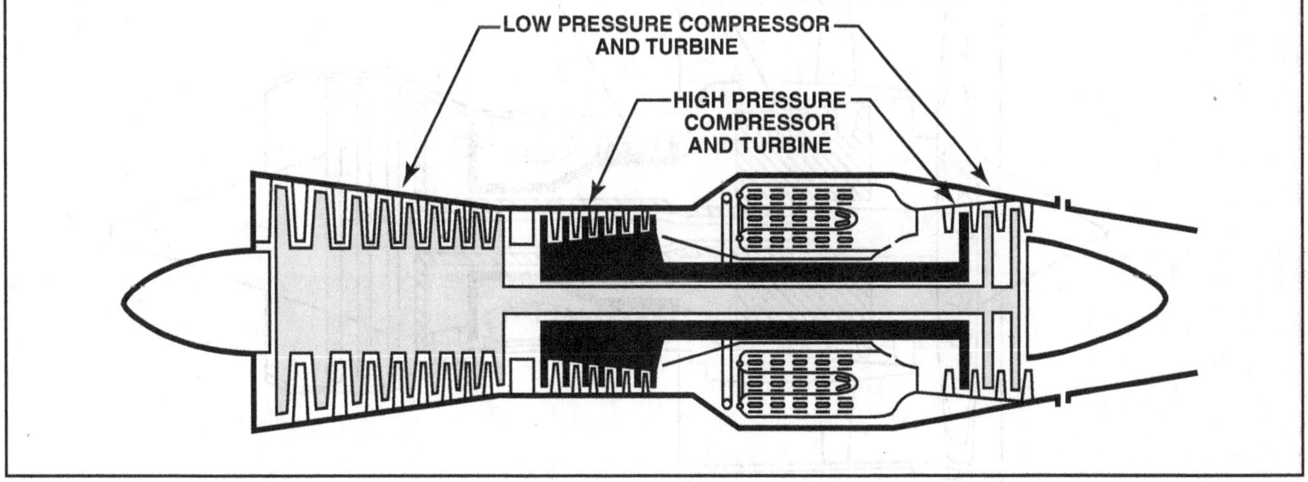


**Figure 3-36. The low-pressure turbine in a dual-spool, axial flow engine drives the low-pressure compressor while the high-pressure turbine drives the high-pressure compressor. By splitting the compressor, two rotating groups, each with considerably less mass than a single-spool compressor, enable the compressors to respond more quickly to power lever inputs and to perform better at high altitudes.**

speed of the high-pressure compressor is relatively constant based on the setting of the fuel control governor. With a constant level of energy at the turbine, the speed of the low-pressure compressor increases or decreases with changes in the inlet air flow caused by atmospheric pressure fluctuations or flight maneuvering. For example, low-pressure compressors increase in speed as an aircraft gains altitude because the atmosphere is less dense and more rotational speed is necessary to force the required amount of air through the engine. Conversely, as an aircraft descends, air becomes more dense and easier to compress and the low-pressure compressor slows. The low-pressure compressor supplies a high-pressure compressor with a constant air pressure and mass airflow for each power setting.

Many turbofan engines have a compressor section divided into three sections, referred to as a **triple-spool compressor**. In this arrangement, the fan is referred to as the low-speed, or $N_1$ compressor. The next compressor is called the **intermediate**, or **N2 compressor**. The innermost compressor is called the **high-pressure**, or **N3 compressor**. The low-speed compressor is typically driven by a multiple stage, low-pressure turbine. The intermediate and high-pressure compressors are driven by single stage turbines. [Figure 3-37]

## COMPRESSOR STALL

As discussed earlier, compressor blades are actually small airfoils, and are subject to the same aerodynamic principles that apply to aircraft wings. Like a wing, a compressor blade has an angle of attack. The angle of attack of a compressor blade is a result of inlet air velocity and a compressor's rotational velocity. These two forces combine to form a vector that defines the airfoil's actual angle of attack with regard to the approaching inlet air. Like an aircraft wing, the angle of attack of a compressor blade can change.

A **compressor stall** can be described as an imbalance between two vector quantities: inlet velocity and compressor rotational speed. Compressor stalls occur when the compressor blade angle of attack exceeds the critical angle of attack. At this point, smooth airflow is interrupted creating turbulence and pressure fluctuations. Compressor stalls cause the air flowing in the compressor to slow down and stagnate, sometimes reversing direction. In its mildest form, a compressor stall can be heard as a pulsing or fluttering sound. In a developed state, a compressor stall sounds like a loud explosion. Cockpit gauges do not always indicate a mild or **transient compressor stall**, but they will indicate a developed stall. Typical instrument indications include fluctuations in engine speed and an increase in exhaust gas temperature. Most transient stalls are not harmful to the engine and can correct themselves after one or two pulses. However, severe, or **hung, stalls** can significantly impair engine performance and result in engine damage.

The only way to overcome a compressor stall is to reduce the angle of attack on the rotor blades. This can be accomplished by **variable inlet guides** as well as stator vanes that change the direction of air contacting the rotor blades. For example, as the rotational speed of a compressor decreases, the sta-

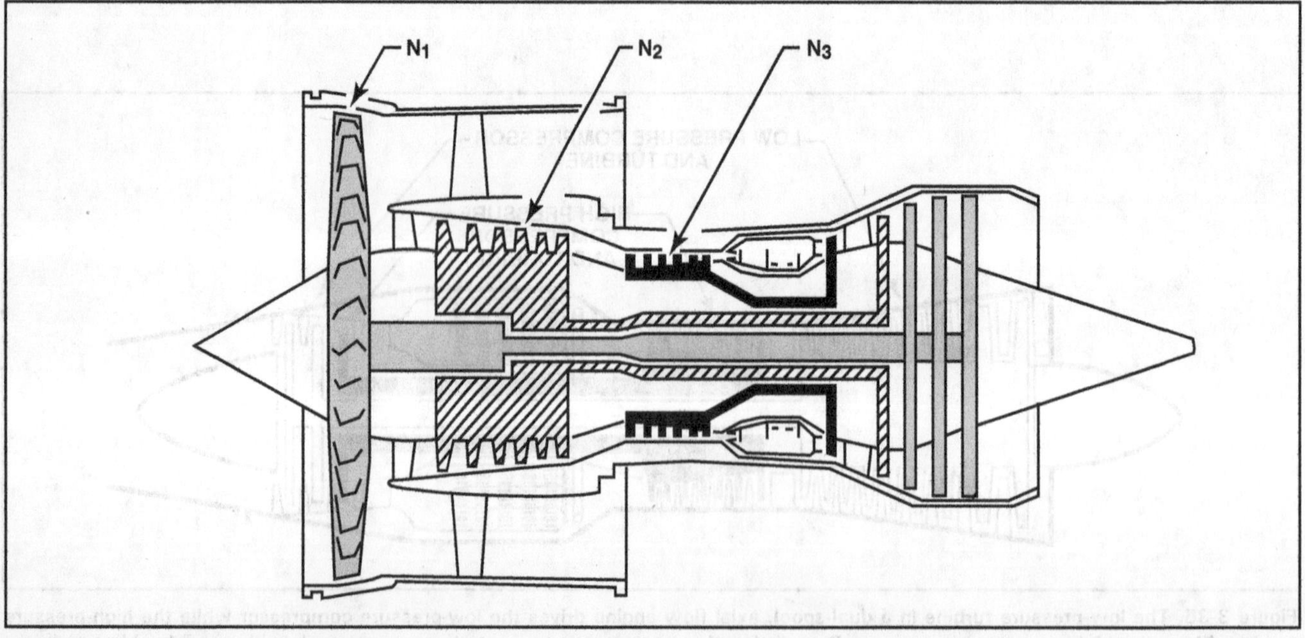


**Figure 3-37. The triple-spool compressors on many turbofan engines enable each compressor section to reach its optimum speed for varying power requirements and flight conditions.**

tor vanes are progressively closed to maintain the appropriate airflow angle to the proceeding rotor blades. The position of stator vanes is controlled automatically by the fuel control unit. To accomplish this, the fuel control unit monitors compressor inlet temperature and engine speed.

Another way to change the angle of attack of compressor blades is by bleeding off air pressure from within the compressor. Some engines incorporate automatic air-bleed valves that operate during low speed conditions and engine startup. The automatic valves open to relieve pressure caused by air piling up at the compressor's high-pressure end. Regulating air pressure helps prevent a compressor from stalling and makes engine starting easier.

Compressor stalls typically occur when engine inlet air is disrupted, such as when an aircraft flies through areas of severe turbulence or performs abrupt flight maneuvers. A pilot can induce a compressor stall if excessive fuel flow is produced by sudden engine acceleration with an incompatible engine speed and airflow combination. Physical contamination or damage to compressor blades, stator vanes, or turbine components can also disrupt airflow and cause a compressor stall.

## COMBINATION COMPRESSORS

Hybrid axial flow-centrifugal flow compressors combine the best features of both centrifugal and axial compressors and to eliminate some of their respective disadvantages. This design is currently in use with some smaller engines installed on business jets and helicopters. [Figure 3-38]

## COMPRESSOR AIR BLEEDS

In addition to supplying air for combustion, a compressor supplies high-pressure, high-temperature air for various secondary functions including cabin pressurization, heating, and cooling. Compressor air can also be used for deicing, anti-icing, and pneumatic engine starting. This air is referred to as **bleed air**, or **compressor bleed air**, and is tapped from the compressor through bleed ports in various locations. A **bleed port** is a small opening adjacent to the compressor stage used to collect bleed air supply. The choice of which compressor stage to bleed air from depends on the pressure and temperature required for a particular function. Air bled from the

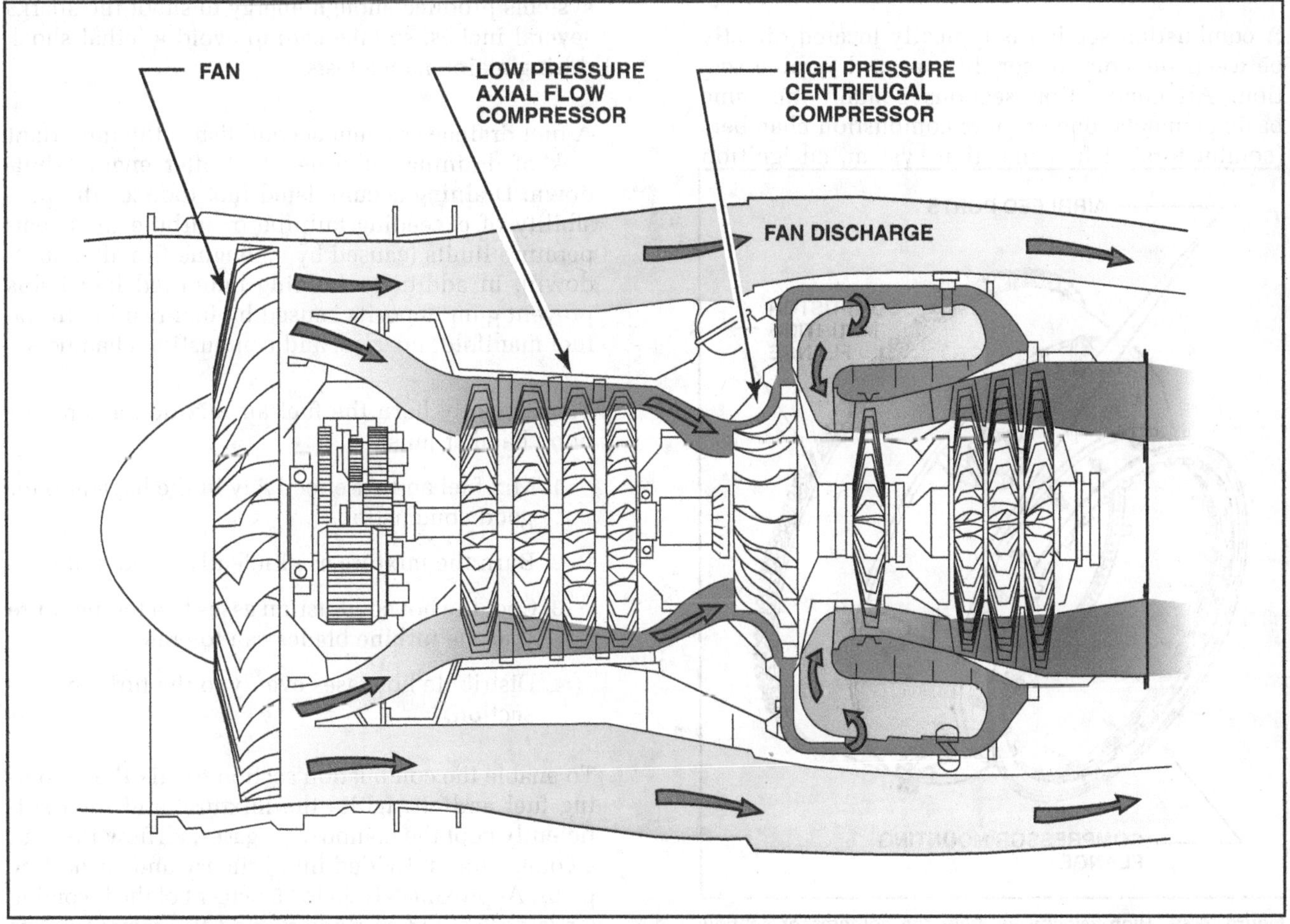


**Figure 3-38. The Garrett TFE731 engine has a two-stage compressor that uses an axial flow compressor for the low-pressure stage and a single stage centrifugal compressor for the high-pressure stage.**

final or highest-pressure stage often requires cooling, because the act of compression can heat the air to temperatures in excess of 650 degrees Fahrenheit.

Bleeding air from the compressor causes a small but noticeable drop in engine power. Sometimes power loss can be detected by observing the engine pressure ratio (EPR) indicator. For example, selecting the engine inlet anti-ice function causes a drop in EPR and engine speed if the engine power lever is left in a fixed position. Exhaust gas temperature (EGT) readings might change as well.

### DIFFUSER

When air leaves an axial flow compressor toward the combustion section, it travels at speeds up to 500 feet per second. This is too fast for combustion and must be slowed significantly. The divergent shape of a diffuser slows compressor discharge while increasing air pressure to its highest value in the engine. The diffuser is typically a separate section bolted to the rear of the compressor case, ahead of the combustion section. [Figure 3-39]

## COMBUSTION SECTION

A combustion section is typically located directly between the compressor diffuser and turbine section. All combustion sections contain the same basic elements: one or more combustion chambers (combustors), a fuel injection system, an ignition source, and a fuel drainage system.

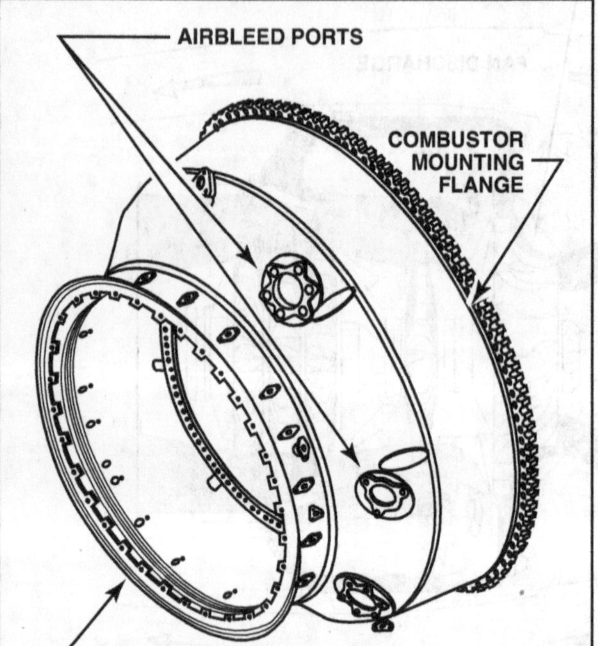


**Figure 3-39. High-velocity air from the compressor section enters the diffuser, where air velocity decreases and air pressure increases to a maximum.**

The **combustion chamber** or **combustor** in a turbine engine is where fuel and air are mixed and burned. A typical combustor consists of an outer casing with a perforated inner liner. The perforations are various sizes and shapes, all having a specific effect on the propagation of the flame within the liner.

The fuel injection system meters the appropriate amount of fuel through the fuel nozzles into the combustors. Fuel nozzles are located in the combustion chamber case or in the compressor outlet elbows. Fuel is delivered through the nozzles into the liners in a finely atomized spray. This ensures thorough mixing with the incoming air. The finer the spray, the more rapid and efficient the combustion process is.

A typical ignition source for gas turbine engines is the **high-energy capacitor discharge system**, consisting of an exciter unit, two high-tension cables, and two spark igniters. This ignition system produces 60 to 100 sparks per minute, resulting in a ball of fire at the igniter electrodes. Some of these systems produce enough energy to shoot the sparks several inches, so take care to avoid a lethal shock during maintenance tests.

A fuel drainage system accomplishes the important task of draining unburned fuel after engine shutdown. Draining accumulated fuel reduces the possibility of exceeding tailpipe or turbine inlet temperature limits (caused by an engine fire after shutdown). In addition, draining unburned fuel helps prevent gum deposits caused by fuel residue in the fuel manifold, nozzles, and combustion chambers.

To efficiently burn the fuel/air mixture, a combustion chamber must:

1. Mix fuel and air effectively in the best ratio for good combustion.
2. Burn the mixture as efficiently as possible.
3. Cool the hot combustion gases to a temperature that the turbine blades can tolerate.
4. Distribute hot gases evenly to the turbine section.

To enable the combustion section to mix the incoming fuel and air, ignite the mixture, and then sufficiently cool the combustion gases, airflow through a combustor is divided into primary and secondary paths. Approximately 25 to 35 percent of the incoming air is designated as primary, and the remaining air is designated as secondary. Primary, or **combustion air**, is directed inside the liner in the front end of a combustor. As this air enters the combustor, it passes through a set of **swirl vanes**, which slow the air down to five or six feet per second and impart a vortex motion. The reduction in airflow velocity is important because kerosene-based fuels have a slow flame propagation rate. An excessively high-velocity airflow could literally blow the flame out of the engine. Such a condition is known as a **flameout**. The vortex created in the flame area provides the turbulence required to mix the fuel and air properly, after which the combustion process is complete in the first third of a combustor.

The secondary airflow in the combustion section flows at a velocity of several hundred feet per second around the combustor's periphery. This flow of air forms a cooling air blanket on both sides of the liner and centers the combustion flames to prevent contact with the liner. Some secondary air slows and enters the combustor through the perforations in the liner. This air supports the combustion of any remaining unburned fuel. Secondary air also mixes with the burned gases and cool air to provide an even distribution of energy to the turbine nozzle at a temperature that the turbine section can withstand. [Figure 3-40]

The three basic types of combustion chambers are the multiple-can type, the annular (basket) type, and the can-annular type. They are the same functionally, but their design and construction are different.

## MULTIPLE-CAN COMBUSTORS

The multiple-can combustion chamber consists of a series of individual combustor cans that function as individual burner units. This type of combustion chamber is well suited to centrifugal compressor engines because of the way compressor discharge air is equally divided at the diffuser. Each can is constructed from a perforated stainless steel liner inside an outer case. The inner liner is highly heat resistant and easily removed for inspection. Each combustion can has a large degree of curvature that provides high resistance to warpage. However, this shape is inefficient because of the volume of space it requires and the additional weight.

The individual combustors in a typical multiple-can combustion chamber are interconnected with small **flame propagation tubes**. The combustion starts in the two cans equipped with igniter plugs; the flame travels through the tubes to ignite the fuel/air mixture in the other cans. Each flame propagation tube consists of a small tube surrounded by a larger tube (or jacket). The small inner tube contains the flame and the outer tube contains cooling and insulating airflow between the cans. A typical multiple-can

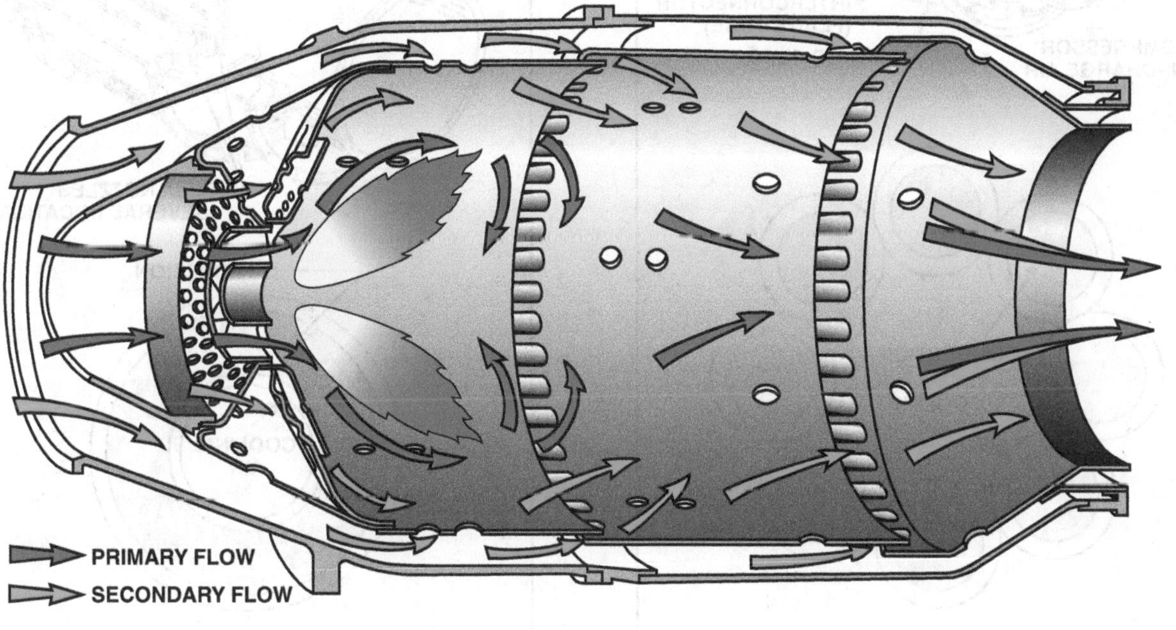


**Figure 3-40. As air flows into the combustion section, it separates into primary and secondary flows. The primary flow supports combustion, and the secondary flow cools the hot gases before they enter the turbine section.**

combustion section includes 8 or 10 cans. On most American-built engines, cans are numbered clockwise with the number one can on the top when facing the rear of the engine. All of the combustor cans discharge exhaust gases into an open area at the turbine nozzle inlet. [Figure 3-41]

## ANNULAR COMBUSTORS

Today, annular combustors are commonly used in both small and large engines. From a standpoint of thermal efficiency, weight, and physical size, the annular combustor is the most efficient. An annular combustion chamber consists of a housing and perforated inner liner, or basket. The liner is a single unit encircling the outside of the turbine shaft housing. The shroud is shaped to contain one or more concentric baskets. An annular combustor with two baskets is known as a double-annular combustion chamber. Normally, the ignition source consists of two spark igniters similar to the type found in multiple-can combustors.

In a conventional annular combustor, airflow enters at the front and is discharged at the rear and primary and secondary airflow are much the same as the multiple-can design. However, unlike can combustors, an annular combustor must be removed as a single unit for repair or replacement. This usually involves complete separation of the engine at a major flange. [Figure 3-42]

Some annular combustors are designed with a reverse direction airflow. **Reverse-flow combustors** work the same as conventional flow combustors, except that the air flows around the chamber and enters from the rear. This causes the combustion gases to flow through the engine opposite the

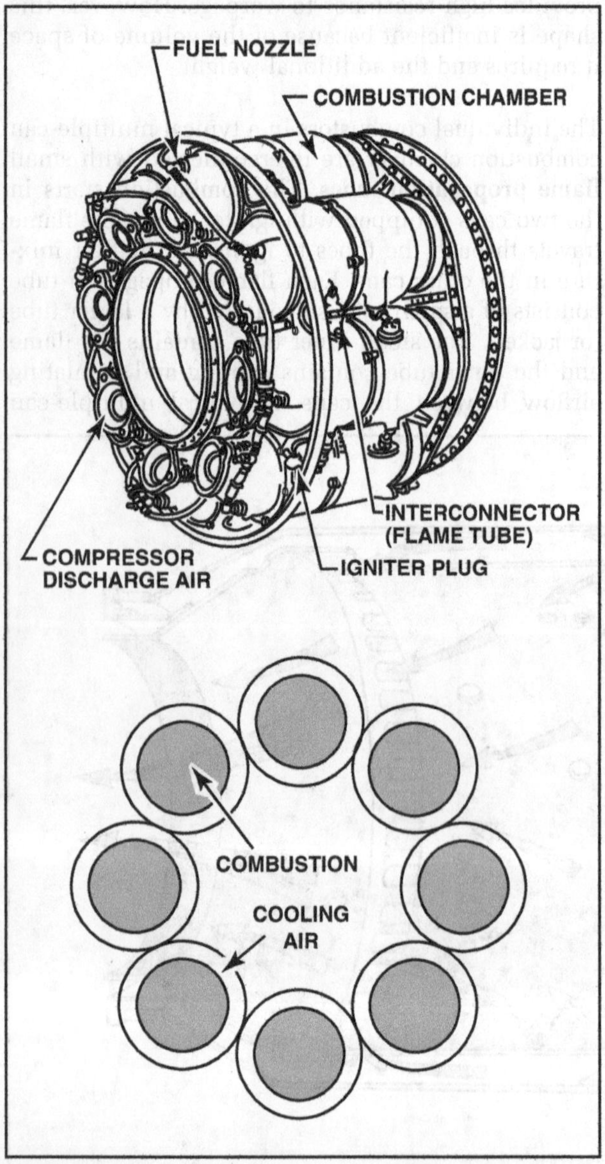


Figure 3-41. Used primarily in early turbine engine designs, multiple-can combustors consisted of a series of individual burner cans arranged radially around an engine. The multiple-can design has the advantage of easy removal of any combustor for maintenance or replacement.

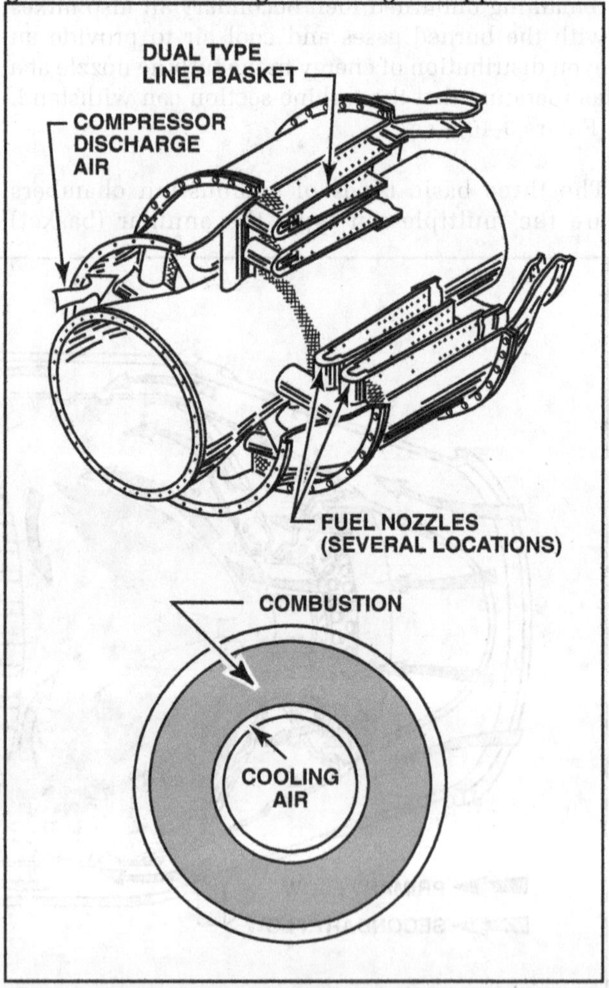


Figure 3-42. An annular combustor is the most efficient for its weight of any combustor design. However, the engine must be disassembled to repair or replace an annular combustor. Also, the shallow curvature makes this combustor more susceptible to warping.

normal airflow. This idea was first employed by Whittle in his early designs.

In a typical reverse-flow annular combustor, the turbine wheels are inside the combustor instead of downstream, as with the conventional flow designs. This design allows for a shorter and lighter engine that uses the hot gases to preheat the compressor discharge air. These factors help make up for the loss of efficiency caused by the gases passing through the combustor in the reverse direction. [Figure 3-43]

## CAN-ANNULAR COMBUSTORS

Can-annular combustion sections are a combination of the multiple-can and the annular type combustors. The can-annular combustor was invented by Pratt & Whitney and consists of a removable steel shroud that encircles the entire combustion section. Inside the shroud, or casing, multiple burner cans are assembled radially about the engine axis with bullet-shaped perforated liners. A fuel nozzle cluster is attached to the forward end of each burner can, and pre-swirl vanes are placed around each fuel nozzle. The pre-swirl vanes enhance combustion by promoting a thorough mixing of fuel and air and slowing the velocity of axial air in the burner can. Flame propagation tubes connect the individual liners, and two igniter plugs initiate combustion. Each can and liner is removed and installed as a single unit for maintenance. This design combines

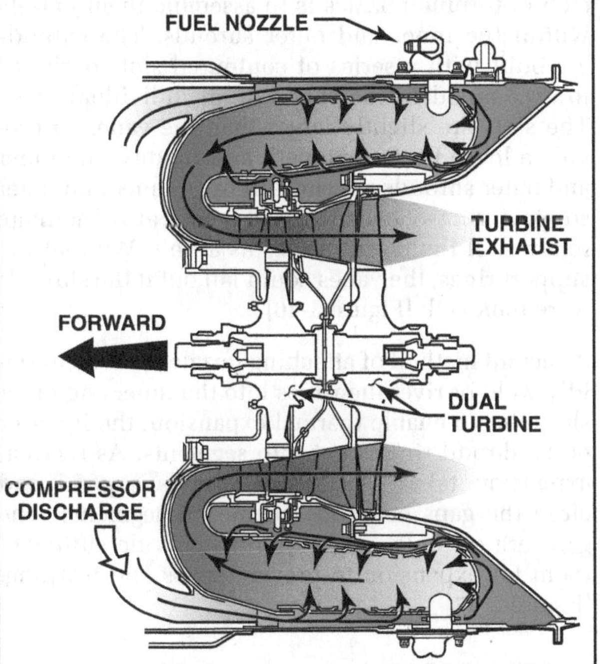


**Figure 3-43. A reverse-flow combustor is light and compact. The turbine wheels are contained within the combustor rather than behind it.**

the ease of overhaul and testing of the multiple-can arrangement with the compact design of the annular combustor. [Figure 3-44]

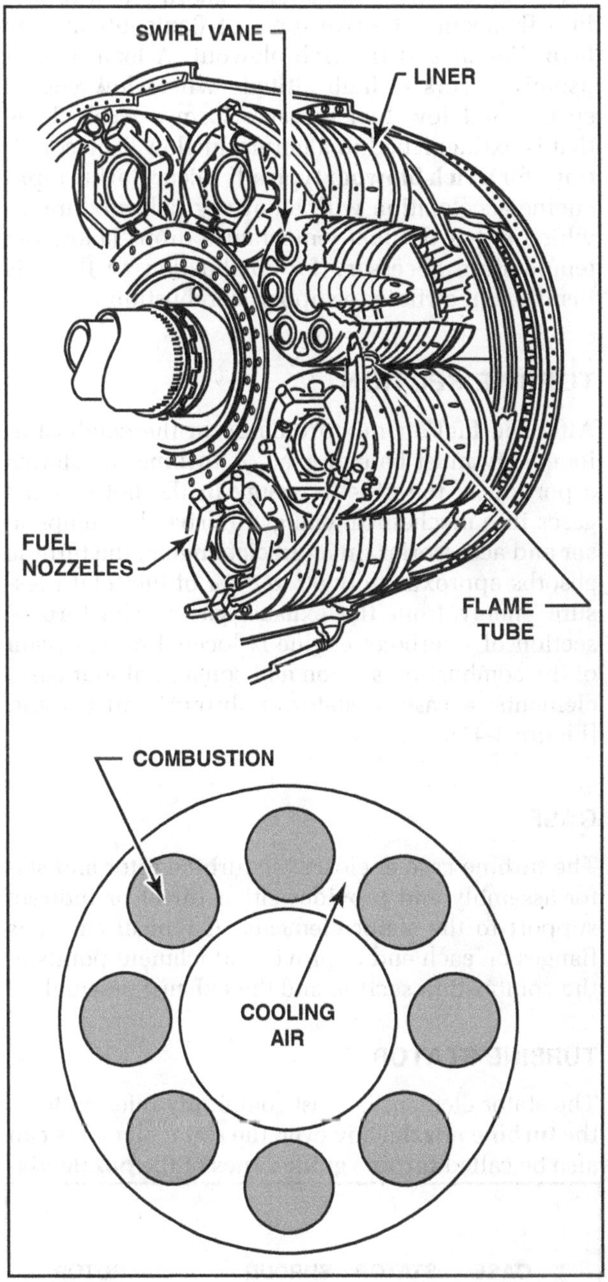


**Figure 3-44. A can-annular combustor contains individual burner cans in an annular liner. The short burner cans combine the compact efficiency of the annular combustor with the ease of maintenance of the multiple-can combustor.**

## FLAMEOUT

As mentioned earlier, the combustion flame can be extinguished by high airflow rates. Additionally, excessively slow airflow rates can cause this problem. Although flameout is uncommon in modern engines, combustion instability still occurs and occasionally causes a complete flameout. The correct set of circumstances (turbulent weather, high altitude, slow acceleration, and high-speed maneuvers) can induce combustion instability that results in a flameout. The two types of flameouts are the **lean die-out** and the rich blowout. A lean die-out usually occurs at high altitude where low engine speeds and low fuel pressure form a weak flame that is extinguished in a normal airflow. The conditions for a **rich blowout** typically occur during rapid engine acceleration with an overly rich mixture, in which either the fuel temperature drops below the temperature necessary for combustion or there is insufficient airflow to support combustion.

## TURBINE SECTION

After the fuel/air mixture burns in the combustor, its energy must be extracted. A **turbine** transforms a portion of the kinetic energy in the hot exhaust gases into mechanical energy to drive the compressor and accessories. In a turbojet engine, the turbine absorbs approximately 60 to 80% of the total pressure energy from the exhaust gases. The turbine section of a turbojet engine is located downstream of the combustion section and consists of four basic elements: a case, a stator, a shroud, and a rotor. [Figure 3-45]

### CASE

The turbine case encloses the turbine rotor and stator assembly and provides either direct or indirect support to the stator elements. A typical case has flanges on each end to provide attachment points to the combustion section and the exhaust assembly.

### TURBINE STATOR

The stator element is most commonly referred to as the **turbine nozzle**; however, the stator elements can also be called **turbine guide vanes** or the **nozzle diaphragm**. The turbine nozzle is located directly aft of the combustion section and immediately ahead of the turbine wheel. Because of its location, the turbine nozzle is typically exposed to the highest temperatures within a gas turbine engine.

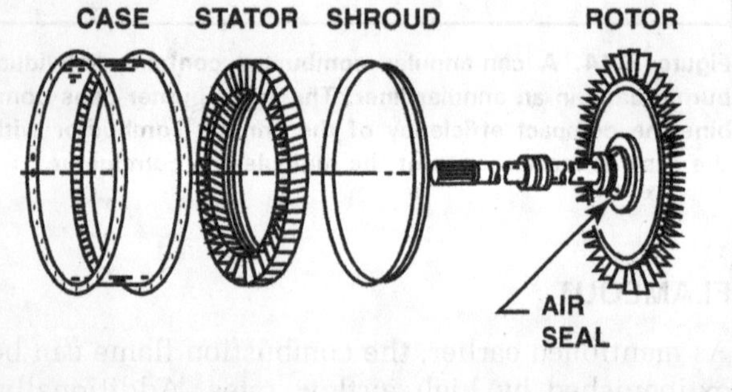

**Figure 3-45. The four basic elements of the turbine assembly in a gas turbine engine are the case, stator, shroud, and rotor.**

The purpose of the turbine nozzle is to collect the high-energy airflow from the combustors and direct the flow to strike the turbine rotor at the appropriate angle. The vanes of a turbine nozzle are contoured and positioned to form a number of converging nozzles that convert some of the exhaust gas pressure energy to velocity energy. Furthermore, the angle of the stator vanes is set in the direction of turbine wheel rotation to most efficiently convert the velocity into mechanical energy.

### SHROUD

The turbine nozzle assembly consists of an inner and outer shroud that retains and surrounds the nozzle vanes. The number of vanes employed varies with the type and size of an engine. The turbine nozzle vanes are assembled between the outer and inner shrouds (or rings) in a variety of ways. Although the actual elements might vary slightly in their configuration and construction, one aspect is common to all turbine nozzles: the nozzle vanes are constructed to permit thermal expansion. Otherwise, the rapid temperature changes imposed by the engine would cause severe distortion or warping of the nozzle assembly.

One way that designers address the thermal expansion of turbine nozzles is to assemble them loosely within the inner and outer shrouds. The shrouds are built with a series of contoured slots designed to accommodate the shape of an individual vane. The slots are slightly larger than the vanes to provide a loose fit. For strength and rigidity, the inner and outer shrouds are encased in an inner and outer support ring. These support rings also facilitate removal of the nozzle vanes as a unit. Without the support rings, the vanes could fall out if the shrouds were removed. [Figure 3-46]

A second method of attaching nozzle vanes is to rigidly weld or rivet the vanes into the inner and outer shrouds. To enable thermal expansion, the inner or outer shroud ring is cut into segments. As thermal expansion takes place, the shrouds expand and close the gaps between the shroud segments. The gaps are carefully engineered to provide sufficient room for expansion to prevent stress and warping. [Figure 3-47]

### TURBINE ROTOR

The rotating elements of a turbine section consist of a shaft and a turbine rotor, or wheel. The **turbine**

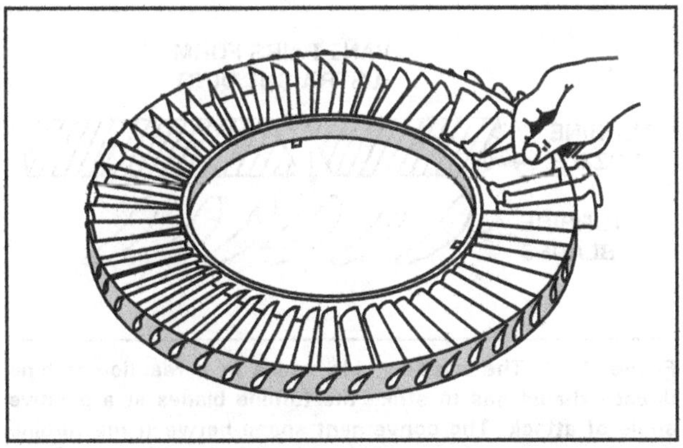

Figure 3-46. A loose fit between the vanes and shrouds permits thermal expansion without warping the turbine nozzle assembly.

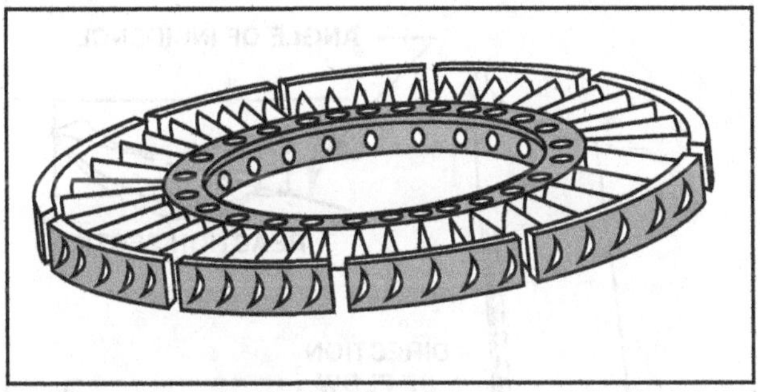

Figure 3-47. When vanes are riveted or welded into segmented shrouds, the gaps between shroud segments permit thermal expansion.

**wheel** is a dynamically balanced unit consisting of blades attached to a rotating disk. The **turbine disk** anchors the turbine blades and is bolted or welded to the main shaft. The shaft rotates in bearings lubricated by oil between the outer race and bearing housing. This arrangement reduces vibration and allows for a slight misalignment in the shaft.

As the high-velocity gases pass through the turbine nozzle and hit the turbine blades, the turbine wheel rotates. In some engines, a single turbine wheel cannot absorb sufficient energy from the exhaust gas to drive the compressor and accessories. Therefore, many engines use multiple turbine stages, each stage consisting of a turbine nozzle and wheel.

The severe centrifugal loads imposed by the high rotational speeds, as well as the elevated operating temperatures exert extreme stress on the turbine blades. At times, these stresses can cause turbine blades to expand in length. If left unchecked, this expansion (or creep) can result in the turbine blades rubbing against the engine's outer casing.

## TURBINE BLADES

Turbine blades are airfoil-shaped components designed to extract the maximum amount of energy from the flow of hot gases. Blades are either forged or cast, depending on their alloy composition. Early blades were manufactured from steel forgings; however, today most turbine blades consist of cast nickel-based alloys. In either case, after a blade is forged or cast, it must be finish-ground to the desired shape. As an alternative to metal turbine blades, the development of blades manufactured from reinforced ceramic materials are being developed. Because of ceramic's ability to withstand high temperatures, greater engine efficiencies might be possible. Their initial application is likely to be in small, high-speed turbines operating at very high temperatures.

Turbine blades fit loosely into a turbine disk when an engine is cold, but expand to fit tightly at normal operating temperatures. The most commonly used method for attaching turbine blades is by **fir tree slots** cut into the turbine disk rim and matching bases cast or machined into the turbine blade base. [Figure 3-48]

After it is installed, a turbine blade is retained in its groove either by peening, welding, rivets, or lock tabs. The peening method is used frequently in various ways. A common application of peening requires a small notch to be ground in the edge of the blade's fir tree root prior to installation. After the blade is inserted into the disk, the notch is filled by the disk metal, which is peened into it by a small

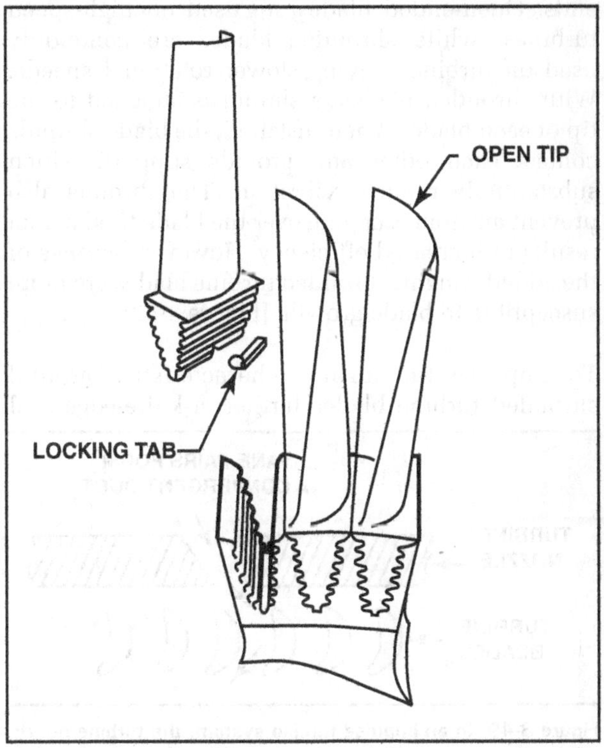


Figure 3-48. The loose fit of a fir tree base permits the base of a turbine blade to expand as it heats to operating temperature.

punch mark made in the disk adjacent to the notch. A tool similar to a center punch is used for this job.

Turbine blades are generally classified as impulse, reaction, or combination impulse-reaction. In a turbine that uses **impulse blades**, the blades merely change the direction of airflow coming from the turbine nozzle and cause relatively no change in gas pressure or velocity. The turbine wheel simply absorbs the force required to change the direction of airflow and converts it to rotary motion. [Figure 3-49]

**Reaction turbine blades** produce a turning force based on an aerodynamic action. To do this, the turbine blades form a series of converging ducts that increase gas velocity and reduce pressure. The result is similar to what happens to an airfoil, in that the reduced pressure produces a lifting force. However, in a turbine, the force is exerted in the direction of rotation. [Figure 3-50]

To more evenly distribute the workload along the length of the blade, most modern turbine engines incorporate **impulse-reaction turbine blades**. With this type of blade, the blade base is impulse-shaped while the blade tip is reaction-shaped. This design results in a uniform velocity and pressure drop across the entire blade length. [Figure 3-51]

Turbine blades can be open or shrouded at their ends. Open-ended blades are used on high-speed turbines, while shrouded blades are commonly used on turbines having slower rotational speeds. With shrouded blades, a shroud is attached to the tip of each blade. When installed, the blade shrouds contact each other and provide support, which substantially reduces vibration. The shrouds also prevent air from escaping over the blade tips, which results in increased efficiency. However, because of the added weight, shrouded turbine blades are more susceptible to blade growth. [Figure 3-52]

To improve the airflow characteristics around shrouded turbine blades further, a knife-edge seal is machined around the outside of the shroud to reduce air losses at the blade tip. The knife-edge seal fits with a close tolerance into a shrouded ring mounted in the outer turbine case.

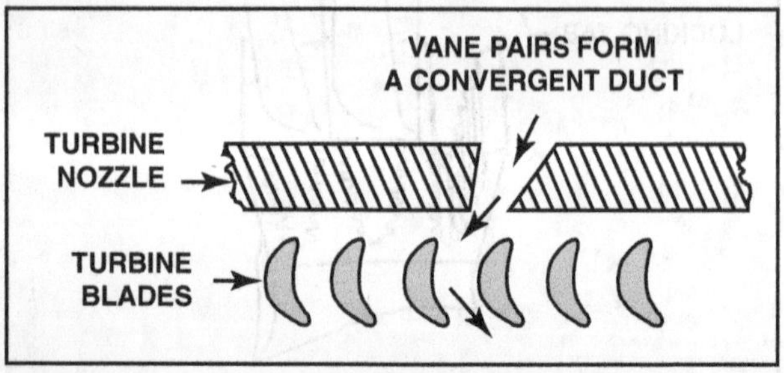


**Figure 3-49. In an impulse turbine system, the turbine nozzle vanes form a series of converging ducts that increase the velocity of the exhaust gases. The impulse turbine blades extract energy from the gases as the blades redirect the flow of high-velocity gases.**

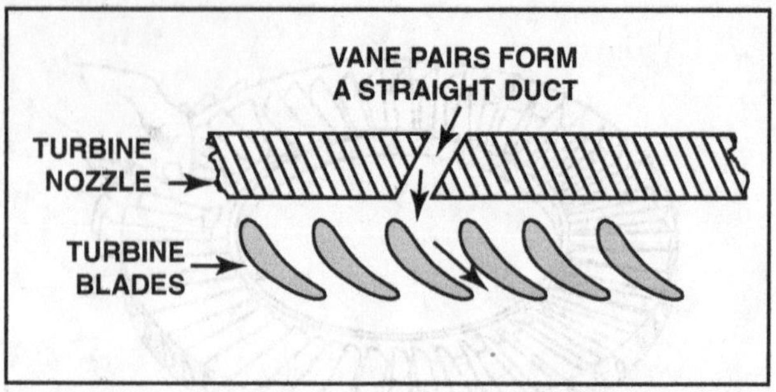


**Figure 3-50. The nozzle guide vanes in a reaction turbine direct exhaust gas to strike the turbine blades at a positive angle of attack. The convergent shape between the turbine blades increases gas velocity and decreases its pressure to create a component of lift that rotates the turbine wheel.**

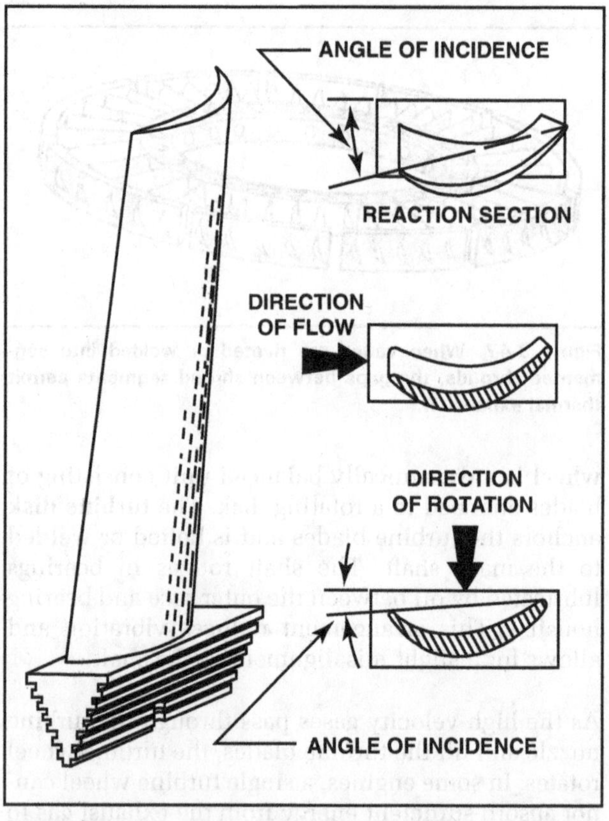


**Figure 3-51. To help account for the different rotational speeds along the length of a turbine blade, most turbine engines use impulse-reaction turbine blades. This type of blade is constructed with an impulse section at its base and a reaction section at its tip.**

## COOLING

Temperature control is an important consideration in the design of a turbine section. The temperature of the turbine section is the most limiting factor in the operation of a gas turbine engine. However,

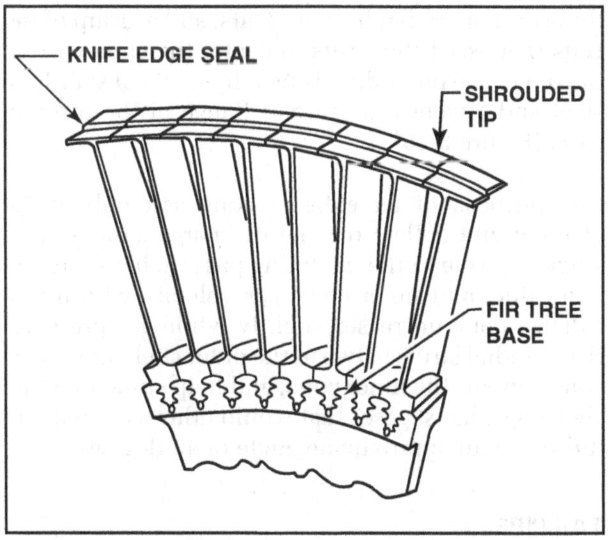


**Figure 3-52. Shrouded blades form a band around the turbine wheel perimeter to reduce blade vibration and increase efficiency.**

the higher an engine raises the temperature of the incoming air, the more power, or thrust, an engine can produce. Therefore, the effectiveness of a turbine engine's cooling system significantly affects engine performance. Through the design of cooling systems, many cooling systems enable the turbine vane and blade components to operate in a thermal environment 600 to 800 degrees Fahrenheit above the temperature limits of their metal alloys.

One of the most common ways of cooling the components in the turbine section is by using engine bleed air. Because turbine disks absorb heat from hot gases passing near their rim and from the blades through conduction, disk rim temperatures are normally well above the temperature of the disk portion nearest the shaft. To limit the effect of these temperature variations, cooling air is directed over each side of the disk.

To cool turbine nozzle vanes and turbine blades, compressor bleed air can be directed in through the hollow blades and out through holes in the tip, leading edge, and trailing edge. This type of cooling is known as **convection cooling** or **film cooling**. [Figure 3-53]

In addition to drilling holes in a turbine vane or blade, some stationary nozzle vanes are constructed of a porous, high-temperature material. In this case, bleed air is ducted into the vanes and exits through the porous material. This type of cooling is known as **transpiration cooling**.

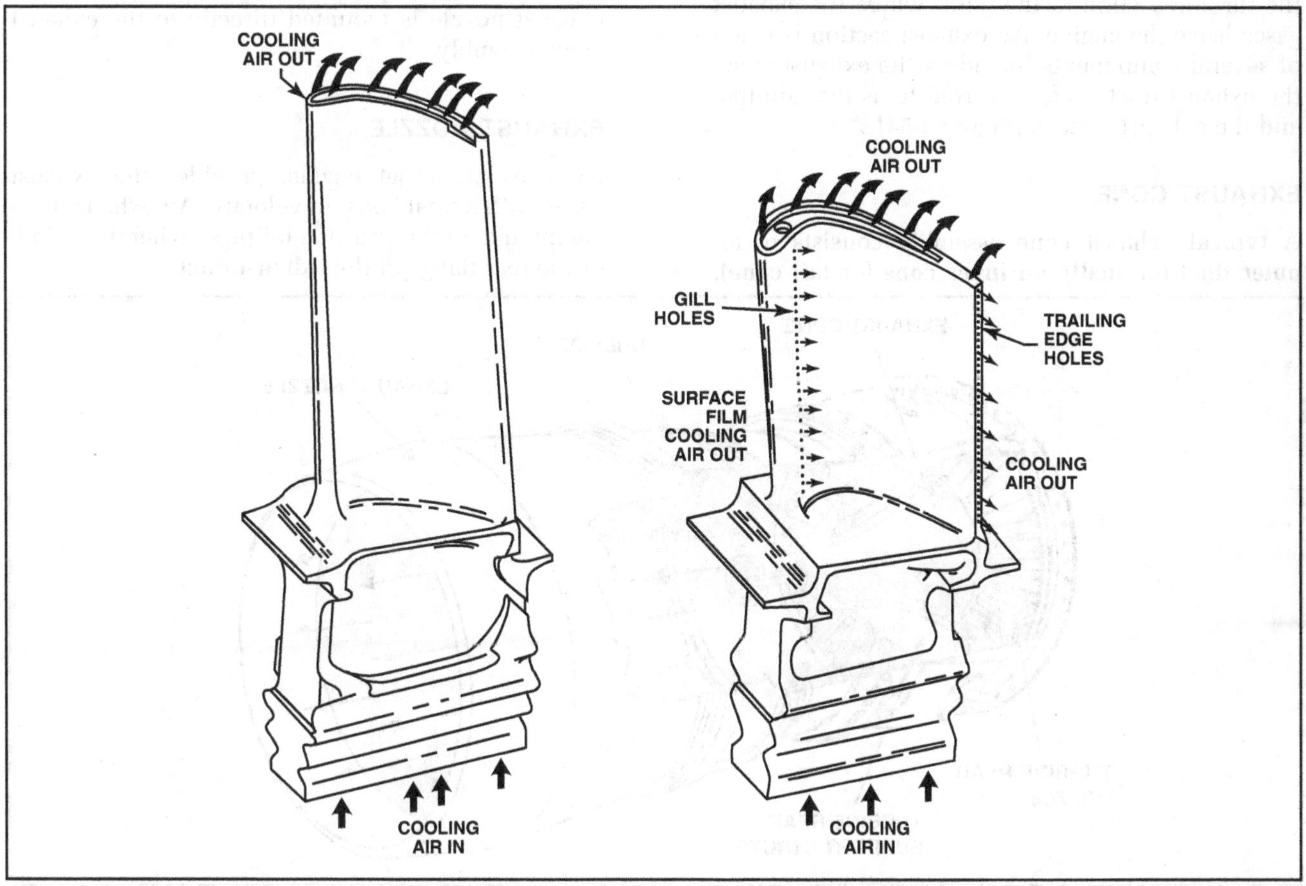


**Figure 3-53. An internally cooled blade receives cooling air at the root and expels it at the tip or through holes in the leading and trailing edges.**

Modern engine designs incorporate a combination of air cooling methods using low- and high-pressure air for both internal and surface cooling of turbine vanes and blades. To provide additional cooling, the turbine vane shrouds might also be perforated with cooling holes.

### COUNTER-ROTATING TURBINES

While not common in large engines, some small turboshaft engines feature counter-rotating turbine wheels. Counter-rotating turbines are used for their effectiveness in dampening gyroscopic effects and reducing engine vibration, but this design provides no aerodynamic advantage.

## EXHAUST SECTION

The design of the exhaust section a turbojet engine directly affects the amount of thrust developed.

For example, the shape and size of an exhaust section and its components affect the temperature of the air entering the turbine (**turbine inlet temperature**), the mass airflow through the engine, and the velocity and pressure of the exhaust jet.

A typical exhaust section extends from the rear of the turbine section to the point where the exhaust gases leave the engine. An exhaust section is made of several components including the exhaust cone, the exhaust duct—often referred to as the tailpipe, and the exhaust nozzle. [Figure 3-54]

### EXHAUST CONE

A typical exhaust cone assembly consists of an **outer duct** (or **shell**), an **inner cone** (or **tail cone**), three or more radial hollow **struts**, and a group of **tie rods** that assist the struts to center the cone within the duct. The outer duct is usually made of stainless steel and attaches to the rear flange of the turbine case. [Figure 3-55]

The purpose of an exhaust cone assembly is to channel and collect turbine discharge gases into a single jet. Due to the diverging passage between the outer duct and inner cone, gas velocity within the exhaust cone decreases slightly while gas pressure rises. Radial struts between the outer shell and inner cone support the inner cone, and help straighten the swirling exhaust gases that would otherwise exit the turbine at an approximate angle of 45 degrees.

### TAILPIPE

A tailpipe is an extension of the exhaust section that directs exhaust gases safely from the exhaust cone to the exhaust, or jet nozzle. A tailpipe reduces engine operating efficiency due to heat and duct friction losses. A drop in exhaust gas velocity reduces thrust. Tailpipes are used almost exclusively with engines installed within a fuselage, in which case the tailpipe protects the surrounding airframe. Engines installed in a nacelle (or pod) typically do not require a tailpipe, in which case the exhaust nozzle is mounted directly to the exhaust cone assembly.

### EXHAUST NOZZLE

An exhaust, or jet nozzle, provides the exhaust gases with a final boost in velocity. An exhaust nozzle mounts to the rear of a tailpipe, when installed, or the rear flange of the exhaust duct.

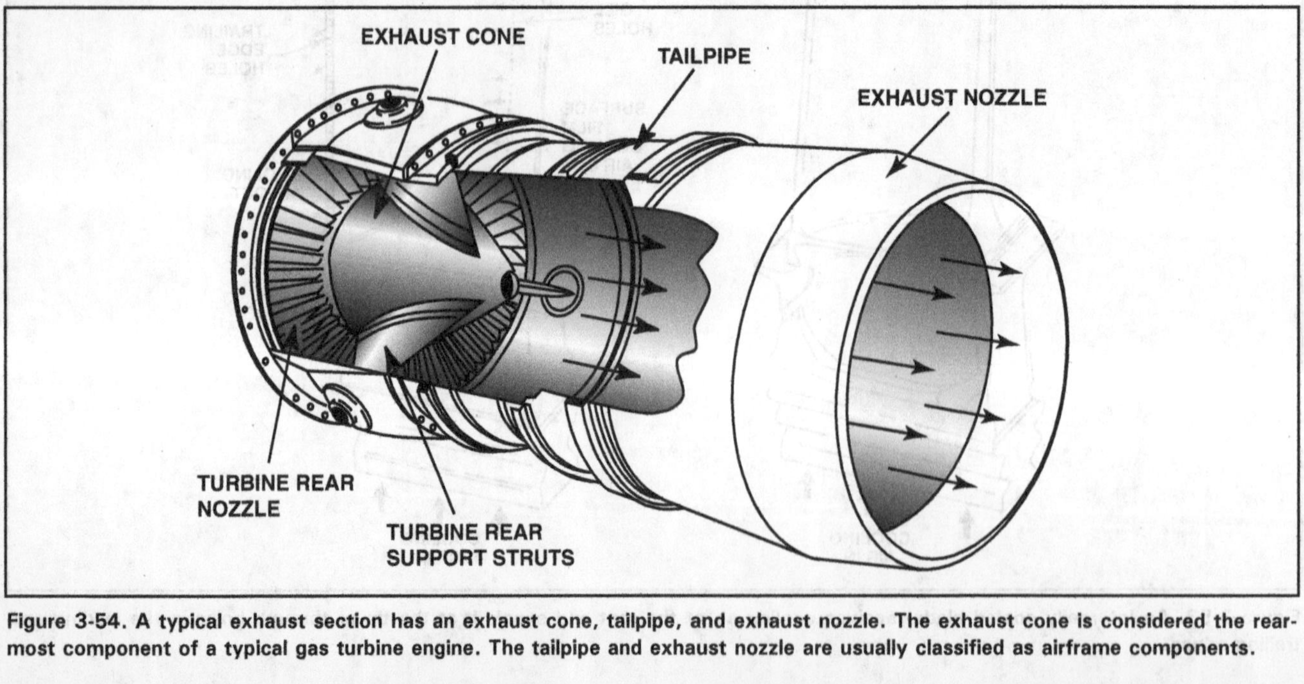


**Figure 3-54. A typical exhaust section has an exhaust cone, tailpipe, and exhaust nozzle. The exhaust cone is considered the rear-most component of a typical gas turbine engine. The tailpipe and exhaust nozzle are usually classified as airframe components.**

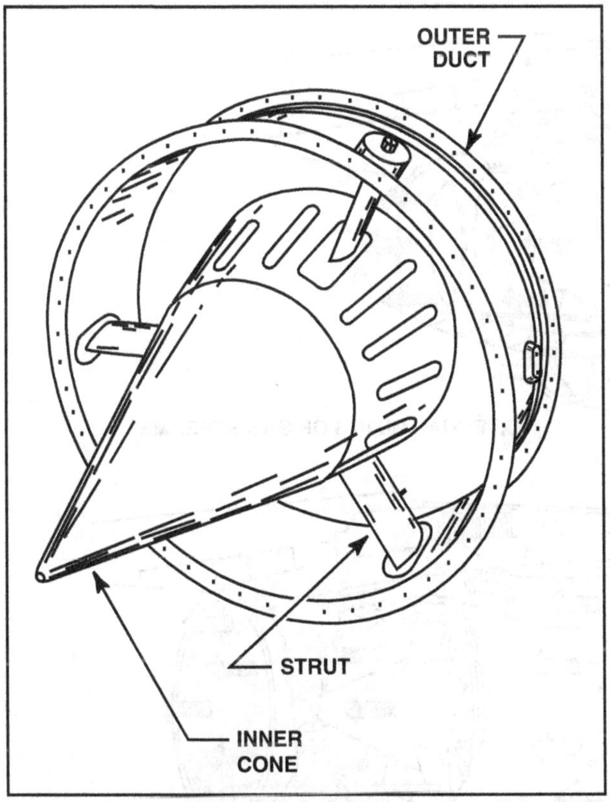


Figure 3-55. The exhaust cone is the rearmost engine component. It straightens and smoothes exhaust gas to extract the greatest possible thrust.

The two types of exhaust nozzle design are the converging design and the converging-diverging design. On a converging exhaust nozzle, the nozzle diameter decreases from front to back. This convergent shape produces a venturi that accelerates the exhaust gases and increases engine thrust.

From front to back, the diameter of a converging-diverging duct decreases and then increases. The converging portion of the exhaust nozzle accelerates the turbine exhaust gases to supersonic speed at the narrowest part of the duct. After the gases are moving at the speed of sound, they are accelerated further in the nozzle's divergent portion and the exhaust gases exit the nozzle well above the speed of sound. For additional information on both convergent and convergent-divergent exhaust nozzles, refer to Chapter 6, Section B.

On fan or bypass engines, two gas streams are vented to the atmosphere. High-temperature gases are discharged by the turbine, while a cool air mass is moved rearward by the fan section. In a low by-pass engine, the flow of cool and hot air is combined in a mixer prior to exiting the engine. High-bypass engines typically exhaust the two streams separately through two coaxial nozzles. However, on some high-bypass engines a common (or integrated) nozzle begins mixing the gases before they exit the nacelle. [Figure 3-56]

The area of an exhaust nozzle opening can be fixed or variable. A variable geometry nozzle is sometimes necessary on engines that use an afterburner. Variable nozzles are typically operated with pneumatic, hydraulic, or electric controls.

## AFTERBURNERS

Afterburners are used to accelerate the exhaust gases to increase thrust. An afterburner is typically installed immediately aft of the last stage turbine and forward of the exhaust nozzle. The components that make up an afterburner include the fuel manifold, an ignition source, and a flame holder. [Figure 3-57]

An afterburner on a gas turbine engine can operate because the gases in the tailpipe still contain a large percentage of oxygen. If you recall, approximately 25 percent of a compressor's discharge air supports combustion, while the remaining 75 percent is used for cooling. After cooling air passes through an engine, a portion is mixed with the exhaust gases at the rear of the turbine section. The tailpipe entrance is fitted with a **fuel manifold** with afterburner nozzles (or **spray-bars**) to inject fuel into the tailpipe. The fuel and air mix, ignite, and burn in the afterburner. The additional heat generated by combustion accelerates the exhaust gases and creates additional thrust.

To ensure thorough fuel-air mixing, a tubular grid or spoke-shaped obstruction, called a **flame holder**, is placed downstream of the fuel nozzles. The flame holder creates turbulence, which causes the approaching gases to swirl and mix thoroughly.

The use of an afterburner dramatically increases the temperature and thrust produced by an engine. Therefore, when an afterburner is being used, the area of an exhaust nozzle must be increased. If not, back pressure would be created at the rear of the turbine, which would increase turbine temperature beyond a safe level. By increasing the size of the exhaust nozzle, exhaust gas temperature can be held to tolerable limits.

Afterburners are primarily used on military aircraft to assist in takeoff or produce rapid climb-out speeds. Afterburners can provide as much as a 100 percent increase in thrust; however, the increase in fuel flow is three to five times higher than normal.

## THRUST REVERSERS

On most turbine engine aircraft, the brakes are unable to adequately slow the aircraft during land-

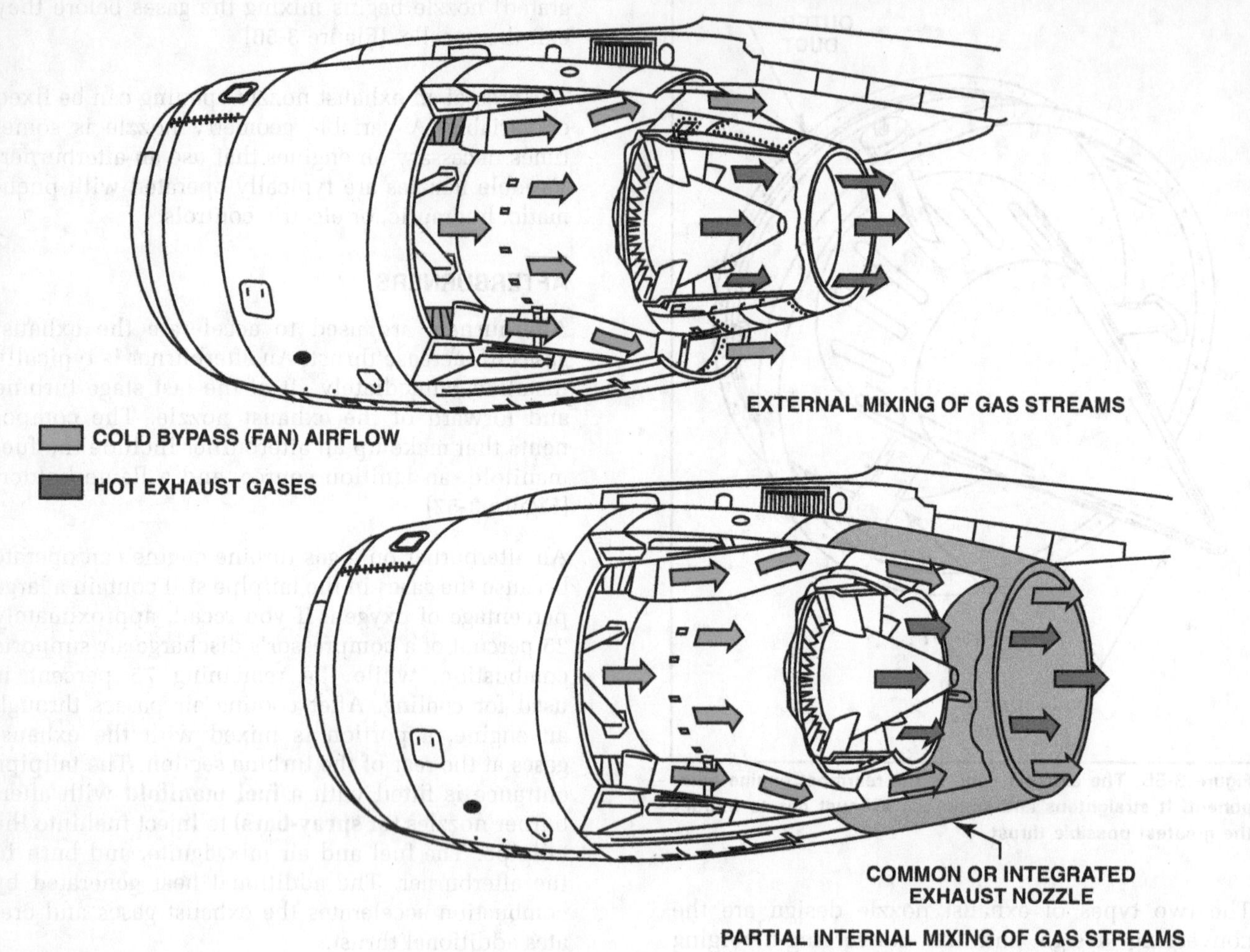


**Figure 3-56. On some high-bypass engines, cold bypass air mixes with hot exhaust gases after they exit the engine. Other high-bypass engines use a common or integrated exhaust nozzle that partially mixes the gas streams internally.**

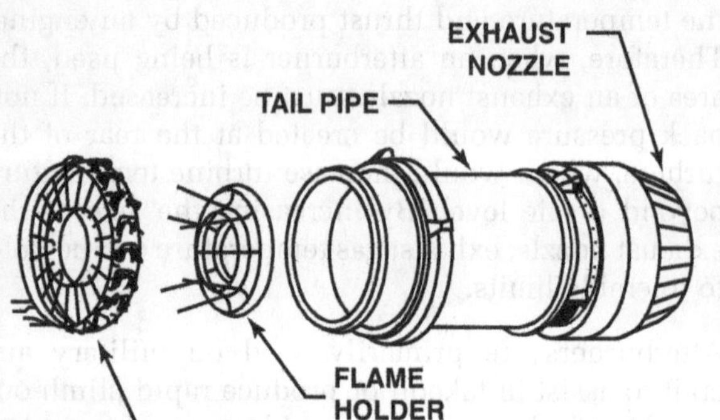


**Figure 3-57. An afterburner increases thrust. The system consists of a fuel manifold, an ignition source, and a flame holder.**

ing rollout. The amount of kinetic energy that must be dissipated is so great that the use of brakes alone would cause significant brake wear. Additionally, the heat buildup in the wheel area generated by braking could lead to a brake fire. Therefore, most turbojet and turbofan powered aircraft are fitted with thrust reversers to assist in braking. Thrust reversers redirect the flow of exhaust gases to provide thrust in the opposite direction and slow forward motion. For further information on the various types of thrust reverser systems, refer to Chapter 6, Section B.

## ACCESSORY SECTION

The accessory section, or **accessory drive gearbox**, of a gas turbine engine is used to drive engine and aircraft accessories including electric generators, hydraulic pumps, fuel pumps, and oil pumps. Secondary functions include acting as an oil reservoir (or sump) and housing the accessory drive and reduction gears.

The location of an accessory drive gearbox is designed to maintain a streamlined engine profile. Accessory drives may be located on the front, midsection, or rear of an engine. Inlet and exhaust locations typically dictate the location of the accessories. Rear-mounted gearboxes typically provide for the narrowest engine diameter and lowest drag configuration. [Figure 3-58]

Typically, the power needed to drive accessories is taken from an engine's main power shaft. Beveled gears drive an accessory shaft to turn the gears in an accessory gearbox. The accessory gearbox provides mounting locations for each accessory. Because turbine engines operate at high speeds, reduction gearing is necessary to drive the accessories at the appropriate speed. In some installations, an **intermediate** or **transfer gearbox** is necessary to obtain the appropriate reduction gearing necessary for the accessories. [Figure 3-59]

The number of accessories on an engine determines the amount of power required to drive the accessory gearbox. For example, the accessory drive system on a large, high-bypass engine can take up to 500 horsepower from the engine.

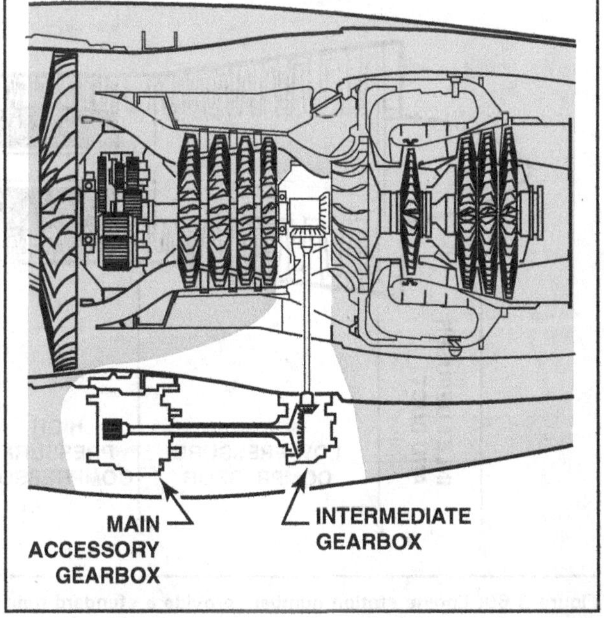


**Figure 3-59. With a typical waist-mounted accessory section, a radial shaft geared to the main engine shaft transfers power to the drive pads through an intermediate gearbox.**

## ENGINE STATION NUMBERING

Engine manufacturers usually assign station numbers at several points along a turbine engine's gas path. These numbered locations are similar to fuselage stations, providing a technician with a quick and accurate way to locate certain areas during maintenance. Station numbers establish the locations for taking pressure and temperature readings. For example, engine pressure ratio, or EPR, compares air pressure at the engine inlet and after the last turbine rotor to determine engine thrust. Standard labels identify the locations for EPR readings because different engines have different types of inlet and exhaust ducts. The engine inlet is station $P_{t2}$, which means pressure total at station 2. Similarly, turbine discharge pressure is taken at station $P_{t7}$. Engine pressure ratio is therefore expressed by the ratio $P_{t7}$:$P_{t2}$. Engine stations are also designated by the label $T_t$, meaning temperature total for engine instruments that require temperature information. For example, engine inlet temperature is taken at station $T_{t2}$. [Figure 3-60]

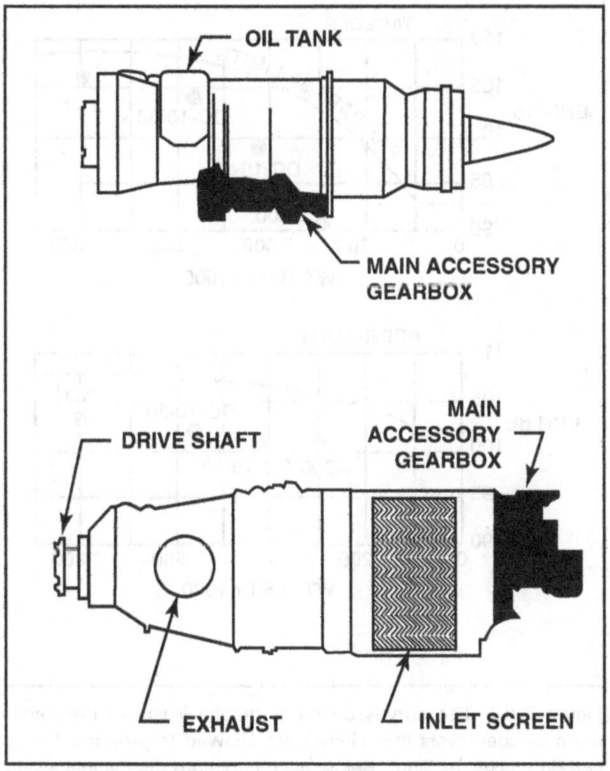


**Figure 3-58. Accessory drives typically blend with the engine profile to minimize drag.**

## NOISE SUPPRESSION

Noise is an unintended byproduct of burning fuel in a jet engine. Noise control around densely populated areas is a significant issue that engine designers and operators work to minimize. Much of the noise produced by a turbine engine results from mixing hot, high-velocity gases and cold, low-velocity air surrounding the engine. The resulting noise includes both low- and high-frequency vibrations; the low frequencies are predominant.

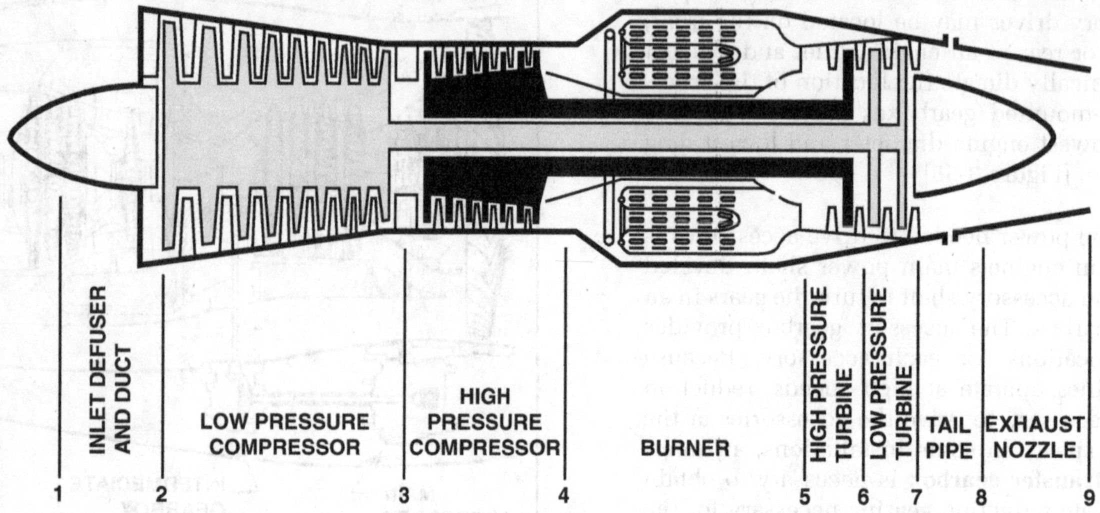


**Figure 3-60. Engine station numbers provide a standard means of identifying points along an engine.**

The increasing use of turbofan engines has significantly reduced noise levels inside the aircraft cabin and on the ground. Turbofan engines seldom require noise suppressors because the hot and cold gas streams are mixed prior to release into the atmosphere, which significantly reduces exhaust noise.

Turbojet engines, especially earlier designs, frequently require additional noise suppression equipment. This equipment typically includes a device to disrupt airflow behind the tail cone, and using new materials for sound insulating. In addition, some airframe components have been redesigned or modified with noise reduction kits to meet new regulations. [Figure 3-61]

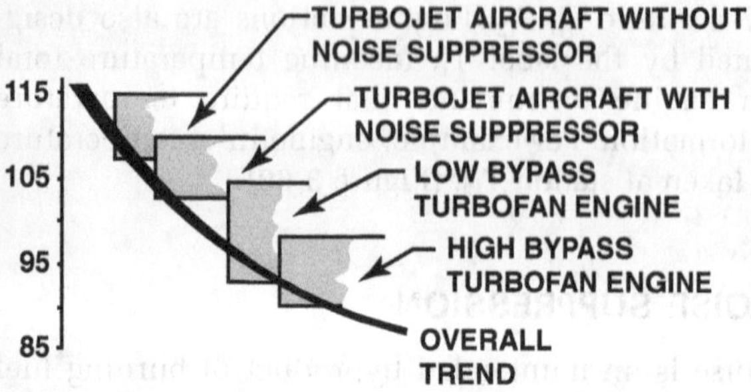


**Figure 3-61. The noise level of early turbojet aircraft without noise suppressors typically exceeded 110 decibels. In comparison, modern high-bypass turbofan engines produce less than 100 decibels of sound.**

To address concerns about noise around airports, the Federal Aviation Administration and other regulatory agencies have established guidelines for aircraft operators that specify maximum noise limits based on aircraft weight. [Figure 3-62]

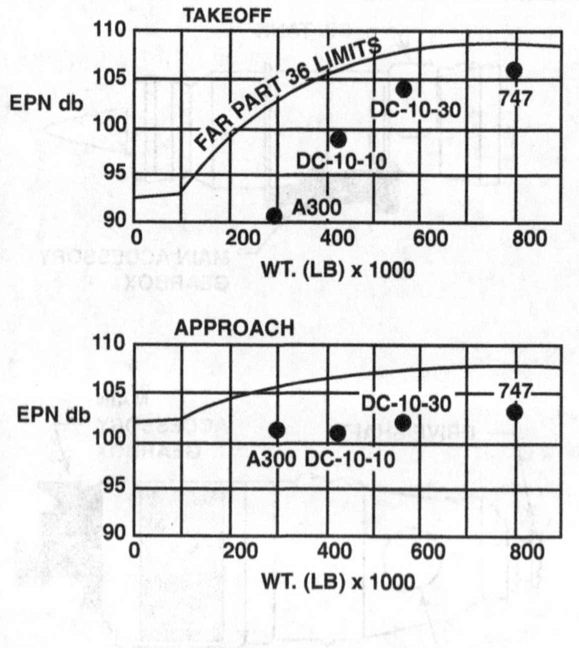


**Figure 3-62. The curves on these graphs illustrate the maximum decibel levels that aircraft are allowed to produce during certain phases of flight. Below each curve are the decibel levels produced by particular models of aircraft.**

## ENGINE MOUNTS

The design and construction of mounts for gas turbine engines is relatively simple. Because gas turbine engines produce little torque, they do not need heavily constructed mounts. The mounts primarily support the engine's weight and transfer engine stresses to the aircraft structure. On a typical wing-mounted turbofan engine, the engine is attached to the aircraft by two to four mounting brackets.

Because of induced propeller loads, a turboprop develops higher torque loads; as a result, engine mounts are proportionally heavier. For similar reasons, turboshaft engines used in helicopters are stronger and equipped with more mount locations. [Figure 3-63]

## BEARINGS

The shaft for the compressor and turbine rotors must be adequately supported. Engine bearings are located along the length of the rotor shaft to support it. The number of bearings is partly determined by the length and weight of the rotor shaft. For example, a split-spool axial compressor with its many rotating components requires more main bearings than a centrifugal compressor.

Generally, ball and roller bearings are used to support the main rotor shaft. Both ball and roller bearing assemblies are encased in strong housings with inner and outer races that provide support and hold lubricating oil. These types of bearings are ideal because they:

- Offer minimal rotational resistance.
- Enable precision alignment of rotating elements.
- Tolerate high momentary overloads.
- Are relatively inexpensive, easily replaced, and simple to cool, lubricate, and maintain.
- Accommodate both radial and axial loads.
- Resist high temperatures.

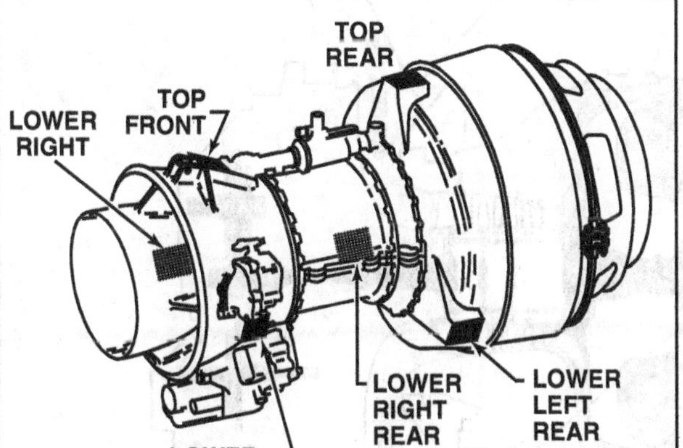


Figure 3-63. Turboshaft engines experience high torque loads and require stronger engine mounts.

The disadvantages of these bearings are vulnerability to damage caused by foreign matter and a tendency to fail without appreciable warning. Proper lubrication and sealing against contaminants is essential for engine reliability. Commonly used types of oil seals are labyrinth, helical thread, and carbon.

A **labyrinth seal** does not press or rub against another surface. Instead, each seal is made of a series of rotating fins that come very close, but do not touch a fixed, abradable race. With this type of seal, air leaks past each fin and air pressure decreases. By the time the air reaches the far side of the seal, its pressure is nearly zero. Therefore, the positive air pressure prevents oil from leaking past the seal. [Figure 3-64]

**Helical seals** are similar to labyrinth seals except that helical seals depend on reverse threading to prevent oil leakage. **Carbon seals** function differently; they are spring-loaded to hold the carbon ring against the rotating shaft, much like carbon brushes in an electric motor.

# TURBOPROP ENGINES

A turboprop engine is a gas turbine engine that rotates a propeller to produce thrust. Turboprops,

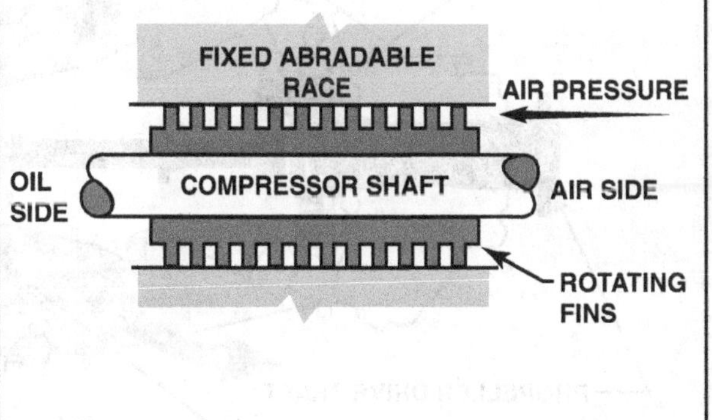


Figure 3-64. The rotating fins of a labyrinth seal do not touch their outer fixed race to create a seal. Instead, air pressure prevents oil from leaking past the seal.

like all gas turbine engines, have a compressor section, combustion section, turbine section, and exhaust section. These sections carry out the same functions as if they were installed in a turbojet engine. However, a turboprop engine has a few significant differences. The turbine in a turboprop engine extracts more energy from exhaust gases than blades found in a turbojet engine. A turboprop uses multiple stage turbines to extract up to 85 percent of an engine's total power to rotate the propeller.

In addition to the turbine used to drive the compressor and accessories, most turboprop engines use a **free turbine** to drive the propeller. The free turbine is independent—that is, it is not mechanically connected with the main turbine. This free (or **power) turbine** is in the exhaust stream, downstream from the main turbine, and drives only the propeller. [Figure 3-65]

Another method to transfer exhaust gas energy to the propeller is through a fixed shaft. In this case, the main turbine has an additional turbine wheel to extract the energy needed to drive a propeller. With a **fixed shaft engine**, the main power shaft goes directly into a reduction gearbox to convert the high-speed, low-torque turbine output into low-speed, high-torque energy to drive the propeller.

To prevent the propeller on a turboprop engine from driving the turbine, a sophisticated propeller control system adjusts propeller pitch to match the engine's output. For example, in normal cruise flight, both the propeller and engine speed remain constant. Therefore, in order to maintain a constant-speed condition, the propeller's blade angle and fuel flow must be adjusted simultaneously; when fuel flow is increased, the propeller blade pitch must also increase.

## TURBOSHAFT ENGINES

Turboshaft engines are gas turbine engines that operate something other than a propeller by delivering power to a shaft. Turboshaft engines are similar to turboprop engines, and in some instances, use the same design. Like turboprops, turboshaft engines use almost all of the energy in the exhaust gases to drive an output shaft. The power can be taken directly from the engine turbine, or the shaft can be driven by a free turbine. Like free turbines in turboprop engines, the free turbine in a turboshaft engine is not mechanically coupled to the engine's main rotor shaft; thus, it can operate at its own speed. Free turbine designs are used extensively in current production model engines. Turboshaft engines are frequently used to power helicopters and auxiliary power units aboard large commercial aircraft.

## AUXILIARY POWER UNITS

Turbine-powered transport aircraft require large amounts of power to start and operate. To meet a demand for ground power when the aircraft engines are not running, most large turbine aircraft are equipped with **auxiliary power units**, or **APUs.** Engine starting and ground air conditioning require a high-pressure, high-volume pneumatic air source that is not always available at remote airports. Additionally, large amounts of electrical power are

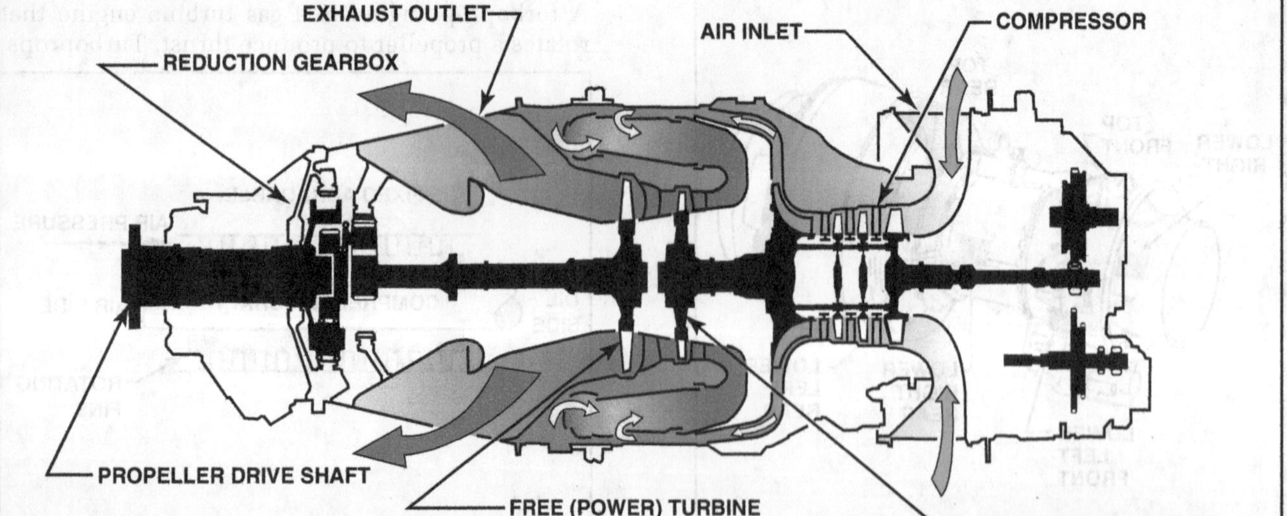


**Figure 3-65. Propellers driven by a free turbine rotate independently of the compressor turbine.**

needed for passenger amenities such as lighting, entertainment, and food preparation.

A typical APU consists of a small turbine powerplant driving an electric generator identical to those mounted on the aircraft's engines. Additionally, an APU compressor supplies bleed air to a load compressor for heating, cooling, anti-ice, and engine starting. As with other gas turbine engines, the bleed air load imparted on an APU is greater than any other load.

An APU is typically started using its own electric starter motor and aircraft battery power. With fuel supplied from one of the aircraft's main fuel tanks, an APU can start up, provide electric power, heat or cool the cabin, and start the main engines without the need for a ground power source.

After an APU starts, it runs at its rated speed regardless of the electrical and pneumatic loads imposed. To accomplish this, its fuel control unit automatically adjusts the fuel flow. For example, if APU bleed air is used to start an aircraft engine, the APU's fuel control unit automatically meters additional fuel to satisfy the load increase, which keeps the APU at its rated speed. A heavily loaded APU (running near its maximum exhaust gas temperature) is protected by a load control valve that modulates the pneumatic load to maintain a safe operating temperature. As the APU temperature approaches a critical level, the pneumatic load is reduced automatically to prevent overheating.

To prevent APU damage, most manufacturers specify a cool-down period before the APU is shut down. This minimizes the possibility of thermal shock that can occur when a heavily loaded, hot APU engine is abruptly shut down. The cool-down procedure typically requires closing the bleed valve until the exhaust gas temperature (EGT) stabilizes. A typical cool-down period is three minutes. [Figure 3-66]

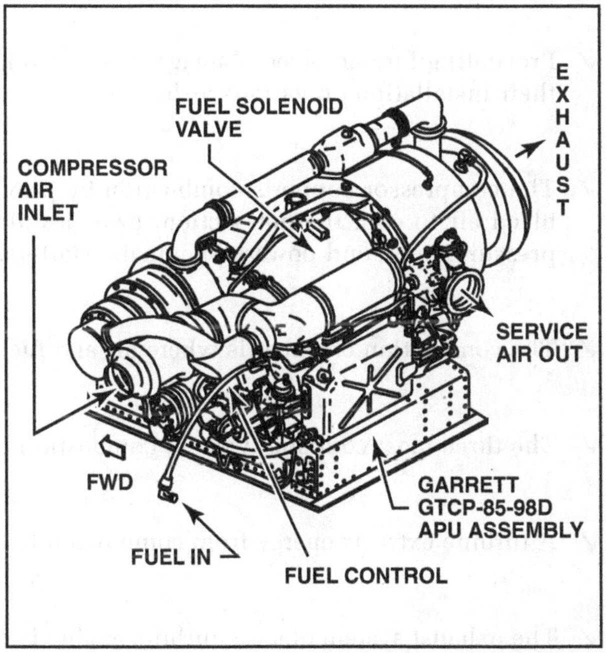


**Figure 3-66. The Garrett GTCP-85-98D APU assembly provides on-board aircraft electrical and pneumatic power for ground operations.**

# SUMMARY CHECKLIST

✓ Five varieties of gas turbine engines are turbojets, turboprops, turboshafts, turbofans, and unducted fans.

✓ The seven sections of a gas turbine engine are the air inlet duct, compressor section, combustion section, turbine section, exhaust section, accessory section, and auxiliary systems (for example, start, lubrication, fuel, anti-ice, cooling, and pressurization).

✓ Preventing foreign object damage (FOD) is a key consideration in the design of gas turbine engines and their installation on various airframes.

✓ The compressor supports combustion by providing the air necessary to produce thrust; it also supplies bleed air to cool the hot section, provides airframe anti-icing, provides fuel anti-icing, provides cabin pressurization, and powers pneumatic starters.

✓ The combustion chamber is where air and fuel are mixed and ignited.

✓ The three most common types of combustion chambers are multiple-can, annular, and can-annular.

✓ A turbine extracts energy from combustion to drive the compressor and accessories.

✓ The exhaust system of a gas turbine engine is designed to move the engine air mass from the turbine section out of the engine and away from the aircraft structure.

✓ An exhaust nozzle provides a final boost in velocity to the exiting gasses.

✓ Standard locations on an engine are identified by the manufacturer through a system of engine stations.

✓ In addition to providing thrust for an aircraft, gas turbine engines can be installed on an airframe as an auxiliary power unit (APU) to provide a power source to start the main engines and operate aircraft systems on the ground.

# KEY TERMS

aeolipile
solid-propellant rockets
liquid-fuel rocket
athodyd
aero-thermodynamic-duct
engine pressure ratio
EPR
shaft horsepower
forward-fan engines
aft-fan engines
thrust ratio
bypass ratio
ducted fan
fan pressure ratio
aspect ratio
ultra-high bypass propfan
UHB propfan
unducted fan engines

UDF engines
ducted ultra-high bypass engines
hot section
cold section
ram recovery
pressure recovery
ram effect
divergent inlet
convergent-divergent inlet
vortex dissipater
vortex destroyer
blow-away jet
compressor pressure ratio
radial outflow compressor
impeller
rotor
single-stage compressors
double-stage compressors
double-sided impeller
double-entry impeller
plenum chamber
auxiliary air-intake doors
blow-in doors
diffuser
compressor manifold
outlet ducts
outlet elbows
combustion chamber inlet ducts
turning vanes
cascade vanes
rotor
stator
pressure stage
root
bulb
fir tree
dovetail
shroud
flat machine tips
profile tips
end bend
inlet guide vanes
outlet vane assembly
single-spool compressor
dual-spool compressor
twin-spool compressor
triple-spool compressor
low pressure compressor
low speed compressor
$N_1$ compressor
intermediate compressor
$N_2$ compressor
high-pressure compressor
$N_3$ compressor
compressor stall
transient compressor stall
hung stall
variable inlet guides
bleed air
compressor bleed air
bleed port
combustion chamber
combustor
high-energy capacitor discharge system
combustion air
swirl vanes
flameout
flame propagation tubes
reverse flow
lean die-out
rich blowout
turbine
turbine nozzle
turbine guide vanes
nozzle diaphragm
turbine wheel
turbine disk
creep
fir tree slots
impulse blades
reaction turbine blades
impulse-reaction turbine blades
convection cooling
film cooling
transpiration cooling
turbine inlet temperature
outer duct
shell
inner cone
tail cone
struts
tie rods
fuel manifold
spray-bars
flame holder
accessory drive gearbox
intermediate gearbox
transfer gearbox
labyrinth seal
helical seals
carbon seals
free turbine
power turbine
fixed shaft engine
auxiliary power units
APU
accessory drive gearbox

# QUESTIONS

1. The first flight by a jet propelled aircraft took place in ______ (what year).

2. Jet propulsion is a practical application of Newton's ______ (first, second, or third) law of motion.

3. The four types of gas turbine engines are the ______, ______, ______, and the ______.

4 Both turboprop and turboshaft engines must use a ______ ______ between the engine and the propellers/ rotors.

5. A gas turbine engine that delivers power through a shaft to operate something other than a propeller is referred to as a ____________ engine.

6 A high bypass ratio turbofan engine has a bypass ratio of ______ to 1 or greater.

7. Engines that use a separate turbine that is not mechanically connected to a compressor to drive a propeller are called ______ ______ engines.

8. Turbofans are generally divided into what three classifications?

   a. ______

   b. ______

   c. ______

9. With modern high bypass engines, most of the engineís thrust is produced by the ______ rather than from the ______ exhaust ______.

10. Bypass ratios of 30:1 are obtainable by what is called an ______ High Bypass (UHB) engine.

11. The inlet duct of a turbine engine is normally considered to be a part of the ______ (airframe or engine).

12. When subsonic air passes through a section of a duct that has a divergent shape, its velocity will ____________ (increase or decrease).

13. Subsonic inlet ducts are usually of a fixed geometry and ____________ (converging or diverging) in shape.

14. Supersonic aircraft typically utilize a ____________-____________ inlet duct.

15. What is the primary function of the compressor section of a gas-turbine engine?

16. The two basic types of compressors used on turbine engines are:

   a. ____________

   b. ____________

17. The three main components of a centrifugal compressor are:

    a. _______________

    b. _______________

    c. _______________

18. More than _______ (what number) stages of compression is not practical using a centrifugal compressor.

19. Modern centrifugal compressors can obtain a compression ratio as high as _______:1.

20. The two main elements of an axial flow compressor are:

    a. _______________

    b. _______________

21. Axial flow compressors have a pressure rise per stage of approximately _______:1.

22. The rotating elements of an axial flow compressor are referred to as _______ (blades or vanes).

23. The stationary elements of an axial flow compressor are referred to as _______ (blades or vanes).

24. Multi-spool axial flow compressors have the advantages of:

    a. _______________

    b. _______________

    c. _______________

    d. _______________

25. Compressor blades which have a reduced thickness at the tips are called _______________ tips.

26. _______________ vane segments may be used to minimize vibration.

27. On a multi-spool engine, the low-pressure compressor ($N_1$) will _______________ (speed up or slow down) with an increase in altitude.

28. What two factors determine the angle of attack of a compressor blade?

    a. _______________

    b. _______________

29. Compressor stalls may cause the air flowing in the compressor to _______________, or stagnate. In some cases the air may reverse direction.

30. Design factors which contribute to the prevention of compressor stalls include:

    a. _______________

    b. _______________

    c. _______________

31. The special set of vanes located at the discharge end of the compressor form the outlet vane assembly. The purpose of this assembly is to help straighten the airflow and eliminate any ____________.

32. To take advantage of the good points of both the centrifugal flow and axial flow compressors, some engines may use a ____________ compressor.

33. High temperature, high pressure air taken from the compressor for various purposes is known as ______ air.

34. Some current applications of bleed air are:

a. ____________

b. ____________

c. ____________

d. ____________

e. ____________

35. The section of a turbine engine directly behind the compressor is known as the ____________.

36. The pressure in the ______ section of a gas turbine engine is the highest of any section in the engine.

37. As primary air flow enters a combustor, it passes through a set of ______ ______, which give the air a radial motion.

38. The three types of combustion chambers that may be found in turbine engines are:

a. ____________

b. ____________

c. ____________

39. Annular combustors which reverse the direction of the airflow are ____________ combustors.

40. The two types of flameout that can occur in a gas turbine engine are refered to as:

a. ____________

b. ____________

41. Approximately ______ (what percentage) of the total pressure energy from the exhaust gasses is absorbed by the turbine section is used to turn the compressor and drive the accessories.

42. What are the two functions of the turbine nozzle?

a. ____________

b. ____________

43. When turbine blades are installed on a turbine disk, the unit is known as a turbine ______.

44. The most common method of attaching turbine blades to the disk is the ______ ______ method.

45. The three classifications used to describe turbine blades are:

 a. ______________

 b. ______________

 c. ______________

46. Turbine blades may be open or ______ at their tips.

47. The primary air, or the air that enters into the combustion process, amounts to about ______ percent of the total air that flows through a gas turbine engine.

48. The jet nozzle imparts a final ______________ (increase or decrease) in the velocity to the gases.

49. Afterburning can produce as much as a 100% increase in thrust, with fuel flows increasing by ______ to ______ times.

50. Turbofan engines ______ (often or seldom) require noise suppression.

51. Gas turbine engine rotors are usually supported by either ______ or ______ (what type) bearings.

52. The turbine of a turboprop engine extracts up to ______ percent of the engines total power output to drive the propeller.

# SECTION B

## OPERATING PRINCIPLES

### ENERGY TRANSFORMATION

A gas turbine engine is a form of **heat engine** that converts the chemical energy of fuel into heat energy. Heat energy causes an increase in gas pressure that is converted into kinetic energy in the form of a high velocity stream of air. The kinetic energy is transformed to mechanical energy as the gases rotate a series of turbine wheels to drive a compressor and accessories. In the case of turboprop or turboshaft engines, the expanding gases can also drive a second power turbine to drive a propeller or gearbox.

### ENERGY TRANSFORMATION CYCLE

The energy transformation cycle in a gas turbine engine is known as the **Brayton cycle** (or **constant pressure cycle**). Similar to the four-stroke Otto cycle, the Brayton cycle has intake, compression, combustion, and exhaust events. However, unlike a piston engine, all four events occur simultaneously and continuously in a gas turbine engine. A gas turbine engine is able to produce power continuously. To support the continuous production of power, a gas turbine engine must burn a great deal of fuel. [Figure 3-67]

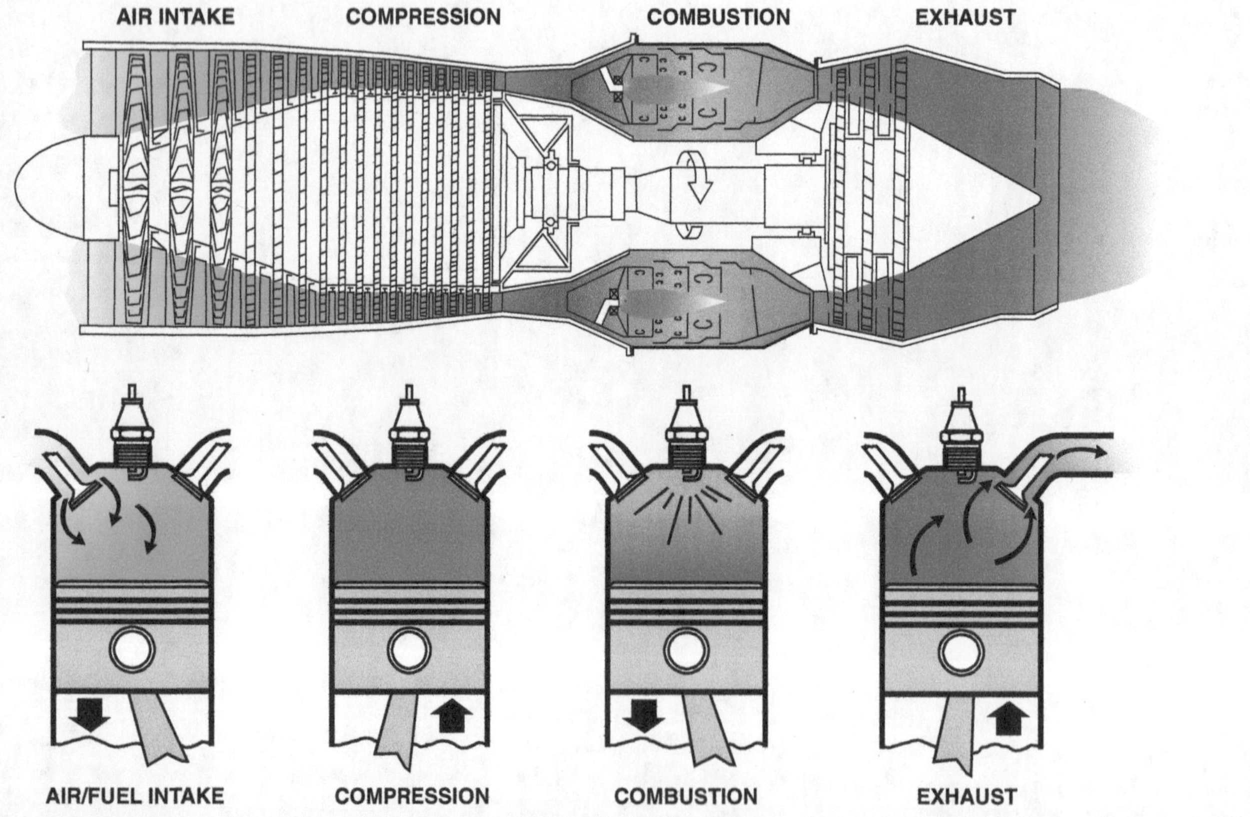


**Figure 3-67. In a gas turbine engine, air is drawn in through an air inlet, compressed in the compressor, mixed with fuel and ignited in the combustors, and exhausted through the turbines and exhaust nozzle. A gas turbine engine performs the same functions as a cylinder and piston in a reciprocating engine. In a turbine engine, these four events happen continuously.**

The continuous intake event in a gas turbine engine draws ambient air into the engine through an inlet duct to the first compressor stage. Each compressor stage increases static air pressure. In the combustor, fuel is sprayed into the incoming airflow and ignited, resulting in continuous combustion. The resulting release of heat energy increases the volume of the air while maintaining a relatively constant pressure. When exhaust air exits the combustion chamber, it passes through the turbine where static air pressure drops and air volume continues to increase. Because the flow of expanding gases is relatively unobstructed, the velocity increases dramatically. [Figure 3-68]

## PRODUCING THRUST

Recall that a gas turbine engine produces thrust based on Newton's third law of motion: for every action, there is an equal and opposite reaction. In a turbojet engine, the acceleration of a mass of air by the engine is the action, and forward movement is the reaction.

### VELOCITY AND PRESSURE

As air passes through a gas turbine engine, its velocity and pressure change to produce thrust. For example, in the compressor, static air pressure increases while velocity remains nearly constant. After combustion, gas velocity must be increased again to rotate the turbine. The most common way to induce a velocity or pressure change is an application of Bernoulli's principle. **Bernoulli's principle** states that when a fluid or gas is supplied at a constant flow rate through a duct, the sum of the potential (or pressure) and kinetic (or velocity) energy is constant. Simply stated, as air velocity increases, air pressure decreases and as air velocity decreases, air pressure increases.

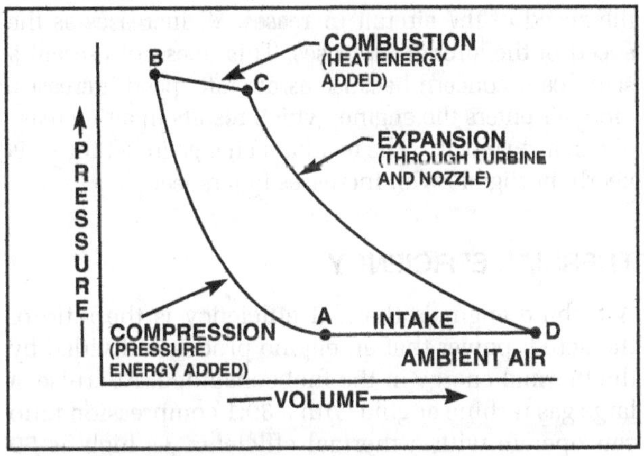


**Figure 3-68. This chart illustrates the changes in pressure and volume during engine operation. Point A represents the condition of the air just before it enters the compressor. After it enters the compressor, its pressure increases and its volume decreases. Point B represents the pressure and volume of the air as it leaves the compressor. At point C, heat energy expands the volume of the air mass with little or no change in pressure. After it is heated, the air expands and loses pressure as it flows through the turbine section to point D.**

As an example of Bernoulli's principle, consider a quantity of air flowing through a converging duct. As the duct decreases in diameter, the air must accelerate if it is to flow through the smaller opening. This increases the kinetic energy of the air. Because energy cannot be created or destroyed, the air's potential energy (pressure) decreases. Likewise, if a quantity of air passes through a diverging duct, the air's potential energy (pressure) increases because its kinetic energy (velocity) decreases.

Remember that, in an air mass, when one form of energy is converted to another, the temperature of the air mass changes. When air pressure decreases, air temperature also decreases. [Figure 3-69]

### THRUST CALCULATIONS

A jet engine produces thrust by accelerating an air mass to a velocity higher than the incoming air. The thrust becomes the propelling force to move the aircraft. Newton's second law of motion states that force is proportional to the product of mass

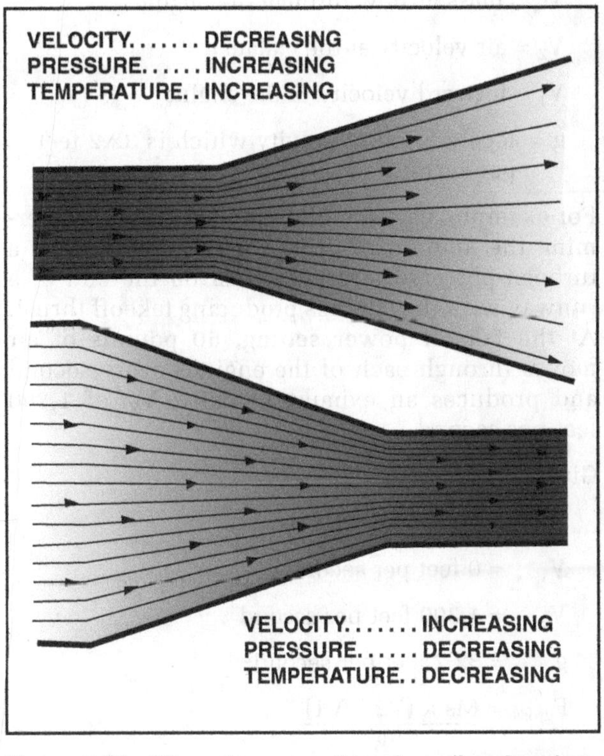


**Figure 3-69. When air passes through a diverging duct, air velocity decreases while air pressure and temperature increase. When air passes through a converging duct, air velocity increases while air pressure and temperature decrease.**

times acceleration. Furthermore, the acceleration produced when a force acts on a mass is directly proportional to the force and is inversely proportional to the mass. This relationship is expressed by the formula:

$F = M \times A$

Where:

F = force

M = mass

A = acceleration

To calculate the acceleration of an air mass through a gas turbine engine, you must determine the difference between the speed of the jet exhaust and that of the intake air. After you calculate acceleration, you must compare it to a constant. The most widely used constant when discussing acceleration is the gravitational constant of 32.2 feet per second squared. After you incorporate the gravitational constant, you use the following formula to calculate the force required to accelerate a given mass of air:

$$F = \frac{Ms\ (V2 - V1)}{g}$$

Where:

F = engine thrust in pounds

$M_s$ = mass airflow through the engine

$V_2$ = air velocity at the exhaust

$V_1$ = forward velocity of the engine

g = acceleration of gravity which is 32.2 feet per second$^2$

For example, use the following variables to determine the amount of **gross thrust** produced by a turbojet-powered aircraft at rest on the end of a runway with the engines producing takeoff thrust. At the takeoff power setting, 50 pounds of air moves through each of the engines every second and produces an exhaust velocity, $V_2$, of 1,300 feet per second.

Given:

$M_s$ = 50 pounds per second

$V_1$ = 0 feet per second

$V_2$ = 1,300 feet per second

g = 32.2 feet per second$^2$

$$F_{gross} = \frac{Ms \times (V2 - V1)}{g}$$

$$= \frac{50 \text{ lbs./sec.} \times (1{,}300 \text{ ft./sec.} - 0)}{32.2 \text{ ft./sec.}^2}$$

$$= \frac{65{,}000 \text{ lb.-ft./sec.2}}{32.2 \text{ ft./sec.2}}$$

$$= 2{,}018.6 \text{ pounds}$$

In this example, one engine produces 2,018.6 pounds of gross thrust. However, during flight, the engine will be moving forward, greatly reducing the velocity change across the engine. Consider the same aircraft in the previous example, but now flying at 500 miles per hour (734 feet per second). You can use the basic formula to calculate its net thrust as follows:

Given:

$M_s$ = 50 pounds per second

$V_2$ = 1,300 feet per second

$V_1$ = 734 feet per second

$$F_{net} = \frac{Ms \times (V2 - V1)}{g}$$

$$= \frac{50 \times (1{,}300 - 734)}{32.2 \text{ ft./sec.}^2}$$

$$= \frac{50 \times 566}{32.2 \text{ ft./sec.}^2}$$

$$= 878.9 \text{ pounds net thrust}$$

The formula illustrates that the net thrust produced by a gas turbine engine can be increased by two methods—either by increasing the mass flow of air through the engine or by increasing exhaust velocity.

If the velocity of a turbojet engine remains constant with respect to the aircraft, exhaust thrust decreases when the speed of the aircraft increases. $V_1$ increases as the speed of the aircraft increases. This does not present a significant concern because as aircraft speed increases, more air enters the engine, which results in an increase of exhaust velocity. The resultant change in net thrust is nearly negligible with increases in airspeed.

## THERMAL EFFICIENCY

A turbine engine's thermal efficiency is the ratio of the actual power that an engine produces divided by the thermal energy in the fuel consumed. At cruise, a large gas turbine engine with a 30:1 compression ratio can operate with a thermal efficiency as high as 50 percent. In comparison, as discussed in Chapter 1, the thermal efficiency of a typical reciprocating engine is between 30 and 40 percent.

Three primary factors determine the thermal efficiency of a gas turbine engine: turbine inlet temperature, compression ratio, and compressor and turbine component efficiencies.

As described earlier, the higher that a gas turbine engine raises the temperature of the incoming air, the more thrust it can produce. The primary limiting factor to increasing the temperature of the air is the amount of heat the turbine section can withstand. Therefore, if the turbine inlet temperature limits on a given engine can be increased, higher thermal efficiencies will result. [Figure 3-70]

Furthermore, the more a gas turbine engine compresses incoming air, the more thrust an engine can produce. Engines with higher compression ratios force more air into the engine, which enables more heat energy from the burning fuel to be transferred to the internal airflow. An increase in the amount of heat energy transferred from the fuel to the air improves an engine's thermal efficiency.

High compressor and turbine efficiencies in a gas turbine engine promote higher thermal efficiencies. Compressor and turbine efficiency directly affect the compression ratio of a given engine, which directly affects thermal efficiency. [Figure 3-71]

## FACTORS THAT AFFECT THRUST

The amount of thrust that a given engine can produce is affected by a number of environmental, design, and operational factors. For example, temperature, altitude, and airspeed directly affect inlet air density, and, consequently, thrust. The combination of these three variables is sometimes represented by a single variable, called **stagnation density**. Operating speed and the efficiency of the fan design are additional factors that contribute directly to the amount of thrust an engine produces.

### TEMPERATURE

The air mass flowing through a turbine engine is the working fluid that an engine uses to produce thrust. The denser the air passing through an engine, the more thrust the engine can produce. Air density is inversely related to temperature. In other words, as outside air temperature (OAT) increases, air density decreases. Anytime the density of the air entering a gas turbine engine decreases, engine thrust also decreases. Conversely, thrust output improves with a reduction in outside air temperature. Engine manufacturers base their thrust calculations on a standard temperature of 59 degrees Fahrenheit or 15 degrees Celsius. This provides a reference point to use when calculating thrust and compensating for temperature variations. In the field, however, all performance calculations are adjusted for nonstandard temperatures. [Figure 3-72]

To counteract the detrimental effects of hot weather on thrust, some early engine designs included a thrust augmentation system. In a water injection **thrust augmentation** system, water, or a mixture of water and alcohol, is injected directly into the compressor inlet or into the combustion chamber.

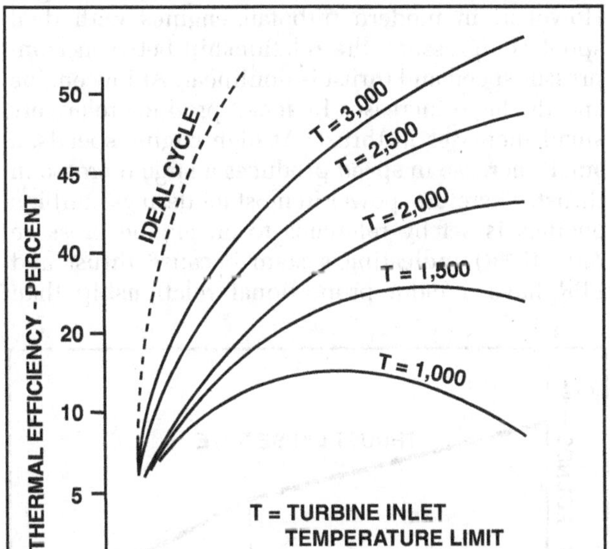


**Figure 3-70. Turbine inlet temperature (TIT) readings between 2,500 and 3,000 degrees Fahrenheit with compression ratios near 32:1 provide thermal efficiencies of 50 percent or better.**

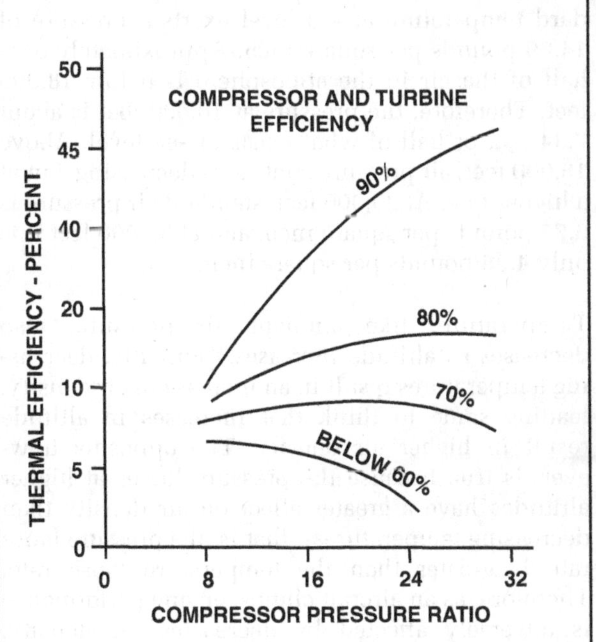


**Figure 3-71. Compressor and turbine efficiency near 90 percent is necessary to reach thermal efficiencies above 20 percent.**

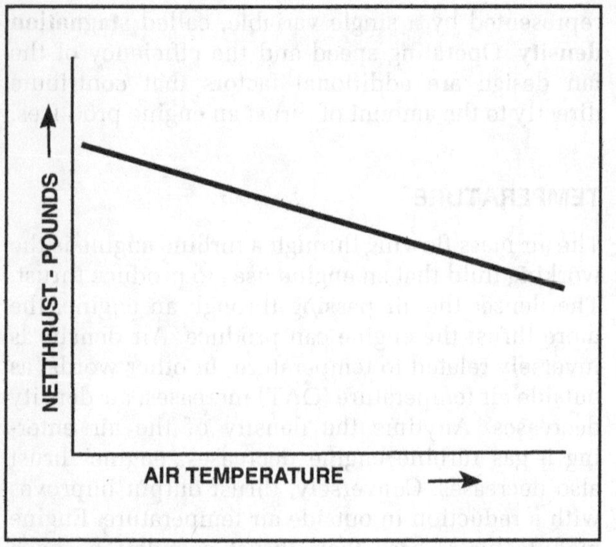


**Figure 3-72. Air density decreases as temperature rises; the lower the density of the air, the less thrust an engine can produce.**

Not only does **Water injection** cool the air mass to enable more fuel to be burned without exceeding turbine inlet temperature limits but the additional water molecules also increase the density of the air mass. Chapter 7 provides more information about water injection systems.

## ALTITUDE

As altitude increases, air pressure drops. Air at standard temperature at sea level exerts a pressure of 14.69 pounds per square inch. Approximately one-half of the air in the atmosphere is below 18,000 feet. Therefore, the pressure at 18,000 feet is about 7.34 psi, or half of what exists at sea level. Above 18,000 feet, air pressure continues decreasing, but at a higher rate. At 20,000 feet, standard air pressure is 6.75 pounds per square inch, and at 30,000 feet it is only 4.36 pounds per square inch.

Temperature, like ambient air pressure, also decreases as altitude increases. Normally, decreasing temperatures result in an increase in air density, leading some to think that increases in altitude result in higher air density. The opposite, however, is true because the pressure losses at higher altitudes have a greater effect on air density than decreasing temperatures—that is, the pressure lapse rate is greater than the temperature lapse rate. Therefore, as an aircraft climbs, engine performance is adversely affected by decreasing air density, despite the relatively cooler air.

At approximately 36,000 feet, air temperature stabilizes at –69.7 degrees Fahrenheit and remains at that temperature up to approximately 80,000 feet. This layer in the atmosphere divides the troposphere from the stratosphere and is called the tropopause. Between these altitudes, the air density no longer increases due to the decreasing temperatures. As a result, as altitude increases above 36,000 feet, air density decreases quite rapidly. Because of this, long-range jet aircraft are often flown at an optimal altitude of 36,000 feet. Below this altitude, dense air creates more aerodynamic drag and above this altitude, the rapidly dropping density decreases engine thrust output. [Figure 3-73]

## AIRSPEED

As previously noted, when forward airspeed increases, the air mass acceleration in the engine decreases with the result that less thrust is produced. However, as the aircraft speeds up, more air is forced into the engine. This is known as **ram effect** and results in an increase in air pressure in an engine, producing more thrust. Therefore, increasing aircraft speed causes two opposing results; a decrease in thrust from the reduction in air mass acceleration and an increase in thrust from ram effect. The net effect on thrust is determined by subtracting the thrust lost from thrust realized. This result is referred to as ram recovery. [Figure 3-74]

## ENGINE SPEED

Early turbojet engines had a relatively linear relationship between compressor speed and thrust. Because of this; engine power output on these engines was set using a tachometer (or r.p.m. gauge). However, in modern turbofan engines with dual spool compressors, the relationship between compressor speed and thrust is nonlinear. At low engine speeds, large increases in speed produce relatively small increases in thrust. At high engine speeds, a small increase in speed produces a large increase in thrust. Therefore, power in most modern gas turbine engines is set by reference to an engine pressure ratio (EPR) indicating system because thrust and EPR have a more proportional relationship than

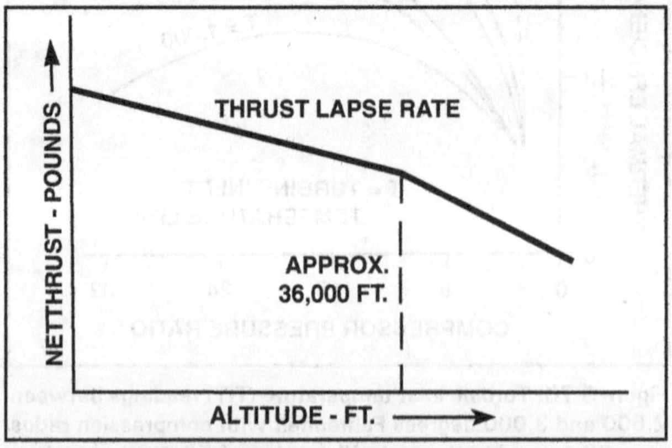


**Figure 3-73. Air density decreases with altitude; as an aircraft climbs, engine thrust decreases.**

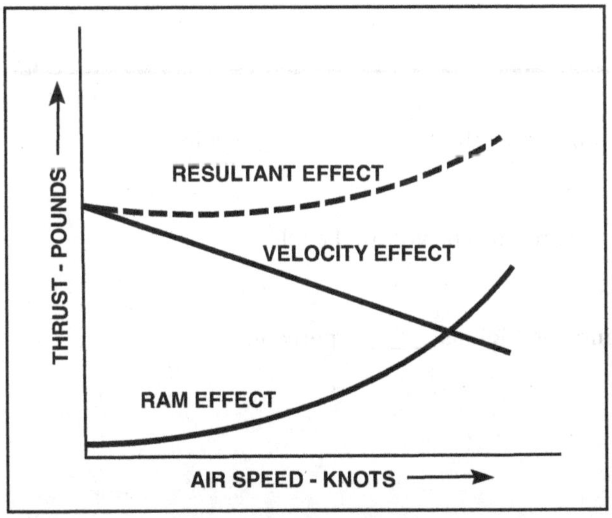


**Figure 3-74. As airspeed increases, the amount of air that an engine can accelerate decreases. As airspeed increases, ram effect increases. The resultant effect, called ram recovery, is a slight increase in engine thrust.**

thrust and engine speed.

Compressor aerodynamics limit engine speed because compressor efficiency begins to drop when blade tips reach the speed of sound. Therefore, efficient compressor design requires engine operation at a speed that does not let the blades reach supersonic speeds and produce disruptive shockwaves. The longer a compressor blade is, the higher the tip rotational speed is for a given speed. This explains why most large-diameter compressors turn at relatively slow rotational speeds. In contrast, small diameter turbine engines can rotate at compressor speeds in excess of 50,000 r.p.m.

### FAN EFFICIENCY

Turbofan engines have replaced turbojet engines on most transport and business jet aircraft. The turbofan engine design is quieter and more fuel efficient. For example, given a turbojet and a turbofan engine with the same rated thrust, the turbofan engine will burn less fuel because of the greater propulsive efficiency of the fan. Fan efficiency directly affects the thrust that an engine can produce.

# SUMMARY CHECKLIST

✓ The energy transformation cycle of a gas turbine engine is known as the Brayton cycle (or constant pressure cycle).

✓ In the Brayton cycle, intake, compression, combustion, and exhaust occur simultaneously and continuously.

# KEY TERMS

heat engine
Brayton cycle
constant pressure cycle
Bernoulli's principle
gross thrust
stagnation density
thrust augmentation
water injection
ram effect

# QUESTIONS

1. The operating cycle of events used by turbine engines is known as the _______________-cycle.

2. The Brayton cycle is known as a constant _______________ (pressure or volume) cycle.

3. A large turbine engine can operate with a thermal efficiency as high as _______ percent.

4. Warm air is _______ (more or less) dense than cool air.

5. As the temperature of the air at the intake of a turbine engine increases, the amount of thrust produced will _______________ (increase or decrease).

6. To counteract the effects of high intake temperatures, some engines use a _______________ thrust augmentation system.

7. Net thrust of a turbine engine will _______________ (increase or decrease) with an increase in altitude.

8. The net effect of airspeed on thrust is that the thrust _______ (will or will not) increase as airspeed increases.

9. The speed at which the ram air pressure rise cancels the pressure drop inside the inlet duct is known as the _______ _______________ point.

10. In most modern engines, power is set using the _______ indicator.

# TURBINE ENGINE OPERATION, INSTRUMENTS, MAINTENANCE, AND OVERHAUL

CHAPTER 4

## INTRODUCTION

As a powerplant technician, you are expected to operate, maintain, and overhaul turbine engines. To adequately perform these tasks, you must be able to distinguish between normal and deteriorating engine performance. Additionally, you must acquire knowledge and experience to effectively troubleshoot and repair turbine engines. The following discussion provides information to help develop your understanding of turbine engine operation, maintenance, and overhaul procedures.

# SECTION A

## ENGINE OPERATION, INSTRUMENTS, AND MAINTENANCE

### OPERATION

An aviation maintenance technician should be thoroughly familiar with the procedures necessary to operate a gas turbine engine. This includes understanding the engine instrumentation, ground run procedures, and safety items associated with starting and running a turbine aircraft engine. For any aircraft that you are required to run, first familiarize yourself with the location and movement of the engine controls. [Figure 4-1]

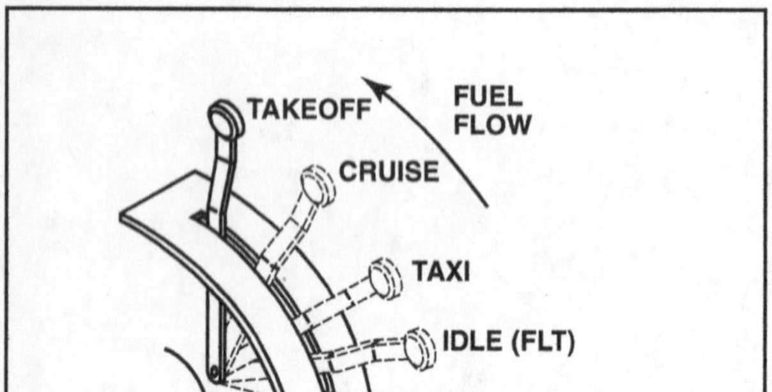


**Figure 4-1. Most turbojet and turbofan engines have a single power lever that controls fuel and engine speed. Most turboprop engines employ a power lever for engine speed control, a condition lever for fuel cutoff, and a propeller control to change propeller blade pitch.**

In addition to the engine controls, locate all of the engine instruments. Be sure to read all placards and other markings on or near the instruments. The engine instruments display important engine operating information that you must monitor during an engine run. It is critical that you are able to interpret instrument readings and avoid engine damage during ground operations.

### ENGINE INSTRUMENTATION

Instruments that indicate oil pressure, oil temperature, engine speed, exhaust gas temperature, and fuel flow are common to both turbine and reciprocating engines. However, gas turbine engines include a few unique instruments. These instruments display engine performance data including engine pressure ratio, turbine discharge pressure, and torque. Most gas turbine engines have multiple temperature sensing instruments to provide temperature readings in and around the turbine section. Some of the common temperature indications include turbine inlet temperature (TIT), turbine gas temperature (TGT), interstage turbine temperature (ITT), and turbine outlet temperature (TOT). As the operator and troubleshooter of a turbine engine, you must understand the operation of all turbine engine instruments to determine the engine's level of performance.

### COMPRESSOR SPEED

Turbine compressor speed is displayed on a tachometer calibrated in percent r.p.m. Each compressor section has a separate tachometer. For an engine with a twin-spool compressor, the $N_1$ tachometer indicates the speed of the low-pressure compressor and the $N_2$ tachometer indicates the speed of the high-pressure compressor. [Figure 4-2]

For engines with a centrifugal compressor, r.p.m. provides a direct indication of thrust being produced. However, for engines with an axial-flow compressor, compressor r.p.m. is used primarily to monitor engine speed during starting and to help a pilot identify an overspeed condition.

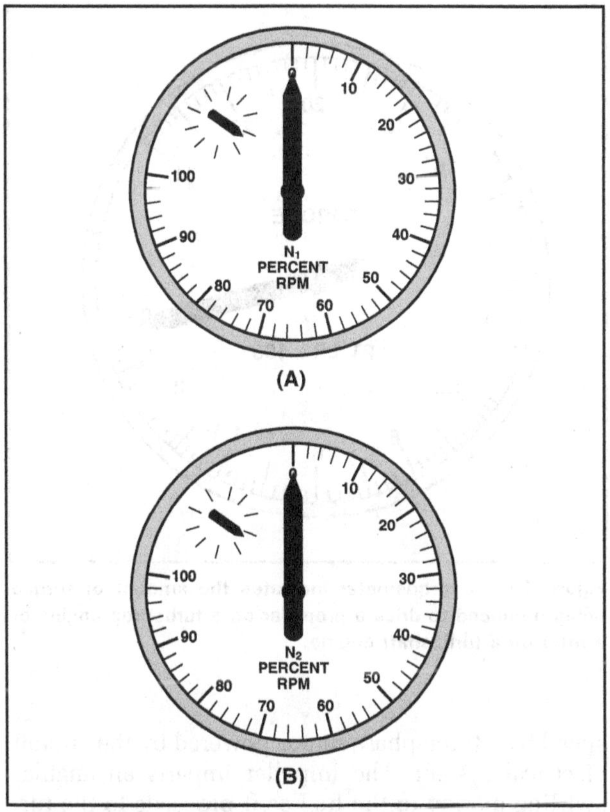


**Figure 4-2. (A) The $N_1$ tachometer indicates fan or low-pressure compressor speed. (B) The $N_2$ tachometer indicates high-pressure compressor speed.**

With turboprop engines that incorporate a free turbine, the $N_g$ tachometer indicates engine speed; the $N_p$ tachometer indicates propeller, or free-turbine, speed.

Turbine engines have two slightly different kinds of electronic tachometers. The first type senses fan speed to measure fan and the low-pressure compressor r.p.m. The sensor contains a coil of wire that generates a magnetic field. The sensor is mounted in the shroud so that each passing fan blade interrupts its magnetic field. An electronic circuit measures the frequency of the interruptions and transmits it to a gauge in the cockpit.

Another type of electronic tachometer for turbine engines consists of a gear-driven shaft that turns a rotor with a permanent magnet past a stationary pickup coil. Each rotation of the permanent magnet cuts across the coil induces voltage. An electronic circuit measures the frequency of the induced voltage and positions the pointer on the tachometer.

## ENGINE PRESSURE RATIO

Engine pressure ratio (EPR) indicates the amount of thrust produced in many turbofan-powered aircraft. EPR represents the relationship between turbine discharge pressure and compressor inlet pressure. Probes installed in the engine inlet $Pt_2$ and at the exhaust $Pt_7$ record the pressure. A differential pressure transducer compares the information from each probe to determine the EPR indicated on a gauge in the cockpit. [Figure 4-3]

EPR system design automatically compensates for the effects of airspeed and altitude. However, changes in ambient temperature require a correction to ensure accurate information for adjusting engine power settings.

## TURBINE DISCHARGE PRESSURE

In some aircraft, an individual $Pt_7$ gauge indicates turbine discharge pressure. This instrument displays the total engine internal pressure just aft of the last turbine stage. When corrected for varia-

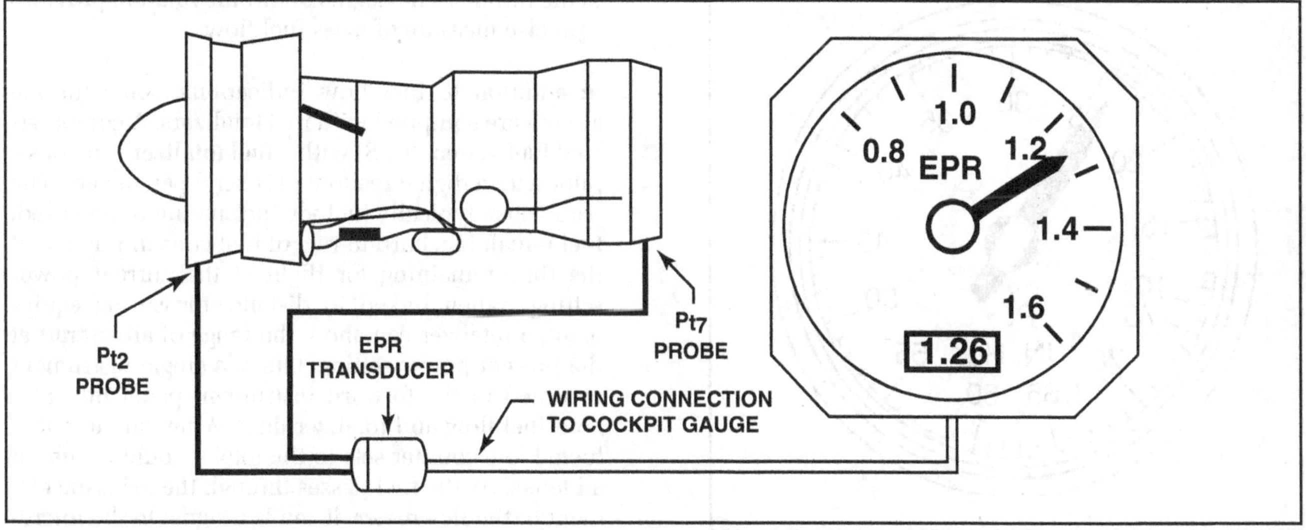


**Figure 4-3. An engine pressure ratio (EPR) gauge provides a reliable indication of thrust by calculating the ratio of turbine discharge pressure $Pt_2$ to compressor inlet pressure $Pt_7$.**

tions in inlet pressure caused by airspeed, altitude, and ambient air temperature, turbine discharge pressure provides an accurate indication of thrust. [Figure 4-4]

## TORQUEMETER

Turboprop and turboshaft engines produce torque to rotate a propeller or rotor and often provide information about engine power output on a torquemeter. Torquemeters are normally calibrated in percentage units or foot-pounds; however, some torquemeters are calibrated in shaft horsepower or p.s.i. [Figure 4-5]

There are different ways to measure engine torque. One technique uses sensors on a driveshaft to measure the amount of shaft twist caused by torque. Sensor data is processed and displayed on the cockpit indicator.

Another technique measures torque pressure. A small, oil-filled cylinder and piston sensor in the reduction gearbox is sensitive to torque reaction force. Pressure on the piston increases proportionally with an increase in torque reaction force. Pressure is measured and the torque is displayed on the instrument indicator.

## FUEL FLOW INDICATOR

Fuel flow for a gas turbine engine is indicated in pounds of fuel per hour. Because the volume of jet fuel changes with temperature, fuel flow is normally measured in terms of mass, not volume. A typical mass flow system consists of two cylinders, an impeller, and a turbine mounted in the main fuel line to the engine. The impeller is driven at a constant

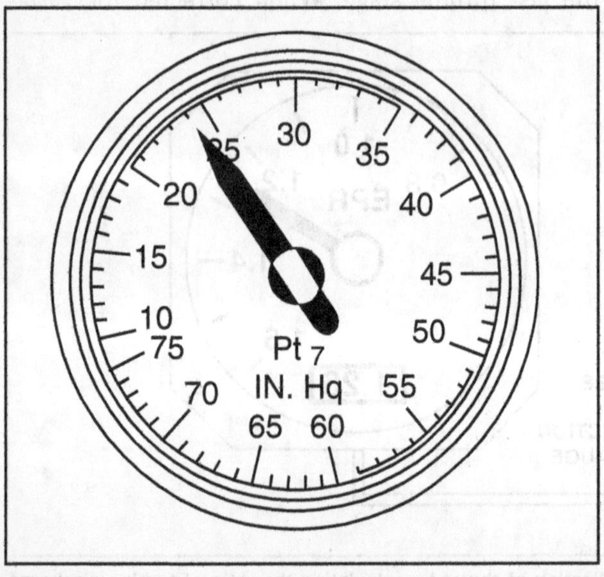


**Figure 4-4. Thrust indications in some aircraft are provided by a $Pt_7$ turbine discharge pressure gauge.**

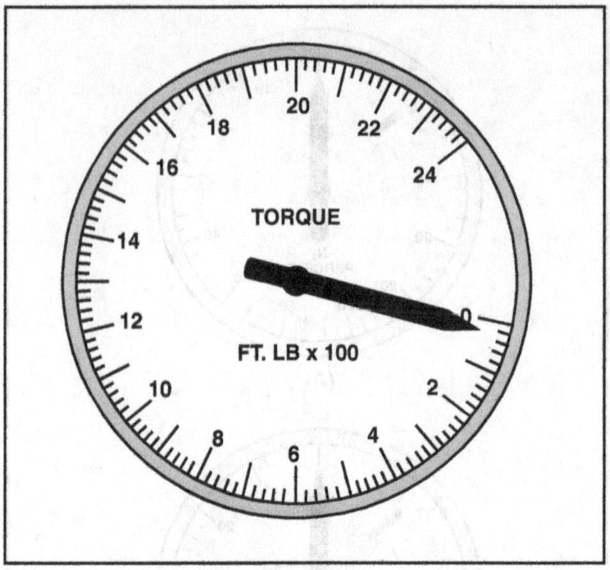


**Figure 4-5. A torquemeter indicates the amount of torque being produced to drive a propeller on a turboprop engine or a rotor on a turboshaft engine.**

speed by a three-phase motor powered by the aircraft electrical system. The impeller imparts an angular swirling motion to the fuel as it proceeds to the turbine. As fuel impacts the turbine, it rotates until the force of a calibrated restraining spring balances the rotational force. The deflection of the turbine aligns a permanent magnet in a transmitter to a position corresponding with the fuel flow in the line. The position of the permanent magnet is transmitted to a permanent magnet in a receiver to position the indicator needle in the cockpit. This system is by far the most accurate means of monitoring fuel flow because it accounts for changes in fuel viscosity and volume related to changes in temperature. For example, as fuel density increases, more spin energy is imparted to the turbine. The degree of turbine rotation provides a precise measure of mass fuel flow.

In addition to fuel flow indications, some turbine aircraft are equipped with fuel totalizers. A computerized fuel system (CFS) with a **fuel totalizer** provides a pilot with a digital readout of several parameters. The parameters typically include the amount of fuel used, fuel remaining, current rate of fuel consumption, and the time remaining for flight at the current power setting. When linked to distance-measuring equipment, a totalizer can show the range of an aircraft at the present power setting. Often, a single instrument mounted in the forward instrument panel indicates both fuel flow and totalizer data. When an aircraft is fueled, the counter sets to the total amount of fuel in all tanks. As the fuel passes through the metering element of the flowmeter, it sends a signal to the microprocessor to calculate the amount of fuel remaining.

## EXHAUST GAS TEMPERATURE

A critical limiting factor for operating a gas turbine engine is the temperature of the turbine section. The temperature of a turbine section must be monitored to prevent overheating the turbine blades and other exhaust section components. A common way to monitor the temperature of the turbine section is with an exhaust gas temperature (**EGT**) gauge. [Figure 4-6]

The differentiating characteristic of EGT Systems is the location of the temperature sensors. Common turbine temperature sensing gauges include turbine inlet temperature (**TIT**), turbine outlet temperature (**TOT**), interstage turbine temperature (**ITT**), and turbine gas temperature (**TGT**).

The **turbine inlet temperature** gauge senses temperature at the inlet to the power turbine, which is the most critical engine parameter. However, on some large engines, it is not practical to measure turbine inlet temperature. These engines typically have temperature thermocouples installed at the turbine discharge that measure **turbine outlet temperature**. For all practical purposes, turbine outlet temperature is the same as a turbine's exhaust gas temperature; both provide a relative indication of turbine inlet temperature. Even though the temperature of the gases exiting a turbine is lower than at the inlet, it provides pilots with a gauge of the engine's internal operating condition. On other engines, the temperature sensing probes are placed at some other location within the turbine section. For example, when the probes are placed between two turbine stages, the indicator in the cockpit displays **interstage turbine temperature**. Interstage turbine temperature is directly proportional to the turbine inlet temperature.

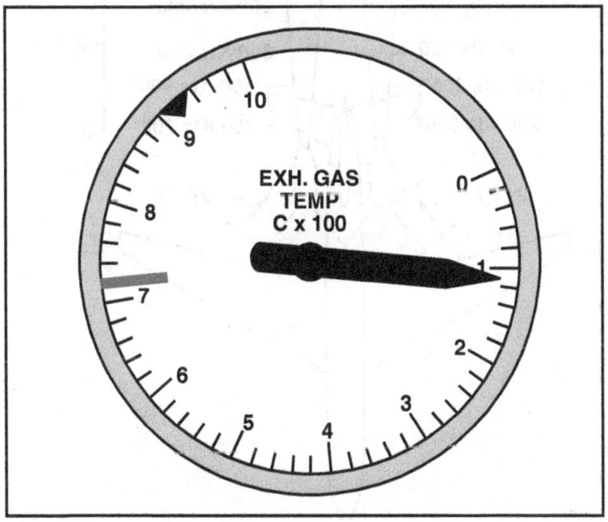


**Figure 4-6. The exhaust gas temperature gauge on a gas turbine engine is essential for monitoring the temperature of the turbine section. Most turbine engine temperature-monitoring gauges include limit markings for different operating parameters. In this figure, the radial line, usually red, indicates the maximum temperature limit for continuous operation, whereas the triangle indicates the maximum transient temperature limit during start.**

All EGT systems use multiple thermocouples positioned around the circumference of the engine exhaust section casing. Due to high pressures and temperatures involved, chromel-alumel thermocouples are typically used. An EGT indicator in the cockpit shows the average temperature measured by the thermocouples.

## ENGINE INDICATING AND CREW ALERTING SYSTEM

Engine parameters on most modern business jets and transport aircraft are displayed electronically on a liquid crystal display (**LCD**) or a cathode ray tube (**CRT**). The most common electronic system is the **engine indicating and crew alerting system**, or **EICAS**. A typical EICAS uses two displays mounted in the middle of an instrument panel. The system displays all primary and secondary powerplant instruments. The primary instrument indications of EPR, $N_1$, and EGT are presented with both digital and analog movements on the top display. The secondary engine instrument indications of $N_2$, $N_3$, fuel flow, engine vibration and oil pressure, temperature, and quantity are presented on the lower display. In addition, a crew alerting function monitors engine parameters and displays system faults and warning messages to the crew. Other airframe system indications that are often included in an EICAS include the aircraft's electrical, hydraulic, bleed air, and pressurization systems. [Figure 4-7]

During routine cruise operations, the lower screen might be blank. However, when a fault is detected, the upper screen displays the warning, and a representation of the instrument for the faulty system appears on the lower screen. An EICAS reduces crew workload because it does not display secondary information during normal operations. If a display fails, all necessary information appears on the operable display. In this case, information appears in a digital format and the system is automatically converted to a compact mode. In the unlikely event that the second CRT fails, the critical engine information appears on a backup display.

# GROUND OPERATIONS

As a maintenance technician, you will often operate a gas turbine engine. For example, troubleshooting a discrepancy reported by the flight crew might require you to operate the engine to attempt to duplicate and analyze the fault. You will operate the engine to test its performance before and after

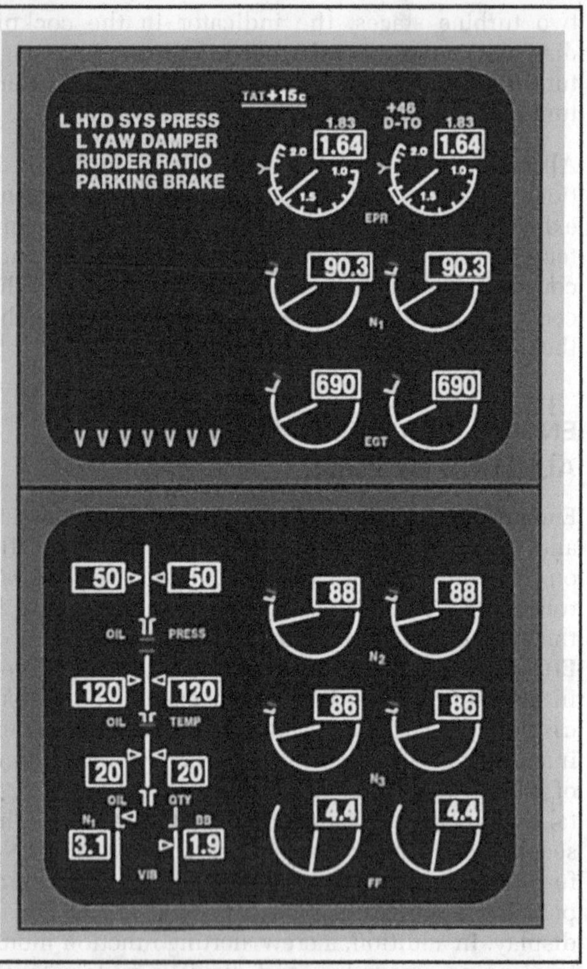


Figure 4-7. EICAS displays engine monitoring instrumentation as well as alert messages in a dual CRT or LCD format. The upper screen displays primary engine instrumentation and alerting functions while the lower screen displays secondary engine instrumentation.

inspection and maintenance or to reposition an aircraft by taxiing. The following discussion provides a basic overview of turbine engine starting and runup operations. For specific information regarding a particular engine and airframe, always consult the checklist and instructions provided by the aircraft manufacturer.

Operate turbine engines in an area specifically designated for that purpose to reduce hazards to personnel, hangars, and other equipment. If possible, always run a gas turbine engine in front of a blast shield, so the jet blast is deflected upward. Whenever the aircraft does not need to move during the ground run, chock the wheels and set the brakes.

Prepare for an engine run by removing the engine inlet and exhaust covers; then check for proper oil levels, adequate fuel, and fluid leaks that could pose a fire hazard. To prevent foreign object damage, remove loose objects from the ramp around the engine and remove any tools or other loose objects from the turbine inlet before starting. Be sure that all ground support equipment, such as auxiliary power carts, hydraulic service units, and fire extinguishers, is positioned a safe distance from the aircraft. Observe all warnings to keep people safely outside the turbine intake and exhaust danger arcs when the engine is running. [Figure 4-8]

Inspect the condition of the compressor and turbine, and verify freedom of motion. Additionally, check the operation of communications equipment between the cockpit and ground safety personnel.

## ENGINE STARTING

Upon entering the cockpit, verify that the master switch is OFF, the landing gear handle is in the DOWN position, and the generator switches are OFF. Additionally, check to make sure the power levers are in the cutoff or fuel shutoff position, and the starter and ignition switches are OFF. If using

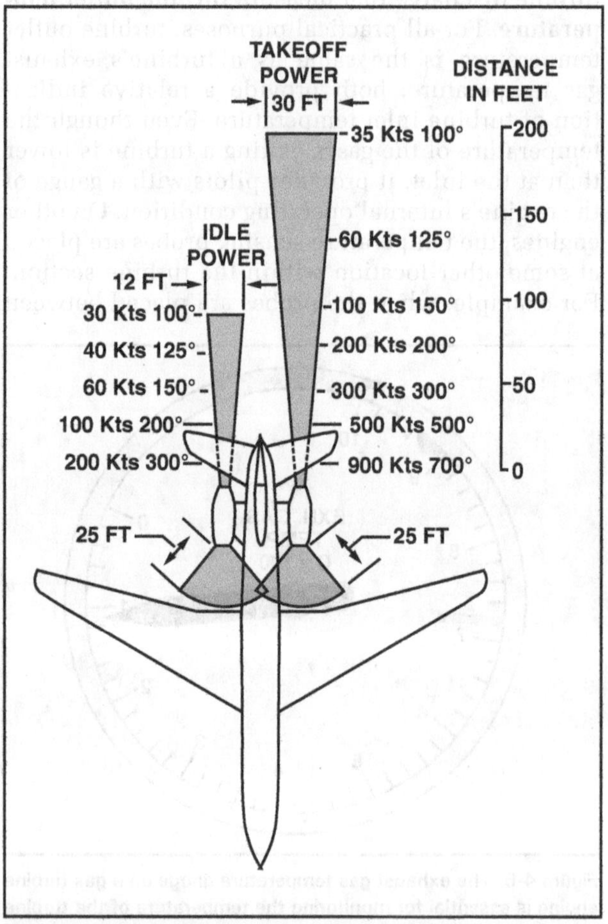


Figure 4-8. Ground personnel must be cautious when near operating turbojet and turbofan engines. Intake safety arcs are established to prevent injury to personnel and engine damage due to ingestion. Likewise, exhaust safety arcs are designed to prevent damage to surrounding equipment and personnel from jet blast.

a ground power unit to start the engine, verify that the correct voltage is being supplied to the aircraft. When ground personnel indicate that conditions are safe for engine start, turn the master switch and battery (or external power) switches ON, and turn on the fuel boost pumps.

Operation of the starter, ignition, and fuel control is usually based on $N_1$ or $N_2$ indications and time. Observe the engine instruments and elapsed time during the engine start procedure. A typical start sequence requires starter engagement before switching on the ignition. After the engine reaches a specified speed, open the fuel valve. Check the fuel flow indicator to confirm fuel flow, and then monitor the EGT indicator to confirm combustion. A sharp rise in EGT indicates the start has commenced. Watch the EGT indicator to verify that temperature does not exceed published limits and result in a hot start.

A **hot start** occurs when an excessively rich fuel/air mixture is ignited. If a hot start continues, the exhaust gas temperature will exceed the operational limit and the engine will likely sustain damage. To minimize the possibility of a hot start, monitor the exhaust gas temperature, turbine inlet temperature, or interstage turbine temperature gauge during start. If any temperature exceeds its operational limit, immediately shut off fuel to the engine. Consult the engine manufacturer's maintenance manual for inspection or overhaul requirements following a hot start.

A **hung start** occurs when the engine startup is normal and exhaust gas temperature is within limits, but the engine fails to accelerate or reach idle speed. Hung starts occur when the starter cuts out too soon, or the starting power source fails to provide enough energy to rotate the engine at sufficient speed. If a hung start occurs, shut down the engine and correct the cause of the insufficient starting speed before you attempt another start.

When an engine starts and becomes self-accelerating, release the start switch and monitor the engine instrument indications. Following a successful engine start, the engine should idle between 40 and 70 percent, depending on the engine model. Monitor the EGT, fuel flow, oil and fuel temperatures, oil pressure, and tachometer readings and compare them to their operational ranges. Be aware that fuel flow indications might be unreliable at idle speeds because of inherent inaccuracies in fuel flowmeters at low speeds.

## ENGINE FIRE

In the event of an engine fire (or if the fire warning light illuminates during the start cycle), cut off fuel flow to the engine and continue motoring it with the starter. If the fire persists, small amounts of $CO_2$ can be discharged into the inlet duct while the engine is being motored. Be careful not to discharge excessive amounts of $CO_2$ directly into a hot engine. The cooling effect produced by large amounts of $CO_2$ can contract the turbine housing around the turbine blades, which could result in engine disintegration.

## POWER CHECK

If an engine idles well and the engine parameters appear normal, verify that the engine is capable of producing takeoff thrust. Based on the prevailing atmospheric conditions, calculate the EPR or discharge pressure value for full power. In most cases, the engine manufacturer provides a takeoff thrust setting curve to make these calculations. [Figure 4-9]

Ambient environmental conditions dramatically affect turbine performance; therefore, compressor inlet air temperature and pressure measurements must be accurate for computing takeoff thrust. Measure air temperature a few feet above the runway surface at the height of the compressor inlet. The free air temperature indicator in an aircraft can be used at airports that do not provide a runway temperature measurement. For an accurate thrust computation, measure the actual temperature with a calibrated, handheld thermometer in the shade of the airplane.

Turbine engine performance is partly based on the actual air pressure sensed at the compressor inlet. Air pressure at the compressor inlet of a stationary aircraft is the same as the field barometric pressure. Altimeter settings provided by air traffic control are field barometric pressure corrected to sea level, which is unusable for computing engine performance. Field barometric pressure is obtained by setting the aircraft altimeter to field elevation and reading the altimeter setting on the face of the instrument.

The effect of relative humidity is negligible on the thrust of a turbojet engine. Measuring relative humidity is unnecessary when checking gas turbine engine performance.

After you know the calculated takeoff EPR, adjust the throttle to obtain takeoff power. While advancing the power lever to the takeoff EPR, carefully observe the EGT, tachometer, fuel flow, and oil pressure readings to avoid exceeding operational

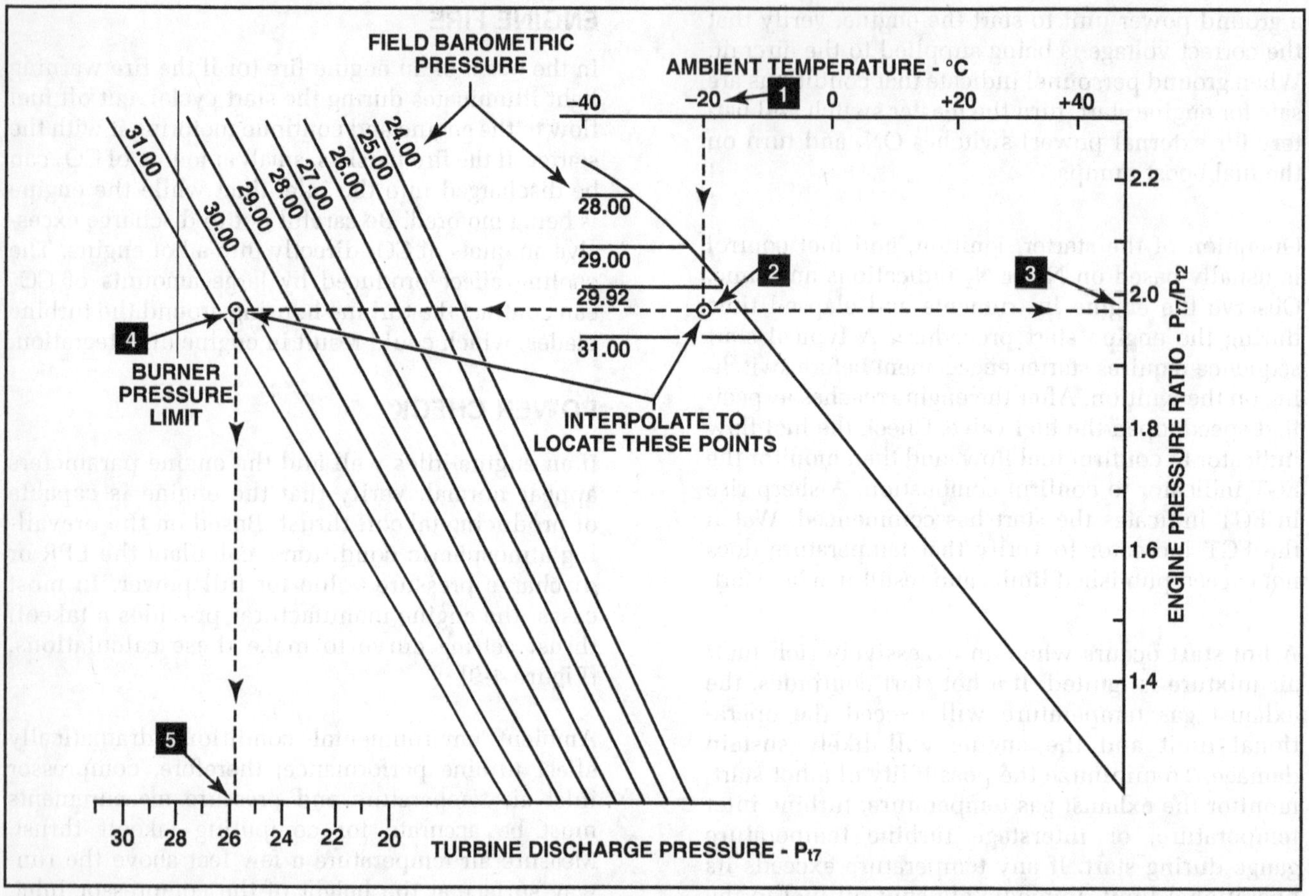


**Figure 4-9. Given an ambient temperature of –20°C and a field barometric pressure of 30.50 in. Hg., you can determine the takeoff EPR and turbine discharge pressure. First, locate the ambient temperature line (1) and move downward to intercept the barometric pressure scale (2). Project a horizontal line to the right that intercepts the engine pressure ratio axis (3). To determine turbine discharge pressure, return to the intersection of the ambient temperature and barometric pressure (2) and project a line left to a second barometric pressure scale (4). Drop downward to arrive at the value for turbine discharge pressure (5).**

limits. To make precise thrust measurements using a takeoff thrust setting curve, the aircraft must be stationary and engine operation stabilized. If the predetermined EPR reading is achieved and all other engine instruments are within their proper ranges, the engine is producing takeoff thrust.

## ENGINE SHUTDOWN

After you complete the engine run, follow the appropriate shutdown procedures. Typically, before you shut down a gas turbine engine, you permit the engine to idle for at least 30 seconds so component temperatures can stabilize and oil system scavenging can occur. After the recommended time period passes, move the power lever to the cutoff or fuel shutoff position. When combustion ceases, move the fuel boost, fuel valve, generator, battery, external power, and master switches to their OFF positions. If you do not follow the appropriate shutdown procedures, uneven engine cooling could result. Furthermore, a rapid shutdown can lead to incorrect oil quantity indications as a result of poor scavenging.

## COLD WEATHER OPERATIONS

A cold-soaked gas turbine engine that has been sitting in cold weather requires special starting procedures. For example, a ground power supply should be used to start a cold-soaked engine, to ensure adequate rotational speed. A typical turbojet requires an $N_2$ speed of at least 10 percent for a successful start. Note that if you have no indication of fan rotation on the $N_1$ tachometer, ice buildup could be interfering with fan rotation.

When you achieve a successful engine start in cold weather, EGT indications might be much lower than during warm weather starts. Furthermore, because oil viscosity increases as temperature decreases, oil pressure indications might run at full scale until the oil warms. In addition, a filter blocked warning light could illuminate until oil temperature rises.

## ENGINE PERFORMANCE

Turbine engine performance is based on standards established by the Society of Automotive Engineers (SAE). These standards are known as engine power ratings and are listed on an engine's Type Certificate Data Sheet. In most cases, engine power ratings are expressed in values of EPR, percent $N_1$, or torque. Because aircraft and engine maintenance manuals often use engine power-rating terminology to define engine performance, it is important that you be familiar with the different ratings.

Power ratings common to most modern commercial gas turbine engines include takeoff power, maximum continuous power, maximum cruise power, cruise power, maximum climb power, ground idle, and flight idle. A **takeoff power rating** represents the amount of power that an aircraft engine is permitted to produce for takeoff. In most cases, a takeoff power setting is time-limited; you must exercise caution during engine runs to ensure that ground operation time limits are followed. If you exceed the time limits for takeoff power, the turbine section could overheat.

**Maximum continuous power** is a power level used at the discretion of the pilot for unusual or emergency situations. Depending on the engine model, maximum continuous power might be synonymous with **maximum cruise power.** As the name implies, a maximum continuous power setting is not subject to any time limitations. However, both max continuous and max cruise power settings result in increased fuel burns, which decrease the aircraft's range.

A **cruise power** rating provides the best fuel economy during flight and extended range. There is no time limit on this power setting.

An engine's **maximum climb power rating** is used for normal climb to cruise altitude. This power rating is higher than a cruise power rating and is not subject to time limitations. As with other maximum ratings, when an engine is run at maximum power, it consumes a significant quantity of fuel.

**Ground idle** is the lowest engine speed permitted for ground operation. A typical ground idle rating is between 50 and 70 percent. The ground idle speed on a single-spool engine is indicated on the $N_1$ tachometer. However, if the engine has a dual or triple-spool compressor, the ground idle speed is indicated on the $N_2$ or $N_3$ tachometers.

**Flight idle** is the lowest engine speed permitted in flight and is used primarily for descent, approach, and landing. On many engines, flight idle speed is approximately 10 percent r.p.m. higher than ground idle speed. This slightly higher idle speed provides greater stall protection and quicker response to power needs. Some aircraft are equipped with power controls that automatically reset flight idle speed for the increased idle r.p.m. necessary at higher altitudes.

### DERATED ENGINE

When the power output of an engine is intentionally limited to less than the maximum power that the engine can produce, the engine is said to be derated. An engine might be derated when it is installed in an aircraft that does not require the engine's maximum rated power or to accommodate a component limitation, such as a rotorcraft transmission. Derating an engine can also increase engine life.

### PART-THROTTLE ENGINE

Part-throttle **(flat-rated)** engines produce takeoff thrust under standard sea-level conditions before the power lever is advanced to the full-throttle position. When a part-throttle engine is operated in atmospheric conditions above standard, takeoff thrust is obtained by advancing the power lever further forward than when operating at sea level conditions. Be careful that you do not exceed the takeoff thrust setting when conducting a ground run on a part-throttle engine. This is especially critical on cold days when the amount of thrust an engine can produce increases. Most commercial turbine engines are configured as part-throttle engines.

### FULL-THROTTLE ENGINE

With a full-throttle engine, takeoff power is obtained when the power lever is advanced to the full throttle position on a standard sea level day. However, with this type of engine, total thrust output decreases as temperatures increase and increases as temperatures decrease. A typical full-throttle engine is equipped with automatic limiting devices in the fuel control system to prevent engine damage caused by overspeed or overtemperature conditions. Therefore, when operating a full-throttle engine, the power lever is advanced to the full forward stop for each takeoff regardless of ambient conditions. Most military aircraft use engines configured as full-throttle engines.

## MAINTENANCE

Because of the hundreds of different gas turbine engine models in use today, it is impractical to list and explain the various maintenance procedures for all of them. Instead, you must consult each specific engine maintenance manual. The following discussion explores general maintenance practices common to most turbine engines.

Engine manufacturers are responsible for providing maintenance and overhaul information in the **Instructions for Continued Airworthiness** section in the maintenance manuals that they produce. In addition, Federal Aviation Regulations require that each set of maintenance manuals provides detailed servicing information, troubleshooting guides, and schedules for cleaning, inspecting, adjusting, testing, and lubricating engine parts. Additionally, an FAA-approved set of maintenance manuals must include a section entitled **Airworthiness Limitations,** which establishes mandatory replacement times, inspection intervals, and component cycle limits.

The two general classifications of maintenance performed on gas turbine engines are line maintenance and shop maintenance. **Line maintenance** is any maintenance that can be performed while the engine is installed on an aircraft. **Shop maintenance** requires engine removal. Because shop maintenance includes most of the maintenance performed during an overhaul, it is covered in greater detail in Section B of this chapter.

## LINE MAINTENANCE

Line maintenance tasks include performing inspections, troubleshooting, cleaning, trimming, verifying instrumentation readings, checking fluid levels, and replacing accessories. The following topics introduce you to these tasks and provide you with procedures common to several makes and models of turbine engines.

### FIELD CLEANING

As with other aircraft components, the interior of a gas turbine engine must be cleaned periodically. Otherwise, the aerodynamic efficiency of compressor blades will decrease with the accumulation of dirt, oil, and soot. Decreased efficiency leads to poor acceleration, reduced EPR, and excessive exhaust gas temperatures. Aircraft operated near salt water also require frequent cleaning to prevent corrosion caused by salt deposits.

The two most common methods for removing dirt and salt deposits from the inside of a turbine engine are a fluid wash and an abrasive grit blast. With a **fluid wash**, clean demineralized water or an emulsion cleaner is sprayed into an engine's intake. Water alone is typically used to remove salt deposits and is often referred to as a **desalinization wash**. An emulsion cleaner, followed by a water rinse, is typically used to remove dirt and soot deposits. This type of wash is known as a **performance recovery wash**. To determine how often an engine should be cleaned, manufacturers typically provide a recommended wash schedule. [Figure 4-10]

When performing a fluid wash, it is imperative to follow the manufacturer's instructions. On turboprop engines, a fluid wash is usually accomplished by spraying or pouring the washing liquid into the compressor inlet duct while the engine is motored with the starter. This is known as a **motoring wash** and typically accomplished at speeds between 10 and 25 percent. For large turbo jet and turbofan aircraft a fluid wash is accomplished by spraying the washing liquid into the engine's inlet duct while the engine idles at approximately 60 percent. [Figure 4-11]

When compressor contamination is too heavy to be effectively removed by an internal engine wash, a more vigorous **abrasive grit blast cleaning** is available. This heavy cleaning procedure involves injecting an abrasive grit such as Carboblast into the engine intake at selected power settings. Carboblast typically contains ground walnut shells or apricot pits. Always follow the engine manufacturer's recommended procedure and use only the type and amount of material specified for a particular engine. The greater cleaning capability of grit blast cleaning provides a longer interval between cleanings as compared to the solvent and water methods. However, an abrasive grit cleaning is minimally effective at cleaning turbine blades and vanes; most of the cleaning grit burns up before it reaches the turbines. [Figure 4-12]

### ENGINE TRIMMING

Engine trimming refers to the process of adjusting an engine's fuel control unit to enable the engine to produce its maximum rated thrust. Trimming is normally performed after you change an engine or fuel control unit or whenever an engine is not producing its maximum thrust.

Manual trimming procedures vary widely between engine models. Before you attempt to trim an engine, review the specific procedures in the engine maintenance manual. A typical trimming procedure requires you to install calibrated instruments for reading turbine discharge pressure or EPR. In addition, a calibrated tachometer must be installed to read $N_2$ r.p.m. After you install the instruments, point the aircraft into the wind. Keep in mind that if the velocity of the wind blowing into the intake is too great, elevated compression and turbine discharge pressures will result. This condition will produce a low trim setting. When trimming an engine, be sure to measure the barometric pressure

| OPERATING ENVIRONMENT | NATURE OF WASH | RECOMMENDED FREQUENCY | RECOMMENDED METHOD | REMARKS |
|---|---|---|---|---|
| Continuously salt laden | Desalination | Daily | Motoring | Strongly recommended after last flight of day. |
| Occasionally salt laden | Desalination | Weekly | Motoring | Strongly recommended. Adjust washing frequency to suit condition. |
| All | Performance Recovery | 100 to 200 hours | Motoring or Running. | Strongly recommended. Performance recovery required less frequently. Adjust washing frequency to suit engine operating conditions as indicated by engine condition monitoring system. Motoring wash for light soil and multiple motoring or running washes for heavy soil is recommended. |

**Figure 4-10. As indicated in the wash schedule, engines operated in a salt-laden environment should be washed frequently. However, for these aircraft, the need for a performance recovery wash is less frequent.**

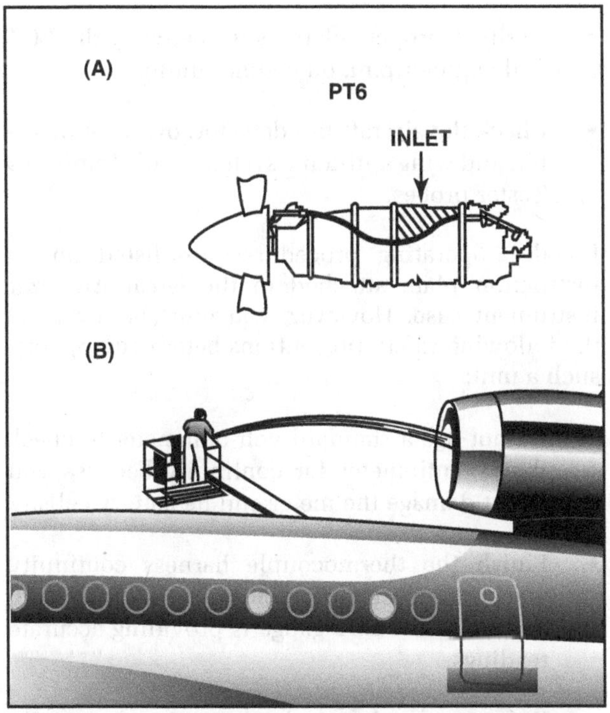


**Figure 4-11. (A) A fluid wash conducted on a typical turboprop engine is accomplished by pouring or spraying a cleaning fluid into the compressor inlet duct. (B) A fluid wash done on a large turbojet or turbo fan engine is accomplished by spraying large quantities of wash fluid into an engine as it idles.**

at the engine inlet and the ambient temperature so you can correct performance readings for standard sea-level conditions. The ideal conditions for trimming a turbine engine are an absence of wind, low humidity, and standard temperature and pressure.

After you have calculated the maximum power output for the engine you are trimming, start the engine and let it idle as specified to permit the engine to stabilize. To ensure an accurate trim setting, turn off all engine bleed air. Bleeding air off the compressor has the same effect as decreasing compressor efficiency. If you make a trim adjustment with the bleeds on, an inaccurate, overtrimmed condition will result.

With the engine running at idle and then at maximum power, observe the turbine discharge or EPR readings to determine how much trimming is necessary. If trimming of either the idle or maximum settings is necessary, it is typically accomplished by

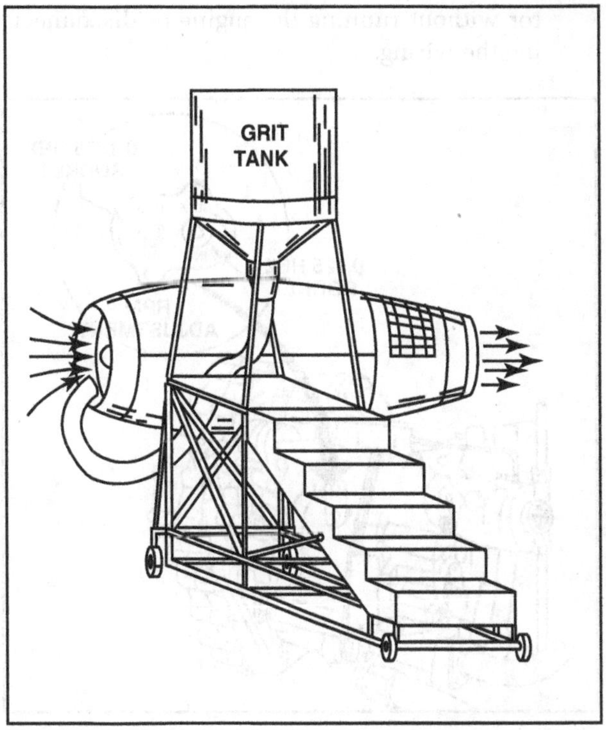


**Figure 4-12. Use abrasive grit blast cleaning to remove heavy engine contamination. To perform an abrasive grit blast, an engine is run while a specific type and quantity of abrasive grit is fed into the engine.**

turning a screw-type adjustment on the fuel control unit. [Figure 4-13]

## EGT AND TACHOMETER CHECKS

Keep in mind that two of the most important factors affecting turbine engine life are EGT and engine speed. If the cockpit indications of these two variables are inaccurate, serious engine damage can result. For example, excessively high exhaust gas temperatures can reduce turbine blade life by as much as 50 percent, while low exhaust gas temperatures significantly reduce turbine engine efficiency and thrust. Additionally, inaccurate r.p.m. indications can lead to unintentional overspeed conditions that can result in premature engine failures. To help protect against EGT and r.p.m. discrepancies, these instrument systems are checked periodically.

One way to check the accuracy of an engine's EGT and r.p.m. indicating systems is with a **jet calibration test unit (Jetcal® Analyzer)**. Jetcal is the trade name for several models of a widely used jet calibration test units manufactured by Howell Instruments, Inc. One model of Jetcal Analyzer consists of a portable EGT and r.p.m. test unit. [Figure 4-14]

Specifically, a portable Jetcal Analyzer enables you to:

- Functionally check the aircraft EGT system ferror without running the engine or disconnecting the wiring.

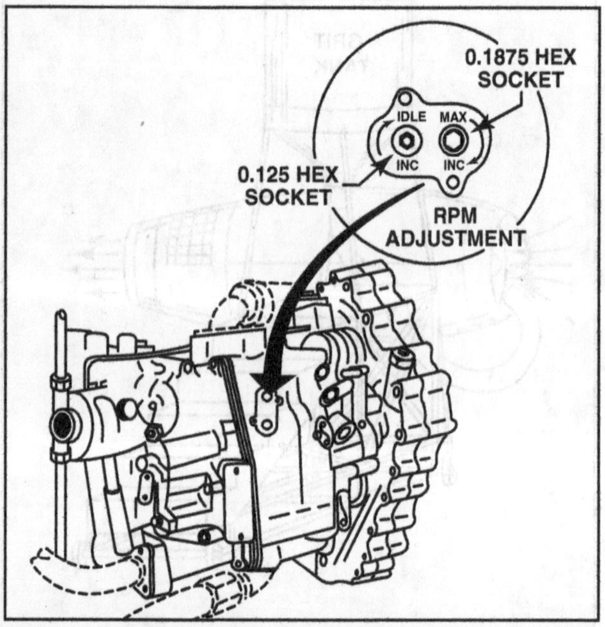


**Figure 4-13. A typical turbine engine fuel control unit is equipped with adjustment screws for trimming the engine. Trimming procedures enable you to adjust both idle speed and maximum rated thrust.**

- Detect inoperative or inaccurate thermocouples either in or out of the wiring harness.
- Check the wiring harness for continuity, resistance, and accuracy, as well as identify breaks in harness wiring and poor or dirty electrical connections.
- Check the insulation on the circuit wiring for short circuits to ground or short circuits between leads.
- Check EGT indicators for error, either in the instrument panel or removed from the system.
- Determine engine speed with an accuracy of ±0.1 percent during engine run-up while checking and troubleshooting the aircraft tachometer system.
- Verify a proper relationship between the EGT and engine r.p.m. on engine run-up.
- Check the aircraft fire detector, overheat detector, and wing anti-icing systems with Tempcal® Tester probes.

Usually, operating procedures are listed on an instruction plate attached to the Jetcal Analyzer instrument case. However, you must be aware of the following safety precautions before you operate such a unit:

- Do not use a standard volt-ohmmeter to check the potentiometer for continuity because you might damage the meter and its battery cells.
- Finish the thermocouple harness continuity and accuracy checks before engine run-up to be certain the EGT gauge is providing accurate readings.
- Be sure the Jetcal Analyzer is electrically grounded when using an AC power supply.
- Use the appropriate heater probes on the engine thermocouples that you intend to test. The temperature gradients vary with the design of the heater probes. Therefore, be certain you never attempt to modify a heater probe for testing other types of thermocouples.
- Do not leave heater probe assemblies in the tailpipe during engine run-up.
- To prevent damage to the Jetcal Analyzer and heater probe assemblies, do not allow the heater probes to exceed 900°C.

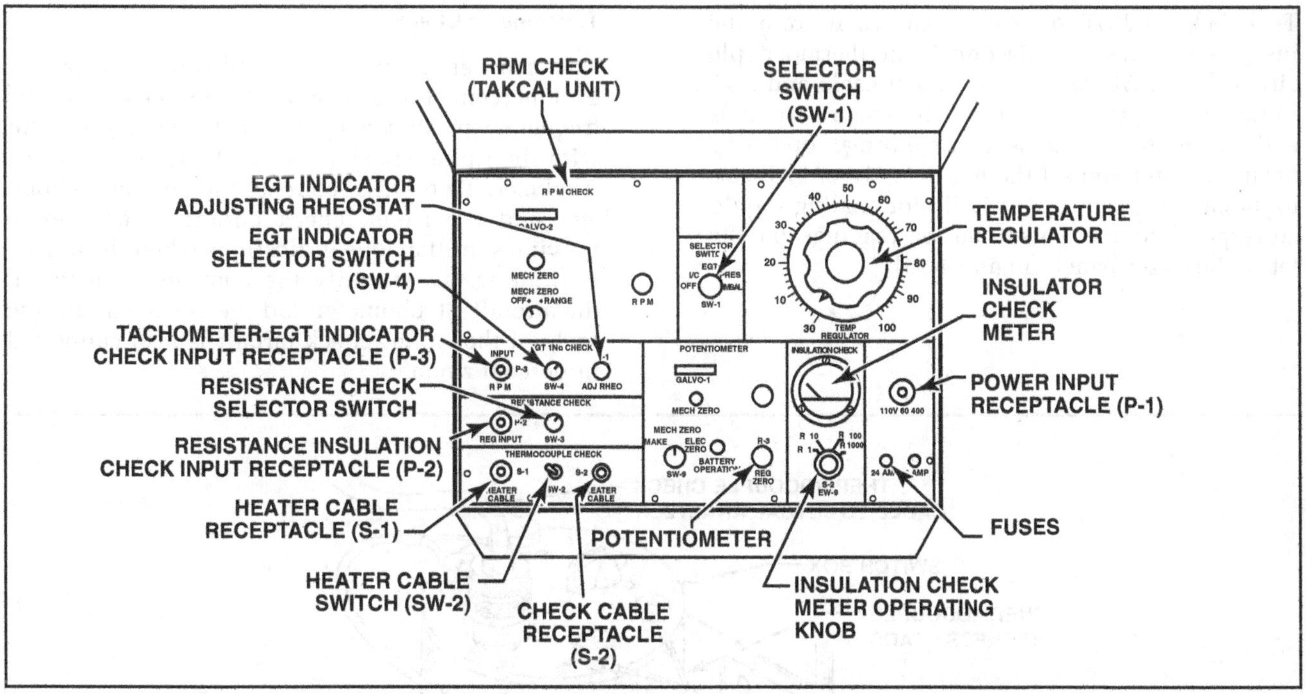


**Figure 4-14. The instrument compartment on a Jetcal Analyzer is conveniently marked to easily identify the controls used for checking r.p.m., EGT, wire resistance, and insulation breaks.**

### EGT Circuit Checks

Continuity checks of the EGT circuit detect errors caused by one or more inoperative aircraft thermocouples. A continuity check is made by raising the temperature of a heater probe between 500 and 700°C, then placing the hot probe over each the aircraft thermocouple. As each thermocouple heats up, the EGT gauge for that engine registers a temperature rise for each functionally correct thermocouple. Detecting a rise on the EGT gauge may be difficult for systems with eight or more thermocouples in a single harness because of the electrical characteristics of the parallel circuit in which the thermocouples operate. In such cases, Howell Instruments provides instructions for alternative ways to test aircraft thermocouples.

When you verify the continuity of an EGT circuit, the next step is to perform a functional check of the EGT circuit. The time required to test an EGT system depends on several factors, including the number of engines, the number of thermocouples in a harness, the position of the harness in an engine, the number of errors found, and the time required to correct any errors. A normal functional test on a single engine can typically be performed in 10 to 20 minutes.

During an EGT circuit functional check and a thermocouple harness check, the Jetcal Analyzer is guaranteed to be accurate within ±4°C. A functional check is made by heating the engine thermocouples in the tail pipe to the engine test temperature. The heat is supplied by heater probes. When the engine thermocouples are hot, their temperatures will register on the aircraft EGT indicator. At the same time, a set of thermocouples embedded in the heater probes are also sensing and registering the temperature of the probes. If the temperature indicated on the aircraft's EGT gauge is within the specified tolerance of the temperature reading on the Jetcal Analyzer, the EGT circuit is operating properly. However, if the difference exceeds the published tolerance, you must inspect and troubleshoot the aircraft system to determine which parts are malfunctioning.

You also use the Jetcal Analyzer to test the electrical resistance and insulation of an EGT thermocouple during the functional test. The resistance and insulation check circuits make it possible to analyze and isolate any error in the aircraft's EGT system. Because variations in resistance affect the amount of current flow in a thermocouple circuit, the resistance of a thermocouple harness must conform to a narrow tolerance. Erroneous temperature readings caused by incorrect harness resistance can result in overtemperature damage to the turbine and tailpipe.

To check an EGT indicator, remove it from the instrument panel and disconnect the thermocouple circuit leads. Attach the instrument cable and EGT indicator adapter leads to the indicator terminals and place the indicator in its normal operating position. After you set the Jetcal Analyzer switches to the proper position, the indicator reading should correspond to the potentiometer readings on the Jetcal Analyzer panel. [Figure 4-15]

**Tachometer Check**

You can verify tachometer indications to within ±0.1 percent during engine run by measuring the frequency produced by the tachometer generator with the r.p.m. check (or takcal) circuit in a Jetcal Analyzer. To do this, connect the aircraft tachometer and the r.p.m. check circuit in parallel to provide simultaneous indications when the engine is running. To simplify the comparison between the aircraft's tachometer and the check circuit, the scale of the r.p.m. check circuit is also calibrated in percent r.p.m.

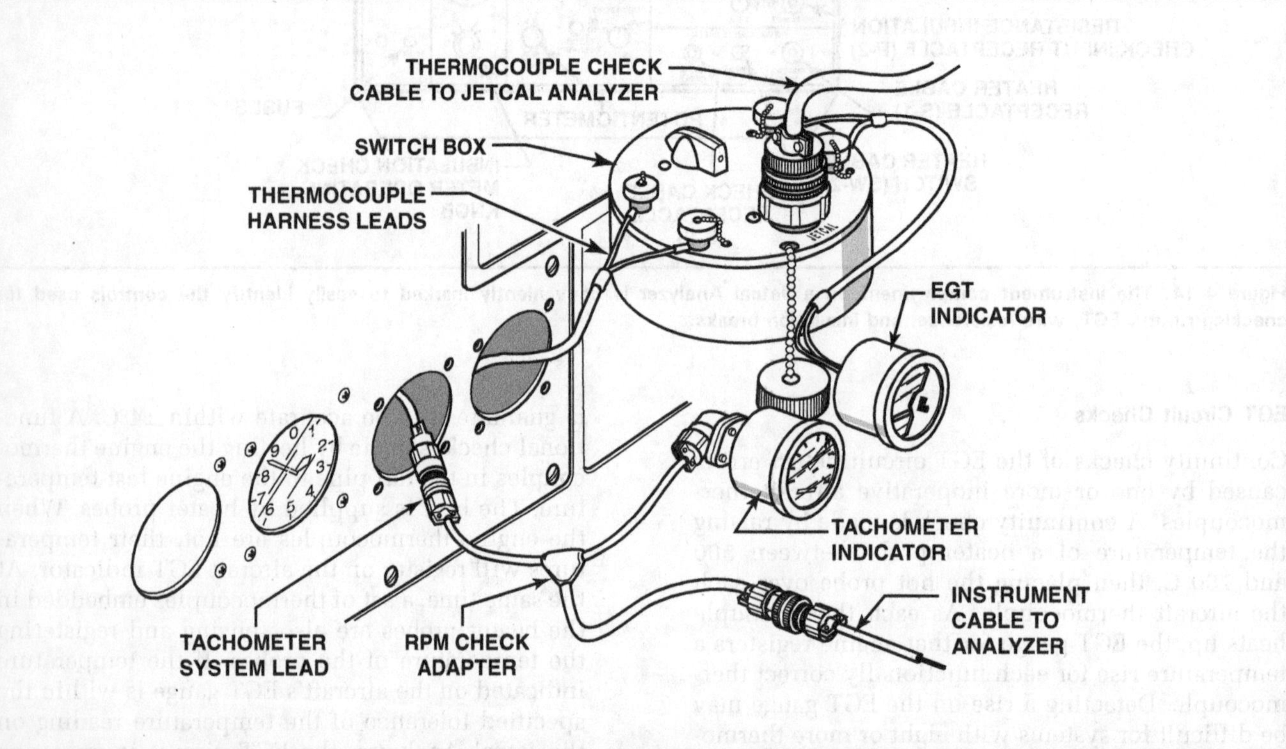


**Figure 4-15. To test an EGT indicator, remove the indicator from the aircraft instrument panel and attach the Jetcal Analyzer adapter cable. Then attach the aircraft thermocouple harness leads and Jetcal Analyzer cable to the Jetcal Analyzer's switch box.**

# SUMMARY CHECKLIST

✓ The tachometer of a gas turbine engine displays speed as a percentage of power from various locations, depending on the type of engine.

✓ The engine pressure ratio (EPR) gauge indicates thrust produced by an engine.

✓ Depending on the location of the sensor, the exhaust gas temperature (EGT) of a gas turbine engine might be displayed as turbine inlet temperature (TIT), turbine outlet temperature (TOT), or interstage turbine temperature (ITT).

✓ An engine indicating and crew alerting system (EICAS) is a digital, multifunction display of engine performance data; critical data is always displayed for the pilot.

✓ A hot start refers to ignition of an excessively rich fuel/air mixture in a gas turbine engine. If a hot start is not terminated, significant damage to the engine is likely.

✓ A hung start refers to a gas turbine engine that does not accelerate to reach idle speed.

✓ A fluid wash, either water or an emulsion cleaner sprayed into an engine with its compressor turned to low power, removes salt, dirt, or soot deposits from a gas turbine engine.

✓ Abrasive grit blast cleaning can be used to clean compressor blades if a fluid wash is insufficient.

✓ Trimming a gas turbine engine is adjusting an engine's fuel control unit to ensure development of maximum thrust. Maximum speed must be calculated before making any adjustments.

# KEY TERMS

fuel totalizer
turbine inlet temperature
TIT
turbine outlet temperature
TOT
interstage turbine temperature
ITT
engine indicating and crew alerting system
EICAS
hot start
hung start
takeoff power rating
maximum continuous power
maximum cruise power
cruise power
maximum climb power rating
ground idle
flight idle
flat-rated engine
instructions for continued airworthiness
ICA
airworthiness limitations
line maintenance
shop maintenance
fluid wash
desalinization wash
performance recovery wash
motoring wash
abrasive grit blast cleaning
jet calibration test unit
Jetcal Analyzer

# QUESTIONS

1 Engine pressure ratio is the ratio between readings from the compressor inlet and the ______ stage turbine.

2. Match each of these descriptions with the appropriate turbine engine instrument.

a. ______ Indicates the total engine internal pressure immediately aft of the last turbine stage

b. ______ Is an indication of the thrust being developed by the engine

c. ______ Indicates the torque being developed by a turboprop engine

d. ______ Indicates r.p.m. in percent of maximum

e. ______ Indicates exhaust gas temperature

1. Torquemeter
2. Tachometer
3. EGT gauge
4. Turbine discharge pressure
5. EPR gauge

3. The start of a turbine engine is indicated by a rise in the ______ ______ ______.

4. When an engine start produces a temperature that exceeds the limit, it is known as a ______ ______.

5. A hot start inspection typically ______ (does or does not) require engine removal.

6. When an engine has a normal start, but cannot accelerate or reach idle r.p.m., it is called a ______ ______.

7. If an engine fire occurs during the start of a turbine engine, you should immediately move the fuel control lever to the "off" position and ______ ______.

8. Gas turbine engine thrust may be rated using several different terms, match each description with the appropriate rating.

a. ______ This is the maximum allowable thrust for takeoff.

b. ______ This rating is the maximum continuous thrust.

c. ______ This is the maximum thrust approved for normal climb.

d. ______ This is the maximum thrust approve for cruising.

1. Normal rated power
2. Takeoff power
3. Maximum cruise power
4. Maximum continuous power

9. One takeoff and one landing constitutes one ______ ______.

10. A turbine engine is divided into two sections; a ______ and a ______ section.

11. Compressor ______ occurs from ingestion of sand, dirt, dust, and other fine airborne contaminants.

12. The most frequent discrepancy found while inspecting the combustion section is ______.

13. The inside of a gas turbine engine may be inspected with a ______ (what instrument) without disassembling the engine.

14. Engine trimming consists of adjusting the engines ______ ______ ______ after replacement or when an engine does not produce maximum thrust.

15. A water wash performed solely to remove salt deposits on compressor components of aircraft operated over or near the ocean is known as ______.

16. Compressor cleaning using abrasive grit is accomplished while the engine is ______ (operating or being motored by the starter).

17. The two methods used to remove dirt, salt and corrosion deposits from compressor components are:

a. ______

b. ______

18. ______ ______ is the trade name for an EGT and rpm system test unit.

19. Monitoring performance and mechanical systems over time to provide an overview of engine condition is called ______ ______.

20. Within certain limitations, the internal condition of an engine can be evaluated by the ______ analysis of lubricating oil samples.

# SECTION B

# ENGINE REMOVAL AND OVERHAUL

## ENGINE REMOVAL

Many gas turbine powerplants are removed from an airframe as a **quick engine change assembly**, or **QECA.** Designed to reduce the time an aircraft is out of service, a QECA is a powerplant with the appropriate accessories installed. Be sure to follow the aircraft manufacturer's instructions when removing an engine. Following are some general guidelines that apply to most gas turbine engines.

### REASONS FOR REMOVAL

Several scenarios require an engine to be removed from an aircraft. For example, the engine might have accumulated the hours or cycles recommended for overhaul or performance might have degraded. Additional reasons include serious damage from foreign objects or debris, damage from a hot start, or an inspection that reveals excessive metal particles in the oil. Even some routine maintenance and repairs can require engine removal. Whatever the case, before removing or replacing an engine, always consult the applicable manufacturer's instructions to determine whether removal is required.

#### ENGINE LIFE SPAN

Turbine engines are highly reliable powerplants with long service lives. Time between overhaul (TBO) is not always specified for a turbine engine in the same way that it is for a reciprocating engine. For example, instead of establishing a TBO for the entire engine, some manufacturers establish a recommended operating time between overhauls for individual components or engine sections. Furthermore, many aircraft operators obtain permission from the FAA to operate their engines beyond TBO limits. Permission is based on the part of the Federal Aviation Regulations under which the aircraft operates, the approved inspection program, the submission of trend analysis data, and the use of engine manufacturer data.

#### FOREIGN OBJECT DAMAGE

Foreign object damage (FOD) can occur any time that something is drawn into a gas turbine engine. When a FOD incident occurs, the engine must be inspected. The level of inspection depends on the severity of the damage. For example, if an external inspection reveals little damage, only a borescope inspection might be necessary. If the damage to the fan blades, vanes, or compressor is minor, and no other damage exists within the engine, you can make repairs while the engine remains on the aircraft. However, if substantial damage is clearly visible, you will likely have to remove the engine and sent it to an overhaul facility for repair.

#### HOT START

A hot start is ignition with an excessively rich fuel/air mixture. If a hot start continues, the exhaust gas temperature will exceed the operational limit and the engine will be damaged. A hot start always requires an engine inspection. Many overtemperature inspections can be accomplished with the engine installed on the aircraft. However, if you observe significant damage during the inspection, you will probably have to remove the engine for repair.

### PREPARATION FOR REMOVAL

In some ways, turbine engine removal procedures are similar to those for reciprocating engines. Both involve hazardous chemicals and the procedure should be performed in a well-ventilated area with a fire extinguisher nearby. After the aircraft is parked, chock the main gear wheels to keep the aircraft from rolling during maintenance. Check the maintenance manual for requirements to see whether support is required when the engines are removed. For example, on some tricycle gear aircraft, the tail must be supported to prevent the aircraft from tipping when the engine weight is removed. On some aircraft, you must deflate the landing gear shock struts to prevent damage from over-extension when you remove the engine weight.

#### IGNITION, FUEL, AND BATTERY DISARMING

Before starting the engine removal process, make sure the ignition system is disconnected. On engines with high-voltage ignition units, you must disconnect the voltage supply to the ignition unit and allow the unit to discharge for the manufacturer's prescribed time to avoid a lethal shock.

To help prevent fuel leaks, make sure that all shutoff valves are closed. Fuel selector valves are either manually or electrically operated. If an electric solenoid-operated shutoff valve is installed, you might need to apply battery power to close the valve. After ensuring that the fuel is shut off, disconnect the battery to reduce the possibility of electrical sparks.

## PROPELLER REMOVAL

Before removing a turboprop engine, remove the propeller. When removing a large constant speed propeller, it is essential to use a propeller sling with a hoist. In addition, be sure to have one or two additional people assist you to prevent damage to the propeller or the surrounding equipment. In every case, follow the manufacturer's instructions for propeller removal.

## FLUID LINE DISCONNECTION

The types of fluid lines used with gas turbine engines include flexible hoses, aluminum alloy tubing, and stainless steel tubing. Due to the temperatures radiated by a turbine engine, as well as the fluid pressures required for operation, rigid tubing is frequently used on turbine engines. To simplify removal, most main fuel lines are readily accessible through an access panel. [Figure 4-16]

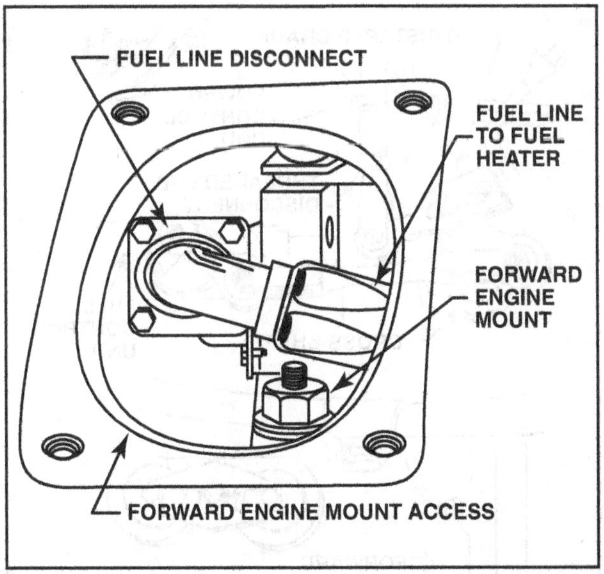


**Figure 4-16. To disconnect the main fuel line on many turbine engines, remove the bolts from the hose flange. On some aircraft, a fuel line might have a quick disconnect at the firewall.**

After you drain a fuel line, plug or cover the ends with moisture-proof tape to prevent insects, dirt, or other foreign matter from entering the line and to prevent any residual fluids from dripping out. Be sure to label all lines and fittings to eliminate any doubt about location when you reinstall them on the new engine.

## ELECTRICAL DISCONNECTION

Depending on the type of engine and the equipment installed, you might disconnect electrical leads either at the accessory or at the engine firewall. AN and MS connectors are often used to simplify disconnecting electrical leads at the firewall,. A typical AN or MS electrical connector consists of a plug and receptacle assembly for multiple wires. To help prevent accidental disconnection during aircraft operation, the plug assembly screws to the receptacle assembly and is secured with safety wire. [Figure 4-17]

Wrap the exposed ends of connectors with moisture-proof tape to protect them from contamination, after you disconnect them. Also, coil loose cables and secure conduits out of the way to prevent damage when the engine is removed. If the wires are not clearly identified, label them to facilitate the installation process of the new engine.

## ENGINE CONTROL DISCONNECTION

The engine control rods and cables enable operation of the throttle and mixture from within the cockpit. On a typical control rod, one or both ends are threaded with a clevis or rod end bearing. On most aircraft, a rod end bearing is connected to the

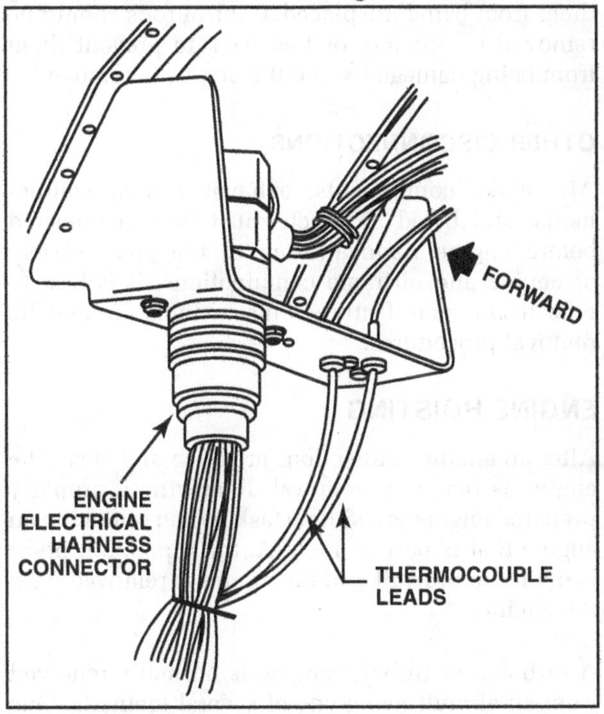


**Figure 4-17. Most electrical connections are grouped in bundles and are disconnected at the firewall or junction by separating an AN or an MS electrical connector.**

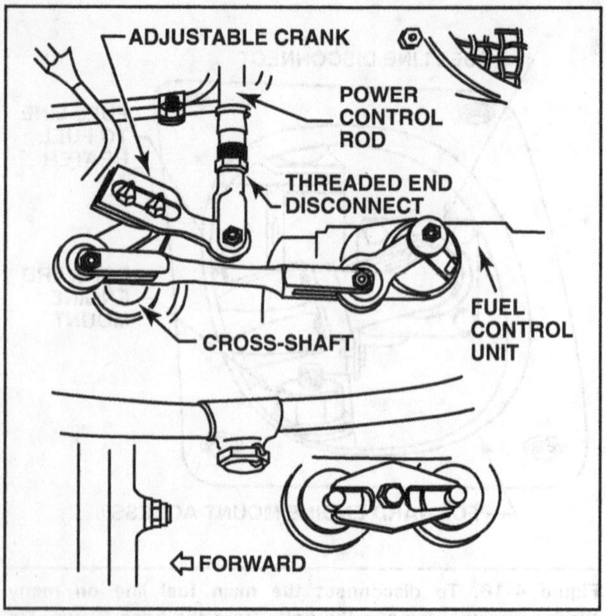


**Figure 4-18. On engines controlled by a single power lever, you must separate only one control rod and end before you remove the engine. When removing a turboprop engine, disconnect the power lever, condition lever, and propeller controls.**

fuel control unit by a bolt secured with a lock nut. [Figure 4-18]

After you disconnect the engine control linkages, inspect the hardware for wear. You must replace the cotter pins, but if the nuts and bolts are airworthy, reinstall them in the control rod end to prevent them from being misplaced. Control rods should be removed completely or tied back to prevent them from being damaged when the engine is removed.

## OTHER DISCONNECTIONS

Air intake components, exhaust system components, and bleed air ducts must be disconnected before engine removal. Due to the great variety of engine and airframe combinations, it is best to refer to the manufacturer's instructions for specific removal procedures.

## ENGINE HOISTING

After all engine connections are open and clear, the engine is ready for removal. Removing a properly prepared engine is a simple task. When removing an engine that is part of a QECA, the separation point is often the firewall and the mount is removed with the engine.

A turbofan or turbojet engine is normally removed from an aircraft using one of several methods. One method uses an engine dolly made of an engine buildup stand mounted on a hydraulic lift. The dolly is positioned under the engine; the hydraulic lift raises the mount for attachment to the engine. After the engine is securely bolted onto the dolly, the dolly is slowly raised until all the engine weight is supported by the dolly. Then, the engine mount attachment hardware is removed in the order specified in the manufacturer's instructions. Before the last nuts are removed, be sure the engine is steady and secure without any lateral load. Remove the remaining hardware and gently move the engine free of the mount attachments. If the engine binds at any point, investigate the reason and maneuver the engine as necessary until it slips free. After the engine is moved clear of the airframe, carefully lower it onto an engine stand and secure it with the appropriate hardware. [Figure 4-19]

Another removal method uses a hoist and a sling above the engine nacelle (or pylon). After mounting, the hoist is connected to the designated points on the engine mounts through the access ports in the pylon. After the engine is secured to the hoist, slowly remove the slack in the cables until they support the engine weight. Remove the fastening hardware, verify that all engine disconnections have been made, and lower the engine onto an engine buildup stand and transport truck. Operate the hoist in a manner that keeps the cables properly tensioned. [Figure 4-20]

When removing a turboprop engine, a conventional hoist is typically used to lift the engine from the aircraft. Before you begin, always verify that the hoist has sufficient capacity to lift the engine safely. When using a conventional hoist hoist, attach the sling to the engine at the prescribed points. For your safety, carefully inspect the sling and hoist before lifting the engine.

**Figure 4-19. On an Airbus A320, an engine dolly is positioned under the engine and raised with a hydraulic lift to support the engine.**

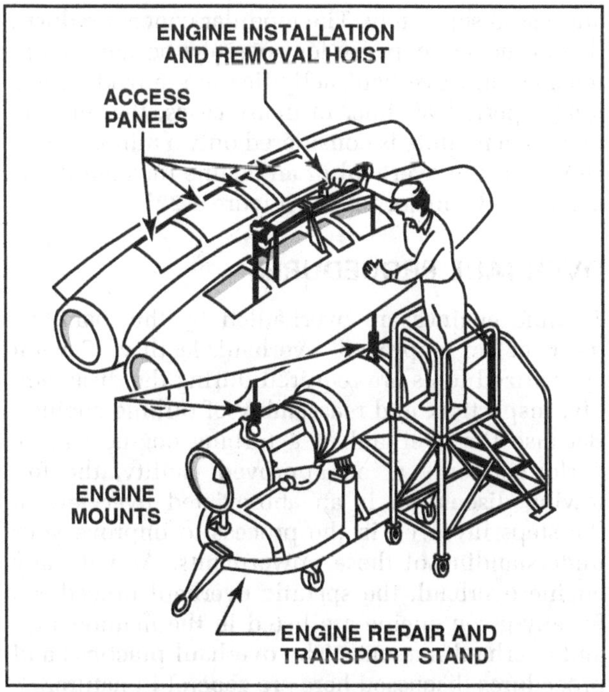


**Figure 4-20. Pod-mounted engines such as those on a Lockheed Jetstar can be removed and lowered onto a transport truck by a two-cable hoist. The hoist attaches to the engine mount structure.**

Some engine hoisting frames are fitted with power-operated hoists. Use a power hoist if only if you have been trained in its operation. An inexperienced operator can cause considerable damage.

## ENGINE COMPARTMENT

Whenever an engine is removed from an aircraft, thoroughly inspect the engine compartment and make repairs as necessary. Examine the engine nacelle for corrosion, cracks, missing rivets, or any other visible defects. Many cracks in aluminum cowlings or ducts can be stop-drilled or patched if they do not exceed limits specified in the manufacturer's structural repair manual.

Check engine controls for integrity and freedom of movement. Additionally, inspect cables for broken wire strands and cable pulleys for binding, flat spots, and chipped edges. Inspect pulley bearings for excessive play. The antifriction bearings in control rods should move freely and the rods should not be deformed. Inspect areas where cables and rods pass through bulkheads or panels for evidence of chafing and misalignment.

Check the outer surface of all exposed electrical wiring for breaks, chafing, deteriorated insulation, or other damage. In addition, inspect crimped and soldered terminals for security and cleanliness. Examine the connector plugs for damage, corrosion, and overall condition. Check bonding straps for fraying, loose attachments, and corrosion at terminal ends. Ensure that all hydraulic and pneumatic tubing is from dents, nicks, and kinks and that all connections are secure. Check all air ducts for dents and the condition of the fabric or rubber antichafing strips at their joints. Work out any dents and replace any antichafing strips that have pulled loose or no longer form a tight seal.

Thoroughly inspect all hoses and replace any that have been damaged by weather checking or cold flow. **Weather checking** is a cracking of the outside covering of hoses that sometimes penetrates to the reinforcement webbing. **Cold flow** refers to deep and permanent impressions or cracks caused by hose clamps. Both types of damage weaken hoses and could cause leaks to develop.

## ENGINE MOUNTS

Before installing a new or overhauled aircraft engine, you must inspect the engine mount structure. For turboprop engines, check the mounts for bends, dents, flat spots, or elongated bolt holes. Typically, dye penetrant inspection is used to identify cracks, porous areas, or other defects. Check ferrous parts, such as engine mounting bolts, by magnetic particle inspection.

The strength and integrity of a turbine engine mount is critical. Because of the propeller, the construction of a turboprop mount is very different than the mount for the typical turbofan or turbojet engine. Because of the large variety of engine-airframe combinations, the type and location of engine mount fixtures also varies.

For example, wing-mounted engines are typically suspended on pylons, and aft-fuselage mounted engines are attached to the aircraft on thrust struts. On aircraft such as the Boeing 727, Lockheed L1011, and the McDonnell-Douglas DC-10 or MD-11 the engine is fastened directly to the internal airframe structure in the vertical stabilizer. [Figure 4-21]

### REMOVAL OF ACCESSORIES

If you must remove a turbine engine that is not part of a QECA, you must remove the engine accessories. Take care to note the location and attachments of accessories before removal to expedite buildup of the replacement powerplant. Hold the accessories aside for reinstallation on the replacement engine or send them out for overhaul, as required. Regardless of whether accessories are to be sent out for overhaul or placed in storage, preserve them in accordance with the manufacturer's instructions. Be sure to attach all of the required accessory identification

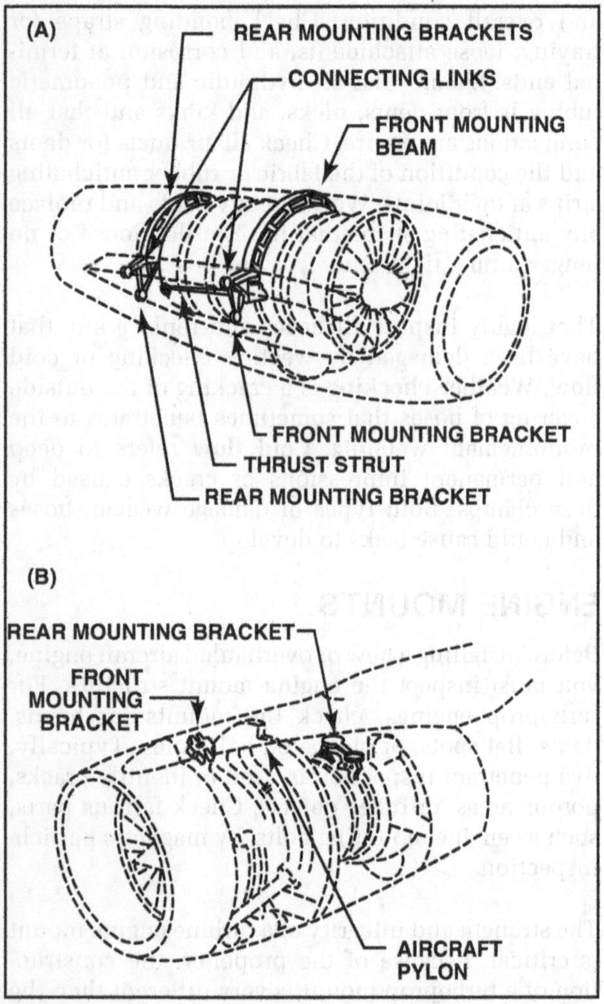


**Figure 4-21. (A) Many business jet aircraft have engines mounted on short thrust struts extending from the sides of the aft fuselage. The thrust struts support mounting brackets and beams with attachment points for an engine. (B) Large transport category aircraft with engines mounted on wing pylons typically have mounting fixtures that support the engine at the front and rear.**

and record cards to each component you remove, and cover all exposed drives and ports to prevent contamination.

## ENGINE OVERHAUL

Many turbine engines are maintained and overhauled based on the limits of the parts. For example, the life limit of a hot section is different from the life-limit of an accessory drive gearbox. A single life-limit, or TBO, is seldom established for a gas turbine engine. The reliability and modular construction of turbine engines provide a variety of options related to time between overhaul. **Modular construction** means that an engine is designed as a set of separate modules (or sections) assembled together. The inspection, line maintenance, and overhaul requirements of each module can be addressed separately. The modular concept reduces downtime and expense for operators because maintenance and overhaul activities are spread over a longer period of time. In many cases, the replacement of a module is considered only a minor repair. However, the overhaul of an engine (or module) is considered a major repair. [Figure 4-22]

### OVERHAUL PROCEDURES

Turbine engines are overhauled by the manufacturer or an approved overhaul facility. Several specialized tools are required during the disassembly, inspection, and reassembly of turbine engines. Because the overhaul of a turbine engine can be performed only at an approved facility, the following discussion is an abbreviated overview of the steps involved in the process to improve your understanding of these powerplants. As with any engine overhaul, the specific overhaul procedures for any given engine are listed in the maintenance and overhaul manuals. The overhaul practices and procedures discussed here are general in nature.

### DISASSEMBLY

Turbine engines are disassembled either vertically or horizontally. On vertically disassembled engines, the forward part of the engine is typically mounted in a fixture facing downward. A small engine can be mounted on a fixture with casters for easy movement from one work area to another. Large engines are often mounted vertically on a stationary fixture, surrounded by a scaffold. Another vertical mounting method for large engines involves securing the engine to an elevator that can be lowered into the shop floor. Scaffolds and elevators permit access to any point along the engine's length. Horizontally disassembled, engines might be mounted in a stand that permits the engine to be turned over for access to all external engine areas.

**Figure 4-22. The modular design of some turboprop engines makes it possible to perform many maintenance tasks with the engine attached to the aircraft.**

After it is mounted on a stand, the engine is dismantled into modules, or main subassemblies. Each module is then attached to a separate stand and moved to an area for further disassembly, cleaning, inspection, and overhaul. Large or heavy modules such as the compressor section and turbine section are lifted from the mounted engine by cranes or hoists.

## CLEANING

After disassembly, engine components are cleaned so that flaws and defects are more easily detected. Cleaning also removes oxide deposits and dirt to prepare the components for special applications such as plating, anodizing, or painting before they are placed back in service.

Engine components are cleaned with approved methods and agents to prevent unintentional damage. Always use the process and materials recommended by the manufacturer; some cleaning solutions can strip plating from a part or cause a reaction with a base metal. Likewise, refrain from cleaning titanium components with trichloroethylene, residual traces of which can cause corrosion. Some common cleaning methods include washing with organic solvents, vapor degreasing, steam cleaning, and tumbling in a grit solution. An effective cleaning method for hot section components uses a series of controlled acid or alkali baths and water rinses. Grit blasting is also used to clean some cold or hot section components.

## BEARINGS

Turbine engine bearings require special handling during the cleaning process to prevent the onset of surface corrosion when a bearing is removed from an engine. Most turbine engine overhaul instructions specify that bearings should be cleaned in an environmentally controlled room. Due to close design tolerances, even the slightest corrosion damage is unacceptable. For this reason, never leave the turbine engine bearings unprotected.

To properly handle bearings, use lint-free cotton or synthetic rubber gloves to keep the acids, oils, and moisture on your hands from contaminating any bearing surface. Furthermore, clean each bearing in a separate container filled with fresh cleaning solvent. Never use shop cleaning vats and vapor degreasing because of a risk of residual contamination from other parts.

Never use shop air to blow a turbine bearing dry; moisture in the air supply could corrode the bearing. The best method is to use a lint-free cloth and then let the bearing air-dry. After the bearing is completely dry, immediately lubricate it with the specified lubricant.

## VISUAL INSPECTION

Heavy maintenance inspections performed during overhaul start with a thorough visual examination after the engine parts are cleaned. Typically, an inspection light and magnifying glass are used for close visual inspections.

Before conducting the inspection, you should review an engine's operation logs for entries made since the last inspection. Entries of hot starts or hung starts, oil- and fuel-pressure fluctuations, and overspeed or overtemperature incidents provide indications regarding what type of defects are likely to be found.

The terms used to describe defects and damage found in turbine engines are similar to the terms used to describe damage found in reciprocating engines. However, some terms are unique to turbine engines, including:

**Blending** — A method of filing compressor or turbine blades and vanes to remove damage and reestablishing the appropriate contour for an aerodynamic shape.

**Blistering** — Raised areas that indicate a separation of a surface layer from a base metal. Blistering is often evident as peeling (or flaking) of a metal plating.

**Bow** — A stress-induced bend or curve in a blade's contour.

**Bulge** — An outward bending or swelling caused by excessive pressure or weakening due to excessive heat.

**Compression** — A squeezing force produced by two opposing forces acting on a part.

**Creep** — A condition of permanent elongation in rotating airfoils resulting from thermal stress and centrifugal loading. Creep is also referred to as growth.

**Dynamic Balancing** — A procedure used to balance the main rotating assembly of a turbine engine along both its rotational plane and the rotor axis.

**Electrolytic Action** — Breakdown of surfaces caused by electrical activity between dissimilar metals. Electrolytic action is also known as galvanic corrosion.

**Flowing** — The spreading out of a plated or painted surface caused by poor adhesion to the base or excessive loading on the part's surface.

**Galling** — The fretting (or chafing) of a mating surface by sliding contact with another surface or body. The heat friction causes the material from one surface to be welded or deposited onto the other, ultimately damaging the surface area.

**Glazing** — The development of a hard, glossy surface on bearing surfaces in the presence of oil, heat, and pressure.

**Growth** — A term synonymous with creep.

**Guttering** — Deep concentrated erosion that results from an enlargement of cracks or repeated exposure to a concentrated flame.

**Profile** — The contour or aerodynamic shape of a blade or surface.

**Shear** — A tearing force produced by two opposing, parallel forces acting on a part.

**Static Balancing** — A procedure that balances the main rotating assembly of a turbine engine to reduce vibration.

**Tension** — A force that tends to pull an object apart.

**Untwist** — A straightening and loss of blade curvature that results from gas loads, thermal stress, and centrifugal loading.

## COMPRESSOR SECTION

A turbine engine's fan blades (or first stage compressor blades) are vulnerable to damage caused by ingestion of foreign objects and erosion. Therefore, compressor blades and vanes are visually examined to identify cracks, dents, gouges, and other defects caused by FOD. Detecting and correcting blade defects is critically important because a single blade failure can lead to total engine failure. [Figure 4-23]

Light or minor foreign object damage can often be repaired by removing the damage and blending the blade. However, severe damage to the blade or any damage to its root requires blade replacement.

Blade and vane erosion result from ingestion of sand, dirt, dust, and other fine airborne contaminants. The abrasive effect of repeated ingestion events can wear through a blade's surface coating and into the base metal. Slipstreams around the engine core of modern high bypass engines reduce blade erosion by directing many of the contaminants around, rather than through, a compressor. However, because wing-mounted turbofan engines

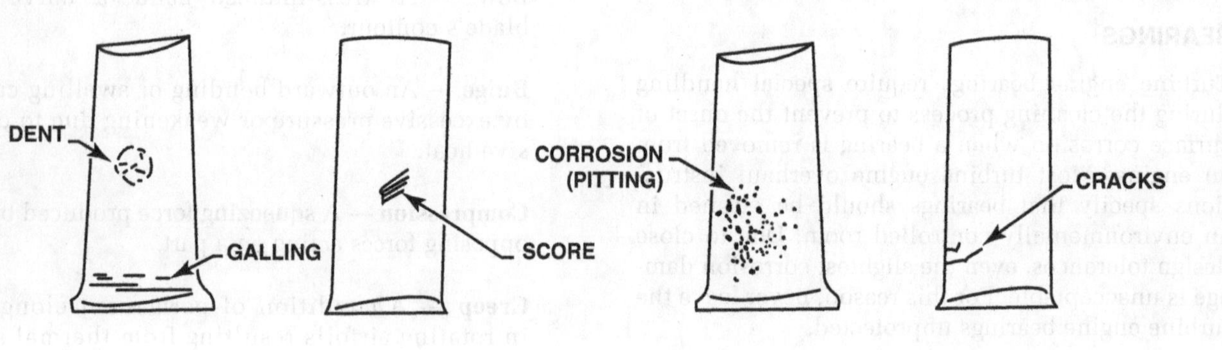


**Figure 4-23. Compressor blades are subject to stress, metal fatigue, and FOD-related defects ranging from light scratches and small dents to critical defects such as cracks and deep gouges.**

often have little ground clearance, they are more vulnerable to blade erosion during ground operations. [Figure 4-24]

For a compressor to perform efficiently, the clearance between a compressor blade and the compressor case liner must be as small as possible. However, accumulative compressor blade creep, or growth, eventually causes the blade tips to rub against the lining. Rubbing causes galling on compressor blade tips, which reduces blade efficiency and strength.

## COMBUSTION SECTION

The types of defects acceptable for a given combustion section vary according to engine model. Therefore, you must understand and follow the manufacturer's instructions when inspecting the combustion chamber. Typically, a combustion section is examined for the same types of damage in both line maintenance and shop maintenance inspections. However, the method of inspection often differs. For example, when inspecting a combustion chamber during line maintenance, you need a borescope. However, during an overhaul, you disassemble the entire combustion sections, which enables you to conduct a detailed visual inspection with normal magnification.

Some of the more common defects found during an inspection include cracks, burner-can shift, hot spots or scorched areas, warpage, and erosion. Combustion liners should also be checked for excess weld material (or slag) around all welded seams. If the welded material is not thoroughly fused into the base metal, a weld should be removed and reapplied. Otherwise, pieces of excess weld could break loose and damage turbine components downstream. Similarly, you must repair or replace a liner that has two or more converging cracks progressing from a free edge to prevent a piece of metal from breaking free and causing damage elsewhere. Minor cracks in the baffling around a fuel nozzle support seat should be repaired whenever

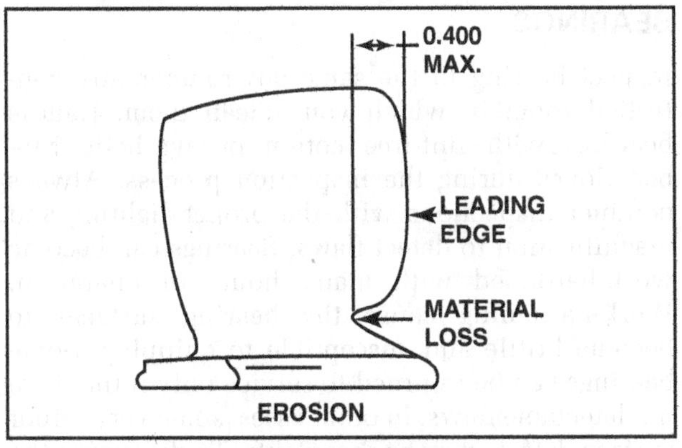


**Figure 4-24. Blade erosion is cumulative and occurs over many hours of operation. Erosion is evident by a loss of material on a blade's leading edge and near its root.**

a single crack connects more than two air holes. You should also repair minor cracks in a liner or around igniter boss pads. However, any cracks in a cone or swirl vane are cause for replacement of the combustion liner.

A malfunctioning fuel nozzle can cause significant damage to a combustion liner. Typically, hot spots or scorched areas on a combustion liner are the result of flame contact from a malfunctioning or misaligned fuel nozzle. For example, a partially clogged fuel nozzle often causes damage known as hot streaking in a combustion section. Hot streaking typically appears as burn marks along the length of a combustion section, which results from unatomized fuel contacting the combustion liner and then burning. Severe hot streaking can result in a flame passing through the entire turbine section to the tailpipe.

## TURBINE SECTION

The turbine section of an engine is subjected to great heat and stress, with damage often occurring in the form of cracking, warping, erosion, and burning. Cracking is the most common type of damage found in a turbine engine, followed by erosion caused from the flow of gases as well as impurities in the air mass that impinge on internal components. To ensure a comprehensive inspection of the complete turbine section, you should inspect the turbine nozzle vanes, turbine disk, and turbine blades separately.

### Turbine Nozzle Vanes

As noted earlier, the hottest gases in a turbine engine pass through the first set of turbine nozzle vanes. Because of this, small cracks are frequently found there. Depending on the size and orientation of the cracks, some cracking might be acceptable. Because stress is initially relieved by the development of small cracks, the weakness resulting from a small crack progressing in a nonmoving part is negligible. However, whenever cracks appear to be converging, you must replace the cracked component to prevent major engine damage.

In addition to cracking, the intense thermal stress and high-speed gases impacting a set of vanes over time can cause bowing and warping. The amount that a given vane has bowed is measured on the trailing edge using a flat plate fixture and a thickness gauge. Vanes that are bowed more than the allowable limits must be replaced or repaired in accordance with overhaul instructions. Typically, bowing is greater on a trailing edge than on a leading edge. Therefore, if the trailing edge is within serviceable limits, the leading edge is likely within limits as well. [Figure 4-25]

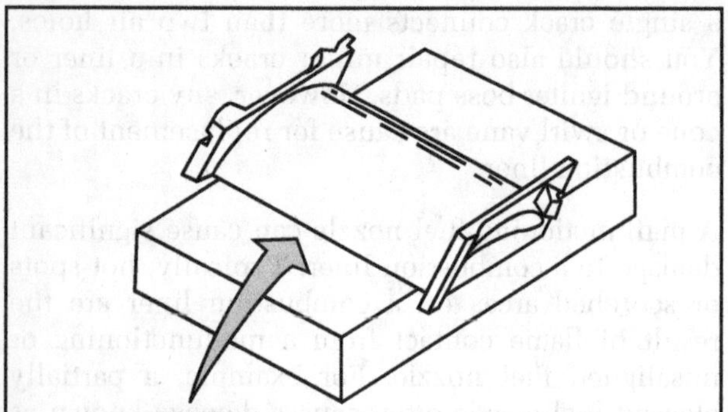


**Figure 4-25. To check a vane for bowing, place it on a flat plate fixture and insert a thickness gauge under the leading and trailing edges.**

### Turbine Disk

A turbine disk is typically inspected visually with a strong inspection light and magnifying glass. Because of the centrifugal forces a turbine wheel is subjected to, any cracks found on a turbine disk are cause for rejection and replacement. However, some manufacturers allow continued use of a turbine disk with slight pitting if the damage can be blended out by stoning and polishing.

### Turbine Blades

Turbine blades routinely incur damage because of the extreme environment in which they operate. Because catastrophic engine failure is likely if a turbine blade fails, cracking is not permitted in these parts. Of particular concern during visual inspections are stress rupture cracks on turbine blade leading and trailing edges. Stress rupture cracks are identifiable as fine hairline cracks that appear perpendicular to the blade length. Typical causes of stress rupture cracks include excessive temperatures or centrifugal loading.

Turbine blades are more prone to blade creep than compressor blades because of the high temperatures and centrifugal loads imposed during an engine cycle. A turbine engine cycle consists of start and shutdown. Each engine cycle subjects turbine blades to high heat and high rotational speeds. As a result, every turbine blade becomes slightly longer with each engine cycle. Although the additional length might be only millionths of an inch, the accumulative effect produced by numerous engine cycles eventually eliminates the necessary blade-to-case clearance.

Blade creep is divided into three stages, or classifications—primary, secondary, and tertiary. **Primary creep** occurs during an engine's first run; this is when new blades experience operational stresses for the first time. **Secondary creep** occurs slowly during many hours of operation. Engine manufacturers take secondary creep into consideration when establishing a turbine's service life. **Tertiary creep** occurs at an accelerated rate after a period of secondary creep. The onset of tertiary creep is attributed to hot starts, overtemperature events, extended operation at high power settings, and blade erosion.

Loads imposed by the flow of gases across turbine blades and vanes can cause them to untwist. When turbine blades and vanes begin untwisting, the efficiency of the turbine system decreases and engine performance deteriorates. Blades and vanes must be removed during engine tear down to check for untwisting. After they are removed, they are measured in special shop fixtures. After you inspect a blade, reinstall it in the exact slot from which it came to maintain turbine wheel balance.

Curling of blade tips is often acceptable if no sharp bends exist and the curling is within prescribed limits, which are typically not to exceed an area of one-half square inch at the tip while trailing edge limits are much less. Cracking or breaking of a blade tip often results from sharp bends at the tip. Blades with sharp bends must be replaced.

## EXHAUST SECTION

The exhaust section of a turbine engine is subject to the same high stresses and corrosive environment as the turbine section. Therefore, warping, buckling, and cracking are common defects found during inspections. A malfunctioning fuel nozzle or combustion chamber can produce hot spots or hot streaking on the exhaust cone and tailpipe. If secondary airflow does not properly control the flame zone, the combustion flame can contact the exhaust cone or tailpipe. Warping in an exhaust duct liner generally indicates the occurrence of a severe overtemperature event.

## BEARINGS

Inspect bearing in the same environmentally controlled room in which you clean them. Handle bearings with lint-free cotton or synthetic rubber gloves during the inspection process. Always conduct inspections with the proper lighting and magnification to detect flaws. Bearings can become work-hardened with many hours of operation. Work-hardening cause the bearing surfaces to become brittle and susceptible to chipping. Some bearings can be returned to service only if there are no detectable flaws. In other cases, some very minor surface defects may be acceptable. To determine the exact type and number of defects permissible, refer to the manufacturer's specifications.

After the inspection is complete and a bearing is determined to be serviceable, perform a magnetism check. Research shows that a bearing can become magnetized from rotation at high speeds, lightning strikes absorbed by an aircraft, and arc welding on the engine with improper grounding. A magnetic field detector is used to determine if a bearing has been magnetized. Any bearing with residual magnetism must be degaussed, or demagnetized. The degaussing procedure destroys the magnetic field in a part. The process of degaussing a part includes placing the part near or through an electromagnetic coil with alternating current that creates alternating magnetic fields. When a part is brought into close proximity to a degausser, the magnetic domains in a part are disrupted until there is no longer a magnetic field in the part. After a bearing has been degaussed and passes the magnetism check, it should be stored in vapor-proof packaging until engine reassembly.

## MARKING PARTS

A method for identifying areas that need repair on cold and hot section components is essential during the inspection process. This saves time by providing a technician with a visual cue to the area that needs repair. Approved marking materials for both cold and hot sections include chalk, special layout dye, and some commercial felt-tip applicators and marking pencils. Wax or grease marking pencils are acceptable only for marking parts that are not directly exposed to extreme heat.

Use only approved marking materials when marking parts that are directly exposed to an engine's hot gas path, including turbine blades and disks, turbine vanes, and combustion chamber liners. Never use a common graphite-lead pencil or any marker that leaves a carbon, copper, zinc, or lead deposit. These deposits can be drawn into the metal when heated, causing intergranular stress. In addition, layout dye, like Dykem® Steel Blue® Layout Fluid, can be potentially dangerous to hot section components if not completely removed. For these reasons, specific marking procedures and materials specified by an engine manufacturer take precedence over general marking practices.

## STRUCTURAL INSPECTION

Structural inspections are conducted using nondestructive test methods such as magnetic particle, fluorescent or dye penetrant, radiography, eddy current, and ultrasonic inspection. The purpose of a structural inspection is to discover hidden flaws that are undetectable by visual inspection. For example, a hairline crack in a hot section component might be visible only with a dye penetrant inspection. Likewise, defects that exist below the surface of a component can be detected only through magnetic particle, radiography, eddy current, or ultrasonic testing.

Magnetic particle testing can be used only on ferrous materials. The particles can be applied in either a dry form or wetted in a solvent solution. The dry form works best on cast or forged parts with rough surfaces. A wet solution with fluorescent particles and an ultraviolet lamp is better for detecting fine cracks in smooth surfaces.

Dye penetrant test kits are available with red dye or green dye. Red dye is convenient for daylight use because the developer can be sprayed from a can on the tested part. The developer causes penetrant trapped in a surface defect to turn red. The red mark or line on the part's surface becomes clearly visible. Green dye works best on parts that are removed and placed in a drip tray. After the part is clean, the green fluorescent penetrating fluid is sprayed on and permitted to dry. An ultraviolet lamp illuminates defects, which show up as bright yellow-green lines.

Radiography is a testing method that uses X-rays or Gamma rays to penetrate a part and reveal hidden flaws. This testing method requires special training and licensing because it is potentially hazardous to personnel and requires certain safety precautions. Radiography will typically detect defects that visual and dye-penetrant methods miss. This method is occasionally used to verify suspected defects in an area that is not easily inspected. Radiography has several inherent limitations and its usefulness in engine overhaul is limited.

An eddy current inspection locates both surface and subsurface discontinuities in metal parts. Specialized test equipment supplies alternating current at a specific frequency to a test coil applied to the part being tested. The magnetic field produced by the test coil induces a secondary field in the part. This secondary magnetic field causes eddy currents to flow in the part. The currents are measured and analyzed. A discontinuity in a component disrupts the induced magnetic field, and test equipment detects the anomaly.

Ultrasonic testing introduces high-frequency sound waves through a part to detect discontinuities. The two types of ultrasonic test equipment available are the immersion and the contact types. Immersion equipment is heavy and stationary while contact equipment is small and portable. Both types beam sound waves through a part and display the response on a CRT for analysis. By comparing results with those of a standard response pattern, you can detect discontinuities and flaws in a part.

## DIMENSIONAL INSPECTION

The close tolerances and fits of parts in a turbine engine make dimensional inspections critically important for determining serviceability. For example, correct clearance between the compressor and turbine blades in the engine housing is crucial for engine efficiency. Blade tip clearances are usually measured with a thickness gauge. Additional components that must be dimensionally checked during an overhaul are listed by manufacturers for each engine model in the overhaul manual. When specified, you must use special tools provided by the engine manufacturer to obtain accurate readings. [Figure 4-26)

## REPAIRS

The decision to repair or replace a turbine engine component is based on a variety of factors. For example, mandatory replacement is specified for certain parts in the overhaul manual instructions. However, some parts can be inspected for serviceability and repaired or replaced as necessary. If repairs can restore a part to serviceability, remaining service life projections must be considered to determine whether repair or replacement is the better option. Repairs that must be built up (or welded) to achieve service limits often require specialized equipment and facilities.

Plasma coating is a popular technique for building up a component and restoring it to its original dimensions. The plasma coating process is a proven method for extending the service life of blades and vanes and reducing overhaul costs. Plasma coating involves spraying an atomized metallic material onto the base metal of a part at a high velocity and at a high heat. For example, a compressor blade is built up by spraying the blade with ionized argon gas heated to 50,000°F at a velocity over 2,200 feet per second. Metallic powder is then introduced into the gas stream, causing a coat of molten metallic particles to bond to the airfoil. The process is controlled in such a way as to produce multiple coatings as thin as 0.00025 inch each. Each coating is thoroughly fused to the base metal with excellent adhesion characteristics. After the coating process is complete, the blade or vane airfoil is ground to new part dimensions.

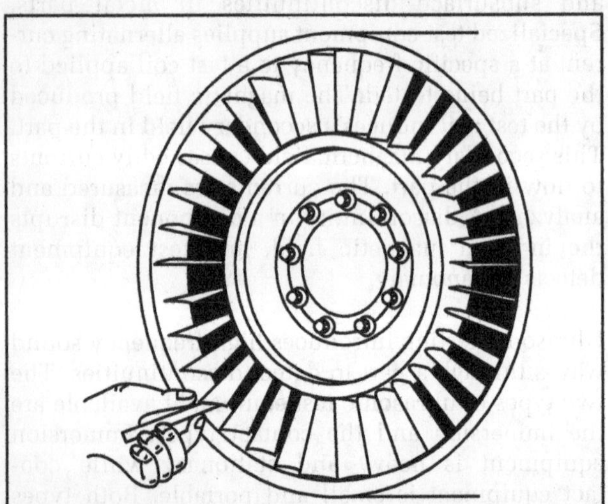

**Figure 4-26. You can use a thickness gauge to check clearances between turbine blades and the shroud unless the manufacturer requires a special tool.**

A variation of this process is referred to as ceramic coating and applies corrosion prevention to compressor parts. Additionally, the ceramic coating produces a smooth surface that reduces air friction and surface drag, which improves compressor performance. Ceramic materials can be applied to many of an engine's hot section components, including combustors, turbine nozzle diaphragms, turbine disks, turbine blades, and vanes.

Several welding methods are also used to make engine repairs. One method is called electron beam welding. Electron beam welding is used to make repairs to compressor airfoils constructed from titanium alloys. When done properly, a blade repaired with electron beam welding is as strong or stronger than a new blade or vane, making it possible to rework some compressor airfoils that would normally be rejected.

The primary difference between electron beam welding and other conventional welding techniques is that electron beam welding produces a very narrow bead. Because this welding process is completed in a vacuum chamber, the oxygen level is tightly controlled. Heat is concentrated in a small area and stress on the base metal and weld is less than in other methods. You can sometimes use this type of repair when damage to an airfoil exceeds the limits that can be repaired by blending. Typically, new material is welded in place and ground to the original airfoil shape. As with most welding procedures, heat-treatment procedures are used to relieve stress in the area of the weld.

## COMPRESSOR SECTION

One of the most common repairs made to a compressor section is the removal of foreign object damage from blades and vanes by blending. Blending is performed parallel to the length of a blade using smooth contours to minimize stress points. Common files, emery or crocus cloth, and Carborundum stones are commonly used in blend repairs. Power tools are not permitted when blending because heat stress may build up and cause damage to adjacent areas.

A typical blend repair has a length to depth ratio of approximately four to one and is completed in several steps. First, the damaged area is scalloped by filing enough material away to create a saddle or dished out shape. Next, a stone or finish file is used to smooth out score marks and radius the edges of the repair. Finally, the repair is polished with emery or crocus cloth to restore the original finish. Usually, repaired blades must be inspected by magnetic particle or dye penetrant methods to verify that all damage was removed. Repaired areas are often marked with a felt tip dye marker to help maintenance personnel identify reworked areas during future inspections.

The amount of damage permissible on engine fan blades, inlet guide vanes, and compressor blades varies from engine to engine. Therefore, you must refer to the manufacturer's repair instructions before you make any repairs. As a general rule, nicks, dents, erosion, and scoring on the face of a fan blade do not require repair as long as the damage does not exceed 0.030 inch. The area where the deepest damage is permitted is on a fan blade leading edge outboard of a mid-span shroud. Damage in this area can typically extend into a blade up to 0.060 inch. No damage is permitted around the fillets at the blade's base and where a shroud meets the blade face. [Figure 4-27]

The amount of damage permitted on a hollow inlet guide vane is much less than that for a compressor fan blade. Because vanes are hollow and the walls are constructed of thin material, blending out damage can result in inadvertently penetrating the vane wall. Furthermore, no attempts to repair an inlet guide vane by straightening, brazing, welding, or soldering are usually permitted.

As a general rule, any sharp, V-shaped dent or any cracking and tearing of a guide vane requires vane replacement. However, small, shallow dents can sometimes be left unrepaired if they are rounded, have a gradual contour, or otherwise fall within the manufacturer's specifications. Additionally, trailing edge damage of an inlet guide vane can be blended if one-third of the weld seam remains after a repair is made. You can usually reuse rubber-filled guide vanes, even if some cracking exists, as long as the cracks extend inward from the outer airfoil and do

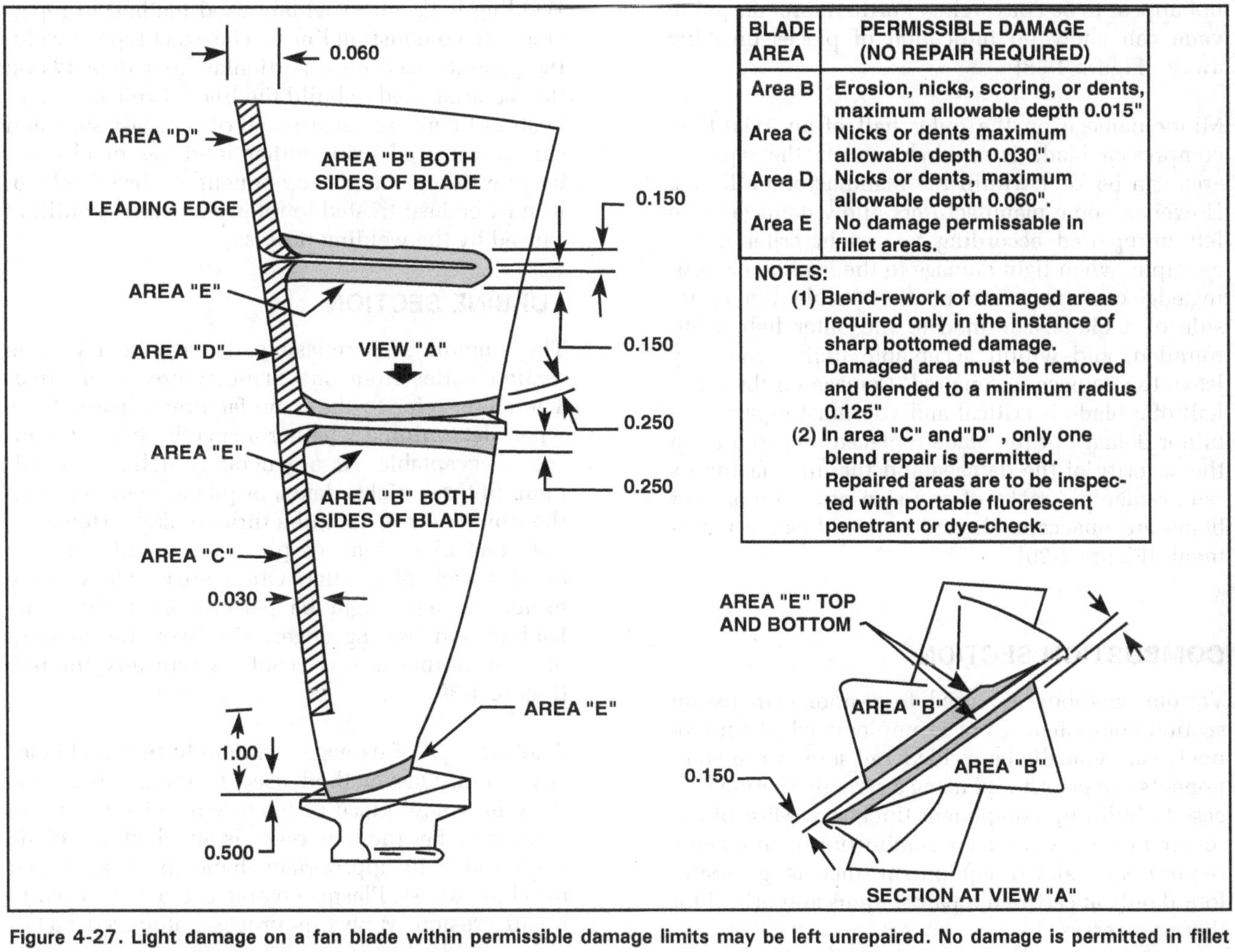


| BLADE AREA | PERMISSIBLE DAMAGE (NO REPAIR REQUIRED) |
|---|---|
| Area B | Erosion, nicks, scoring, or dents, maximum allowable depth 0.015" |
| Area C | Nicks or dents maximum allowable depth 0.030". |
| Area D | Nicks or dents, maximum allowable depth 0.060". |
| Area E | No damage permissable in fillet areas. |

NOTES:
(1) Blend-rework of damaged areas required only in the instance of sharp bottomed damage. Damaged area must be removed and blended to a minimum radius 0.125"
(2) In area "C" and"D" , only one blend repair is permitted. Repaired areas are to be inspected with portable fluorescent penetrant or dye-check.

**Figure 4-27. Light damage on a fan blade within permissible damage limits may be left unrepaired. No damage is permitted in fillet areas and cracks require replacement of a fan blade.**

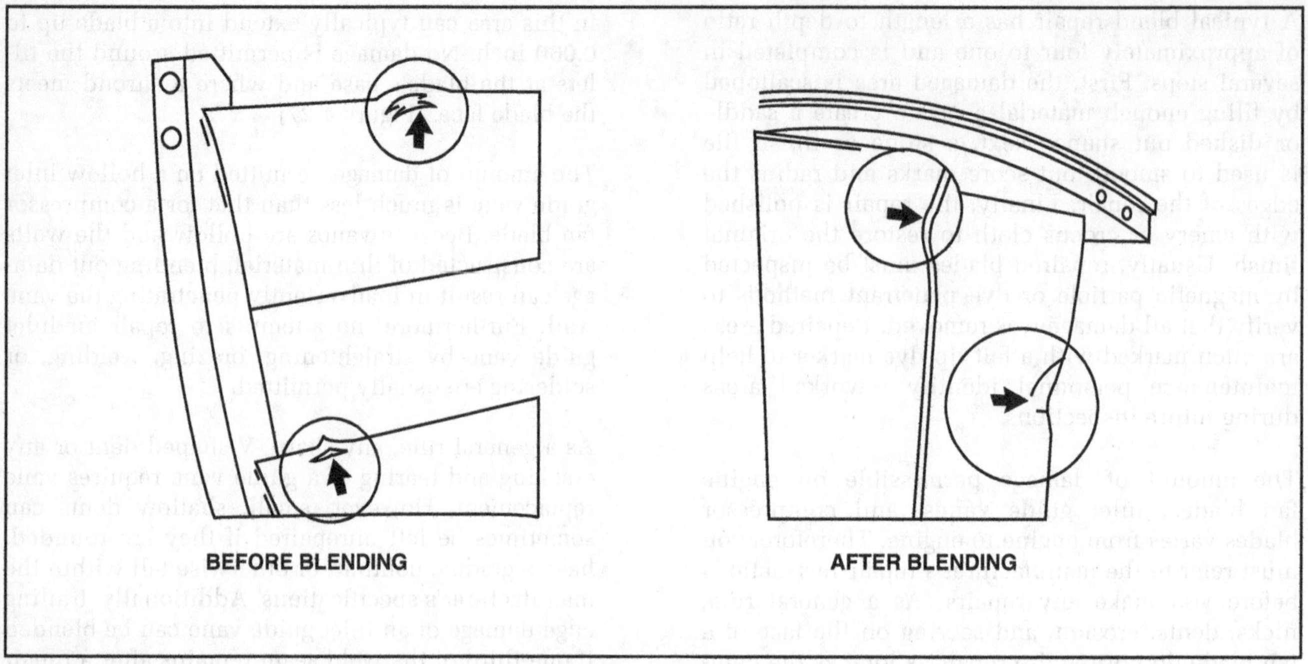


**Figure 4-28. If an inlet guide vane becomes damaged, and the damage does not penetrate the outer shell of the vane, you can blend and contour it.**

not appear to be converging. Furthermore, the guide vane can show no indication of pieces breaking away. [Figure 4-28]

Minor damage on the outer half of an axial-flow compressor blade is repairable when the repaired area can be kept within the manufacturer's limits. However, some manufacturers allow damage to be left unrepaired according to certain criteria. For example, when light damage to the leading or trailing edge of a compressor blade is visible from either side of a blade, confined to the outer half, well-rounded, and within acceptable limits, you may leave the damage unrepaired. Damage on the inner half of a blade is critical and you must repair even minor damage or the blade replaced, depending on the severity of the damage and the manufacturer's requirements. Cracks of any size on a compressor blade are unacceptable and require blade replacement. [Figure 4-29]

## COMBUSTION SECTION

Various methods are used to restore combustion section components. For example, cracked components can typically be welded and some worn components can be restored using a ceramic coating process to build up component thickness. Most of the repair processes used on combustion components require specialized equipment that is generally found only at certified repair stations authorized for these processes.

Welding is the most widely used method to repair cracks in combustion liners. The exact type of welding process used on a particular liner depends on the material used to build the liner. Typically, combustion liners are constructed of stainless steel and can be repaired using either inert gas or electron beam welding. After a component has been welded, it must be heat-treated to relieve any stress buildup caused by the welding process.

## TURBINE SECTION

The amount of permissible damage in a turbine section varies from one manufacturer to another. Therefore, refer to the manufacturer's instructions when determining whether a specific type of damage is acceptable. As a general guideline, a maximum of three nicks, dents, or pits are permitted on the front and rear face of a turbine blade. However, only one nick, dent, or pit is permitted within a quarter inch of a fillet. Other areas where some minor damage might be permissible include the leading and trailing edges. However, the amount of damage that is serviceable is typically limited. [Figure 4-30]

Another type of damage common to turbine blades is erosion. One method used to repair erosion is to weld a new piece of blade with electron beam welding. After the new piece is attached, the blade is ground to its appropriate shape and heat treated to relieve stress. Plasma coating can also be used to repair erosion. With this process, atomized metal-

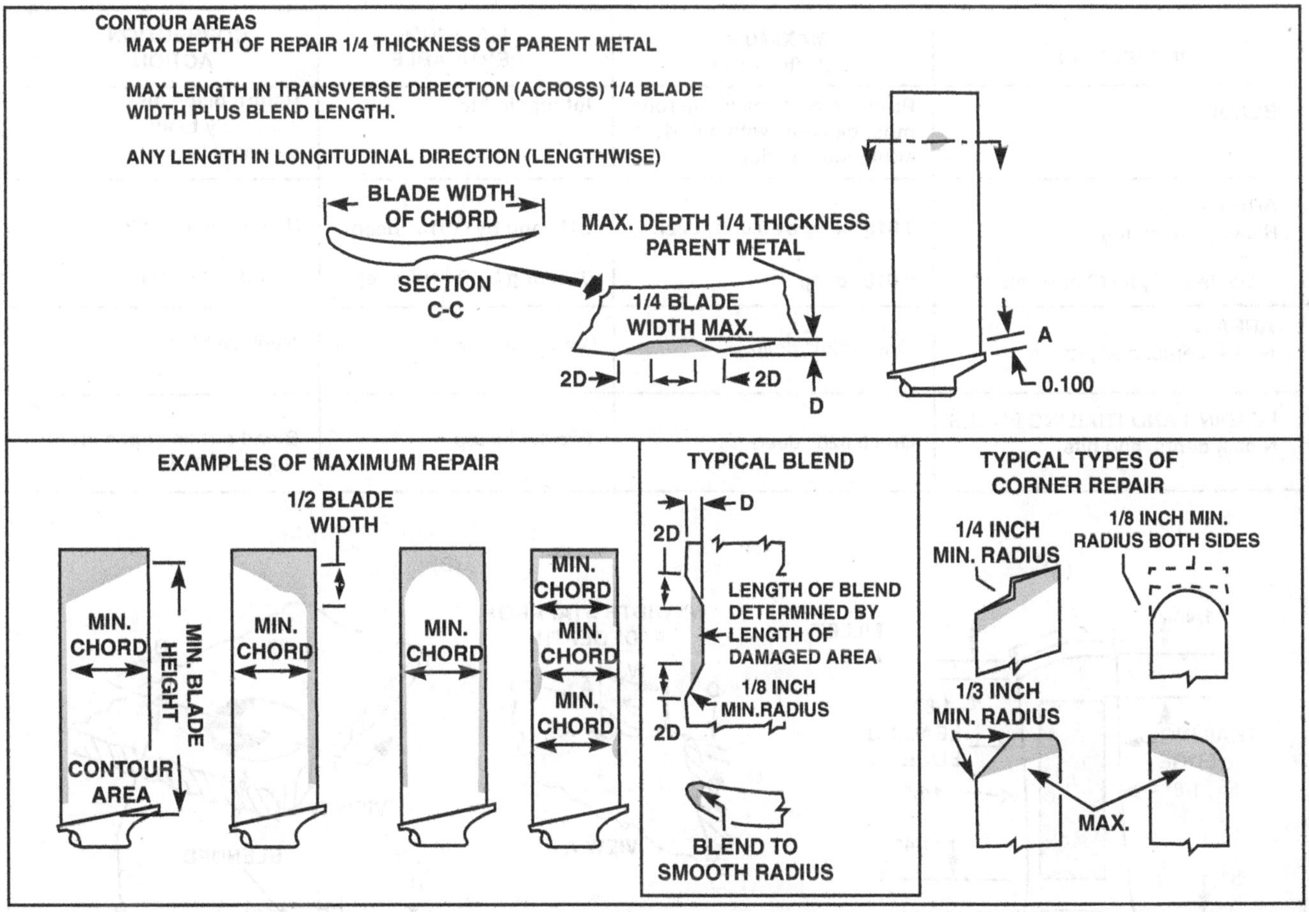


**Figure 4-29. Compressor blade repairable limits and blended repairs are based on blade width, length, and chord dimensions. Typically, most leading and trailing edge damage as well as tip damage is repairable provided you maintain a minimum chord and height.**

lic material is sprayed onto the eroded section of a turbine blade in multiple coats. After the coating process is complete, the blade is ground to its original shape.

Additional turbine components that often require repair during overhaul are turbine nozzle vanes. Typical damage that can be repaired on turbine nozzle vanes includes nicks, dents, scratches, bowing, and cracking. Most nicks, dents, and scratches are repaired using simple blending and contouring techniques to relieve stress concentrations and maintain a smooth airflow. You can usually straighten a bowed turbine nozzle vane, but the material used to build some nozzle vanes cannot withstand the straightening process. In situations where straightening is not a permissible repair, the bowed area can be cut away and a new piece of blade material welded in place. After the new material is welded in place, the vane is ground to the proper shape and heat-treated to relieve stress. [Figure 4-31]

Because turbine nozzle vanes do not rotate, they are not subject to the extreme stresses that turbine blades encounter. Therefore, minor cracking might be permissible in nozzle vanes. Multiple factors determine whether you can leave a crack (or multiple cracks). To determine the exact criteria for permissible cracking, refer to the specific manufacturers' overhaul manuals. [Figure 4-32]

## EXHAUST SECTION

Repairable damage in an exhaust section typically includes minor warping, buckling, and cracking. Warping and buckling are generally repaired by straightening and cracks are normally welded. Additional welding repairs include filling small holes and replacing larger areas of damage by welding a new piece of material in place. Typically, inert gas or electron beam welding techniques are used to repair engine exhaust sections constructed of stainless steel.

| INSPECTION | MAXIMUM SERVICEABLE | MAXIMUM REPAIRABLE | CORRECTION ACTION |
|---|---|---|---|
| BLADE SHIFT | Protrusion of any blade root must be equal within 0.015"' either side of disk. | Not repairable | Return blade disk assembly to an overhaul facility. |
| AREA A<br>Nicks (3 maximum) | 0.015" long by 0.005" deep | .015 long by 0.010" deep | Blend out damage |
| Dents and pits (3 maximum) | 0.010" deep | .015 long by 0.010" deep | Blend out damaged |
| AREA B<br>Nicks, dents, and pits | One 0.020" deep | Not repairable | Replace blade |
| LEADING AND TRAILING EDGES<br>Nicks, dents, and pits | One 0.020" deep | Two 1/8" deep | Blend out damaged area/<br>Replace blade |

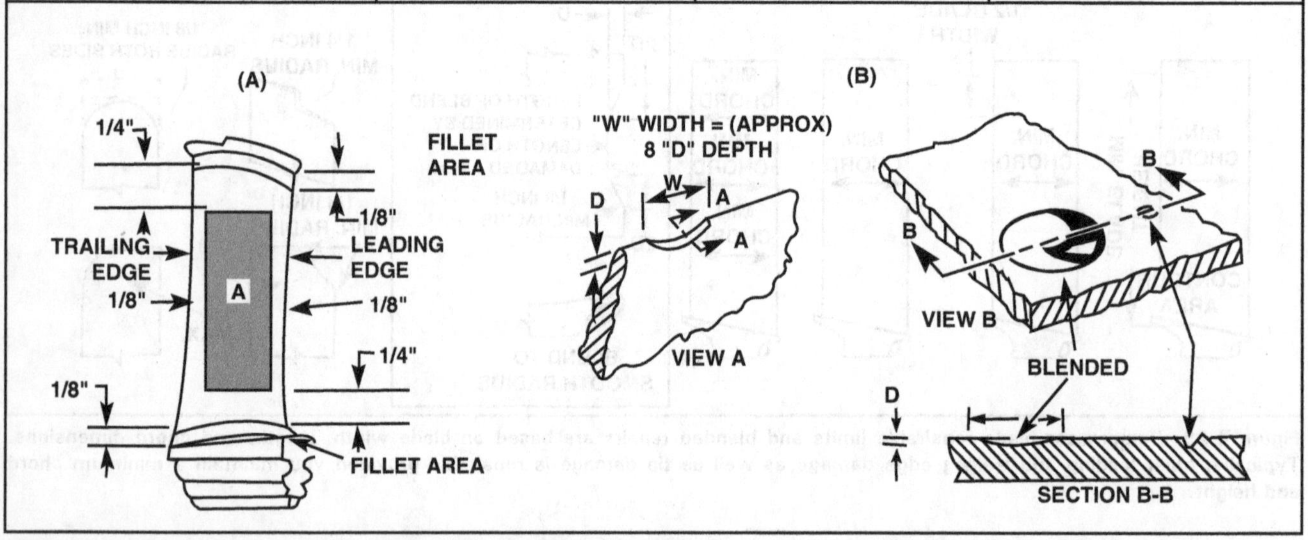


**Figure 4-30. (A) Both the chart and the first figure indicate the location and type of damage that is generally repairable on a turbine blade. However, if any crack or rippling on a trailing edge exists, blade replacement is required. (B) As a rule, whenever you repair a repair a turbine blade, the width of the repair should be approximately eight times the depth.**

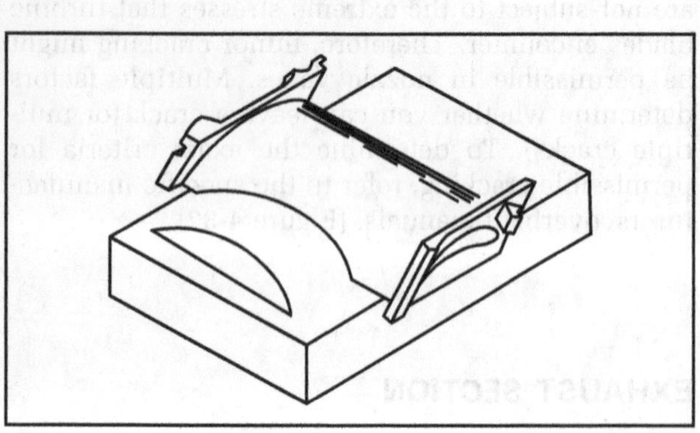

**Figure 4-31. A badly damaged turbine nozzle vane is repaired by removing the damaged area and welding in a new piece of material.**

## BALANCING

Approved turbine engine repair procedures are designed to maintain the original strength and balance of the engine. Balance is critical because of the high rotational speeds that turbine engines operate. If the main rotating assembly of a turbine engine is unbalanced it can cause severe vibration. To help ensure proper balance, you must replace compressor and turbine in a specific way. Typically an engine manufacturer restricts the number of blades that can be replaced in a given stage and on a single rotor without rebalancing the rotor.

A single blade replacement is generally accomplished by installing a new blade with an equal moment-weight. To determine the moment-weight of a single blade, each compressor or turbine blade is marked with a code indicating moment-weight in inch-ounces or inch-grams. If a new blade with the same moment-weight as a damaged blade is not available, you must replace multiple blades. For example, on a compressor or turbine wheel with an even number of blades, you replace both the damaged and opposite (180 degrees away) blades with blades of equal moment-weight. For a dam-

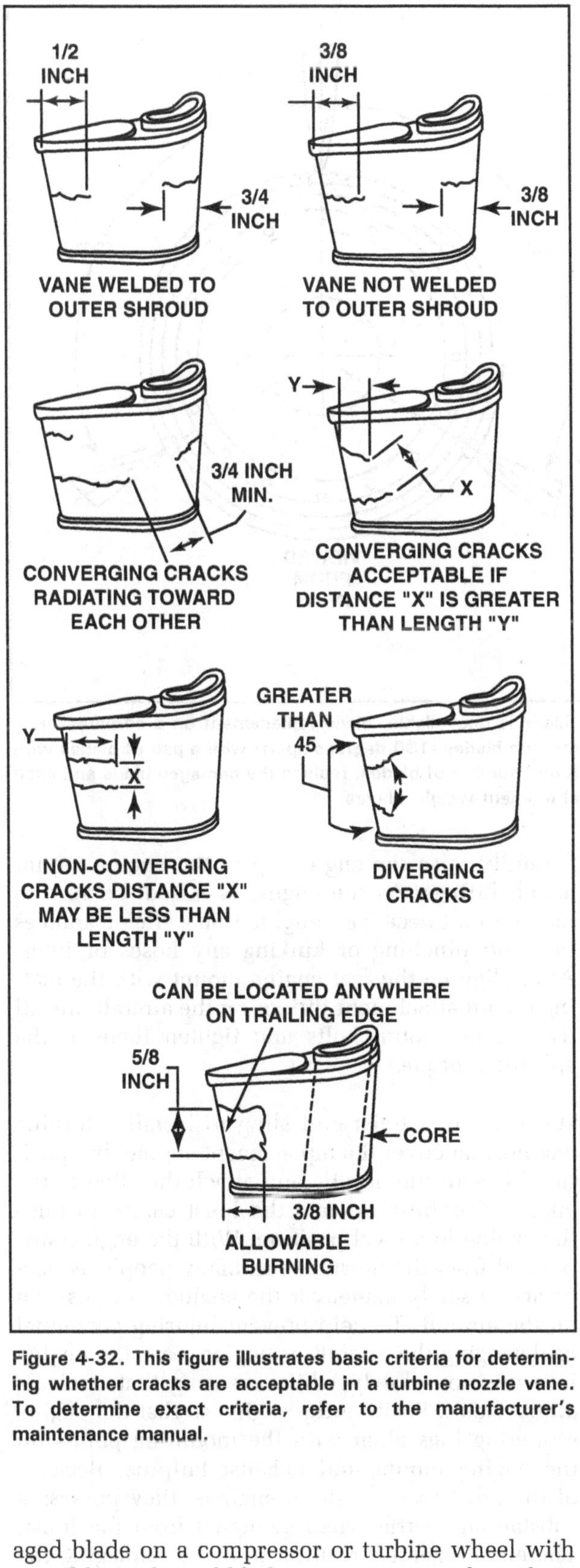


**Figure 4-32. This figure illustrates basic criteria for determining whether cracks are acceptable in a turbine nozzle vane. To determine exact criteria, refer to the manufacturer's maintenance manual.**

aged blade on a compressor or turbine wheel with an odd number of blades, you must replace three blades with equal moment-weights—the damaged blade and the blades 120 degrees to the right and left. [Figure 4-33]

Most engines are limited to a maximum speed that is below the speed at which a rotating assembly begins to vibrate. However, if repairs are improperly done, the speed at which vibration begins might fall to within the engine's normal operating range. Vibrations in one assembly can induce vibrations in other assemblies with the same natural frequency. Severe vibrations can eventually lead to complete engine destruction. To prevent this, you normally check both the static and dynamic balance of a turbine engine during the repair process. Static balancing procedures ensure balance on the rotational plane; dynamic balancing procedures ensure that the rotating assembly is balanced both in the rotational plane and along the rotor axis.

## REASSEMBLY

Generally, you use the same fixtures and tooling to reassemble a gas turbine engine after heavy maintenance or overhaul that you used to disassemble it. In addition, torque wrenches and other torque measuring tools ensure that components are properly fastened to manufacturer specifications. The closely-machined mating surfaces and tight clearances typical of turbine engine construction require the utmost care during reassembly.

Turbine engines can be reassembled vertically or horizontally. Reassembly procedures are the reverse of disassembly. Reassembly does require more time to ensure proper fit and tightening of hardware. Following the specified hardware tightening sequences is crucial to prevent incorrect torque settings. A turbine engine has many circular bolt-ring sets, and special assembly procedures are often stipulated by the engine manufacturer. Remember to check the airworthiness tags and appropriate paperwork for all modules, sections, and components before reassembly.

A typical overhaul manual specifies the parts that you must replace when reassembling an engine. Some examples of parts that are normally replaced during an overhaul include bearings, seals, gaskets, O-rings, lockwire, lockwashers, tablocks, and cotter pins.

### ENGINE TESTING

The final step in the overhaul process is to test the engine. Engine performance is evaluated with a block test in a test cell with specialized test equipment and standard engine instruments. Operational test procedures vary with individual engines. For all engines, the failure of any internal

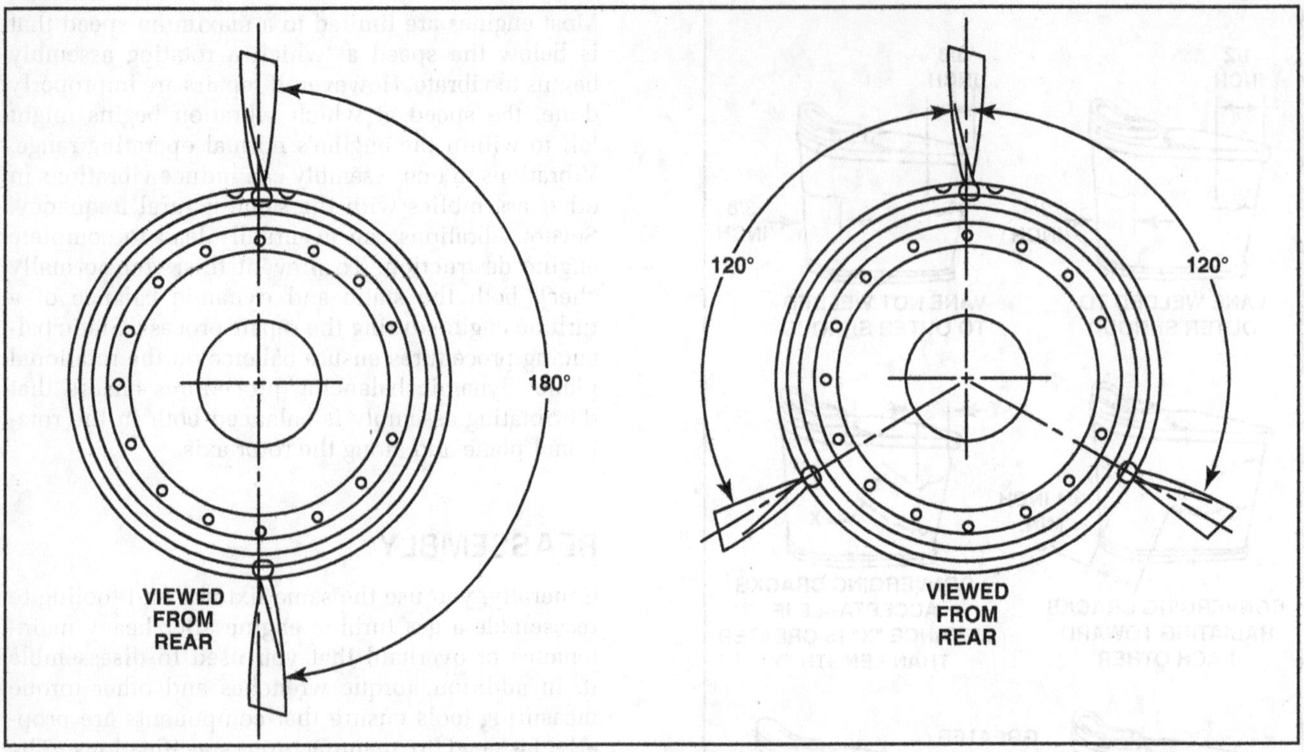


**Figure 4-33. If a blade having the exact moment-weight the damaged blade is unavailable, blade replacement on a compressor or turbine wheel with an even number of blades is accomplished by replacing two blades (180 degrees apart) with a pair of blades with equal moment-weight. However, if a compressor or turbine wheel has an odd number of blades, replace the damaged blade and each blade 120 degrees to the left and right of the damaged blade with equal moment-weight blades.**

part during run-in requires disassembly and repair. If an engine accessory fails, install a new accessory and continue the block test. Following successful completion of block test requirements, engines not slated for immediate installation on an aircraft should receive a corrosion prevention treatment and be placed in storage.

## ENGINE INSTALLATION

A repaired, overhauled, or replaced engine must be prepared for installation. This preparation typically entails returning the engine to the configuration it was in immediately after it was removed. However, if an engine being installed is shipped new from the factory, additional assembly might be required. For example, if an engine was preserved for storage, you must follow the depreservation procedures required by the manufacturer.

### MOUNTING THE ENGINE

Before mounting an engine on an aircraft, be sure you have the appropriate hardware nearby and that you have inspected the engine mount structure and shock mounts for integrity. When using an engine dolly to install an engine, observe the precautions and instructions on the dolly's ground handling instruction placards. With the dolly in position, carefully raise the engine up to the engine mount attach fittings. As the engine is raised, be sure to maintain all necessary engine-to-nacelle clearances to avoid pinching or kinking any hoses or lines. After aligning the rear engine mount with the mating mount attachment fittings on the aircraft, install the engine mount bolts and tighten them to the specified torque.

When using a hoist and sling to install a turbine engine, maneuver the replacement engine into position beneath the nacelle and attach the sling to the engine. Carefully operate the hoist cables to raise the engine in a level position. With the engine suspended from the hoist, use as many people as necessary to safely maneuver the engine into position on the aircraft. To help prevent injuring personnel or damaging the aircraft or engine, ease the engine into position slowly while ensuring that it clears all obstacles. Position the engine so that the engine mounting lugs align with the mounting points on the engine mount and exhaust tailpipe. Because of the great mass of these engines, they possess a substantial inertia when swinging from the hoist. Therefore, exercise caution to avoid damaging the nacelle framework, ducts, or firewall connections.

After the engine is correctly aligned, insert the mounting bolts and secure them with the appropriate nuts. Then torque the engine mounting nuts to the manufacturer's recommended value. The applicable manufacturer's instructions outline the appropriate sequence for tightening the mounting bolts to ensure security. While the nuts are being tightened, the hoist should support the engine weight and permit proper mounting bolt alignment. Otherwise, the weight of the engine on the mounting bolts could affect your ability to properly tighten the nuts to the correct torque. Improper alignment can result in false torque readings. After the nuts are properly tightened to the specified torque, safety them according to the manufacturer's specifications.

## CONNECTIONS AND ADJUSTMENTS

After the engine is mounted, the air conditioning duct can be connected between the pylon and engine bleed air duct. Tighten the duct connections to the proper torque and remove the dolly (or hoist and sling) from the engine. With the engine supported by the aircraft, connect the electrical leads and fluid lines necessary for operation to the engine and accessories. Generally there are no rules that govern the order in which the accessories are connected. However, be sure to follow the manufacturer's instructions for an efficient installation.

Hoses in low-pressure systems are generally attached and secured in place with clamps. Before reinstalling clamps, examine them carefully and replace any that are badly distorted or defective. After a hose is installed, it must be adequately supported and routed away from parts that could cause damage. Usually, rubber-lined supporting clamps, called Adel clamps, are installed at specified intervals to provide protection and support.

Before installing metal tubing with threaded fittings, make sure that the threads are clean and in good condition. If specified in the instructions, apply the appropriate thread-sealing compound to the fitting before installation. Exercise care to prevent cross-threading any fittings and be sure to use the correct torque. Overtightening a fitting increases the likelihood of leaks and failures.

When you connect electrical leads to an accessory, make sure that all connections are clean and secure. When leads are secured on a threaded terminal post with a nut, insert a lock washer under the nut to prevent the nut from backing off. When required, knurled connector plugs are secured with steel safety wire to prevent accidental disconnection. To help prevent electrical leads within the engine nacelle from chafing, all wiring must be anchored appropriately to provide a secure installation.

Each aircraft model has an engine control system specifically designed for a particular combination of airframe and engine. Typical engine controls consist of rigid push-pull rods, flexible push-pull wire encased in a coiled wire sheath, cables and pulleys, or any combination of the three. Regardless of type, all engine controls must be accurately adjusted to ensure instantaneous response to a control input. Therefore, all adjustments must be made in accordance with the procedures outlined in the manufacturer's instructions.

Before rigging an engine's fuel and power controls, inspect all bellcranks for looseness, cracks, or corrosion, and examine all rod ends for damaged threads. After you rig a control, check for the correct number of visible threads after final adjustment. In addition, examine cable drums for wear and cable guards for proper position and tension.

The power lever control cables and push-pull rods in the airframe between the cockpit and engine pylon are not usually disturbed during an engine change, so they sometimes require no rigging. However, you must re-rig the portion of the engine control system from the pylon to the engine after each engine or fuel control change. [Figure 4-34]

Before adjusting the power controls at the engine, be sure that the power lever is free from binding and the controls have full-throw at the console. If they do not have full-throw or are binding, check their path through the airframe and repair discrepancies. A properly adjusted engine control must have a degree of cushion, or springback, at its fully open and closed positions. In other words, the stops for the power and condition levers on a fuel control must be reached before the power or condition controls reach their stop in the cockpit. The presence of a cushion ensures that the power and fuel valves fully open and close. Without a cushion, a pilot cannot determine whether a power or condition valve is fully opened or closed. Power controls on multiengine aircraft must have equal amounts of cushion so that the control levers align in any selected power setting. This reduces the likelihood of having to set each control individually while synchronizing engine operations.

After you install and adjust a turboprop engine, you can install the propeller. Obtain the proper gaskets or O-rings prior to installation. Large propellers require the use of an appropriate sling and hoist arrangement due to their size and weight. Never attempt to lift a propeller into place with inadequate personnel or equipment. Always follow the manufacturer's recommended installation procedure.

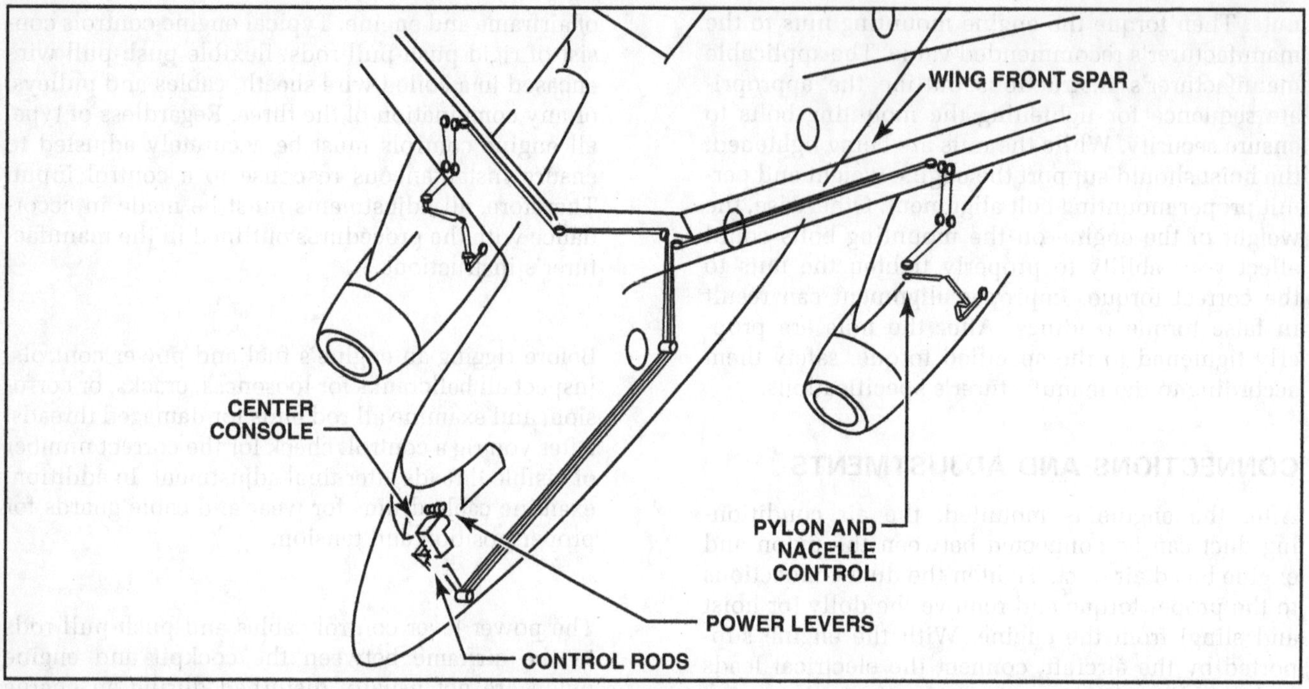


**Figure 4-34. The control system components in the airframe generally remain undisturbed during an engine change. However, the controls in the engine pylon must always be rerigged.**

## ENGINE ALIGNMENT AND TRIMMING

After you install a new or replacement turbine engine in a helicopter, it is very important to check the alignment of the engine and the transmission. This is critical to avoid placing excessive stress on the main input shaft couplings. Alignment is normally accomplished by shimming the mount legs between the fuselage and the engine mount. This procedure might not be required if the engine mounts are not disturbed during an engine change. However, whenever the engine mounts are changed or the drive shaft shows excessive wear, alignment checks should be accomplished. Some maintenance shop operators check the alignment at every engine installation for an added margin of safety. [Figure 4-35]

Trimming an engine involves adjusting the idle and maximum r.p.m. setting on the engine fuel control. Engine trimming was described in detail in section A of this chapter.

## ENGINE PRESERVATION

Engines that are placed in storage or transported to an overhaul facility must be preserved and protected to prevent corrosion and other forms of damage. Whether an engine is waiting to be overhauled or is newly overhauled, damaging rust and other forms of corrosion can occur unless the engine is protected. Preservation is also recommended when an engine remains on the aircraft if engine operation is limited (or suspended) for an extended period of time. For example, to protect an engine's fuel system, fuel lines can be filled with corrosion-preventive oil and all openings sealed. To protect an engine as a whole, it can be sealed in a bag or container that contains a desiccant. The desiccant absorbs moisture within a sealed enclosure to prevent the onset of corrosion.

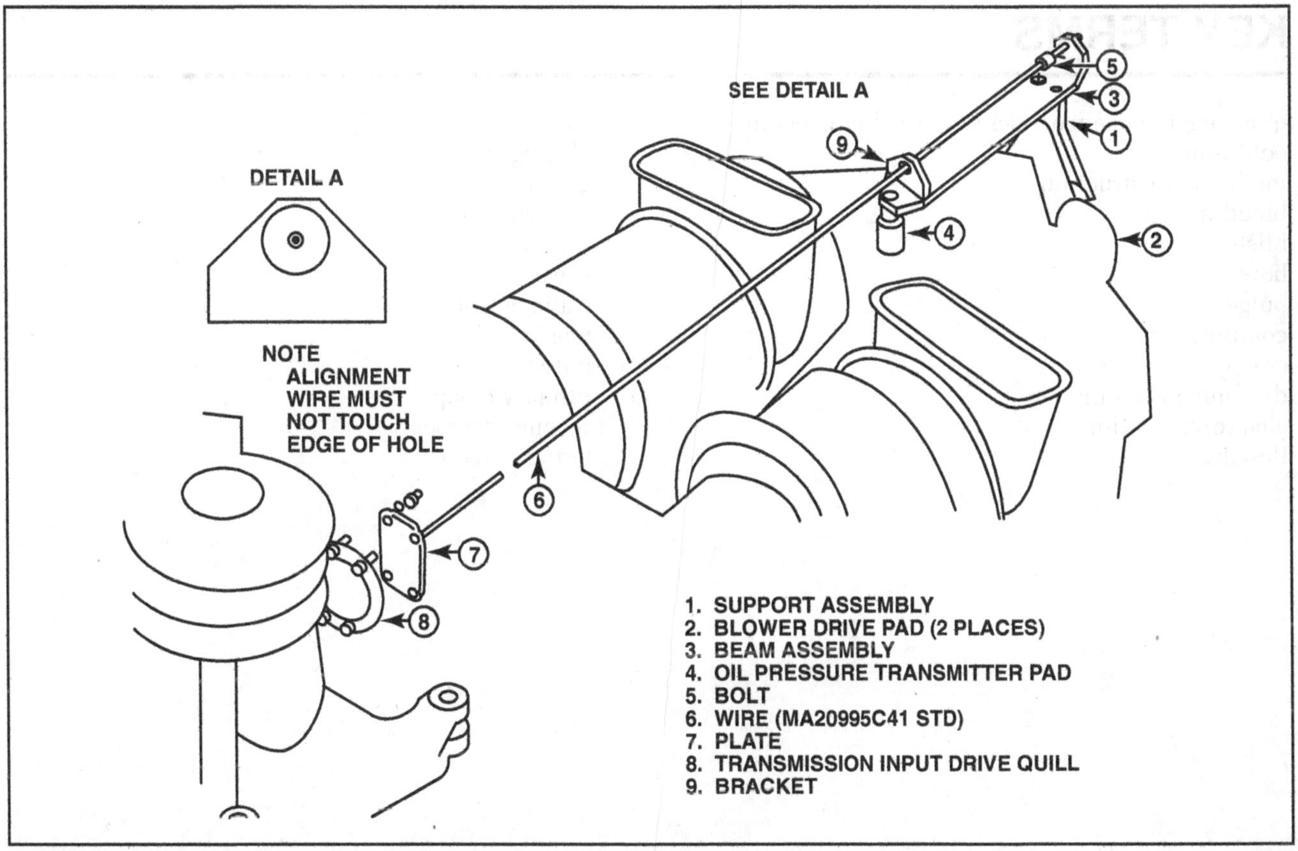


**Figure 4-35. To check engine-to-transmission alignment, a beam assembly is typically mounted to an engine drive pad. A piece of safety wire is then strung from the beam assembly to a plate on the transmission. The wire passes through a target hole in a bracket attached to the beam assembly. When the wire is taut, it should pass through the target hole without touching the side of the hole. If it touches, the mounts should be shimmed until the correct alignment is obtained.**

# SUMMARY CHECKLIST

✓ Because the removal and installation of a gas turbine engine is different for every engine and airframe combination, always follow the manufacturer's published instructions.

✓ Only the manufacturer or an approved overhaul facility can overhaul a gas turbine engine.

✓ When an overhauled engine is reinstalled on an aircraft, it must be aligned and trimmed.

# KEY TERMS

quick engine change assembly weather checking
cold flow
modular construction
blending
blistering
bow
bulge
compression
creep
dynamic balancing
electrolytic action
flowing
galling
glazing
growth
guttering
profile
shear
static balancing
tension
untwist
primary creep
secondary creep
tertiary creep

# QUESTIONS

1. Typically, a turbine engine _______ (does or does not) have a TBO rating like a reciprocating engine.

2. The most common damage to a compressor is from _______.

3. What do the initials QECA stand for?

4. The overhaul of an engine module is considered to be a _______ (major or minor) repair.

5. Properly cleaned bearings should be dried with a lint-free cloth or allowed to _______dry.

6. Minor damage to engine compressor and fan blades _______ (are or are not) repairable.

7. A partially clogged fuel nozzle causes a condition known as _______ _______.

8. Stress rupture cracks in a turbine blade appear ______________(at right angles to, along) the blade length.

9. Primary creep occurs on a turbine blade ____________(slowly, during the first run, after 100 hours operation).

10. The most common dye penetrant for daylight use is colored _______ (red, green, orange).

11. If a blade having a higher or lower moment weight must be used for replacement, a turbine wheel with an even number of blabes will take at least _______ blades, while a turbine wheel with an odd number of blades will require at least _______blades.

12. Stress rupture cracks on a turbine engine normally run ______________ (perpendicular or parallel) to the length of the blade.

13. Stress rupture cracks and rippling of the trailing edge of turbine blades are usually caused by excessive ______________.

14. Blade _______ (creep or untwist) occurs in both turbine blades and turbine vanes as a result of excessive gas loads on their surfaces.

15. Blade _______ (creep or untwist) is a term used to describe the permanent elongation of turbine blades.

16. A common graphite lead pencil _______ (is or is not) an acceptable marking device for hot section components.

17. Plasma coating is primarily used to build up parts to their _______ diminsions.

18. Compressor blade to engine housing clearances are normally measured with a _______ _______.

19. After a combustion liner has been repaired by welding, it must be _______ _______ to relieve built-up stresses.

20. Turbine blade ______________ (cracking or erosion) is the result of the wearing away of metal, either from the gas flow across the surface or the impingement of impurities in the gases on internal components.

21. If a turbine blade is replaced, the new blade must have a ______________ ______________ that is equal to the old blade.

22. After installing a turbine engine in a helicopter, it may be necessary to check the alignment of the engine to the ______________.

23. When properly adjusted, engine controls will have a small amount of ______________ ______________ at each end of their travel.

24. The term ______________ refers to adjustments that are made to a turbine engine fuel control.

25. When is it usually necessary to trim a turbine engine fuel control?

    a. ______________

    b. ______________

    c. ______________

26. Trim adjustments generally include only the ______________ and the ______________ speed of the turbine engine.

27. Substances that can absorb moisture from the atmosphere are referred to as ______________.

28. Trimming a turbine engine fuel control allows it to produce ______________ ______________.

# CHAPTER 5

# INDUCTION SYSTEMS

## INTRODUCTION

The induction system is designed to supply air to an engine to support combustion. On reciprocating engines, air enters an air intake and is routed to a carburetor or another fuel metering device. The air (sometimes mixed with fuel) is delivered to the cylinders for combustion. In a turbine-engine induction system, large quantities of air enter through an inlet into a compressor. After compression, the resulting high-pressure airmass is diffused, mixed with fuel, and ignited in a combustion chamber to produce thrust. Because a turbine engine consumes large quantities of air, the induction system plays a significant role in overall engine efficiency.

# SECTION A

## RECIPROCATING ENGINES

The primary purpose of an induction system in a reciprocating engine is to provide a sufficient quantity of air to support normal combustion. Reciprocating engine induction systems are broadly classified as normally aspirated, supercharged, and turbocharged.

## NORMALLY ASPIRATED SYSTEMS

The typical induction system on a normally aspirated engine consists of four major components, or sections: air intake, induction air filter, fuel metering system, and induction manifold. Additional subsystems such as an alternate air source, an ice removal or prevention system, and a temperature indicating system are often included to provide the pilot with information and limited control of the system.

### AIR INTAKES

An air intake, sometimes referred to as an air scoop, collects ambient air from outside of the aircraft. To take maximum advantage of ram air pressure, the location of an intake is typically found in the propeller slipstream because of the extra velocity the propeller imparts to the airstream. By taking advantage of ram air pressure, the pressure within the intake is typically higher than at any other point in a normally aspirated induction system. Because of this pressure rise, a well-designed intake scoop can have a substantial effect on an engine's power output.

### AIR FILTERING

For reliable engine operation and a long service life, the induction air must be free of foreign material. Induction filters are typically installed to prevent dust, sand, abrasive materials, and other contaminants from entering the engine.

Dust carried into the engine cylinders by induction air can be particularly detrimental to an aircraft engine. Dust particles can cause accelerated wear on cylinder walls and piston rings, foul the spark plugs with silicon, and contaminate the oil. If dust contaminates the oil, the particles are carried throughout the engine, causing further wear on bearings and gears. In extreme cases, dust accumulation can clog an oil passage, ultimately causing oil starvation. Dust can also collect in a fuel-metering device and disrupt its ability to provide the proper fuel/air mixture at all power settings.

#### Filter Maintenance

The efficiency of any filtration system depends on proper maintenance and service. Periodic removal, cleaning, or replacement of filter elements is essential to ensure proper engine performance. Many early air filters were constructed from screen wire that was filled with a reusable fiber material known as **flock**. To maintain such a filter, clean and service it by washing it in an approved solvent. Then soak the filter element in a mixture of engine oil and preservative oil. After all the fibers are thoroughly saturated, suspend the filter and permit the excess oil to drain.

Newer types of air filters include paper filters similar to the ones used in automobiles. As air passes through the porous paper filter element, dust and sand particles become trapped on the filter surface. Some manufacturers approve a method of cleaning paper filters by blowing the dust out in the opposite direction to the normal airflow. Some paper filters can be washed in a mild soap and water solution and permitted to dry. However, when servicing this type of filter; be sure to follow the manufacturer's recommendations or restrictions.

Another type of filter available today is a polyurethane foam filter impregnated with a glycol solution. The glycol solution makes the filter sticky so that contaminants stick to the element. This type of filter element is particularly effective. Avoid attempting to clean an impregnated foam filter. To service this type of filter, remove and discard the used foam element and install a new one.

### FUEL METERING SYSTEM

The fuel delivery system on a normally aspirated engine is either a carburetor or fuel injection system. The purpose of a fuel delivery system is to meter the amount of fuel based on the volume of air delivered to the cylinders. A complete discussion about fuel metering is in Section B of Chapter 7.

## INTAKE MANIFOLD

The intake manifold typically includes ducting from the fuel metering device to the individual cylinders. On a typical horizontally opposed engine, the intake manifold provides the connecting point of all the individual pipes that deliver air (sometimes mixed with fuel) to the cylinders. One end of each cylinder's intake pipe is typically bolted to the cylinder intake port and the other end is attached to the manifold with a short section of synthetic rubber hose or rubber packing and a packing nut. Both methods permit some movement between the intake pipes and manifold as the cylinders expand and contract. In some installations, the intake manifold is routed through the oil sump before it branches to each cylinder. This increases the temperature of the fuel/air mixture which, in turn, promotes better fuel vaporization.

In large radial engines, even distribution of the fuel/air mixture is difficult to achieve. To help ensure equal distribution, some radial engines have a **distribution impeller** attached directly to the rear of the crankshaft. As the fuel/air mixture enters the center of the distribution impeller, centrifugal force distributes the mixture to the cylinders. Because the impeller is attached directly to the crankshaft, it operates at the same speed and does not boost the pressure in the manifold.

One important characteristic of an intake manifold is that it must be airtight. If all seals are not maintained, unfiltered air will leak into the intake manifold and inadvertently cause the mixture to become lean, which can result in rough engine operation. Small induction leaks are most noticeable at idle because the pressure differential between the manifold and atmosphere is greatest at low speed.

# INDUCTION SYSTEM ICING

Induction system icing occurs when water freezes in an induction system and restricts airflow to the engine. When this happens, the engine might run rough, lose power, or even quit in flight. Complaints of poor engine performance in flight that cannot be verified on a postflight ground check might indicate that induction system icing occurred while in flight. When ice accumulation causes poor engine performance, the problem disappears when the ice melts. It is critical for both pilots and aircraft maintenance technicians to understand how induction icing forms, what the indications are, and how to prevent or remove it.

Induction ice can form when an aircraft flies through clouds, fog, rain, sleet, snow, or even clear air when relative humidity is high. Induction icing is generally classified as one of three types: fuel evaporation, throttle, and impact.

## FUEL EVAPORATION ICE

Fuel evaporation ice, sometimes referred to as **carburetor ice**, is a result of the temperature drop that occurs when fuel is vaporized. In a carburetor, as fuel is released into the airstream, it turns into a vapor and absorbs heat from the surrounding air. This can cause a drop in air temperature of 30 degrees Fahrenheit or more. In some cases, this loss of heat is enough to cause the moisture in the air to condense and freeze. Because of this phenomenon, a carburetor typically accumulates ice before any other part of an aircraft in flight. In fact, carburetor ice can occur at ambient air temperatures as high as to 70 degrees Fahrenheit and when relative humidity is as low as 50 percent. Optimum conditions for carburetor ice exist when the outside air temperature is between 30° and 40° Fahrenheit and the relative humidity is above 60 percent.

In a fuel injection system, fuel is injected and vaporized at or near the intake port of each cylinder. In this case, the heat of combustion offsets the temperature drop caused by fuel vaporization. Therefore, fuel evaporation icing is typically not a concern in fuel injected engines.

## THROTTLE ICE

Throttle ice forms on the downstream side of a throttle, or **butterfly valve,** when it is in a partially closed position. Air flowing across and around the throttle valve creates an area of low pressure on the downstream side. This has a cooling effect on the fuel/air mixture, which can cause moisture to accumulate and freeze on the downstream side of the butterfly valve. Because throttle icing typically occurs when the butterfly valve is partially closed, a small amount of ice can cause a relatively large reduction in airflow and a corresponding loss of engine power. In severe cases, a large accumulation of ice can jam the throttle and render it immovable. Because the temperature drop created by the low pressure area is not that great, throttle ice seldom occurs at temperatures above 38 degrees Fahrenheit.

## IMPACT ICE

Impact ice is caused by visible moisture striking an aircraft and then freezing. The air intake and air filter are the areas most susceptible to impact icing. However, impact ice can also collect at points in an induction system where the airflow changes direction or where dents and protrusions exist. Whenever an induction system encounters impact icing, air flow is restricted to the rest of the system . Severe cases of impact icing can cause a total blockage to airflow and lead to complete engine failure.

## ICE DETECTION AND REMOVAL

Because the accumulation of ice in an induction system restricts the amount of air that can enter an engine, the first indication of icing is a decrease in engine power. On an aircraft equipped with a fixed-pitch propeller, the decrease in engine power is indicated by a drop in speed followed by engine roughness. However, if an aircraft has a constant-speed propeller, the first indication of induction ice is a decrease in manifold pressure with no change in engine speed.

To prevent engine performance from degrading because of induction icing, it is necessary to prevent or remove carburetor icing. The most commonly used method is to direct warm air into the carburetor. With this type of ice removal system, known as a **carburetor heat** system, unfiltered air is drawn from within the engine cowling through a sheet metal shroud surrounding an exhaust pipe. The shroud is commonly called a **heater muff** and functions as an air-to-air heat exchanger that warms the intake air and then directs it to a **carburetor air box.** [Figure 5-1]

A carburetor heat system applies heat at the first sign of carburetor icing, after which, engine output will increase. On engines with a fixed-pitch propeller, the increase in power output is indicated by an increase in speed shortly after carburetor heat is applied. On engines equipped with a constant-speed propeller, an increase in manifold pressure indicates increased power output.

Although carburetor heat is extremely effective at eliminating carburetor ice, improper or careless use can damage an engine. For example, because carburetor heat air is unfiltered, excessive use increases the chance of dirt and foreign material entering the engine. For this reason, carburetor heat should always be in the cold position when the aircraft is on the ground. This is especially true when operating in sandy or dusty locations. As another precaution, the carburetor heat control should be left in the "cold" position when starting an engine. If the heat control is placed in the "hot" position, damage to a carburetor heat air box could result if the engine backfires.

Remember that warm air is less dense than cold air. When carburetor heat is applied, the fuel/air mixture becomes richer and its weight is reduced. A reduction in volumetric efficiency causes a noticeable loss in power. Furthermore, high intake air temperatures that result from using carburetor heat can

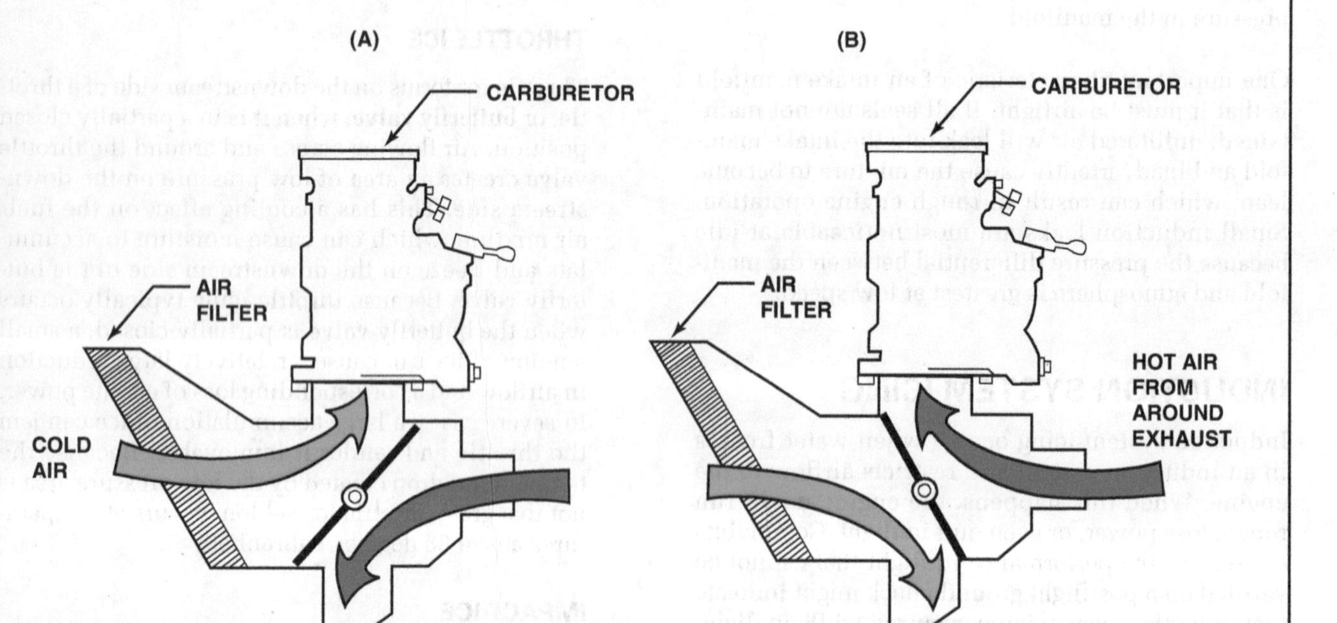


**Figure 5-1. (A) When the carburetor heat control is in the cold position, filtered ram air entering the main air scoop is ducted to the carburetor while heated air is ducted overboard. (B) In the hot position, the air door is repositioned to route hot, unfiltered air into the carburetor.**

lead to detonation, especially during takeoff or other high-power operations.

Any time that an engine fails to develop full power, a possible cause is the inadvertent application of carburetor heat, possibly from an improperly rigged carburetor heat control. Whenever you troubleshoot an engine that is not developing full power, verify the position of the carburetor heat control and rigging before assuming that another component is at fault.

Another type of system used to eliminate induction icing works by spraying a deicing fluid into the air stream ahead of the carburetor. This type of system often uses alcohol as a deicing fluid. A typical system includes an alcohol reservoir, an electric pump, a spray nozzle, and cockpit controls.

Although the use of heated air and deicing fluid is effective at removing both carburetor and throttle ice, little can be done to remove impact ice when it blocks an air intake. To address that problem, an alternate air supply must be provided. On carbureted engines, a carburetor air box provides an **alternate air supply** that can draw air from the main intake or from inside the cowling. However, because fuel-injected engines do not use a carburetor air box, an **alternate air door** must be installed. When opened, the alternate air door lets warm, unfiltered air flow into the induction system. The operation of an alternate air door can be controlled manually from the cockpit or automatically. [Figure 5-2]

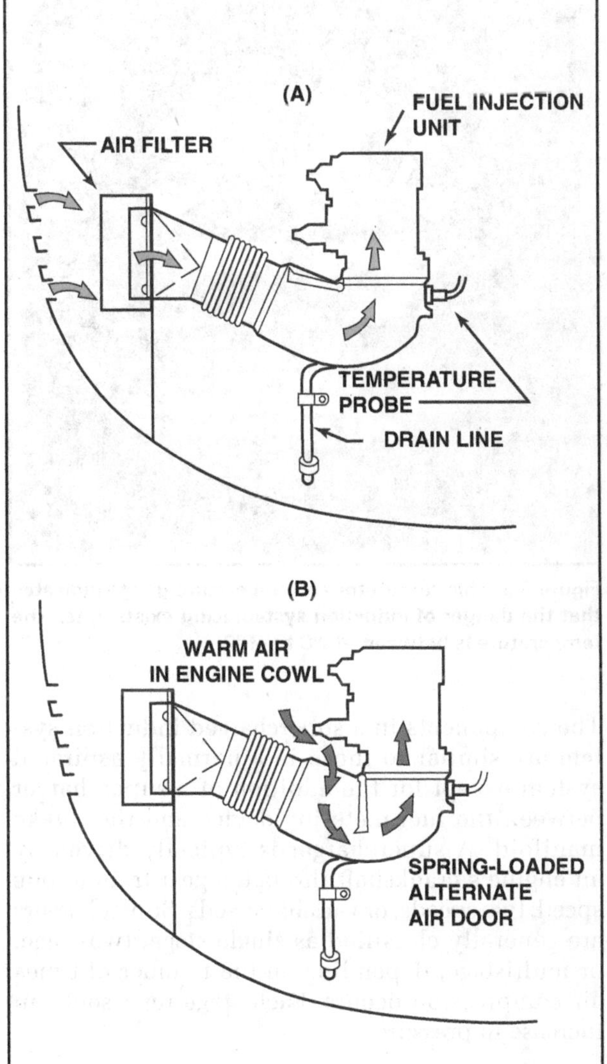


**Figure 5-2. (A) Under normal conditions, the induction system on a fuel injected engine ducts filtered air into the fuel injection unit. (B) If the filter or intake becomes clogged with ice or other debris, a spring-loaded alternate air door opens and permits unfiltered air from inside the cowling to enter the induction system.**

## TEMPERATURE INDICATING SYSTEMS

To help inform a pilot when the temperature at the carburetor can support the formation of ice, some aircraft are fitted with a **carburetor air temperature gauge**, or **CAT gauge**. With this type of system, carburetor air temperature is measured at the carburetor entrance by a temperature-sensing bulb in the ram air intake duct. The bulb senses air temperature in the carburetor and sends a signal to a cockpit instrument that is calibrated in degrees. [Figure 5-3]

In addition to identifying the conditions necessary for ice formation, CAT gauges also indicate excessively high carburetor air temperatures, which can indicate the onset of detonation. For example, if a CAT gauge has a red line identifying a maximum operating temperature, engine operation above that temperature increases the chance of detonation.

# SUPERCHARGED INDUCTION SYSTEMS

The higher an airplane climbs, the less oxygen is available in the atmosphere to support combustion. As an aircraft powered by a reciprocating engine climbs, the power output of the engine decreases. To limit this natural loss of engine power, more oxygen must be supplied to the engine. One way to supply more air to an engine is with a supercharger. A **supercharger** is an engine-driven air pump that increases manifold pressure. The higher the manifold pressure, the denser the fuel/air mixture is and the more power the engine can produce. A typical supercharger is capable of boosting manifold pressure above 30 inches of mercury while producing a volumetric efficiency that exceeds 100 percent.

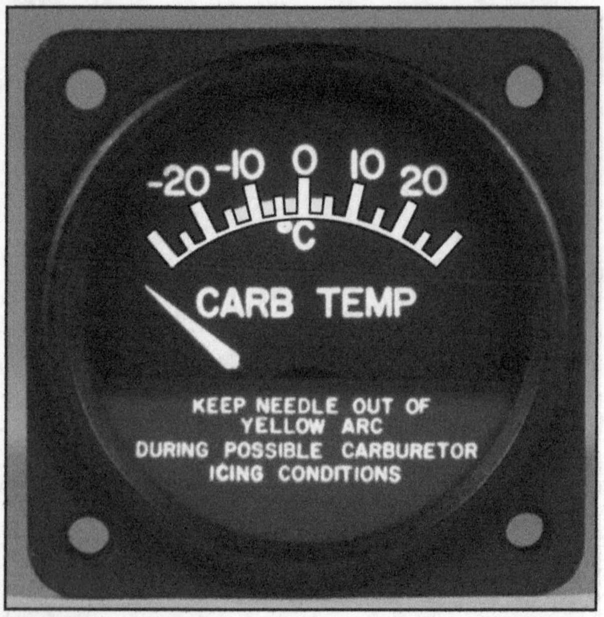


**Figure 5-3. This carburetor air temperature gauge indicates that the danger of induction system icing exists when the temperature is between –15°C to +5°C.**

The components in a supercharged induction system are similar to those in a normally aspirated system except for the addition of a supercharger between the fuel metering device and the intake manifold. A supercharger is typically driven by an engine's crankshaft through a gear train at one speed, two speeds, or variable speeds. Superchargers are generally classified as single-stage, two-stage, or multistage, depending on the number of times air compression occurs. Each stage represents an increase in pressure.

On all supercharged engines, a manifold pressure gauge sensor is installed after the supercharger to measure the pressure of the fuel/air mixture before it enters the cylinders. Knowing the pressure of the mixture before it enters the cylinders provides an accurate indication of engine performance.

## SINGLE STAGE, SINGLE-SPEED SUPERCHARGER

An early version of a single stage, single-speed supercharger is known as a sea-level supercharger, or **ground boost blower**. This type of supercharger has a single gear-driven impeller that increases the power produced by an engine at all altitudes. The drawback is that engine power output still decreases with an increase in altitude in the same way that it would with a normally aspirated engine. [Figure 5-4]

Single-stage, single-speed superchargers are found on many radial engines and use an air intake that

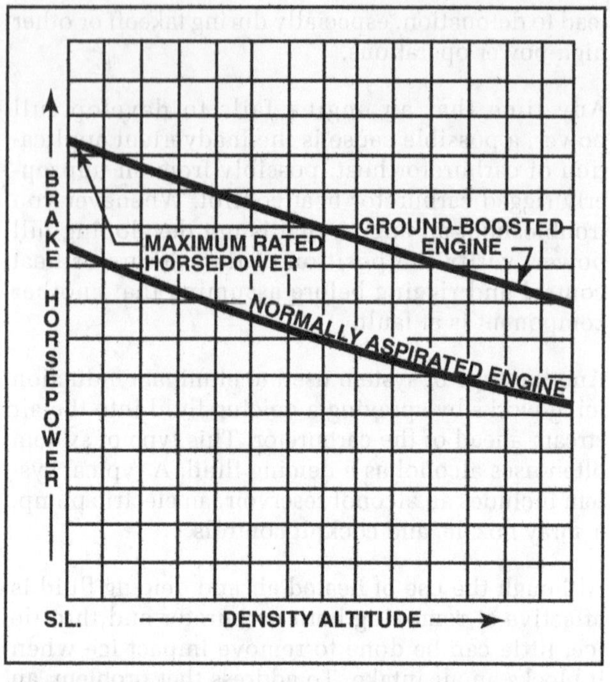


**Figure 5-4. The lower curve illustrates how the power output of a normally aspirated engine declines as altitude increases. The upper curve illustrates how a ground-boosted engine has a higher power output at all altitudes but still decreases as altitude increases.**

faces forward so that the induction system can take full advantage of the ram air. Intake air passes through ducts to a carburetor where fuel is metered in proportion to the airflow. The fuel/air charge is then ducted to the supercharger, or **blower** impeller, which accelerates the fuel/air mixture radially in the same manner as a centrifugal compressor used on a turbine engine. After it undergoes acceleration, the fuel/air mixture passes through a diffuser, where air velocity is converted to pressure energy. After it is compressed, the resulting high pressure fuel/air charge is directed to the cylinders. [Figure 5-5]

The gear ratio of a typical single-stage impeller gear train varies from approximately 6:1 to 12:1. This means that the impeller speed on an engine equipped with a 10:1 impeller gear ratio operating at 2,600 r.p.m. would be 26,000 r.p.m. This high speed rotation requires that an impeller be forged out of a high grade aluminum alloy.

## SINGLE STAGE, TWO-SPEED SUPERCHARGER

Some of the large radial engines used through World War II used a single-stage, two-speed supercharger. With this type of supercharger, a single impeller can be operated at two speeds. At the low speed, the impeller gear ratio is approximately 8:1 and at the high speed, the impeller gear ratio is stepped up to approximately 11:1. The lower impeller speed is

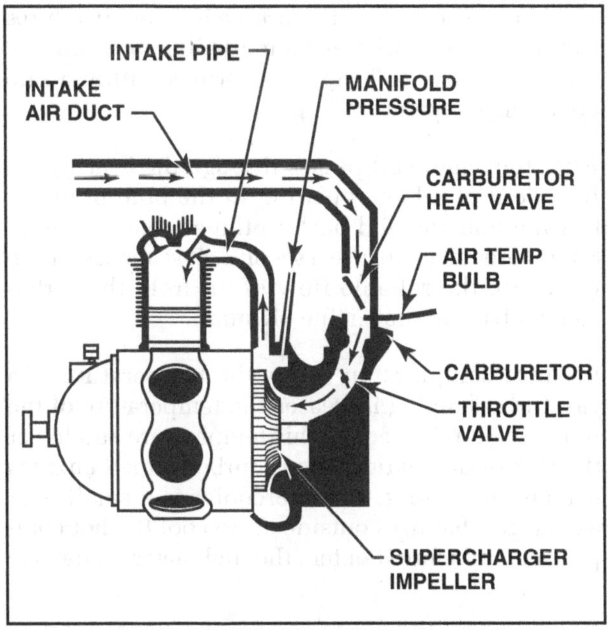


**Figure 5-5. This simplified figure traces the path of induction air from the intake to the cylinders in a single stage, single-speed supercharger induction system.**

often referred to as the **low blower** setting while the high impeller speed is called the **high blower** setting. On engines equipped with a two-speed supercharger, a lever or switch in the cockpit activates an oil-operated clutch that changes the speed of the supercharger.

Under normal operations, the supercharger is in the low blower position for takeoff. In this mode, the engine performs as a ground-boosted engine and the power output decreases as the aircraft gains altitude. However, after the aircraft reaches a specified altitude, the pilot reduces power and switches the supercharger control to the high blower position. The throttle is then reset to the desired manifold pressure. Engines equipped with this type of supercharger are called altitude engines. [Figure 5-6]

## TURBOCHARGER SYSTEMS

A drawback of gear-driven superchargers is that they use a large amount of the engine's power output for the amount of power increase that they produce. This problem is avoided with a turbosupercharger, or turbocharger, because the turbochargers are powered by engine exhaust. In other words, a turbocharger recovers energy from a source that would otherwise be lost.

Turbochargers can be controlled to maintain an engine's rated sea-level horsepower from sea-level up to the engine's critical altitude. Critical altitude is defined as the maximum altitude that a turbocharged engine can produce its rated horsepower under standard atmospheric conditions. In other

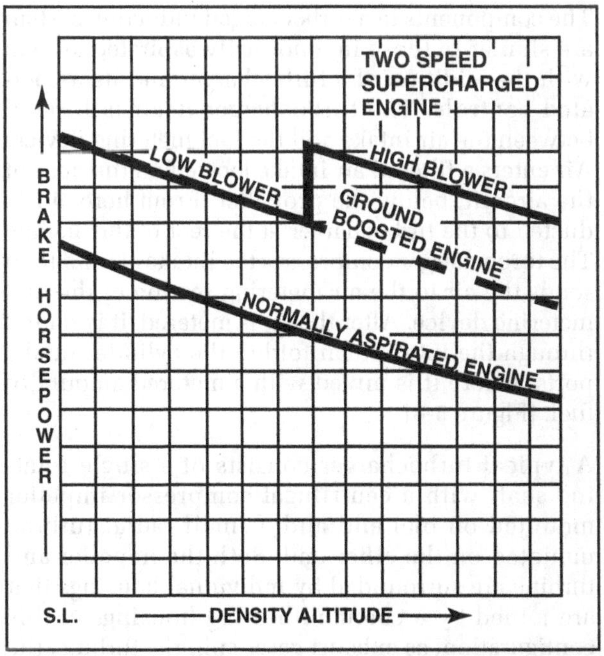


**Figure 5-6. On engines equipped with a two-speed supercharger, when the low blower speed is selected, the engine's brake horsepower is boosted above that of a normally aspirated engine. However, power output still decreases as the aircraft climbs. To help compensate for this, the high blower setting can be selected after the aircraft reaches a higher altitude.**

words, when a turbocharged engine exceeds critical altitude, power output begins to decrease like a normally aspirated engine. [Figure 5-7]

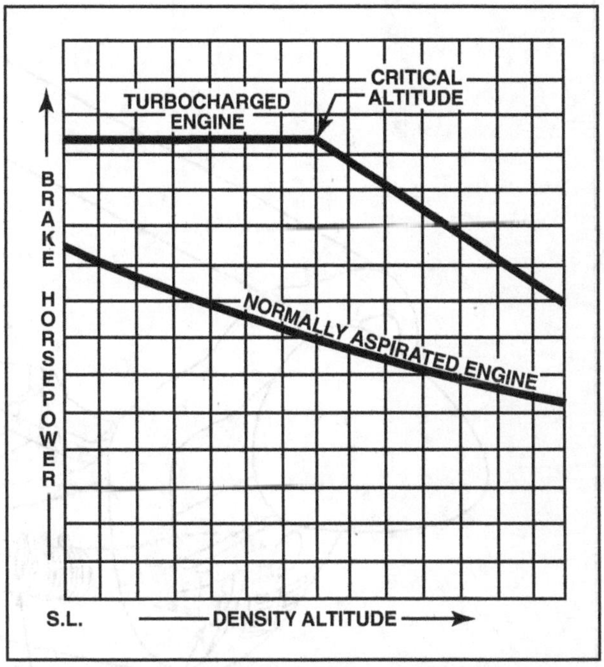


**Figure 5-7. With a turbocharged engine, the turbocharger enables an engine to produce its rated sea-level horsepower up to the engine's critical altitude. Above the critical altitude, the engine's power output decreases similar to that of a normally aspirated engine.**

The components in a turbocharged induction system are similar to those in a normally aspirated system with the addition of a turbocharger and its associated controls. The turbocharger itself is located between the air intake and the fuel metering device. Air enters a filtered air intake located on the nose of the aircraft, below the propeller. From here, air is ducted to the turbocharger at the rear of the engine. The turbocharger compresses the intake air and then sends the air to the air metering section of the fuel metering device. After the air is metered, it is routed through the intake manifold to the cylinder intake ports, where it is mixed with a metered amount of fuel. [Figure 5-8]

A typical turbocharger consists of a single rotating shaft with a centrifugal compressor impeller mounted on one end and a small radial turbine mounted on the other end. Both the impeller and turbine are surrounded by individual housings that are joined by a common bearing housing. In this configuration, as exhaust gases spin the turbine, the impeller draws in air and compresses it. [Figure 5-9]

The friction caused by high rotation speeds, exhaust gases flowing through the turbine, and the compression of intake air all cause heat in turbochargers . Therefore, a continuous flow of engine oil must be pumped through the bearing housing to cool and lubricate the bearings. Approximately four to five gallons of oil per minute flow through a typical turbocharger bearing housing to lubricate the bearings and remove heat. Because turbine inlet temperatures can reach 1,600 degrees Fahrenheit, a large flow of oil is necessary to keep the bearings within a safe operating temperature.

After the engine oil passes through the bearings, it flows out of a large opening in the bottom of the bearing housing and back to the engine oil sump. Some turbochargers use a second oil scavenge pump to ensure the reliable flow of oil from the turbocharger back to the engine oil sump.

Because compression raises the temperature of a gas, turbocharging increases the temperature of the induction air. To reduce this temperature and lower the risk of detonation, many turbocharged engines use an intercooler. An intercooler is a small heat exchanger that uses outside air to cool the hot compressed air before it enters the fuel metering device.

## TURBOCHARGER CONTROL SYSTEMS

If all of an engine's exhaust gases passed through the turbine of a turbocharger, excessive manifold pressures, or overboosting would result. If the amount of exhaust gases that flow to a turbocharger is limited, performance would be excessively limited at higher altitudes. Turbocharger systems are designed to control the amount of exhaust gases that pass through the turbocharger's turbine.

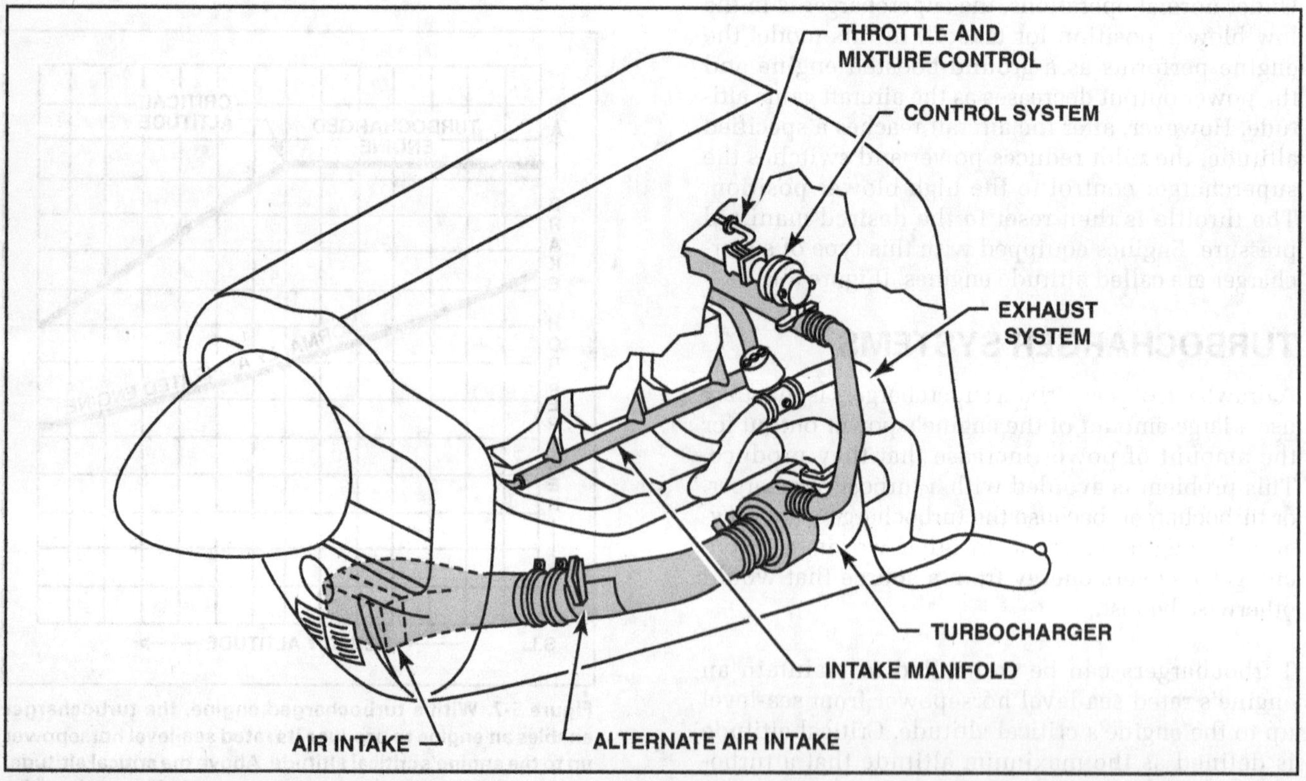


**Figure 5-8. This illustration shows the components of a typical turbocharger induction system installed in a light aircraft.**

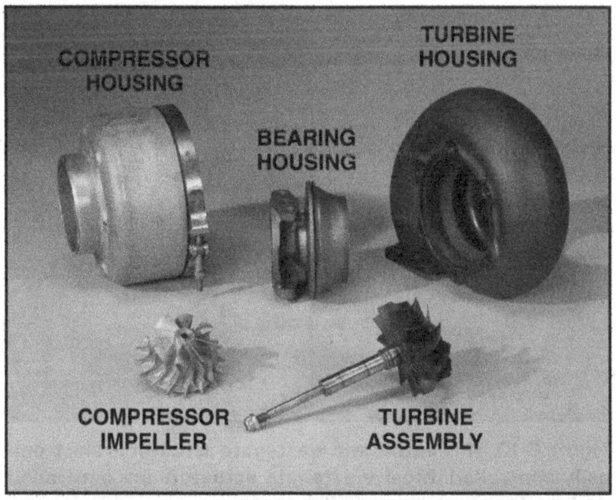


**Figure 5-9. A turbocharger consists of a compressor impeller and a turbine mounted on a single rotating shaft. Both the impeller and turbine are surrounded by separate housings joined by a common bearing housing.**

To control the amount of exhaust gases that flow past a turbocharger turbine, a valve known as a wastegate is used. When a wastegate is fully open, all of the exhaust gases bypass the turbocharger and pass out the exhaust stack. Conversely, when a wastegate is fully closed, all of the exhaust gases are routed through the turbine before they exit through the exhaust. Depending on the system, the position of the wastegate can be adjusted either manually or automatically. [Figure 5-10]

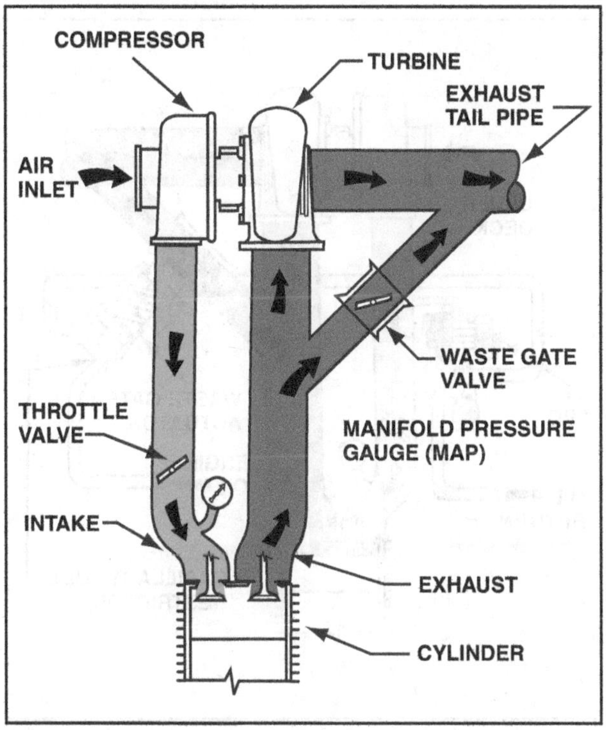


**Figure 5-10. A wastegate is used to direct the exhaust gases to a turbocharger. When the wastegate is fully open, all exhaust gases bypass the turbocharger. However, when the wastegate is fully closed, all exhaust gases are directed through the turbocharger.**

## MANUAL CONTROL SYSTEMS

One of the simplest forms of turbocharger control uses a mechanical linkage between the engine throttle valve and the wastegate valve. For takeoff at low density altitudes, the throttle is advanced until the engine develops full takeoff power as indicated on the manifold pressure gauge. At this point, the wastegate will be fully or nearly fully open. As the aircraft gains altitude, engine power decreases, which requires the pilot to advance the throttle forward to partially close the wastegate. The gradual closure of the wastegate proportionally increases manifold pressure, and the engine produces its rated horsepower. This process continues as the aircraft climbs to its critical altitude. At the engine's critical altitude, the throttle is fully forward and the wastegate is fully closed.

A second type of manual control system enables the pilot to set the position of the wastegate using a control in the cockpit. With this type of system, the engine is started with the wastegate in the fully open position. Prior to takeoff, the throttle is advanced full forward and the wastegate is slowly closed with the cockpit control until full engine power develops. After the aircraft takes off and begins to climb, the pilot must monitor the engine performance and close the wastegate as necessary to maintain the desired power output.

The final type of manual wastegate controller uses an adjustable restrictor in the exhaust section that bypasses the turbocharger. The amount that the restrictor is threaded in or out of the exhaust pipe determines the amount of exhaust gas that is forced to flow through the turbocharger. With this type of system, no adjustments to the restrictor can be made from the cabin. [Figure 5-11]

On aircraft equipped with this type of control system, the wastegate restrictor is adjusted so the engine develops its rated horsepower under standard conditions with a wide open throttle. By doing this, the maximum obtainable manifold pressure decreases as the aircraft gains altitude, and the induction system is protected from being overboosted. To provide additional protection against an overboost condition when temperatures and pressures are below standard, this type of system typically has a pressure relief valve. When manifold pressure rises to within approximately one inch of its rated pressure, the relief valve begins to rise off its seat. This way, by the time maximum manifold pressure is reached, the pressure relief valve is open enough to bleed off excess pressure.

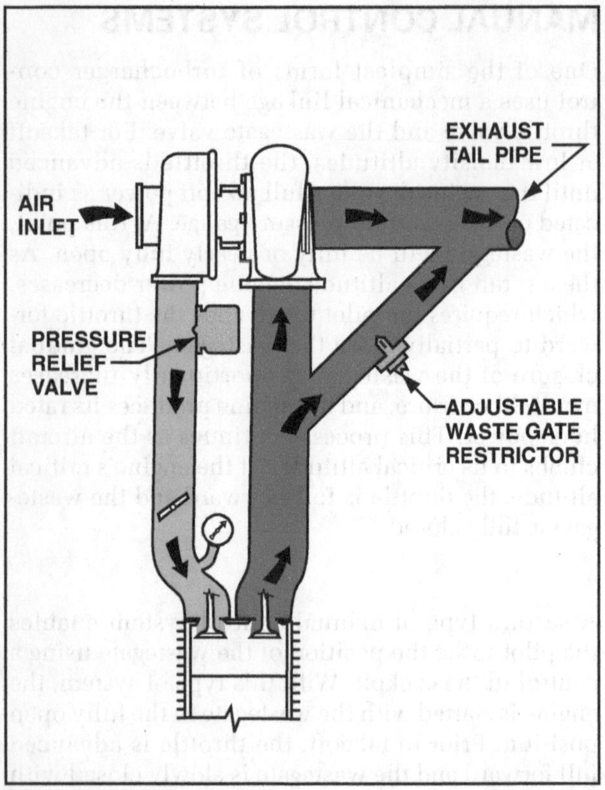


**Figure 5-11. On turbocharging systems equipped with an adjustable wastegate restrictor, the amount that the restrictor is threaded in or out determines how much of the exhaust bypasses the turbocharger.**

## AUTOMATIC CONTROL SYSTEMS

As the name implies, an automatic turbocharger control system automatically positions the wastegate so the engine maintains the selected power output level. To do this, these systems use a combination of several components including a wastegate actuator, an absolute pressure controller, a pressure-ratio controller, and a rate-of-change controller.

### WASTEGATE ACTUATOR

The wastegate in an automatic control system is positioned by a wastegate actuator. For most wastegate actuators, the wastegate is held open by spring pressure and closed by oil pressure that acts on a piston. Oil pressure is supplied to the actuator from the engine's oil system. Some wastegates are controlled electronically with electrical actuators. [Figure 5-12]

### ABSOLUTE PRESSURE CONTROLLER

On Teledyne Continental Motors engines, the wastegate actuator is controlled by an **absolute pressure controller**, or **APC**. An APC consists of a bellows

**Figure 5-12. This automatic wastegate actuator is electronically controlled. Most wastegate actuators are controlled with spring pressure and oil pressure.**

and a variable restrictor valve. The bellows senses the absolute pressure of the air before it enters the fuel metering device. This pressure is commonly referred to as **upper deck pressure.** As the bellows expands and contracts, it moves the **variable restrictor valve** to control the amount of oil that flows out of the wastegate actuator. [Figure 5-13]

With this automatic control system, oil flows into the wastegate actuator through a **capillary tube restrictor.** After the actuator chamber fills, the oil flows out of the actuator to the APC and then back to the engine.

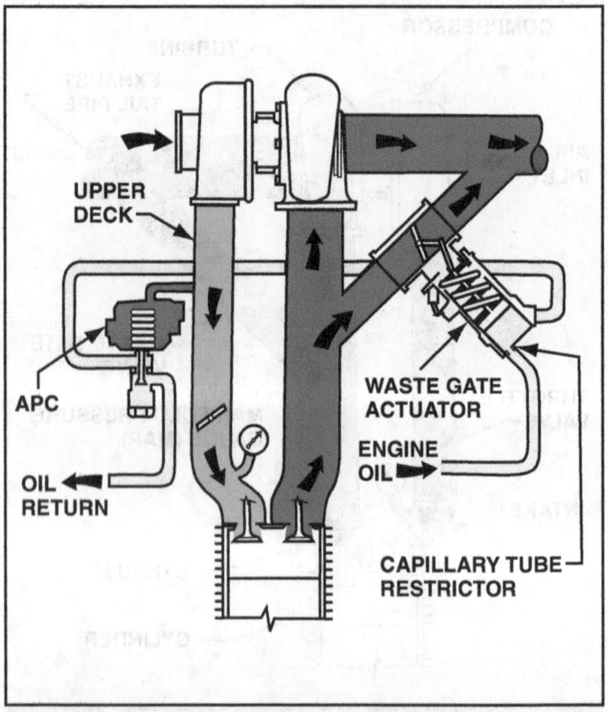


**Figure 5-13. The automatic control system used with several turbocharged Teledyne Continental Motors engines uses a wastegate actuator that is controlled by an absolute pressure controller.**

The rate at which the oil flows through the APC and back to the engine is determined by the position of the variable restrictor valve.

When the engine is not running, no oil pressure exists, and the spring pressure inside the wastegate actuator holds the wastegate in the fully open, or bypass position. In addition, because the upper deck pressure is low, the bellows holds the variable restrictor valve closed. After engine start, engine oil flows into the wastegate actuator cylinder and the APC. Because the restrictor valve in the APC is closed, oil pressure builds in the system until it can partially overcome the spring pressure in the wastegate actuator. As oil pressure continues to build, the wastegate begins to close and direct some of the exhaust to the turbocharger. This process continues until the upper deck pressure builds enough to compress the APC bellows and open the restrictor valve. After the restrictor valve opens, oil is permitted to flow back to the engine. Because oil is supplied to the wastegate actuator through a restricted opening, oil flows out of the actuator faster than it flows in. This permits the oil pressure within the actuator to decrease rapidly and let spring force open the wastegate until the two forces balance.

In this type of system, when the throttle is advanced to obtain takeoff power, the increased flow of exhaust gases through the turbocharger causes an increase in upper deck and manifold pressure. When the upper deck pressure increases to approximately one inch above the desired manifold pressure, the APC bellows contracts and causes the restrictor to open partially and drain oil back into the engine sump. The reason that the APC is set to open approximately one inch above the maximum manifold pressure is to account for the pressure drop across the throttle body. As some of the exhaust gases bypass the turbocharger, the turbine speed decreases enough to hold the desired manifold pressure.

As the aircraft climbs, the air becomes less dense and the upper deck pressure starts to decrease. The APC senses the decrease and closes the variable restrictor valve enough to slow the oil flow from the wastegate actuator. This increases the oil pressure within the actuator, which repositions the wastegate to direct more exhaust gases through the turbocharger.

As the aircraft continues to ascend, the wastegate valve continues to close in response to decreasing upper deck pressure. When the aircraft reaches critical altitude, the wastegate is fully closed and all exhaust gases flow through the turbocharger. If the aircraft climbs above this altitude, manifold pressure will decrease.

A variation of the absolute pressure controller is the **variable absolute pressure controller**, or **VAPC**. A VAPC functions similarly to an APC, but instead of using a bellows to control the position of a restrictor valve, the position of the restrictor valve seat is controlled by a cam that is actuated by the throttle control.

## PRESSURE-RATIO CONTROLLER

Some engines are restricted to a maximum altitude at which they are allowed to maintain their maximum rated manifold pressure. On engines that are limited in this way, a secondary control device known as a pressure-ratio controller is installed in parallel with the absolute pressure controller. The pressure-ratio controller monitors both the ambient and upper deck pressures to prevent the turbocharger from boosting upper deck pressure more than 2.2 times the ambient pressure. [Figure 5-14]

To explain how a pressure-ratio controller works, assume an aircraft is equipped with a turbocharging system that has a manifold pressure limit of 36 inches of mercury at 16,000 feet. As the airplane takes off and begins climbing, the absolute pressure controller slowly closes the wastegate so that the manifold pressure remains at 36 inches. As the aircraft approaches 16,000 feet, the wastegate will

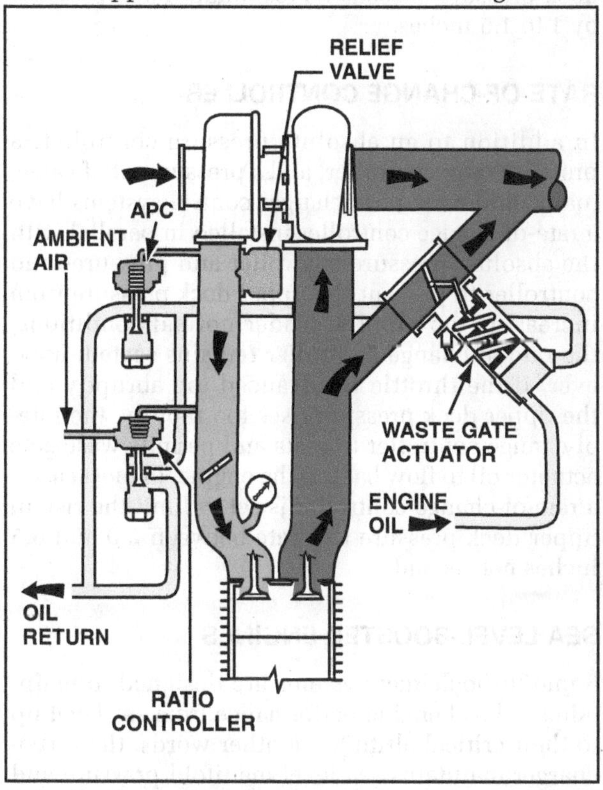


**Figure 5-14. On turbocharging systems that are restricted to a maximum differential between manifold and ambient pressures, a pressure ratio controller is installed in parallel with the absolute pressure controller in the oil line between the wastegate actuator and the engine sump.**

be fully or almost fully closed to maintain the 36 inches of manifold pressure. The atmospheric pressure at 16,000 feet is approximately 16.22 inches of mercury; therefore, at 16,000 feet, the pressure-ratio controller begins to unseat because the upper deck pressure (37 inches) will exceed 2.2 times the ambient pressure (16.22 x 2.2 = 35.68 in Hg). If the aircraft continues to climb to 18,000 feet, where the ambient pressure is approximately 14.95 in. Hg., the pressure-ratio controller will unseat as necessary to maintain an upper deck pressure of 32.89 inches of mercury (14.95 x 2.2 = 32.89).

A typical pressure-ratio controller consists of a bellows that adjusts a variable restrictor valve. One side of the bellows senses upper deck pressure while the opposite side senses ambient pressure within the cowl. When the upper deck pressure exceeds 2.2 times the ambient pressure, the bellows expands enough to open the restrictor valve and bleeds off some of the wastegate actuator oil.

As a backup to the pressure-ratio controller, most turbocharger systems incorporate a **pressure relief valve**. A typical pressure relief valve consists of a spring loaded pop-up valve that is mounted to the upper deck near the compressor output. In most cases, the relief valve remains seated until the upper deck pressure exceeds its maximum rated pressure by 1 to 1.5 inches.

## RATE-OF-CHANGE CONTROLLER

In addition to an absolute pressure controller, a pressure ratio controller, and a pressure relief valve, many automatic turbocharger control systems have a rate-of-change controller installed in parallel with the absolute pressure controller and pressure-ratio controller to prevent the upper deck pressure from increasing too rapidly. Under normal conditions, the rate-of-change controller remains seated; however, if the throttle is advanced too abruptly and the upper deck pressure rises too rapidly, the rate-of-change controller unseats and permits wastegate actuator oil to flow back to the engine. In most cases, a rate-of-change controller is set to limit the rise in upper deck pressure to a rate between 2.0 and 6.5 inches per second.

## SEA LEVEL-BOOSTED ENGINES

Some turbocharger systems are designed to maintain sea level engine performance from sea level up to their critical altitude. In other words, the turbocharger maintains sea level manifold pressure and does not boost manifold pressure above that level. Engines that are equipped with this type of turbocharger system are referred to as sea level-boosted engines.

The turbocharger system in all sea level-boosted engines is controlled automatically. However, the components used in this type of system differ from those used in other automatic control systems. The three units that permit automatic control include an exhaust bypass valve assembly, a density controller, and a differential pressure controller.

The **exhaust bypass valve assembly** functions in a manner similar to the wastegate actuator. Engine oil pressure acts on a piston, which is connected to the wastegate valve through a mechanical linkage. Increased oil pressure on the piston moves the wastegate valve toward the closed position to direct exhaust gases through the turbocharger. Conversely, when oil pressure decreases, spring tension moves the wastegate valve toward the open position to permit the exhaust gases to bypass the turbocharger. The amount of oil pressure acting on the exhaust bypass valve assembly is controlled by the density controller and differential pressure controller. [Figure 5-15]

The **density controller** regulates the bleed oil flow from the exhaust bypass valve assembly only during full throttle operation. To do this, a density controller uses a nitrogen-filled bellows that senses the density of the upper deck air. The bellows is contained in a rigid housing that extends into the upper deck airstream. If the density of the air is insufficient to produce full engine power, the density controller adjusts the oil pressure acting on the exhaust bypass valve assembly so more exhaust is directed to the turbocharger.

To regulate the oil pressure within the exhaust bypass valve assembly, the bellows in a density controller positions a metering valve to bleed off the appropriate amount of oil. If the density of the upper deck air is too low to produce full power, the bellows in the density controller expands and positions the metering valve to stop the flow of oil back to the engine. However, if upper deck air density is too high, the bellows contracts and positions the metering valve to permit oil to flow back to the engine.

When a sea level-boosted engine is operated at less than full throttle, the **differential pressure controller** regulates turbocharger output. A differential pressure controller consists of a diaphragm that controls the position of an oil-metering valve. One side of the diaphragm is exposed to upper deck pressure and the other side is exposed to manifold pressure. In this configuration, the differential pressure controller monitors the pressure differential, or drop, across the throttle body. A typical differential pressure controller is set to allow a two- to four-inch pressure drop across the throttle body. If this differential is exceeded, the diaphragm positions the metering valve to bleed oil from the exhaust bypass valve assembly, reducing the degree of turbocharge boost. However, if the pressure differential decreases below the preset valve, the diaphragm positions the metering valve to stop the flow of oil out of the exhaust bypass valve assembly, which forces the wastegate closed and increases the degree of turbocharged boost.

In addition to controlling the degree of turbocharged boost during part throttle operations, the differential pressure controller reduces the duration of a condition known as bootstrapping. **Bootstrapping** occurs when a turbocharger system senses small changes in temperature or speed, or both, and continually changes the turbocharger output in an attempt to establish equilibrium. Bootstrapping typically occurs during part-throttle operation and is characterized by a continual drift or transient increase in manifold pressure.

## OPERATIONAL CONSIDERATIONS

When operating a turbocharged engine, you should be aware of some additional considerations. For example, as a rule, because turbocharged engines are more sensitive to throttle movements than normally aspirated engines, avoid rapid throttle movements when operating a turbocharged engine. If throttle movements are not controlled, engine or turbocharger damage could result. Advancing the throttle too rapidly could cause the turbocharger to **overboost** the induction system. A severe overboost condition could damage the intake manifold or even the pistons and cylinders.

Rapid throttle movements can also cause what is know as an **overshoot**. In this case, the turbocharger controllers cannot keep up with the throttle movement and the manifold pressure overshoots the desired value, which requires the operator to retard the throttle as appropriate. Although not as serious as an overboost, an overshoot can increase the operator's workload. To avoid an overshoot, make gradual throttle movements that permit the turbocharging system to find a new equilibrium.

## ADDITIONAL TURBOCHARGER USES

In addition to compressing intake air to improve engine performance, turbocharger systems also perform several other tasks. For example, upper deck pressure is used as a reference to regulate the operation of fuel discharge nozzles, fuel pumps, and fuel flow gauges. Furthermore, turbocharger discharge air can be used for cabin pressurization. However, in this case, the amount of air entering the cabin must be limited. To do this, the turbocharger air used for pressurization must pass through a **sonic venturi**. As turbocharger air passes through a sonic venturi, it accelerates to transonic speed to produce a shock wave. The shock wave slows the remaining airflow in the venturi, thereby limiting the amount of air entering the cabin.

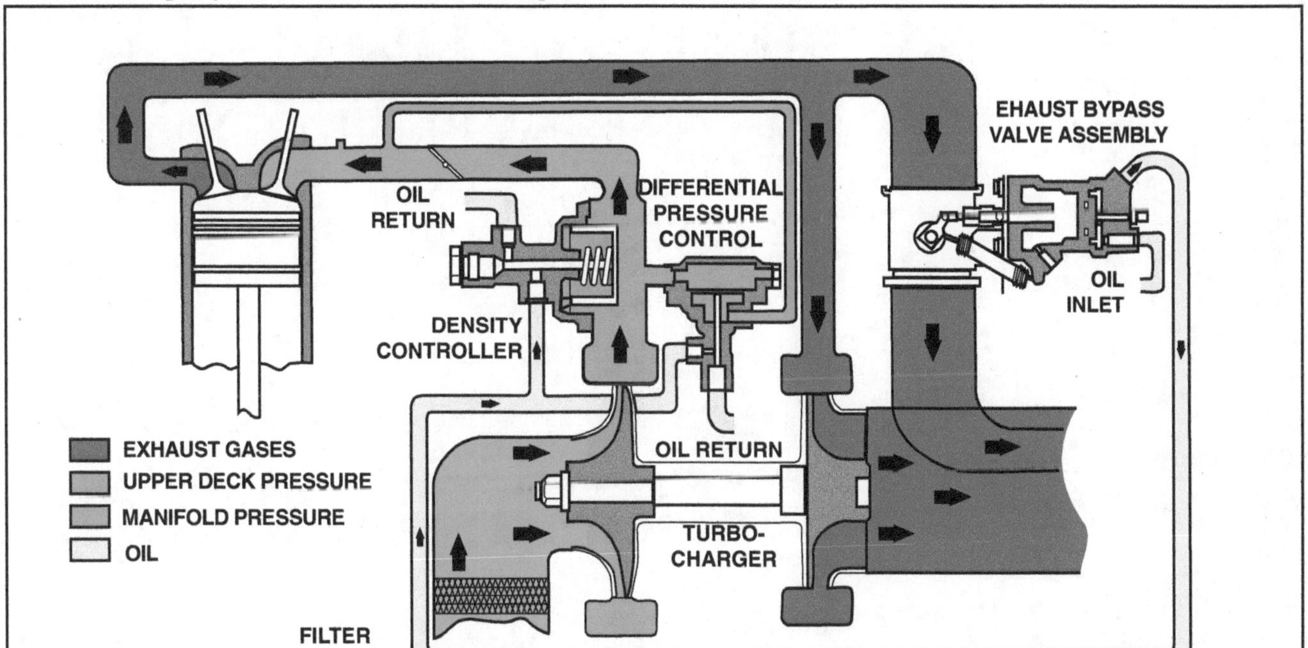


**Figure 5-15. A sea level-boosted turbocharger system maintains an engine's sea level performance up to the engine's critical altitude. To do this, the turbocharging system uses an exhaust bypass valve assembly, a density controller, and a differential pressure controller.**

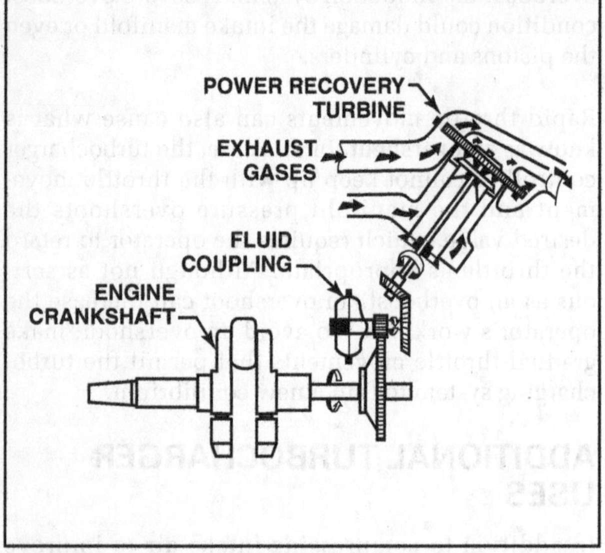


**Figure 5-16. The turbocharger system used in many general aviation aircraft not only supplies induction air, but also serves as a reference pressure. The fuel discharge nozzles, fuel pump, and fuel flow gauge all use upper deck pressure as a reference pressure to perform fuel metering functions properly. In addition, on many aircraft, the turbocharger provides air for cabin pressurization.**

## TURBOCOMPOUND SYSTEMS

A turbocompound engine is a reciprocating engine in which exhaust driven turbines are coupled to the engine crankshaft. This system of obtaining additional power is sometimes called a **power recovery turbine** system, or **PRT**. It is not a supercharging system, and it is not connected in any manner to the air induction system of the aircraft. Instead, a PRT system enables an engine to recover energy from the velocity of the exhaust gases that would be lost if they were ducted overboard. Depending on the type of engine, the amount of horsepower recovered varies with the amount of input horsepower. A typical PRT in a large radial engine has three turbines that can recover up to 390 horsepower from the exhaust gases.

On engines that have a power recovery turbine, an exhaust collector nozzle directs the exhaust gases onto a turbine wheel. As the turbine spins, a turbine wheel shaft transmits the recovered power to the engine crankshaft through gears and a fluid coupling. The fluid coupling is necessary to prevent torsional vibration from being transmitted to the crankshaft. [Figure 5-17]

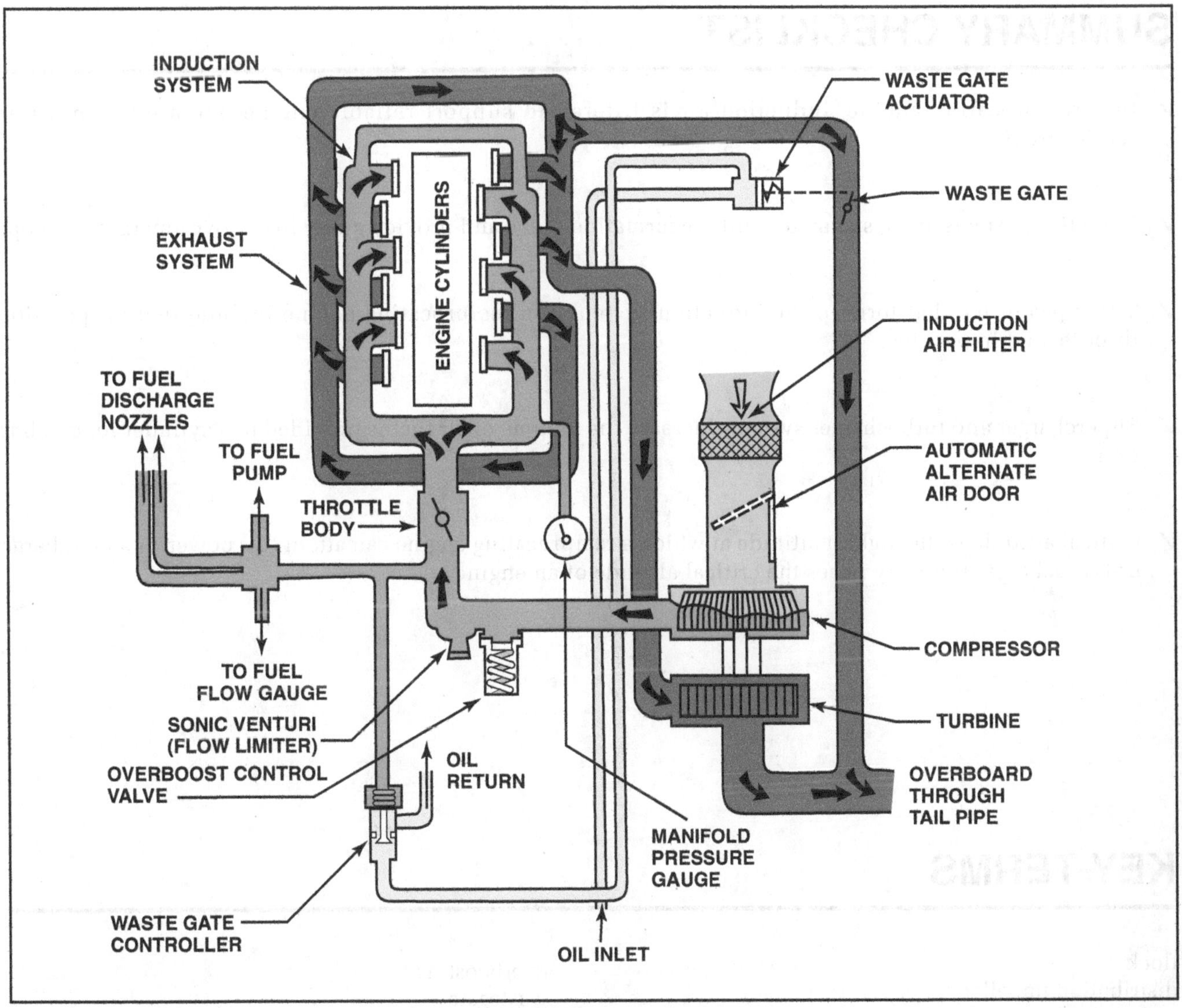


**Figure 5-17. On engines equipped with a power recovery turbine, the engine's exhaust gases are directed to a series of turbine wheels that transmit rotational energy back to the crankshaft.**

# SUMMARY CHECKLIST

✓ In a reciprocating engine, induction air is filtered to support reliable engine operation and a long service life.

✓ Induction systems are designed to limit the formation of ice and provide a way to remove any that develops.

✓ The types of ice that form in the induction system of a reciprocating engine include fuel evaporation, throttle, and impact ice.

✓ Supercharger and turbocharger systems increase the volume of air that is provided to a cylinder for combustion.

✓ Critical altitude is the highest altitude at which a reciprocating engine can attain full power. A supercharger or turbocharger typically raises the critical altitude of an engine.

# KEY TERMS

flock
distribution impeller
carburetor ice
butterfly valve
carburetor heat
heater muff
carburetor air box
alternate air supply
alternate air door
carburetor air temperature gauge
CAT gauge
supercharger
ground boost blower
blower
low blower
high blower
critical altitude
compressor impeller
turbine
intercooler
overboosting
wastegate
absolute pressure controller
APC
upper deck pressure
variable restrictor valve
capillary tube restrictor
variable absolute pressure controller
VAPC
pressure relief valve
exhaust bypass valve assembly
density controller
differential pressure controller
bootstrapping
overboost
overshoot
sonic venturi
power recovery turbine
PRT

# QUESTIONS

1. The induction system consists of these four major components:

   a. ______________

   b. ______________

   c. ______________

   d. ______________

2. What three types of air filter systems have been used on aircraft?

   a. ______________

   b. ______________

   c. ______________

3. Reciprocating engine induction systems can be broadly classified as:

   a. ______________

   b. ______________

4. Some modern horizontally opposed engines that use float carburetors have the carburetor mounted directly to the bottom of the engine _______ _______, and the induction pipes pass through the warm oil.

5. Two advantages of passing the fuel/air mixture through the engine oil sump are:

   a. ______________

   b. ______________

6. Air supplied for carburetor heat _______ (is or is not) filtered.

7. The carburetor heat control should always be in the _________ (hot or cold) position when operating on sandy or dusty surfaces.

8. Warm air is __________ (more or less) dense than cool air.

9. Engines equipped with fuel injection systems are not susceptible to carburetor icing, but are equipped with an ______________ air system to allow airflow in case of filter clogging or impact icing.

10. Alternate air doors may be operated _______________ or _______________.

11. Internally driven superchargers are located _______________ (upstream or downstream) of the fuel metering device.

12. Manifold pressure of a turbocharged engine is measured on the _____________ (engine or turbocharger) side of the throttle valve.

13. An aircraft engine whose rated horsepower has been increased by using a supercharger is called a/an _______ _________________ engine.

14. An aircraft whose engines are equipped with a two-speed supercharger will use the _______ (high or low) blower position for takeoff.

15. An aircraft engine that can develop its rated sea level horsepower to a given altitude is called a/an ______________ engine.

16. Superchargers which are powered by the energy of the exhaust gases are called ____________.

17. The turbocharger is located ______________ (upstream or downstream) of the fuel metering device.

18. The three sections of a turbocharger are:

a. ______________

b. ______________

c. ______________

19. "The turbocharger shaft is supported in ball bearings." This statement is ______ (true or false).

20. Two important functions of the oil that flows through the center housing of a turbocharger are:

a. ______________

b. ______________

21. Causing an engine to produce an excess of manifold pressure is called ______________ the engine.

22. The valve that is used to control the amount of exhaust gases routed to the turbocharger is known as a ______ ______________.

23. When the waste gate is fully closed ______________ (all or none) of the exhaust gases must pass through the turbocharger.

24. Turbocharger bearings are cooled by a contineous flow of engine ____________.

25. Another name for turbocharger discharge pressure is ___________ ____________ pressure.

26. The waste gate actuator used with a turbocharger system controlled with an absolute pressure controller is _______ (opened or closed) by oil pressure acting on the piston.

27. The capillary tube restrictor is on the ___________ (inlet or outlet) oil line inside the waste gate actuator.

28. A ratio controller of a turbocharger system is installed in ______________ (series or parallel) with an absolute pressure controller.

29. The variable automatic pressure controller (VAPC) maintains a constant upper deck pressure for each position of the ______________ valve.

30. The two pressures sensed by the ratio controller are:

a. ______________

b. ______________

31. The ratio controller controls the manifold pressure at ________________ (high or low) altitudes.

32. Should the pressurer-ratio controller fail, the ______ ______ ______, found in most systems, will prevent overboosting.

33. Engines using turbochargers that are designed to operate from sea level up to their critical altitude are referred to as ______ ______ ______ engines.

34. The three basic components of a sea level boosted turbocharger system are:

a. ____________

b. ____________

c. ____________

35. The density controller regulates "bleed oil" only at the ______ ____________ position.

36. The ____________ ____________ (what device) on a turbocharger used for pressurizing an aircraft limits the amount of air that can be supplied to the cabin.

37. Rapid throttle movement can cause a temporary overboost known as an ____________.

38. The differential pressure controller reduces the unstable condition known as ____________.

39. Bootstrapping ________ (is or is not) detrimental to engine life.

40. A reciprocating engine in which exhaust-driven turbines are coupled to the engine crankshaft is known as a ____________ system.

# SECTION B

# TURBINE ENGINES

Turbine engine induction systems are substantially different from the induction systems on reciprocating engines. Turbine engines consume much more air than reciprocating engines, generally operate at faster airspeeds, and the distance from the inlet to a turbine engine is extremely short.

Typically, the air inlet duct on a turbine engine is considered an airframe component. However, because the supply of air is essential to the operation of a turbine engine, it is important to discuss this topic in the context of engine operation.

## TURBOJET AND TURBOFAN INLETS

A gas turbine engine consumes between six and ten times the volume of air per hour as a reciprocating engine of equivalent size, so the air inlet of a turbine engine is correspondingly larger. Additionally, to ensure optimum performance, the air inlet duct on a turbojet or turbofan engine must provide a relatively smooth, high energy supply of air to the compressor. If this is not done, improper combustion, excessive turbine temperatures, or a compressor stall can occur. In fact, given the speeds at which turbine aircraft travel, even a small aerodynamic disruption in an air inlet duct will result in a large decrease in engine performance.

The air inlet duct to a turbine engine has several functions, one of which is to recover as much of the total pressure of the free airstream as possible and deliver this pressure to the compressor. This is known as **ram recovery** or **pressure recovery**. In addition to recovering and maintaining the pressure of the free airstream, many inlet ducts are shaped to raise the air pressure above atmospheric pressure. This **ram effect** results from forward movement, which causes air to pile up in the inlet. The faster an aircraft flies, the more air piles up, and the greater the inlet air pressure rises above ambient.

The air inlet duct must also provide a uniform supply of air to the compressor for efficient operation. To do this, an inlet duct must create minimal drag. If an inlet duct is to deliver its full volume of air with a minimum of turbulence, it must be maintained as close to its original condition as possible. Therefore, any repairs to an inlet duct must maintain the duct's original, smooth aerodynamic shape. Poor workmanship resulting in protruding rivet heads or inferior sheet metal repairs can destroy the efficiency of an otherwise acceptable duct installation. To help prevent damage or corrosion to an inlet duct, an inlet cover should be installed any time the engine is not operating.

Air inlet ducts are designed to operate at different airspeeds. To maintain an even airflow and minimize pressure losses caused by friction, inlet ducts are designed with straight sections. Some of the most common locations where engine inlets are mounted are on the engine, in the wing, and on the fuselage.

The types of inlet ducts on modern turbojet and turbofan aircraft depend on the locations of the engines. For example, engines mounted on wing or fuselage pylons have an air inlet duct that is directly in front of the compressor and mounted to the engine. This provides the shortest possible inlet duct with a minimum of pressure loss. [Figure 5-18]

Some aircraft with engines mounted inside the wings feature air inlet ducts in the wing's leading edge. Aircraft such as the Aerospatiale Caravelle, de Havilland® Comet, and de Havilland Vampire all use wing-mounted inlet ducts. Typically, wing-mounted inlet ducts are positioned near the wing root area. [Figure 5-19]

**Figure 5-18. A Boeing 757 has wing-mounted engines that use engine-mounted inlet ducts directly in front of the compressor.**

**Figure 5-19. The Hawker-Siddeley 801 Nimrod was developed from the de Havilland Comet airframe and uses wing-mounted air inlets that are aerodynamically shaped to reduce drag.**

Engines mounted inside a fuselage typically use air inlet ducts located near the front of the fuselage. For example, many early military aircraft were designed with an air inlet duct in the nose of the fuselage. In addition, some modern supersonic military aircraft have inlet ducts located just under the aircraft nose. Although using an air inlet of this type enables the aircraft manufacturer to build a more aerodynamic aircraft, the increased length of the inlet duct makes it more inefficient. [Figure 5-20]

Some military aircraft use air inlet ducts mounted on the sides of the fuselage. This arrangement works well for both single- and twin-engine aircraft. By mounting an intake on the sides of the aircraft, the duct length can be shortened without adding a significant amount of drag to the aircraft. A disadvantage to this arrangement is that some abrupt flight maneuvers can cause an imbalance in ram air pressure between the intakes. The air pressure imbalance acting on the compressor face can result in a slight loss of power.

**Figure 5-20. The single-entrance inlet duct takes full advantage of ram effect much like engine-mounted air inlets. Although the aircraft is aerodynamically clean, the length of the duct makes it slightly less efficient than the shorter length of side-mounted types or those ahead of wing-mounted engines.**

## SUBSONIC INLETS

A typical subsonic air inlet consists of a fixed geometry duct whose diameter progressively increases from front to back. This **divergent** shape works like a **diffuser**—the intake air passes through the duct and spreads out. As the air spreads out, its velocity decreases and its pressure increases. In most cases, subsonic inlets are designed to diffuse the air in the front portion of the duct. This enables air to progress at a consistent pressure before it enters the engine. [Figure 5-21]

A turbofan inlet duct is similar in design to a turbojet duct except that the inlet discharges only a portion of its air into the engine. The remainder of inlet air passing through the fan flows around, or bypasses, the engine core to create thrust in a manner similar to a propeller. In addition, the bypass air helps cool the engine and reduce noise.

A turbofan engine uses one of two types of inlet duct designs. One type is a short duct that permits a large percentage of fan air to bypass the engine core and produce thrust. This type of duct is typically used on high-bypass engines. The other type of duct design forms a shroud around the engine core and is used on low- and medium-bypass engines. Full fan ducts reduce aerodynamic drag and noise emissions. In addition, a full duct generally has a converging discharge nozzle that produces reactive thrust. Full ducts are not used on high-bypass engines because the weight incurred by such a large diameter duct would offset the benefits. [Figure 5-22]

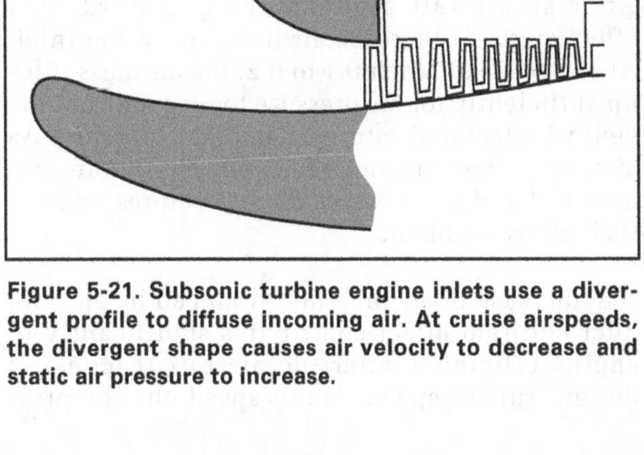

**Figure 5-21. Subsonic turbine engine inlets use a divergent profile to diffuse incoming air. At cruise airspeeds, the divergent shape causes air velocity to decrease and static air pressure to increase.**

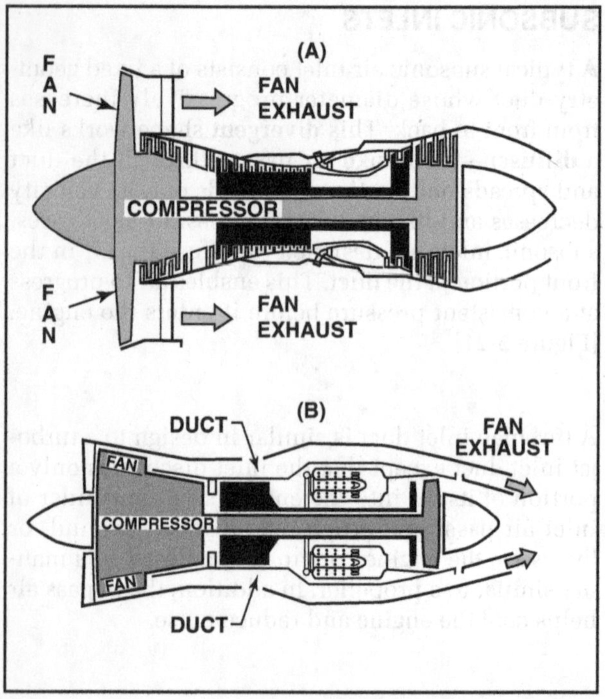


**Figure 5-22. (A) A high-bypass turbofan engine uses a short duct that permits a large portion of the incoming air to bypass the engine. (B) Some low- and medium-bypass engines use long inlet ducts that reduce surface drag of the fan discharge air and enhance thrust.**

### RAM EFFECT

In addition to the pressure rise created by the divergent shape of an inlet duct, turbine engines realize an additional pressure rise from ram effect. The resulting pressure rise causes an increase in mass airflow and jet velocity, which increases engine thrust.

Without ram effect, the compressor must pull air in through the inlet. The more air that is drawn in, the faster the air must flow through the inlet. Recall that whenever air is accelerated, its pressure decreases. Therefore, an aircraft inlet, when the aircraft is stationary, introduces air into the compressor below ambient pressure.

After an aircraft begins moving forward, ram effect starts to increase air pressure in the inlet. At airspeeds of Mach 0.1 to 0.2, the air mass piles up sufficiently for air pressure to recover from the venturi effect and return to ambient pressure. As airspeed increases, ram effect becomes more pronounced and air pressure at the compressor inlet rises above ambient.

The increase in air pressure produced by an inlet duct and ram effect contributes significantly to engine efficiency after the aircraft reaches its design cruising speed. At this speed, the compressor reaches its optimum aerodynamic efficiency and produces the most compression for the best fuel economy. At this design cruise speed, the inlet duct, compressor, combustor, turbine, and exhaust duct are designed to match each other as a unit. If damage, contamination, or ambient conditions cause a mismatch between the sections, engine performance suffers.

## SUPERSONIC INLETS

Air entering the compressor on a turbine engine must flow slower than the speed of sound. Therefore, the inlet duct on a supersonic aircraft must decrease the speed of inlet air before it reaches the compressor. To understand how a supersonic inlet does this, you must first understand how supersonic airflow reacts to converging and diverging openings.

### AIRFLOW PRINCIPLES

Air flowing at subsonic speeds is considered to be incompressible while air flowing at supersonic speeds is compressible. Because of this, air flowing at supersonic speeds reacts differently when forced to flow through either a convergent or divergent opening. For example, when supersonic airflow is forced through a convergent duct, it compresses, or piles up, and its density increases. This causes a decrease in air velocity and a corresponding increase in pressure. On the other hand, when supersonic airflow passes through a divergent duct, it expands and its density decreases. As it expands, its velocity increases, and its pressure decreases. [Figure 5-23]

In addition to understanding the velocity and pressure changes that occur with supersonic airflow, remember that whenever something travels through air at the speed of sound, a shock wave forms, any air flowing through the shock wave slows to a subsonic speed, and its pressure increases.

### INLET DESIGN

To slow the inlet air to subsonic velocity, all supersonic aircraft use convergent-divergent, or CD inlet ducts. With a CD duct, the diameter of the duct progressively decreases, then increases from front to back. The velocity of supersonic air entering the convergent portion of the duct decreases as it moves to the narrowest part of the inlet. At the narrowest point, the air has slowed to the speed of sound and a shock wave forms. As the air passes through the shock wave, it enters the divergent portion of the inlet where velocity continues to decrease and pressure increases. After the air reaches the compressor, its velocity is well below sonic speed, and its pressure has increased. [Figure 5-24]

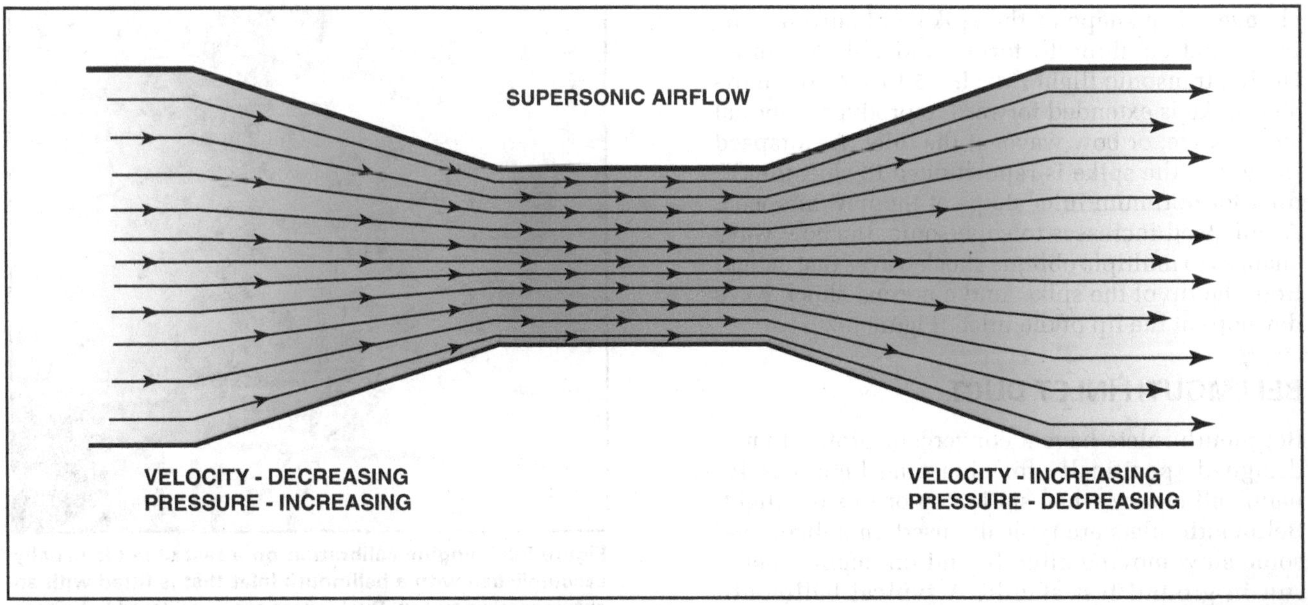


**Figure 5-23. When air moving at supersonic speeds flows through a convergent duct, its velocity decreases while its pressure increases. Conversely, when air moving at supersonic speeds flows through a divergent duct, its velocity increases and its pressure decreases.**

An engine inlet duct on a supersonic aircraft must perform efficiently at subsonic, transonic, and supersonic speeds. Because the optimum inlet shape changes for each range of airspeeds, a typical supersonic aircraft has an inlet duct with variable geometric construction. There are several ways to change the geometry of an inlet duct; one method is a movable wedge that is retracted during slow speed flight. As the aircraft accelerates to supersonic speeds, the wedge is extended into the inlet airstream to produce a convergent-divergent shape. [Figure 5-25]

In addition to the movable wedge, this type of inlet duct uses a dump valve and a spill valve. During subsonic flight, the dump valve is opened into the airstream to permit more air into the diverging portion of the inlet. At the same time, the spill valve is open to help prevent turbulence. During supersonic flight, both the dump and spill valves are opened to vent excess airflow to the atmosphere.

Another method used to vary the geometry of an inlet duct is a movable spike, or plug, which is positioned to alter the shape of the inlet as aircraft speed

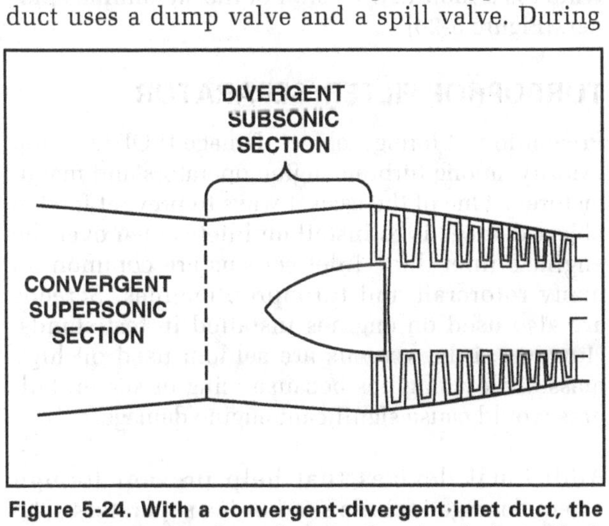


**Figure 5-24. With a convergent-divergent inlet duct, the convergent section slows the incoming air velocity to Mach 1.0 at its narrowest point and forms a shock wave. The divergent section then reduces the air velocity further while increasing air pressure.**

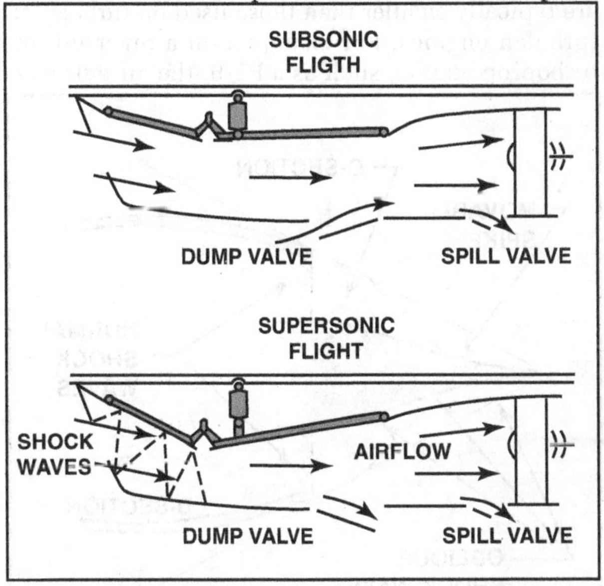


**Figure 5-25. Some supersonic aircraft use a variable geometry inlet that maintains efficient airflow at subsonic, transonic, and supersonic speeds. At subsonic speeds, the wedge is retracted to take full advantage of ram effect. When the aircraft reaches supersonic speeds, the wedge is extended to produce a convergent-divergent shape.**

changes. The shape of the spike and surrounding inlet duct combine to form a movable CD inlet. During transonic flight (Mach .75 to 1.2), the movable spike is extended forward to produce a normal shock wave, or bow wave, at the inlet. As airspeed increases, the spike is repositioned to shift the CD duct for optimum inlet shape at the new airspeed. As airspeed increases to supersonic, the bow wave changes to multiple oblique shock waves that extend from the tip of the spike, and a normal shock wave develops at the lip of the inlet. [Figure 5-26]

## BELLMOUTH INLET DUCT

Bellmouth inlets have a convergent profile that is designed specifically for obtaining high aerodynamic efficiency when stationary or in slow flight. Bellmouth inlets are typically used on helicopters, some slow-moving aircraft, and on engines being run in ground test stands. A typical bellmouth inlet is short, with rounded shoulders that reduce air resistance to a minimum. The efficiency of a bellmouth duct makes it an excellent duct to use while determining engine performance data during ground testing. However, because their shape produces significant drag in forward flight, bellmouth inlets are typically not used on high speed aircraft. [Figure 5-27]

**Figure 5-27. Engine calibration on a test stand is usually accomplished with a bellmouth inlet that is fitted with an anti-ingestion screen. Duct losses are considered to be zero because of the smooth rounded edges of this type of inlet.**

# TURBOPROP INLETS

Turboprop engines develop the majority of their thrust with a propeller rather than by jet propulsion. Therefore, the air inlet ducts on turboprop engines are typically smaller than those used on turbojet or turbofan engines. For example, on a reverse-flow turboprop engine, such as a PT-6, the air entrance to the compressor is located toward the rear of the engine. Depending on the aircraft installation, an air scoop located at the front of the nacelle below the propeller might be used to duct air back to the engine inlet. In such installations, ducting similar to that used on reciprocating engines routes intake air to the engine.

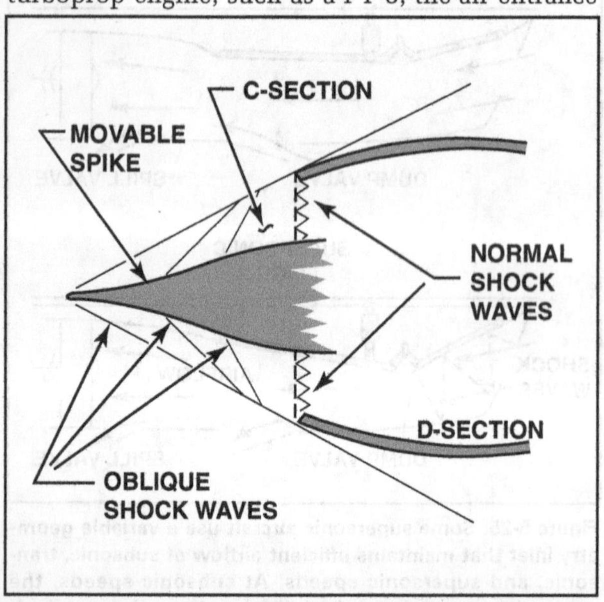


**Figure 5-26. One method of varying the geometry of an inlet duct uses a movable spike. The spike can be repositioned in flight to alter the inlet shape for maximum inlet efficiency.**

On turboprop engines with an intake at the front of the engine, a ducted spinner is generally considered to be the best inlet design. However, ducted spinners are heavier, more difficult to maintain, and harder to deice than a conventional streamlined spinner. Another option is to use a conical spinner, which is a modified version of the streamline spinner. [Figure 5-28]

## TURBOPROP FILTER/SEPARATOR

Prevention of foreign object damage (FOD) is a top priority among turbine engine operators and manufacturers. One of the easiest ways to prevent foreign object damage is to install an inlet screen over the engine's inlet duct. Inlet screens are common on many rotorcraft and turboprop engines. Screens are also used on engines installed in test stands. However, inlet screens are seldom used on high mass airflow engines because icing or screen failures would cause significant engine damage.

Additional devices that help prevent foreign object damage include sand or ice separators. The basic design of a sand or ice separator consists of an air intake with at least one venturi and a series of sharp bends. The venturi is used to accelerate the flow of incoming air and debris so that the

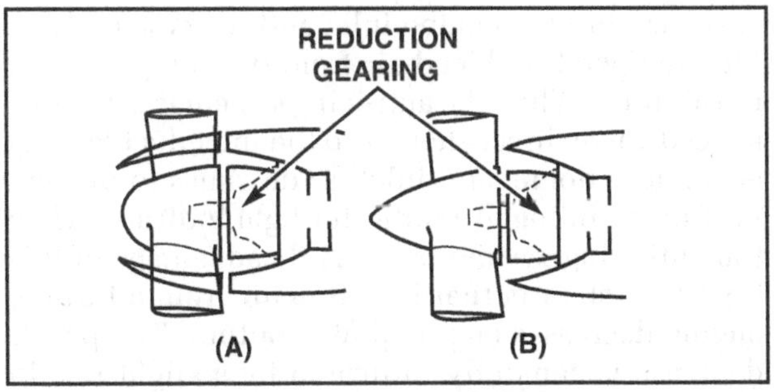


**Figure 5-28. (A) A ducted spinner inlet is the most efficient design for turboprop engines. (B) Although less efficient than ducted spinners, conical spinner inlets present fewer design problems.**

inertia of the debris prevents it from making the bends in the intake, channeling it instead away from the compressor.

Another type of separator used on some turboprop aircraft incorporates a movable vane that extends into the inlet airstream. After it is extended, the vane creates a prominent venturi and a sudden turn in the engine inlet. Combustion air follows the sharp curve but, due to inertia, sand and ice particles cannot. The movable vane is operated by the pilot with a control handle in the cockpit. [Figure 5-29]

## TURBOSHAFT FILTER/SEPARATOR

A critical aspect of air inlet system design for a turboshaft engine is the prevention of foreign object damage to the compressor. This is especially difficult in helicopter operations where landings are often conducted in unimproved areas. Therefore, many helicopters are fitted with a **particle separator** on the engine inlet.

One type of particle separator relies on a venturi and sharp directional changes in airflow to filter sand and ice particles out of the induction air. The venturi accelerates the flow of incoming air and debris so the debris has enough inertia that it cannot follow the bends in the intake. Instead, the debris is channeled away from the compressor and into a sediment trap. [Figure 5-30]

In another type of particle separator, several individual filter elements act as a **swirl chamber**. With this type of system, as incoming air passes through an element, helical vanes create a swirling motion of the air. The swirling motion creates enough centrifugal force to throw the dirt particles

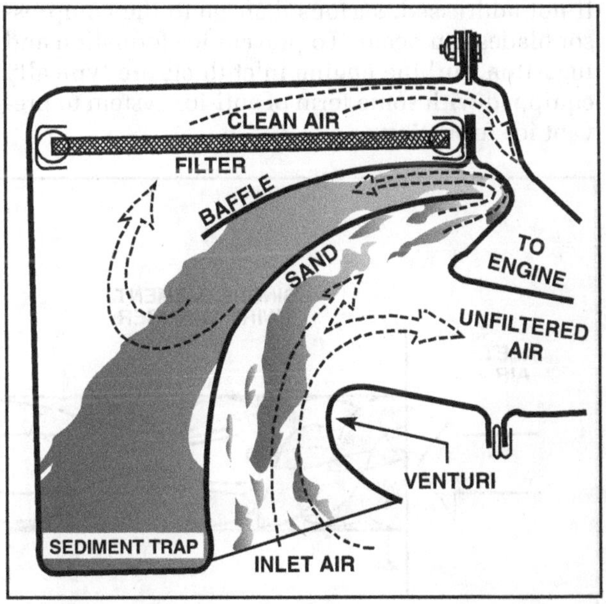


**Figure 5-30. This particle separator is typical of the type found on turbine-powered helicopters. The venturi in the air inlet accelerates the air and sand, so the sand has too much inertia to make the turn leading to the engine.**

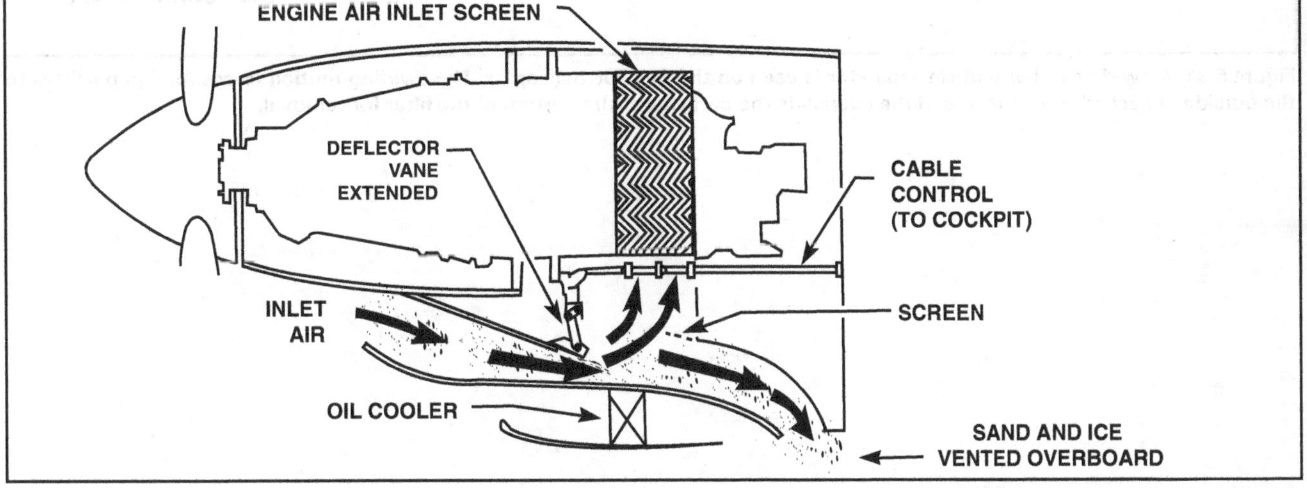


**Figure 5-29. A typical turboprop induction system filter/separator uses a deflector vane to produce a venturi. The venturi accelerates sand, ice, and other debris and carries it overboard.**

to the outside of the chamber. The particles then drop to the bottom of the separator where compressor bleed air blows them overboard Because the foreign particles are swirled out of the intake air, clean air then passes through the filter into the engine inlet. [Figure 5-31]

## INLET ANTI-ICE SYSTEMS

When a turbine-powered aircraft flies through icing conditions, ice can build up in the engine's inlet duct and on the inlet guide vanes. Ice disrupts airflow into the compressor and reduces engine efficiency. There is significant potential for large pieces of ice to form and break off into the engine; if not addressed, serious damage to the compressor blades can occur. To prevent ice formation and ingestion, turbine engine inlet ducts are typically equipped with some form of anti-ice system to prevent ice formation.

A typical turbine engine inlet anti-ice system ducts high temperature bleed air from the compressor to the air inlet. When the anti-icing system is activated, a bleed valve directs hot air to the inlet duct leading edge, nose dome, and inlet guide vanes to prevent ice from building. An indicator light indicates when the anti-icing system is on. A disadvantage of this type of system is that bleeding air from a turbine engine decreases engine power output. The power decrease is generally indicated by a slight rise in EGT and a shift in both EPR and fuel flow.

One way that manufacturers avoid the power loss associated with a bleed-air anti-ice system is to install an electric system. With an electric anti-ice system, electric heating elements are embedded in a rubber boot or placed behind a metal leading edge surrounding the intake.

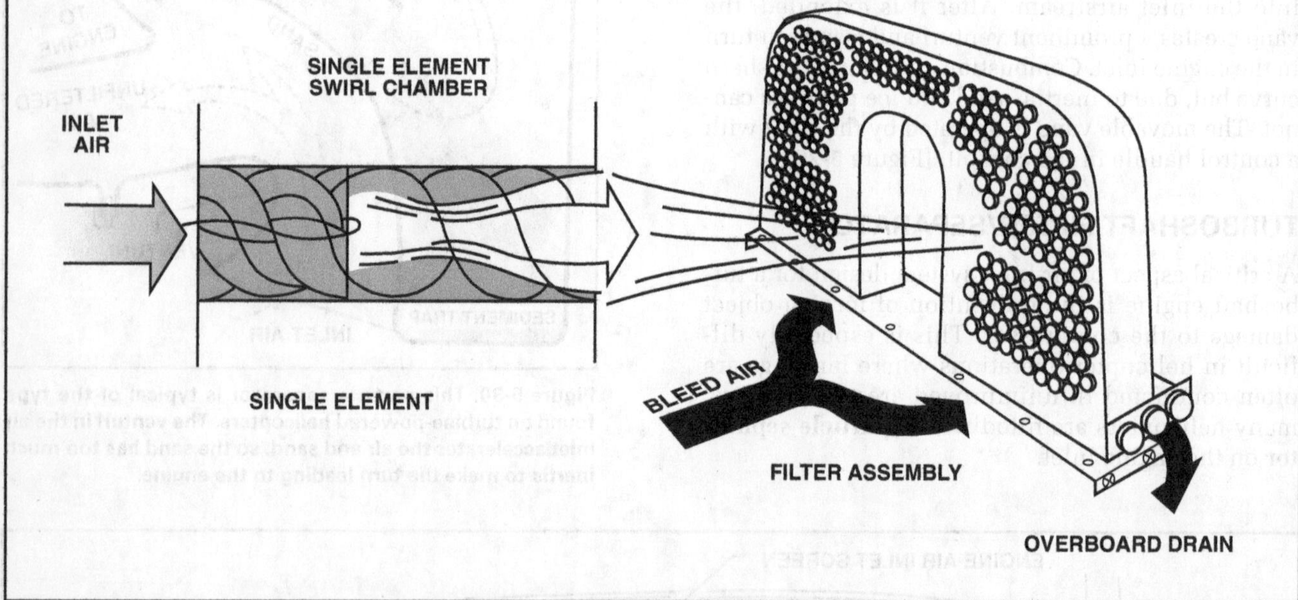


**Figure 5-31. A swirl chamber particle separator is used on the Bell 206 helicopter. The swirling motion forces foreign particles to the outside of each filter element, and then deposits the particles at the bottom of the filter for removal.**

# SUMMARY CHECKLIST

✓ The air inlet on a turbojet engine provides a large volume of smooth, high-energy air to the compressor.

✓ At subsonic speeds, air flowing through the ducts of a turbine engine behaves according to Bernoulli's principle.

✓ Turboprop and turboshaft engines use different types of separators to remove particles by changing the direction of airflow before the compressor stage.

✓ Inlet anti-ice systems direct bleed air to the leading edge of the inlet duct to prevent or remove the formation of ice.

# KEY TERMS

ram recovery
pressure recovery
ram effect
divergent
diffuser
particle separator
swirl chamber

# QUESTIONS

1. In a ______________ duct air velocity decreases and air pressure ______________.

2. The air entering the first stage of compression on a supersonic airplane must be at a speed below ______________.

3. In flight, the forward motion of the aircraft produces an increase in intake air pressure known as the ______________ ______________.

4. The inlet for a turbofan is similar in design to that for a turbojet except that it discharges only a portion of its air into the engine, the remainder passes through the ______________.

5. Supersonic inlet ducts must be designed to operate in three speed modes:

   a. ______________

   b. ______________

   c. ______________

6. Supersonic aircraft will use a ______________ ______________ (what shape) inlet duct.

7. The inlet duct on a subsonic turbojet powered aircraft is a form of ______________ (converging or diverging) duct.

8. When turbine engines are calibrated on a test stand, a ______________ (what shape) inlet is typically installed.

9. Helicopter operations may require the use of a ______________ ______________ on the inlet of the engine.

# CHAPTER 6

# EXHAUST SYSTEMS

## INTRODUCTION

In both reciprocating and turbine engines, the purpose of an exhaust system is to route spent combustion gases overboard. Exhaust systems must function properly because a system failure could have disastrous results, such as a fire or the introduction of poisonous gases into the cabin. For an engine to operate at its maximum efficiency and safety, you must inspect and maintain the exhaust system according to the manufacturer's recommendations.

# SECTION A

## RECIPROCATING ENGINES

A byproduct of combustion in a reciprocating engine is high-temperature, noxious gases. Due to the corrosive nature of exhaust gases and the wide range of temperatures that the system experiences, modern exhaust system components are typically made of nickel-chromium steel or other corrosion- and heat-resistant alloys.

## TYPES OF EXHAUST SYSTEMS

Two basic types of exhaust systems are in use on reciprocating aircraft engines: the short stack (or open system) and the collector system. The short stack system was used on nonsupercharged and low power engines. The collector system used on most modern engines improves nacelle streamlining and provides easier maintenance in the nacelle area. It is also found on all turbo-supercharged engines that collect and route the exhaust gases to the turbine. A disadvantage of the collector system is an increase in exhaust system back pressure, which reduces horsepower. However, the increased horsepower achieved by turbo-supercharging overcomes the power lost from increased back pressure.

### SHORT STACKS

Early in-line and V-engines often used straight stacks, which were short sections of steel tubing welded to a flange and bolted to the cylinder exhaust port. Short stacks were effective at getting exhaust out of the engine compartment, but provided no silencing capability. When an aircraft was side-slipped, cold air could flow into these stacks and warp the exhaust valves.

The short stack system is relatively simple; removal and installation includes little more than removing and installing the hold-down nuts and clamps.

### COLLECTOR SYSTEMS

The types of collector systems for reciprocating engines are defined by the type of engine. The following sections discuss the opposed engine exhaust manifold and the radial engine collector rings.

#### OPPOSED ENGINE EXHAUST MANIFOLD

The typical exhaust system on a horizontally opposed engine consists of risers from each cylinder and an exhaust collector on each side of the engine. The risers are attached to each cylinder with brass or special heat-resistant locknuts. [Figure 6-1]

On some systems, a crossover tube connects the exhaust stacks on the left side of the engine with the stacks on the right side. Sections of the exhaust system are usually joined together with spring-loaded ball joints. When properly installed, the ball joints are loose enough to allow expansion movement but tight enough to prevent leakage. Ball joints also

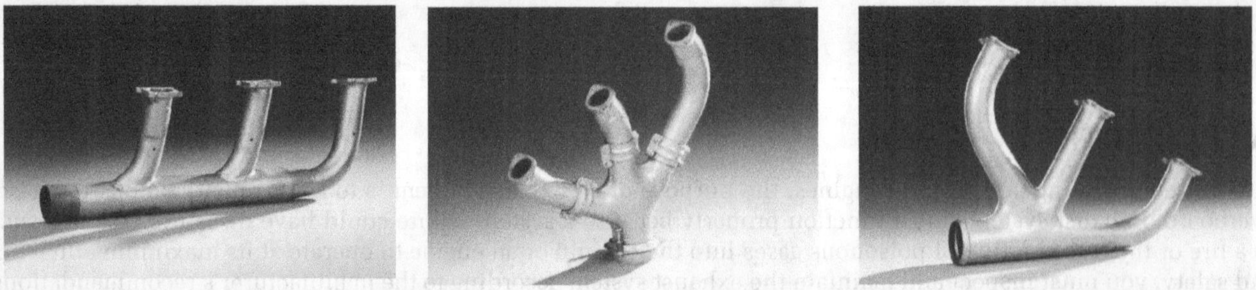

**Figure 6-1. Risers and collectors can be constructed as a unit; the risers can be connected to the collector with ring clamps, or each riser can be a separate part of the collector system.**

compensate for slight misalignment of the parts. The exhaust collector tube might be routed to a turbocharger, a muffler, or an exhaust augmenter before being routed overboard. [Figure 6-2]

### RADIAL ENGINE EXHAUST COLLECTOR RINGS

Radial engines use an exhaust manifold made up of pieces of tubing that are fitted together with loose slip joints. In addition to aiding in aligning exhaust components, slip joints accommodate exhaust tube expansion when an engine is running to prevent leakage.

Each section of the collector is bolted to a bracket on the blower section of the engine and is partly supported by a sleeve connection between the collector ring ports and the short stack on the engine exhaust ports. The exhaust tailpipe is joined to the collector ring by a telescoping expansion joint; this provides enough slack to remove segments of the collector ring without removing the tailpipe. [Figure 6-3]

## MUFFLERS AND HEAT EXCHANGERS

Engine noise abatement is an important issue that has received increasing attention in aircraft design over time. A significant amount of research has been conducted to find practical ways of increasing the frequency and reducing the intensity of engine noise. A large portion of the total noise is generated by the propeller, but the noise through the exhaust is an appreciable amount.

The earliest exhaust collectors carried the gases away from the engine, but had a negligible effect

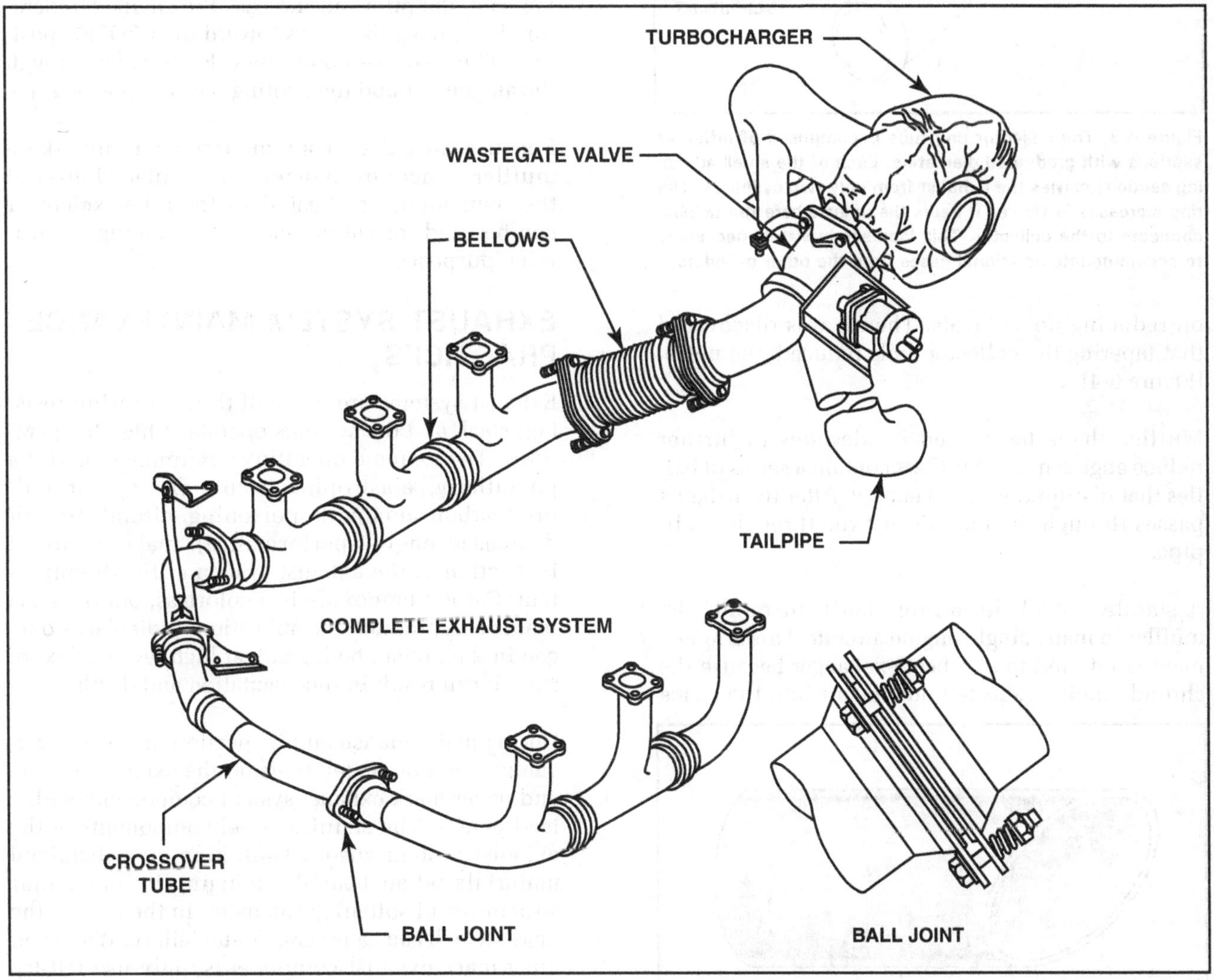


**Figure 6-2. This illustration shows the exhaust system of a turbocharged, six-cylinder, horizontally opposed engine. At each location where expansion and contraction occur, bellows are installed to permit changes in physical dimensions without any leakage. The hydraulically controlled waste gate valve permits exhaust gases to pass directly through the tail pipe or directs them to the turbocharger turbine section. The turbocharger in this installation is wrapped in a heat blanket to improve efficiency and decrease air temperatures inside the cowling.**

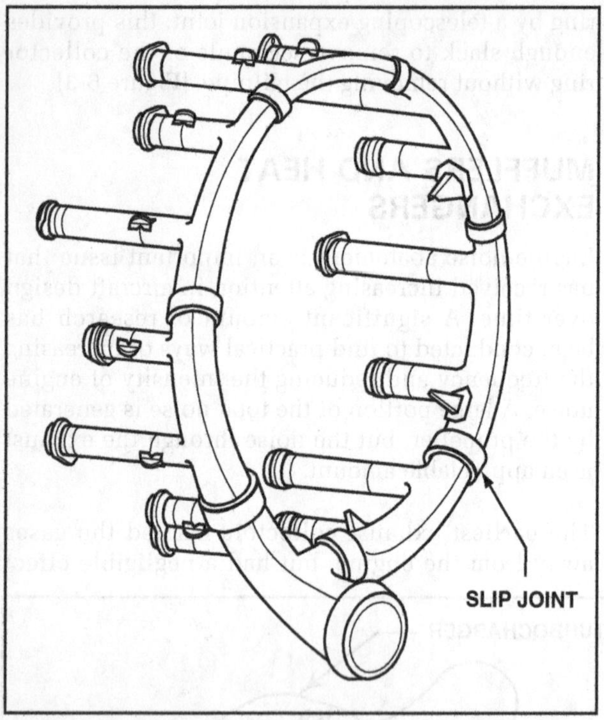


**Figure 6-3. The collector ring tube is composed of different sections with graduated diameters. Each of the small adjoining sections carries the exhaust from only two cylinders. The ring increases in size as it nears the point where the tailpipe connects to the collector. This increase in size is necessary to accommodate additional gases from the other cylinders.**

on reducing noise levels. Then it was discovered that tapering the collector ends reduced, the noise. [Figure 6-4]

Mufflers have been used for decades to further reduce engine noise. Mufflers contain a series of baffles that disrupt the sound energy. After the exhaust passes through the muffler, it exits through a tailpipe.

A stainless steel shroud (or shell) surrounds the muffler in many single-engine aircraft. This arrangement is referred to as a heat exchanger because the shroud admits unheated outside air into the space

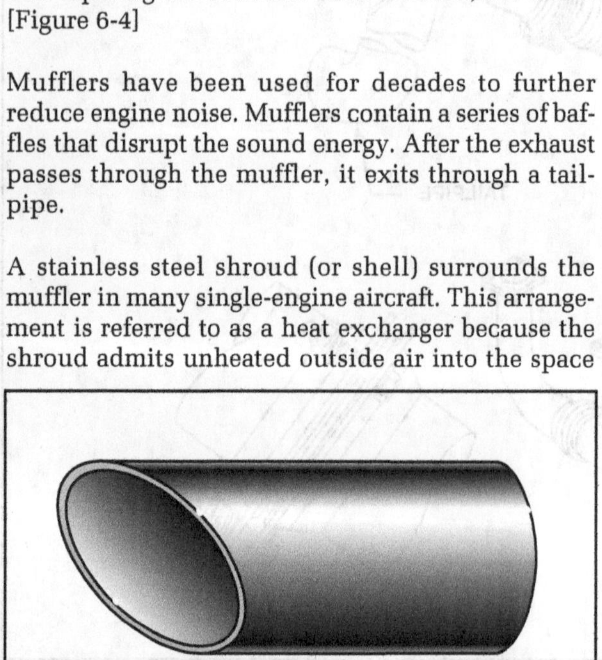

**Figure 6-4. Exhaust discharged through a tapered opening, called a bayonet, creates an area of slightly lower pressure that reduces exhaust back pressure and noise.**

between the muffler and the shroud where the exhaust gases heat the muffler and the air within the shroud. This heated air can be used to heat the cabin or for deicing or anti-icing systems. Maintenance personnel can easily remove the shroud to inspect the muffler. [Figure 6-5]

## EXHAUST AUGMENTERS

On some engines, exhaust augmenters aid in engine cooling. Exhaust augmenters use the velocity of the exiting exhaust gases to produce a venturi effect to increase airflow over the engine. [Figure 6-6]

Some exhaust augmenters are adjustable using an augmenter vane located at the exit end of each augmenter. When the vane is fully closed, the cross-section of the augmenter tube is reduced by approximately 45 percent. If an engine is running too cool, the pilot can increase the engine temperature by moving the vanes toward the CLOSED position. This decreases both the velocity of air through the augmenter and the cooling effect on the engine.

Because an exhaust augmenter heats up like a muffler, a heat exchanger can be placed around the augmenter. The heated air from the exchanger can be used for cabin heat or for deicing or anti-icing purposes.

## EXHAUST SYSTEM MAINTENANCE PRACTICES

Exhaust systems are made of thin, corrosion-resistant steel, and the systems operate at high temperatures. The extreme operating environment and the potentially catastrophic results of a system failure (carbon monoxide poisoning, aircraft fire, or decreased engine performance), make a careful inspection of the exhaust system critically important. Carbon monoxide is a colorless, odorless gas that is a byproduct of combustion. It displaces oxygen in the human body, and, at high levels of exposure, it can result in incapacitation and death.

During maintenance and inspection, never use galvanized or zinc-plated tools on the exhaust system, and never mark exhaust system components with a lead pencil. The stainless steel components of the exhaust system absorb lead, zinc, or galvanized materials when heated, changing its molecular structure and softening the metal in the area of the mark, which can cause cracks and failure. When you must mark exhaust components, only use felt-tip markers, India ink, or Prussian blue.

Some exhaust system components are coated with a corrosion-resistant ceramic material. Use only a degreasing solution to clean these units. To avoid

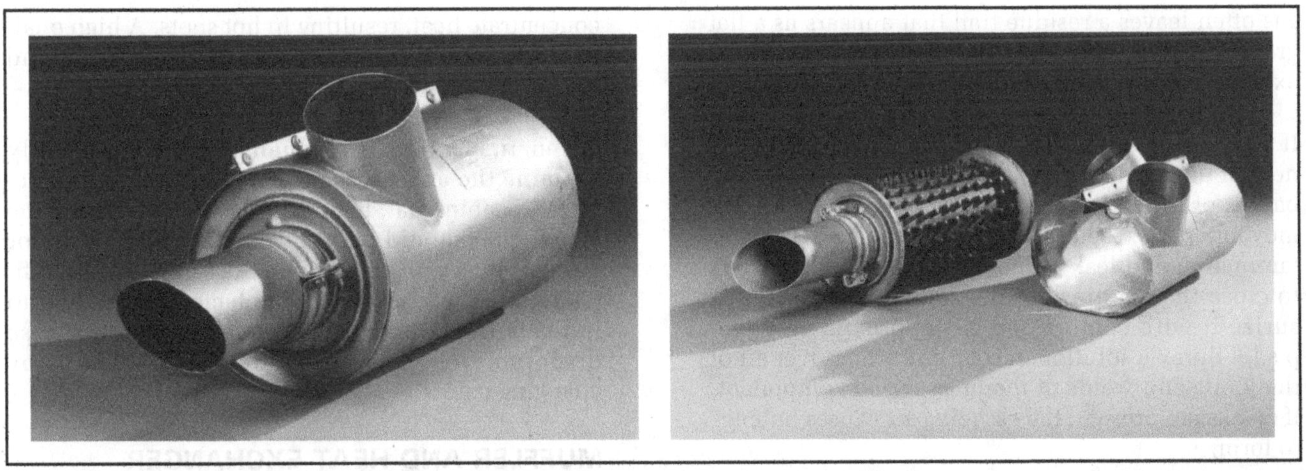

Figure 6-5. On the left, the shroud is installed on the muffler. The shroud is typically held to the muffler with stainless steel screws. On the right, the shroud is removed. The knobs on the muffler transfer heat from the muffler to the air space within the shroud.

damage to the ceramic coating, never sand blast these components or use alkaline cleaners. Corrosion-resistant steel can be cleaned with abrasive media as long as it has not been previously used to clean iron or steel materials. Used sand often contains metal particles that can become embedded in the metal and cause corrosion.

## EXHAUST SYSTEM INSPECTION

During an inspection of the exhaust system, look for any cracks, dents, or missing parts. A pick or a similarly pointed instrument is useful for probing areas where damage is suspected. Cracks are the most commonly identified exhaust system discrepancy. A crack will permit exhaust gas to escape. Escaping

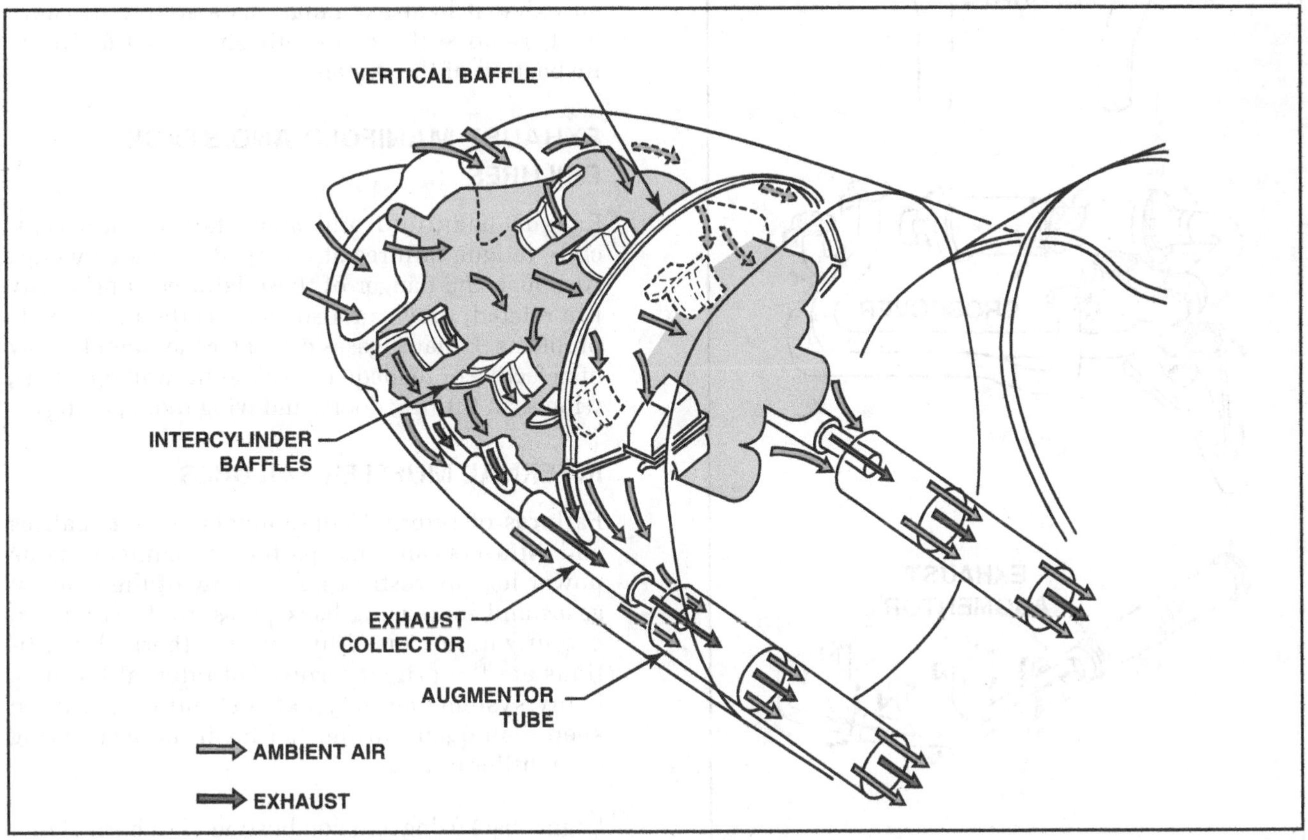


Figure 6-6. The exhaust from the cylinders on each side of the engine flows through a collector and discharges into the inlet of a stainless steel augmenter tube. This flow of high velocity gas creates low pressure that draws air through the cylinder fins.

gas often leaves a residue trail that appears as a flat gray or a sooty black streak on the outside of an exhaust stack or muffler. [Figure 6-7]

If you are unable to thoroughly inspect a component of the exhaust system visually (such as internal baffles or diffusers) or if a part is hidden by nonremovable parts, remove the system to check for contamination and leaks. One way to check for leaks is to close the openings of the component and pressurize it with compressed air (approximately two p.s.i.). Spray a solution of soap and water over all of the joints and welds of the pressurized component. If cracks are present, the escaping air causes bubbles to form.

The expansion and contraction of various components make welds a likely area for cracks to form. Poor quality weld beads protrude internally and concentrate heat, resulting in hot spots. A high quality weld tapers smoothly into the base metal and evenly dissipates heat.

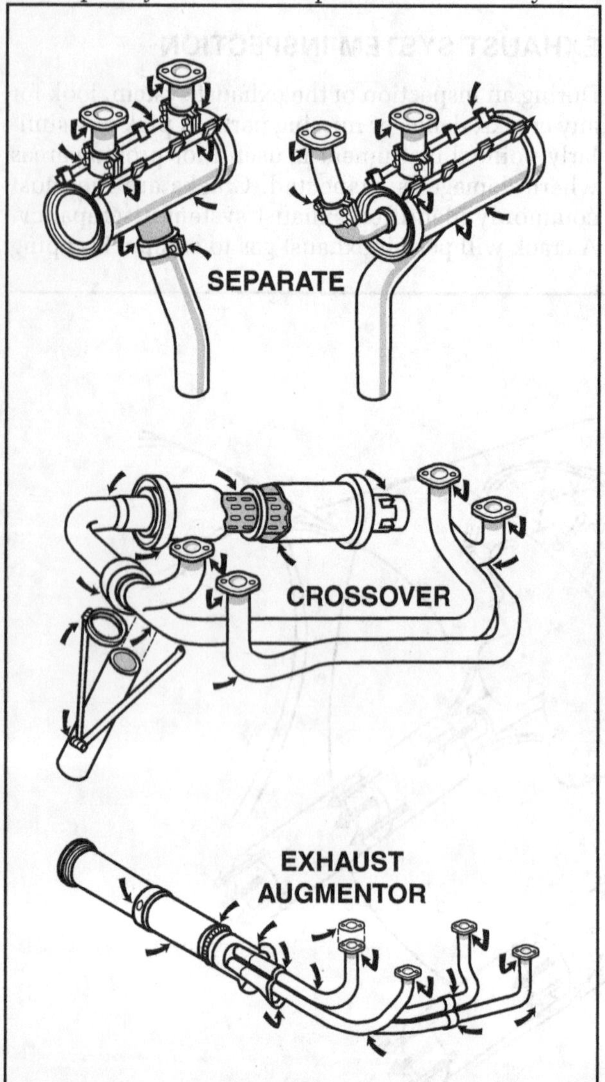


**Figure 6-7. The arrows indicate the primary inspection points on these different types of exhaust systems.**

When inspecting the exhaust system, carefully examine the areas that heat air for carburetor deicing and cabin heat. In addition, when operating the engine you should periodically check the cabin for the presence of carbon monoxide. In many aircraft, a simple carbon monoxide detector is installed to indicate the presence of carbon monoxide. These disposable detectors indicate the deadly gas by changing color.

## MUFFLER AND HEAT EXCHANGER FAILURES

Many muffler and heat exchanger failures can be traced to cracks or ruptures in the surfaces that provide heat for the cabin and carburetor. Failures in the heat exchanger surface, usually in the outer wall, permit exhaust gases to escape directly into the cabin heat system. Exhausted gases drawn into the engine induction system can cause engine overheating and loss of power. In most cases, a failure in the exhaust system is a result of the high exhaust temperatures. Defects expand as a result of thermal and vibration fatigue. On aircraft using an exhaust heat exchanger as a source of cabin heat, remove the heater air shroud to facilitate inspection of the system.

## EXHAUST MANIFOLD AND STACK FAILURES

Exhaust manifold and stack failures are typically fatigue failures at clamped points or welds. Although the danger of these failures is primarily fire related, they can also cause carbon monoxide problems. Exhaust gases can enter the cabin by way of defective or inadequate seals at firewall openings, wing strut fittings, doors, and wing root openings.

## INTERNAL MUFFLER FAILURES

Failures of internal components such as baffles and diffusers can cause partial or complete engine power loss by restricting the flow of the exhaust gases and increasing back pressure. Erosion and carburization caused by extreme thermal conditions are the primary causes of internal failures. Many systems employ exhaust outlet guards to keep dislodged muffler baffles from obstructing the muffler outlet.

Engine backfiring and combustion of unburned fuel within the exhaust system are probable contributing factors to internal muffler failure. In addition, local hot spot areas caused by uneven exhaust gas flow can result in burning, bulging, or rupturing of the outer muffler wall.

### TURBOCHARGER EXHAUST SYSTEMS

The exhaust system of a turbocharged engine operates under conditions of greatly increased temperature and pressure, so the inspection and maintenance of a turbocharged exhaust system is even more critical. During high-altitude operation, the exhaust system pressure is maintained at or near sea level values, and, because of this pressure differential, any leaks permit exhaust gases to escape with a torch-like intensity that can damage adjacent components or structures.

Coke deposits, or carbon buildup, are a common cause of waste gate malfunction, which causes erratic system operation. Excessive deposit buildup can cause the waste gate to stick in the closed position, causing an over-boost condition. Coke deposit buildup in the turbine itself will cause a gradual loss of power in flight and low manifold pressure readings prior to takeoff. Clean, repair, overhaul, and adjust the system components and controls according to the manufacturer's service instructions.

### AUGMENTER EXHAUST SYSTEM

Inspect exhaust systems equipped with augmenter tubes at regular intervals for proper alignment, security of attachment, and general overall condition. Even when augmenter tubes do not contain heat exchanger surfaces, you should inspect them for cracks along with the rest of the exhaust system.

### EXHAUST SYSTEM REPAIRS

Exhaust stacks, mufflers, tailpipes, and so on, should be replaced with new or reconditioned components instead of being repaired in the field. The attempt to perform welded repairs to exhaust system components is complicated by the difficulty of accurately identifying the base metal so you can correctly select the appropriate repair materials.

Do not use steel or other low-temperature, self-locking nuts as a substitute for brass or high-temperature locknuts used by the manufacturer. The majority of exhaust system gaskets should never be reused. Always replace gaskets with new ones of the same type provided by the manufacturer.

## SUMMARY CHECKLIST

✓ Muffler baffles disrupt the noise energy of aircraft exhaust.

✓ Because the muffler is used as a heat exchanger to heat small aircraft powered by reciprocating engines, mufflers must be inspected for cracks to ensure that carbon monoxide does not enter the cabin.

✓ Only approved repair facilities may perform welded repairs to exhaust system components.

# QUESTIONS

1. The two general types of exhaust systems used on reciprocating aircraft engines are:

   a. ____________

   b. ____________

2. ____________ allow for expansion and contraction of the exhaust system.

3 The purpose of the ____________ surrounding the muffler is to capture heat for other systems.

4. Spring-loaded ____________ allow for movement without leakage, and slight misalignment of exhaust components.

5. Exhaust ____________ use the velocity of the exiting exhaust gases to produce a venturi effect.

6. Exhaust system parts should never be marked with a ________ pencil.

7. A crack on an exhaust system component will often show as a ________ gray or ________ black streak on the outside of the part.

8. Exhaust system failure almost always creates what hazards?

   a. ____________

   b. ____________

9. Carbon buildup in the waste gate unit of a turbocharged engine is often referred to as ____________ deposits.

10. A turbocharger system places a ____________(higher or lower) pressure on the exhaust components.

## TURBINE ENGINES

The exhaust system of a turbine engine must withstand very high temperatures, and it is usually manufactured from nickel or titanium. The engine heat must not be permitted to transfer to nearby airframe components or structures. The airframe structures are protected by routing ventilating air around the exhaust pipe and by covering the exhaust pipe with an insulating blanket. An insulating blanket has an inner layer of insulating material under a stainless steel skin, which is dimpled to increase its strength. This assembly prevents the heat from leaving the engine anywhere except for the exhaust.

## TURBOJET EXHAUST SYSTEM

The exhaust section of a turbojet engine is located directly behind the turbine section. The exhaust section components direct the flow of gases aft to prevent turbulence and to increase the exit velocity of the gases. [Figure 6-8]

### CONE ASSEMBLY

The exhaust cone collects the gases discharged from the turbine and gradually converts them into a single jet. The collected gases are delivered directly to the jet nozzle, or through a tailpipe.

### TAIL PIPE OR EXHAUST DUCT

The term *exhaust duct* refers to the engine exhaust pipe, or tail pipe, which connects the turbine outlet to the jet nozzle of a non-afterburning engine. If engine exhaust gases could be discharged directly into the outside air in an exact axial direction at the turbine exit, an exhaust duct might not be necessary, but this is not practical. Engine thrust can be increased if the gases are discharged from the aircraft at a higher velocity than that produced by the turbine outlet alone, and an exhaust duct collects and straightens the gas flow out of a turbine and increases the velocity of the gas before discharging it from the exhaust nozzle, which increases momentum and thrust.

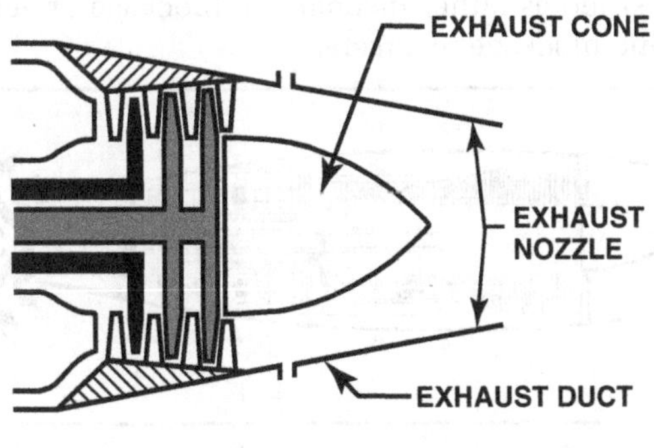


**Figure 6-8. The components of the exhaust section include the exhaust cone assembly, the exhaust duct (or tailpipe) when required, and the exhaust (or jet) nozzle.**

The exhaust duct is essentially a simple conical or cylindrical stainless steel pipe. The assembly also includes an engine tail cone and the struts inside the duct. The tail cone and the struts add strength to the duct, impart an axial direction, and smooth the gas flow.

Immediately aft of the turbine outlet, and usually just forward of the flange to which the exhaust duct is attached, one or more sensors monitor the turbine discharge pressure. Because measuring the inlet turbine temperature on large engines is often impractical, exhaust gas temperature thermocouple probes might be attached at the turbine outlet.

### EXHAUST NOZZLES

The rear opening of a turbine engine exhaust duct is called the exhaust nozzle. The nozzle acts as an orifice whose size determines the density and velocity of exiting gases. Nozzle shapes are either convergent or convergent-divergent.

### CONVERGENT EXHAUST NOZZLE

Most aircraft that produce exhaust gas at subsonic velocity use a convergent exhaust nozzle to increase exhaust gas velocity.

Adjusting the area of an exhaust nozzle changes both engine performance and exhaust gas temperature. Some engines are trimmed to their correct exhaust gas temperature by altering the exhaust nozzle area. To do this, you can bend small tabs to change the area or fasten small adjustable pieces, called mice, around the perimeter of the nozzle.

## CONVERGENT-DIVERGENT EXHAUST NOZZLE

Whenever the engine pressure ratio is high enough to produce supersonic exhaust gas velocities, a convergent-divergent nozzle will produce more thrust. The advantage of a convergent-divergent nozzle is greatest at high Mach numbers because of the resulting higher pressure ratio across the engine exhaust nozzle. [Figure 6-9]

To ensure that a constant weight (or volume) of gas flows past any given point at sonic velocity, the rear part of a supersonic exhaust duct is enlarged to accommodate the additional weight or volume of a gas flowing at supersonic rates. Otherwise, the nozzle would not operate efficiently.

# TURBOFAN EXHAUST

The bypass engine has two gas streams that must be ejected to the atmosphere—the cool fan air and the hot gases discharged from the turbine. In a low-bypass engine, a mixer unit typically combines these two flows and discharges them through the same nozzle. In a high-bypass engine, the fan air is usually discharged separately from the hot gases.

# TURBOPROP EXHAUST

In a typical turboprop exhaust system, exhaust gases pass from the turbine section through a tail pipe assembly into the atmosphere. The exhaust arrangement used depends on the type of engine. Turboprop engines using a through-flow burner typically expel the gases straight out the back of the engine and out the nacelle. This extracts the maximum amount of thrust from the velocity of the hot gases. Engines

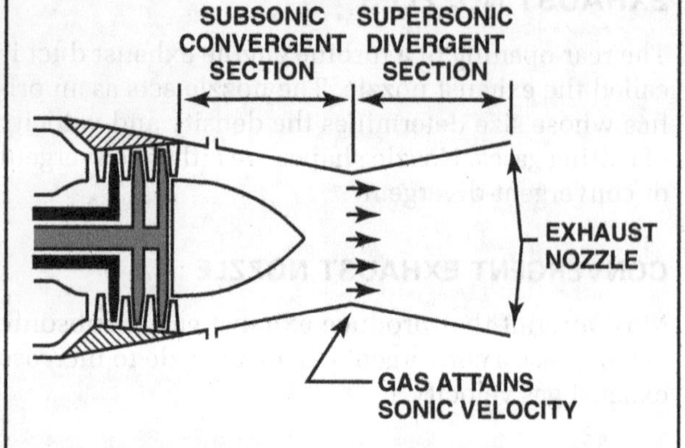


**Figure 6-9. The convergent section in a convergent-divergent nozzle handles gases at subsonic speeds and funnels them to the throat of the nozzle as they attain sonic velocity. The divergent section accelerates the Mach 1 gas to supersonic speed.**

that use a reverse flow combustor might exhaust the hot gases near the front of the engine. This design collects the exhaust gases and vents them overboard through exhaust stacks. This arrangement provides a negligible amount of additional thrust.

# THRUST REVERSERS

Transport category aircraft powered by turbojets and turbofans, most commuter aircraft, and an increasing number of business jets are equipped with thrust reversers to:

- Aid in braking and directional control during normal landing and reduce brake maintenance.
- Provide braking and directional control during emergency landings and balked takeoffs.
- Back an aircraft out of a parking spot in a power-back operation.

Although some thrust reversers are electrically powered, most large transport category aircraft use hydraulic or pneumatic actuators. The pilot controls the thrust reversers with a cockpit lever. In a typical system, the pilot retards the power levers to ground idle and selects reverse thrust. Then the pilot advances the power levers to takeoff power to slow the aircraft as required. When the aircraft slows, the pilot retards the power levers to ground idle and deselects reverse thrust. [Figure 6-10]

Although thrust reversers provide approximately 20 percent of the braking force under normal conditions, they must be capable of providing 50 percent of rated thrust in the reverse direction. Exhaust gas typically exits the reverser at an angle to the engine's thrust axis. As such, maximum reverse thrust capability is always less than forward thrust capability. Operating with thrust reversers at low ground speeds can cause compressor stalls due to the reingestion of hot gases. It can also cause ingestion of fine sand and other runway debris. Most thrust reversers are classified as either mechanical-blockage or aerodynamic-blockage reversers.

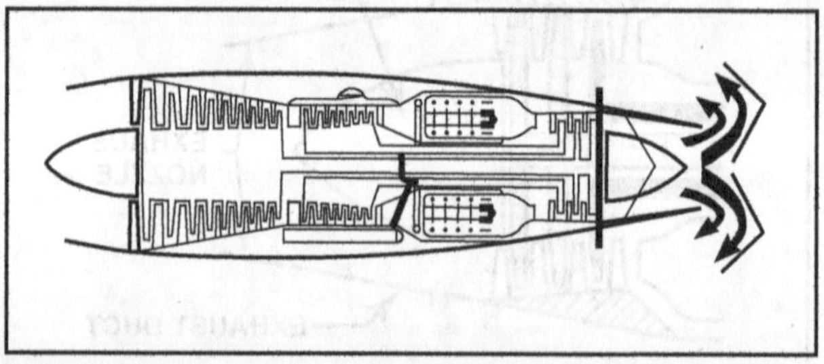

**Figure 6-10. Thrust reversers change the direction of exhaust gas flow from a rearward to a more forward direction. This illustration shows a mechanical blockage thrust reverser.**

## MECHANICAL-BLOCKAGE REVERSERS

Mechanical blockage is accomplished by placing a movable obstruction in the exhaust gas stream either before or after the exhaust exits the duct. The engine exhaust gases are mechanically blocked and diverted to a forward direction by an inverted cone, half-sphere, or other device. The mechanical blockage system is sometimes referred to as the clamshell thrust reverser because of its shape.

## AERODYNAMIC-BLOCKAGE REVERSER

The aerodynamic-blockage thrust reverser uses thin airfoils or obstructions placed in the gas stream. These vanes, often referred to as cascades, redirect the escaping exhaust gases forward, which results in rearward thrust. Some aircraft use a combination of the aerodynamic-blockage and the mechanical-blockage reversers.

Mixed exhaust turbofans are configured with one reverser, while unmixed or bypass exhaust turbofans often have both cold stream and hot stream reversers. Some high-bypass turbofans use only cold stream reversing because most of the thrust is present in the fan discharge; a hot stream reverser would add system weight but provide minimal value. [Figure 6-11]

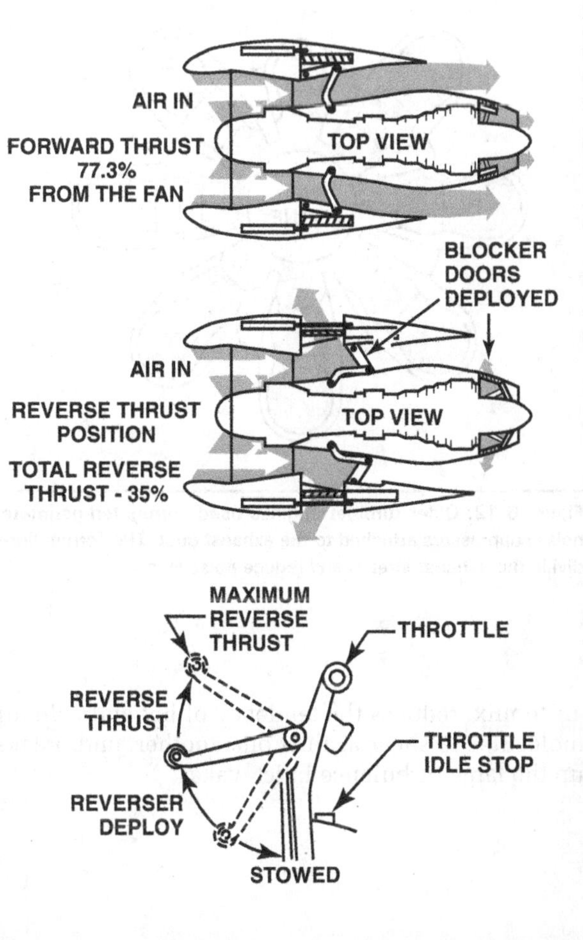


**Figure 6-11. This illustration of the aerodynamic-blockage reverser on a DC-10 shows the reverser doors stowed when the engine produces forward thrust. When deployed, the reverser doors divert both cold and hot stream air. To deploy the thrust reversers, the pilot retards the power lever to the idle stop, then raises the reverser lever from its stowed position, and advances the power lever to decelerate the aircraft as necessary.**

# NOISE SUPPRESSORS

Because most major airports are located near large cities, the need to minimize turbine exhaust noise is obvious. Aircraft and engine manufacturers have worked with regulators and operators to improve noise reduction technologies and techniques with each generation of products. When possible, new technologies and techniques are retrofitted to earlier designs to reduce noise.

Noise suppressors used on the ground include portable devices positioned near the rear of an engine during periods of prolonged ground operation. Most large airports have blast fences and designated run-up areas, and aircraft operations are restricted to certain times of the day.

Older turbojet engines produce a combination of noise frequencies at very high levels. Although a turbojet compressor produces a great deal of high frequency sound, this noise decreases rapidly as the distance from the source increases. Turbojet exhaust also produces noise at a wide range of frequencies and at very high energy levels. This noise is damaging to human hearing and audible over great distances. One solution to turbojet exhaust noise is the use of a corrugated perimeter noise suppressor that helps break up the exhaust flow and raises its noise frequency. Some older engines can be fitted with hush kits that reduce their noise emissions. [Figure 6-12]

Newer engines use a variety of techniques to reduce harmful noise. For example, some turbofan engines blend fan discharge air with the exhaust gases to reduce sound emission. On these engines, the sound at the inlet is likely to be louder than sound from the tail pipe. In addition, the inlet and exhaust ducts on turbofan engines are lined with sound-attenuating materials that reduce noise levels. [Figure 6-13]

Because low frequency noise can linger at a relative high volume, increasing the frequency of the sound often reduces noise. Frequency change is accomplished by increasing the perimeter of the exhaust stream. This provides more space for cold and hot

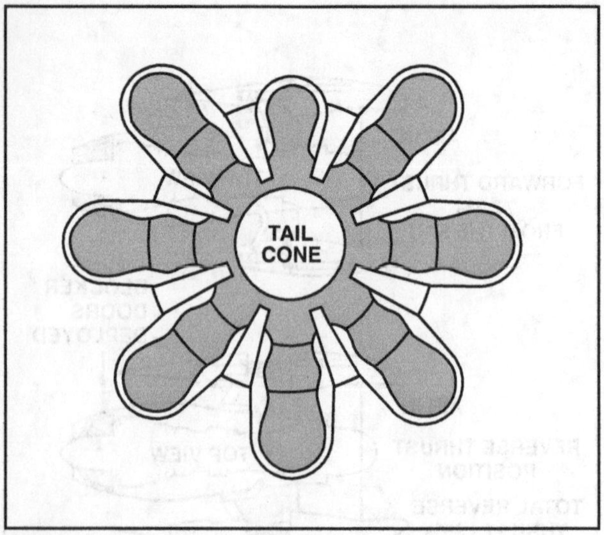


**Figure 6-12. Older turbojet engines used corrugated-perimeter noise suppressors attached to the exhaust duct. The corrugations divide the exhaust stream and reduce noise levels.**

air to mix, reduces the tendency of hot and cold air molecules to shear against one another, and breaks up the large turbulence in jet wake.

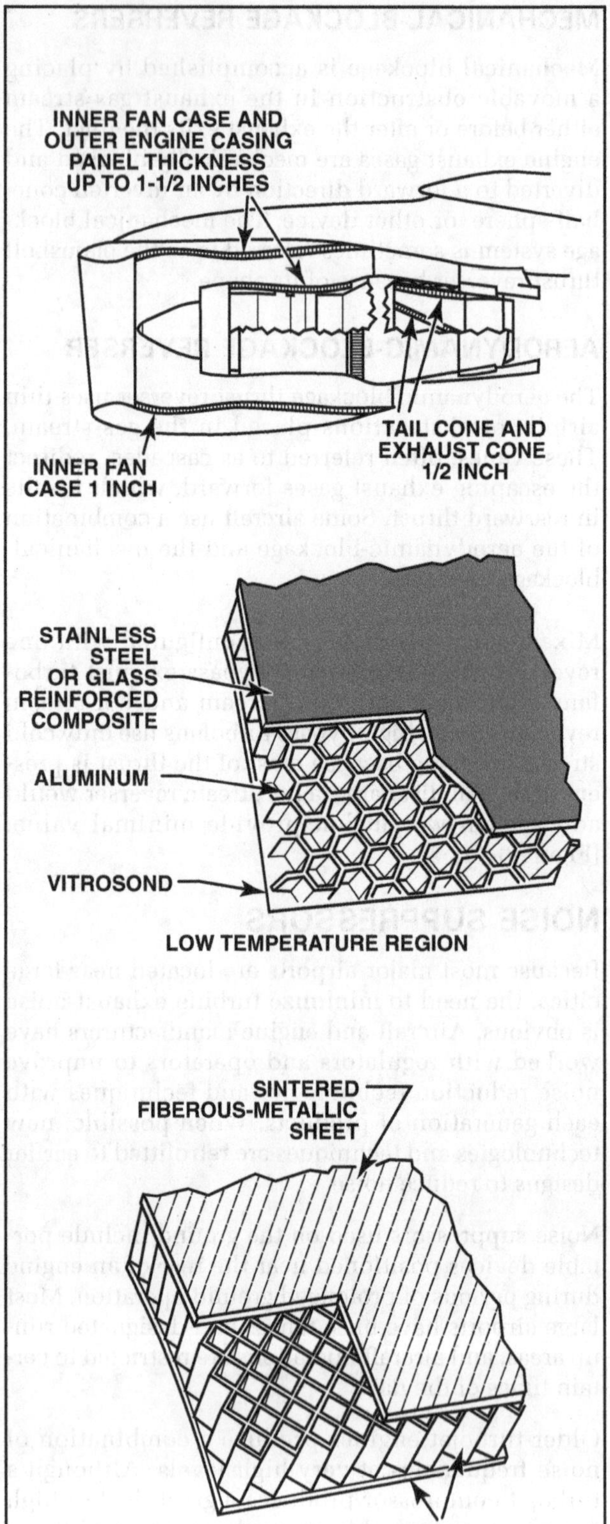


**Figure 6-13. High-bypass turbofan engines employ sound-absorbing materials at specific locations to minimize noise emissions. The materials and patterns used depend on the temperatures present at various locations.**

# SUMMARY CHECKLIST

✓ An exhaust nozzle on a turbine engine controls the density and velocity of exiting gas.

✓ Thrust reversers redirect exhaust to slow an aircraft on landing or to enable it to back up during taxi.

# QUESTIONS

1. A greater amount of thrust can be obtained from a turbojet engine if the exhaust gases are discharged from the aircraft at a velocity _________ (higher or lower) than that at the turbine outlet.

2. Subsonic engines will use a ______________ (converging or C-D) jet nozzle.

3. A ________________ (what shape) tail pipe is used on most subsonic aircraft.

4. Supersonic aircraft utilize a ________________ ________________ (what shape) type of tail pipe.

5. Turboprop exhaust gases provide _________________ (increased or very little) additional thrust.

6. The three functions of thrust reversers are:

   a. ____________________

   b. ____________________

   c. ____________________

7. A thrust reverser system can provide about ______% of the total braking force under normal conditions.

8. There are two types of thrust reversers; _________blockage and __________blockage.

9. High bypass turbojets frequently use only __________stream air for reverse thrust.

10. Unmixed exhaust turbofan engines may have both _________ stream and __________ stream reversers.

11. Some high bypass engines may only have ________ (hot or cold) stream reversing.

12. Older engine installations may have _______ _______retrofitted in order to reduce noise to acceptable levels.

13. The noise generated by a turbofan is ______ (greater or less) than that generated by a turbojet.

CHAPTER 7

# ENGINE FUEL SYSTEMS

## INTRODUCTION

For an aircraft to operate reliably in every phase of flight and in all expected environments, its fuel system must store and maintain a sufficient quantity of fuel and deliver it to the powerplant without interruption or contamination. The entire fuel system can be divided in three functional areas: storage, delivery, and distribution. The earliest systems were very simple, including a tank, fuel lines, a selector valve, and a carburetor. Over time, powerplant technology advanced, and with increased power came more complexity and more specific demands for distributing fuel. Fuel systems are designed to efficiently meet the design requirements of an aircraft powerplant with particular considerations for safety. Aviation maintenance technicians must be thoroughly familiar with the design, operation, and maintenance of the aircraft fuel system before inspecting or performing maintenance.

# SECTION A

## FUEL STORAGE AND DELIVERY

Aircraft fuel systems have two basic sections; airframe and powerplant. The airframe section consists of all the parts associated with storage and delivery, including the parts from the fuel tanks to the engine-driven pump. The powerplant section consists of the distribution parts, beginning after the engine-driven fuel pump and concluding at the point where air and fuel are mixed for combustion (inside a carburetor or in the combustion chamber of a cylinder or turbine engine). While many components in an aircraft fuel system are specific to the airframe, the sole purpose of the fuel system is to provide fuel to the engine(s). This section focuses on the airframe components and the types of fuel. Additional information on these topics is available in the Jeppesen *A&P Technician Airframe Textbook.* The engine components are discussed in the next two sections about fuel metering for gasoline-powered reciprocating and turbine engines.

## FUEL SYSTEM REQUIREMENTS

The fuel systems of aircraft certified or registered in the US must be designed to meet specific operating requirements in 14 CFR Part 23 of the Federal Aviation Regulations. Some of these requirements are:

- Each fuel system must be constructed and arranged to ensure fuel flow at a rate and pressure established for proper engine and auxiliary power unit functioning under all likely operating conditions. (FAR 23.951)
- Each fuel system must be arranged so that no pump can draw fuel from more than one tank at a time, or provisions must be made to prevent air from being drawn into the fuel supply line. (FAR 23.951)
- Turbine-powered aircraft must be capable of sustained operation with 0.75 cubic centimeter of free water per gallon of fuel at 80 degrees Fahrenheit. In addition, an engine must be capable of sustained operation when the fuel is cooled to its most critical condition for icing. (FAR 23.951)
- Each fuel system of a multiengine aircraft must be arranged so that the failure of any one component (except a fuel tank) will not result in the loss of power of more than one engine or require immediate action by the pilot to prevent the loss of power. (FAR 23.953)
- If a multiengine airplane has a single tank or assembly of interconnected tanks, each engine must have an independent tank outlet with a fuel shutoff valve at the tank. (FAR 23.953)
- A way to rapidly shut off fuel in flight to each engine of a normal category aircraft must be provided to appropriate flight crewmembers. The engine fuel shutoff valve cannot be located on the engine side of any firewall. (FAR 23.995)
- On multiengine aircraft, the closing of an individual fuel shutoff valve for any engine shall not affect the fuel supply to the other engines. (FAR 23.1189)
- Tanks used in multiengine fuel systems must have two vents arranged so that is unlikely that both become plugged at the same time. (FAR 23.953)
- All filler caps must be designed so that they are unlikely to be installed incorrectly or lost in flight. (FAR 23.953)
- The fuel systems must be designed to prevent the ignition of fuel vapors by lightning. (FAR 23.954)
- The fuel flow rate of a gravity-feed system must be 150 percent of the takeoff fuel flow when the tank contains the minimum fuel allowable. The same requirement exists when the airplane is in the attitude that is most critical for fuel flow. (FAR 23.955)
- The fuel flow rate of a pump-feed fuel system for each reciprocating engine must be 125 percent of the takeoff fuel flow required. (FAR 23.955)
- If an aircraft is equipped with a selector valve that enables an engine to operate from more

than one fuel tank, the system must not cause a loss of power for more than ten seconds for a single-engine (or twenty seconds for a multi-engine) aircraft between the time one tank runs dry and the time fuel is supplied by the other tank. (FAR 23.955)

- A turbine-powered aircraft must have a fuel system that will supply 100 percent of the fuel required for operation in all flight attitudes with uninterrupted flow as the fuel system automatically cycles through all of its tanks (or fuel cells). (FAR 23.955)
- If a gravity-feed system has interconnected tank outlets, it should not be possible for fuel from one tank to flow into another and cause it to overflow. (FAR 23.957)
- The amount of unusable fuel in an aircraft must be determined and made known to the pilot. Unusable fuel is the amount of fuel in a tank when the first evidence of malfunction occurs. The aircraft must be in the attitude that is most adverse for fuel flow. (FAR 23.959)
- The fuel system must be designed with a means to prevent vapor lock (fuel vapor that blocks flow) when fuel is at critical temperature (with respect to vapor formation) under the most critical operating conditions. (FAR 23.961)
- Each fuel tank compartment must be adequately vented and drained to prevent the accumulation of explosive vapors or liquid. (FAR 23.967)
- No fuel tank can be on the engine side of a firewall; it must be at least one-half inch away from the firewall. (FAR 23.967)
- Each fuel tank must have an expansion space of at least two percent that cannot be filled with fuel. However, if a fuel tank vent discharges clear of the airplane, no expansion space is required. (FAR 23.969)
- Each fuel tank must be vented from the top part of its expansion space. In addition, if more than one fuel tank has interconnected outlets, the airspace above the fuel must also be interconnected. (FAR 23.975)
- Each fuel tank must have a drainable sump located where water and contaminants will accumulate when the aircraft is in its normal ground attitude. In addition, each reciprocating engine fuel system must have a drainable sediment bowl with a capacity of one ounce for every 20 gallons of fuel. (FAR 23.971)
- Provisions must be made to prevent fuel spilled during refueling from entering the aircraft structure. (FAR 23.973)
- For aircraft with reciprocating engines, the filler opening of an aircraft fuel tank must be marked at or near the filler opening with the word "Avgas" and the minimum grade of fuel. For turbine-powered aircraft, the tank must be marked with the word "Jet Fuel" and with the permissible fuel designation. If the filler opening is for pressure fueling, the maximum permissible fueling and defueling pressures must be specified. (FAR 23.1557)
- All fuel tanks are required to have a strainer at the fuel tank outlet or at the booster pump inlet. For a reciprocating engine, the strainer should have an element of 8 to 16 meshes per inch. For turbine engines, the strainer should prevent the passage of any object that could restrict fuel flow or damage any of the fuel system components. (FAR 23.977)
- For engines that require fuel pumps, each engine must have one engine-driven fuel pump. (FAR 23.991)
- At least one drain must be available to permit safe drainage of the entire fuel system when the airplane is in its normal ground attitude. (FAR 23.999)
- If the design landing weight of the aircraft is less than that permitted for takeoff, there must be provisions in the fuel system for jettisoning fuel to bring the maximum weight down to the design landing weight. (FAR 23.1001)
- The fuel-jettisoning valve must be designed to enable personnel to close the valve during any part of the jettisoning operation. (FAR 23.1001)

## FUEL SYSTEM TYPES

Depending on the design of an aircraft fuselage, one of two fuel delivery systems is used. The simplest form of aircraft fuel system is the **gravity-feed system.** Used on many high-wing, carbureted, single-engine aircraft, the typical gravity-feed system has two fuel tanks, a fuel selector valve, a fuel strainer, a primer, and a carburetor. [Figure 7-1]

On low-wing aircraft, the fuel metering device is higher than the fuel tanks. Therefore, a pump is necessary to supply the engine with fuel. A **pressure-feed system** uses a pump to supply fuel to the engine. All turbine-powered aircraft use fuel pumps. Additionally, all high-wing aircraft with a reciprocating engine using fuel-injection or a pressure

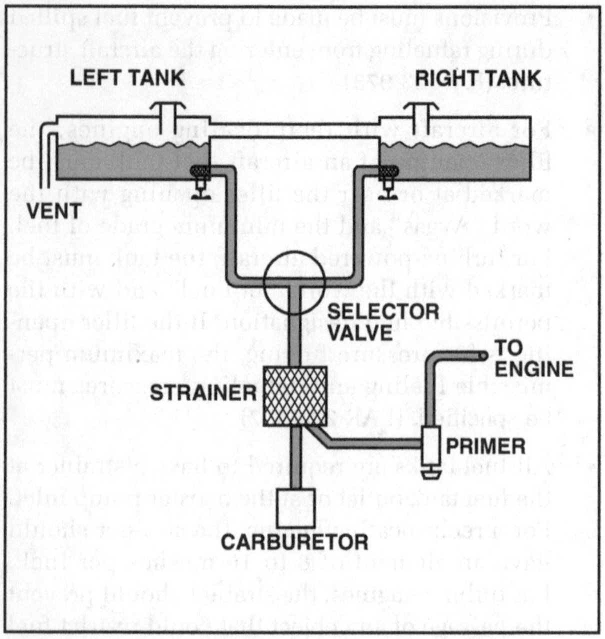


**Figure 7-1. A typical gravity-feed fuel system consists of two fuel tanks, a selector valve, a strainer, a primer, and a carburetor.**

carburetor require fuel pumps as well. For these aircraft, an auxiliary pump is necessary to supply the engine should the engine-driven pump fail. [Figure 7-2]

Many multiengine aircraft use a **crossfeed** system to transfer fuel between tanks. This system feeds fuel to any engine from any tank and provides a means for balancing the fuel load to maintain aircraft stability. Turbine aircraft fuel systems can also include provisions for single-point refueling.

## FUEL SYSTEM COMPONENTS

A typical fuel system includes multiple fuel tanks, lines, filtering units, pumps, gauges, and a priming system. Systems that are more complex include dump valves, a means for transferring fuel, and single-point refueling provisions. Although these components are considered airframe components, failure of any component can contribute to engine problems. By gaining a thorough understanding of each component, you will understand how certain component failures affect engine operation.

### FUEL STORAGE

Fuel tank construction varies significantly between types of aircraft. The basic types of tank include *welded (or riveted) metal tanks* in a wing or fuselage cavity, *composite tanks* in a wing or fuselage cavity, *wet wings* (tanks formed by sealing a section of the aircraft structure), and *bladder tanks* (Neoprene-impregnated fabric).

Maintaining fuel storage components in an airworthy condition is critical. Improperly maintained fuel tanks (or cells) can contaminate fuel, which can lead to damaged components or restricted flow.

Corrosion in fuel storage systems is a significant concern. Even when corrosion-resistant materials are used, fuel cells and related components are not corrosion-proof. Any time that water enters a fuel compartment, corrosion can occur within the system. Corroded parts might fail to work as designed or release debris and contaminate fuel.

Fuel storage compartments deteriorate over time. As gaskets, sealants, hoses, and bladders age, they become brittle, and debris from their breakdown can contaminate fuel. Contaminants can lead to engine malfunction by restricting or blocking fuel flow.

Fuel tanks are designed with features to alleviate fuel contamination and its corresponding operational hazards. Fuel tanks are required to have a sump and drain installed at their lowest point. A sump collects water and sediment, and provides a convenient location to drain and inspect fuel before maintenance or flight.

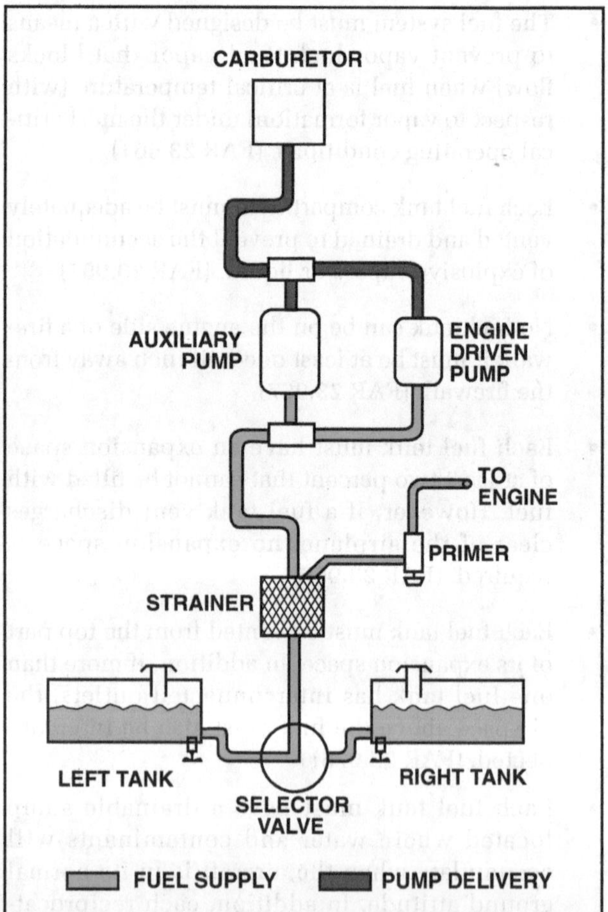


**Figure 7-2. Pressure-feed fuel systems are used in aircraft where the fuel supply is located below the fuel metering device.**

Regulations dictate that fuel tanks must be vented and contain adequate space for fuel expansion. Venting prevents tank pressurization and permits air to displace the fuel delivered to the engine. If a fuel vent becomes blocked (either partially or completely), an area of low pressure forms in the tank as the fuel is consumed. Eventually, low pressure will reduce or stop fuel flow from the tank. If an engine is not receiving an adequate amount of fuel, especially at high power settings, a restricted vent might be the cause. The expansion space provides room for the fuel to expand when ambient temperatures increase.

To prevent fuel from entering the aircraft during refueling, a scupper and drain are sometimes installed near the filler neck of the tank. A **scupper** collects overflowing fuel and directs it to an overboard drain. If the scupper drain becomes blocked, water and other contaminants can enter the tank when you remove the filler cap.

## FUEL DELIVERY

Fuel delivery and vapor return take place through fuel lines (rigid and flexible) and fittings. The manufacturer determines the size of a fluid line based on the engine's fuel flow requirements. The installation and routing of fuel lines through the airframe and nacelle must follow these requirements.

- Route the fuel lines separate from other systems and components. If this is not possible, ensure that the fuel line is installed below electrical wiring. In addition, ensure that the wiring is attached to the airframe. Never clamp a wiring bundle to a fuel line.
- Support fuel lines in a manner to avoid stress on the fittings; never rely on pulling a line into place by tightening its fittings.
- Ensure that rigid tubing has at least one bend to compensate for slight misalignments and vibration. A bend also relieves tension caused by expansion and contraction due to changes in temperature and pressure.
- Bond all metal fuel lines at each structural attachment point with bonded and cushioned clamps.
- Ensure that fuel lines are installed in a manner that protects them from being used as a handhold while maintenance is performed.
- Route fuel lines along the top or sides of compartments to prevent them from being damaged by people or cargo.
- Prevent vapor lock by avoiding sharp curves, steep rises, and steep falls when installing fuel lines.

Fuel lines routed in an engine compartment require additional considerations because of their environment. Heat, vibration, and corrosive elements are greater in an engine compartment than other locations. If a fuel line in the nacelle fails during flight, not only is engine operation affected, but a fire or explosion may occur.

### FLEXIBLE FUEL LINES

In modern aircraft, flexible fuel lines are hoses constructed from synthetic materials like Neoprene and Teflon®. These materials are used for their durability and chemical resistance. To reduce the likelihood of fire, a fire resistant device can be installed over the line. A **fire sleeve** is a hollow, silicone-coated fiberglass tube installed during fabrication. The sleeve is secured to the hose by stainless steel bands wrapped around each end. To protect against chemicals, a sleeve's ends can be dipped in a silicone-type sealer before final assembly. Fire sleeves provide invaluable protection to flexible lines, but they do limit your ability to inspect the hose. Because of this, you must follow the manufacturer's recommended replacement intervals.

In addition to fire shields, stainless steel heat shields can be positioned to reflect heat away from flammable fluid lines. A damaged or missing heat shield can allow fuel within a line to vaporize and cause vapor lock, interrupting engine performance.

Flexible fuel lines can be bent, but not twisted. Twisting weakens the part, which leads to premature failure. In addition, a twisted hose will try to return to its original form. This torque, combined with vibration, can cause the end fittings to loosen. To help identify a twisted hose, most hoses are manufactured with a lay line. When a flexible hose is installed properly, the lay line is straight, not spiraled. [Figure 7-3]

Teflon fuel lines provide a high degree of heat and chemical resistance. When exposed to high temperature, Teflon hoses can assume a permanent

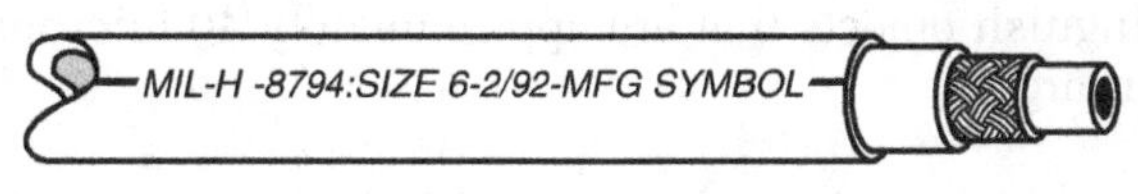


**Figure 7-3 A lay line provides a visual reference to identify whether a hose is twisted. Some manufacturers use their identification markings instead of a solid lay line.**

set. If you need to remove and reinstall a serviceable Teflon hose, prevent cracking and splitting by tying a support wire across the ends to maintain the radius until reinstallation.

## RIGID FUEL LINES

Rigid lines may be constructed from a number of materials, including copper, aluminum, and stainless steel. Copper lines are slightly weaker than aluminum ones, but transfer heat well. A copper fuel line may be coiled for flexibility and to accommodate thermal expansion and contraction. Copper lines tend to work-harden and can eventually crack. Copper lines are typically used for manual engine primer lines for carbureted engines.

The majority of rigid fuel lines are constructed from 5052-O aluminum alloy. This material has good corrosion resistance, is reasonably easy to fabricate, and weighs less than materials of comparable strength. However, because aluminum does not conduct heat well, it is rarely used within a nacelle.

Stainless steel tubing is used when high temperatures and corrosive conditions are present or high strength is required. Stainless fuel lines are used extensively on turbine engines.

## FUEL STRAINERS AND FILTERS

Regulations require that a fuel strainer (or fuel filter) be installed to remove contaminants and to provide a means to drain contaminants from the system. The strainer represents the lowest point in a fuel system and is located between the fuel tank and the engine (specifically the fuel-metering device or engine-driven fuel pump). Water and solid contaminants collect in the sediment bowl and drain through a valve. A fine mesh screen (or other filter element) provides fuel filtering within the strainer. [Figure 7-4]

**Figure 7-4. A fuel strainer is located at the lowest point of an aircraft's fuel system and must be checked periodically for contaminants that could restrict fuel flow to the engine.**

Most turbine engine fuel systems use both coarse and fine filter elements. A coarse mesh filter is typically installed between the supply tank and the fuel pump, and a fine mesh filter is installed between the fuel pump and the fuel control unit. Filter effectiveness is measured in microns. One micron is equal to one millionth of a meter, or approximately .000039 inch. For perspective, the human eye is able to distinguish objects that are approximately 40 microns or larger.

In turbine engines, the passages in fuel control units are extremely small and easily plugged. To ensure an uninterrupted supply of clean fuel, most turbine engines use micron filters. A typical cellulose fiber micron filter element is capable of removing particles between 10 and 25 microns.

Another type of filter uses a stack of wire mesh disks made from bronze, brass, or stainless steel. This type of filter is reusable and well suited to withstand high operating pressures. [Figure 7-5]

Two-stage filters meet the requirements for both coarse and fine filtration in a single unit. The typical two-stage filter contains a pleated mesh element (rated at 40 microns) that filters the main system fuel to the combustor. A cylindrical mesh element (rated at 10 microns) provides fine filtration for reliable operation of the fuel control unit in the servo mechanism. [Figure 7-6]

## ENGINE-DRIVEN FUEL PUMPS

Engine-driven fuel pumps are the primary source of pressure in a pressure-feed fuel system; they deliver a continuous supply of fuel at the necessary pressure for engine operation.

### RECIPROCATING ENGINES

On reciprocating engines, a positive-displacement pump delivers a specific quantity of fuel for every crankshaft revolution. The vane-type fuel pump is widely used. The typical vane-type fuel pump is an accessory, driven by a splined shear-shaft. The pump housing contains a steel sleeve with an off-center bore. The spline turns a hollow steel rotor and the four vanes slide freely; during rotation, the volume between vanes increases and decreases, drawing fuel in and pushing it out. [Figure 7-7]

Vane-type fuel pumps deliver more fuel to the fuel-metering device than necessary. To prevent over-pressurization of the fuel-metering unit, engine-driven fuel pumps are typically designed

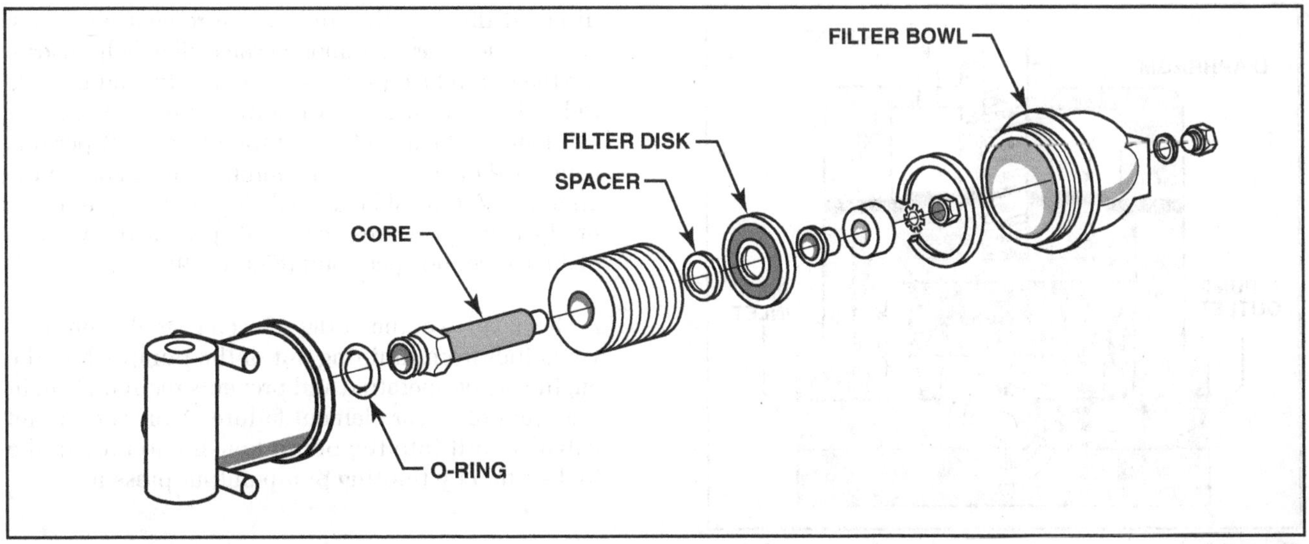


**Figure 7-5. A typical screen disk filter element consists of several thin wafer disks constructed of fine wire mesh capable of filtering extremely small particles.**

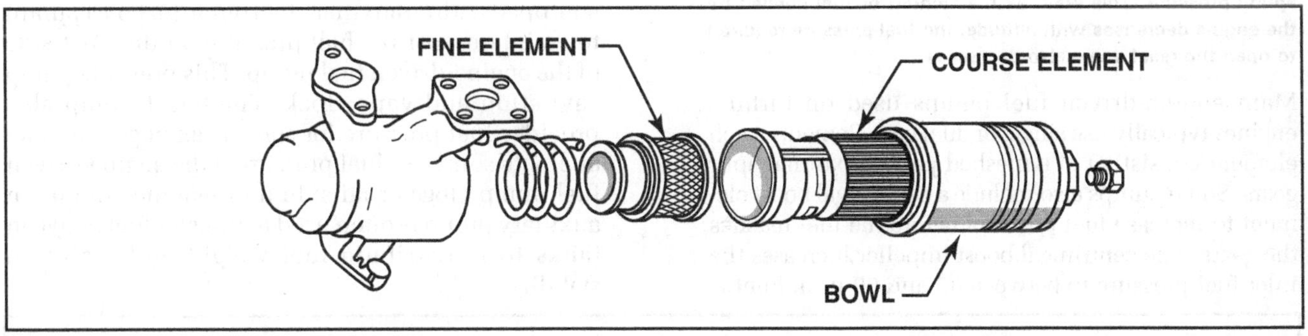


**Figure 7-6. A two-stage filtration unit combines the requirements for coarse filtration and fine filtration in a single unit.**

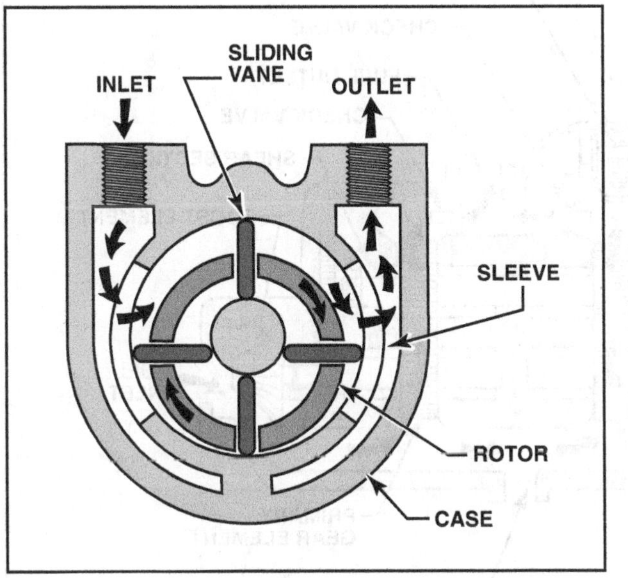


**Figure 7-7. In a vane-type pump, a set of vanes slide in and out of a rotor as it rotates in a pump housing. Because the rotor is offset in the pump housing, the volume between each set of vanes alternately increases and decreases, allowing the pump to pull fluid in on one side and force it out the other.**

with a spring-loaded valve that routes excess fuel to the inlet side of the fuel pump. Most fuel pumps have an adjusting screw for adjusting the spring tension of the valve. A properly set relief valve minimizes fuel pressure fluctuations during throttle movement, and the pressure remains within safe limits.

An altitude-compensating fuel pump adjusts the fuel pressure delivered to the fuel-metering unit according to changes in altitude and atmospheric pressure. A diaphragm, sensing atmospheric pressure, controls fuel flow to the metering unit by counteracting or supplementing the force of the relief valve spring. [Figure 7-8]

## TURBINE ENGINES

The main fuel pump on most turbine engines is an engine-driven, positive-displacement pump. The amount of fuel delivered by the pump is directly related to engine speed. A continuous supply of fuel is provided to the fuel control unit in excess of the engine's need. Surplus fuel is returned to the tanks or another location ahead of the fuel pump inlet.

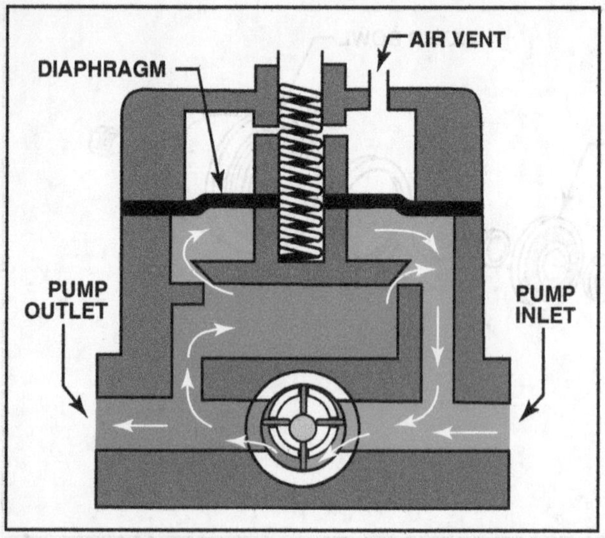


**Figure 7-8. A vane-type fuel pump with a balanced relief valve has a diaphragm that allows either atmospheric or carburetor inlet pressure to act on the relief valve in combination with spring pressure. This way, as the amount of fuel needed by the engine decreases with altitude, the fuel pressure required to open the relief valve also decreases.**

Main engine-driven fuel pumps used on turbine engines typically use single or dual gear elements, each element consisting of a meshed pair of external spur gears. Some pumps also include a centrifugal boost element to increase fuel pressure before the fuel reaches the gears. The centrifugal boost impeller increases the inlet fuel pressure to between 30 and 60 p.s.i. Fuel is directed through the high-pressure gear elements. Dual elements are common because they help distribute the pump load (to increase longevity) and provide redundancy in case of a failure of one or the other element. A shear section on the drive shaft permits continued operation of one pump element should the other fail. A typical large dual-element gear pump can produce fuel pressures up to 1,500 p.s.i. with a volume of 30,000 pounds per hour. [Figure 7-9]

A check valve at the outlet of each gear element prevents fuel from draining out of the pump when the engine is not operating and prevents recirculation in the event of a gear element failure. A pressure relief valve is built into the pump housing to protect the fuel system by limiting pump output pressure.

## AUXILIARY FUEL PUMPS

An aircraft with an engine-driven pump is also equipped with an auxiliary fuel pump (or boost pump) to maintain positive fuel pressure on the inlet side of the engine-driven fuel pump. This prevents pump cavitation and vapor lock. The boost pump also provides fuel pressure for starting an engine and an alternate source of fuel pressure if the engine-driven fuel pump clogs or fails. In multiengine aircraft an auxiliary pump is often used to transfer fuel between tanks to redistribute fuel weight and maintain stability.

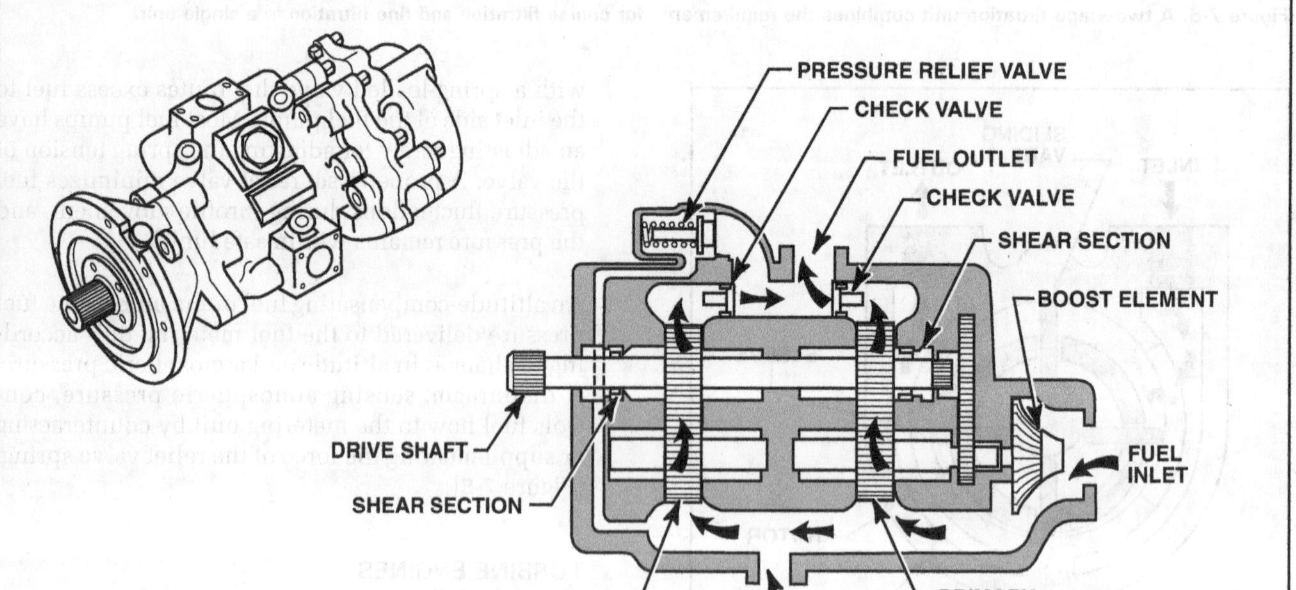


**Figure 7-9. A typical engine-driven fuel pump for a turbine engine contains a centrifugal boost pump impeller, dual gear pump elements, check valves, and a relief valve.**

When operating boost or auxiliary fuel pumps, it is important to follow the aircraft and engine manufacturer's operating procedures closely. Depending on the design of the fuel system, some boost pumps operate only intermittently while others are in continuous operation. In addition, some electric boost pumps have different switch positions to vary the fuel flow delivery rate.

## MANUAL PUMPS

Some light aircraft use manual pumps in the fuel system. These are the manual primer and wobble pump. A **manual primer** is typically installed as a branch from the fuel strainer, parallel to the main fuel line. A manual primer is simply a small cylindrical tube that, when pulled, draws fuel through a check valve and into a chamber. After the chamber fills, the primer is pushed forward to force fuel through a second check valve and into the engine cylinders.

Manual primers are reliable pumps that require little maintenance. Be aware that if a primer is not locked when the engine is running, suction produced in the cylinders can draw fuel through the primer to the engine. Additional fuel affects the fuel/air mixture in the cylinders and the engine may run rough or even stop.

For radial engines, priming is usually restricted to the upper cylinders. If fuel were pumped into the lower cylinders, a liquid lock condition could occur.

The typical wobble pump consists of a handle that pivots vanes around a drilled shaft assembly. The vane and shaft move within a four-chambered pump housing with flapper valves. As the handle is pumped back and forth, the vanes draw fuel into two chambers while simultaneously pumping fuel out of the other two chambers. [Figure 7-10]

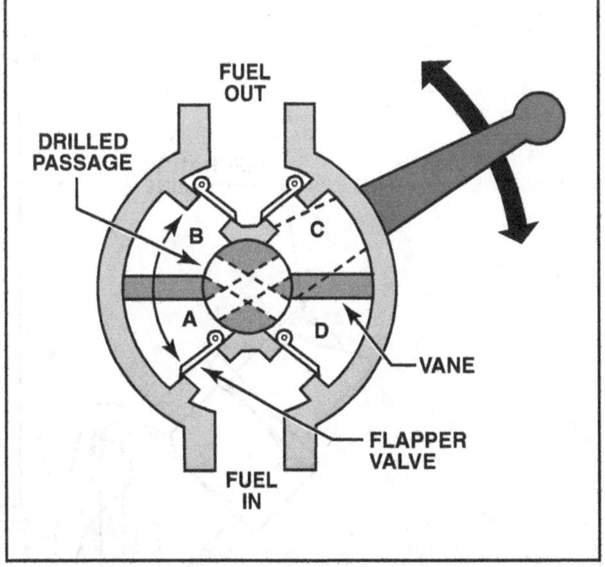


**Figure 7-10. A typical wobble pump consists of two vanes attached to a rotating shaft with two drilled passages. When installed in its housing, these two vanes create four chambers that alternately draw fuel into and push fuel out of the pump.**

In some aircraft, a wobble pump is the backup to the engine-driven pump and is used to transfer fuel between tanks. A wobble pump can also be used to pressurize the fuel system for starting and priming the engine.

## CENTRIFUGAL PUMPS

A centrifugal pump is an auxiliary pump driven by an electric motor. Most centrifugal boost pumps have two operating speeds: high and low. High speed is typically used during takeoff, high engine power settings, and at high altitudes, and low speed is used for engine start. The pumps can be mounted to the aircraft structure or submerged in a fuel tank.

For safety, submerged pumps have seals that prevent fuel from leaking into the motor and the motor chamber of submerged pumps is vented to outside air. This way, any fumes or liquid fuel that seeps into the motor section are vented overboard.

The high-speed impeller pumps fuel at a high velocity. The pump's high rotational speed swirls the fuel, removing air before it enters the fuel line. The high velocity, combined with high fuel pressure, significantly reduces the possibility of vapor lock. Centrifugal pumps are not positive displacement pumps; whenever fuel pressure passes a predetermined threshold, the pump continues operating but flow to the engine stops. [Figure 7-11]

## PULSATING ELECTRIC PUMPS

Some light aircraft use a pulsating electric pump as an auxiliary fuel pump. These pumps use a similar design to pumps used in automotive fuel systems. Pulsating electric pumps are normally installed in parallel with an engine-driven fuel pump. This arrangement permits either pump to provide fuel pressure to the engine regardless of the condition of the other pump.

In a typical pump, a solenoid coil encircles a steel plunger with a brass passage connecting the fuel inlet chamber and fuel outlet chamber. A calibrated spring pushes the plunger upward while electromagnetic force from the coil pulls it down. A check

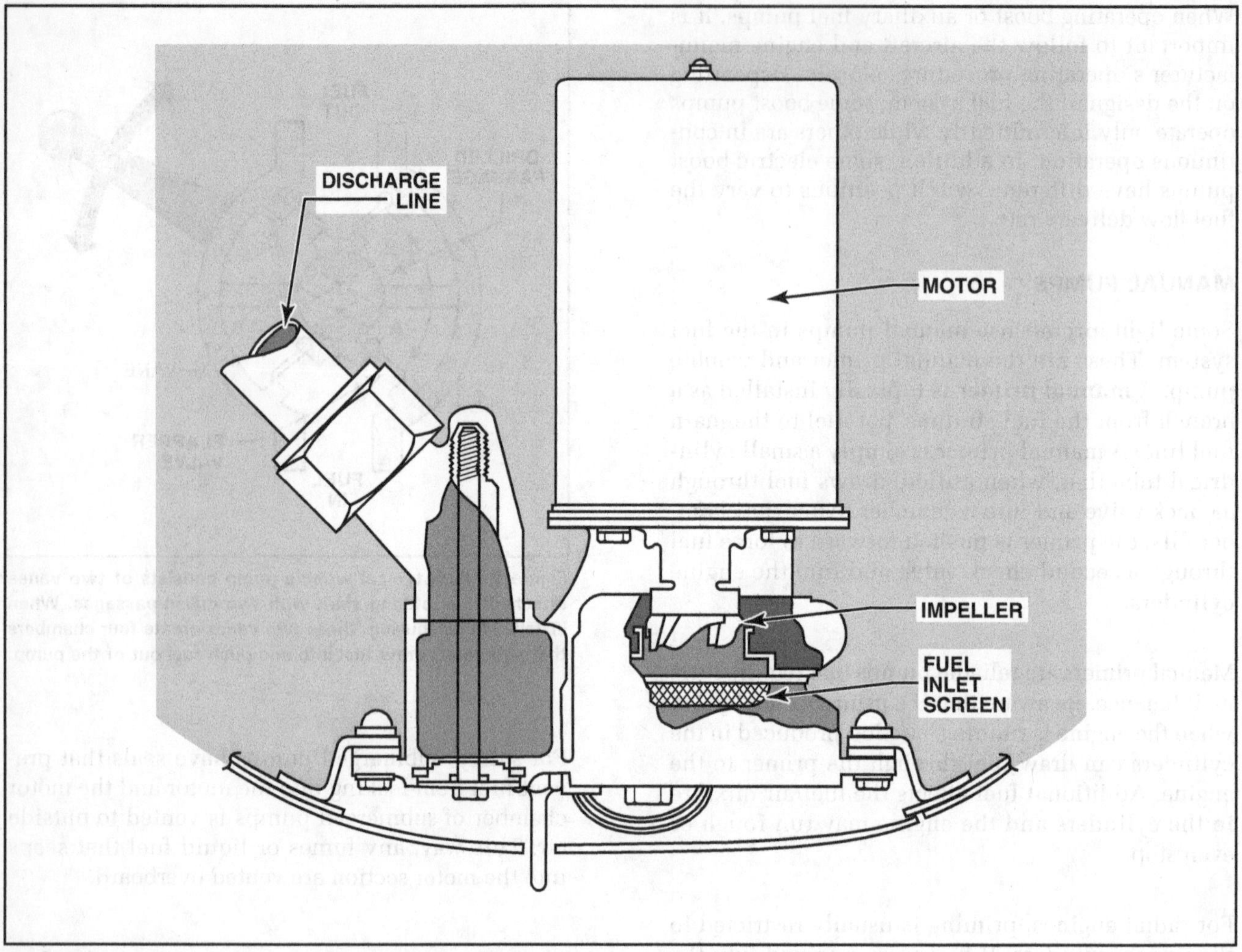


**Figure 7-11. A centrifugal boost pump uses an impeller driven by an electric motor.**

valve at the brass tube inlet admits fuel when the plunger slides up and a check valve at the outlet permits fuel to pass through when the plunger slides down. [Figure 7-12]

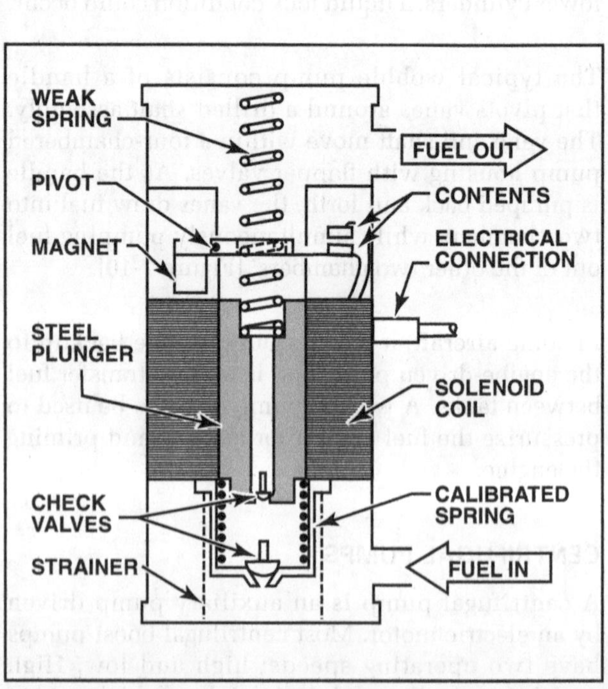


**Figure 7-12. A pulsing boost pump uses a calibrated spring and an electromagnet to force a plunger up and down to pump fuel.**

## BYPASS VALVE

If an engine has both an engine-driven fuel pump and a boost pump, bypass valves (when pumps are in series) or check valves (when pumps are parallel) must be incorporated into the fuel system. These valves let fuel bypass the engine-driven pump during engine start or if the pump fails. In most cases, a bypass valve includes a spring-loaded valve installed in conjunction with a pressure-relief valve. The spring tension of a bypass valve is calibrated to permit the valve to open whenever the boost pump pressure exceeds the engine-driven pump pressure. [Figure 7-13]

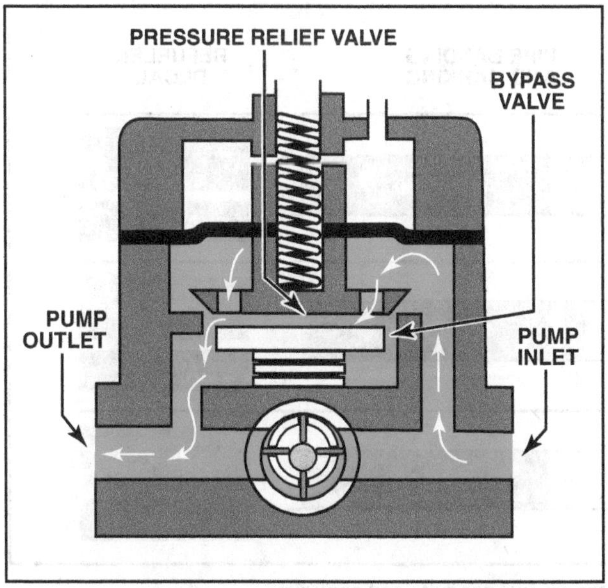


**Figure 7-13. On engines that use both an engine-driven pump and a boost pump, a bypass valve is typically installed in conjunction with a pressure relief valve. When boost pump pressure exceeds engine-driven pump pressure, fuel flows directly to the engine.**

# FUEL TYPES

## AVIATION GASOLINE

The dynamics of internal combustion require certain gasoline properties. Because of the wide range of atmospheric conditions that aircraft operate in, the requirements are more stringent. The **volatility** of aviation gasoline (or Avgas) measures the fuel's ability to change from a liquid into a vapor. Volatility is usually expressed in terms of **Reid Vapor Pressure**, which represents the partial pressure of 100LL gasoline at 100 F degrees. If the partial pressure (for a given temperature) is less than the measured pressure in a closed system the gasoline will evaporate. The vapor pressure of 100LL avgas is approximately 7 pounds per square inch at 100 degrees Fahrenheit. By contrast, lower-grade automotive gasoline has a Reid vapor pressure of between about 7.8 and 9 p.s.i., typically adjusted seasonally to account for warmer and cooler temperatures.

Avgas must vaporize readily to burn evenly in a cylinder. Fuel that is not fully atomized results in hard starting and rough running. However, if fuel vaporizes too readily, evaporation occurs in the fuel lines and results in vapor lock. In carbureted engines, highly volatile fuel causes extreme cooling and increases the possibility for the formation of carburetor ice.

Aviation gasoline is graded (numbered) according to its ability to resist detonation (or knocking). The higher the number, the more resistant it is to detonation. The **octane** number compares the anti-knock properties of a fuel to a mixture of iso-octane and normal heptane. For example, grade 80 fuel has the same anti-knock properties as a mixture of 80 percent iso-octane and 20 percent heptane.

Fuel used to be described with two performance numbers (avgas 100/130). The first number was the lean mixture rating and the second number the rich mixture rating. To avoid confusion and minimize handling errors when working with different grades of avgas, common practice designates fuel only by its lean mixture performance number. The common types of aviation gasoline available are avgas 80, 100, and 100LL. Avgas 100LL and 100 perform identically, the "LL" indicates a lower lead content than avgas 100.

One ingredient that petroleum companies use to reduce engine detonation is **tetraethyl lead (TEL)**. However, it causes corrosion on components in the combustion chamber. To prevent corrosion, ethylene bromides are added to the fuel; this additive combines with lead oxides, and the corrosive byproducts are discharged from the cylinders during engine operation. Due to scientific evidence about negative health and environmental effects from the use of TEL, research continues on alternative additives and fuels for aircraft engines.

In addition to numeric grading, color is used to identify fuel and the markings on fuel-related components. Avgas 80 is dyed and marked red. Avgas 100 is dyed and marked green. Avgas 100LL is dyed and marked blue. [Figure 7-14]

Aircraft fuel pumps and trucks are marked with color-coded fuel identification decals on each side of the tank. Fuel trucks are also marked on the dashboard in the cab. Likewise, aircraft fuel filler ports are labeled so that all items related to aircraft fueling are similarly coded to prevent filling with the improper grade or type of fuel.

## TURBINE FUELS AND ADDITIVES

Turbine powered aircraft use a kerosene-type fuel called "jet fuel." JET A and JET A-1 are common in civil use. JET B, which is a blend of gasoline and kerosene, is less common. Jet fuel designations, unlike those for avgas, simply identify a particular fuel; they do not describe performance characteristics. To determine which type of turbine fuel is approved for an engine; check the engine type certificate data sheet or the aircraft specifications.

The primary difference between types of jet fuel is the freezing point. JET A freezes at –40°C (–40°F). JET A-1 freezes at –47°C (–52.6°F). JET B freezes at –50°C (–58°F).

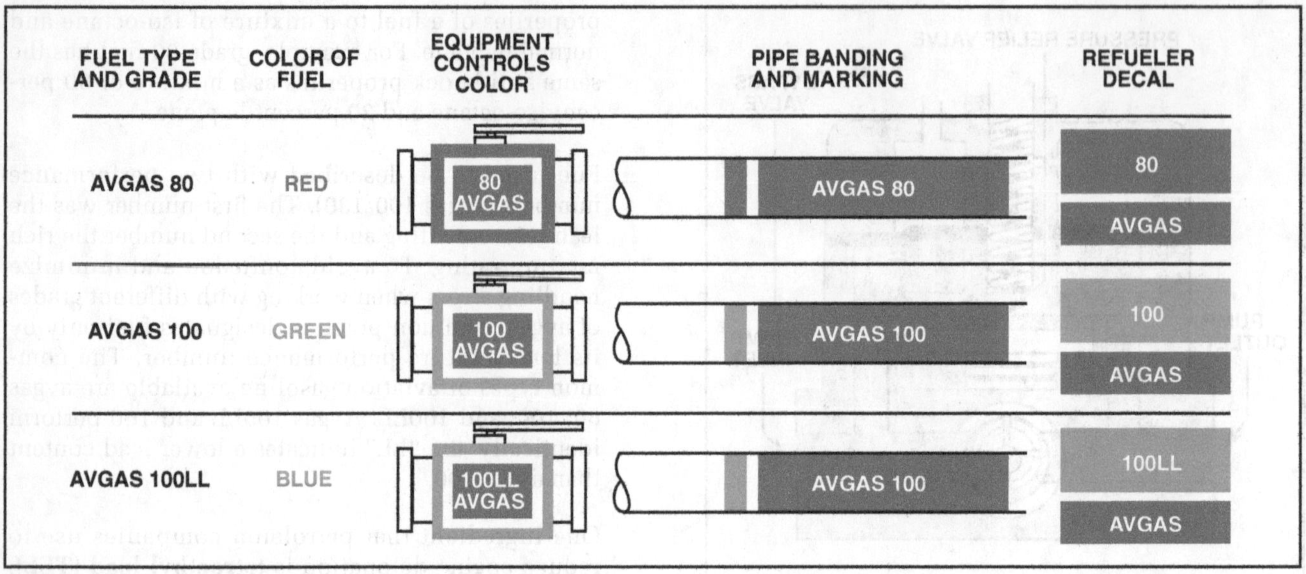


**Figure 7-14. This illustration depicts the colors and types of markings used on fuel conduits and controls.**

Jet fuels are colorless or have a light straw color. Differently colored jet fuel might indicate an unapproved fuel. Verify the suitability of fuel before using it to service an aircraft. Markings for equipment that stores and dispenses approved turbine fuels are white letters on a black background. [Figure 7-15]

Jet fuel is more viscous than avgas. As a result, the fuel acts as a lubricant in pumps and fuel-control units. The downside of this attribute is that jet fuel holds water and solid material that does not easily settle into sumps. Any time water is present in a fuel, the potential for fuel icing or microbial growth is significant. Many aircraft and engine manufacturers recommend the use of anti-icing and antimicrobial fuel additives. Except in extremely low temperatures, anti-icing additives are effective at preventing water from freezing in the fuel system. Antimicrobial agents kill microbes, fungi, and bacteria. These microorganisms tend to form slime (or matted waste) inside fuel tanks that can accumulate and clog filters and fuel lines as well as corrode fuel cells.

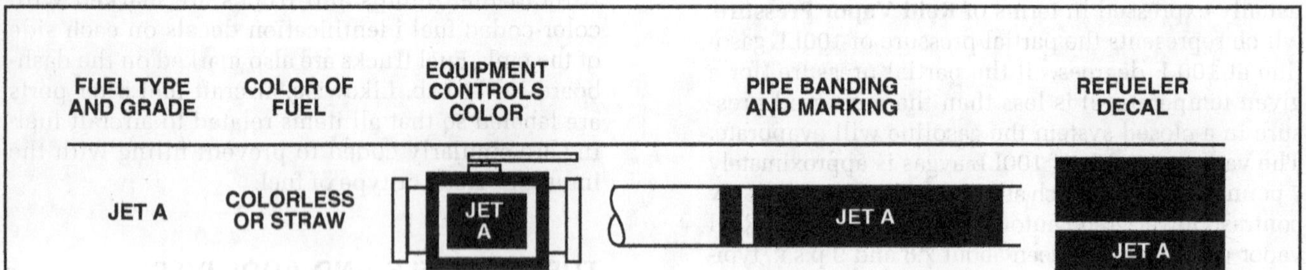


**Figure 7-15. This illustration depicts the colors and types of markings used on turbine fuel conduits and controls.**

Fuel additives are often premixed in the fuel by the distributor. When fuels are supplied without additives, the appropriate quantity of additives is metered while refueling the aircraft. If metering equipment is not available, pour the additives into the fuel tanks just before refueling. The turbulence created by refueling adequately mixes the additives with the fuel. The type and amount of additive used must be approved by the aircraft manufacturer to maintain the fuel system's airworthiness. To determine the approved fuel additives for a turbine engine, check the engine type certificate data sheet or the aircraft specifications. PRIST® Hi-Flash™ is a commonly used additive containing both anti-icing and antimicrobial agents.

## SPECIFIC TURBINE ENGINE COMPONENTS

Turbine fuel systems require components not used with reciprocating engines. Some aircraft have an approved landing weight that is less than the approved takeoff weight; this requires a special valve so a pilot can rapidly jettison fuel in an emergency. Additional components special to a turbine engine are a fuel heater, fuel transfer ejectors, and a water injection system.

### FUEL HEATER

A fuel heater eliminates the potential of fuel metering problems caused by ice crystals. Typical fuel heaters use a heat exchanger with oil or bleed air to warm the fuel. [Figure 7-16]

In a typical unit, fuel flows continuously while the heat source is regulated. Fuel heat is normally used when the fuel temperature is about 32 degrees Fahrenheit (or less) or a fuel filter bypass warning occurs. Some systems are automatic and others require activation by a switch in the cockpit.

Improper use of fuel heat can cause vapor lock, and high temperature can damage the fuel control unit. Manually operated fuel heating systems typically have operating restrictions. For example, fuel heat may be operated for one minute prior to takeoff, and then an additional minute during each successive 30 minutes of flight, or fuel heat should not be operated during takeoff, approach, or go-around. The risks of using the fuel heater during these times include engine surging and flameout.

Automatic systems are normally set to activate for fuel temperatures between 35°F and 37°F. An electric timer and gate valve control the cycle time. As the system cycles on and off, oil temperature and

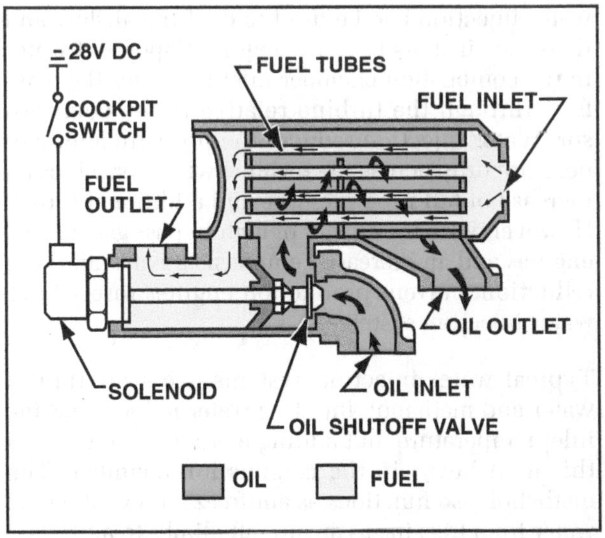

Figure 7-16. One type of fuel heater uses engine oil to heat turbine fuel and melt any ice crystals suspended in the fuel.

engine pressure ratio (EPR) gauges fluctuate. For a fuel heater that uses engine oil to heat the fuel, oil temperatures should drop when fuel heat is activated. For a system that uses bleed air as a heat source, EPR readings generally decrease when fuel heat is in use.

### FUEL TRANSFER EJECTORS

Some systems use fuel transfer ejectors, sometimes called jet pumps, to scavenge fuel from a fuel tank and ensure the transfer of fuel from the main tank to a boost pump sump. Transfer ejectors are usually located at the lowest point in a fuel tank and remain submerged until the tank is almost empty. Transfer ejectors have no moving parts; the ejector is a tube with a constrictor that works on the Bernoulli principle. When a fuel pump pulls fuel through a transfer ejector, an area of low pressure develops at the restriction. In turn, this area of low pressure pulls more fuel from the tank into the line and boost pump sump. This arrangement enables a pump to transfer virtually all the fuel from the tank, greatly reducing unusable fuel, and a pilot has greater control for balancing the aircraft fuel load.

### WATER INJECTION

Water injection augments thrust in a gas turbine engine. The maximum thrust that a turbine engine can produce depends, in part, on the weight (or density) of air moving through the engine, with a direct relationship between air density and thrust. As the density of air passing through an engine decreases, thrust decreases. During flight, ambient air pressure can decrease and increased air temperature can reduce density. To counteract these conditions, water injection can be used to cool the airflow and increase air density in an engine. Vaporized water in the combustion chamber inlet increases the mass flow through the turbine relative to the compressor. Water injection reduces the pressure and temperature drop across the turbine, which provides an increase of tail pipe pressure and additional thrust. However, with the advent of high-bypass gas turbine engines and an increased emphasis on aircraft noise reduction, current production engines rarely have water injection systems.

Typical water injection systems use a mixture of water and methanol. Injecting water reduces turbine inlet temperature, but adding methanol counteracts this as it burns in the combustion chamber. The methanol also functions as antifreeze, preventing the water from freezing as an aircraft climbs to altitude.

Water can be injected directly into the compressor inlet or into the diffuser ahead of the combustion chamber, or both. Injecting water at the engine inlet poses a risk of ice formation at the compressor inlet at takeoff speed when ambient temperatures are below 40 degrees Fahrenheit. For an engine with an axial flow compressor, injecting water in the diffuser section provides more even distribution and enables a greater quantity of water to be used.

On systems that use water injection both at the compressor inlet and at the diffuser, full thrust augmentation is achieved by activating both injection nozzles. However, there is a limit to the amount of fluid injection any compressor or combustor can efficiently use. [Figure 7-17]

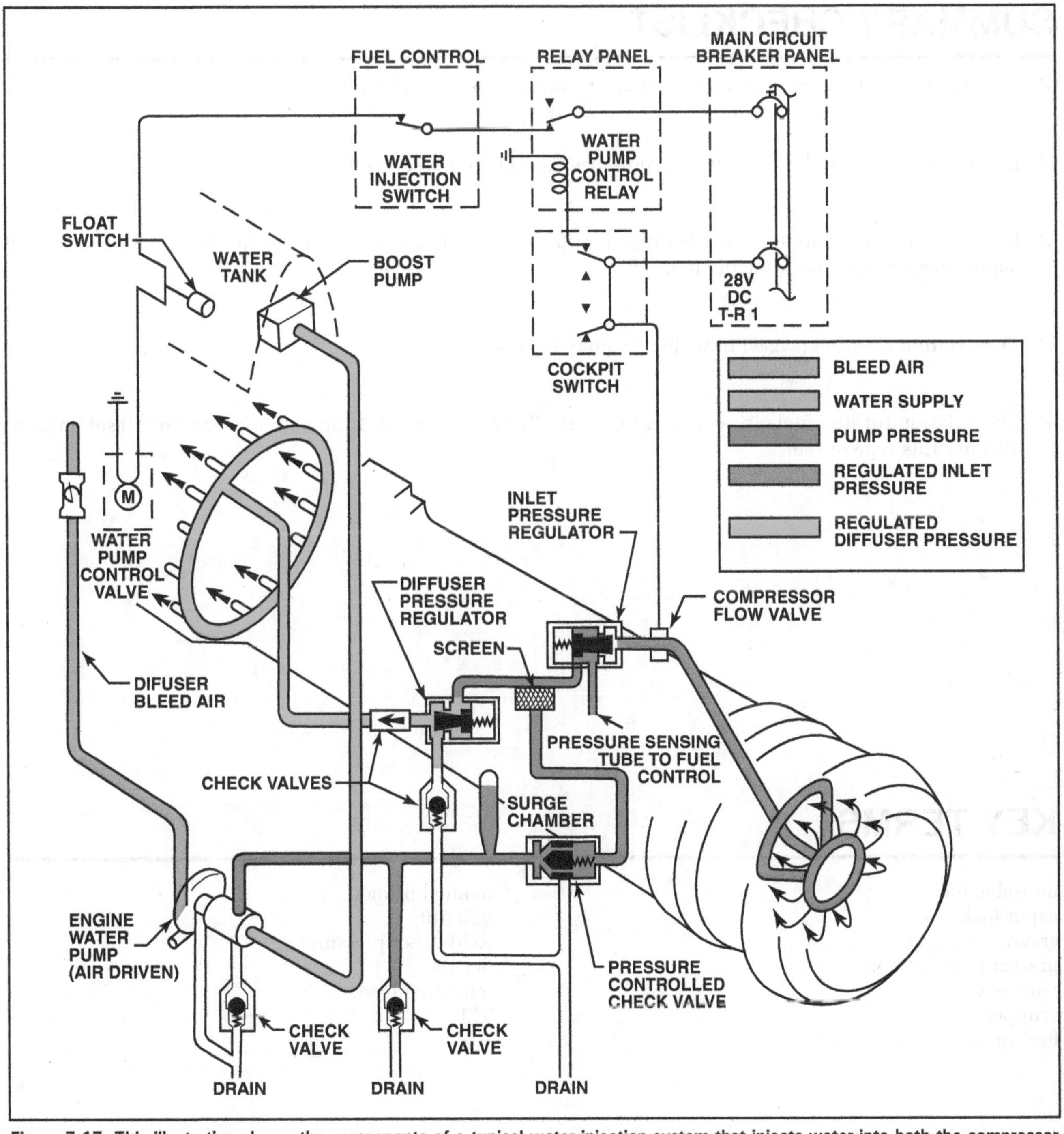


**Figure 7-17. This illustration shows the components of a typical water injection system that injects water into both the compressor inlet and the diffuser.**

# SUMMARY CHECKLIST

✓ The three functional areas of a fuel system are storage, delivery, and distribution.

✓ Every aircraft uses either a gravity- or pressure-feed fuel delivery system.

✓ Multiengine aircraft are typically equipped with a crossfeed system to transfer fuel between tanks so any engine can receive fuel from any tank.

✓ The aviation gasoline (avgas) in wide use today is 100LL.

✓ The aviation turbine fuels in wide use today are JET A and JET A-1. Some reciprocating diesel engines also use this type of fuel.

# KEY TERMS

unusable fuel
vapor lock
gravity-feed system
pressure-feed system
crossfeed
scupper
fire sleeve
manual primer
volatility
Reid vapor pressure
octane
tetraethyl lead
TEL

# QUESTIONS

1. The partial or complete interruption of fuel flow due to the presence of vapor in fuel lines is called ______ ______.

2. Fuel which vaporizes too readily can cause ______ ______.

3. The primary purpose of a boost pump is to prevent main fuel pump ______ and system ______ ______.

4. The three basic types of turbine engine fuels are:

   a. ______
   
   b. ______
   
   c. ______

5. The main fuel pumps used with turbine engines are generally the ______ type.

6. A ______ (what type) boost element may be built into the engine driven fuel pump.

7. The two most common types of filtering elements found in turbine engine fuel systems are:

   a. ______
   
   b. ______

8. What two sources of heat may be used to warm the fuel of a turbine engine?

   a. ______
   
   b. ______

9. How many levels of filtration are normally required in turbine engine fuel systems? ______

10. The fluid used in a water injection system is a mixture of water and ______.

11. Water injection in a turbine engine is a means of ______ augmentation.

12. The two locations where water may be injected into a turbine engine are:

    a. ______ ______
    
    b. ______ ______

# SECTION B

# RECIPROCATING ENGINE FUEL METERING

This section discusses the distribution of fuel to a reciprocating engine. The components involved in fuel distribution meter and deliver fuel to the cylinders for combustion. For engines with carburetors, fuel is mixed with air in the induction system. For engines with fuel injection, mixing occurs in the cylinder assembly. Fuel distribution components are a powerplant subsystem.

Because the metering device affects engine performance and fuel economy, it must function reliably through a wide range of operating and environmental conditions. Fuel distribution components are necessary to atomize fuel for complete and even burning in the cylinders. If fuel is not properly atomized, it will not burn completely

## TYPES OF METERING DEVICES

Modern aircraft with reciprocating engines meter fuel either by carburetion or by fuel injection. Designs vary according to engine type and aircraft requirements. The two types of carburetors are float and pressure-injection. The three types of fuel injection are direct, continuous-flow, and the electronically controlled system.

## METERING PRINCIPLES

Familiarity with basic laws of physics and fluid mechanics is essential to understanding how fuel metering devices work. Bernoulli's principle is significant in these systems. Bernoulli's principle states that a fluid (gas or liquid) flowing through a venturi speeds up in the restricted area while pressure decreases. The area of low pressure produced in a venturi is used in several different applications in the fuel system. [Figure 7-18]

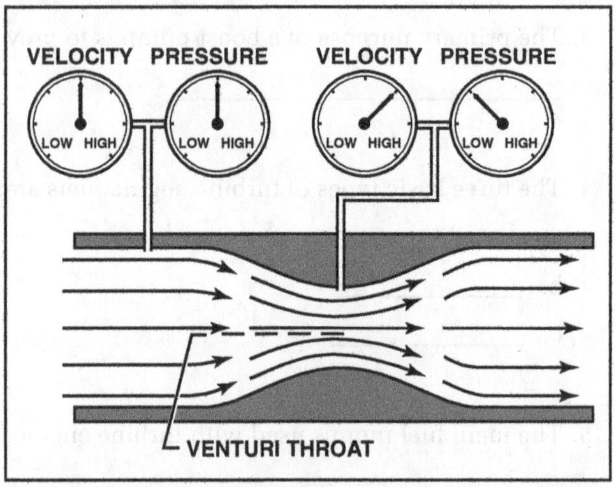


**Figure 7-18. As air flows through the throat of a venturi, its speed increases and pressure decreases. This creates a pressure differential that can be used to meter the amount of fuel needed to produce a combustible mixture.**

For gasoline or diesel fuel to burn, it must be atomized and mixed with oxygen from the air. For complete combustion, the ratio of fuel and air must be within a certain range. This range is governed by the chemical composition of the atmosphere and the fuel.

### ATMOSPHERIC CONTENT

In the atmosphere, the composition of air is approximately seventy-eight percent nitrogen and about twenty-one percent oxygen. The remaining one percent is a combination of other gases, primarily argon and carbon dioxide. Nitrogen, an inert gas, does not support combustion. The oxygen content is critical, and slight atmospheric changes can have a dramatic effect on combustion.

The density of air (and vaporized fuel) is dramatically affected by temperature, pressure, and humidity. Density is defined as the mass (or weight) of a substance per unit of volume. The only accurate way to measure a fuel/air ratio is in terms of weight.

The International Civil Aviation Organization (ICAO) defines standard atmosphere as a pressure of 29.92 in. Hg. (1013.25 mb) at a temperature of 59 degrees Fahrenheit (15 degrees Celsius) at sea level. In this environment, air weighs approximately 0.0765 pounds per cubic foot. The ICAO standard does not address humidity. Any change in pressure, temperature, altitude, or humidity affects air density. A decrease in air density for a given fuel/air mixture yields a richer mixture. Conversely, an increase in air density results in a leaner mixture. If the fuel/air mixture ratio is maintained, increased air density results in improved engine performance because more fuel and air can be drawn into the engine. Because water is incombustible, an increase in humidity degrades engine performance by reducing the engine's volumetric efficiency.

## AIR/FUEL RATIO

The amount of fuel and air entering an engine for combustion is described in terms of an air/fuel ratio. For example, 12 pounds of air and 1 pound of fuel is described as 12 to 1 (12:1). Mixture is also expressed as a decimal. The air/fuel ratio of 12:1 is equivalent to a .083 fuel/air mixture. As a general rule for aviation gasoline engines, an air/fuel ratio between 8:1 and 16:1 will burn.

Theoretically, the perfect combustible mixture is 1 pound of air for 0.067 pounds of fuel (aviation gasoline); this is an air/fuel ratio of 15:1 (or a fuel/air mixture of 0.067). This ratio defines a **stoichiometric mixture**. With a stoichiometric mixture, all available fuel and oxygen are used in combustion, releasing the maximum amount of heat from the fuel. Although a stoichiometric mixture enables an engine to operate at best economy, reciprocating engines are not typically operated with a stoichiometric mixture. Because these engines are relatively inefficient, they need a richer mixture to provide necessary engine performance. A typical reciprocating engine develops maximum power with an air/fuel ratio of approximately 12:1.

## MIXTURE TERMINOLOGY

Two common terms that describe an air/fuel mixture are **lean** and **rich**. These terms are relative, describing variations in mixture. Lean indicates that air was added or fuel removed from a mixture. For example, an air/fuel mixture ratio of 10:1 is leaner than 8:1. Rich indicates that air was removed or fuel added to a mixture; an air/fuel ratio of 8:1 is richer than 10:1.

For most reciprocating engines, the pilot adjusts the mixture control in the cockpit to obtain the desired fuel/air mixture. Terms that describe adjustments of the mixture control are full rich, idle-cutoff, lean best power, rich best power, and best economy.

**Full rich** refers to the full forward position of the mixture control, which provides maximum fuel flow from the fuel metering device. For maintenance purposes, this is the normal position for ground operations, except for high elevation airports.

**Idle-cutoff** refers to the full aft position of the mixture control, which completely cuts off fuel flow the engine. The recommend method of shutting down a reciprocating engine is to move the mixture control to the idle-cutoff position. The fuel supply is stopped, and all of the fuel in the intake manifold and cylinders is consumed. This greatly reduces the risk of an inadvertent engine start if the propeller is rotated by hand.

**Lean best power** and **rich best power** refer to mixture settings that provide the maximum speed or manifold pressure for a given throttle position. The same engine performance is provided across the range, with a lean best power setting using slightly less fuel than a rich best power setting.

**Best economy** refers to the mixture ratio that develops the greatest amount of engine power for the least amount of fuel flow. This position is determined differently depending on aircraft instrumentation. The most common method is to slowly pull the mixture control aft until exhaust gas temperature and engine speed peak. Although this setting provides the best fuel economy, it could result in engine overheating if used for extended periods of time. Most engine manufacturers recommend using the best power mixture settings for normal operations.

## LEANING TECHNIQUES

The mixture control enables the pilot to adjust fuel mixture to compensate for varying atmospheric and operating conditions. For example, as an aircraft climbs, air density decreases, which causes the mixture to become rich. To maintain the desired engine performance, the mixture must be leaned. On some aircraft, the fuel metering device performs this action automatically. However, most reciprocating engines require operator action.

Fuel mixture is set according to engine instruments. Aircraft equipment determines which instrument should be used. The Pilot Operating Handbook (POH) or Aircraft Flight Manual (AFM) describes the appropriate leaning procedure. The instruments that you typically refer to when adjusting fuel mixture include the tachometer, the manifold pressure gauge, and the exhaust gas temperature (EGT) gauge, if available. In some aircraft, digital processors and instrumentation enable the avionics to provide a pilot with directions to obtain the ideal fuel mixture for current operations.

For an aircraft with a fixed-pitch propeller, the tachometer can be used to adjust fuel mixture. Watch the tachometer while slowly pulling the mixture control aft. The engine speed will increase slightly when the fuel is set for best economy. For best power, slightly richen the fuel mixture by pushing the mixture control forward.

For an aircraft equipped with a constant-speed propeller, the tachometer cannot be used to adjust fuel mixture. Instead, use the manifold pressure gauge. The manifold pressure indication peaks when the fuel is set for best economy. For best power, slightly richen the fuel mixture by pushing the mixture control forward.

The EGT gauge is the most accurate instrument for setting fuel mixture for both fixed-pitch and constant-speed propeller aircraft. An EGT gauge uses a temperature-sensing thermocouple to measure the temperature of exhaust gasses. As the fuel/air mixture is leaned, exhaust gas temperature increases. This gauge enables you to set the fuel mixture for either best economy or best power. Unless the manufacturer provides different instructions, the common way to identify best power is to find best economy (peak EGT) and then enrich the mixture by pushing the mixture control forward until the EGT gauge indicates a decrease of approximately 25 degrees Fahrenheit.

## SPECIFIC FUEL CONSUMPTION

The specific fuel consumption of an engine is the number of pounds of fuel burned per hour to produce one horsepower. This performance measure relates to efficiency. To compare an engine to the manufacturer's specifications, you will have to perform an engine runup. Because it is difficult to accurately measure the brake horsepower of an engine, other performance data can be used in conjunction with the manufacturer's charts to determine fuel consumption. For example, by running an engine at a specific speed for a specific length of time and, by monitoring fuel flow, you can ascertain the engine's fuel consumption. [Figure 7-19]

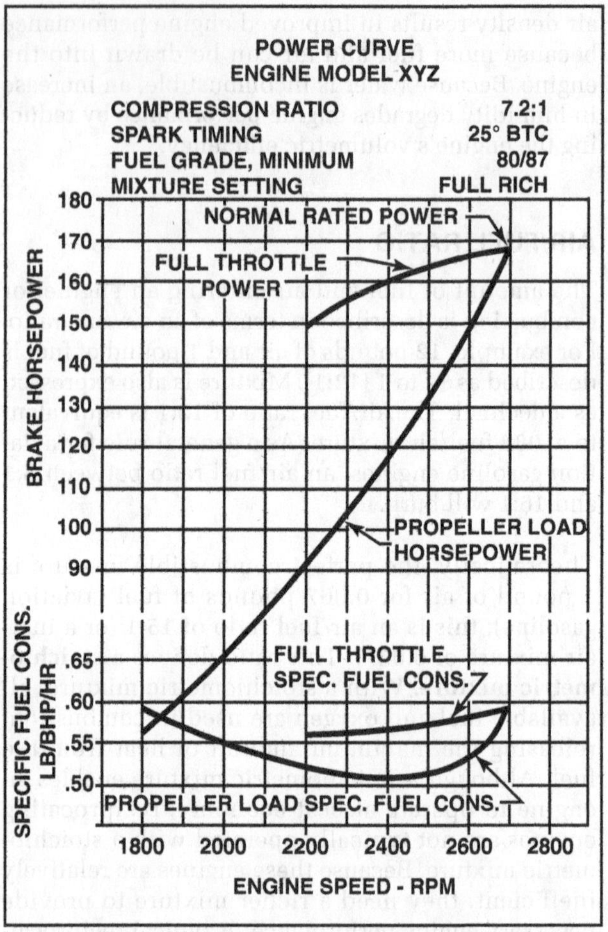


**Figure 7-19. Monitoring the rate of fuel flow while operating an engine for a given time at a specific speed allows you to determine overall engine performance and confirm operation of a fuel-metering device.**

## COMBUSTION ANOMOLIES

During normal combustion, the fuel/air mixture burns in a controlled and predictable way. The action occurs in a fraction of a second: a spark plug ignites the mixture and it evenly burns outward until all of the fuel is consumed. The dual spark plug configuration common to most aircraft reciprocating engines creates a wave by providing two sparks at the same time. The result is a smooth increase in temperature and pressure, providing maximum force to the piston at exactly the right moment in the power stroke.

**Detonation** is the uncontrolled, explosive ignition of the fuel/air mixture in a cylinder. Detonation induces high cylinder temperatures and pressures, which cause the engine to run rough, overheat, and lose power. Detonation is destructive and causes the failure of pistons, cylinders, and valves. Operating an aircraft an excessively lean mixture or gasoline with a lower than specified octane rating results in detonation.

**Preignition** is the early burning of the fuel/air mixture caused by a hot spot in the cylinder, not by the normal ignition spark. Common hotspots include carbon particles, overheated valve edges, silica deposits on a spark plug, or faulty spark plug electrodes. Hot spots typically result from poor engine cooling, dirty induction filters, or improper shutdown procedures. If an engine continues running after the ignition is turned off, preignition might be the cause. Detonation and preignition can occur simultaneously, and one may even cause the other. Operationally, it is difficult to distinguish between the two; both are destructive to an engine.

**Backfiring** describes the fuel/air mixture burning in the induction system. An extremely lean fuel/air mixture can burn slowly. With a slow-burning fuel/air mixture, it is possible for the fuel mixture to remain burning when the intake valve opens for the next cycle. As the next fuel/air charge enters the cylinder, it is ignited before the intake valve closes and the fuel burns within the induction manifold, fuel metering unit, and induction air filter.

**Afterfiring** is the burning of fuel in the exhaust system. In most cases, afterfiring is the result of an excessively rich fuel/air mixture. The relative lack of oxygen causes the mixture to burn slowly; unburned fuel mixes with air in the exhaust system and ignites. This may cause flames to appear out of the exhaust stacks.

## CARBURETORS

Carburetors are classified as **updraft** or **downdraft** depending on the direction air flows through the device. Most carburetors are the updraft type. All carburetors meter fuel and atomize it into the air to make a combustible mixture. In theory, the fuel/air mixture reaching each cylinder is identical in volume and composition. In reality, both the volume and composition vary because of the different distances traveled through the induction manifold and pressures exerted by the exhaust system.

### CARBURETOR VENTURI PRINCIPLES

All carburetors depend on the differential pressure created by a venturi to meter the proper amount of fuel for a volume of air. When air flows through a venturi, its speed increases while both pressure and temperature decrease. To control the volume of air that passes through a venturi, all carburetors are equipped with a throttle valve. The **throttle valve** (or butterfly valve) is a pilot-controllable restrictor plate installed between the venturi and the engine. When the throttle valve is fully opened (parallel to the airflow), the maximum volume of air and fuel enter the engine. In this case, the only component that limits the volume of air entering the engine is the venturi. However, as the throttle valve is moved to its closed position (perpendicular to the airflow) less air is admitted and engine power is reduced. [Figure 7-20]

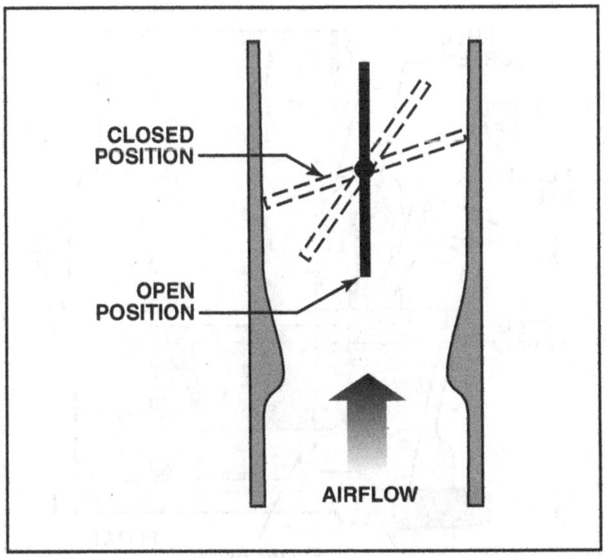


**Figure 7-20. When the throttle valve is parallel to the airflow, the maximum volume of air and fuel enters the engine. When the throttle valve is near perpendicular to the airflow, less air and fuel enter the engine.**

The size and shape of the venturi is designed for the requirements of the engine. Carburetors on similar engines might appear to be identical, but the size of the venturi could be different. Always ensure that you are installing the correct device on an engine.

### CARBURETOR SYSTEMS

To provide an engine with the necessary fuel for proper operation under various engine loads, speeds, and air densities, most carburetors include the following five systems:

- Main metering
- Idling
- Mixture control
- Accelerating
- Power enrichment or economizer

The construction and principle of operation of each of these systems varies depending on the type of carburetor. The following topics describe each system in relation to its use in float-type and pressure-injection carburetors.

### FLOAT-TYPE CARBURETORS

The float-type carburetor is named after the component used to regulate the fuel that enters the carburetor. Fuel is stored in a **float chamber**, the amount controlled by a float-operated **needle valve** installed in the fuel inlet. As fuel enters the chamber, the float rises and the needle valve begins to close. After the fuel reaches an established level, the position of the float completely closes the needle valve and the flow of fuel stops. [Figure 7-21]

The carburetor float is typically constructed of brass or a composite material. Brass floats are hollow, and the air sealed inside provides buoyancy. A composite float can be hollow or solid. When the float solid, air trapped in the pores of the composite material provides buoyancy.

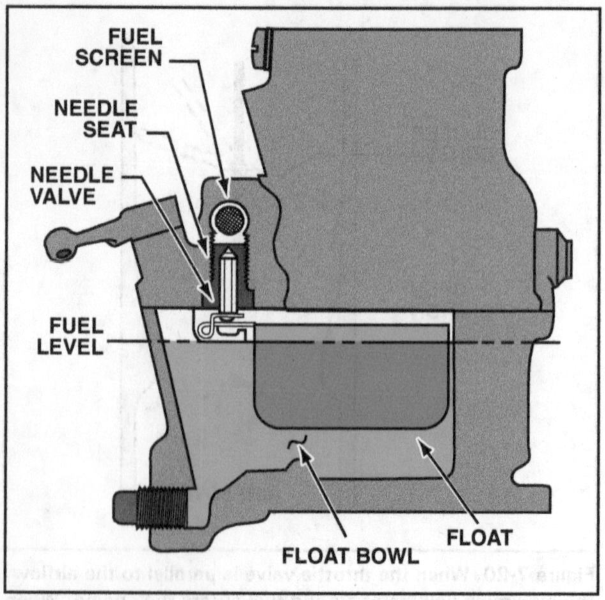


**Figure 7-21. Float carburetors store a quantity of fuel in a float chamber. The amount of fuel in the float chamber is controlled by a float-actuated needle valve.**

As the volume of fuel changes in a float chamber, the volume of air also changes. A vent maintains ambient pressure in the float chamber as the fuel level rises and falls. All float chambers are vented to ambient pressure.

## MAIN METERING

The main metering system supplies the engine with the correct amount of fuel for all speeds above idle. The system consists of one or more venturi tubes, the main metering jet and discharge nozzle, and the throttle valve. [Figure 7-22]

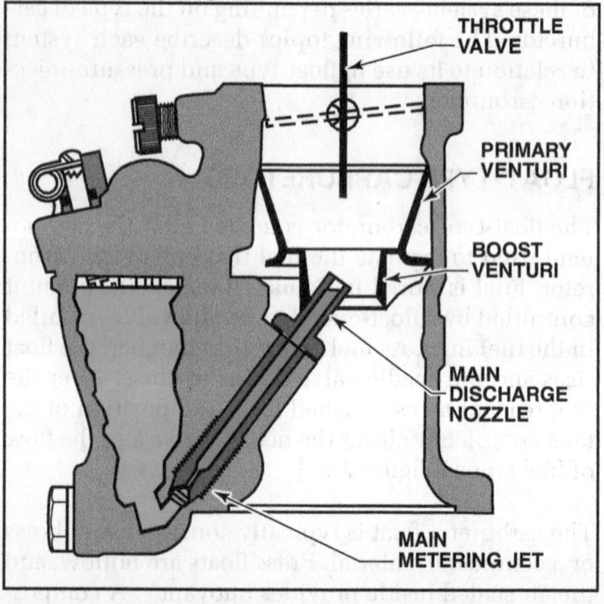


**Figure 7-22. The primary components of the main metering system of a float carburetor include one or more venturi tubes, a metering jet and discharge nozzle, and a throttle valve.**

Fuel metering begins at the venturi. In some carburetors, a single venturi is insufficient to create an adequate pressure drop to meter fuel. In this case, a **boost venturi** is installed forward of the **primary venturi**.

The **discharge nozzle** delivers fuel from the float chamber to the intake air. For an engine at rest, the fuel in the discharge nozzle is even with the level in the float chamber. In most cases, the fuel level is approximately 1/8 inch below the opening of the discharge nozzle. This distance is referred to as the **fuel metering head** and is designed to prevent fuel from leaking from the carburetor when the engine is not operating.

The discharge nozzle transfers fuel based on the differential pressure between air in the venturi and float chamber. For example, when no air flows through the venturi, the pressure in the float chamber and venturi are the same. However, when air flows through the venturi, pressure decreases. Differential air pressure causes fuel to flow through the discharge nozzle into the airstream. The size of the pressure differential determines the amount of fuel transferred. However, the maximum amount of fuel that can flow through the discharge nozzle is limited by the size of the **main metering jet**. [Figure 7-23]

A pressure differential of at least 0.5 in. Hg. is typically required to raise the fuel past the fuel metering head. At high power settings, the pressure differential is sufficient to ensure a continuous flow of fuel. However, at low power settings, the pressure differential is marginal and surface tension may hinder fuel delivery. **Surface tension** is a physical property of fluids created by molecular cohesion. Liquids

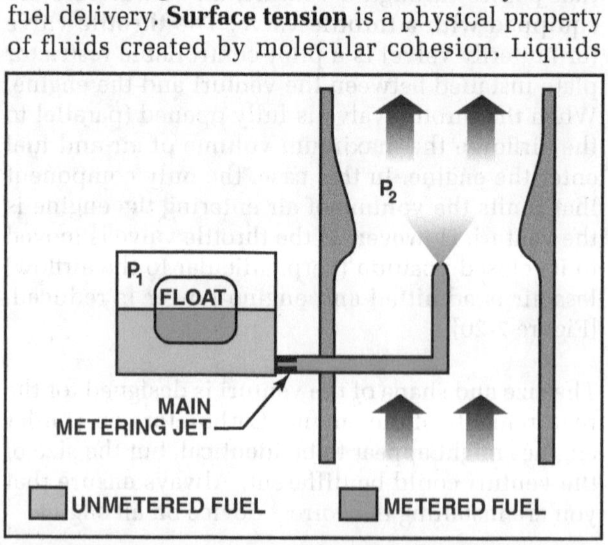


**Figure 7-23. When intake air passes through the venturi, the pressure in the venturi ($P_2$) is less than the pressure in the float chamber ($P_1$). The pressure differential forces fuel from the discharge nozzle into the airstream. The greater the pressure differential between $P_1$ and $P_2$, the greater the amount of fuel discharged.**

Figure 7-24. The surface tension of a liquid is a result of molecular cohesiveness and tends to prevent a liquid from readily breaking apart. Surface tension is observed in the convex shape of a liquid in this slightly overfilled container.

tend to hold together. The liquid in a slightly overfilled container is an example of surface tension. [Figure 7-24]

Because surface tension causes fuel to adhere to itself and to the walls of the discharge nozzle, the fuel discharges from the nozzle in large intermittent droplets instead of a fine, continuous spray. To disrupt the effects of surface tension, an air bleed system is often incorporated in the carburetor design.

An **air bleed** is a vented passage with a small, calibrated orifice. One end of the passage opens into the metered fuel near the base of the discharge nozzle. The other end is vented above the float level to ambient pressure behind the venturi. The air bleed passage is matched to the discharge nozzle to provide the proper airflow. Figure 7-25 describes and illustrates how this system works.

In addition to drawing fuel out of the float chamber, the low pressure in the venturi also draws air from behind the venturi. The bleed air and the fuel mix together in the discharge nozzle, where the fuel is emulsified and surface tension is disrupted. With its surface tension disrupted, the fuel is discharged from the nozzle in a fine, uniform spray that promotes vaporization. [Figure 7-26]

## IDLING SYSTEM

When an engine operates at idle speed, the throttle valve is nearly closed, air velocity through the venturi is limited, and differential pressure is weak. In some cases, the differential can be so low that sufficient fuel cannot be drawn through the main discharge nozzle. To ensure consistent engine operation at idle, a small passage (or series of passages) is drilled in the carburetor barrel near the edge of the throttle valve where air flows. These **idle discharge ports** (or **idle jets**) are connected to the main metering jet by an idle emulsion tube. An idle metering jet in the emulsion tube regulates the amount of fuel that can be drawn from the main discharge system and an idle air bleed emulsifies the fuel. The throttle plate creates a venturi at the discharge ports. The resulting low pressure draws fuel from the idle discharge ports and enables fuel to be discharged into the airstream. [Figure 7-27]

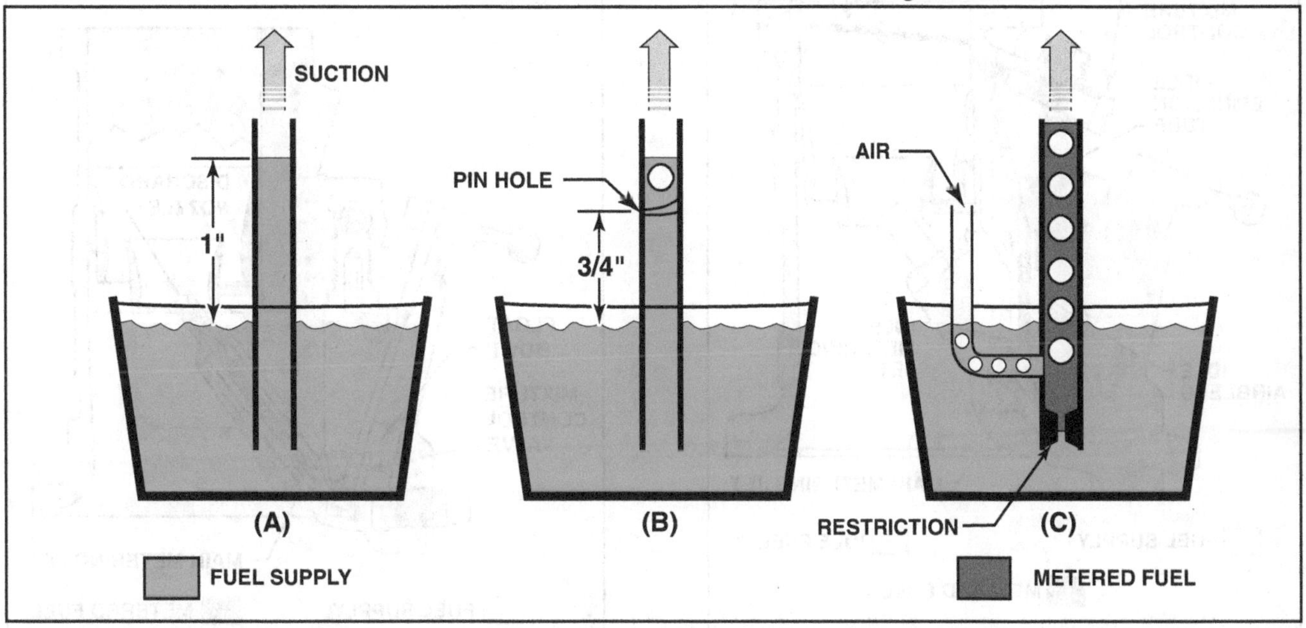


Figure 7-25. (A) Air pressure pushing down on a fluid in an open container moves a solid stream of fluid up a straw when a vacuum is applied to the straw. (B) A pin hole in the side of the straw introduces a small amount of air into the liquid stream, disrupting the solid stream and greatly reducing the amount of fluid that can be drawn through the straw. (C) When air is introduced below the liquid level and a metering orifice is added, the fluid and the air emulsify better, resulting in a finely broken fluid/air charge that can rise in the straw.

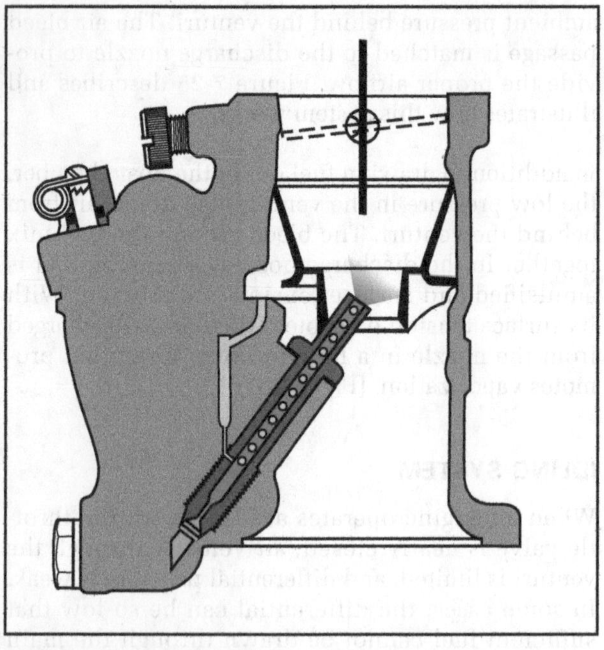

Figure 7-26. The incorporation of an air bleed in the main metering system decreases fuel surface tension, which improves fuel atomization.

Most carburetors include a maintenance-adjustable needle valve to control the fuel discharged into the airstream through the upper idle discharge port. Turning the thumbscrew in leans the idle mixture by reducing the amount of fuel discharged. Turning the thumbscrew out richens the idle mixture by increasing the amount of fuel discharged. Generally, the idle mixture is richer than the normal mixture. Because an engine operating at idle has little airflow over the cylinders for cooling, the richer mixture partially offsets this loss.

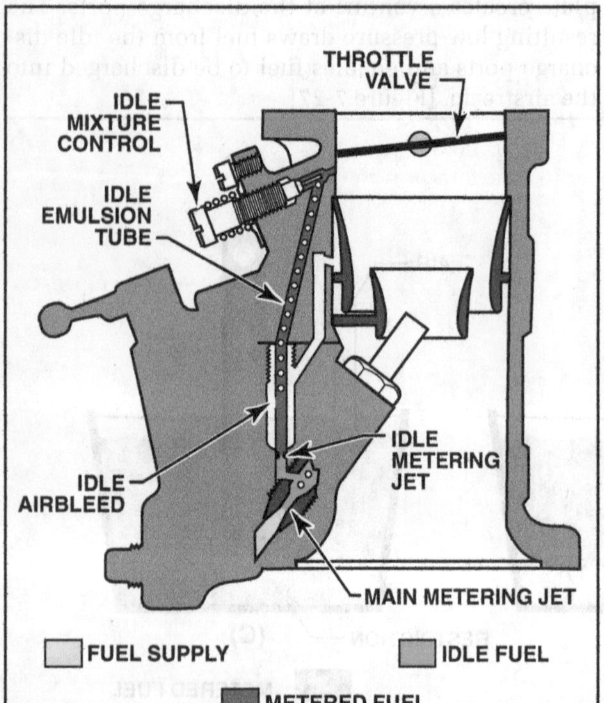


Figure 7-27. A typical idling system consists of multiple discharge ports in the carburetor barrel near the edge of the throttle valve.

In a multiple-port idle discharge system, the number of active ports increases as the throttle is opened. As more ports become exposed, more fuel is drawn into the throat of the carburetor. Multiple ports provide a smooth transition between idle speed and the higher power settings at which the main discharge nozzle becomes effective.

## MIXTURE CONTROL

The mixture control system provides the pilot with a method of adjusting the mixture supplied to an engine. Inside of a carburetor the fuel available to the main metering jet can be controlled with a variable orifice or by back suction. Some carburetors also include an automatic mixture control.

### Variable Orifice Mixture Control

In a variable orifice mixture control system, the mixture control is attached to a valve in the float chamber to control the size of a passage between the float chamber and the main metering jet. Some carburetors use a needle valve while others use a step-cut rotary valve. In either case, the valve is installed in series with the main fuel metering jet. [Figure 7-28]

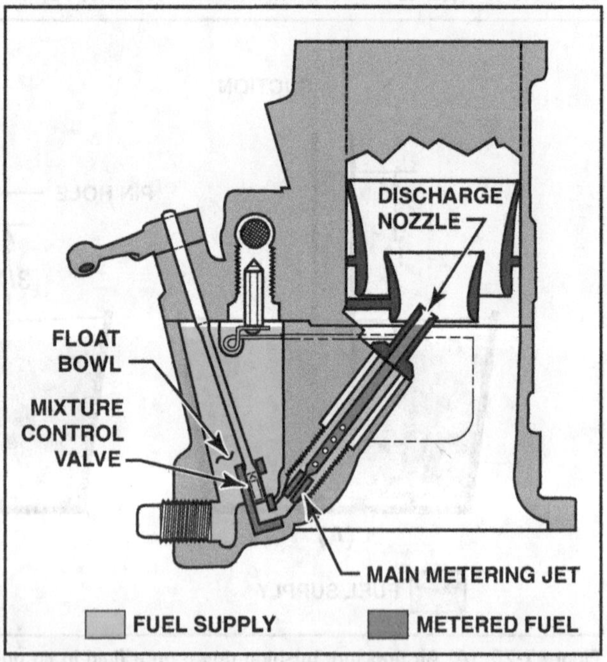


Figure 7-28. In a carburetor with a variable orifice mixture control, the mixture ratio is adjusted by changing the size of the passage between the float chamber and metering jet.

When the mixture control valve is in the idle-cut-off position, no fuel flows to the main metering jet. When the valve is in the full rich position, the amount of fuel available to the engine is restricted only by the main metering jet. Between those positions, the valve controls the amount of fuel that can flow to the discharge nozzle.

#### Back Suction Mixture Control

In a back suction mixture control system, differential pressure controls fuel delivered to the discharge nozzle. The mixture control is attached to a valve in the carburetor that changes how and where the fuel float chamber is vented. [Figure 7-29]

Depending on the position of the valve, the float chamber is vented to either the atmosphere or a low pressure area in the venturi, or a combination of the two. When the mixture control is in the full rich position, the float chamber is fully vented to the atmosphere. This venting creates the largest possible pressure differential between the float chamber and discharge nozzle, which permits the greatest flow of fuel to flow to the discharge nozzle. When the mixture control is placed in the idle-cutoff position, the float chamber is vented to low pressure air in the venturi. This venting eliminates any pressure differential between the float chamber and the discharge nozzle, which stops fuel flow. When the mixture control is placed in an intermediate position, the float chamber is vented to a combination of the atmospheric and venturi air. The differential of the resultant air pressure to pressure in the venturi controls the amount of fuel through the discharge nozzle.

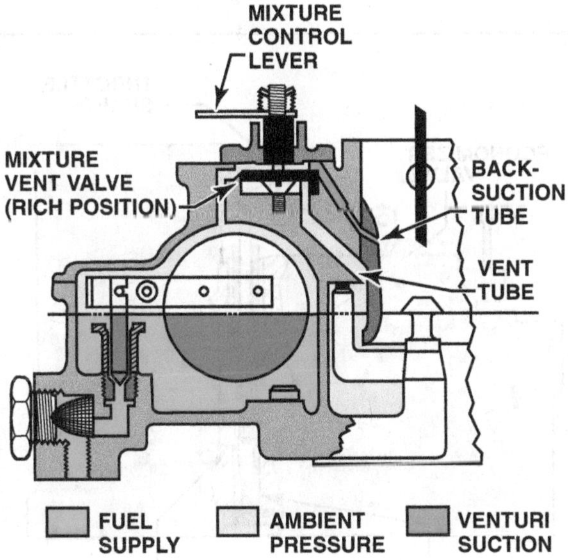


**Figure 7-29. With a back-suction mixture control system, the position of a mixture-control vent valve changes the pressure differential between the discharge nozzle and the float chamber.**

#### Automatic Mixture Control

Some carburetors have an automatic mixture control system that continuously adjusts the fuel/air mixture during flight. With this system, the mixture is leaned as the aircraft climbs, enriched as the aircraft descends, and otherwise adjusted for normal changes in atmospheric pressure during flight.

An **automatic mixture control** (AMC) system uses a sealed bellows to actuate a variable orifice or back-suction valve. As atmospheric pressure decreases (such as during a climb), the bellows expands, which leans the fuel/air mixture. When atmospheric pressure increases (such as during a descent), the bellows contracts, which richens the fuel/air mixture.

## ACCELERATION SYSTEM

When a throttle valve opens rapidly, airflow through the carburetor increases before the discharge nozzle provides the necessary corresponding increase in fuel flow. This delay causes a sudden, momentary leaning of the fuel/air mixture, which results in the engine hesitating before accelerating. Many carburetors are equipped with an acceleration system to prevent this. A quick, supplemental charge of fuel is provided to the carburetor until the discharge nozzle can deliver fuel at a rate proportional to the airflow. Two commonly used acceleration systems are the acceleration well and the accelerator pump.

#### Acceleration Well

The simplest acceleration system has an annular chamber around the main discharge nozzle. If an engine is running at a steady speed, a small volume of fuel is stored in this acceleration well. When the throttle valve is opened rapidly, the fuel from the well is drawn into the venturi to provide sufficient fuel for smooth operation until the main metering system can meet demand. [Figure 7-30]

#### Accelerator Pump

The accelerator pump consists of a piston (typically a leather packing and a spring) in a fuel-filled chamber. The pump is linked to the throttle control. When the throttle valve is closed, the movement of the accelerator pump causes the pump chamber to fill with fuel. When the throttle valve opens rapidly, the piston forces fuel past a check valve, discharging it into the airstream. [Figure 7-31]

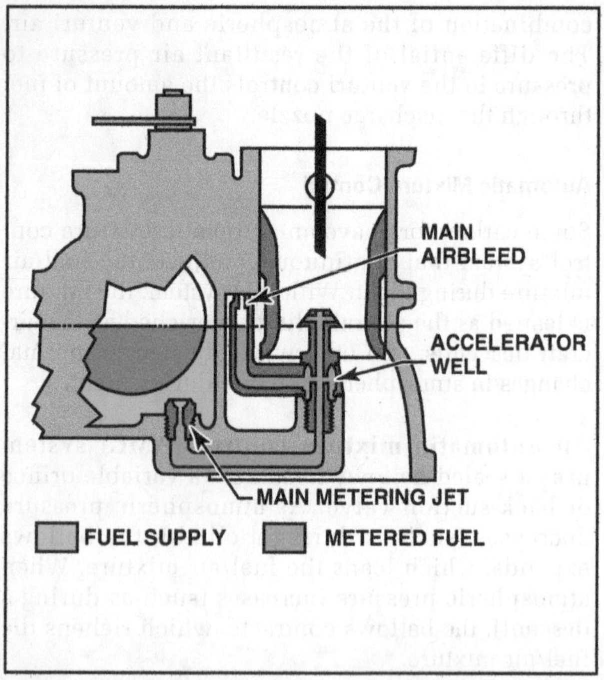


**Figure 7-30. An acceleration well consists of an annular chamber that stores a charge of fuel around the main discharge nozzle. With this type of system, when the throttle is advanced rapidly, the fuel in the acceleration well is discharged into the airstream, temporarily enriching the mixture.**

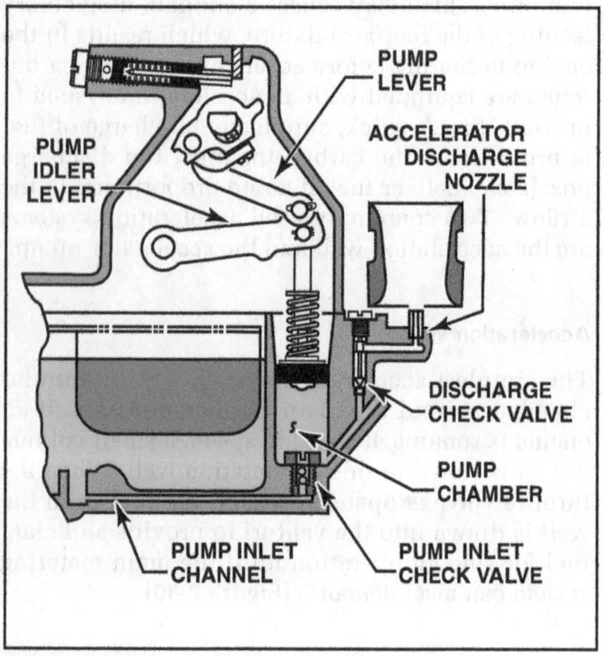


**Figure 7-31. On carburetors equipped with an accelerator pump, rapid throttle advance causes an accelerator pump piston to force stored fuel into the airstream through a dedicated discharge nozzle.**

## POWER ENRICHMENT/ECONOMIZER SYSTEM

Aircraft engines are designed to produce the maximum amount of power for their weight. However, the heat generated by operating at maximum power can be more than air-cooling can dissipate. One way to dissipate excess heat is a power enrichment system that provides a richer fuel/air mixture at high power settings; the excess fuel in the mixture helps cool the cylinders.

Power enrichment systems typically function at throttle settings above cruise power. Not only does a power enrichment system increase fuel flow at high power settings, it also permits the pilot to use a leaner mixture at cruise power. For this reason, this system is sometimes referred to as an **economizer system.**

### Needle Type

The needle-type economizer system uses an enrichment metering jet and nozzle parallel with the main metering jet and nozzle. The needle valve is operated by a link to the throttle shaft. When the engine operates at any power setting less than full throttle, a spring holds the valve on its seat, and the economizer jet provides no additional fuel to the engine. However, when the throttle plate is fully open, the valve is lifted off its seat and fuel flows through the economizer jet and through the discharge nozzle. [Figure 7-32]

### Air Bleed Type

Instead of using a dedicated economizer metering jet and discharge nozzle, the air bleed economizer system adjusts the size of the air bleed for the main discharge nozzle. Changing the size of the air bleed orifice adjusts the fuel/air mixture.

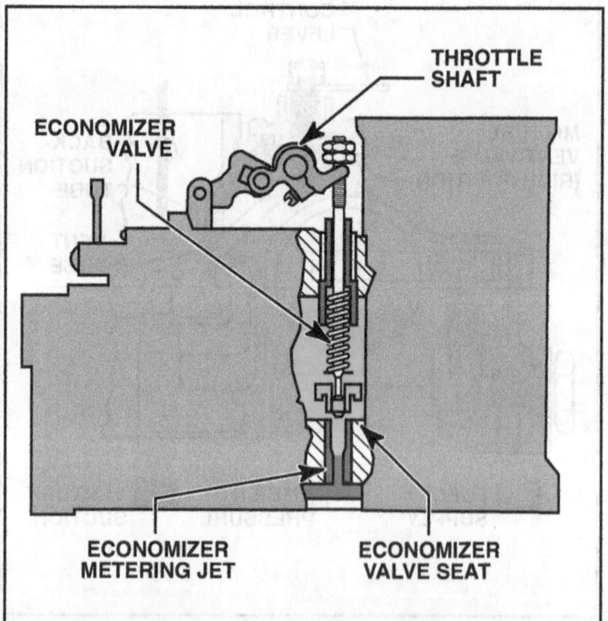


**Figure 7-32. A needle-type economizer admits additional fuel through the economizer metering jet when the needle valve is pulled off its seat at full throttle settings.**

A needle valve and seat are installed at the air bleed entrance. When the engine operates at cruise power, a spring holds the needle valve off of its seat, and the orifice retains its normal size. When the throttle valve is fully opened, a lever presses the needle valvo. By restricting the air bleed, additional fuel is supplied to the discharge nozzle, which provides a richer fuel/air mixture. [Figure 7-33]

## CARBURETOR LIMITATIONS

Float-type carburetors are reliable and relatively easy to maintain, but they have several distinct disadvantages. Because float-type carburetors use low operating pressures, incomplete vaporization and inadequate fuel flow from the discharge nozzle can occur. In addition, a float-type carburetor does not respond well to sudden maneuvers or unusual aircraft attitudes. Float-type carburetors also have a tendency to accumulate ice. **Carburetor ice** occurs when water freezes in the venturi and restricts airflow to the engine. This can cause an engine to run rough, lose power, or even quit in flight. The two categories of carburetor ice are fuel evaporation and throttle ice.

**Fuel evaporation ice** can occur when fuel is discharged in the venturi. Vaporized fuel absorbs heat from the surrounding air, causing air temperature to drop 30 degrees Fahrenheit or more. In some cases, this loss of heat allows moisture in the air to condense and freeze. A carburetor is typically the first component of an aircraft to accumulate ice during flight. Carburetor ice can occur at ambient air temperatures up to 70 degrees Fahrenheit with relative humidity as low as 50 percent. The flight conditions

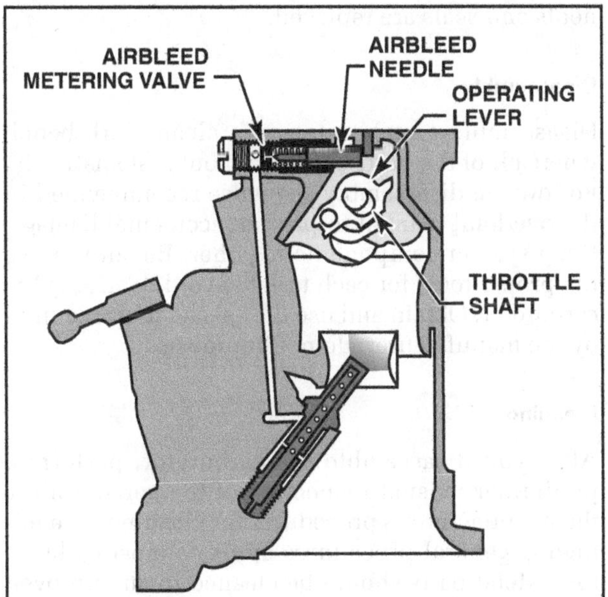


**Figure 7-33. An air bleed economizer enriches the fuel/air mixture at high power settings by controlling the size of the air bleed opening.**

most likely to result in the development of carburetor ice are when the outside air temperature is between 30 and 40 degrees Fahrenheit and the relative humidity exceeds 60 percent.

**Throttle ice** forms on the backside of a partially closed throttle valve. As air flows across and around a throttle valve, an area of low pressure is created downstream. This has a cooling effect on the fuel/air mixture that can cause moisture to freeze on the backside of the valve. Because the throttle valve is partially closed, a small amount of ice causes a relatively large reduction in airflow and a corresponding loss of power. In a severe case, a large accumulation of ice can jam the throttle and make it immovable. Because the temperature drop at the throttle valve is small, throttle ice seldom occurs at temperatures above 38 degree Fahrenheit.

## FLOAT-TYPE CARBURETOR MAINTENANCE

You can perform most basic maintenance for a float-type carburetor while it is installed on the engine. For example, you can check the control linkages for freedom of movement and full range of motion. Be sure to clean and lubricate all moving parts. Verify that all safety wire and cotter pins are present and secure. You should also inspect the fuel lines and air hoses for leaks, kinks, or other damage. Check the fuel filter and strainer regularly.

You will need to verify the security of the carburetor mounting on the engine. Pay special attention to the mounting flange and gasket, looking carefully for signs of cracks or leaks. A leak between the carburetor and engine will affect the fuel/air mixture. Depending on the severity of a leak, the fuel/air mixture can become so lean that the engine operates rough at idle and does not produce full power. A severe leak can even cause detonation and engine damage.

Although not considered a part of a carburetor, you should also check the induction air box and filter for security, cleanliness, and air leaks around the filter. Furthermore, check the carburetor heat valve for proper travel and a positive seal. A carburetor heat leak will lower the density of air entering the carburetor, which decreases engine power output.

### Idle Mixture Adjustment

The idle mixture must be adjusted correctly for an engine to operate smoothly at low speed. The idle mixture on most carburetors is controlled by a needle valve that is constructed with a spring-loaded thumb screw (or knurled knob) for adjustments. [Figure 7-34]

To check idle mixture, run the engine until cylinder head temperature is in the normal range. Slowly

**Figure 7-34. The idle mixture valve of a float carburetor is typically adjusted by a screw head or knurled knob. The adjustment screw is generally spring-loaded to maintain its setting.**

pull the mixture control aft while watching the tachometer. If the idle mixture is adjusted properly, engine r.p.m. will increase slightly (between 25 and 50 r.p.m.) before dropping off rapidly. An immediate decrease in r.p.m. indicates that the idle mixture is too lean. However, a momentary increase greater than 50 r.p.m. indicates that the idle mixture is too rich. For aircraft equipped with a manifold pressure gauge, you should note a manifold pressure decrease (approximately 1/4 inch) just before an increase as the engine stops operating.

If the idle mixture check reveals a lean or rich condition, increase or decrease the idle fuel flow as appropriate. Continue checking and adjusting the idle mixture until the desired idle fuel mixture is obtained. After each adjustment, briefly operate the engine at a high speed to prevent spark plug fouling. After you believe the idle mixture is set correctly, repeat the idle mixture check several times to verify a consistent response.

#### Idle Speed Adjustment

After you set the idle mixture, check the engine idle speed. Check the aircraft manufacturer's maintenance instructions for the appropriate speed. The typical range for idle speed is 600 to 800 r.p.m. Most carburetors are equipped with a spring-loaded adjustment screw for setting idle speed. [Figure 7-35]

The engine should be at normal operating temperatures before you make any adjustments. Additionally, check the operation of the ignition system. Briefly operate the engine at a high speed to prevent spark plug fouling; then close the throttle and allow the speed to stabilize. If the engine does not idle at the appropriate speed, adjust the idle speed screw and recheck idle speed. Briefly operate the engine at a high speed after each adjustment.

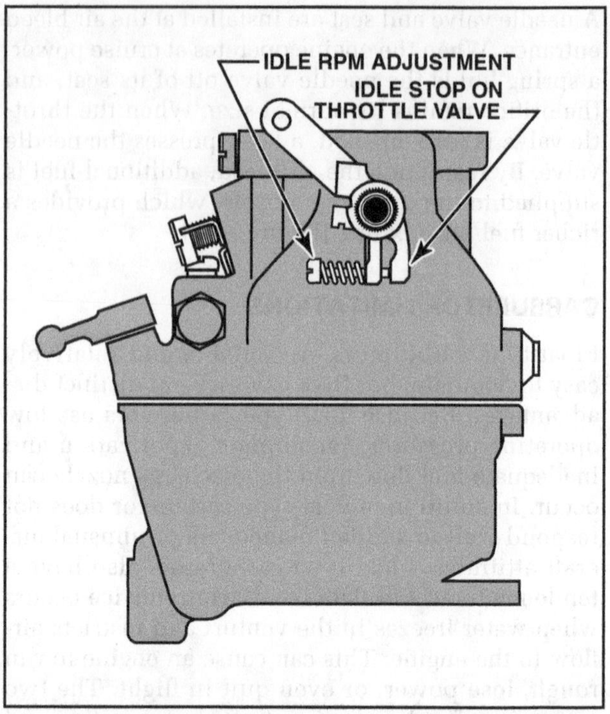


**Figure 7-35 To adjust the idle speed on most carburetors, a spring-loaded screw is rotated to provide a contact for the idle stop on the throttle valve linkage.**

## CARBURETOR OVERHAUL

Carburetor overhaul is commonly performed concurrently with engine overhaul. Overhaul procedures require a complete disassembly of the carburetor and a visual inspection of all internal components. Additionally, dimensional checks are made to determine serviceability of reusable components and seals are replaced.

#### Disassembly

Disassemble a carburetor on a clean work bench where all of the parts can be laid out systematically. Follow the disassembly sequence recommended in the overhaul manual to prevent accidental damage. Keep system components together. Be sure to use the proper tools for each task to avoid damaging the carburetor. Obtain and use the special tools required by the manufacturer; do not improvise.

#### Cleaning

After you disassemble the carburetor, perform a preliminary visual inspection of the parts. Follow the manufacturer's procedures for cleaning. The following general procedures apply to most carburetors. Metal parts should be cleaned in an approved carburetor cleaner (such as Stoddard Solvent) to remove grease, oil, and varnish from gasoline additives. After rinsing in fresh solvent, air-dry all parts.

Do not dry with cloths or shop rags because lint or threads could obstruct metering jets and cause close-fitting parts to bind.

Removal of carbonized or gummy deposits requires a decarbonizing solution. Be aware that certain decarbonizers degrade materials used in carburetor components. Only use decarbonizers approved by the manufacturer and follow their instructions for use. Decarbonizing fluids can pose a health hazard, so wear the appropriate personal protective equipment during use.

After soaking a part in a decarbonizer bath, rinse the parts with hot water and dry them with clean, dry, compressed air. Give special attention to the internal passages, bleeds, and recesses when rinsing and drying. Carbon deposits remaining on aluminum parts may be removed with No. 600 wet sandpaper and water. Additionally, corrosion on aluminum parts should be removed by immersion in an alkaline cleaner or an equivalent agent recommended by the manufacturer.

#### Inspection

Visually inspect clean parts to determine the serviceability of each component. Look for corrosion, cracks, bent parts, and damaged threads. Any parts subjected to wear should be dimensionally checked (compared against a table of limits) or replaced.

Use a magnifying glass and light to inspect fuel and air passages. Never insert a piece of wire into a passage because the wire could become stuck or cause damage to the component, rendering it useless.

Check the float assembly for freedom of motion, proper fit, and proper clearance. Inspect the fulcrum pin for binding. Inspect the float assembly for leaks and buoyancy; if a float loses buoyancy, it will sink and allow the fuel level to rise. If this happens, the carburetor can supply an excessively rich mixture. A leaking float must be replaced.

Inspect the float needle valve and seat for wear, grooves, scratches, and pits. If wear is visible, the valve may not seat properly. A leaking needle valve can result in fuel leaks at the discharge nozzle or carburetor flooding. The typical needle valve is constructed of hardened steel and the seat is made from bronze. Needle valve seats typically wear faster than the needles. In some carburetors, the needle valve has a synthetic rubber tip to provide a more effective seal and reduce wear between the parts.

The fuel level in a carburetor is determined by the position of the float. Limited reassembly of a carburetor is necessary to check the float level. The fuel level in a float-type carburetor is typically between 3/16 and 1/8 inch below the top of the discharge nozzle.

The method used to check float level depends on the carburetor model. For example, on carburetors where the float is suspended from the throttle body, the float level can be measured with a ruler or slipping the shank of the proper size twist drill between the gasket and float with the throttle body inverted. When the float level is correct, the drill should barely touch the float without causing it to rise. Be sure to check the float level on both sides. [Figure 7-36]

For other models of carburetor, the float and needle valve assembly are mounted in the float bowl and fuel is necessary to check the float level. Level the carburetor body on a flow bench and attach a fuel supply at the correct pressure to the fuel inlet. As the float bowl fills, the float should close the needle valve. After the valve is closed, use a depth gauge to measure the distance between the carburetors's parting surface and the surface of the fuel. Measure the fuel level away from the edges to minimize the effect of surface tension. If the fuel level is incorrect, make adjustments by inserting or removing shims below the needle valve seat.

After the proper fuel level is established, some manufacturers require a check of total float travel. Permit the float to rest in its lowest position. The distance between the throttle body parting surface and the top of the float is referred to as float drop. Float travel is calculated by subtracting float level from float drop. [Figure 7-37]

After float travel is correct, some manufacturers require you to check the side clearance between the float and the walls of the float chamber. Attach a special cutaway float bowl fixture to the bottom of the throttle body. Then measure the distance between the float and test fixture with a drill rod gauge of

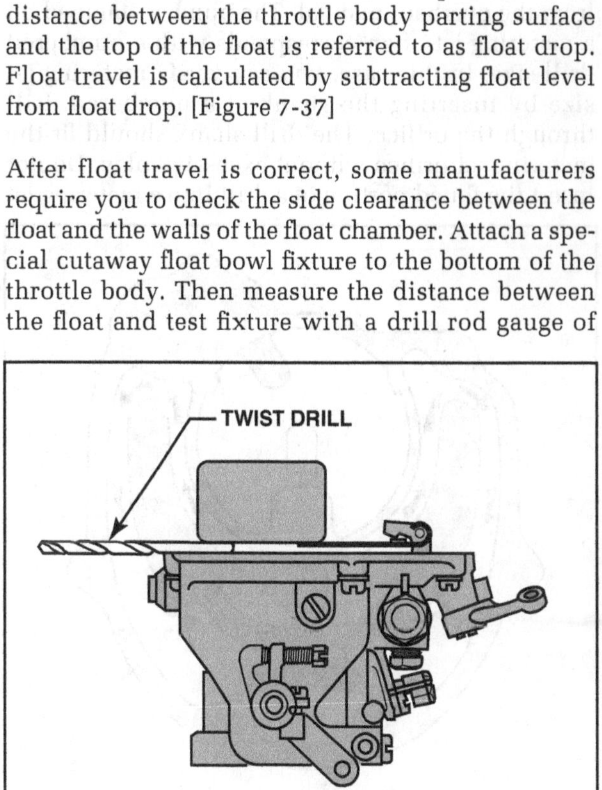


**Figure 7-36. The float clearance on some carburetors is measured with a ruler or by inserting the shank of the proper size twist drill between the gasket and float with the throttle body inverted.**

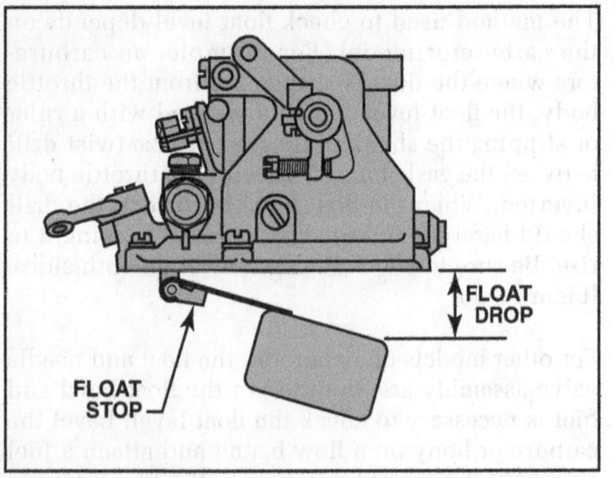


**Figure 7-37. To determine the float drop, hold the throttle body in an upright position and measure the distance between the mounting flange and the top of the float. After you determine the float drop, calculate the total float travel by subtracting the float clearance from the float drop.**

the specified size. The gauge must pass completely around the float without binding. [Figure 7-38]

Visually inspect and dimensionally check the main metering system components. Verify the size of a metering jet by comparing it with specifications from the overhaul manual. The number stamped on a metering jet often corresponds with a numbered drill size. In this case, you can verify metering jet size by inserting the shank of a numbered drill through the orifice. The drill shank should fit the metering jet orifice without excessive play. Do not insert the fluted portion of a drill into a metering jet

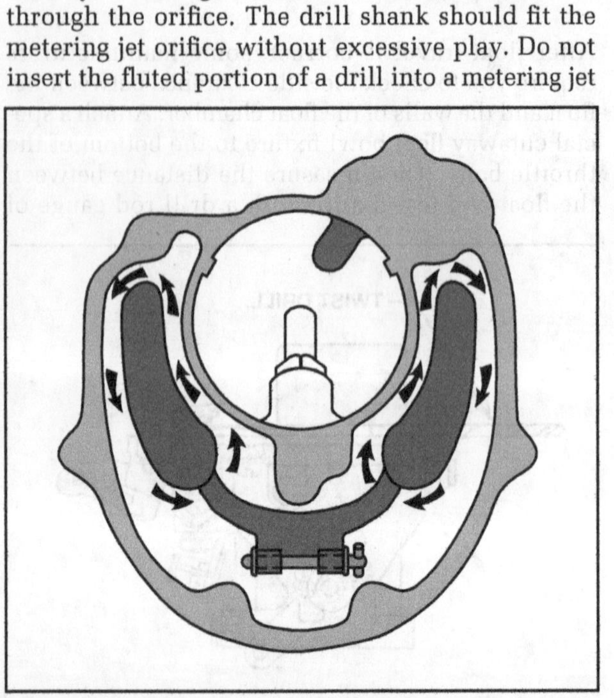

**Figure 7-38. To check the side clearance between the float and float bowl, you must use a special test fixture that enables you to pass a drill rod of a specified size completely around the float.**

because it could scratch or score the orifice. Inspect the main discharge nozzle for obstructions, kinks, and bent sections.

Verify that the throttle valve moves freely through its full range of motion and check the throttle valve shaft and bushings for excessive wear and play. Check the bleed air passages for obstructions and examine the venturi for corrosion, deep scratches, and scoring. When a boost venturi is installed inside the primary venturi, check for broken or bent support arms.

Closely examine the idle discharge jet and the idle system bleeds for obstructions, nicks, and dents that could narrow the openings. Verify that the mixture control shaft moves freely in the housing. After completing the visual inspection, check the dimensions of mixture control components called out in the overhaul manual.

Visually inspect the security of the accelerator pump linkage and check the moving parts for proper travel and freedom of motion. You must make several dimensional checks on the accelerator pump, including the dimension of the spring-loaded telescoping shaft and its corresponding hole in the throttle body. Check for proper spring tension and inspect the condition of the leather packing. When a carburetor is equipped with a power enrichment or economizer system, complete the visual and dimensional inspections as required. The valve, valve seat, and metering jet measurements should be within the permissible limits listed in the maintenance manual tables.

## REASSEMBLY AND INSTALLATION

The carburetor should be reassembled in the sequence outlined in the overhaul manual. Use any required special tools to prevent damage to components.

Most carburetor bodies are made of cast aluminum alloy, the threaded openings of which are easily damaged. A drop or two of thread lubricant on threaded fittings before installation prevents damage. Be sure to insert at least one thread of the fitting or screw into the casting before lubricant is applied to prevent plugging jets or other small passages. Be sure to tighten threaded components to the specified torque settings. Apply a small amount of lubricating oil to moving components (such as the accelerator pump telescoping shaft and seals) to ease reassembly. After you have assembled all components and tightened hardware to the specified torque, safety the components with wire or other specified safety lock mechanisms, as required.

After you reassemble the carburetor, perform a final check of the fuel level and verify proper operation of the float and needle valve assembly. This check ensures that you reassembled the carburetor properly, and that no binding of the float and needle valve assembly exists. To perform this check, level the carburetor on a flow bench. Attach a sight glass tube to the carburetor fuel drain port with a piece of flexible rubber hose. Align the glass tube vertically and secure it; then, using a ruler, mark a line on the glass tube extending from the carburetor parting surface. Now attach a fuel supply at the correct pressure to the fuel inlet. After the float bowl fills to the correct level, the float should seat the needle valve and fuel flow should stop. Measure the distance from the fuel surface in the center of the glass tube to the parting surface mark and compare with specified limits. [Figure 7-39]

Before installing a carburetor, review the appropriate installation instructions. In most installations, the first step involves installing a gasket and mounting the carburetor to the engine. After the carburetor is securely attached and safetied, connect the fuel lines and controls. Tighten fittings according to the specified torque values. To prevent imprecise control movement, replace worn hardware when attaching the control linkages and rods.

After you have attached and safetied the controls, check for freedom of movement and full range of motion in the cockpit and at the carburetor. For most installations, the mechanical control stops on the carburetor should be reached before the controls reach their stops in the cockpit. The amount of control travel possible between the carburetor stop and the cockpit stop is called **springback**. An equal amount of springback should be present at both fully open and fully closed positions.

After installation is complete, perform an engine runup to verify proper operation. Check and set idle mixture and idle speed. If adjustments are required, make them using the procedures described earlier. After you set the idle adjustments, apply full throttle briefly to confirm that the engine can achieve full-rated power. After completing the engine runup, move the mixture control to idle-cutoff to verify a prompt engine shutdown.

## PRESSURE-INJECTION CARBURETORS

Pressure-injection carburetors are not widely used on modern reciprocating engines. This fuel metering device was used extensively during WWII. Pressure-injection carburetors are still used in classic, aerobatic, and experimental racing aircraft. A basic understanding of how a typical

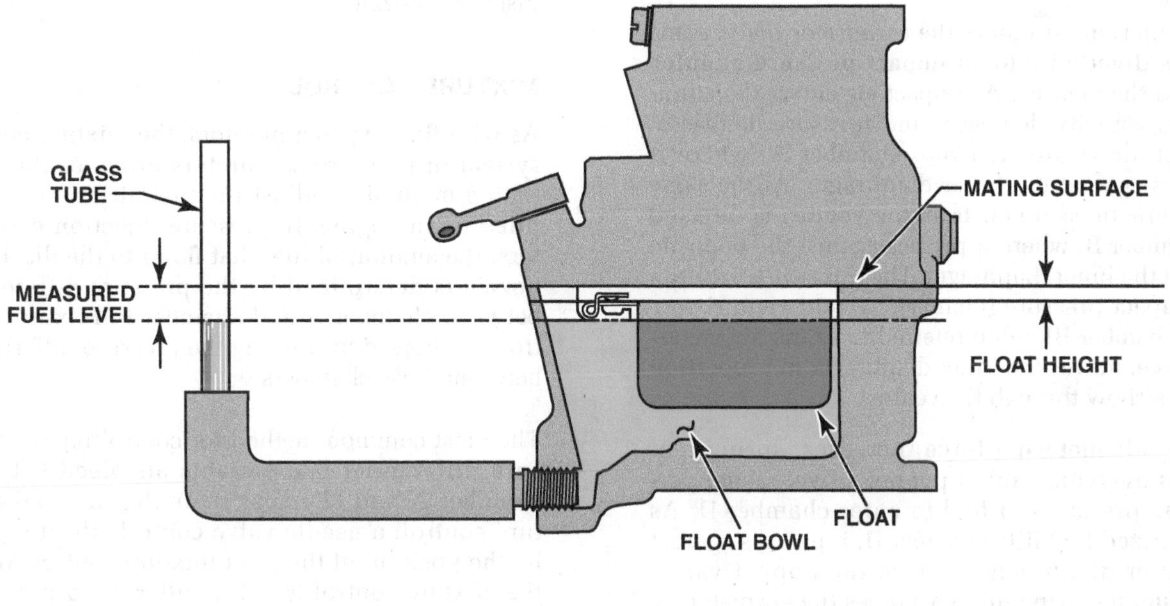


**Figure 7-39. After you mark a line level with the carburetor's parting surface on a sight glass, measure the distance between the fuel level and parting surface. This check verifies the correct fuel level and the proper functioning of the float and needle valve assembly.**

pressure-injection carburetor functions is important if you encounter these aircraft, but also to better understand the modern fuel injection systems that came later.

Pressure-injection carburetors differ from float-type carburetors in several ways. Instead of a float chamber to store fuel, pressure-injection carburetors receive fuel under pressure from a pump. Fuel pressure, not differential air pressure, causes fuel to exit the discharge nozzle; so the discharge nozzle does not directly discharge into a venturi. This design reduces the potential for carburetor icing and improves fuel vaporization.

Despite significant design and operational differences, a pressure-injection carburetor also contains systems for fuel metering, mixture control, idling, acceleration, and power enrichment. Because of the differences, each system is described in detail. [Figure 7-40]

## MAIN METERING

The main metering system supplies the correct amount of fuel to the engine. The main metering system consists of a fuel regulator (fuel control unit), a main metering jet, and a throttle valve.

The **fuel regulator** (**fuel control unit**) meters the appropriate amount of fuel for engine operation. A typical fuel control unit consists of five distinct chambers separated by an inner and outer diaphragm, a poppet valve assembly, and a main metering jet. [Figure 7-41]

As induction air enters the carburetor body, some of it is diverted into an **impact pressure annulus** around the venturi. As impact air enters the annulus, its velocity decreases and pressure increases. Impact air is directed into chamber A, where it presses against the inner diaphragm. At the same time, low pressure air from the venturi is directed to chamber B, where it presses against the opposite side of the inner diaphragm. The difference between the impact pressure (chamber A) and venturi suction (chamber B), often referred to as the **air metering force**, moves the inner diaphragm in proportion to the airflow through the venturi.

As the air metering force increases, spring tension is overcome and a poppet valve opens, permitting pressurized fuel to enter chamber D. As pressurized fuel fills chamber D, it presses against the outer diaphragm to close the poppet valve. This **fuel metering force** balances the air metering force to regulate fuel in proportion to the airflow through the venturi.

When the engine operates at idle speed, insufficient airflow passes through the venturi to control the poppet valve that regulates fuel. To compensate, a spring in chamber A supplements the air metering force. At idle speed, spring tension opens the poppet valve to permit sufficient fuel pressure for operation.

The regulated fuel in chamber D passes through a metering jet to enter chamber C. From this point forward, fuel is metered at a constant pressure for all engine operations. From chamber C, the metered fuel passes through an idle needle valve on its way to the discharge nozzle. [Figure 7-42]

At power settings above idle, a combination of spring pressure and low pressure on the back side of a diaphragm hold the idle needle valve open far enough to permit adequate fuel flow, and fuel metering is controlled by the main metering jet. The discharge nozzle valve is spring loaded in the closed position; it is opened by a combination of metered fuel pressure and low pressure (venturi suction) acting on the discharge valve diaphragm. The discharge valve diaphragm maintains constant fuel pressure after the main metering jet. Additionally, the spring provides a positive fuel cutoff when the mixture control is placed in the idle-cutoff position.

Because fuel pressure, rather than venturi suction, delivers fuel, the discharge nozzle is downstream from the venturi and throttle valve to avoid icing problems. To aid fuel vaporization, air from the impact pressure annulus is mixed with fuel in the discharge nozzle.

## MIXTURE CONTROL

As with float-type carburetors, the mixture control system in pressure carburetors provides the pilot with a method to adjust the fuel/air mixture supplied to an engine. In pressure-injection carburetors, the amount of fuel that flows to the discharge nozzle is determined by the pressure differential between chamber A and chamber B. Mixture control is achieved by varying the pressure differential between these chambers.

The most common method for controlling the pressure differential is a variable air bleed between chamber A and chamber B. With a manual mixture control, a needle valve controls the air bleed by the position of the pilot mixture control. When the mixture control is in the full rich position, the needle valve is seated, which results in the maximum pressure differential. As the mixture control moves toward the idle-cutoff position, the needle valve begins to open, which decreases the pressure differential. [Figure 7-43]

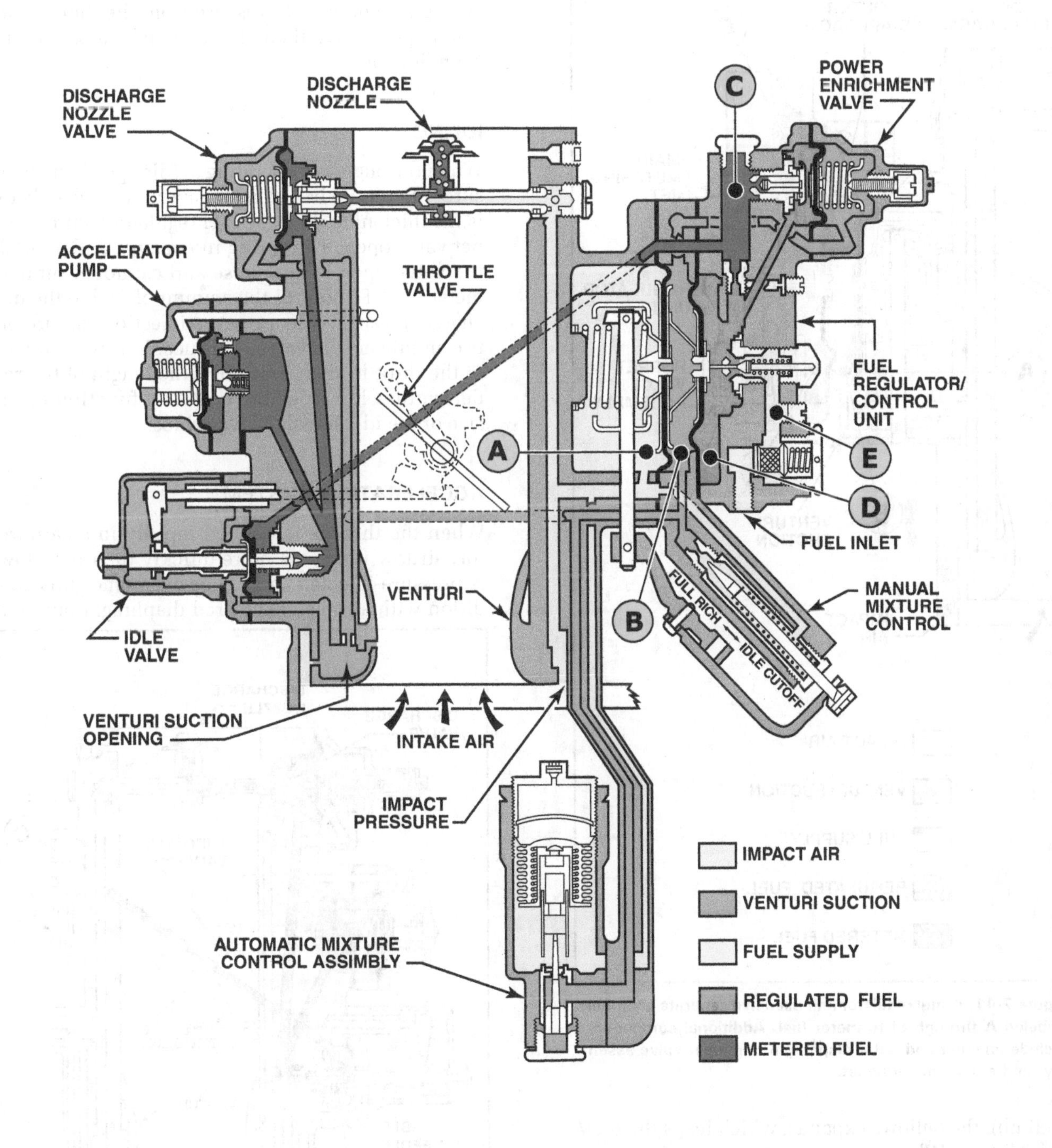


**Figure 7-40. The illustrated Bendix PS7BD pressure carburetor provides an overview of a typical pressure carburetor. A pressure carburetor is different from a float-type carburetor, but they have the same basic systems.**

Some pressure-injection carburetors use an automatic mixture control (or AMC) to continuously adjust the fuel/air mixture during flight. Adjustments compensate for changes in air density caused by any of the following factors: climbing or descending, variations in atmospheric pressure, and changes in temperature. The typical AMC uses a brass bellows filled with helium to actuate a reverse-tapered needle valve. As ambient pressure changes, the bellows expands or contracts, varying the size of the air bleed orifice between chamber A and chamber B. As atmospheric pressure decreases (such as during

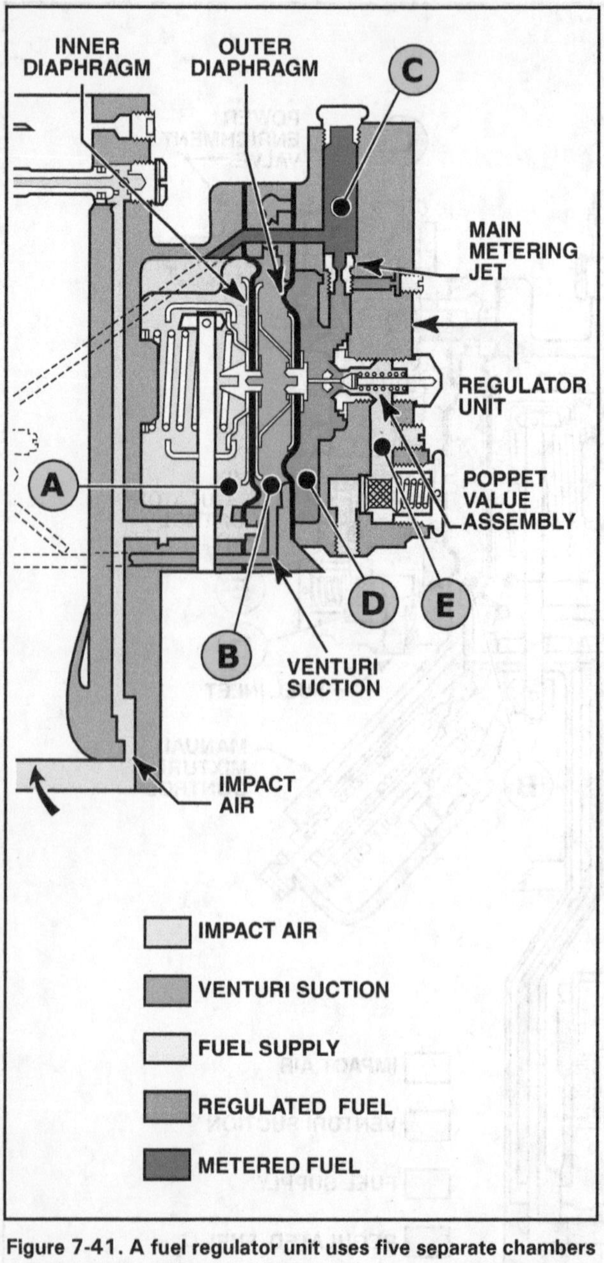


**Figure 7-41. A fuel regulator unit uses five separate chambers (labeled A through E) to meter fuel. Additional components include an inner and outer diaphragm, a poppet valve assembly, and a main metering jet.**

a climb), the bellows expands, which leans the fuel/air mixture. When atmospheric pressure increases (such as during a descent), the bellows contracts, which richens the fuel/air mixture.

When the mixture control is moved to the idle-cutoff position, the flow of fuel to the carburetor stops. The spring in chamber A opens the fuel regulator poppet valve when the engine is at idle speed. A mechanical linkage connects the mixture control with a release lever to allow the poppet valve to close when idle-cutoff is selected; the lever compresses the idle spring to remove all pressure from the diaphragm. The poppet valve then closes, which stops the fuel from flowing.

## IDLING

When the engine is operating at idle speed, the pressure differential between chamber A and chamber B is insufficient to hold the fuel regulator control poppet valve open. The spring in chamber A that holds the valve open is imprecise and cannot accurately meter fuel. To control the amount of fuel to the discharge nozzle at idle, pressure-injection carburetors use an idle needle valve. This needle valve is linked to the throttle shaft assembly; the length of the rod determines idle speed, which is a function of the size of the idle needle valve orifice.

## ACCELERATION SYSTEM

When the throttle is opened rapidly in a carburetor, airflow increases more quickly than fuel flow. A pressure-injected carburetor overcomes this condition with a three-chambered diaphragm pump. A

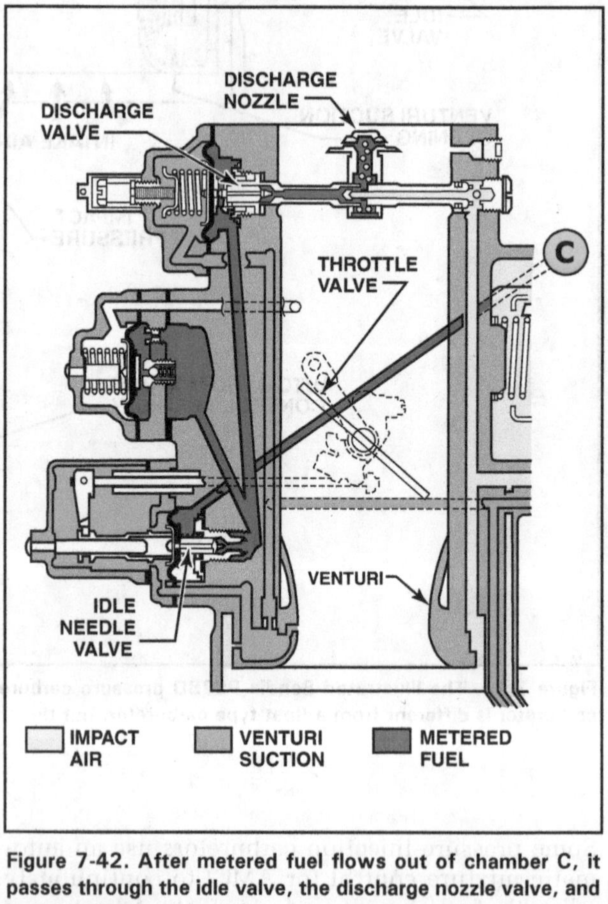


**Figure 7-42. After metered fuel flows out of chamber C, it passes through the idle valve, the discharge nozzle valve, and into the airstream.**

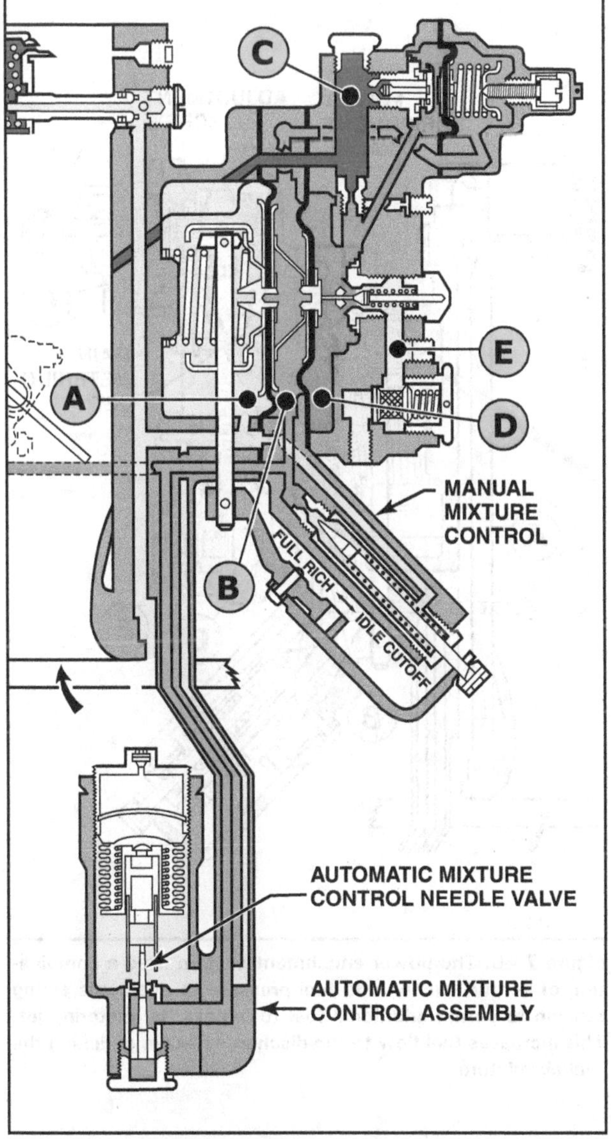


**Figure 7-43. To control the fuel/air mixture, an air bleed is provided between chambers A and B. Controlling the size of the air bleed regulates the pressure differential between the chambers and controls the amount of fuel entering the carburetor.**

diaphragm separates an air chamber from the primary fuel chamber; the primary fuel chamber is separated from the secondary fuel chamber by a rigid divider with a combination check/relief valve and a single fuel bleed orifice. [Figure 7-44]

When the engine is started, manifold pressure decreases, partially compressing the spring in the air chamber. At the same time, fuel fills both fuel chambers. When the throttle opens rapidly, increased manifold pressure on the diaphragm pressurizes fuel in the primary chamber and forces it through the secondary chamber and out through the discharge nozzle. The check/relief valve permits fuel to be quickly discharged when the throttle first opens. The valve does not remain open for long, and the remaining fuel is discharged through the fuel bleed at a slower rate. This system provides supplemental fuel through the main discharge nozzle until the regulatory control valve supplies the necessary fuel flow.

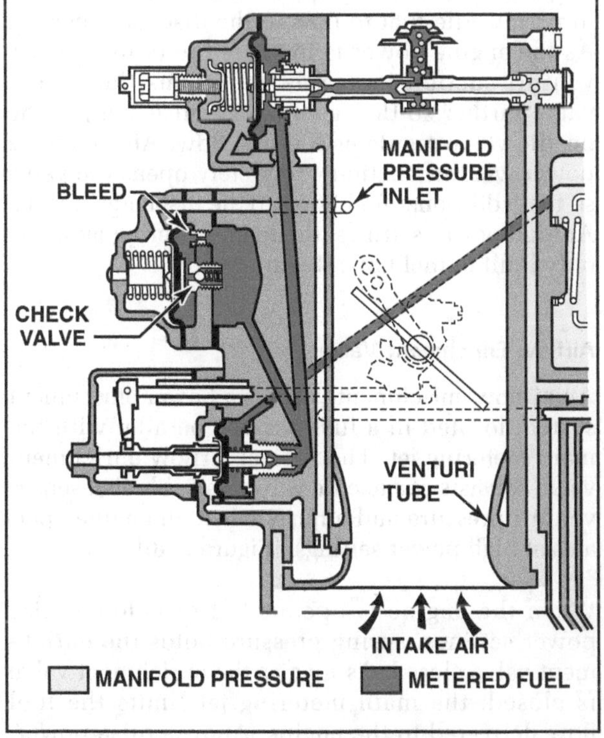


**Figure 7-44. A typical accelerator pump on a pressure injection carburetor consists of a single diaphragm pump with an air chamber that is vented to manifold pressure and two fuel chambers separated by a bleed valve.**

If the throttle is reduced rapidly, the decrease in manifold pressure compresses the pump spring and draws fuel into the primary fuel chamber. To prevent the diaphragm from starving the engine of fuel as the pump fills, the check/relief valve remains closed, and fuel fills the primary fuel chamber through only the fuel bleed orifice.

## POWER ENRICHMENT SYSTEM

The power enrichment system provides extra fuel for operations above cruise power. The extra fuel supplements engine cooling and helps prevent detonation. Power enrichment can be accomplished with either a double-step idle valve or the incorporation of an airflow power enrichment valve.

### Double-Step Idle Valve

A double-step idle valve varies the amount of fuel flowing to the discharge nozzle. At low power settings, the first (or idle step) of the needle valve opens to permit idle fuel to flow to the discharge nozzle. As the engine power is increased to cruise power, venturi suction increases and opens the needle valve further so the second (or cruise step) of the needle valve regulates the fuel flow. Above cruise power, venturi suction completely opens the valve so that additional fuel flows to the discharge nozzle. At high power settings, the main metering jet is the only limit to fuel flow. [Figure 7-45]

### Airflow Enrichment Valve

An airflow enrichment valve is a power enrichment system located in a fuel passage parallel with the main metering jet. The typical airflow enrichment valve consists of a needle valve assembly that senses venturi pressure and adjusts when an engine operates at high power settings. [Figure 7-46]

When the engine is operated at or below cruise power settings, spring pressure holds the enrichment valve closed. As long as the enrichment valve is closed, the main metering jet limits the fuel flow delivered to the engine. Above cruise power, increased airflow through the venturi causes the enrichment needle valve to open, which permits additional fuel to bypass the metering jet and richen the fuel/air mixture.

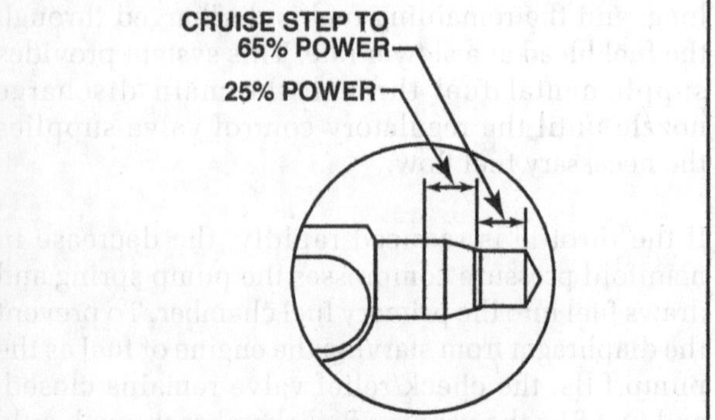


**Figure 7-45. In carburetors that use a double-step idle valve for power enrichment, the needle valve is cut in steps to regulate the amount of fuel that flows to the discharge nozzle for idle and cruise power settings.**

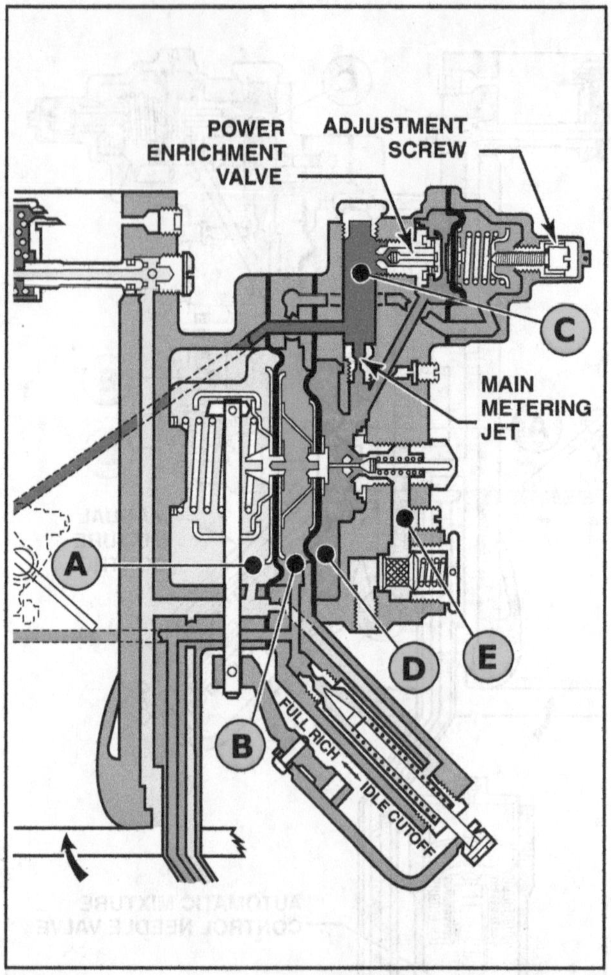


**Figure 7-46. The power enrichment system uses a combination of venturi suction and fuel pressure to overcome spring tension to permit additional fuel to bypass the metering jet. This increases fuel flow to the discharge nozzle, enriching the fuel/air mixture.**

## WATER INJECTION

Water injection systems (also called **anti-detonation injection** or **ADI**) were common on large reciprocating engines with pressure-injection carburetors. The system enabled an engine to produce maximum power without detonation or preignition. With a typical ADI system, water and alcohol were injected into the carburetor to modify the fuel/air mixture to prevent detonation.

On these large reciprocating engines, the carburetor is normally adjusted to provide a somewhat rich fuel/air mixture for high power operations. The extra fuel helps cool the engine and reduce the potential for detonation. The richer fuel/air mixture does not enable an engine to produce its maximum power. When an ADI system is installed, the fuel/air mixture can be leaned to enable an engine to produce maximum power.

### PRESSURE-INJECTION CARBURETOR MAINTENANCE

You need a flow bench and specialized tools to overhaul or perform any internal maintenance on a pressure-injection carburetor, so your maintenance activities are typically limited to inspection, field adjustments, removal, and installation.

With the pressure carburetor installed on the engine, check the same items described for float-type carburetors. For example, check the carburetor for security and for possible leaks around the mating flange. Inspect control linkages for security of installation, freedom of movement, and proper contact with the stops. If all controls are rigged properly, operate the engine to check both the idle mixture adjustment and the idle speed. Both the idle mixture and idle speed are manually adjusted by varying the length of one or more adjustment screws on the side of the metering device. [Figure 7-47]

To check the idle mixture adjustment on a pressure carburetor, use the same procedures as described for a float-type carburetor. While the engine is running at operating temperature, slowly move the mixture control toward the idle-cutoff position while simultaneously observing the tachometer. If the mixture is adjusted properly, engine speed will increase slightly before it drops off rapidly. If the aircraft is equipped with a manifold pressure gauge, you will see that an optimum idle mixture decreases the manifold pressure just before the engine ceases to fire.

After you adjust the idle mixture, adjust the idle speed. Verify that the ignition system is operating properly and that the mixture control is set appropriately. Advance the throttle control to clear the engine and then pull it back to the idle position and allow the engine speed to stabilize. If the engine does not idle at the appropriate speed, adjust the idle speed screw as required and then repeat the procedure.

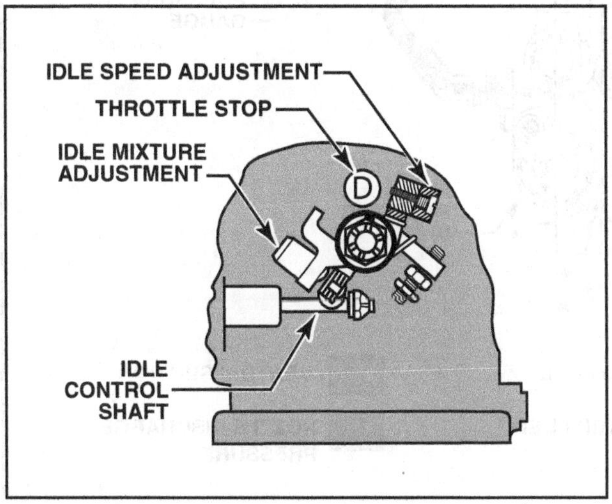


**Figure 7-47. The adjustment screws used to vary the idle mixture and speed are typically located on the throttle valve shaft.**

### PRESSURE-INJECTION CARBURETOR OVERHAUL

As mentioned earlier, the maintenance you can perform on pressure-injection carburetors is limited. In fact, because a flow bench and precision test equipment is required, only the manufacturer or by an approved repair facility overhauls a pressure-injection carburetor.

After an overhaul, the fuel chambers of a pressure-injection carburetor are typically filled with preservative oil. Before installation on an engine, this oil must be removed. Additionally, the manufacturer might require that the entire device be filled with (or submerged in) fuel for a period of time to dilute any residual oil and wet all of the diaphragms and seals. Because installations vary by engine, follow the appropriate manufacturer's installation instructions.

After installation, operate the engine to test and adjust the carburetor. Adjust the idle mixture and idle speed as appropriate. In addition, verify that the carburetor can supply fuel at full power. Recheck idle speed. Pull the mixture control to the idle-cutoff position and verify that the engine shuts down with a positive fuel cutoff.

## FUEL INJECTION SYSTEMS

Carburetors provide a reliable means of metering fuel for an engine; however, they have two major limitations. First, because intake manifolds differ in length and shape, the fuel/air mixture is not evenly distributed to the cylinders of a carbureted engine. Modern, high-performance aircraft engines operating with high compression ratios can be damaged by the introduction of a lean mixture in a cylinder. Second, all carburetors, even those with pressure-injection, are susceptible to carburetor icing.

These limitations were overcome with the incorporation of fuel injection systems on reciprocating aircraft engines. Instead of atomizing fuel in the manifold, a fuel injection system atomizes fuel directly in each cylinder assembly.

When fuel is injected directly into the combustion chamber, the injection system is referred to as a **direct fuel injection system**. This type of fuel injection system was used on early radial engines and offered the benefits of even fuel distribution and a reduced chance of backfiring. The typical direct fuel injection system is similar to a large pressure carburetor that meters the correct amount of fuel into two multi-cylindered piston pumps. These pumps force the metered fuel directly into the combustion chambers of the individual cylinders in timed, high-pressure spurts. Although the system worked well, close manufacturing tolerances and complex components made it impractical for widespread use on aircraft.

A **continuous-flow fuel injection system** is the most common type of fuel injection system in reciprocating aircraft engines. Instead of mixing the fuel and air in the combustion chamber, fuel is continuously injected into each intake port. This ensures fuel is vaporized and well-mixed with air before being drawn into the cylinder when the intake valve opens.

Today, two types of continuous-flow fuel injection systems are used on the majority of U.S.-manufactured reciprocating engines; one is the Precision Airmotive RSA system, and the other is the Teledyne Continental Motors system. The operation and maintenance of both systems are discussed below.

## RSA SYSTEM

Precision Airmotive supports two fuel metering systems (the **RS** and **RSA** system) for use in certified airplanes. The more advanced RSA system is described in this section. The RSA fuel injection system consists of five primary components: a venturi housing, a fuel metering unit, a fuel regulator, a flow divider, and fuel nozzles. Pressurized fuel flows to the fuel metering unit. The positions of the idle lever and mixture control meter fuel to the regulator. Inside the regulator, the combination of air metering force and fuel metering force regulates how much fuel is sent to the flow divider based on the volume of air through the throttle body. [Figure 7-48]

### VENTURI HOUSING

The venturi housing of an RSA fuel injection unit is a single cast-aluminum unit out. A single venturi (also cast-aluminum) is pressed into the bottom of the housing. A throttle valve installed at the top of the venturi housing controls airflow through the venturi. Three holes drilled near the edge of the valve provide adequate airflow for engine idling. [Figure 7-49]

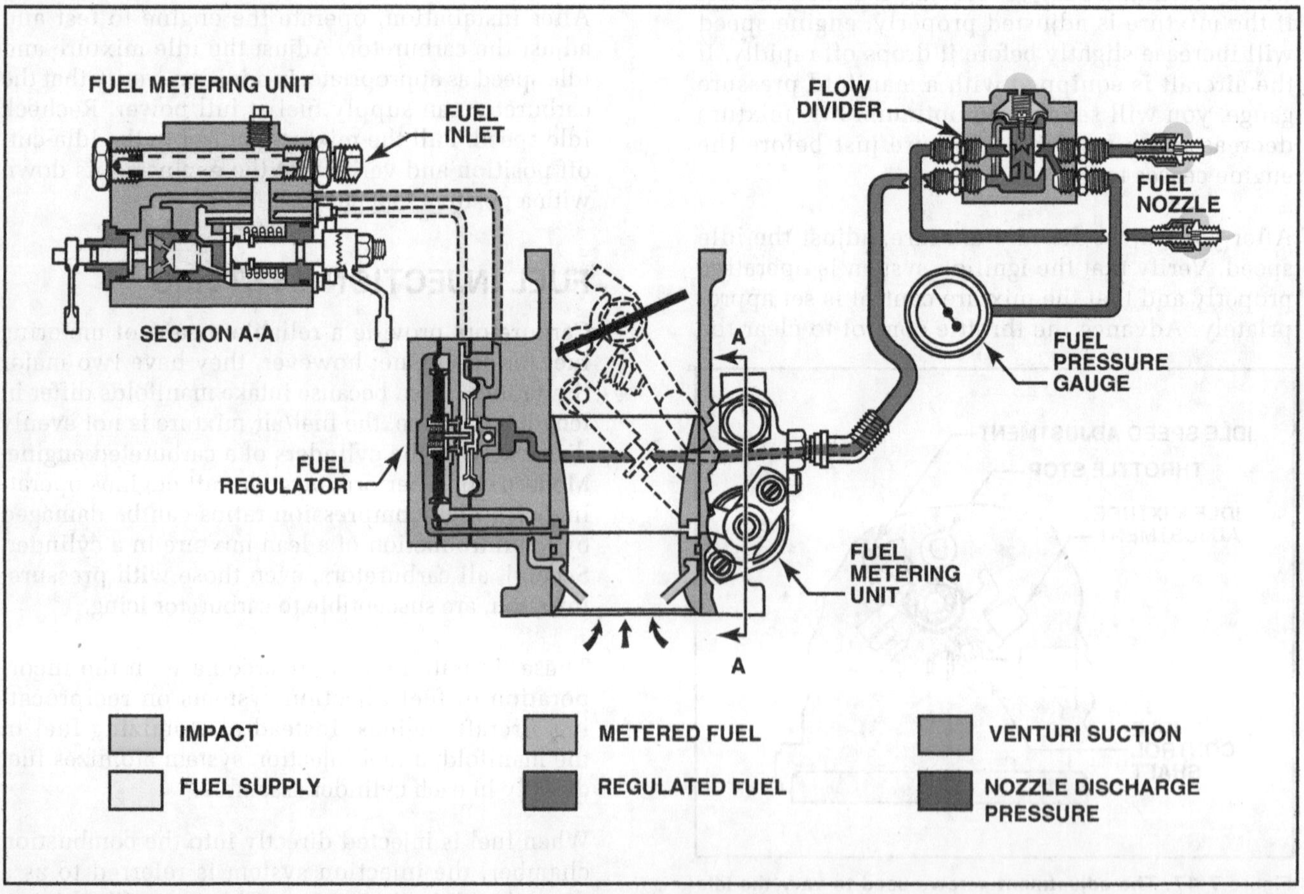


**Figure 7-48. The primary components of an RSA fuel injection system include a venturi housing, fuel metering unit, fuel regulator, flow divider, and several fuel nozzles.**

**Figure 7-49. A typical venturi housing is a single piece of cast aluminum with a venturi pressed into one end. A throttle valve is installed on the other end.**

## FUEL METERING UNIT

The fuel metering unit (part of the venturi housing) consists of a fuel strainer, a mixture control valve, an idle valve, a main metering jet, and an enrichment metering jet. The mixture and idle valves are mechanically actuated, spring-loaded, flat-plate valves that control the amount of fuel flowing through the metering jets. The mixture valve is actuated by the mixture control in the cockpit, and the idle valve is actuated by a mechanical linkage connected to the throttle valve shaft. [Figure 7-50]

Fuel metering is accomplished by fuel flowing through both the mixture control valve and the idle valve. After it passes through the fuel strainer, the fuel passes through a port in the mixture control valve. A typical mixture control valve consists of a flat plate-type valve that is rotated over a passageway leading to the metering jets. With this type of valve, the passageway leading to the metering jet is uncovered as the mixture control in the cockpit is advanced. In the rich position, the opening created by the mixture control is larger than the metering jet, and the jet limits the flow. However, in any intermediate position, the opening is smaller than the main jet, and the mixture control becomes the flow-limiting device. [Figure 7-51]

A second passageway in the mixture control base permits unmetered fuel, or inlet fuel, to flow to the fuel regulator. The pressure of unmetered fuel is used for reference in regulating fuel to the engine.

After fuel flows past the mixture valve, it flows through the metering jets. The position of the idle valve determines the amount of fuel that can flow

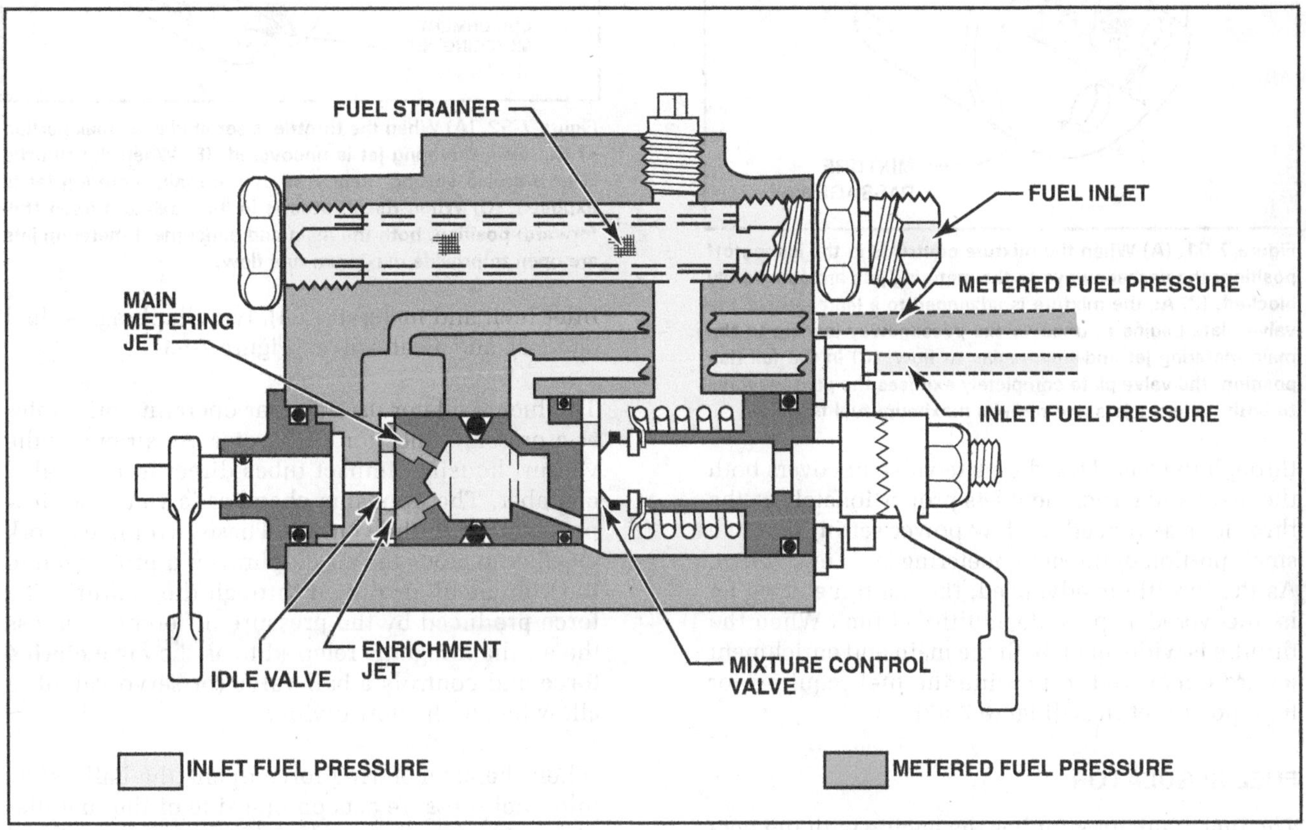


**Figure 7-50. In a typical RSA fuel metering unit, fuel flows through a wire strainer and the mixture control valve before reaching the metering jets. The idle valve position determines the amount of fuel that flows out of the metering jets.**

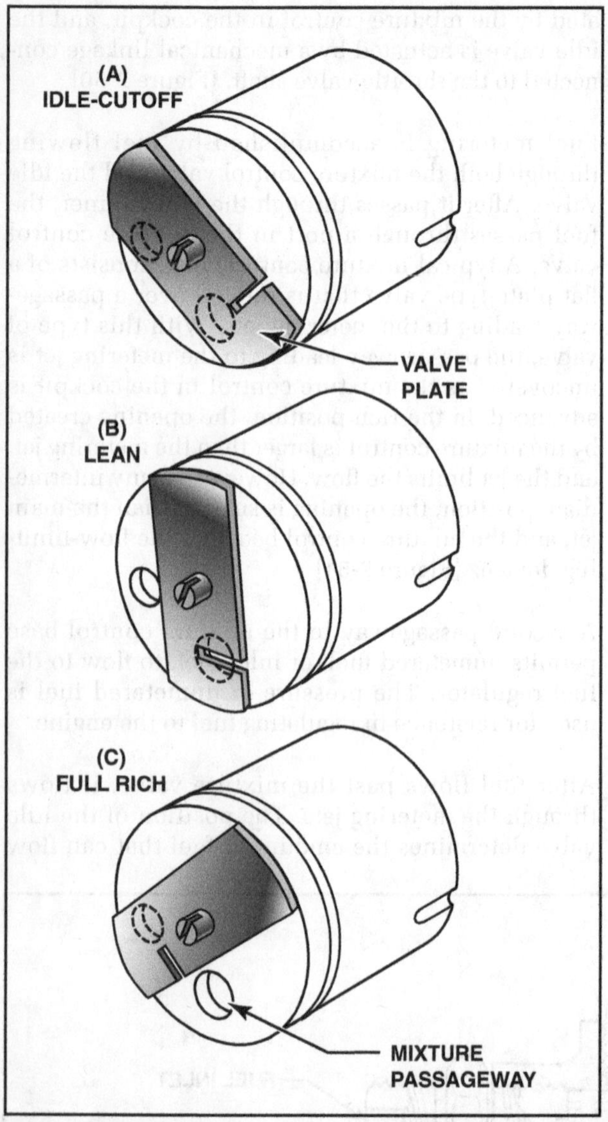


**Figure 7-51. (A) When the mixture control is in the idle-cutoff position, the passageways to the metering jets are completely blocked. (B) As the mixture is advanced to a lean setting, the valve plate begins to uncover the passageway leading to the main metering jet and fuel begins to flow. (C) In the full rich position, the valve plate completely exposes the passageways to both metering jets and permits maximum fuel flow.**

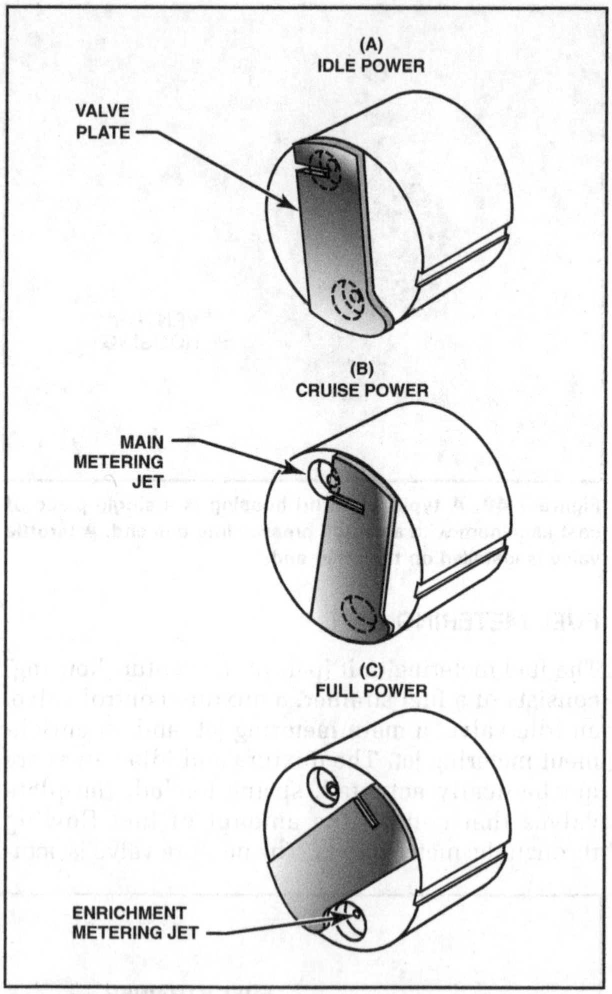


**Figure 7-52. (A) When the throttle is set at idle, a small portion of the main metering jet is uncovered. (B) When the throttle is at a cruise setting, nearly all of the main metering jet is exposed. (C) When the throttle is in its maximum open (full forward) position, both the main and enrichment metering jets are open to provide maximum fuel flow.**

through the jets. The idle plate valve uncovers both the main and enrichment jets proportionately as the throttle is advanced. At low power settings, only a small portion of the main metering jet is uncovered. As the throttle is advanced, the main metering jet is uncovered to provide additional fuel. When the throttle is wide open, both the main and enrichment jet are uncovered to provide the fuel required for high power settings. [Figure 7-52]

## FUEL REGULATOR

The fuel regulator supplies the engine with the necessary amount of fuel. The fuel regulator consists of four distinct chambers (venturi suction, inlet air, inlet fuel, and metered fuel), two diaphragms (fuel and air), and a ball valve. [Figure 7-53]

The fuel regulator uses similar operating principles as a pressure-injection carburetor. As air enters the venturi housing, impact tubes direct it to a sealed chamber. The opposing chamber is vented to low pressure air in the venturi. These two forces work together to move the air diaphragm in proportion to the volume of air drawn through the venturi. The force produced by the pressure differential across the air diaphragm is referred to as the **air metering force** and controls a ball valve (or servo valve) to allow fuel to the flow divider.

When the air metering force opens the ball valve, inlet fuel pressure acts on one side of the fuel diaphragm to close the valve. However, as metered fuel flows past the ball valve into the fuel chamber, it opposes the inlet fuel pressure to create a **fuel**

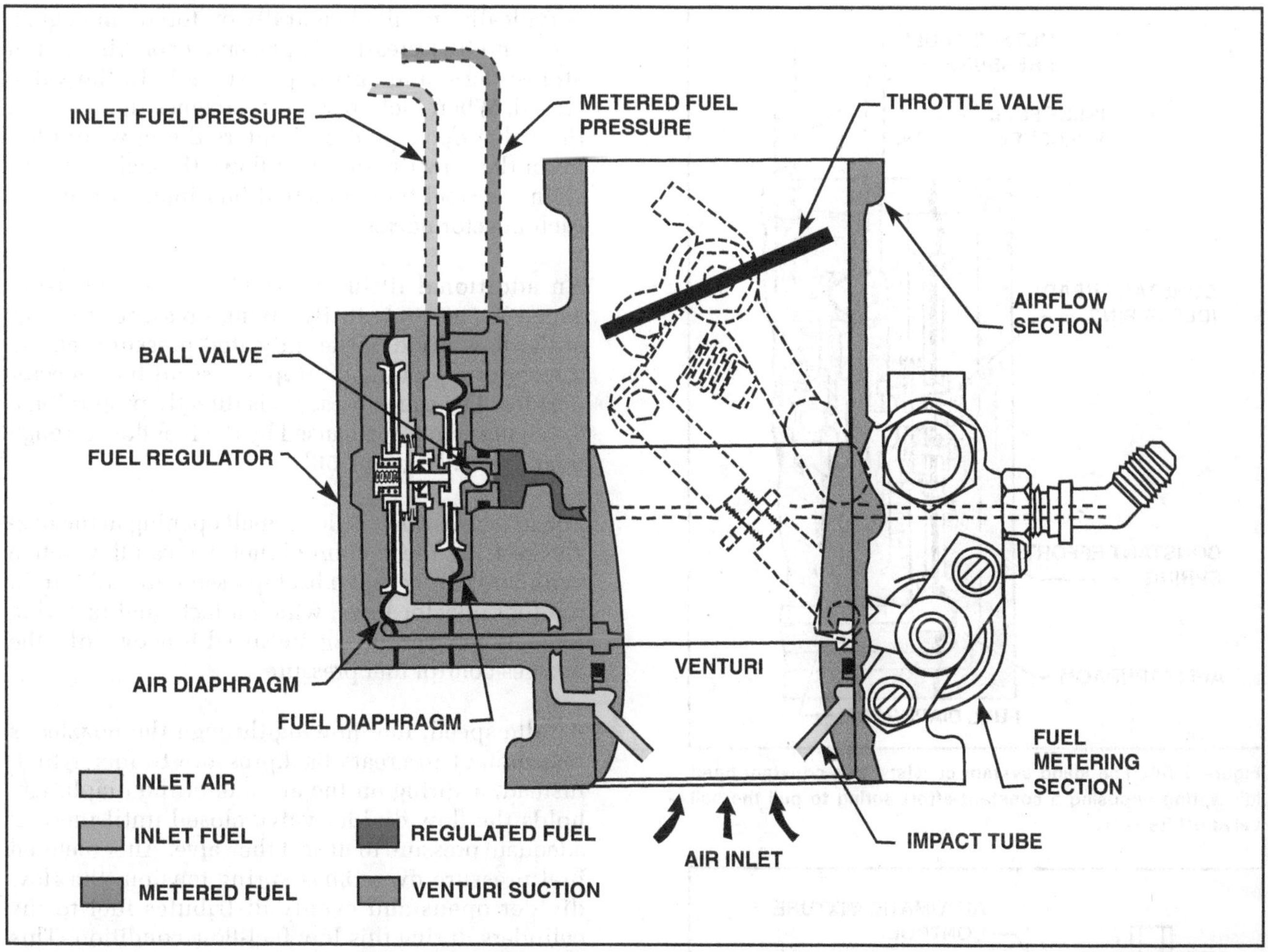


**Figure 7-53. The fuel regulator in an RSA fuel injection system has two air and two fuel chambers, an air diaphragm, a fuel diaphragm, and a ball valve.**

**metering force** that balances the air metering force. Through this interaction, the ball valve creates a pressure differential across the metering jets that is proportional to the airflow through the engine.

## IDLE SYSTEM

At idle, airflow through the engine is low and the air metering force is insufficient to open the ball valve to maintain a pressure differential across the metering jet. In the RSA system, a **constant head idle spring** provides the necessary force required to hold the ball valve off its seat. [Figure 7-54]

At idle, when only a small amount of air flows through the venturi, the spring holds the valve open. After intake air flow increases, the air diaphragm moves to compress the spring. When the diaphragm bushing contacts the stop on the end of the ball valve shaft, the air diaphragm takes over fuel regulation. To provide a smooth transition between idle and cruise power, a constant-effort spring preloads the diaphragm to a neutral position.

## AUTOMATIC MIXTURE CONTROL

To reduce pilot work load, some RSA fuel injection systems are equipped with an automatic mixture control. An automatic mixture control is installed parallel with the manual mixture control. A typical system uses a sealed bellows to move a reverse tapered needle to vary the size of an air bleed orifice between the impact and venturi air chambers. The bellows, filled with helium, expands and contracts with changes in air density. As an aircraft climbs, air density decreases and the bellows expands. Because the bellows connects to a reverse tapered valve, expansion pushes the needle valve off its seat to open the bleed air port. This reduction in the air diaphragm pressure differential partially closes the ball valve, which results in a leaner mixture for combustion. {Figure 7-55}

## FLOW DIVIDER

Metered fuel flows from the regulator through a flexible hose to the flow divider. A flow divider, consisting of a diaphragm-operated valve and a spring,

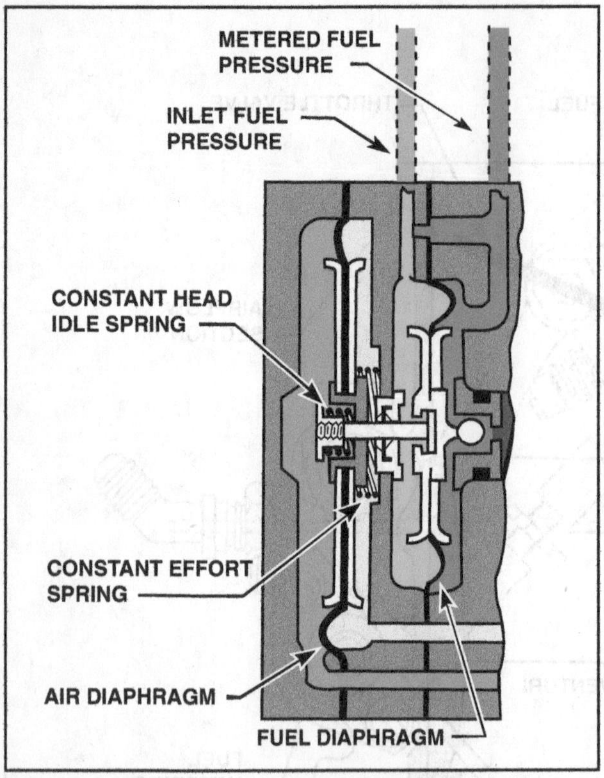


**Figure 7-54. The idling system consists of a constant-head idle spring opposing a constant-effort spring to pull the ball valve off its seat.**

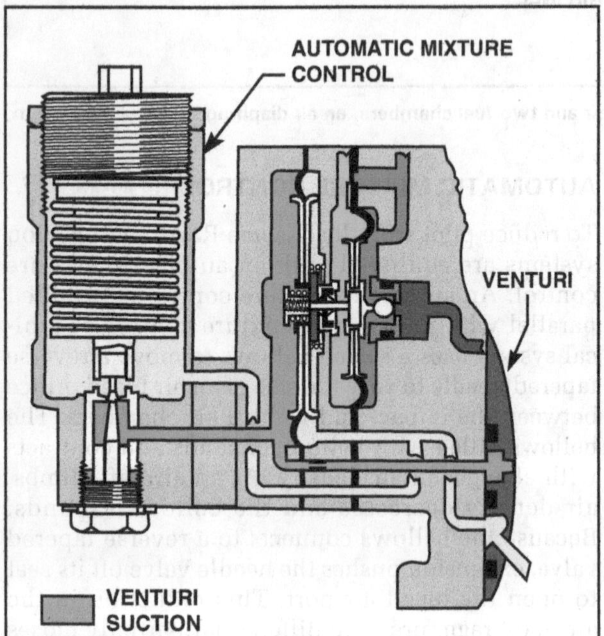


**Figure 7-55. The automatic mixture control that can be installed in an RSA fuel injection system uses a pressure-sensitive bellows assembly to vary the amount of fuel delivered to an engine based on atmospheric pressure.**

is typically installed centrally on top of an engine. When no fuel pressure is present, a combination of atmospheric and spring pressures hold the valve closed. When fuel pressure overcomes these forces, the valve opens and fuel enters the flow divider. From the flow divider, fuel flows through 1/8 inch stainless steel tubing (called fuel injector lines) to each injector nozzle.

An additional fitting is provided for a pressure gauge in the cockpit. By taking pressure readings at the flow divider, the indicated pressure reflects the collective pressure drop across all fuel injector nozzles. The gauge pressure is directly proportional to the pressure drop caused by the fuel flow through the nozzles. [Figure 7-56]

For all speeds above idle, a small opening in the nozzles restricts the amount of fuel that can flow into a cylinder. This causes a back-pressure to build up in the fuel injector lines, which affects fuel metering force. Whenever the engine speed is above idle, the nozzles control fuel pressure.

At idle speed, fuel flowing through the nozzles is insufficient to create backpressure to meter fuel. Instead, a spring on the air side of the diaphragm holds the flow divider valve closed until there is adequate pressure to unseat the valve. After metered fuel pressure overcomes spring tension, the flow divider opens and evenly distributes fuel to the cylinders during this low fuel-flow condition. This arrangement also provides a positive fuel cutoff to the nozzles when the mixture control is in the idle-cutoff position. This action reduces the chance of vapor lock by maintaining fuel in the injector lines.

## INJECTOR NOZZLES

The RSA system uses air bleed nozzles threaded into the cylinder head intake ports. Each nozzle consists of a brass body constructed with a metering orifice, an air bleed hole, and an emulsion chamber. To ensure that no contaminants are drawn into the air bleed hole, a fine mesh metal screen is supported with a pressed steel shroud. For turbocharged engines, an extension that enables the nozzle to receive upper deck air pressure is provided to emulsify the fuel. [Figure 7-57]

Each nozzle incorporates a metering orifice (or jet) that is calibrated to provide a specific flow rate, plus or minus two percent. The jet size is a factor of the available fuel inlet pressure and the engine's maximum fuel flow requirements. Nozzles of the same type are interchangeable between cylinders or engines. The size of the jet is a single letter stamped on the hex flat of the nozzle opposite the air bleed hole. Fuel flows through the metering jet into an

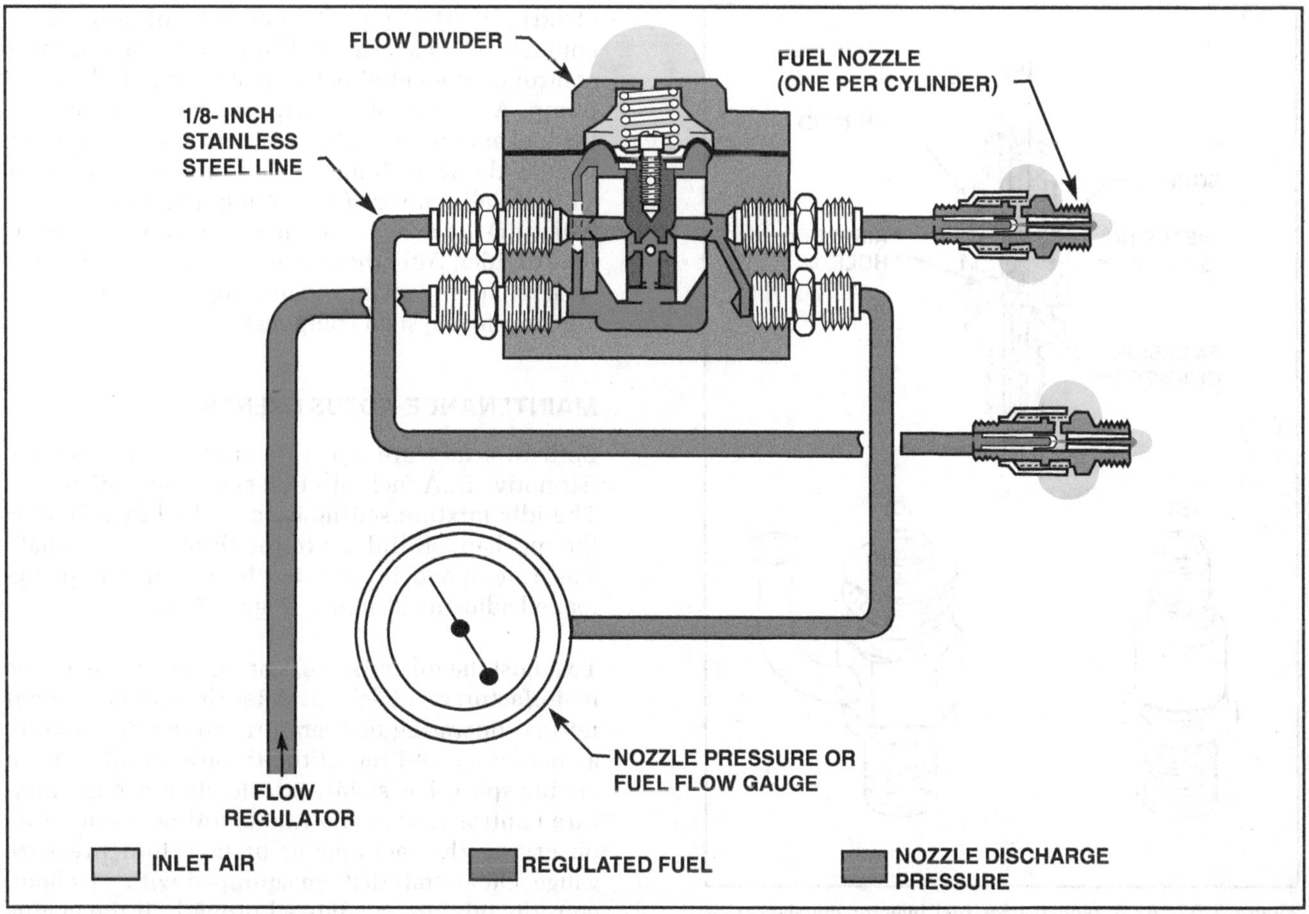


**Figure 7-56. A flow divider ensures equal fuel flow at a regulated pressure to each nozzle. In addition, it provides a convenient location to take a system pressure reading. A pressure gauge connected to the flow divider can be calibrated to display fuel flow.**

emulsion chamber where it is mixed with air. Manifold pressure (on normally aspirated engines) is less than atmospheric pressure, so air is pulled into the nozzle through the air bleed. On a turbocharged engine, manifold pressure typically exceeds atmospheric pressure, so a source of higher pressure air is necessary for the air bleed; in this case, upper-deck pressure is typically used. Fuel atomization occurs as the air and fuel mix in the emulsion chamber.

When installing a fuel nozzle, attempt to position the air bleed hole pointing upward. This reduces the possibility of fuel draining out of the nozzle into the engine. Examine each nozzle carefully to avoid installing a fuel nozzle with a clogged air bleed. If an air bleed should become plugged, the outlet side of the metering jet will sense manifold, not atmospheric pressure. This results in an increased differential pressure across the nozzle metering jet, which causes more fuel to flow through the nozzle. Because the regulator delivers a constant amount of fuel to the flow divider for a given power setting, the nozzle with the clogged air bleed will draw fuel away from the other nozzles; the nozzle with the clogged air bleed will deliver a rich mixture while the others will deliver a lean mixture. Because the fuel pressure gauge is also attached to the flow divider, a clogged air bleed nozzle will indicate a low fuel pressure indication.

Aftermarket manufacturers, such as General Aviation Modifications, Inc. (GAMI), offer injector nozzles that more precisely match air and fuel delivery for each cylinder. GAMI injectors require a Supplemental Type Certificate (STC) for installation.

## RSA SYSTEM INSPECTION AND MAINTENANCE

During an inspection, check the security of all the components. For example, verify the installation of the venturi housing, flow divider, and fuel lines. As with carburetors, inspect the mounting flange for evidence of cracks or leaks. Check all control linkages for freedom and range of movement. Examine the fuel lines for kinks, distortion, or indications of leaks. Verify that all fittings are tight.

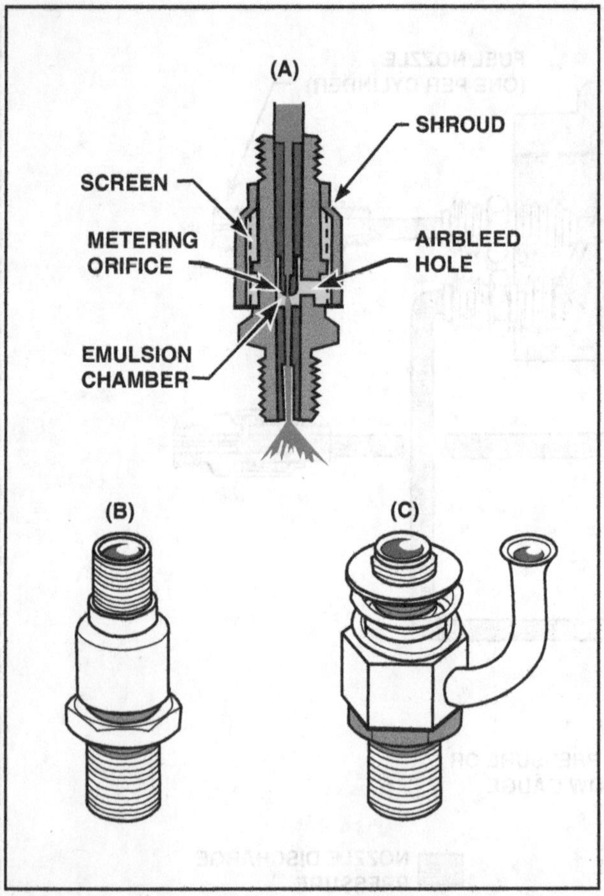


**Figure 7-57 (A) A typical RSA fuel injector consists of a shrouded brass body housing a metering orifice, an air bleed hole, and an emulsion chamber. (B) The nozzles of normally aspirated engines are vented to ambient air that is drawn into the nozzle from under a shroud. (C) Because the manifold pressure in a turbocharged engine often exceeds atmospheric pressure, the nozzles on turbocharged engines accommodate a fitting to receive upper deck air pressure.**

Because the flow divider is vented to the atmosphere, verify that it is unobstructed. If a vent hole were to become plugged, the pressure acting on one side of the diaphragm would not vary with changes in altitude, and an excessively lean mixture would result.

Fuel nozzles must be cleaned according to the manufacturer's maintenance schedule to remove varnish or other contaminants. After you clean the nozzles, visually inspect the metering jet and air bleed for obstructions. If a nozzle is plugged, soak the nozzle in an approved cleaner and then clear the obstruction with compressed air.

Perform a comparison of the fuel flow through the clean nozzles. Install each nozzle on a fuel injection line and direct each nozzle into equal sized containers. With the mixture control in the full rich position and the throttle open, turn on the aircraft's electric boost pump. Operate the pump until the containers are at least half-full. Move the mixture control to idle-cutoff position and turn off the boost pump. After fuel stops dripping from the nozzles, the fuel amount in each container should be approximately the same. If the level of any one container is substantially lower, a restriction might exist somewhere in the nozzle, the fuel injection line, or the flow divider. After the flow test, reinstall the nozzles with an approved anti-seize compound, and secure all other fuel system components.

## MAINTENANCE ADJUSTMENTS

Both idle mixture and idle speed of a Precision Airmotive RSA fuel injection system are adjustable. The idle mixture setting is controlled by adjusting the mechanical linkage to the throttle valve shaft. The idle speed is adjusted by turning a spring-loaded adjustment screw. [Figure 7-58]

To adjust the idle mixture, start the engine using the manufacturer's checklist. After the engine reaches normal operating temperature, adjust the mixture as necessary and retard the throttle to idle. When engine speed has stabilized, slowly move the mixture control toward the idle-cutoff position while observing the tachometer or manifold pressure gauge. On aircraft that are equipped with a tachometer, the mixture is adjusted properly if the engine speed indication increases slightly just before it drops off rapidly. However, on aircraft equipped with a manifold pressure gauge, a decrease in manifold pressure just before the engine ceases to fire indicates an optimum idle mixture.

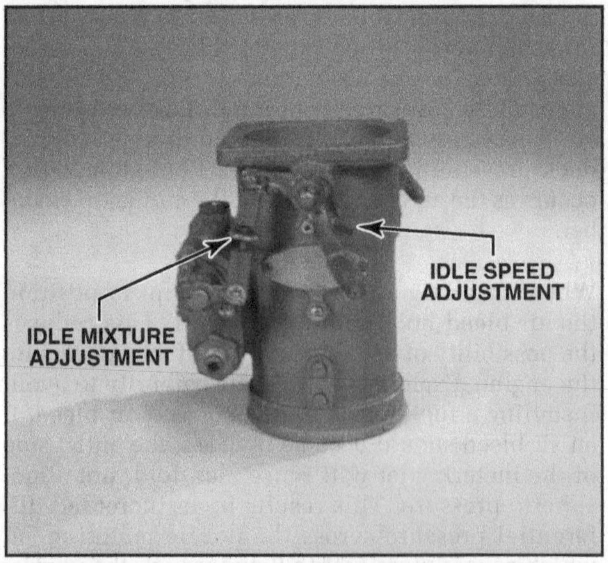


**Figure 7-58. The idle speed on an RSA fuel injection unit is typically changed with a spring-loaded adjustment screw. Idle mixture is adjusted by changing the length of a connecting rod between the idle valve and throttle valve.**

The length of the connecting linkage determines the mixture adjustment. If the idle mixture is too lean, fuel must be added by increasing the length of the linkage. If the idle mixture is too rich, fuel must be decreased by shortening the length of the linkage. After you have adjusted the idle mixture, operate the engine at high engine speed before reducing power to recheck the idle mixture setting.

If the idle speed needs adjustment, rotate the spring-loaded idle screw. If the speed is too low, turn the idle screw clockwise. If the speed is too high, turn the idle screw counter-clockwise.

## TELEDYNE CONTINENTAL MOTORS SYSTEM

Where the RSA system uses both fuel and air metering forces to meter fuel, the Teledyne Continental Motors (TCM) system only uses a fuel metering force to meter fuel. The basic components of a TCM system include an engine-driven injector pump, a fuel/air control unit, a fuel manifold valve, and injector nozzles.

### INJECTOR PUMP

The injector pump used in a TCM system is a shaft-driven, vane pump. The pump housing contains a vapor-separator chamber, a variable orifice, an adjustable relief valve, a vapor ejector, and a bypass valve. [Figure 7-59]

Fuel entering an injector pump is swirled in a vapor-separator chamber to remove vapor. Because the vane pump delivers a specific quantity per revolution, a return passage is included to return fuel back to the pump inlet. A variable orifice in the return line controls pump pressure. When the size of the orifice is increased, the pump output pressure decreases, and when the size of the orifice is decreased, the pump output pressure increases.

The setting of an adjustable orifice works well to control fuel flow when the engine operates at or above cruise power settings. Below cruise power, the orifice is an insufficient restrictor to maintain a constant output pressure. A spring-loaded pressure relief valve downstream from the orifice controls fuel flow at low power settings; resistance offered by the relief valve permits the injector pump to maintain a constant output pressure.

When the throttle is rapidly advanced on a turbocharged engine, the injector pump accelerates and supplies additional fuel before the turbocharger supplies additional air. Uncorrected, this imbalance would cause the mixture to become too rich and the engine would falter. To correct this problem, an injector pump uses an altitude-compensating aneroid bellows to control the metering orifice in the return line. [Figure 7-60]

The aneroid is surrounded by upper deck pressure (or turbocharger discharge pressure). As upper deck

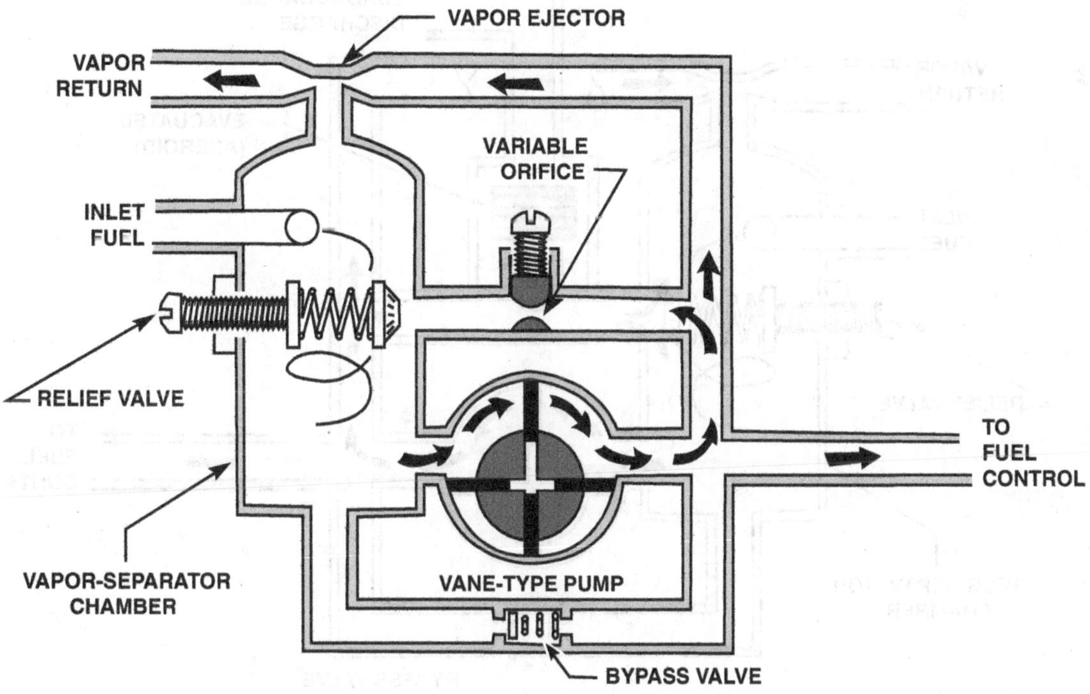


**Figure 7-59. A typical injector pump in a Teledyne Continental Motors fuel injection system consists of a vane pump with a vapor separator, an adjustable orifice and relief valve, a vapor ejector, and a bypass valve.**

pressure fluctuates, the aneroid moves the variable restrictor, which varies output fuel pressure proportionally with upper deck pressure.

To remove excess fuel vapor from the vapor chamber, some of the excess output fuel is routed through a vapor ejector at the top of the vapor chamber. A **vapor ejector** is simply a restriction in the fuel passageway that is open to the vapor chamber. As fuel flows through the restriction, the low pressure area that results draws vapor out of the vapor chamber and returns it to the fuel tanks.

The bypass check valve permits the fuel pressurized by the aircraft boost pump to flow to the fuel control for starting. However, after the engine-driven injector pump pressure exceeds that of the boost pump, the check valve closes and only the injector pump supplies fuel pressure to the fuel control.

To protect the engine in case the injector pump fails, the pump's drive shaft is manufactured with a shear section. Additionally, most injector pumps incorporate a loose-fit coupling to compensate for slight misalignment with the engine drive.

## FUEL/AIR CONTROL UNIT

The fuel/air control unit is mounted on the engine intake manifold. Because the TCM system does not use air metering force, the **air throttle assembly** has no venturi. The **fuel control assembly** is attached to the throttle assembly. The fuel control unit body is made of bronze and houses a mixture valve and a fuel metering valve. Both valves are stainless steel rotary-type valves that rotate in oil-impregnated bushings. [Figure 7-61]

The end of each valve rotates against a fixed bronze metering plug in the center of the fuel control unit. The plug contains a fuel metering jet that meters fuel flow to the engine. The metering plug also contains a passage that connects the fuel inlet with the fuel return outlet and a second passage that connects the mixture control valve chamber with the fuel metering valve chamber. The mixture valve of a TCM fuel control unit acts as a variable selector valve that directs fuel to the metering jet or the fuel pump. [Figure 7-62]

After fuel passes the mixture valve, it flows through the metering jet. The position of the fuel metering valve determines how much fuel can flow out of the main metering jet. The valve plate used with a fuel metering valve proportionately uncovers the outlet of the main jet as the throttle is advanced. Only a small portion of the main metering jet is uncovered at low power setting; as the throttle is advanced, more is uncovered to provide the engine with additional fuel. When the throttle valve is completely open, the completely uncovered main jet provides the maximum amount of fuel. The fuel metering valve is operated with a control arm that is con-

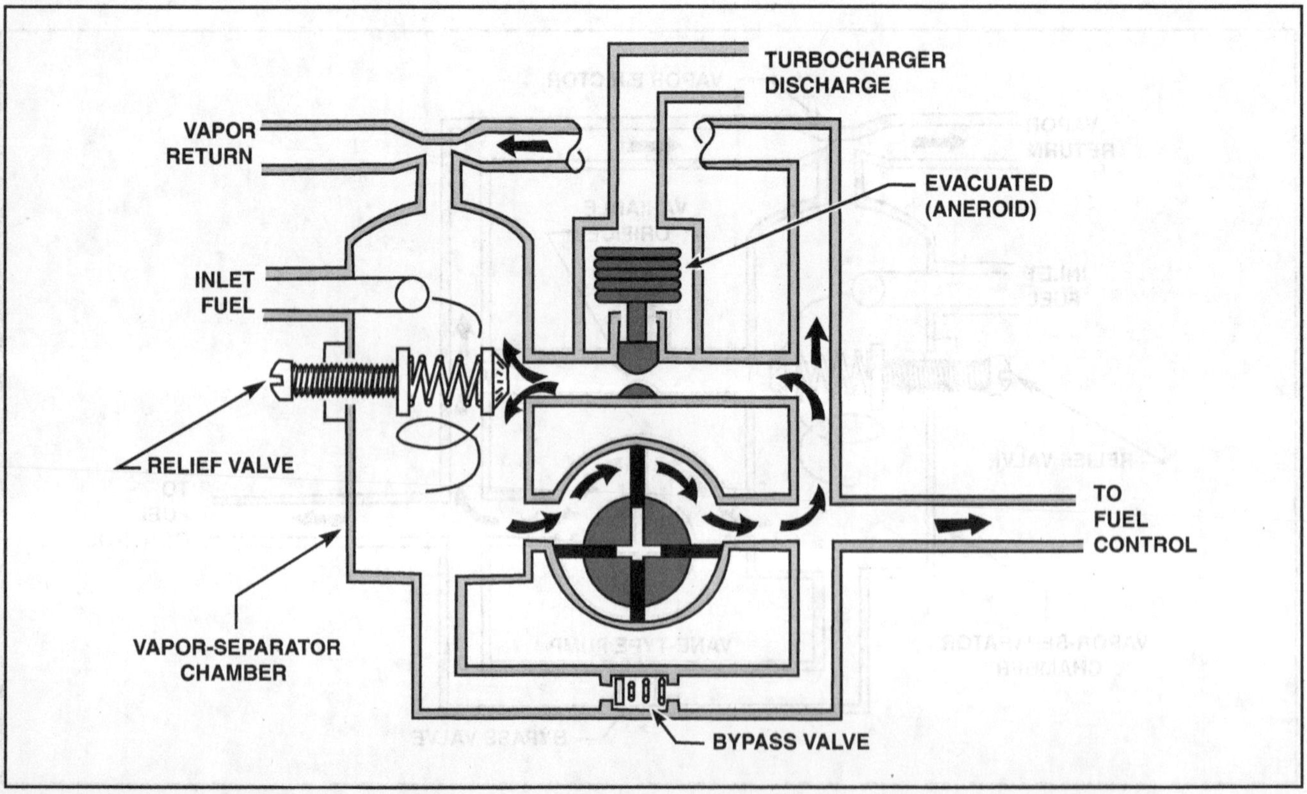


**Figure 7-60. Turbocharged engines are equipped with injector pumps with an aneroid-controlled variable restrictor.**

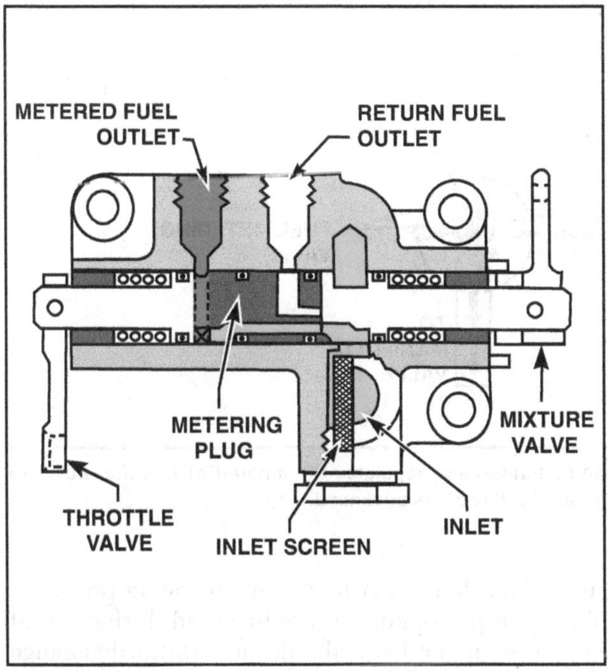


**Figure 7-61. The fuel control assembly contains the manual mixture control valve and fuel metering valve. Both are rotary valves connected to cockpit control levers.**

nected to the cockpit throttle lever. The throttle control actuates both the throttle valve and the fuel metering valve. [Figure 7-63]

## FUEL MANIFOLD VALVE

Fuel flows from the fuel metering valve through a flexible fuel line to the fuel manifold valve. The **fuel manifold valve** (or **distribution valve**) evenly distributes fuel to all cylinders and provides a positive fuel shutoff to the nozzles when the mixture control is moved to the idle-cutoff position. The fuel manifold valve, which is typically mounted atop the engine, includes a fuel inlet, a diaphragm chamber, a poppet valve, and several outlet ports. [Figure 7-64]

When sufficient fuel pressure is supplied by the metering valve, the manifold valve diaphragm moves and opens the cutoff valve. As fuel pressure increases further, the spring-loaded poppet valve is forced open, allowing fuel to flow to the nozzles. The opposition of the poppet valve ensures constant fuel pressure between the main metering jet and manifold valve when the engine is operating at idle speed. At cruise power settings, fuel pressure holds the cutoff and poppet valves fully open, and the restriction in each injector nozzle maintains fuel pressure. When the mixture control is in the idle-cutoff position, fuel pressure to the manifold valve drops and spring tension closes the cutoff valve. This action provides a positive shutoff of fuel and maintains fuel in the fuel injection lines to prevent vapor lock.

The chamber above the diaphragm is vented to ambient air pressure for unrestricted valve movement. To prevent air pressure fluctuations in the chamber above the diaphragm, it is important to prevent ram air from entering the vent. The vent is typically installed pointing to the side or the rear.

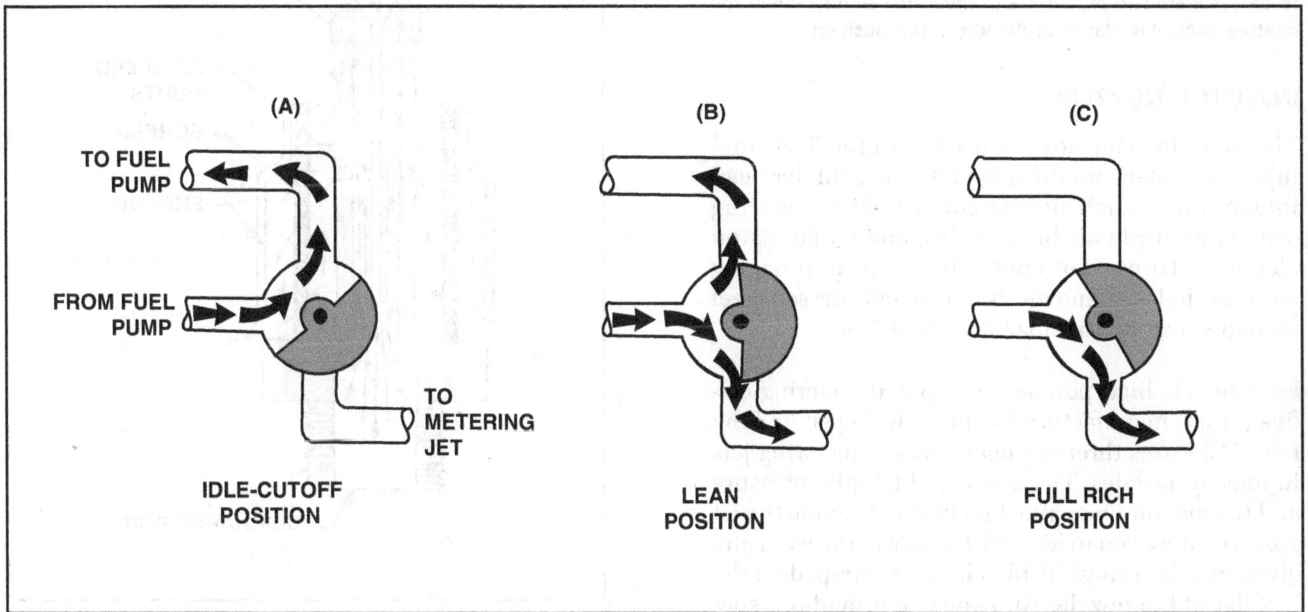


**Figure 7-62. (A) When the mixture valve is in the idle-cutoff position, fuel is routed from the pump outlet back to the pump inlet. (B) When the mixture control is advanced to a lean setting, the mixture valve begins to uncover a portion of the passageway leading to the metering jet. (C) When the mixture control is in the full-rich position, all of the fuel from the injector pump is directed to the fuel manifold valve.**

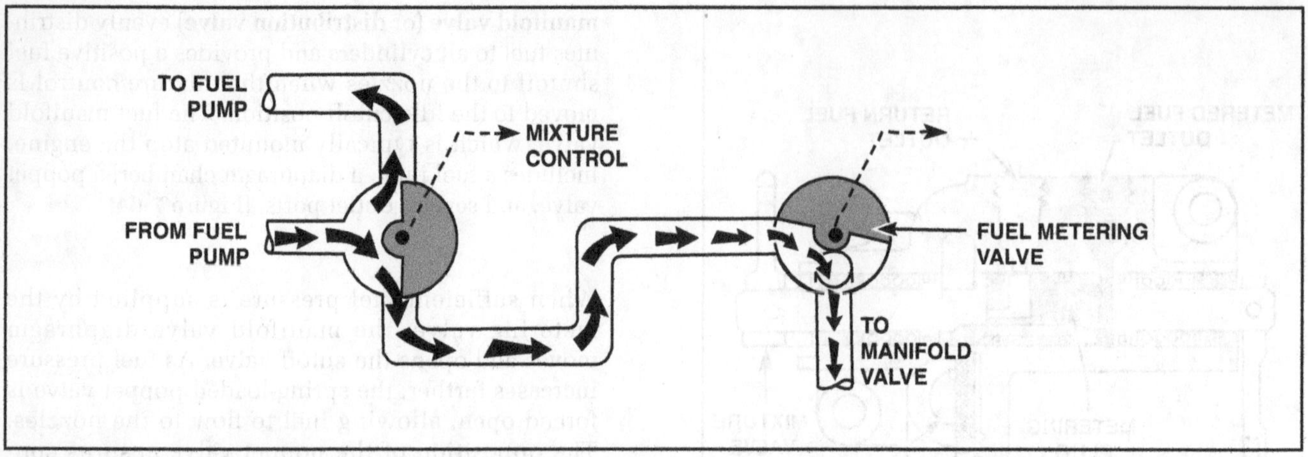


**Figure 7-63. After fuel flows past the mixture valve and metering jet, the metering valve regulates the amount of fuel that flows to the manifold valve for distribution by uncovering the outlet of the main jet as the throttle is advanced.**

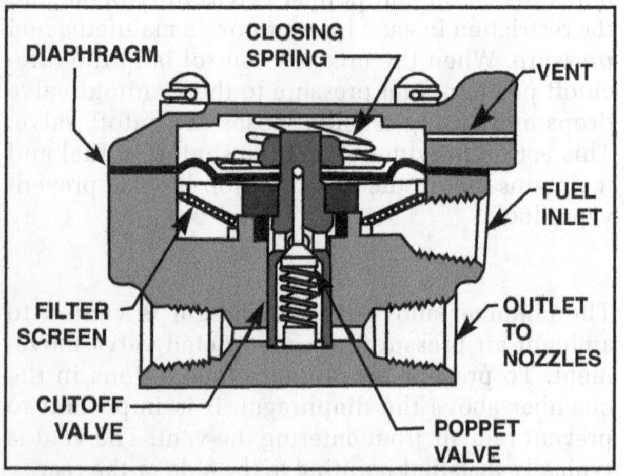


**Figure 7-64. The fuel manifold valve distributes fuel evenly to all cylinders and provides a positive fuel shutoff when the mixture control is placed in the idle-cutoff position.**

## INJECTOR NOZZLES

The brass injector nozzles used with the TCM fuel injection system are threaded into the cylinder head intake ports. Each nozzle consists of a metering orifice, multiple air bleed holes, and an emulsion chamber. To prevent contaminants from plugging air bleed holes, a fine mesh screen and pressed steel shroud surround the nozzle. [Figure 7-65]

Each nozzle incorporates a calibrated metering orifice (or jet) manufactured to provide a specific flow rate. TCM uses three common sizes of metering jets in injector nozzles. The available fuel inlet pressure and the maximum engine fuel flow determine the jet size. To allow you to identify the size of the jet in any given nozzle, a single capital letter is stamped on the hex flat of the nozzle. An A-nozzle provides a specific amount of fuel for a given pressure. A B-nozzle provides one-half gallon more fuel per hour than an A-nozzle at the same pressure. C-nozzles have the largest metering jet and provide one gallon per hour more fuel than an A-nozzle at the same pressure. The appropriate nozzles are installed during initial engine setup, and you should not arbitrarily change this size. Be careful to reinstall nozzles in their original position after cleaning.

Fuel flows through the metering jet into an emulsion chamber where it is mixed with air. Manifold pressure (on normally aspirated engines) is less than atmospheric pressure, so air is pulled into the nozzle through the air bleed. On a turbocharged engine,

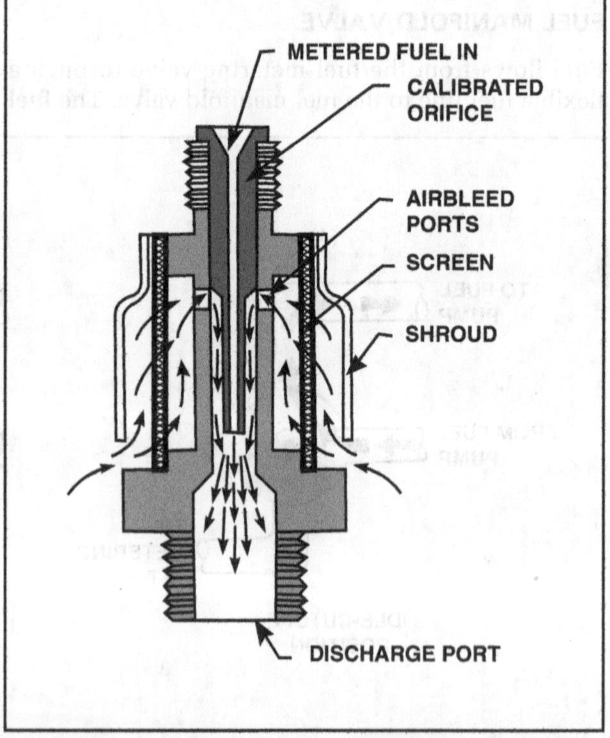


**Figure 7-65. A typical Teledyne Continental Motors fuel injector consists of a shrouded brass body that houses a calibrated orifice, multiple air bleed holes, and an emulsion chamber.**

manifold pressure typically exceeds atmospheric pressure, so a source of higher pressure air is necessary for the air bleed; normally upper deck pressure. As the air and fuel mix in the emulsion chamber, the fuel is atomized.

To accommodate different engine models, TCM manufactures several styles of injector nozzles. Although nozzle styles differ in appearance, their purpose and method of injecting metered fuel is the same.

TCM also offers position-tuned injectors for fuel control that offer increased precision for fuel delivery. General Aviation Modifications, Inc. (GAMI) also offers injector nozzles for TCM systems to more precisely match air and fuel delivery for each cylinder. GAMI injectors require an STC for installation.

## INSPECTION AND MAINTENANCE

A TCM Service Information Directive requires that a functional system check is conducted at the following intervals: every 100-hour or annual inspection; after the replacement of any system component; or whenever performance is outside of published specifications.

A visual inspection includes checking the security and integrity of components. Examine all fuel lines for chafing or leaking. Be aware that all fuel injector lines for a given system are manufactured to the same length. This ensures that each cylinder receives the same amount of fuel at the same pressure. Fuel injection lines cannot be shortened. If a fuel line is longer than the distance between the divider and the nozzle, it should be coiled neatly in the middle.

After you have inspected the fuel lines, check all moving parts for wear and lubricate the ends of the throttle linkage rods with a drop of engine oil. In addition, check and clean the strainer in the fuel control unit and the fuel manifold valve.

Normally, injector nozzles do not require much service; service intervals are commonly between 100 and 300 hours of operation. Nozzle maintenance consists of removal from the engine, soaking in acetone or lacquer thinner, and drying with clean, dry, air. Fuel stains on a cylinder head (or around the nozzle) indicate a clogged nozzle. If a nozzle is clogged, fuel is pushed through the air bleed ports and onto the engine.

Do not use wires, drills, or other cleaning tools to clear out orifice obstructions. Doing so can damage the precision passages and render the nozzle unserviceable. If you cannot clear an obstruction by soaking the nozzle in an approved cleaner and blowing it out with compressed air, manufacturers typically require replacement. After the nozzles are clean, reinstall them with an approved anti-seize compound, and secure all other fuel system components.

While inspecting and cleaning the injector nozzles, remember to inspect the fuel manifold. Ensure the absence of fuel leaks and that the vent hole is free of obstructions.

## FIELD ADJUSTMENTS

Adjustments are normally made during the required functional check. To perform the adjustments, calibrated gauges (or special test equipment) are required. Every time a change is made to a system setting, recheck all previous settings, bearing in mind that every adjustment affects the others. [Figure 7-66]

Measure unmetered fuel pressure with the mixture control in the full rich position and engine operating at a specific idle speed. If required, adjust unmetered fuel pressure by adjusting the low pressure relief screw on the fuel pump. Turn the screw clockwise to increase fuel pressure or counterclockwise to decrease fuel pressure.

To make an idle mixture adjustment, start the engine using the manufacturer's starting checklist. After the engine is at operating temperature, adjust the mixture as necessary and pull the throttle control to the idle position. After engine speed stabilizes, slowly move the mixture control toward the idle-cutoff position. Observe the tachometer or manifold pressure gauge. If you are using a tachometer, note that a properly adjusted mixture will cause engine

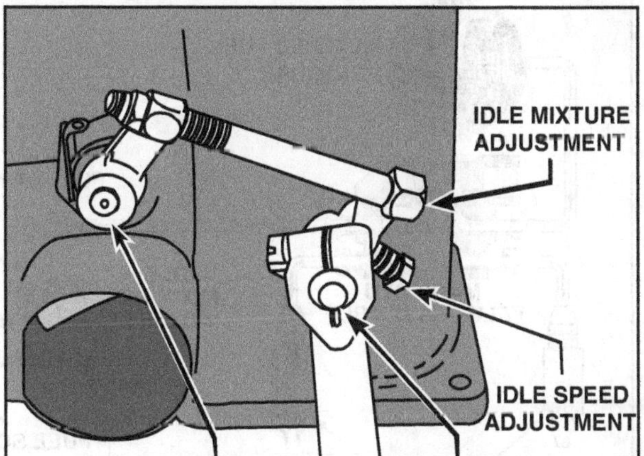


**Figure 7-66. Idle speed on a Teledyne Continental Motors fuel injection unit is adjusted by a spring-loaded adjustment screw. Idle mixture is adjusted by changing the length of the connecting rod between the control arms of the metering and the throttle valves.**

speed to increase slightly before rapidly dropping off. If you are using a manifold pressure gauge, the optimum idle mixture is indicated by a decrease in manifold pressure just before the engine stops running.

If the idle mixture check reveals a mixture that is too lean or too rich, increase or decrease idle fuel flow as required. To increase the fuel flow, shorten the length of the connecting linkage. To decrease fuel flow, increase the length of the connecting linkage. After every adjustment, recheck the mixture using the procedure described above.

After you adjust idle mixture, you might need to adjust idle speed. Rotating the spring-loaded idle screw changes the point at which the throttle shaft contacts the idle stop. To increase idle speed, turn the idle screw clockwise; to decrease idle speed, turn the idle screw counter-clockwise.

After unmetered fuel pressure, idle mixture, and idle speed are within the manufacturer's limits, check the high-power, metered fuel pressure. If the aircraft engine is unable to develop full static power during ground operation, you must apply a conversion factor to the manufacturer's published performance numbers. On engines with an altitude compensating fuel pump (such as the IO-360-ES) or whenever full power is not attained during ground operation, a flight test is required to verify fuel setup and engine performance. High-power, metered fuel pressure should be checked at full throttle and maximum permissible speed after 10 to 15 minutes at a cruise power setting.

Fuel injection system components and adjustment procedures vary depending on whether the engine is normally aspirated or turbocharged. The basic component and system differences can be seen in the schematic diagrams in figures 7-67a and 7-67b.

## TROUBLESHOOTING

Effectively troubleshooting a fuel injection system requires an understanding of the system and its role in the proper operation of an engine. Do not assume that a fault in the fuel injection system is the cause of every rough running engine. A discrepancy with the ignition or induction systems can also cause rough running. The airframe and engine manufacturers typically provide troubleshooting charts to diagnose engine discrepancies.

## OVERHAUL

Fuel injection systems, like carburetors, are normally overhauled during an engine overhaul. Overhaul of these components requires specialized tools, flow benches, and specialized training. Most overhauls are performed either by the manufacturer or by a specially equipped and approved certified repair station.

## ELECTRONICALLY CONTROLLED FUEL INJECTION

The use of electronically controlled fuel injection systems is increasing. Engine sensors provide infor-

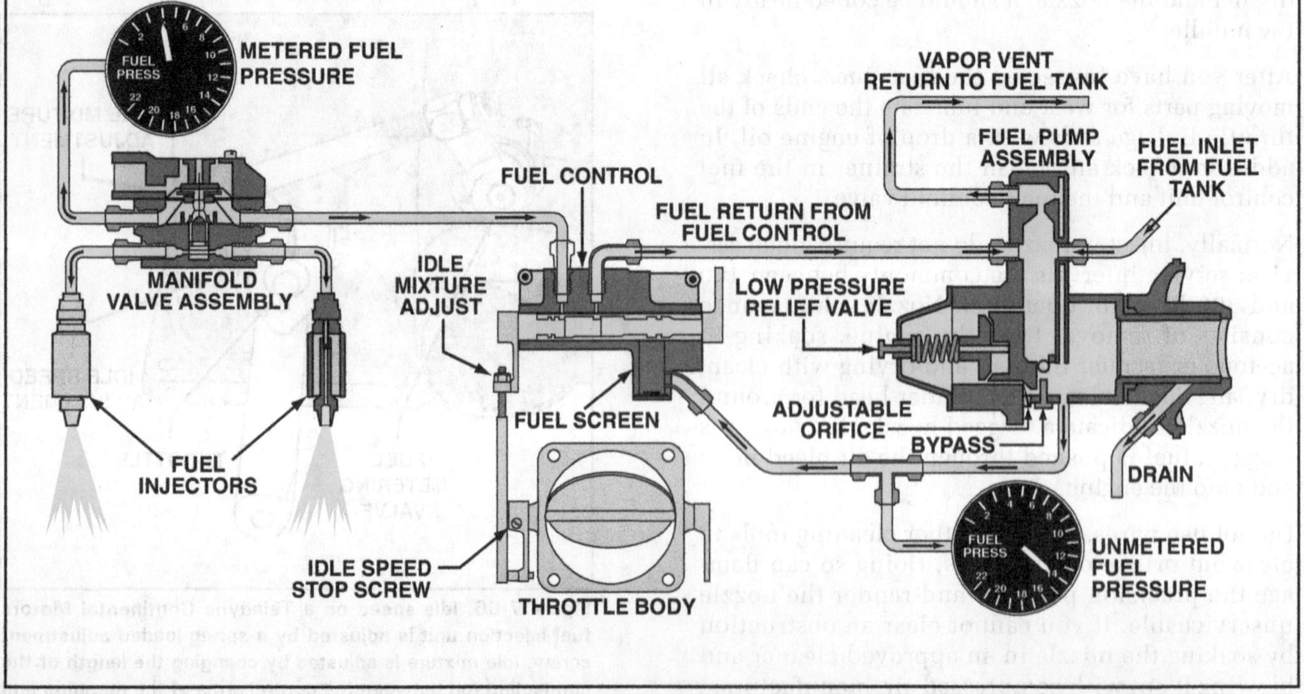


Figure 7-67a. The components of a Teledyne Continental Motors fuel injection system on a typical normally aspirated engine.

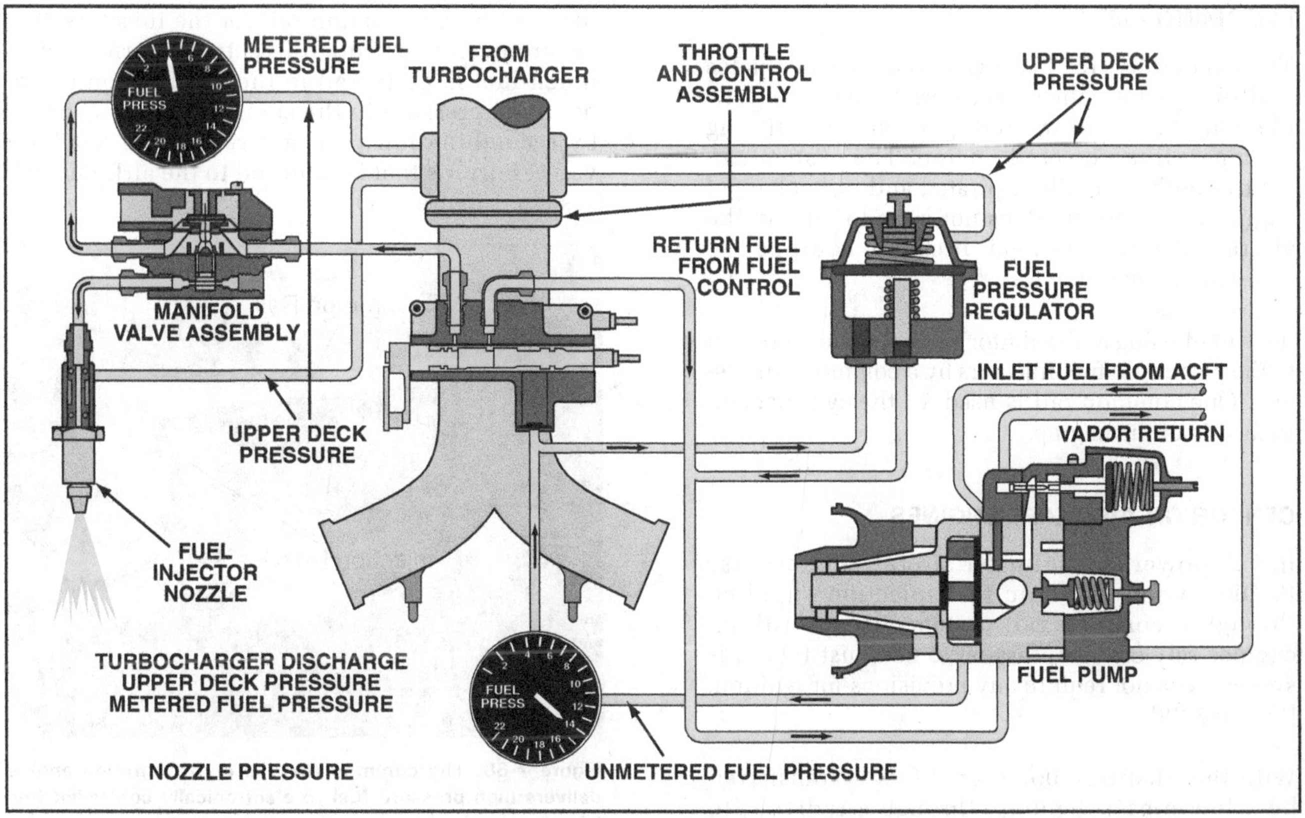


**Figure 7-67b. The components of a Teledyne Continental Motors fuel injection system on a typical turbocharged engine.**

mation to a computer to determine the ideal air/fuel mixture for every combustion event in each cylinder. The amount of fuel injected in a cylinder is controlled by a solenoid valve at the cylinder assembly.

Electronically controlled fuel injection is typically a part of a **Full Authority Digital Engine Control (FADEC)** system. In addition to fuel, the ignition system is also computer-controlled for ideal operation. The air/fuel mixture and ignition timing are adjusted continuously so that each cylinder always operates at peak performance and efficiency. These systems eliminate the need for pilot inputs to adjust the air/fuel mixture during flight. In fact, this system has no pilot mixture control. These systems are used on JET A and 100LL gasoline-powered aircraft. Manufacturers of these systems anticipate the possibility of running on alternative fuels.

Electronically controlled fuel injection systems typically include a data-logging feature, which stores data about engine performance. A trained aircraft maintenance technician with the appropriate equipment can download and analyze this data to monitor aircraft performance over time and diagnose discrepancies. Installation of these systems on legacy aircraft might be possible with the development of supplemental type certificates.

Following are descriptions of three engines with electronically controlled fuel injection:

## TELEDYNE CONTINENTAL MOTORS – POWERLINK™

The TCM PowerLink FADEC system controls fuel injection with microprocessor circuit boards in the base of the electronic control units (ECU). Information is processed from the following components: engine speed sensor; manifold pressure sensors; fuel pressure sensors; throttle position switch; cylinder head temperature (CHT) sensors; exhaust gas temperature (EGT) sensors; and (when equipped) turbine inlet temperature (TIT) sensors for a gasoline-powered engine. [Figure 8-158]

The fuel pump provides fuel directly to the distribution block. The fuel injection distribution lines deliver fuel under pressure to the injector nozzles. Fuel injector solenoids encircling the injector nozzles open and close the valve to control the amount of fuel provided to the cylinder assembly.

The TCM PowerLink FADEC system is powered by the aircraft power supply. To ensure continuous operation of this system in the event of an electrical system failure, a second power supply (typically a backup battery) is required.

## LYCOMING - iE²

The Lycoming - iE² FADEC system also evaluates multiple performance indicators to determine the ideal air/fuel mixture and ignition event timing for a gasoline-powered engine. The system can control both normally aspirated and turbocharged engines. The system does not have to rely on the aircraft electrical system; it can be equipped to generate its own power.

Instead of using a distributor valve, fuel is delivered to the electronic fuel injectors by a common rail system. One common rail is used for the cylinders on each side of the engine.

## CENTURION AIRCRAFT ENGINES

JET A powered Centurion aircraft engines use FADEC with electronic fuel injection supplied through a common rail system. Because diesel engines rely on compression to combust fuel, this system does not require any provisions for ignition. [Figure 7-68]

With the Austro A300, filtered fuel is transferred by a low-pressure pump, through a radiator, to the high-pressure pump. High-pressure fuel is directed to the common rail for the injectors. The electronically controlled injectors determine how much fuel is delivered to the combustion chamber. Fuel pressure in the common rail is managed by a combination pressure relief and regulator valve. Surplus fuel is returned to the airframe fuel system. [Figure 7-69]

**Figure 7-68. The common fuel rail on a Centurion engine delivers high pressure fuel to electronically controlled fuel injection nozzles.**

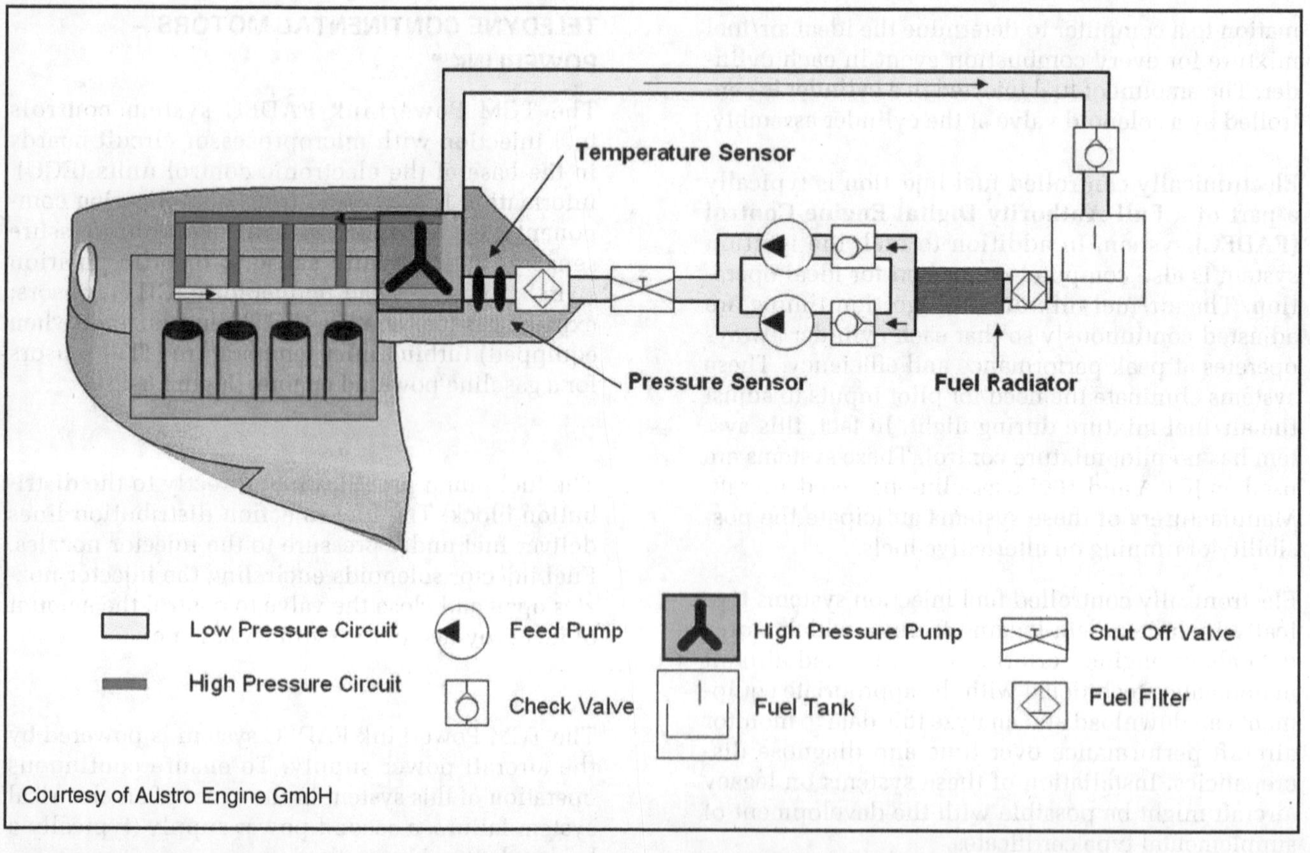


**Figure 7-69. The fuel system of the Austro AE300 is illustrated with this schematic from the operating manual.**

# SUMMARY CHECKLIST

✓ For reciprocating engines, fuel is metered by carburetion or by fuel injection.

✓ Because of changes in density due to environmental factors, fuel and air can not be measured by volume; they can be accurately measured only by weight.

✓ For most reciprocating engines, a pilot uses the mixture control to adjust fuel for changes in atmospheric conditions. Some engines accomplish this automatically.

✓ The throttle valve is a pilot-controllable restrictor plate that meters how much air is permitted into an engine for combustion.

✓ Most carburetors have five main systems: main metering, idling, mixture control, accelerating, and power enrichment (or economizer).

✓ In a direct injection system, fuel is injected directly into the combustion chamber.

✓ In a continuous-flow fuel injection system, fuel is injected continuously into the induction system immediately before the intake valve.

# KEY TERMS

stoichiometric mixture
lean
rich
full rich
idle-cutoff
lean best power
rich best power
best economy
detonation
preignition
backfiring
afterfiring
updraft
downdraft
throttle valve
float chamber
needle valve
boost venturi
primary venturi
discharge nozzle
fuel metering head
main metering jet
surface tension
air bleed
idle discharge ports
idle jets
automatic mixture control
AMC
economizer system
carburetor ice
fuel evaporation ice
throttle ice
springback
fuel regulator
fuel control unit
impact pressure annulus
air metering force
fuel metering force
anti-detonation injection
ADI
direct fuel injection system
continuous-flow fuel injection system
RS
RSA
air metering force
fuel metering force
constant head idle spring
vapor ejector
air throttle assembly
fuel control assembly
fuel manifold valve
distribution valve

# QUESTIONS

1. As the velocity of air increases in the throat of a venturi, the pressure of the air will ______________ (increase or decrease).

2. The chemically perfect mixture of air and fuel (stoichiometric mixture) consists of ________ pounds of air for each pound of fuel.

3. A reciprocating engine will develop maximum power with a mixture of approximately ___________:1.

4. Carburetors tend to run richer at ________________ (altitude or ground level).

5. Carburetors in which the air passes upward through the unit are called ______________ carburetors.

6. The throttle valve of a float-type carburetor is located between the ________________ and the engine.

7. A float-type carburetor discharges the fuel ______________ (upstream or downstream) of the throttle valve.

8. What are the four basic components of the main metering system of a float carburetor?

   a. ______________

   b. ______________

   c. ______________

   d. ______________

9. What is the main function of the venturi? ______________

10. Air bled into the main metering system ______________ (increases or decreases) fuel density and destroys surface tension.

11. The fuel level in the float chamber is usually kept about ______________ inch below the opening in the main discharge nozzle.

12. The ______________ ______________ system determines the ratio of fuel to air in the mixture.

13. The _______ ______________ system is used to shut off the fuel and stop the engine.

14. When a carburetor equipped with a back suction mixture control is in the lean position, the pressure in the float chamber is the same as the pressure at the ______________ ________.

15. The ______________ system supplies extra fuel when the throttle is opened quickly.

16. The power enrichment system is sometimes called an ______________ system.

17. Carburetor controls should be rigged so they have an equal amount of ______________-______________ at both ends of their travel.

18. A pressure carburetor discharges fuel ______________ (upstream or downstream) of the throttle valve.

19. What two factors make up the air metering force in a pressure carburetor?

    a. ________________

    b. ________________

20. The mixture control in a pressure carburetor varies the fuel/air ratio by controlling the ______ (air or fuel) metering force.

21. A water injection system used on reciprocating engines may also be referred to as ______-______________ injection.

22. Field adjustments to carburetors are generally limited to:

    a. ________________

    b. ________________

23. ______________________________ (continuous flow or direct injection) fuel injection systems meter the fuel and deliver it to the intake port of each cylinder.

24. Two functions of the flow divider valve during idle conditions are:

    a. ________________

    b. ________________

25. RSA fuel injector nozzles ________ (are or are not) interchangeable between engines and between cylinders.

26. Lengthening the connecting rod between the throttle fuel valve and the throttle air valve of an RSA injection system ______________ (richens or leans) the idling fuel/air mixture.

27. The adjustable orifice in a Teledyne Continental Motors fuel injection pump adjusts the ______ (high or low) unmetered fuel pressure.

28. The relief valve in the Teledyne Continental Motors fuel injection pump adjusts the ______ (high or low) unmetered fuel pressure.

29. Vapor is removed from the fuel in a Teledyne Continental Motors fuel injection system in the ________________ ______________ (what unit).

30. The orifice in a Teledyne Continental Motors fuel injection pump used with a turbocharged engine is automatically adjusted by an evacuated ______________.

31. The orifice size in a Teledyne Continental Motors fuel injection pump is varied by the amount of upper deck pressure. This pressure is actually the ______________ ______________ pressure.

32. The manual mixture control in a Teledyne Continental Motors fuel injection system is a form of ______________ valve.

33. The ______________________ in the fuel control unit limits the maximum amount of fuel that can flow in a Teledyne-Continental fuel injection system during full-throttle, full-rich operating conditions.

34. Two basic functions of the fuel manifold valve in a Teledyne-Continental fuel injection system are:

a. ______________

b. ______________

35. A set of C-size nozzles will flow one-half gallon of fuel per hour ______________ (more or less) than a set of B-size nozzles.

36. Fuel injector nozzles may be cleaned by soaking them in ______________ or ______________ ______________.

SECTION

C

## TURBINE ENGINE FUEL METERING

Fuel-metering devices for turbine engines meter fuel for reliable ground and air operations. Remember that the power output of a turbine engine varies with the amount of air that is drawn into the compressor and the amount of heat that is generated in the combustion section. The amount of heat produced in the combustors is determined by the amount of fuel that is scheduled (or metered) to the engine. The fuel-metering device must schedule the proper amount of fuel to the engine to obtain a given power output. Inertia of the main turbine and large volumetric changes in airflow associated with power changes limit the ability of turbine engines to respond rapidly to abrupt power lever movements. For example, when an engine is decelerated and the fuel flow is decreased more rapidly than the airflow through the engine, an incombustible fuel/air mixture can result and cause a condition known as a lean die-out. Conversely, if an engine accelerates too rapidly and an excessive amount of fuel is scheduled into the combustors before the main turbine has time to accelerate, a rich blowout can occur. For these reasons, fuel metering-devices for turbine engines must control fuel flow and engine acceleration and deceleration rates. The main components of a typical turbine-engine fuel-metering system are the fuel control unit and the fuel nozzles.

## FUEL CONTROL UNITS

When the pilot makes a power setting with the cockpit controls, the **fuel control unit**, or **FCU**, responds by adjusting fuel flow to the engine. The FCU provides the precise amount of necessary fuel according to the power lever position.

To precisely meter fuel flow, the FCU monitors several engine operating parameters including power lever position, engine speed, compressor inlet air temperature and pressure, and burner or compressor discharge pressure. In addition, many FCUs incorporate several automatic functions to help prevent flameouts, over-temperature occurrences, and overspeed conditions.

In turbine engines, fuel is metered by weight rather than by volume. This is because the heat energy per pound of fuel is constant regardless of its temperature, whereas the heat energy per unit volume of fuel varies. As the temperature of turbine fuel increases, its volume also increases; likewise, as the temperature of turbine fuel decreases, its volume decreases.

FCUs meter the correct amount of fuel into the combustion section to obtain the optimum air-to-fuel mixture ratio of 15:1 by weight. This ratio represents 15 pounds of combustor primary air to one pound of fuel. Remember that the stoichiometric ratio of 15:1 is the theoretically perfect mixture for combustion.

The FCU is typically an engine-driven accessory that meters fuel using either hydromechanical, hydropneumatic, or electronic means. Today, hydromechanical and electronic FCUs are used on most turbojet and turbofan engines. Hydropneumatic units are used on several turboprop engines.

### HYDROMECHANICAL

A typical hydromechanical fuel control unit is divided into a fuel metering section and a computing section. The fuel metering section consists of a fuel pump, a pressure-regulating valve, a single metering valve, and a fuel shutoff valve. The computing section consists of a speed sensitive control (or governor) that responds to the position of the power lever and the speed of the engine. Additional components include a servo valve that controls the rate of engine acceleration and deceleration and two bellows that adjust fuel flow based on burner and inlet air pressure. [Figure 7-70]

#### FUEL METERING SECTION

A hydromechanical FCU meters the appropriate amount of fuel to the combustion section at the correct pressure. The typical fuel metering section uses a positive displacement fuel pump, a main metering valve, and a pressure-regulating valve. In addition, to provide a positive means of stopping the flow of fuel to the engine, there is a fuel shutoff valve downstream from the main metering valve. [Figure 7-71]

Boost pump fuel is directed to the main fuel pump to send unpressurized fuel to the main metering valve. A typical valve uses a tapered shaft to meter

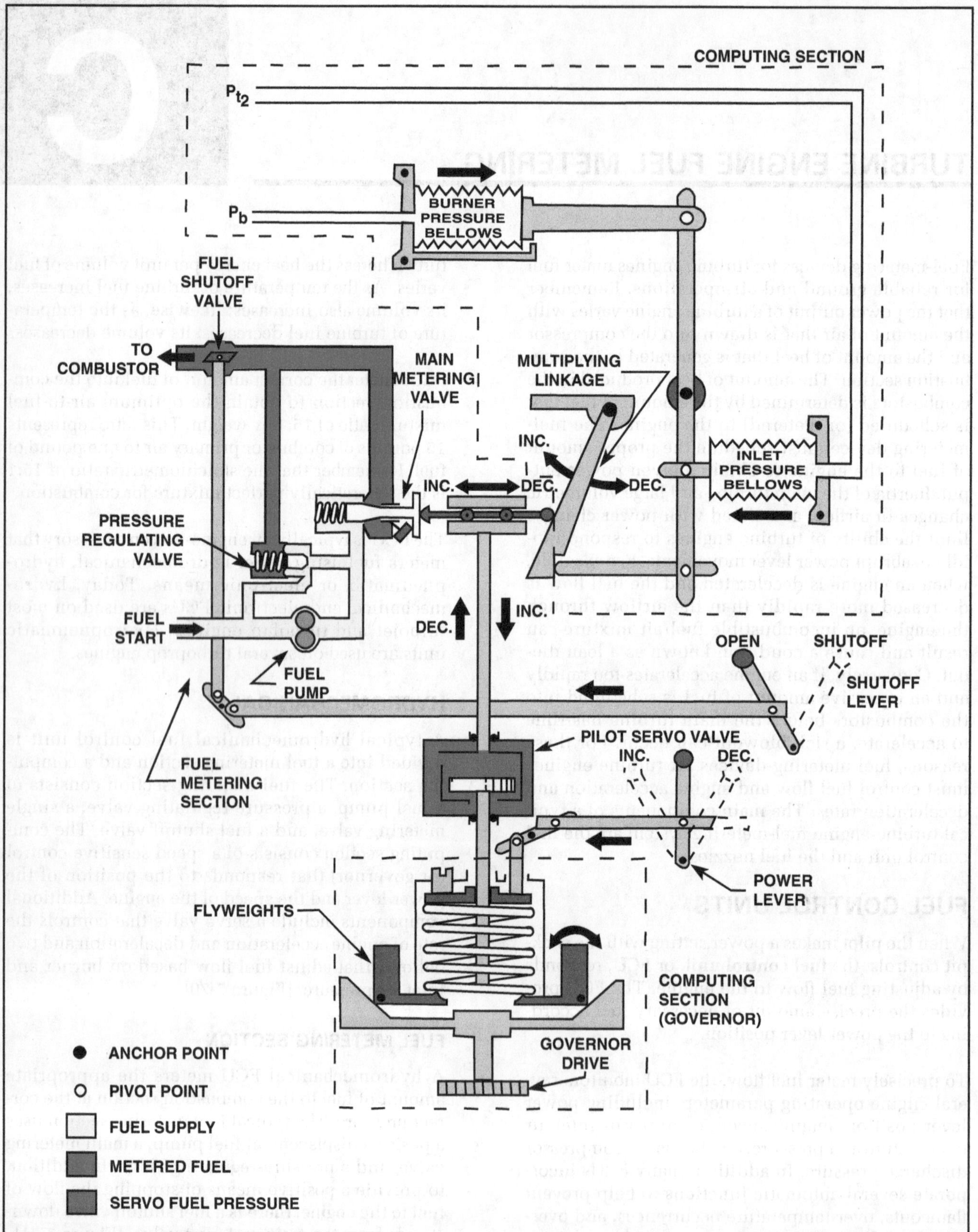


**Figure 7-70. This simplified figure shows the primary components of a hydromechanical fuel control unit. The fuel-metering portion of the unit pumps pressurized fuel to a main metering valve and on to the combustion section. The computing section monitors power lever position, engine speed, burner pressure, and engine inlet pressure to control the amount of fuel permitted through the metering jet to the engine.**

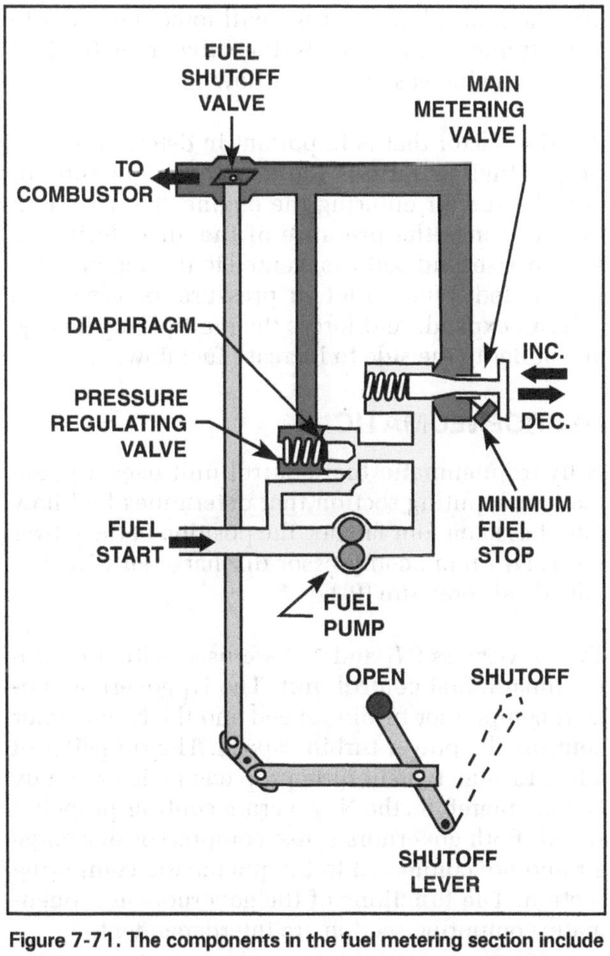


**Figure 7-71. The components in the fuel metering section include a fuel pump, a main metering valve, a pressure regulating valve, and a fuel shutoff valve.**

the fuel flow based on the power lever position and the pressure at the engine inlet and within the burners. A pressure differential occurs as unmetered fuel passes through the metering valve. To meter fuel by weight properly, the system must maintain a constant pressure differential (or drop). A pressure-regulating valve installed in parallel with the main metering valve maintains the pressure differential. Similar to a pressure relief valve, a spring-loaded pressure-regulating valve controls the amount of fuel that is bypassed (returned) to the fuel pump inlet. To maintain a constant pressure differential across the metering valve, a pressure-regulating valve uses a diaphragm exposed to pump pressure on one side and metered fuel pressure on the other. The pressure-regulating valve senses the pressure drop across the metering valve and maintains a predetermined pressure drop based on the spring pressure.

To better understand the function of a differential pressure-regulating valve, consider the following example. For a given power setting, the fuel pump delivers an excess amount of fuel to the metering valve. The pressure-regulating valve continually returns excess fuel to the pump inlet to maintain a specific pressure drop across the metering valve. The amount of fuel that is returned to the pump inlet is determined by the pressure differential across the metering valve and a set, or constant, spring pressure. As engine speed increases, the main metering valve is pushed inward, which causes the metering orifice to become larger. Metered fuel pressure increases while unmetered fuel pressure decreases. This reduced pressure differential across the metering valve causes the pressure-regulating valve to close, enabling less fuel to pass back to the pump inlet. When this occurs, the unmetered fuel pressure builds until the appropriate pressure differential exists across the metering valve. After the pressure differential is established, the pressure-regulating valve opens enough to maintain the same pressure differential for the higher power setting.

To ensure adequate fuel flow during idle power settings, the main metering valve has a minimum-flow stop that prevents the metering valve from closing too far and causing erratic pressure fluctuation across the metering valve during idle operations.

Because the minimum flow stop prevents the metering valve from completely stopping the flow of fuel to the combustors, a fuel shutoff valve is required to provide a positive means of stopping the flow of fuel for engine shutdown. In addition, the shutoff valve also ensures that the correct fuel pressure builds within the FCU during an engine start cycle. A cockpit lever controls the fuel shutoff valve either mechanically, electrically, or pneumatically.

## COMPUTING SECTION

The computing section of the FCU is responsible for positioning the metering valve to obtain the appropriate power output and to control the rate of acceleration and deceleration. A typical computing section uses a speed-sensitive governor, a servo valve, and two pressure-sensitive bellows. [Figure 7-72]

During engine operation, forward movement of the power lever causes the spring cap to slide down the pilot servo valve rod and compress the flyweight speeder spring. This action forces the tops of the flyweights inward, which creates an under-speed condition. Fuel in the pilot servo valve is displaced from top to bottom, which causes the slider to move down. The pilot servo valve is a hydraulic dampener that transforms sudden throttle movements into slow, smooth commands to reposition the main metering valve. As the slider moves down the inclined plane of the multiplying linkage, it moves to the side and forces the metering valve to open. Whenever the

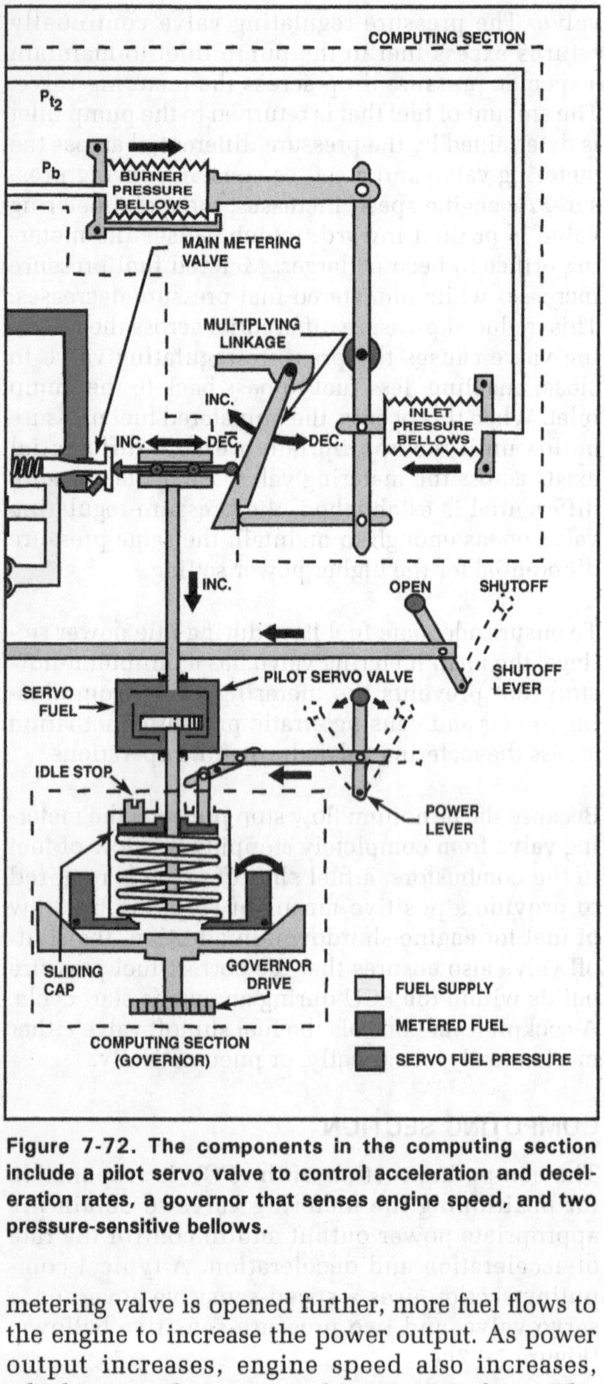


**Figure 7-72. The components in the computing section include a pilot servo valve to control acceleration and deceleration rates, a governor that senses engine speed, and two pressure-sensitive bellows.**

metering valve is opened further, more fuel flows to the engine to increase the power output. As power output increases, engine speed also increases, which causes the governor drive to rotate faster. The increased rotational speed increases the centrifugal force acting on the flyweights causing them to return to an upright position.

On many engines, the static pressure within the combustors is a useful measure of mass airflow. For example, if mass airflow is known, the fuel/air ratio can be more carefully controlled. For this reason, a bellows that is vented to the combustion section is installed in many FCUs. As burner pressure ($P_b$) increases, the burner pressure bellows expands to the right. If the pilot servo valve rod remains stationary, the multiplying linkage will force the slider to the left and open the metering valve to match fuel flow to the increased mass airflow.

Another factor that is important in determining the proper fuel/air ratio is the density or pressure, or both, of the air entering the engine. To permit an FCU to sense the pressure of the air entering an engine, a second bellows, vented to the engine inlet, is installed. When inlet air pressure increases, the bellows expands and forces the multiplying linkage and slider to the side to increase fuel flow.

## HYDROPNEUMATIC

A hydropneumatic fuel control unit uses a pneumatic computing section that determines fuel flow rates based on four factors: the position of the power lever, $N_1$ r.p.m., compressor discharge air ($P_3$), and outside air pressure ($P_0$).

Two governors ($N_1$ and $N_2$) are used with a hydropneumatic fuel control unit. The $N_1$ governor controls compressor turbine speed and the $N_2$ governor controls the power turbine speed. The propeller of a free-turbine type of turboprop engine is driven by $N_2$ and, therefore, the $N_2$ governor controls propeller speed. Both governors sense compressor discharge air and are connected to the pneumatic computing section. The functions of the governors and pneumatic computing section are interdependent.

A **starting flow control unit** is also used with this type of fuel control and is installed between the main metering valve and the fuel nozzles. A starting flow control unit consists of a housing with a ported plunger that slides in a ported sleeve. A rack-and-pinion assembly converts rotational motion of the input lever into linear movement to actuate the plunger. The starting flow control unit ensures the correct fuel pressure to the nozzles and provides a means to drain residual fuel from the fuel manifolds after engine shutdown. This prevents fuel from boiling and fouling the system with carbon due to heat absorption after engine shutdown.

## ELECTRONIC

As turbine engine technology has advanced, scheduling the proper amount of fuel to the engine has become more important. In fact, a modern turbofan engine can achieve its optimum designed efficiency only if the fuel is precisely scheduled. To achieve precision control and monitoring, most modern turbofan engines use an electronic engine control, or EEC, to schedule fuel.

An EEC offers the benefits of increased fuel efficiency, increased reliability, reduced operator workload, and reduced maintenance costs. Furthermore, a properly functioning EEC can prolong engine life by preventing over-temperature and over-speed occurrences. Currently, two types of electronic engine controls are in use: the supervisory engine control system and the full-authority control system.

## SUPERVISORY EEC

A supervisory EEC consists of an electronic control and a conventional hydromechanical fuel control unit. With this type of system, the hydromechanical fuel control unit controls most engine operations including starting, idle, acceleration, deceleration, and shutdown. The ECC monitors several engine operating parameters and adjusts the fuel control unit to obtain the most effective engine operation for a given position of the power lever. After the pilot sets the power lever to obtain a specific engine pressure ratio (EPR), the electronic engine control adjusts the fuel control unit as necessary to maintain the selected EPR as the aircraft changes altitude or as atmospheric conditions change. Additionally, most EECs limit an engine's operating speed and temperature to prevent over-speed and over-temperature occurrences. In fact, some supervisory EECs can be used primarily as an engine speed and temperature limiting control. For example, the supervisory EEC used on a Rolls-Royce RB-211 works on a hydromechanical schedule until the engine is accelerated to near full engine power. However, after the engine nears its maximum rotational speed and operating temperature, the EEC begins operating as a limiter to restrict the amount of fuel that goes to the engine. [Figure 7-73]

As a safety feature, if a supervisory EEC malfunctions, control automatically reverts to the hydromechanical fuel control. Furthermore, a warning light illuminates in the cockpit to warn that the EEC is not providing information to the fuel control unit. Likewise, an aircraft operator can manually revert to the hydromechanical control whenever necessary.

## FULL-AUTHORITY EEC

A full-authority digital engine control, or **FADEC**, performs virtually all functions necessary to support engine operation during all phases of flight. FADEC systems eliminate the need for a hydromechanical fuel control unit. A typical FADEC system consists of a two-channel EEC that can derive information from either channel. In most cases, the EEC receives input on engine speed ($N_1$ and $N_2$), throttle lever position, bleed-air status, aircraft altitude, total inlet air pressure and temperature, stator vane angle, fuel

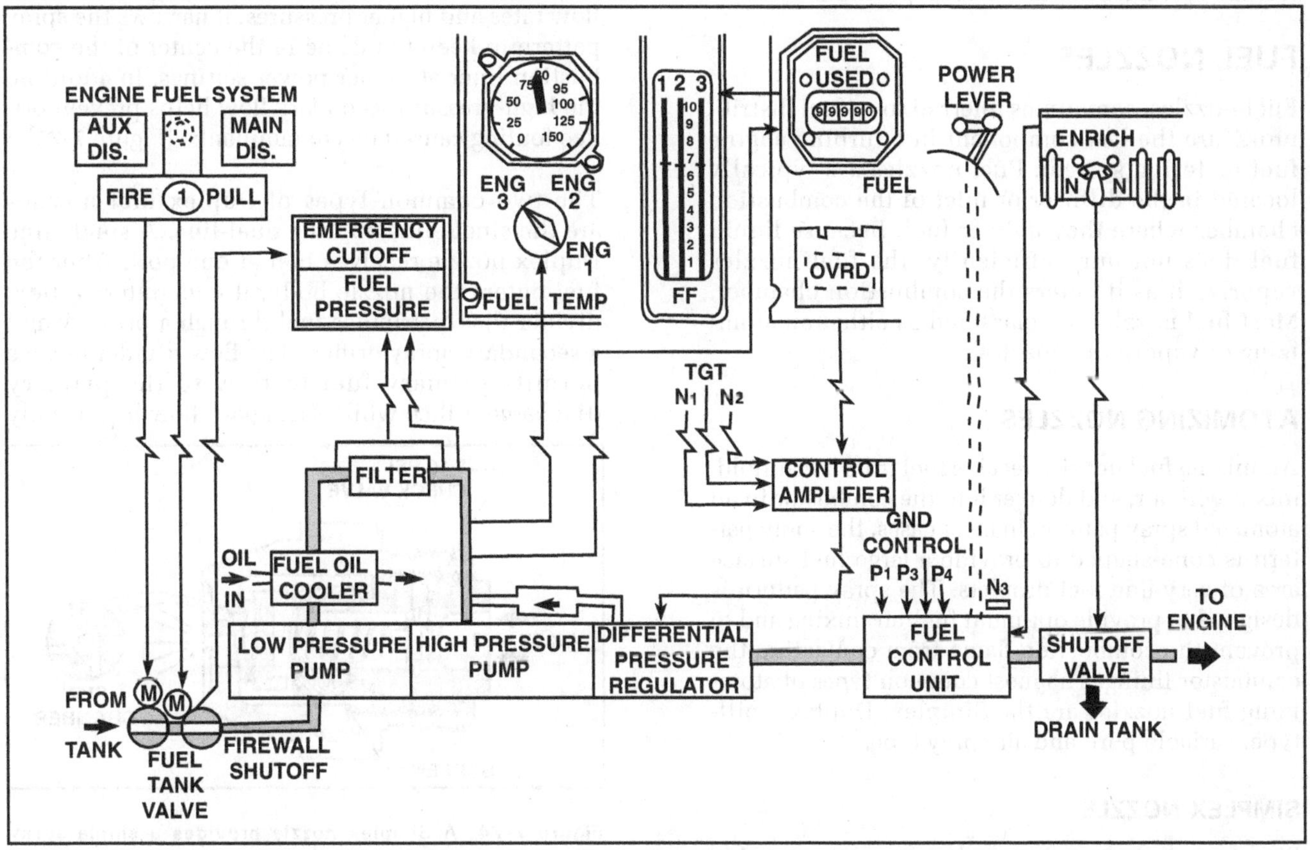


**Figure 7-73. The control amplifier provides electronic control based on inputs received from $N_1$, $N_2$, and turbine gas temperature (TGT). The control operates on a hydromechanical schedule until the engine output approaches its maximum speed. At that point, the electronic circuit begins to function as a fuel limiter. The control amplifier signals the differential pressure regulator how much fuel to divert back to the inlet side of the high pressure pump.**

flow rate, fuel and oil temperature, turbine exhaust pressure and temperature, and burner pressure. The EEC analyzes this information, and then issues a series of commands to a set of actuators that control engine operating parameters.

On a turbine-powered aircraft equipped with a FADEC, the pilot positions the power lever to obtain a desired EPR, or power output; the EEC then automatically accelerates or decelerates to this EPR. In addition, the EEC maintains the EPR as the aircraft changes altitude or as ambient conditions change. FADEC greatly reduces pilot workload as well as under- and overspeed occurrences. Because FADEC closely monitors and controls the engine operating parameters to produce maximum thrust for a given amount of fuel, engines equipped with an EEC are usually more fuel efficient.

For greater reliability, FADEC systems incorporate several redundant and dedicated subsystems. A FADEC EEC has two redundant channels that send and receive data. Each channel has its own processor, power supply, memory, sensors, and actuators. Either channel can use information from the other. An EEC can operate even when several faults exist. As a second backup, if both channels fail, the actuators are springloaded to a failsafe position.

## FUEL NOZZLES

Fuel nozzles, sometimes referred to as fuel distributors, are the last component in a turbine engine fuel metering system. Fuel nozzles are typically located in the diffuser or inlet of the combustion chamber where they deliver fuel. Because liquid fuel does not burn efficiently; the fuel nozzles vaporize it as it enters the combustion chamber. Most fuel nozzles are classified as either an atomizing or vaporizing nozzles.

### ATOMIZING NOZZLES

Atomizing fuel nozzles receive fuel from a manifold, mix it with air, and deliver it to the combustor in an atomized spray pattern. In most cases, the spray pattern is cone-shaped to provide a large fuel surface area of very fine fuel droplets. The spray pattern is designed to provide optimum fuel/air mixing and to prevent the combustion flame from contacting the combustor lining. The most common types of atomizing fuel nozzles are the Simplex, Duplex, spill-type, variable-port, and air-spray type.

#### SIMPLEX NOZZLE

Simplex nozzles, used on early jet engines, provide a single spray pattern. The nozzle itself incorporates an internally fluted spin chamber that imparts a swirling motion to the fuel as it exits the nozzle. The swirling motion reduces the fuel's forward velocity to promote better atomization. To prevent fuel from dribbling out of the fuel manifold and into the combustor after engine shutdown, Simplex nozzles incorporate an internal check valve to stop the flow of fuel at the base of the nozzle. [Figure 7-74]

Because Simplex nozzles do not atomize fuel well, they produce a poor flame pattern at slow engine speeds when the fuel pressure is low. To minimize this problem, some fuel systems incorporate a second set of smaller Simplex nozzles. The small nozzles, sometimes referred to as primers or starting nozzles, spray a very fine atomized mist to improve engine starting.

#### DUPLEX NOZZLE

Duplex nozzles have two independent discharge orifices—one small and the other large. The use of two orifices provides better fuel vaporization and a more uniform spray pattern. The small orifice located in the center of the nozzle discharges pilot, or primary, fuel at a wide angle during engine start and acceleration to idle. The larger orifice encircles the smaller one and discharges main, or secondary, fuel when fuel flow increases above what is needed for idle. Because the secondary fuel is discharged at higher flow rates and higher pressures, it narrows the spray pattern to keep the flame in the center of the combustion liner at higher power settings. In addition, the high-pressure secondary flow helps prevent orifice fouling caused by contaminants. [Figure 7-75]

The two common types of Duplex fuel nozzles are the single-line and the dual-line. A single-line Duplex nozzle receives fuel at one port. After the fuel enters the nozzle body, it encounters a flow divider that distributes fuel through a primary and a secondary spray orifice. The flow divider always permits primary fuel to flow to the primary discharge orifice while secondary flow begins only

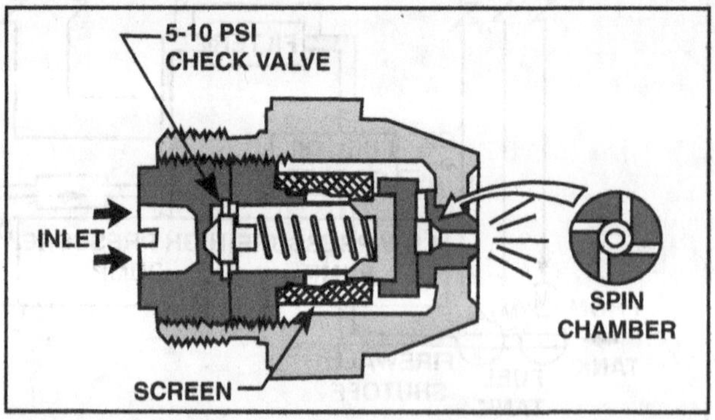


**Figure 7-74. A Simplex nozzle provides a single spray pattern and incorporates an internally fluted spin chamber and a check valve. A Simplex nozzle is typically mounted inside an engine and can be accessed only when a combustor is removed.**

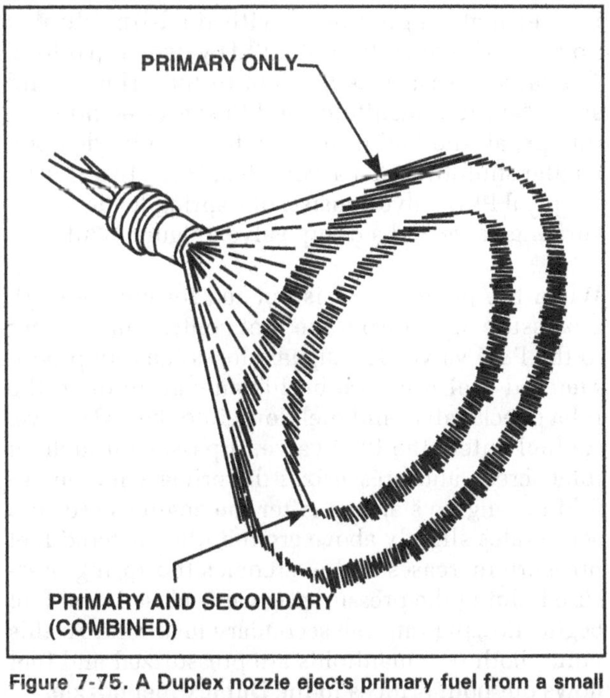


**Figure 7-75. A Duplex nozzle ejects primary fuel from a small center orifice during engine start and acceleration to idle. Above idle speed, higher pressure secondary fuel is ejected out of a larger orifice and combines with the primary fuel flow to create a narrower spray pattern.**

after the inlet fuel pressure increases sufficiently to open the flow divider valve. [Figure 7-76]

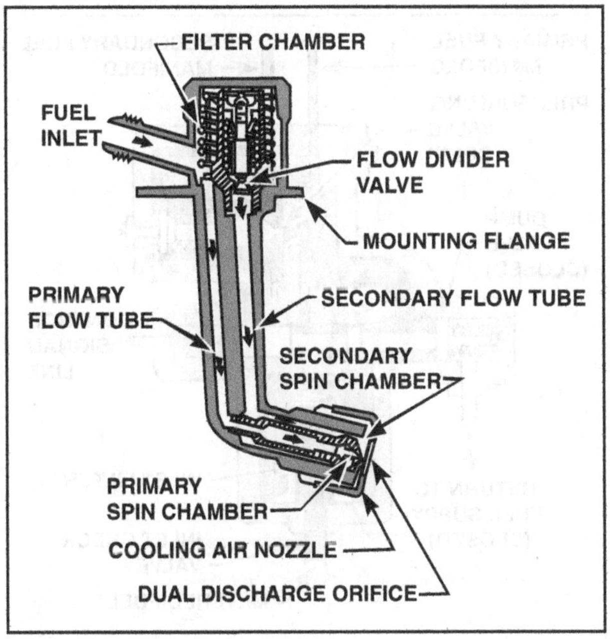


**Figure 7-76. Fuel enters the body of a single line Duplex nozzle and passes through a filter screen and a flow divider. Primary fuel always flows through the flow divider, but secondary fuel flows only when inlet fuel pressure increases sufficiently to open the flow divider valve.**

Duplex nozzles also use spin chambers for each orifice. The head of a Duplex nozzle is designed with air bleed holes to cool and clean the head and spray orifices. Additionally, the air bleed holes provide some primary air for combustion. During engine start with only primary fuel flow, the cooling airflow helps prevent primary fuel from flowing back into the secondary orifice and carbonizing.

## SPILL-TYPE NOZZLE

On some turbine engines high-pressure fuel is supplied to the fuel nozzles at all times. On these engines, spill-type nozzles might be used. A spill-type nozzle is basically a Simplex nozzle with a passage leading away from the spin chamber. This passage, referred to as a **spill passage**, returns the excess fuel supplied during low power operations back to the nozzle inlet. Supplying fuel at high pressure to the nozzle at all times improves atomization at all engine speeds. A disadvantage of this type of nozzle is that recirculating large amounts of fuel at low engine speeds generates extra heat.

## VARIABLE-PORT NOZZLE

A variable-port nozzle, or **Lubbock nozzle**, atomizes fuel over a wide range of fuel flow rates. An internal spring-loaded piston regulates the size of the inlet port swirl chamber according to the fuel flow rate. At low flow rates, the inlet ports are partially covered; at high flow rates, they are fully uncovered. A disadvantage of this type of nozzle is that dirt particles in the fuel tend to make the sliding piston stick.

## AIR-SPRAY NOZZLE

Some Rolls-Royce engines use air-spray nozzles. Openings in the back of this type of nozzle permit primary combustion airflow to aerate the fuel spray. After air enters the nozzle, it passes through a set of inner swirl vanes before entering a swirl chamber. In the swirl chamber, fuel and air are mixed and ejected through an orifice in the center of a set of outer swirl vanes. The turbulence created by the passage of the primary combustion air through the vanes evenly distributes the fuel spray with combustion air.

## VAPORIZING NOZZLES

Instead of delivering fuel directly to the primary air in the combustor, a vaporizing nozzle premixes the primary air and fuel in a vaporizing tube. In most cases, the vaporizing tube extends into the combustion chamber so that when the fuel/air mixture is in the vaporizing tube, the heated air causes the mixture to vaporize before exiting into the combustor flame zone. Some vaporizing type nozzles have only one outlet and are referred to as cane-shaped vaporizers. Other types are T-shaped and provide two outlets. [Figure 7-77]

A shortcoming of vaporizing nozzles is that they do not provide an effective spray pattern for starting. To help alleviate this problem, an additional set of small atomizing-type spray nozzles might be incorporated to aid in engine starting. This system is generally referred to as a primer, or starting, fuel system. The Olympus engine in the Concord SST used vaporizing fuel nozzles with separate primer fuel nozzles.

## NOZZLE MALFUNCTIONS

A normally functioning fuel nozzle produces a spray pattern that holds the flame in the center of the liner. A plugged internal passage or air bleed hole can result in, a distorted spray pattern or incomplete atomization. When spray pattern distortion occurs, the combustion flame can come in contact with the combustion liner. Another undesirable condition occurs if the fuel doesn't atomize properly, which results in a stream of burning fuel that extends beyond the combustion chamber and strikes turbine components. This is referred to as hot streaking and must be corrected immediately. When this condition occurs, burning fuel leaves visible streaks on the components it contacts.

## PRESSURIZATION AND DUMP VALVE

A pressurization and dump valve, commonly referred to as a P&D valve, is frequently included in fuel metering systems with dual-line duplex nozzles. The operation of a P&D valve is two-fold: the valve pressurizes the fuel in the primary and secondary fuel manifolds and the valve empties, or dumps, all the fuel in the two fuel manifolds upon engine shutdown. To accomplish these two things, a typical P&D valve consists of a spring-loaded pressurizing valve and a dump valve. [Figure 7-78]

When the power lever is opened for engine start, a pressure signal from the fuel control unit is sent to the P&D valve. The signal closes the dump port. Metered fuel pressure builds enough to open the inlet check valve, and fuel flows into the P&D valve. As fuel enters the P&D valve, it passes through an inlet screen and pressurizes the primary fuel manifold for engine starting. After the engine starts and accelerates slightly above ground idle, metered fuel pressure increases and overcomes the spring pressure holding the pressurizing valve closed, and fuel begins flowing into the secondary manifold. At this point, both fuel manifolds are pressurized and fuel flows out both orifices in the Duplex fuel nozzle.

When the cockpit fuel cutoff lever is moved to the cutoff position, the fuel control pressure signal is removed. Spring pressure opens the dump valve and the dump port. At the same time, the dump valve blocks the flow of fuel to both fuel manifolds. With the fuel inlet blocked, the remaining fuel in the manifold drains out of the dump port and into

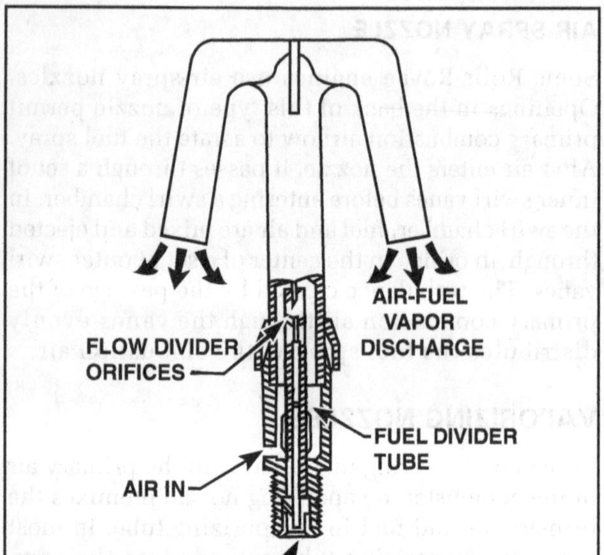


**Figure 7-77. Fuel and air enter the body of a T-shaped vaporizing nozzle and are mixed and vaporized in two vaporizing tubes before being injected into the combustion chamber.**

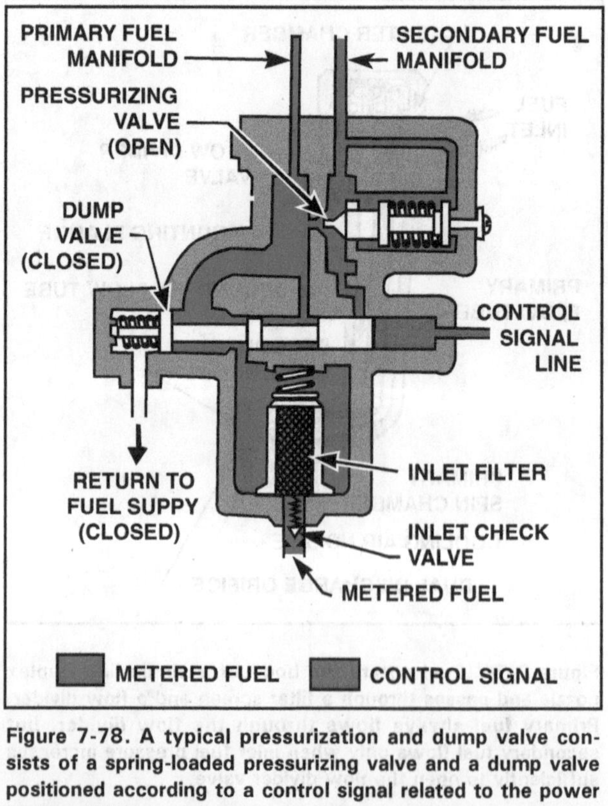


**Figure 7-78. A typical pressurization and dump valve consists of a spring-loaded pressurizing valve and a dump valve positioned according to a control signal related to the power lever position.**

the fuel supply. Because fuel flow through the P&D valve is stopped, spring pressure closes the inlet check valve, leaving metered fuel in the inlet line for the next engine start. [Figure 7-79]

Because the dump valve opens the dump port and stops fuel flow, engine shutdown is nearly instantaneous. Because all of the manifold fuel is dumped at engine shutdown, residual engine heat does not vaporize the fuel in the fuel lines. If the fuel were permitted to vaporize, carbon deposits would form within the lines and manifolds and could clog the finely calibrated passageways.

## DRAIN VALVES

Current EPA regulations prohibit dumping fuel onto the ground or siphoning fuel in flight. Therefore, fuel dumped during engine shutdown must be diverted into a separate storage tank or sent through a recovery system. If dumped to a storage tank, the tank must be drained manually into a container; however, a recovery system eliminates, manual draining. One type of recovery system returns dumped fuel to the supply tank when the fuel cutoff lever is actuated. Another system uses bleed air to force fuel out of the fuel nozzles and into the combustion chamber. This system prolongs combustion slightly before fuel starvation occurs.

A third type of system neither recovers nor burns dump fuel. This system permits fuel to drain out of the lower nozzles and into the combustion chamber on shutdown, where the fuel evaporates in the combustor. This system is used only in engines with no tendency to develop carbon buildup in the fuel nozzles from residual heat.

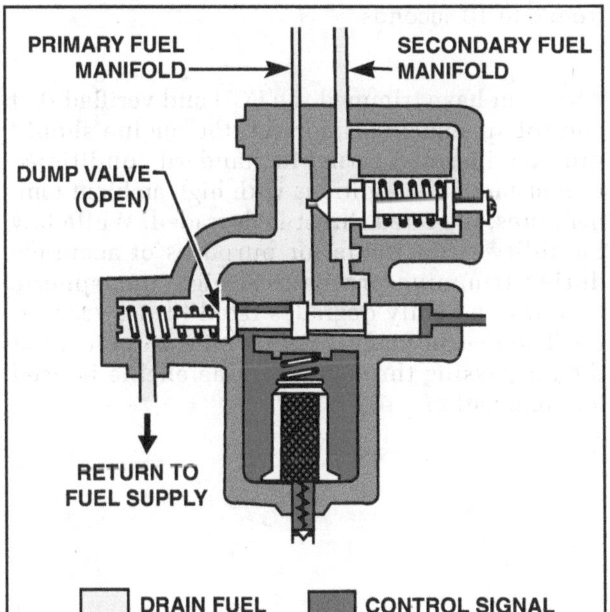


**Figure 7-79. Upon engine shutdown, spring pressure forces the dump valve to close, which blocks the flow of fuel and opens the dump port to drain both fuel manifolds.**

## TURBINE FUEL CONTROL MAINTENANCE

Repairs to turbine engine fuel controls in the field consist of control replacement or occasional field adjustments. Adjustments are typically limited to idle and maximum speed adjustments. The process of adjusting a turbine engine fuel control unit is commonly referred to as trimming. The primary purpose for trimming a fuel control unit is to ensure the availability of maximum thrust output when needed.

Trim checks are completed whenever engine thrust is suspect, and after maintenance tasks prescribed by the manufacturer. For example, an engine change, FCU change, or throttle linkage adjustments (for proper control cushion and spring-back) are all actions that require trimming procedures. An FCU might also need to be retrimmed if engine performance declines due to normal wear in service or when wear and tear on engine control linkages causes misalignment between the cockpit and the engine.

Manual trimming procedures vary considerably between engine models; therefore, review the specific procedures in the engine's maintenance manual. A typical trimming procedure requires installation of calibrated instruments to read turbine discharge pressure or EPR. In addition, a calibrated tachometer is installed to read $N_2$ r.p.m. After the instrumentation is installed, the aircraft should be pointed into the wind. However, if the velocity of the wind is too great, elevated compression and turbine discharge pressures can result, which will produce a low trim setting. Be sure to measure the barometric pressure at the engine inlet and the ambient temperature to correct performance readings to standard sea-level conditions. To obtain a temperature reading, hang a thermometer in the shade of the nose wheel well. The ideal conditions for trimming a turbine engine are no wind, low humidity, and standard temperature and pressure.

After you have calculated the maximum power output for the engine you are trimming, start the engine and let it idle as specified in the maintenance manual. This is necessary to permit the engine time to stabilize. To ensure an accurate trim setting, turn off engine bleed air. Bleeding air off the compressor has the same effect as decreasing the compressor's efficiency. Therefore, if you make a trim adjustment with the bleeds on, an inaccurate or overtrimmed condition will result.

With the engine running at idle and maximum power, observe the turbine discharge or EPR readings to determine how much trimming is necessary. If trimming of either the idle or maximum settings is necessary, it is typically accomplished by turning a screw adjustment on the FCU. However, most manufacturers recommend that to stabilize cams, springs, and linkages within the fuel control, you make final adjustments in the *increase* direction. If you make an over-adjustment, decrease the trim below target values and then increase it to the desired values. [Figure 7-80]

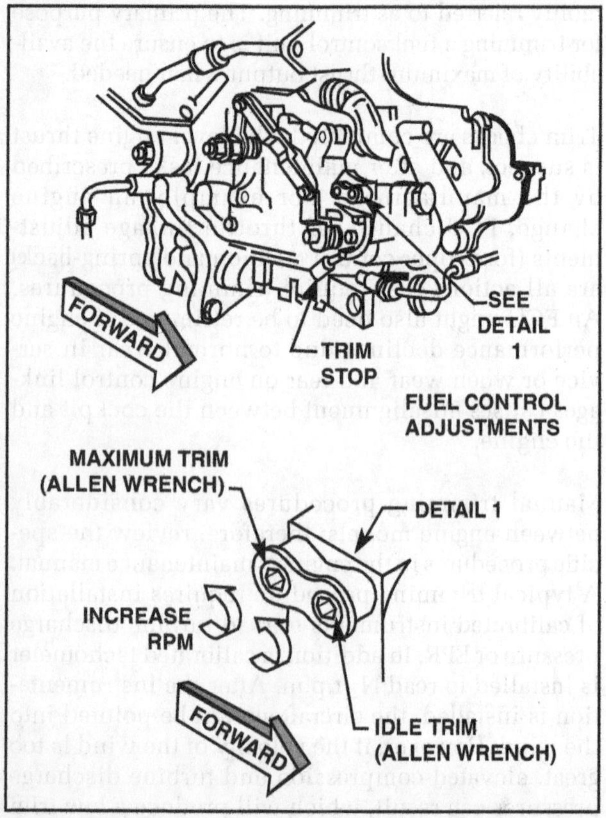


**Figure 7-80. Adjustment screws are typically provided for trimming the FCU. Trimming procedures enable you to adjust both idle speed and maximum rated thrust.**

Typical trim adjustments require only simple hand tools such as an Allen wrench, screwdriver, or wrench. Adjustment components are usually equipped with some sort of friction lock that does not require the use of lockplates, locknuts, or safety wire. Some engines are designed to accommodate remote adjusting equipment. A remote control unit enables you to make the trim adjustments from the cockpit during ground test with the cowls closed.

Another important part of the trim procedure is to check for power lever cushion, or springback. Move the power lever full forward and release it before and after the trim run. The amount of lever springback is measured and compared to the prescribed tolerances. If the cushion and springback are out of limits, you must make the necessary adjustments in accordance with the manufacturer's rigging instructions. Correct power lever springback ensures a pilot that takeoff power will be obtained and that additional power lever travel is available for emergencies. Correct springback is indicated when the fuel control reaches its internal stop before the cockpit power lever reaches its stop.

A trim check normally follows an acceleration check. After completing the trim check, place a mark on the cockpit power lever quadrant at the takeoff trim position. Then, advance the power lever from the idle position to takeoff thrust position and measure the time against a published tolerance. A typical acceleration time from idle to takeoff thrust for a large gas turbine engine ranges from 5 to 10 seconds.

After you have trimmed the FCU and verified that control springback is correct, the engine should produce its rated thrust in standard conditions. In nonstandard conditions with high ambient temperatures, the rated thrust is degraded. While low humidity is desirable for purposes of accuracy during trimming procedures, high atmospheric humidity actually degrades rated thrust very little. The reason for this is that only 25 percent of the air passing through a turbine engine is used for combustion.

# SUMMARY CHECKLIST

✓ A Fuel Control Unit (FCU) meters fuel in a gas turbine engine. The FCU adjusts fuel flow to the engine by calculating power lever position, engine speed, compressor inlet air temperature and pressure, and compressor discharge pressure.

✓ For gas turbine engines, fuel is metered by weight, not volume.

✓ Fuel nozzles, which can be atomizing or vaporizing, deliver the fuel to the combustion chamber.

✓ Trimming an FCU involves adjusting fuel output for idle and maximum speed.

# KEY TERMS

fuel control unit
FCU
starting flow control unit
full authority digital engine control
FADEC
spill passage
Lubbock nozzle

# QUESTIONS

1. Two conditions that the fuel control for a turbine engine must prevent are:
   a. ____________________
   b. ____________________

2. A turbine engine fuel control meters the fuel by ____________________ (weight or volume).

3. The three types of turbine fuel currently in use are:
   a. ____________________
   b. ____________________
   c. ____________________

4. The ________________________ (what device) in a turbine engine fuel control shuts off all flow of fuel to the nozzles when the engine is to be stopped.

5. The fuel control on a Rolls-Royce RB-211 engine operates on a ______________________ (hydromechanical or electronic) schedule until near full engine power.

6. Full Authority Digital Engine Controls (FADEC) replace with electronics most of the ________________ and ________________ elements found in other fuel controls.

7. The two basic types of fuel nozzles used in turbine engines are:

   a. ________________

   b. ________________

8. The type of atomizing nozzle that provides a single spray pattern is known as a ________________ nozzle.

9. The two types of duplex fuel nozzles are:

   a. ________________

   b. ________________

10. The ______________ (what type) fuel nozzle causes the fuel/air mixture to vaporize before it exits the nozzle.

11. Rather than using a flow divider in each fuel nozzle, some engines use a single ____________ valve which acts as a flow divider.

12. Manifold dumping is a procedure which sharply cuts off combustion and also prevents fuel ____________ as a result of residual engine heat.

13. The term used to describe idle speed and maximum thrust adjustments made to a turbine engine fuel control is ______________.

14. Most manufacturers recommend that all fuel control adjustments be made in the ____________ (increase or decrease) direction.

15. If the ______________ (what term) is correct, the fuel control will reach its internal stop before the cockpit quadrant reaches its forward stop.

CHAPTER 8

# ELECTRICAL, STARTING, AND IGNITION SYSTEMS

## INTRODUCTION

As an aviation maintenance technician, you must be familiar with aircraft electrical systems, including ways in which electricity is generated and routed to various aircraft components. By understanding the principles of electricity and electrical system designs, you can effectively diagnose, isolate, and repair malfunctions. However, because the expense of owning the proper tools, test equipment, and current technical publications is prohibitive for most individuals, FAA certified repair stations—or the component manufacturers—service many major electrical components such as generators, motors and inverters. Although you might be required only to remove and replace these items with serviceable units, it is still your responsibility to know how these components operate to be able to troubleshoot and perform routine servicing of the electrical system.

# SECTION A

## GENERATORS

Energy for the operation of most electrical equipment on large aircraft and some small aircraft is supplied by a generator. A **generator** converts mechanical energy into electrical energy by electromagnetic induction. Generators designed to produce direct current are called **DC generators**, and those that produce alternating current are called **AC generators**.

On many older aircraft, the DC generator is the source of electrical energy. In this type of system, the engines drive one or more DC generators to supply power for all electrical equipment and charge the battery. In most cases each engine drives only one generator, but, some large aircraft have two generators driven by a single engine.

### THEORY OF OPERATION

After the discovery that electric current flowing through a conductor creates a magnetic field around the conductor, there was considerable scientific speculation regarding whether a magnetic field could create current flow. In 1831, English scientist Michael Faraday demonstrated that this it. This discovery is the basis for the operation of the generator.

In a simple demonstration of how a magnetic field creates an electric current, several turns of wire are wrapped around a cardboard tube, and the ends of the conductor are connected to a galvanometer. A bar magnet is then moved through the tube. As the magnet's lines of flux are cut by the turns of wire, the galvanometer deflects from its zero position. However, when the magnet is at rest inside the tube, the galvanometer shows a reading of zero, indicating no current flow. When the magnet is moved through the tube in the opposite direction, the galvanometer indicates a deflection in the opposite direction. [Figure 8-1]

You can get the same results by holding the magnet stationary and moving the coil of wire. This indicates that current flows as long as relative motion occurs between the wire coil and the magnetic field. The strength of the induced current depends on both the strength of the magnetic field and the speed at which the lines of flux are cut.

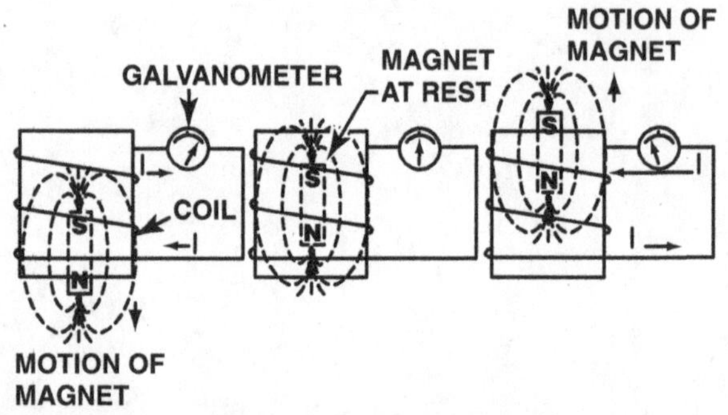


**Figure 8-1. A galvanometer shows the current flow induced into a coil by magnetic flux. The direction of current flow depends on the direction that the magnetic fields cross the conductor.**

When a conductor is moved through a magnetic field, an electromotive force (EMF) is induced into the conductor. The direction the conductor moves in relation to the magnetic flux lines determines the direction, or polarity, of the induced EMF.

The left-hand rule for generators is one way to determine the direction of the induced EMF. When you point your left index finger in the direction of the magnetic lines of flux (north to south), and your thumb in the direction that the conductor moves through the magnetic field, your second finger indicates the direction of the induced EMF, when extended perpendicular to the index finger. [Figure 8-2]

When a conductor in the shape of a single loop is rotated in a magnetic field, a voltage is induced in each side of the loop. Although the two sides of the loop cut the magnetic field in opposite directions, the induced current flows in one continuous direction within the loop. This increases the value of the induced EMF. [Figure 8-3]

When the loop is rotated half a turn so that the sides of the conductor have changed positions, the induced EMF in each wire reverses its direction. This is because the wire, formerly cutting the lines of flux in an upward direction, is now moving downward; and the wire formerly cutting the lines of flux in a downward direction, is now moving upward. In

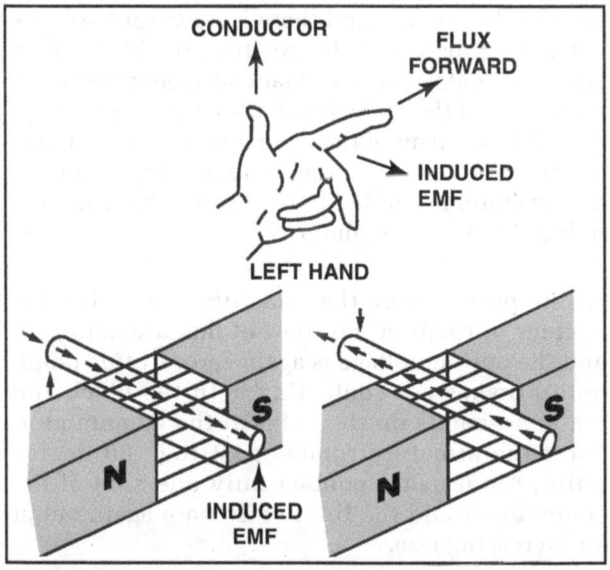


Figure 8-2. According to the generator left-hand rule, the index finger points in the direction of the magnetic flux lines, the thumb shows the direction that the conductor moves, and the middle finger represents the direction of induced EMF.

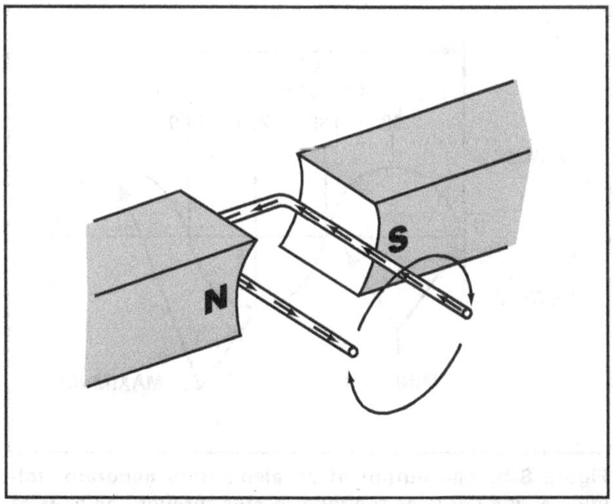


Figure 8-3. When a loop of wire rotates in a magnetic field, the direction of the induced current flow is continuous.

other words, the sides of the loop cut the magnetic field in opposite directions.

In a simple generator, two sides of a wire loop are arranged to rotate in a magnetic field. When the sides of the loop are parallel to the magnetic lines of flux, the induced voltage causes current to flow in one direction. Maximum voltage is induced at this position because the wires are cutting the lines of flux at right angles. This means that more lines of flux per second are cut than in any other position relative to the magnetic field.

As the loop approaches the vertical position, the induced voltage decreases. This is because both sides of the loop become perpendicular to the lines of flux; therefore, fewer flux lines are cut. When the loop is vertical, the wires momentarily travel perpendicular to the magnetic lines of flux and there is no induced voltage.

As the loop continues to rotate, the number of flux lines being cut increases until the 90 degree point is reached. At this point, the number of flux lines cut is maximum again. However, each side of the loop is cutting the lines of flux in the opposite direction. Therefore, the direction, or polarity, of the induced voltage is reversed. Rotation beyond the 90 degree point again decreases the number of flux lines being cut until the induced voltage becomes zero at the vertical position. [Figure 8-4]

When the voltage induced throughout the entire 360 degrees of rotation is shown on an oscilloscope, the

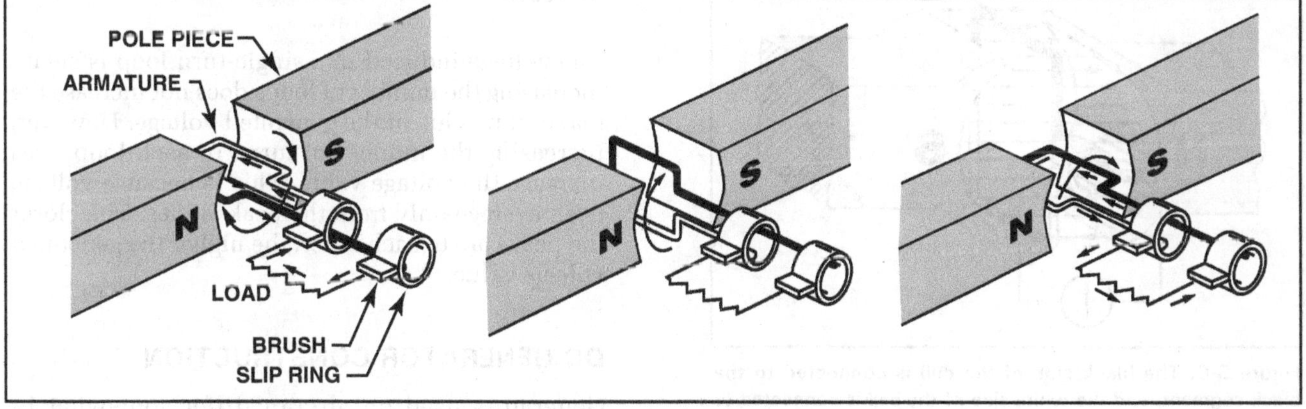


Figure 8-4. In a simple generator, the magnets are called poles and the wire loop is called the armature. A set of brushes ride on a slip ring attached to each end of the loop, completing a circuit through a load. Maximum voltage is induced into the armature when it is parallel with the flux lines. When the armature rotates to a position perpendicular with the flux lines, no lines of flux are cut and no voltage is induced. When the armature rotates another 90 degrees, the maximum numbers of flux lines are cut once again, but in the opposite direction.

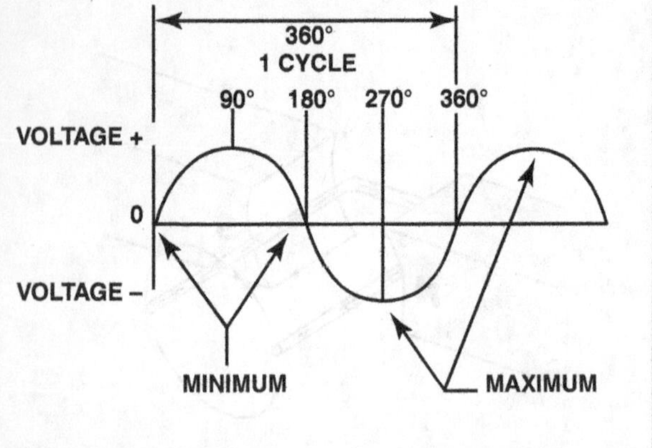


**Figure 8-5. The output of an elementary generator follows a sine curve as the loop rotates through the lines of magnetic flux.**

curve increases from a zero value at zero degrees, to a maximum positive voltage at 90 degrees. After it rotates beyond 90 degrees, the curve decreases until it reaches 180 degrees, at which point the output is again zero. As the curve continues beyond 180 degrees, the amount of negative voltage produced increases up to the 270 degree point, where it is maximum. The amount of negative voltage then decreases to the zero point at 360 degrees. [Figure 8-5]

As the illustration shows, the output produced by a single loop rotating in a magnetic field is alternating current. By replacing the slip rings of the basic AC generator with two half-cylinders, commonly referred to as a single **commutator**, the alternating current is changed to direct current. [Figure 8-6]

To explain how DC current is obtained, start with the armature at zero degrees—the point where no

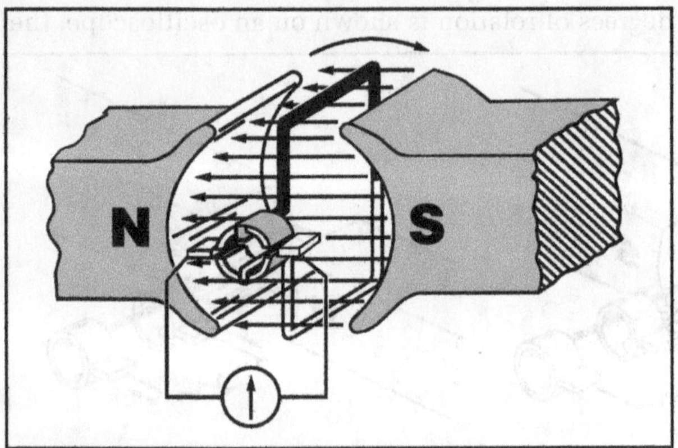


**Figure 8-6. The black side of the coil is connected to the black segment, and the white side of the coil is connected to the white segment. The segments are insulated; two stationary brushes contact the commutator on opposite sides. The brushes are mounted so that each brush contacts a different segment as the loop rotates.**

lines of flux are cut and there is no output voltage. After the armature begins rotating, the black brush comes in contact with the black segment of the commutator, and the white brush comes in contact with the white segment of the commutator. Furthermore, the lines of flux are cut at an increasing rate until the armature is parallel to the lines of flux, and the induced EMF is maximum.

At the point where the armature completes 180 degrees of rotation, no lines of flux are being cut and the output voltage is again zero. At this point, both brushes are contacting both the black and white segments on the sides of the commutator. After the armature rotates past the 180 degree point, the brushes contact only one side of the commutator and the lines of flux are again cut at an increasing rate.

The switching of the commutator permits one brush to stay in contact with that portion of the loop that travels downward through the lines of flux, and the other brush to stay in contact with the half of the loop that travels upward. Although the current reverses its direction in the loop of a DC generator, the commutator action causes current to flow in the same direction. [Figure 8-7]

The variation in DC voltage is called **ripple**, and is reduced by adding more loops (also called windings). As the number of loops increases, the variation between the maximum and minimum values of voltage is reduced. In fact, the more loops that are used, the closer the output voltage resembles pure DC. [Figure 8-8]

Because each loop requires two commutator segments, as the number of armature loops increases, the number of commutator segments must also increase.

The voltage induced in a single-turn loop is small. Increasing the number of loops does not increase the maximum value of the generated voltage. However, increasing the number of turns in each loop does increase the voltage value. This is because voltage is an average only from the peak values. The closer the peaks are to each other, the higher the generated voltage value.

## DC GENERATOR CONSTRUCTION

Generators used on aircraft differ somewhat in design from manufacture to manufacturer. However, all are of the same general construction and operate similarly. [Figure 8-9]

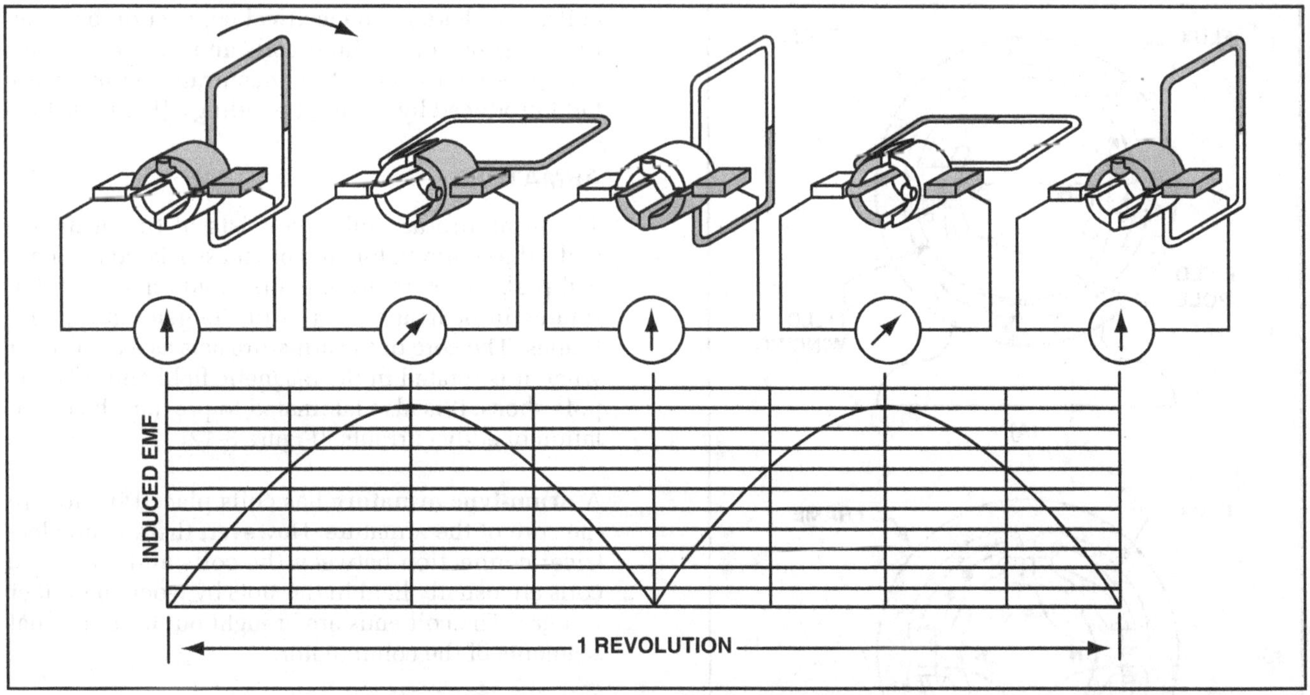


**Figure 8-7. As the armature rotates in a DC generator, the commutator is designed so that one brush always contacts the portion of the loop moving downward through the flux lines and the other brush maintains contact with the portion of the loop moving upward. Commutator action produces pulsing DC voltage that fluctuates from zero to its maximum, twice every revolution.**

## FIELD FRAME

The field frame, or yoke, constitutes the foundation for the generator. The frame has two primary functions: it completes the magnetic circuit between the poles, and it acts as a mechanical support for the other parts. In small generators, the frame is made of one piece of iron; however, in larger generators, it is usually made of two parts bolted together. The frame is highly permeable (that is, magnetic lines of flux pass through it freely) and, together with the pole pieces, forms the majority of the magnetic circuit.

The magnetizing force inside a generator is produced by an electromagnet consisting of a wire coil called a **field coil**, and a core called a **field pole**, or **shoe**. The pole shoes are bolted to the inside of the frame and are usually laminated to reduce eddy cur-

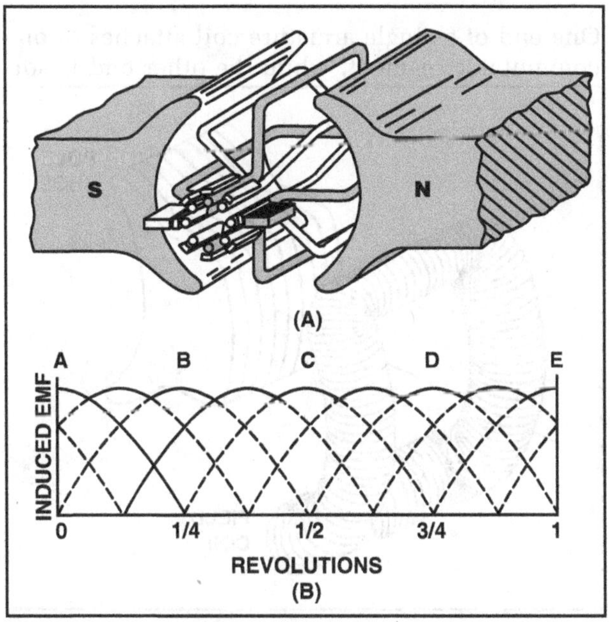


**Figure 8-8. Increasing the number of loops in an armature reduces the magnitude of the ripple in DC voltage.**

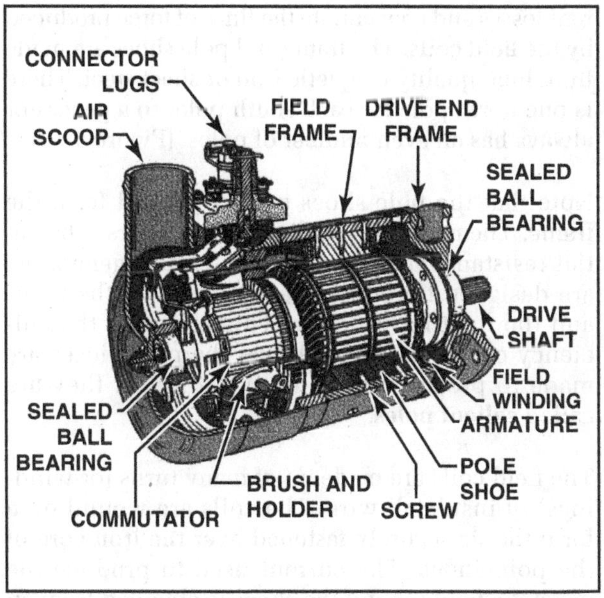


**Figure 8-9. The major parts, or assemblies, of a DC generator include the field frame, rotating armature, commutator, and brush assembly.**

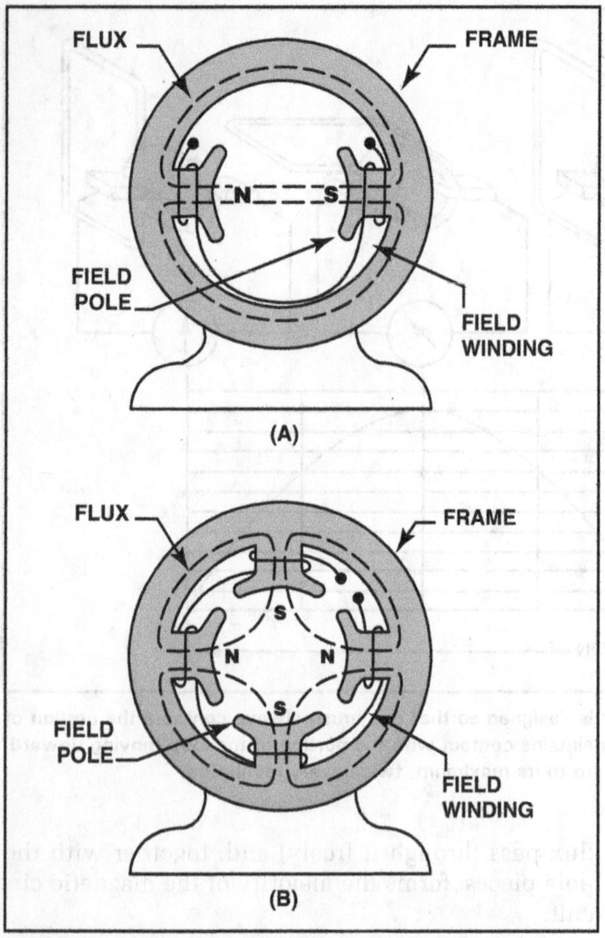


**Figure 8-10. Generator field frames typically house two or four pole shoes. These shoes are not permanent magnets—they rely on the field windings to produce the magnetic field. To produce the necessary magnetic field with permanent magnets would require a significant increase in the size and weight of the generator.**

rent losses and concentrate the lines of force produced by the field coils. The frame and pole shoes are made from high-quality magnetic iron or sheet steel. There is one north pole for each south pole, so a generator always has an even number of poles. [Figure 8-10]

Note that the pole shoes project inward from the frame. The reason is that because air offers substantial resistance to a magnetic field, most generators are designed to reduce the gap between the poles and the rotating armature. This increases the efficiency of the generator. When the pole pieces are made to project inward from the frame, they are called **salient poles.**

The field coils are made up of many turns (or windings) of insulated wire. The coils are wound on a form that is securely fastened over the iron core of the pole shoes. The current used to produce the magnetic field around the shoes is obtained from an external source or from the current generated by the unit itself. The magnetic field is created by the field coils, and there is no electrical connection between the windings of the field coils and the pole shoes. The pole shoes serve to concentrate the magnetic field produced by the field windings. [Figure 8-11]

## ARMATURE

The armature assembly consists of the armature coils, the commutator, and other associated mechanical parts. The armature is mounted on a shaft that rotates in bearings located in the generator's end frames. The core of the armature acts as a conductor when it is rotated in the magnetic field and, like the pole shoes, it is also laminated to prevent the circulation of eddy currents. [Figure 8-12]

A **drum-type armature** has coils placed in slots in the core of the armature. However, there is no electrical connection between the coils and core. The coils are usually held in the slots by wooden or fiber wedges. The coil ends are brought out to individual segments of the commutator.

## COMMUTATORS

The commutator is located at one end of the armature and consists of wedge-shaped segments of hard-drawn copper. Each segment is insulated from the other by a thin sheet of mica. The segments are held in place by steel V-rings or clamping flanges fitted with bolts. Rings of mica also insulate the segments from the flanges. The raised portion of each segment is called the riser, and the leads from the armature coils are soldered to each riser. In some generators, the segments have no risers—the leads are soldered directly to short slits in the ends of the segments. [Figure 8-13]

One end of a single armature coil attaches to one commutator segment, while the other end is sol-

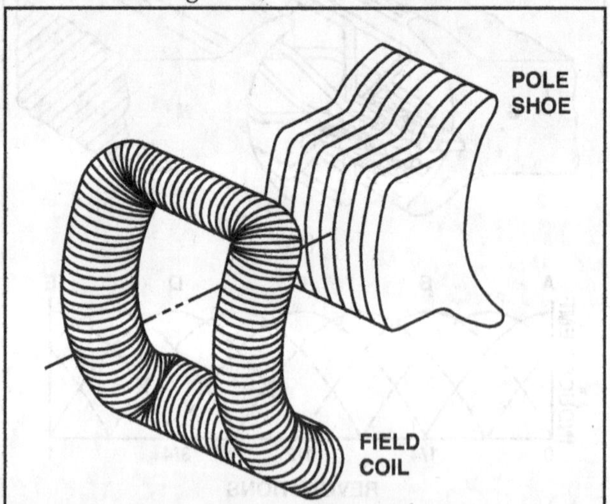


**Figure 8-11. Field coils are form-fitted around the pole shoes so that the north and south poles alternate.**

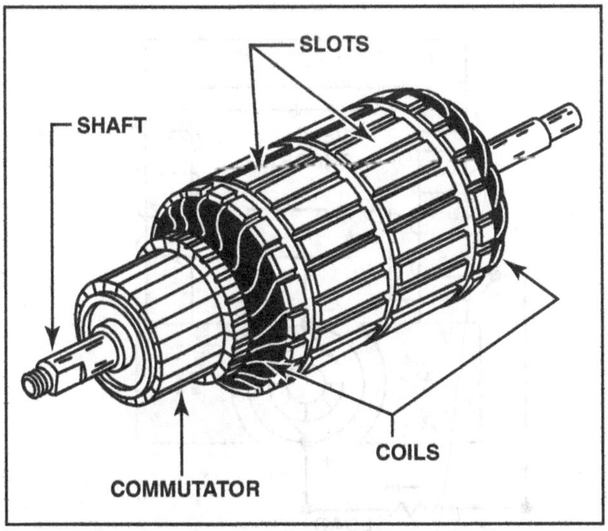


**Figure 8-12. As an armature rotates within the frame assembly, current is induced by the electromagnetic field of the field coils and pole shoes.**

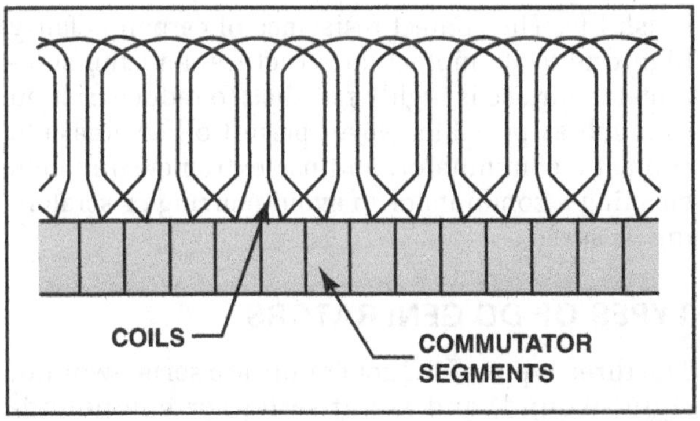


**Figure 8-14. Lap winding connects one end of two coils to each commutator segment; the other end of each coil is attached to one of the adjacent segments.**

dered to the adjacent segment. In this configuration, each coil laps over the preceding one. This is known as lap winding. When an armature rotates at operational speed, the resulting magnetic field lags behind the speed of rotation. Lap winding is a method for stabilizing the armature's magnetic field. [Figure 8-14]

## BRUSHES

Brushes ride on the surface of the commutator and act as the electrical contact between armature coils and an external circuit. A flexible braided-copper conductor, called a pig-tail, connects each brush to the external circuit. The brushes are made of high-grade carbon and held in place by spring-loaded brush holders that are insulated from the frame. The brushes are free to slide up and down in their holders so that they can follow any irregularities in the commutator's surface and compensate for wear. A brush's position is typically adjustable so that the pressure on the commutator can be varied, and so the brush position with respect to the risers can be changed as necessary. The spring tension must be sufficient to ensure good electrical contact between the brush and the rotating commutator, but not so great that is contributes to excessive wear. Conversely, inadequate spring tension results in poor electrical contact that can result in arcing between the brush and the commutator. [Figure 8-15]

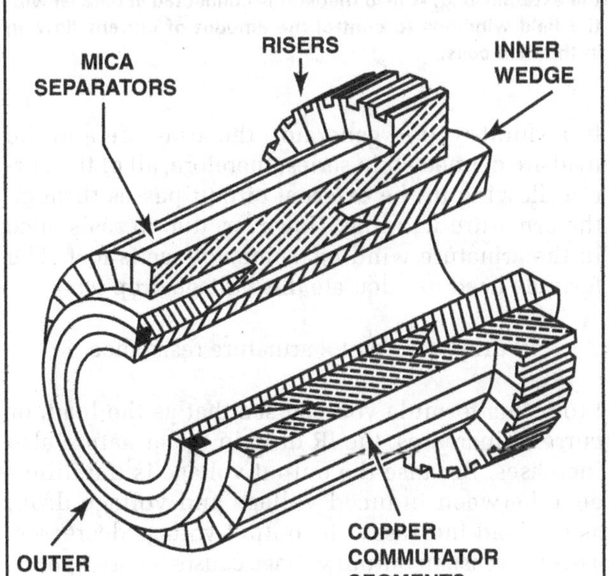


**Figure 8-13. Each segment of a commutator is mounted in a wedge, separated by thin pieces of insulating mica. The leads from the armature coils are attached to the risers.**

The constant making and breaking of connections to armature coils necessitate the use of a brush material that has a definite contact resistance. This material must also have low friction to prevent excessive wear. The high-grade carbon used to make brushes must be soft enough to prevent undue wear to the commutator, yet hard enough to provide reasonable

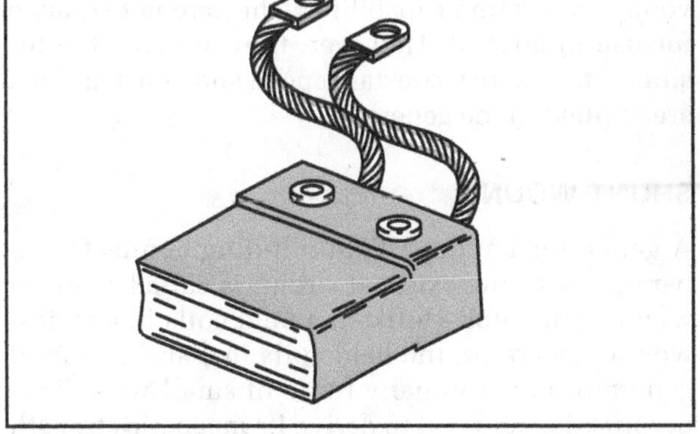

**Figure 8-15. Carbon brushes connect to an external circuit through pig-tails. The brushes are typically adjustable to allow varied pressure on the commutator and position on the segments.**

brush life. The contact resistance of carbon is fairly high due to its molecular structure, and the commutator surface is highly polished to reduce friction as much as possible. Never permit oil or grease to contact a commutator, and use extreme care when cleaning a commutator to avoid marring or scratching its surface.

## TYPES OF DC GENERATORS

The three types of DC generators are series-wound, shunt-wound, and shunt-series, or compound-wound. The difference between each depends on how the field winding is connected to the external circuit.

### SERIES-WOUND

The field winding of a series-wound generator is connected in series with the external load circuit. In this type of generator, the field coils are composed of a few turns of large wire because they must carry the full load current. Magnetic field strength in a series-wound generator is created more because of the large current flow than the number of turns in the coil.

Because of the way that series-wound generators are constructed, they possess poor voltage regulation capabilities. For example, as the load voltage increases, the current through the field coils also increases. This induces a greater EMF that, in turn, increases the generator's output voltage. Therefore, when the load increases, voltage increases; likewise, when the load decreases, voltage decreases.

One way to control the output voltage of a series-wound generator is to install a rheostat in parallel with the field windings. This limits the amount of current that flows through the field coils, thereby limiting the voltage output. [Figure 8-16]

Because series-wound generators have such poor voltage regulation capabilities, they are not suitable for use in aircraft. However, they are suitable for situations where a constant speed and constant load are applied to the generator.

### SHUNT-WOUND

A generator having a field winding connected in parallel with the external circuit is called a shunt-wound generator. Unlike the field coils in a series-wound generator, the field coils in a shunt-wound generator contain many turns of small wire. This permits the field coil to derive its magnetic strength from the large number of turns, rather than from the amount of current flowing through the coils. [Figure 8-17]

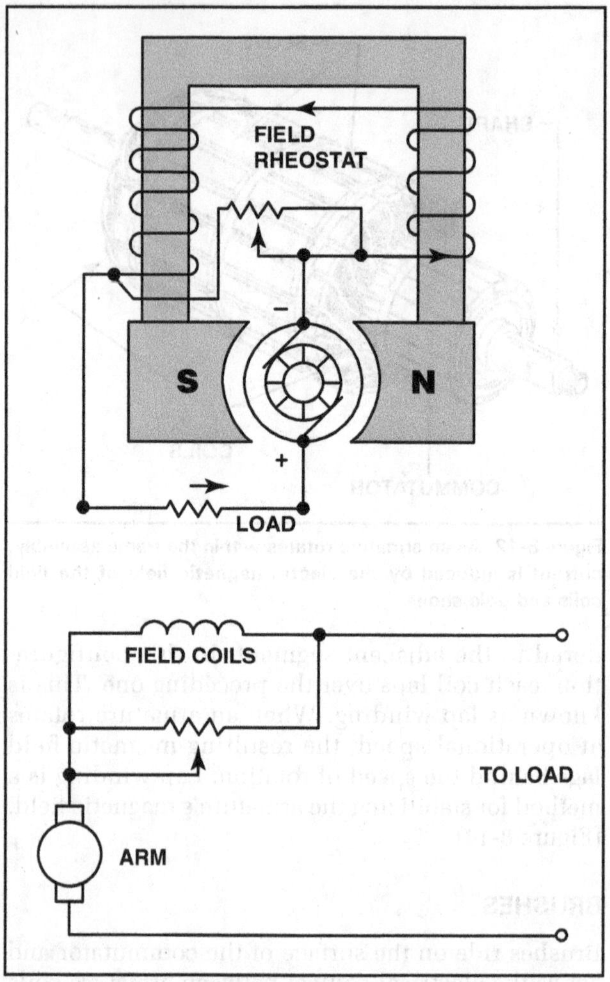


**Figure 8-16. The schematic of a series-wound generator shows that the field windings are connected in series with the external load. A field rheostat is connected in parallel with the field windings to control the amount of current flowing in the field coils.**

In a shunt-wound generator, the armature and the load are connected in series; therefore, all of the current flowing in the external circuit passes through the armature winding. However, due to resistance in the armature winding, some voltage is lost. The formula used to calculate this voltage drop is:

$$\text{IR drop} = \text{current} \times \text{armature resistance}$$

From this formula you can see that as the load, or current, increases, the IR drop in the armature also increases. Because the output voltage is the difference between induced voltage and voltage drop, as the load increases, the output voltage decreases. This decrease in output voltage causes a corresponding decrease in field strength because the current in the field coils decreases with a decrease in output voltage. Similarly, when the load decreases, the output voltage increases accordingly, and a greater current flows in the windings. This action is cumu-

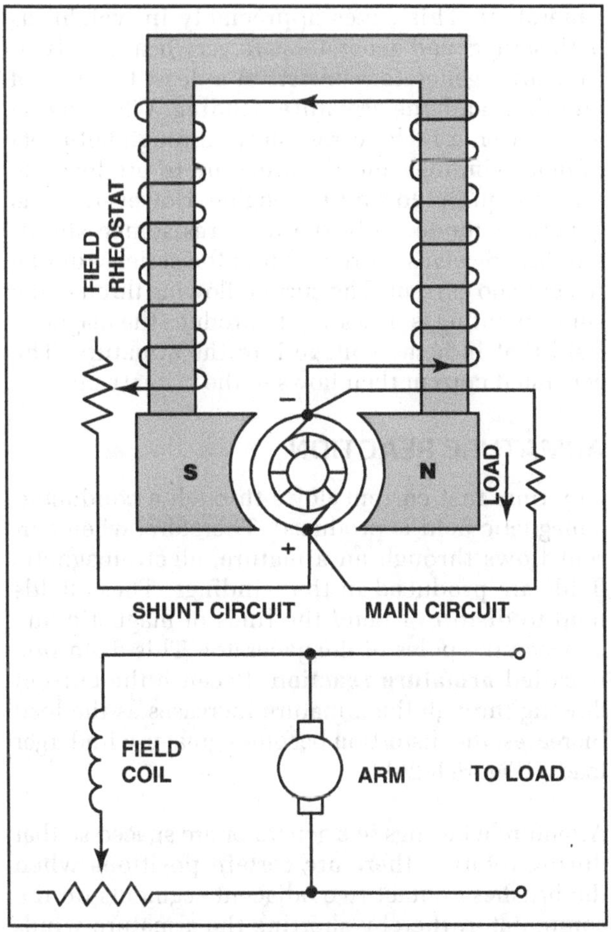


**Figure 8-17. In a shunt-wound generator, the field windings are connected in parallel with the external load.**

lative and, if permitted to go unchecked, the output voltage would rise to a point called **field saturation.** At this point there is no further increase in output voltage. Because of this, a shunt-wound generator is not suitable for rapidly fluctuating loads.

To control the output voltage of a shunt generator, a rheostat is inserted in series with the field winding. In this configuration, as armature resistance increases, the rheostat reduces the field current, which decreases the output voltage. For a given setting on the field rheostat, the terminal voltage at the armature brushes is approximately equal to the generated voltage minus the IR drop produced by the armature resistance. However, this also means that the output voltage at the terminals drops when a larger load is applied. Certain voltage-sensitive devices are available that automatically adjust the field rheostat to compensate for variations in load. When these devices are used, the terminal voltage remains essentially constant.

The output and voltage-regulation capabilities of shunt-type generators make them suitable for light to medium duty use on aircraft. However, DC alternators generally have replaced most of these units.

## COMPOUND-WOUND

A compound-wound generator combines a series winding and a shunt winding to take advantage of the favorable characteristics of each. The series field coils consist of a relatively small number of turns made of large copper conductor, either circular or rectangular in cross-section. As discussed earlier, series field coils are connected in series with the armature circuit. These coils are mounted on the same poles as the shunt field coils and, therefore, contribute to the magnetizing force, or **magnetomotive force**, which influences the generator's main field flux. [Figure 8-18]

If the ampere-turns of the series field act in the same direction as those of the shunt field, the combined magnetomotive force is equal to the sum of the series and shunt field components. Load is added to a compound-wound generator in the same manner as a shunt-wound generator—that is, by increasing the number of parallel paths across the generator. When this is done, the total load resistance decreases, which causes an increase in armature-circuit and series-field circuit current. Therefore, by adding a series field, the field flux increases with an increased load. Thus, the output voltage of the generator

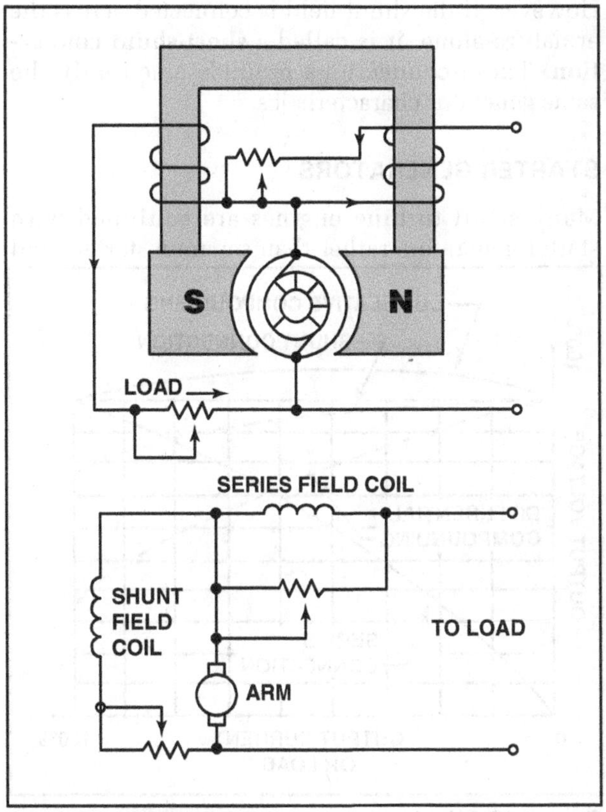


**Figure 8-18. Compound-wound generators use both series and shunt windings.**

increases or decreases with load, depending on the influence of the series field coils. This influence is referred to as the **degree of compounding**.

The amount of output voltage produced by a compound-wound generator depends on the degree of compounding. For example, a **flat-compound** generator is one in which the no-load and full-load voltages have the same value. However, an **under-compound** generator has a full-load voltage less than the no-load voltage, and an **over-compound** generator has a full-load voltage higher than the no-load voltage.

Generators are typically designed to be over-compounded. This design permits varied degrees of compounding by connecting a variable shunt across the series field. Such a shunt is sometimes called a **diverter**. Compound generators are used where voltage regulation is critically important.

If, in a compound-wound generator, the series field aids the shunt field, the generator is said to **be cumulative-compounded**. However, if the series field opposes the shunt field, the generator is said to be **differentially-compounded**. [Figure 8-19]

If the shunt field of a compound-wound generator is connected across both the armature and the series field, it is known as a **long-shunt connection**. However, if the shunt field is connected across the armature alone, it is called a **short-shunt connection**. These connections produce essentially the same generator characteristics.

## STARTER GENERATORS

Many small turbine engines are equipped with starter generators rather than separate starters and generators. This saves appreciably in weight, as both starters and generators are very heavy. A typical starter generator consists of at least two sets of windings and one armature winding. When acting as a starter, a high current flows through both sets of field windings and the armature to produce the torque required to start the engine. However, in the generator mode, only the high resistance shunt-winding receives current, while the series-winding receives no current. The current flowing through the shunt-winding is necessary to produce the magnetic field that induces voltage into the armature. The generated current then flows to the primary bus.

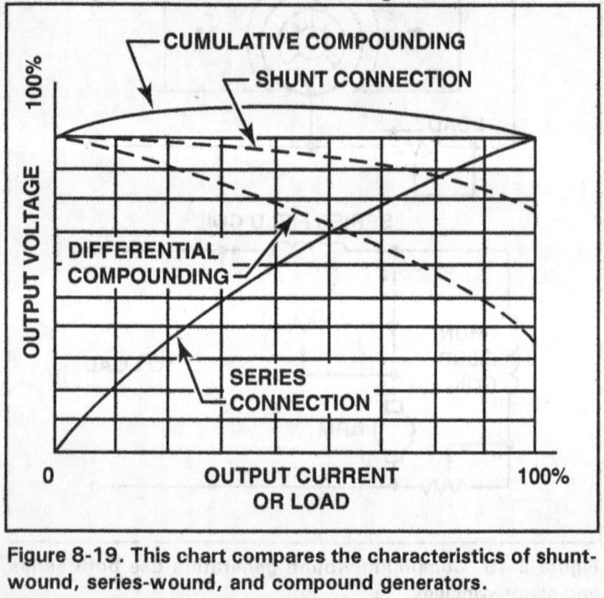


**Figure 8-19. This chart compares the characteristics of shunt-wound, series-wound, and compound generators.**

## ARMATURE REACTION

Any time that current flows through a conductor, a magnetic field is produced. Therefore, when current flows through an armature, electromagnetic fields are produced in the windings. These fields tend to distort or bend the lines of magnetic flux between the poles of the generator. This distortion is called **armature reaction**. Because the current flowing through the armature increases as the load increases, the distortion becomes greater with larger loads. [Figure 8-20]

Armature windings of a generator are spaced so that during rotation there are certain positions when the brushes contact two adjacent segments on the commutator, thereby shorting the armature windings. When the magnetic field is not distorted, no voltage is induced in the shorted windings and no harmful results occur. However, when the field is distorted by armature reaction, a voltage is induced in the shorted windings, and arcing occurs between the brushes and the commutator segments. Consequently, the commutator becomes pitted, the wear on the brushes becomes excessive, and the output of the generator is reduced.

To correct this condition, the brushes are set so that the plane of the coils being shorted is perpendicular to the distorted magnetic field. This is accomplished by moving the brushes forward in the direction of rotation. This operation is called **shifting the brushes** to the neutral plane, or **plane of commutation**. The neutral plane is the position where the plane of the two opposite coils is perpendicular to the magnetic field in the generator. On a few generators, the brushes are shifted manually ahead of the normal neutral plane to the neutral plane caused by field distortion. On nonadjustable brush generators, the manufacturer sets the brushes to minimize arcing.

In some generators, special field poles, called interpoles, counteract some of the effects of field distortion when the speed and load of the generator

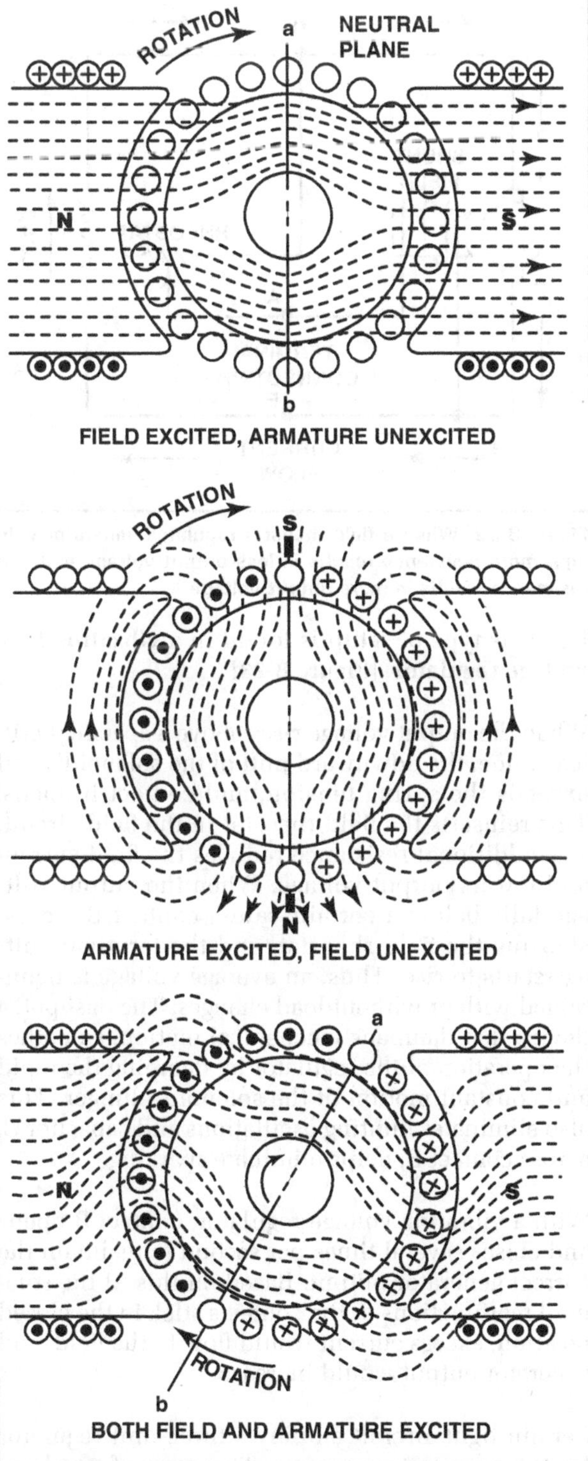


**Figure 8-20. The lines of flux in a field coil flow in a horizontal path from north to south and induce voltage into the armature. Magnetic fields are also produced in the armature, and these tend to distort, or bend, the lines of flux produced by the field coil. This is called armature reaction.**

are changing constantly. An **interpole** is another field pole that is placed between the main poles. [Figure 8-21]

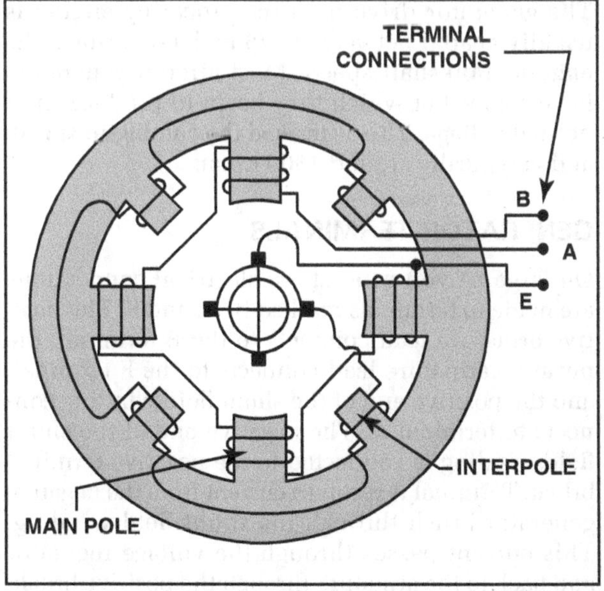


**Figure 8-21. This generator has four poles and four interpoles. Interpoles counteract the effects of armature reaction.**

An interpole has the same polarity as the next main pole in the direction of rotation. The magnetic flux produced by an interpole changes the direction of the current in the armature as the armature winding rotates under the interpole's field. This cancels the electromagnetic fields produced by the armature windings. The interpoles are connected in series with the load and, therefore, the magnetic strength of the interpoles varies with the generator load. Because the field distortion also varies with the load, the magnetic field of the interpoles counteracts the effects of the field around the armature windings and minimizes distortion. In other words, the interpoles keep the neutral plane in the same position for all loads.

## GENERATOR RATINGS

Generators are rated according to their power output. Because a generator is designed to operate at a specified voltage, the rating is usually given as the number of amperes the generator can reliably supply at its rated voltage. For example, a typical generator rating is 300 amps at 28.5 volts. A generator's rating and performance data are stamped on the name plate attached to the generator. When replacing a generator, make sure is the replacement has the proper rating.

Generators rotate either clockwise or counterclockwise, as viewed from the driven end. If no direction is stamped on the data plate, the rotation is marked by an arrow on the cover plate of the brush housing. To maintain the correct polarity, it is important to use a generator with the correct direction of rotation.

The generator drive on a reciprocating engine is usually geared between 1-1/8 and 1-1/2 times the engine crankshaft speed. Most aircraft generators have a speed at which they begin to produce their normal voltage. This is termed the **coming-in speed**, and is typically around 1500 r.p.m.

## GENERATOR TERMINALS

On large 24-volt generators, electrical connections are made to terminals marked B, A, and E. The positive armature lead connects to the B terminal, the negative armature lead connects to the E terminal, and the positive end of the shunt field winding connects to terminal A. The negative end of the shunt field winding is connected to the negative terminal brush. Terminal A receives current from the negative generator brush through the shunt field winding. This current passes through the voltage regulator and back to the armature through the positive brush. Load current, which leaves the armature through the negative brush, comes out of the E lead and passes through the load before returning through the positive brush.

## GENERATOR VOLTAGE REGULATION

Efficient operation of electrical equipment in an aircraft depends on a voltage supply that varies with a system's load requirements. Among the factors that determine the voltage output of a generator, the strength of the field current is the only one that is conveniently controlled.

One way to control the field current is to install a rheostat in the field coil circuit. When the rheostat increases the resistance in the field circuit, less current flows through the field coils and the strength of the magnetic field decreases. Consequently, less voltage is induced into the armature, and generator output decreases. When the rheostat decreases resistance in the field circuit, more current flows through the field coils, and the magnetic field becomes stronger. This allows more voltage to be induced into the armature, which produces a greater output voltage. [Figure 8-22]

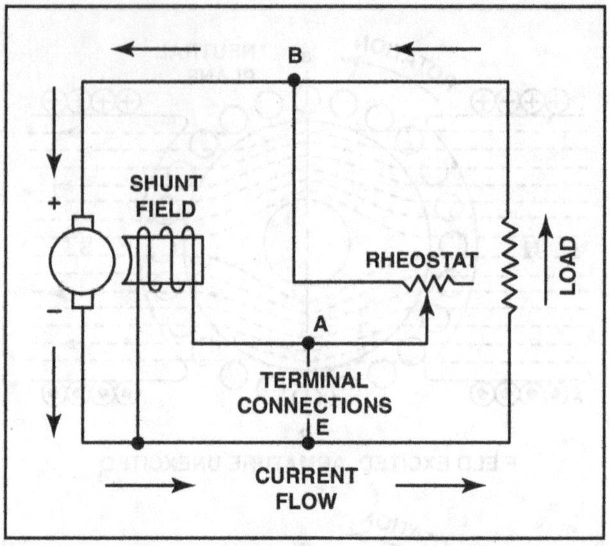


**Figure 8-22. When a field rheostat regulates generator voltage, more resistance results in less output voltage and less resistance results in more output voltage.**

Keep in mind that the weaker the magnetic field, the easier it is to turn the armature. Conversely, if the strength of the magnetic field is increased, more force is required to turn the armature. This means when the load on a generator increases, additional field current must be supplied to increase the voltage output as well as overcome the additional force required to turn the armature.

This principle is further developed by the addition of a solenoid which electrically connects or removes the field rheostat from the circuit as the voltage varies. This type of setup is found in a **vibrating-type voltage regulator**. [Figure 8-23]

When the output voltage rises above a specified critical value, the downward pull of the solenoid's coil exceeds the spring tension, and contact B opens. This reinserts the field rheostat in the field circuit. The additional resistance reduces the field current and lowers output voltage. When the output voltage falls below a certain value, contact B closes, shorting the field rheostat, and the terminal voltage starts to rise. Thus, an average voltage is maintained with or without load changes. The dashpot, a device that dampens mechanical motion, smoothes the operation of the regulator by damping the rapid and constant motion of the solenoid plunger. This also eliminates hunting oscillations and capacitor C, across contact B, helps eliminate sparking.

With a vibrating voltage regulator, contact B opens and closes several times per second to maintain the correct generator output. Based on this, if the solenoid malfunctions or the contacts stick in the closed position, excess current would flow to the field, and generator output would increase.

Certain light aircraft employ a three-unit regulator for their generator systems. This type of regulator includes a current limiter, a reverse current cutout, and a voltage regulator. [Figure 8-24]

The action of the voltage regulator unit is similar to the vibrating regulator described earlier. The **current limiter** is the second of three units, and it limits the generator's output current. The third unit is a **reverse-current cutout**, which disconnects the battery from the generator when the generator output

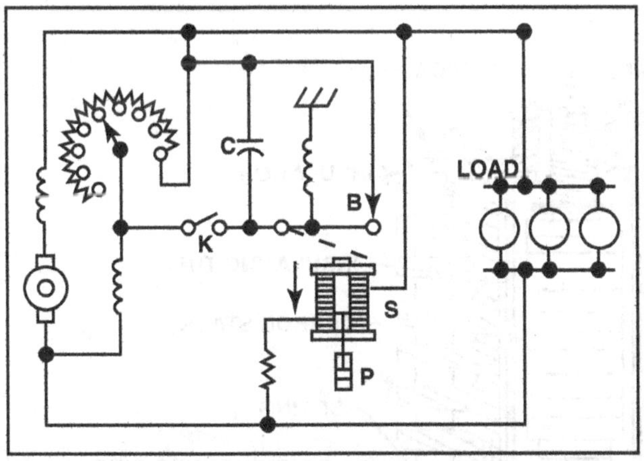


**Figure 8-23. With the generator running at normal speed and switch K open, the field rheostat is adjusted so that the output voltage is about 60 percent of normal. At this level, solenoid S is weak and contact B is held closed by the spring. However, when K is closed, a short circuit is placed across the field rheostat. This action causes the field current to increase and the output voltage to rise.**

is lower than the battery output. If the battery were not disconnected, it would discharge through the generator armature when the generator voltage falls below that of the battery. When this occurs, the battery attempts to drive the generator as a motor. This is called **motoring** the generator and, unless prevented, causes the battery to discharge rapidly.

Because contacts have a tendency to pit or burn when large amounts of current flow through them, vibrating regulators and three-unit regulators cannot be used with generators that require a high field current. Therefore, heavy-duty generator systems require a different type of regulator, such as the carbon-pile voltage regulator. The **carbon-pile** voltage regulator relies on the resistance of carbon disks arranged in a pile or stack. The resistance of the carbon stack varies inversely with the pressure applied. For example, resistance decreases in a compressed stack because less air exists between the carbon disks. However, when the pressure is reduced, more air comes between the disks and causes the resistance to increase.

Pressure on the carbon pile is modulated by two opposing forces: a spring and an electromagnet. The spring compresses the carbon pile, and the electromagnet exerts a pull on the spring that decreases the pressure. [Figure 8-25]

Whenever the generator voltage varies, the pull of the electromagnet varies. If the generator voltage rises above a specific amount, the pull of the electromagnet increases, thereby decreasing the pressure exerted on the carbon pile and increasing its resistance. Because this resistance is in series with the field, less current flows through the field winding with a corresponding decrease in field strength. This results in a drop in generator output.

If the generator output drops below a specified value, the pull of the electromagnet decreases and

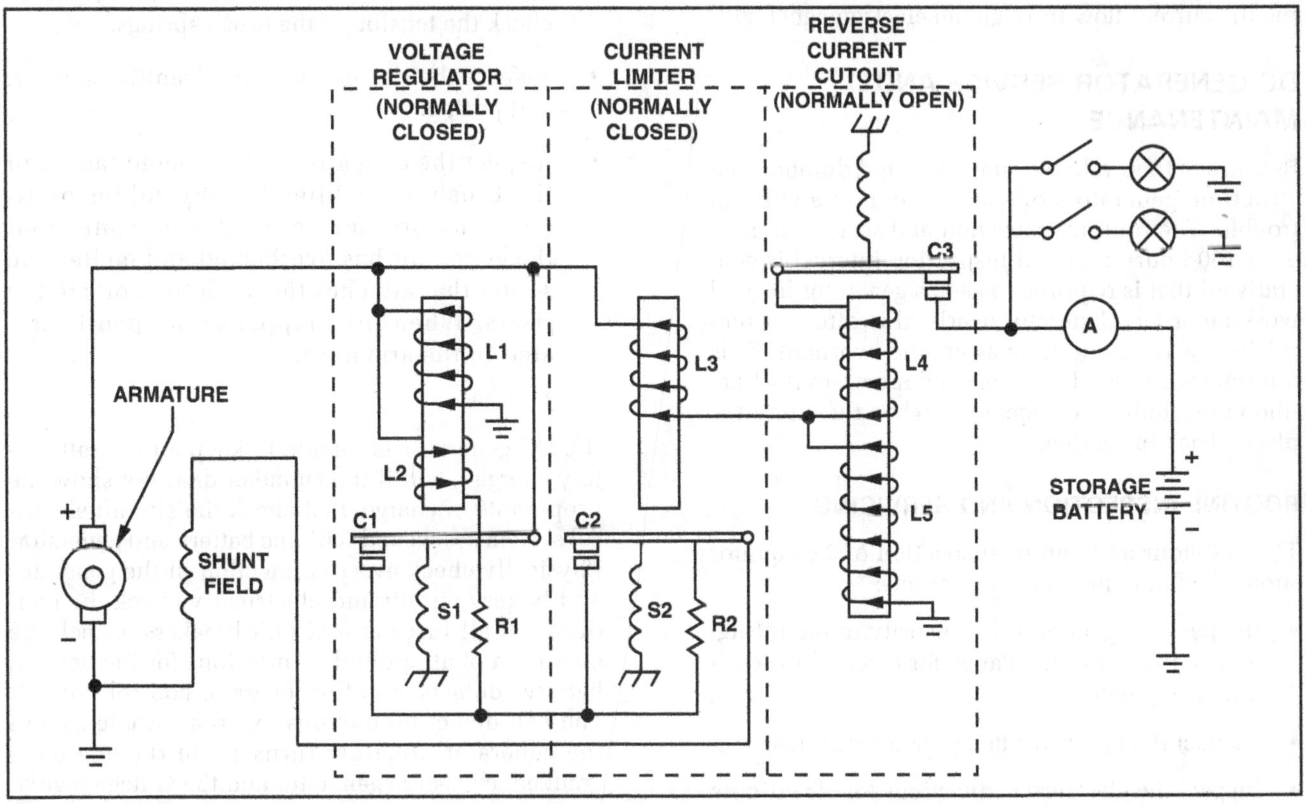


**Figure 8-24. A typical voltage regulator contains three coils: a voltage regulator, a current limiter, and a reverse current cutout.**

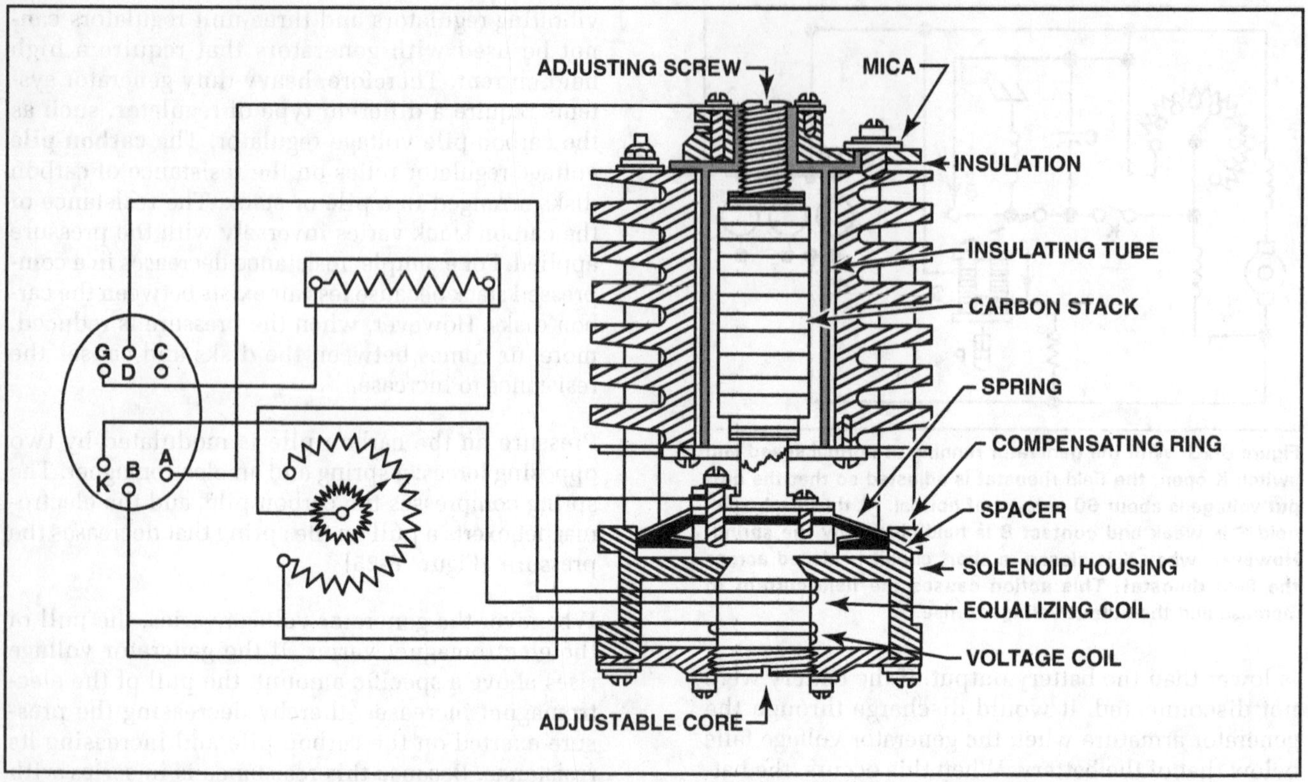


**Figure 8-25. A carbon pile voltage regulator relies on the amount of air space within a stack of carbon disks to control generator voltage. A spring maintains pressure on the disks; an electromagnet controls spring tension.**

the carbon pile places less resistance in the field winding circuit. This results in an increase in field strength and a corresponding increase in generator output. A small rheostat provides a means of adjusting the current flow through the electromagnet coil.

## DC GENERATOR SERVICE AND MAINTENANCE

Because of their relative simplicity and durable construction, generators operate many hours without trouble. The routine inspection and service done at each 100-hour or annual inspection interval is generally all that is required to keep a generator in good working order. Generator overhaul is often accomplished at the same time as engine overhaul. This minimizes aircraft down time and increases the likelihood of trouble-free operation when the aircraft is placed back in service.

### ROUTINE INSPECTION AND SERVICING

The 100-hour and annual inspection of a generator should include the following actions:

- Inspect the generator for security of mounting; check the mounting flange for cracks and loose mounting bolts.
- Inspect the mounting flange area for oil leaks.
- Inspect the electrical connections for cleanliness and security of attachment.
- Remove the band that covers the brushes and commutator. Use compressed air to blow out accumulated dust. Inspect the brushes for wear and freedom of movement. Use a spring scale to check the tension of the brush springs.
- Inspect the commutator for cleanliness, wear, and pitting.
- Inspect the area around the commutator and the brush assemblies for any solder particles. The presence of solder indicates that the generator has overheated and melted the solder that attaches the armature coils to the risers. When this happens, an open is created in the armature.

If a DC generator is unable to keep an aircraft battery charged, and if the ammeter does not show the proper rate of charge, first check the aircraft electrical system associated with the battery and generator. Physically check every connection in the generator and battery circuit and electrically check the condition of all fuses and circuit breakers. Check the condition of all ground connections for the battery, battery contacts, and the generator control units. If you can detect no obvious external problems and the generator armature turns when the engine is cranked, check the generator and the voltage regulator.

One of the easiest ways to determine which unit is inoperative is to connect a voltmeter between the G terminal of the voltage regulator and ground. This checks the generator's output voltage. However, because this check requires the generator to be turning, it must be accomplished with the engine running or on an appropriate test stand. In either case, observe proper safety precautions. Even when the field winding is open, or the voltage regulator is malfunctioning, the generator should produce residual voltage. In other words, the action of the armature cutting across the residual magnetic field in the generator frame and field shoes, produces some voltage. This should be around one or two volts.

If there is no residual voltage, you might need only to restore the generator's residual magnetism through an operation known as **flashing the field.** This is accomplished by momentarily passing current through the field coils in the same direction that it normally flows. The methods vary with the internal connections of the generator, and with the type of voltage regulator used.

For example, for an A circuit generator, you ground the field, and then touch the positive terminal of the battery to the armature. You might also need to insulate one of the brushes by inserting a piece of insulating material between the brush and commutator. To flash the field in an internally grounded B circuit generator, you touch the positive battery terminal to the field. Whatever the case, be certain to follow the specific manufacturer instructions. Failure to do so could result in damage to the generator, the voltage regulator, or both.

If the generator produces residual voltage but no output voltage, the trouble could be with the generator or the regulator. To determine which, operate the engine at a speed high enough for the generator to produce an output, and bypass the voltage regulator with a jumper wire. The method you use varies with the type of generator and regulator being used, and should be done in accordance with the manufacturer's recommendations.

If the generator produces voltage with the regulator shorted, the problem is with the voltage regulator. If this is the case, be sure that the regulator is properly grounded, because a faulty ground connection prevents a regulator from functioning properly. Although it is possible to service and adjust the controls of some vibrator generators, because of the expense, time involved, and test equipment necessary to do the job, most faulty unit are simply replaced with new units. If the generator does not produce an output voltage when the regulator is bypassed, remove the generator from the engine and either overhaul it or replace it with a serviceable unit.

## GENERATOR OVERHAUL

Generator overhaul is accomplished any time a generator is determined to be inoperative, or at the same time the aircraft engine is overhauled. Although an overhaul can be done in some aircraft repair facilities, it is more often the job of an FAA Certified Repair Station licensed for that operation.

The steps involved in the overhaul of a generator are the same for the overhaul of any unit: (1) disassembly, (2) cleaning, (3) inspection and repair, (4) reassembly, and (5) testing.

### DISASSEMBLY

Disassembly instructions for specific units are covered in the manufacturer's overhaul manual and must be followed exactly. Specialized tools are sometimes required for removing pole shoes because the screws holding these in place are usually staked to prevent them from accidentally backing out. Be sure to follow any special instructions when removing bearings. If you fail to use the correct procedures or tools, you can damage the bearings or their seating area.

### CLEANING

Take extra care when cleaning electrical parts. Use the proper solvents, and, in general, do not submerge parts in solvent tanks. Many solvents can remove the lacquer-type insulation used on field coils and armatures, resulting in short circuits after the generator is reassembled.

### INSPECTION AND REPAIR

Inspect components for physical damage, corrosion or wear, and repair or replace them as required. Use a growler and an electrical multimeter to test for proper operation of the electrical components. A **growler** is a specially designed test unit for DC generators and motors and you will use this equipment to perform a variety of tests on the armature and field coils.

Growlers consist of a laminated core wound with many turns of wire that are connected to 110 volts AC. The top of the core forms a V into which the armature of a DC generator fits. The coil and laminated core of the growler form the primary of a transformer, while the generator armature becomes the secondary. Most growlers have a test lamp. This is a simple series circuit with a light bulb that illuminates when the circuit is complete. [Figure 8-26]

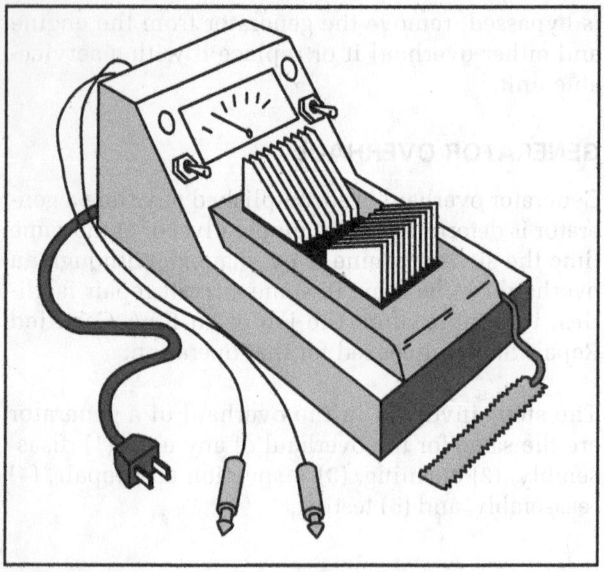

Figure 8-26. A growler tests the armature of a DC generator for open circuits.

To test an armature for an open circuit, place it on an energized growler and then place the test lamp probes on adjacent segments of each armature coil. The lamp should light with each set of commutator bars. Failure of the test lamp to illuminate indicates an open circuit in that coil; in such cases, the only acceptable repair is to replace the entire armature.

Armatures are also tested for shorts by placing them on a growler, energizing the unit, and holding a thin steel strip, typically a hacksaw blade, slightly above the armature. Slowly rotate the armature on the growler. If there are any shorts in the armature windings, the steel strip will vibrate vigorously. [Figure 8-27]

A third test for armature shorts uses the test lamp to check for grounds. To use a test lamp, touch one lead to the armature shaft and touch the second lead to each commutator segment. If a ground exists between any of the windings and the core of the armature, the test lamp illuminates. [Figure 8-28]

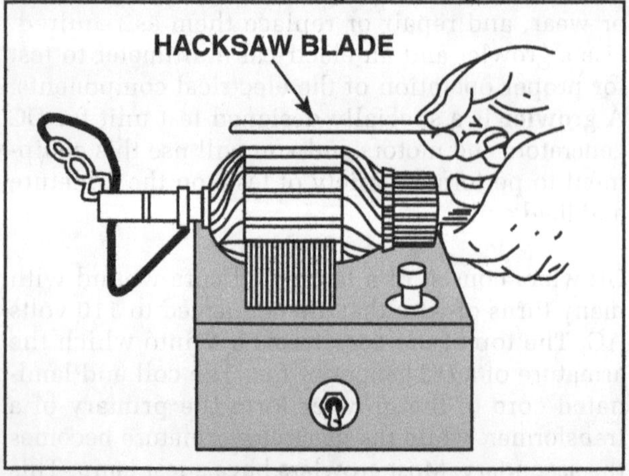


Figure 8-27. When a short exists in the armature windings, the hacksaw blade vibrates vigorously.

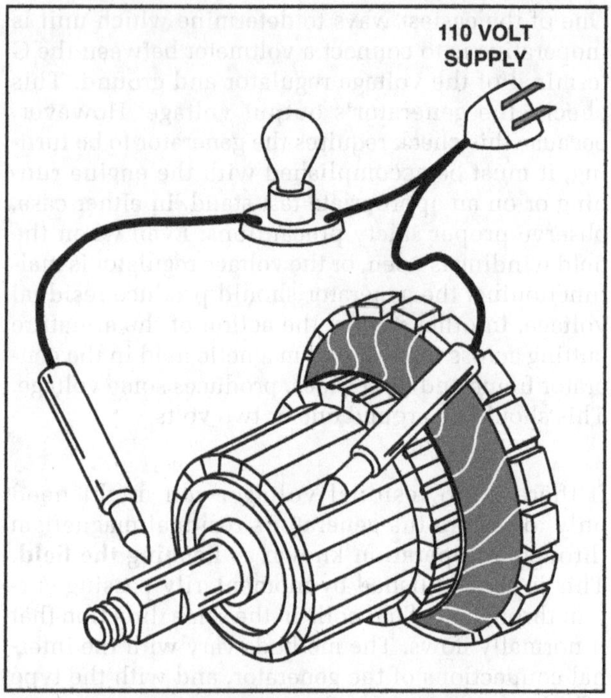


Figure 8-28. When a ground exists between an armature winding and the core, the test light illuminates. This test can also be done with an ohmmeter.

You can also test the generator's field coil for shorts by using a test lamp. To do this, place one probe at the terminal of the field winding and the other probe at the generator frame. If the light illuminates, a short exists. [Figure 8-29]

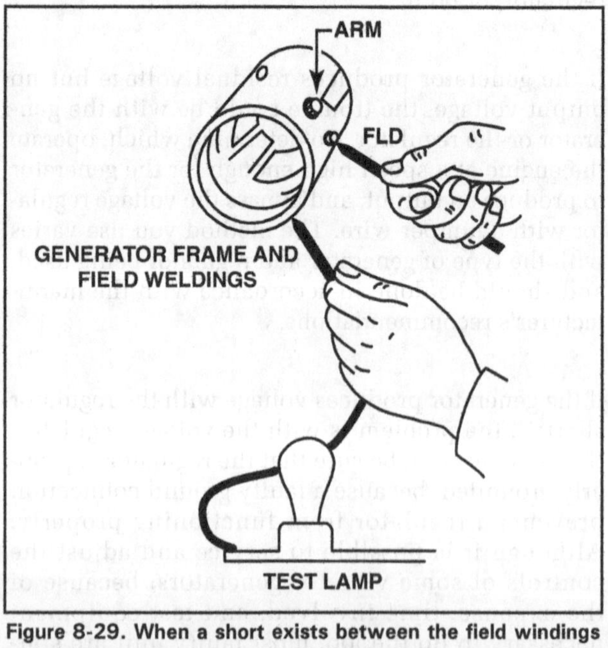


Figure 8-29. When a short exists between the field windings and the frame, a test lamp will illuminate. A successful test indicates an open circuit between these components—that is, the light should not illuminate.

You can test the field coil for continuity with an ohmmeter on a low-ohms scale. A shunt field coil should indicate between 2 and 30 ohms, depending on the specific coil. A series field coil shows almost no resistance. In some cases, the manufacturer specifies a current draw test, which involves connecting a battery of proper voltage across the field coils and measuring the current flow. This value must be within the limits specified in the manufacturer's test specifications. [Figure 8-30]

To resurface a commutator to remove irregularities or pitting, place the armature in a special armature lathe, or an engine lathe equipped with a special holding fixture. When doing this, remove only enough metal to smooth the commutator's surface. If you remove too much material, you jeopardize the security of the coil ends. If the commutator is only slightly roughened, smooth it using No. 000 sandpaper. Never use emery cloth or other conductive material, because you can inadvertently introduce shorts between commutator segments.

You might need to **undercut** the mica insulation between the bars of some commutators. However, when doing this, follow the most current instructions provided by the manufacturer. This operation is accomplished using a special attachment for the armature lathe, or by using a hacksaw blade. Typically, the mica is undercut about the same depth as the mica's width, or approximately .020 inch.

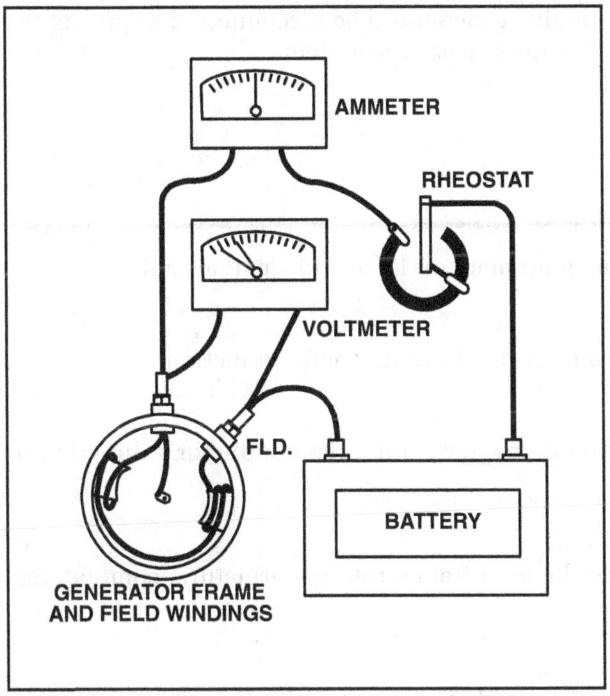


**Figure 8-30. To test for shorted turns in a field coil, measure the field current draw at a specific voltage. The current drawn by the field must be within the manufacturer's prescribed range for the field windings to be considered good.**

## REASSEMBLY

Prior to reassembly, restore the painted finish on the exterior of the frame. In certain cases, you must renew the special insulated coatings on the interior surfaces. Replace all defective parts in accordance with the reassembly procedure specified by the manufacturer.

When reassembling a generator, ensure that all internal electrical connections are properly made and secured, and that the brushes are free to move in their holders. Check the pig-tails on the brushes for freedom, and make sure that they do not alter or restrict the free motion of the brushes. The purpose of the pig-tail is to conduct current and help eliminate any current in the brush springs that could alter its spring action. The pig-tails also eliminate possible sparking caused by movement of the brush within the holder, thus minimizing brush side wear.

Generator brushes are normally replaced at overhaul, or when half-worn. When you install new brushes, be sure to seat them to maximize the contact area between the face of the brush and the commutator. Seat the brush by lifting it slightly to permit the insertion of Number 000 (or finer) sandpaper, rough side out. With the sandpaper in place, pull the sandpaper in the direction of armature rotation, being careful to keep the ends of the sandpaper as close to the commutator as possible to avoid rounding the edges of the brush. When pulling the sandpaper back to the starting point, raise the brush so it does not ride on the sandpaper. [Figure 8-31]

Check the brush spring tension with a spring scale. A carbon, graphite, or light metal brush should exert a pressure of only 1? to 2? pounds on the commutator. If the spring tension is not within the limits set by the manufacturer, replace the springs. When using the spring scale, read the pressure measurement exerted by a brush directly on the spring scale. Attach the scale at the point of contact between the spring arm and the top of the brush, with the brush installed in the guide. Then pull the scale upward until the arm just begins to lift the brush off of the commutator, and read the force on the scale at that moment.

After the generator has run for a short period, the brushes should be inspected to ensure that no pieces of sand are embedded in the brush. Under no circumstance should you use emery cloth or similar abrasive for seating brushes or smoothing commutators because they contain conductive materials.

## TESTING

Carry out operational testing of generators on test benches built for that purpose. Bench testing enables

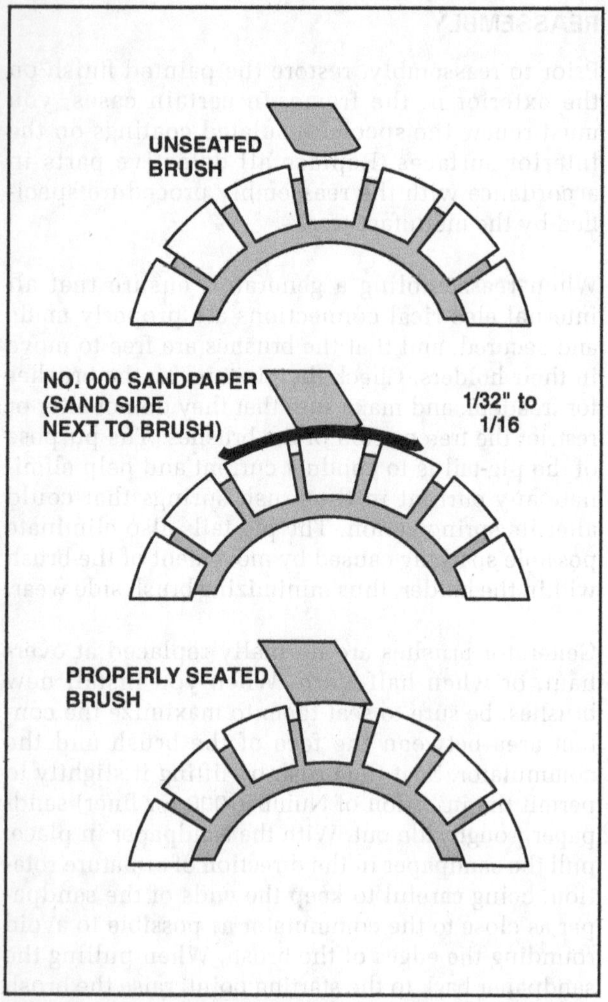


**Figure 8-31. When a new brush is installed in a generator, the brush must be contoured to fit the commutator.**

you to flash the field and ensure proper operation of the unit before installation. Generator manufacturers supply test specifications in their overhaul instructions that should be followed exactly.

## GENERATOR SYSTEMS

When installed on most aircraft, the output of a generator typically flows to the aircraft's bus bar where it is distributed to the various electrical components. In this type of system, the allowable voltage drop in the main power wires coming off the generator to the bus bar is two percent of the regulated voltage when the generator is producing its rated current. As added insurance to make sure that a given electrical load does not exceed a generator's output capability, the total continuous electrical load permitted in a given system is limited to 80 percent of the total rated generator output. For example, if an aircraft has a 60-amp generator, the maximum continuous load that can be placed on the electrical system is 48 amps.

If a generator quits producing current or produces too much current, most aircraft systems have a generator master switch that permits the generator to be disconnected from the electrical system. This feature helps prevent damage to the generator or to the rest of the electrical system. On aircraft that use more than one generator connected to a common electrical system, the Federal Aviation Regulations require individual generator switches that can be operated from the cockpit. This permits a malfunctioning generator to be disconnected to protect the remaining electrical system.

# SUMMARY CHECKLIST

✓ Generators supply operational energy for most electrical equipment on large and small aircraft.

✓ A generator converts mechanical energy into electrical energy by electromagnetic induction.

✓ The left hand rule for generators illustrates the direction of magnetic flux, the conductor's direction of movement, and the direction of induced EMF.

✓ The major components of a generator assembly include the field frame, rotating armature, commutator, and brush assembly.

✓ The three types of DC generators are series-wound, shunt-wound, and shunt-series (compound-wound). Each type is differentiated by the manner in which the field winding is connected to the external circuit.

✓ Armature reaction is the distortion of lines of magnetic flux between the poles of the generator.

✓ A generator rating refers to its power output, usually expressed as the number of amperes that the generator can safely supply at its rated voltage.

✓ Generator voltage can be regulated by controlling the strength of the field current with devices such as rheostats.

✓ A three-unit voltage regulator consists of a current limiter coil, a voltage regulator coil, and a current cutout coil.

✓ A generator is overhauled when the generator is inoperative or the aircraft engine is overhauled. An overhaul of the generator includes disassembly, cleaning, inspection, repair, reassembly, and testing.

✓ A growler is a test unit designed to test the armature of a DC generator.

# KEY TERMS

generator
DC generators
AC generators
commutator
ripple
field coil
field pole
pole shoe
salient poles
drum-type armature
field saturation
magnetomotive force
degree of compounding
flat-compound generator
under-compound generator
over-compound generator
diverter
cumulative-compounded
differentially-compounded
long-shunt connection
short-shunt connection
armature reaction
shifting the brushes
plane of commutation
interpole
coming-in speed
vibrating-type voltage regulator
current limiter
reverse-current cutout
motoring
carbon-pile
flashing the field
growler
undercut

# QUESTIONS

1. Most light aircraft use only a ______ (AC or DC) power system.

2. The three types of DC generators are:
   a. ____________________
   b. ____________________
   c. ____________________

3. Since the ______________________-wound generator has such poor voltage regulation, it is not used as an aircraft generator.

4. Heavy duty DC generators are usually of the ______________________-wound type.

5. If the series field of a compound-wound generator aids the shunt field, the generator is said to be ______________-compounded.

6. Compound generators are used where ______ ______________ is of prime importance.

7. The voltage output of a generator is controlled by controlling the strength of the _______ current.

8. Generator speed is generally ______ to ______ times crankshaft speed.

9. If the points on a vibrating voltage regulator stick closed, the generator output will ______ (increase, decrease, or cease).

10. The three units of a three-unit voltage regulator are:
    a. ______ ______
    b. ______ ______
    c. ______ ______ ______

11. The function of the reverse current cut-out is to prevent the generator from ______________ and discharging the battery.

12. Heavy-duty DC generators will use a __________ __________ (what type) voltage regulator.

13. The operation known as ______________ ______ ___________ is used to restore residual magnetism to the DC generator.

14. New brushes are seated by using ____________________ (silicon carbide, emery, or sandpaper) wrapped over the armature.

# SECTION B

## ALTERNATORS

Two types of alternators are used in today's aircraft: the DC alternator and the AC alternator. DC alternators produce relatively small amounts of current and, therefore, are typically found on light aircraft. Conversely, AC alternators typically found on larger aircraft and military aircraft are capable of producing a great deal of power. Furthermore, because AC electricity can be carried through smaller conductors, AC alternators allow appreciable weight savings.

### DC ALTERNATORS

DC alternators have the same function as DC generators. They produce AC that is then converted to DC before it enters an aircraft's electrical system. The difference is that in an alternator the magnetic poles rotate and induce voltage into a fixed, or stationary winding. Furthermore, the AC current produced is rectified by six solid-state diodes rather than by a commutator. [Figure 8-32]

All alternators are constructed in basically the same way. The primary components of an alternator include the rotor, the stator, the rectifier, and the brush assembly.

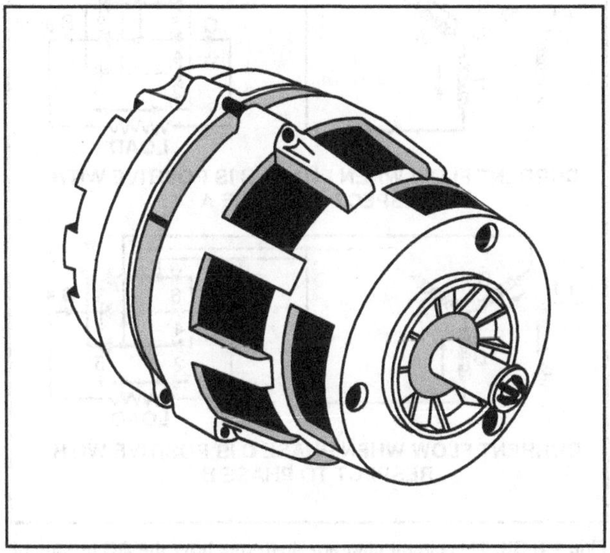

Figure 8-32. Direct current (DC) alternators are sufficient for small to moderate aircraft power needs.

#### ROTOR

An alternator rotor consists of a wire coil wound on an iron spool between two heavy iron segments with interlacing fingers. Rotors have between four and seven fingers. Each finger forms one pole of the rotating magnetic field. [Figure 8-33]

The two coil leads pass through one segment and each lead attaches to an insulated slip ring. The slip rings, segments, and coil spool are all pressed onto a hardened steel rotor shaft that is either splined or machined with a key slot to secure the rotor to the shaft. In an assembled alternator, the rotor shaft is driven by an engine accessory pad or fitted with a pulley and driven by an accessory belt. The slip-ring end of the shaft is supported in the housing with a needle bearing, and the drive end with a ball bearing. Two carbon brushes ride on the smooth slip rings to deliver a varying direct current into the field from the DC exciter and the voltage regulator.

#### STATOR

As the rotor turns, the load current is induced into stationary stator coils. The coils making up the stator are wound in slots around the inside periphery of the stator frame, which is made of thin laminations of soft iron. Most alternators are three-phase alternators. This means that the stator has three separate coils that are 120 degrees apart.

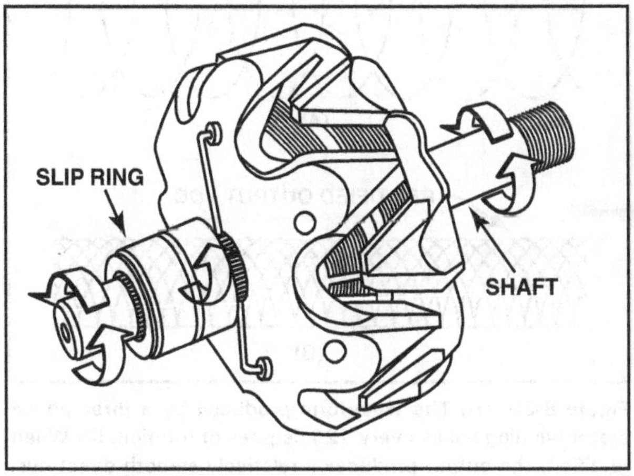


Figure 8-33. The interlacing fingers of a rotor form the poles for the rotating magnetic field.

To do this, one end of each coil is joined at a common junction that forms a Y-connection. [Figure 8-34]

With the stator wound in a three-phase configuration, the output current peaks in each set of windings every 120 degrees of rotation. However, rectified DC output is much smoother. [Figure 8-35]

Because an alternator has several field poles and a large number of stator windings, most alternators produce their rated output at a relatively low speed. This differs from DC generators, which must rotate at a relatively high speed to produce their rated output.

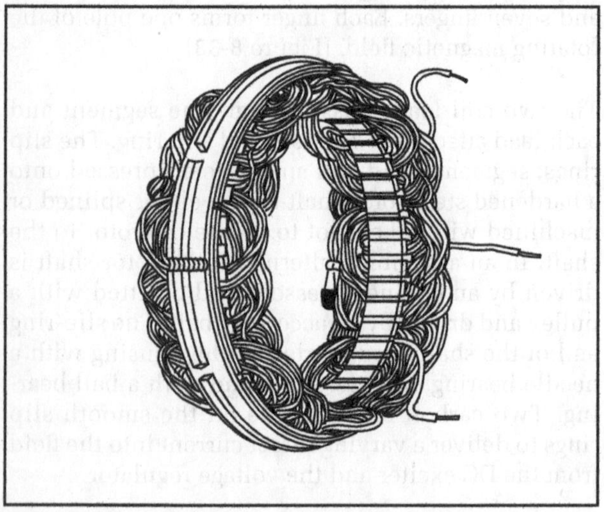

**Figure 8-34. The three sets of coils in a stator are typically joined together with a Y-connection.**

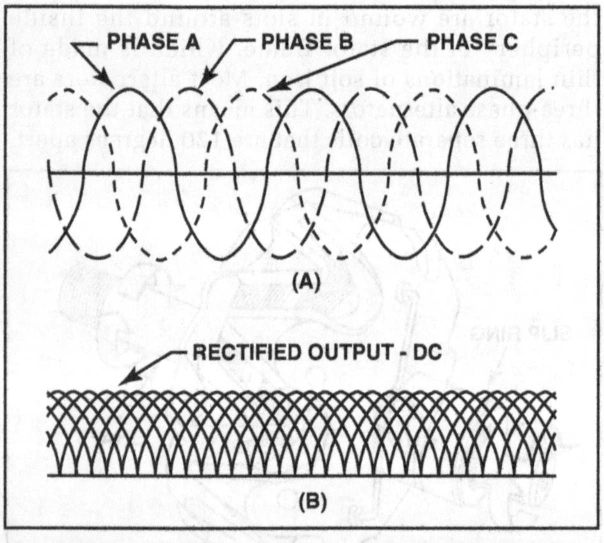


**Figure 8-35. (A) The waveform produced by a three-phase stator winding peaks every 120 degrees of rotation. (B) When rectified, the output produces a relatively smooth direct current, with a low-amplitude, high-frequency ripple.**

## RECTIFIERS

The three-phase, full-wave rectifier in an alternator is made up of six heavy-duty silicon diodes. Three of the diodes are pressed into the slip-ring end frame, and the other three are pressed into a heat sink that is electrically insulated from the end frame. [Figure 8-36]

Figure 8-36 shows that at the instant the output terminal of winding A is positive with respect to the output end of winding C, current flows through diode 1 to the load, and back through diode 2, which is pressed into the alternator end frame. From this diode, it flows back through winding C.

As the rotor continues to turn, winding B becomes positive with respect to winding A, and the current flows through diode 3 to the load, and then back through diode 4 and winding A.

When the rotor completes 240 degrees of rotation, C becomes positive with respect to B. When this occurs, current flows through diode 5 to the load, and then back through diode 6. After 360 degrees of rotation, the process begins again.

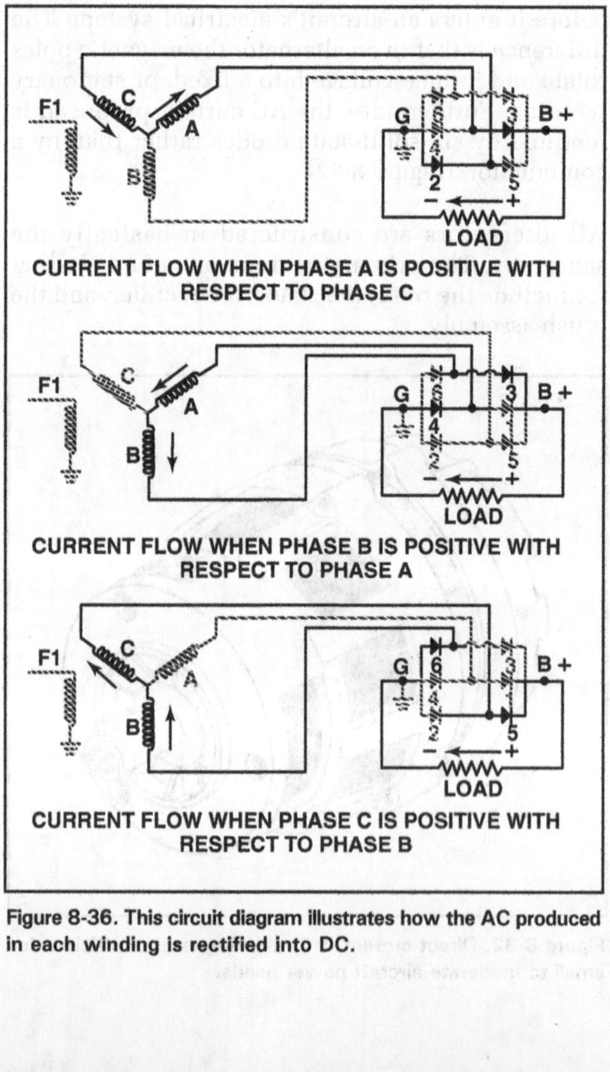


**Figure 8-36. This circuit diagram illustrates how the AC produced in each winding is rectified into DC.**

## BRUSH ASSEMBLY

The brush assembly in an alternator consists of two brushes and their respective brush springs and brush holders. Unlike a generator that uses brushes to supply a path for current to flow from the armature to the load, the brushes in an alternator supply current to the field coils. Because these brushes ride on the smooth surface of the slip rings, the efficiency and service life of alternator brushes is typically greater than on DC generators.

# ALTERNATOR CONTROLS

The voltage produced by an alternator is controlled in the same way as in a generator—by varying the DC field current. When the output voltage rises above the desired value, the field current is decreased. Similarly, when the output voltage drops below the desired value, the field current is increased.

Low-output alternators with vibrator controls increase and decrease the field current by opening a set of contacts. However, a more efficient means of voltage control uses a transistor to control the flow of field current.

The transistorized voltage regulator uses both vibrating points and transistors for voltage control. The vibrating points operate the same as they do in vibrator voltage regulators, but instead of the field current flowing through the contacts, the transistor base current flows through them. Because this current is small compared to the field current that flows through the emitter-collector, there is no arcing at the contacts. [Figure 8-37]

In a completely solid-state voltage regulator, semiconductor devices replace all of the moving parts. These units are very efficient, reliable, and generally have no serviceable components. Therefore, if a completely solid-state unit becomes defective, it is removed from service and replaced.

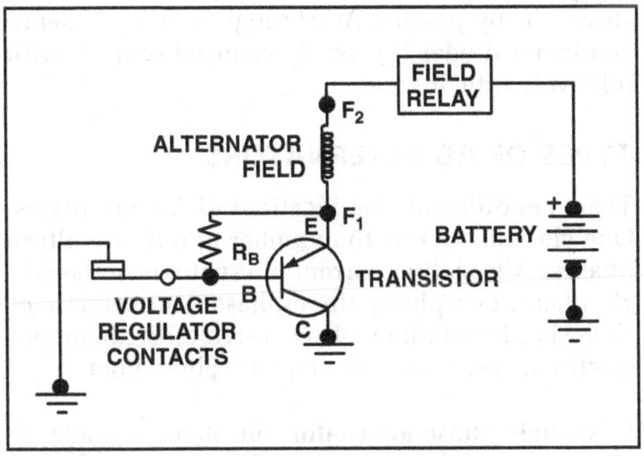


**Figure 8-37. Alternator field current flows from the emitter to the collector only when the voltage regulator contacts are closed and current flows to the base.**

Alternator control requirements are different from those of a generator for several reasons. For example, because an alternator uses solid-state diodes for rectification, current cannot flow from the battery into the alternator. Therefore, there is no need for a reverse-current cutout relay. Furthermore, because the system bus excites the alternator field with a limited voltage, an alternator cannot yield enough current to burn itself out, which eliminates the need for a current limiter.

An alternator requires some means of shutting off the flow of field current when the alternator is not producing power. To do this, most systems use either a field switch or a field relay that is controlled by the master switch. Both permit isolation of the field current and shut it off, if necessary.

Most aircraft alternator circuits use some form of overvoltage protection that permits the alternator to be removed from the bus if a malfunction increases the output voltage to a dangerous level. This function is often handled by an alternator control unit, or ACU, which essentially drops the alternator from the circuit when an overvoltage condition exists.

# DC ALTERNATOR SERVICE AND MAINTENANCE

When an alternator fails to keep the battery charged, first determine that the alternator and battery circuits are properly connected. This includes checking for open fuses or circuit breakers. If everything is connected properly, check for battery voltage at the alternator's battery (B) terminal, and at the "Batt," or "+" terminal of the voltage regulator.

Typically, one of two problems prevents an alternator from producing electrical power. The most likely problem is a shorted or open diode in the rectifying circuit. The other is the possibility of an open circuit in the field windings.

To check for a shorted circuit, measure the resistance between the alternator's B terminal and ground. Set the ohmmeter on the R × 1 scale and measure resistance, then reverse the ohmmeter leads and measure the resistance again. If the diodes are good, there will be relatively low resistance when the diodes are forward-biased and an infinite or very high reading when the diodes are reverse-biased. If the reading is not infinite or very high, one or more of the diodes are shorted. [Figure 8-38]

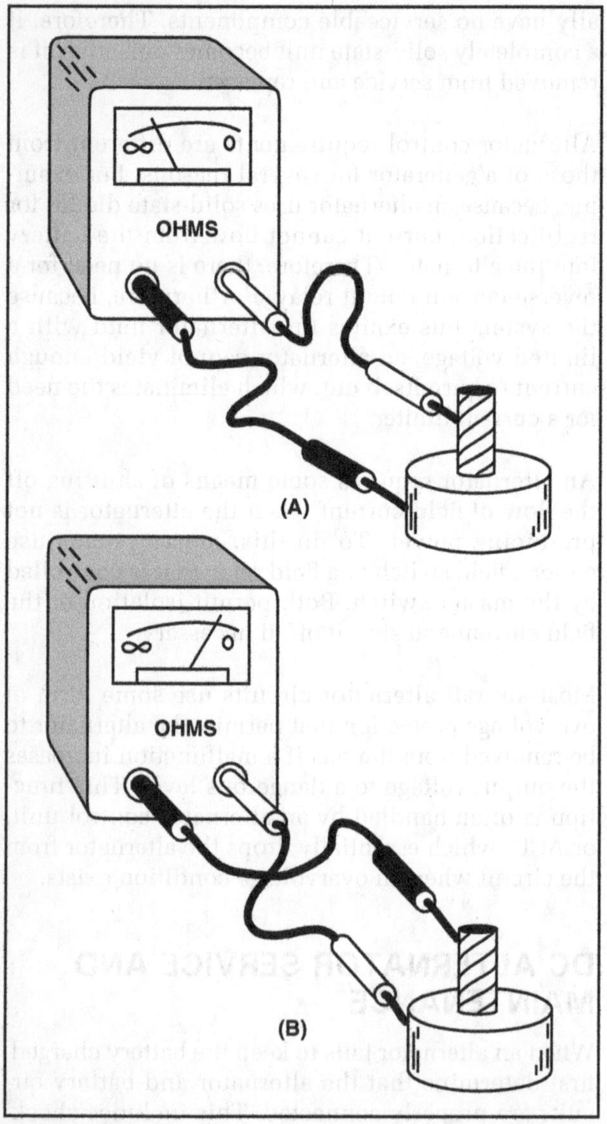


**Figure 8-38. (A) A good diode produces a high resistance reading when reverse-biased. (B) Resistance should be low when forward-biased. A shorted diode typically causes a low resistance reading when checked in the forward- and reverse-biased directions. An open diode produces high resistance readings in both directions.**

Because the diodes in an alternator are connected in parallel, an ohmmeter cannot detect an open diode. However, an ohmmeter will identify an open diode if you check the diodes individually.

Solid-state diodes are quite rugged and have a long life when properly used. However, they can be damaged by excessive voltage or reverse current flow. For this reason, they should never be operated without being connected to an electrical load. Because alternators receive their field current from the aircraft bus and do not rely on residual magnetism to be started, never flash the field or polarize an alternator.

To aid in systematic alternator troubleshooting, some manufacturers have specialized test equipment. This test equipment is usually plugged into the aircraft electrical system between the voltage regulator and the aircraft bus. Through the use of indicator lights, the test equipment shows whether a problem exists in the voltage regulator, the overvoltage sensing circuit, or the alternator field and the associated output circuit. By using this type of test equipment, you can save time and avoid unnecessarily replacing good components.

To avoid burning out the rectifying diodes during installation, it is extremely important that you connect the battery with the proper polarity. *Any* time that you connect an external power source to the aircraft, apply the correct polarity.

## AC ALTERNATORS

Small aircraft use direct current as the main electrical power because it is storable, and aircraft engines use battery power to start. However, large aircraft require elaborate ground service facilities and external power sources for starting. Therefore, they can take advantage of the appreciable weight savings provided by using alternating current as their primary power source.

In addition to saving weight, the voltage in alternating current is easily stepped up or down, so AC can carry current a long distance by raising the voltage with a step-up transformer. This saves additional weight because high-voltage AC is conducted through relatively small wires. At its destination, electricity passes through a step-down transformer where voltage is lowered and current is stepped up to the value needed.

Some situations, such as charging batteries or operating variable speed motors, require direct current. However, by passing AC through a series of semiconductor diodes it is easily changed into DC with relatively little loss.

### TYPES OF AC ALTERNATORS

There are different classifications of AC alternators. One classification is the number of output voltage phases. Alternating current alternators can be single-phase, two-phase, three-phase, and sometimes even six-phase or more. However, almost all aircraft electrical systems use three-phase alternators.

In a **single-phase alternator**, the stator is made up of several windings connected in series to form a single circuit. The windings are also connected so the AC voltages induced into each winding are in phase. This means that to determine the total output of a single-phase alternator, you must add the voltage induced into each winding. Therefore, the total voltage produced by a stator with four windings is four times the single voltage in any one winding. However, because the power delivered by a single-phase circuit is pulsating, this type of circuit is impractical for many applications. [Figure 8-39]

**Two-phase alternators** have two or more single-phase windings spaced symmetrically around the stator, so that the AC voltage induced in one is 90 degrees out of phase with the voltage induced in the other. These windings are electrically separate, so that when one winding cuts the maximum number of flux-lines, the other cuts no flux lines.

Most aircraft alternators use a **three-phase**, or **poly-phase**, circuit. The three-phase alternator has three single-phase windings spaced so that the voltage induced in each winding is 120 degrees out of phase with the voltage in the other two windings. [Figure 8-40]

The three individual phase voltages produced by a three-phase alternator are similar to those generated by three single-phase alternators, whose voltages are out of phase by 120 degrees. In a three-phase alternator, one lead from each winding is connected to form a common junction. When this is done, the stator is Y- or star-connected. A three-phase stator can also be connected so that the phases are end-to-end. This arrangement is called a delta connection.

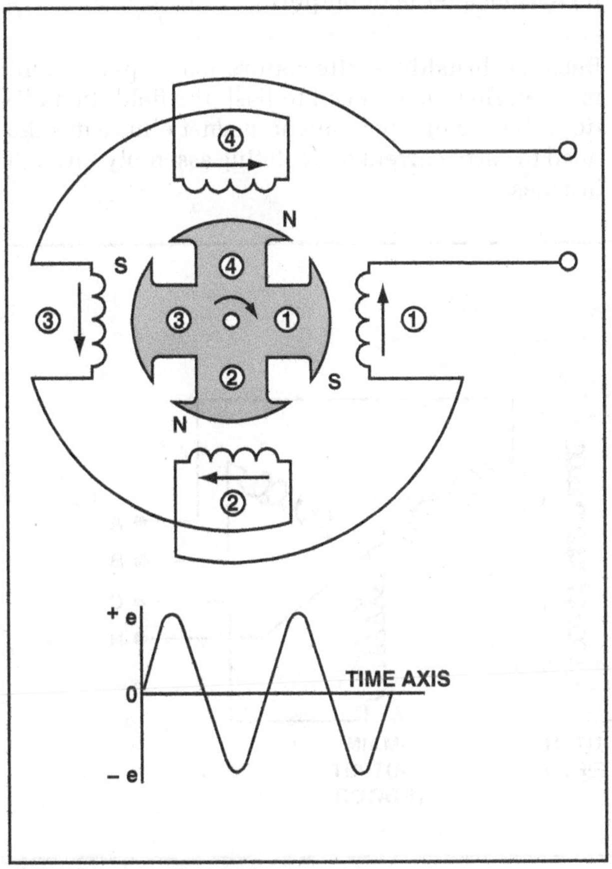

Figure 8-39. In this single-phase alternator, the rotating field induces voltage into the stationary stator. The number of stator windings determines the output voltage.

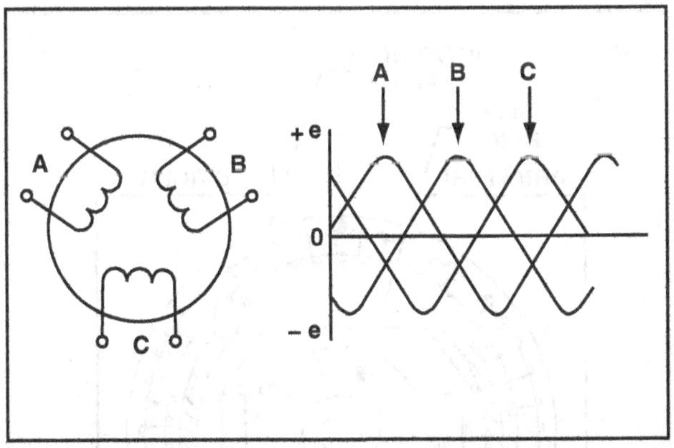

Figure 8-40 Sine wave A is 120 degrees out of phase with sine wave B and sine wave B is 120 degrees out of phase with sine wave C.

Another alternator classification distinguishes between the type of stator and rotor used. In this classification there are two types of alternators: the revolving-armature type, and the revolving-field type.

The **revolving-armature type alternator** is similar in construction to the DC generator, in that the armature rotates within a stationary magnetic field. This setup is typically found only in alternators with a low power rating and generally is not used.

The **revolving-field alternator** has a stationary armature winding (stator) and a rotating-field winding (rotor). The advantage of this configuration is that the armature is connected directly to the load without sliding contacts in the load circuit. Direct connection to the armature circuit makes it possible to use large cross-section conductors that are adequately insulated for high voltage. [Figure 8-41]

The AC alternators used in large jet-powered aircraft are brushless and usually air-cooled. Because the **brushless alternators** have no current flow between brushes or slip rings, they are very efficient at high altitudes, where brush arcing is often a problem.

As discussed earlier, alternator brushes are used to carry current to the rotating electromagnet. However, in a brushless alternator, current is induced into the field coil through an exciter. A brushless alternator consists of three separate fields, a permanent magnetic field, an exciter field, and a main output field. The permanent magnets furnish the magnetic flux to start the generator, producing an output before field current flows. The magnetism produced by these

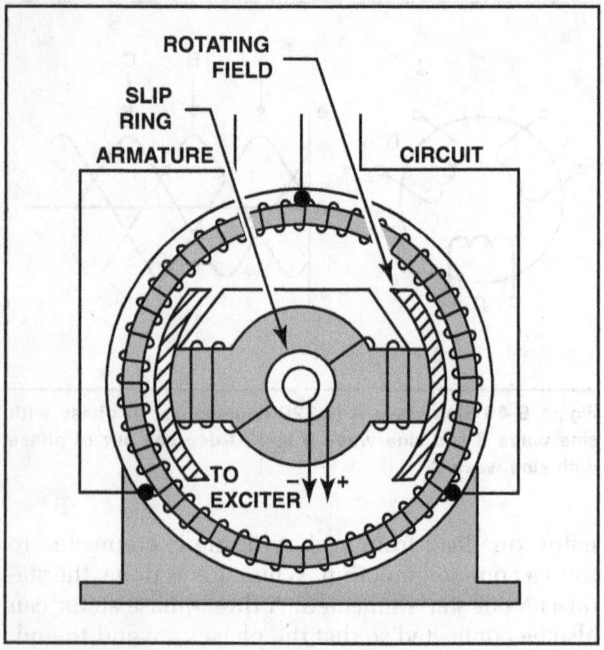


**Figure 8-41. In a revolving-field alternator, the armature is directly connected to the load without the use of sliding contacts. The revolving-field alternator is used widely in aircraft systems.**

magnets induces voltage into an armature that carries the current to a generator control unit, or GCU. Here, the AC is rectified and sent to the exciter field winding. The exciter field then induces voltage into the exciter output winding. The output from the exciter is rectified by six silicon diodes, and the resulting DC flows through the output field winding. From here, voltage is induced into the main output coils.

The permanent magnet, exciter output winding, six diodes, and output field winding are all mounted on the generator shaft and rotate as a unit. The three-phase output stator windings are wound in slots that are in the laminated frame of the alternator housing. [Figure 8-42]

The main output stator winding ends of a brushless alternator are connected in the form of a Y, and in the case of the previous figure, the neutral winding is brought to the outside of the housing along with the three-phase windings. These alternators are usually designed to produce 120 volts across a single phase and 208 volts across two phases.

The GCU monitors and regulates the main generator's output by controlling the amount of current that flows into the exciter field. For example, if additional output is needed, the GCU increases the amount of current flowing to the exciter field winding that, in turn, increases the exciter output. A higher exciter output increases the current flowing through the main generator field winding, thereby increasing alternator output.

Because brushless alternators use a permanent magnet, there is no need to flash the field. In addition, the use of a permanent magnet eliminates the need to carry current to a rotating assembly through brushes.

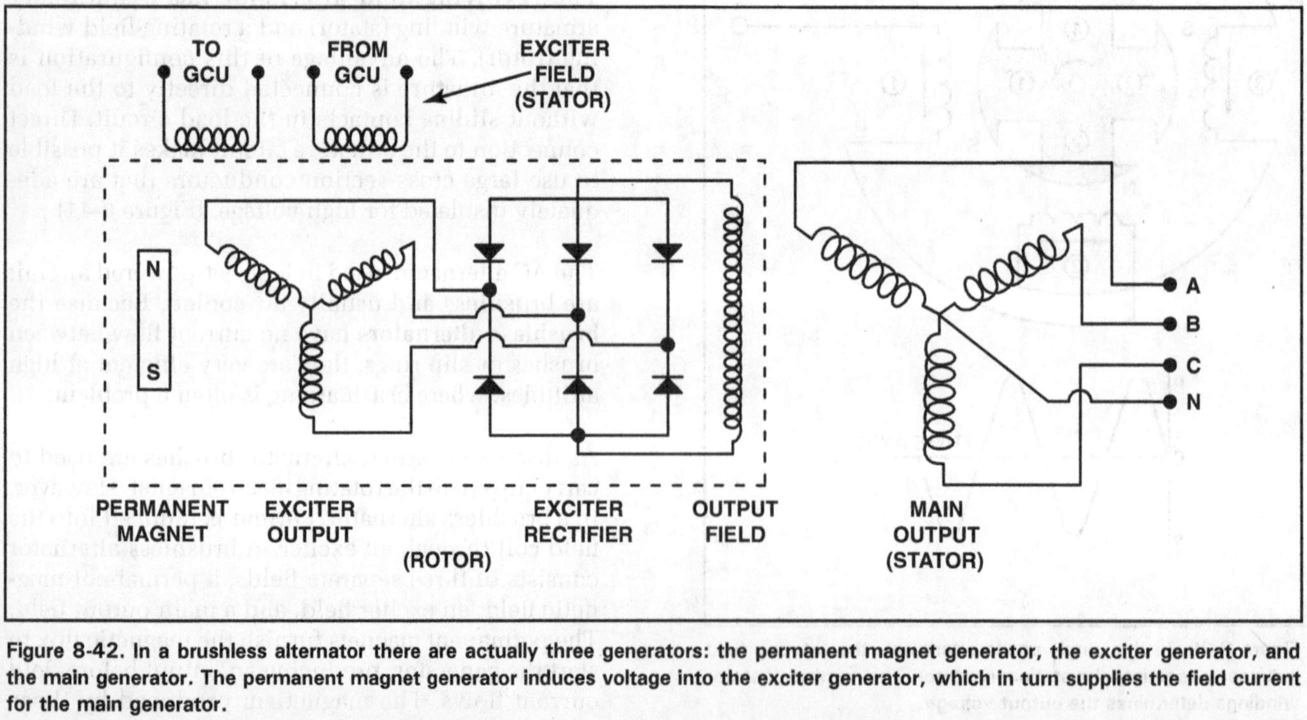


**Figure 8-42. In a brushless alternator there are actually three generators: the permanent magnet generator, the exciter generator, and the main generator. The permanent magnet generator induces voltage into the exciter generator, which in turn supplies the field current for the main generator.**

## ALTERNATOR RATINGS

AC alternators are rated in volt-amps, which is a measure of the apparent power being produced by the generator. Because most AC alternators produce a great deal of power, their ratings are generally expressed in kilovolt-amperes, or KVA. A typical Boeing 727 AC alternator is rated at 45 KVA.

## FREQUENCY

The frequency produced by an AC generator is determined by the number of poles and the speed of the rotor: the faster the rotor, the higher the frequency. Similarly, the more poles on a rotor, the higher the frequency for any given speed. The frequency of AC generated by an alternator is determined using the equation:

$$F = \frac{P}{2} \times \frac{N}{60} = PN$$

Where:
F = Frequency
P = the number of poles
N = the speed in rpm

With this formula you can determine that a two-pole, 3,600 rpm alternator has a frequency of 60 hertz.

$$F = \frac{2 \times 3{,}600}{120} = 60 \text{ Hz}$$

To provide a constant frequency as engine speed varies and to maintain a uniform frequency between multiple generators connected to a common electrical bus, most AC generators are connected to a **constant-speed drive** unit, or **CSD**. Although CSDs come in a variety of shapes and sizes, they all operate the same way. The drive units consist of an engine-driven, axial-piston, variable-displacement hydraulic pump that supplies fluid to an axial-piston hydraulic motor. The motor then drives the generator. A governor that senses the rotational speed of the AC generator controls the pump displacement. The governor action holds the output speed of the generator constant and maintains an AC frequency of 400 hertz, plus or minus established tolerances. [Figure 8-43]

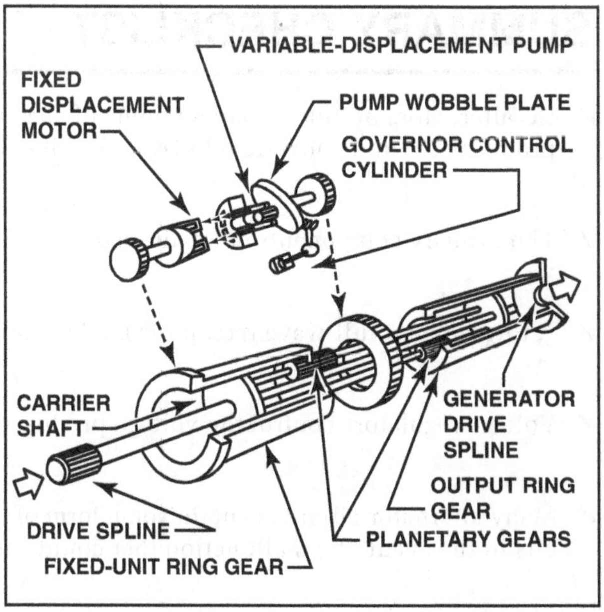


**Figure 8-43. The Sundstrand Integrated Drive Generator uses a constant-speed drive axial-gear differential.**

Some modern jet aircraft produce AC with a generator called an **integrated drive generator**, or **IDG**. The IDG is a high-output generator that uses brushes and slip rings to carry DC exciter current to the rotating field. An IDG comprises a constant speed drive unit and a generator sealed in the same housing. If a problem occurs with an IDG, it is usually not repairable in the field and is simply removed and replaced with a new or serviceable unit. When either a CSD or IDG malfunctions, they can be automatically or manually disconnected in flight. After they are disconnected, they cannot be reconnected in flight; only ground personnel can place them back online. [Figure 8-44]

## AC ALTERNATOR MAINTENANCE

Maintenance and inspection of alternator systems are similar to that of DC systems. The proper maintenance of an alternator requires the unit to be kept clean and all electrical connections tight and in good repair. Alternators and their drive systems differ in design and maintenance requirements; therefore, specific information is found in the manufacturer's service publications and in the maintenance program approved for a particular aircraft.

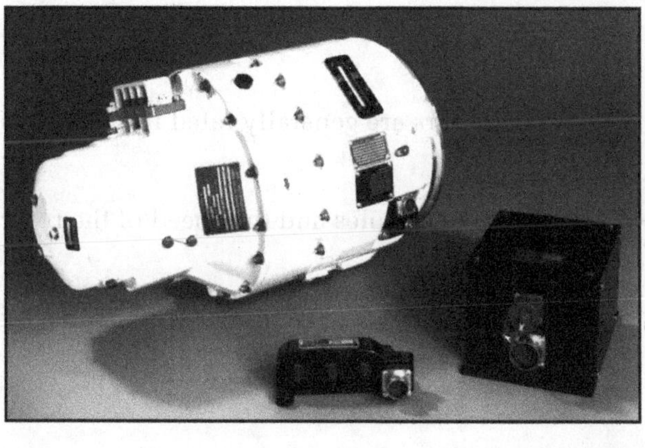

**Figure 8-44. The constant speed drive unit is included in the housing with the Sundstrand Integrated Drive Generator. The generator requires the use of a control unit and a current transformer assembly.**

# SUMMARY CHECKLIST

✓ DC alternators produce small amounts of current and are typically found on light aircraft. A DC alternator produces AC and converts it to DC before it enters the electrical system of the aircraft.

✓ The primary components of an alternator are the rotor, stator, rectifier, and brush assembly.

✓ A three-phase, full-wave rectifier is made of six heavy-duty silicon diodes.

✓ Voltage regulators control the voltage produced in an alternator.

✓ Many alternator circuits contain some form of overvoltage protection that removes the alternator from the bus in the event of a malfunction that could cause an overvoltage situation.

✓ Two common problems that prevent an alternator from producing electrical power are a shorted or open diode in the rectifying circuit or an open circuit in the field.

✓ The voltage produced by an AC alternator can be increased or decreased by means of a step-up or step-down transformer.

✓ AC alternators are classified by output-voltage numbers. They can be single-phase, two-phase, three-phase, or higher. Most aircraft electrical systems are three-phase.

✓ A three-phase alternator circuit has three single-phase windings spaced so that the voltage induced in each winding is 120 degrees out of phase with the other windings.

✓ Large jet-powered aircraft typically use brushless AC alternators that are efficient at high altitudes where brush arcing is a problem.

✓ A brushless alternator contains three generators—a permanent magnet generator, an exciter generator, and a main generator.

✓ AC alternators are generally rated in kilo-volt amperes or KVA.

✓ The number of poles and the speed of the rotor determine the frequency that an AC alternator produces.

✓ Constant speed drives (CSD) are units connected to AC generators to maintain a uniform frequency between multiple generators.

# KEY TERMS

single-phase alternator
two-phase alternator
three-phase alternator
polyphase alternator
revolving-armature type alternator
revolving-field alternator
brushless alternators
constant-speed drive
CSD
integrated drive generator
IDG

# QUESTIONS

1. The DC alternator produces AC and then rectifies it using six _______ (what component).
2. A three phase alternator has stator windings that are _______ degrees apart.
3. To stop the flow of field current, most systems use a field switch activated by the _______ _______.
4. A DC Alternator _______ (will or will not) have a reverse current cut-out relay in the regulator circuit.
5. The two basic problems that would prevent an alternator from producing electrical power are:
   a. _____________
   b. _____________
6. If the airplane's battery polarity is accidentally switched, there is a real possibility of damaging the alternator's _____________
7. It is _______ (sometimes or never) necessary to flash the field of an alternator.
8. When an ohmmeter forward-biases a diode, the resistance will be _______ (high or low).
9. When an ohmmeter reverse-biases a diode, the resistance will be _______ (high or low).
10. Alternating current has the advantage over direct current in that its voltage can be stepped _______ or _______.
11. The value of alternating current can be changed using a _____________ (what device).
12. Large transport catagory aircraft have brushless alternators to reduce _______ at _______.
13. In a brushless alternator, the GCU controls the main generator's output by monitoring and regulating the current in the _______ _______.
14. CSD's, or constant speed drives, are typically driven by a _____________ _______.
15. The main purpose of a CSD is to allow the alternator to produce AC power at a constant _____________.

# SECTION C

## MOTORS AND STARTING SYSTEMS

Motors and starting systems use a power source and mechanical advantage to perform work in aircraft equipment. Most of the components in the following section are electrically operated, but some are powered with compressed air.

### MOTORS

Many components in an airplane, for example, the starter and the autopilot, use electric motors for power. Electric motors can be DC or AC. Both types are described below with information about theory, operation, and maintenance.

#### DC MOTORS

Many devices in an airplane depend on the mechanical energy provided by DC motors. A DC motor is a rotating machine that transforms DC electrical energy into mechanical energy.

#### MOTOR THEORY

The lines of flux between two magnets flow from the north pole to the south pole. At the same time, when current flows through a wire, lines of flux are set up around the wire. The direction that these flux lines encircle the wire depends on the direction of current flow. When the wire's flux lines and the magnet's flux lines are combined, a reaction occurs. For example, when the flux lines between two magnetic poles are flowing from left to right, and the lines of flux that encircle a wire between the magnetic poles flow in a counterclockwise direction, the flux lines reinforce each other at the bottom of the wire. This happens because the lines of flux produced by the magnet and the flow of flux lines at the bottom of the wire are traveling in the same direction. However, at the top of the wire the flux lines oppose, or neutralize, each other. The resulting magnetic field under the wire is strong and the magnetic field above the wire is weak. Consequently, the wire is pushed away from the side where the field is the strongest. [Figure 8-45]

By the same principle, if the current flow through the wire were reversed, the flux lines encircling the wire would flow in the opposite direction. The resulting combination of the magnetic flux lines and wire flux lines would create a strong magnetic field at the top of the wire and a weak magnetic field at the bottom. Consequently, the wire is pushed downward away from the stronger field.

#### PARALLEL CONDUCTORS

Two current-carrying wires in proximity exert a force on each other that is the result of the magnetic fields around each wire. When the current flows in the same direction, the resulting magnetic fields

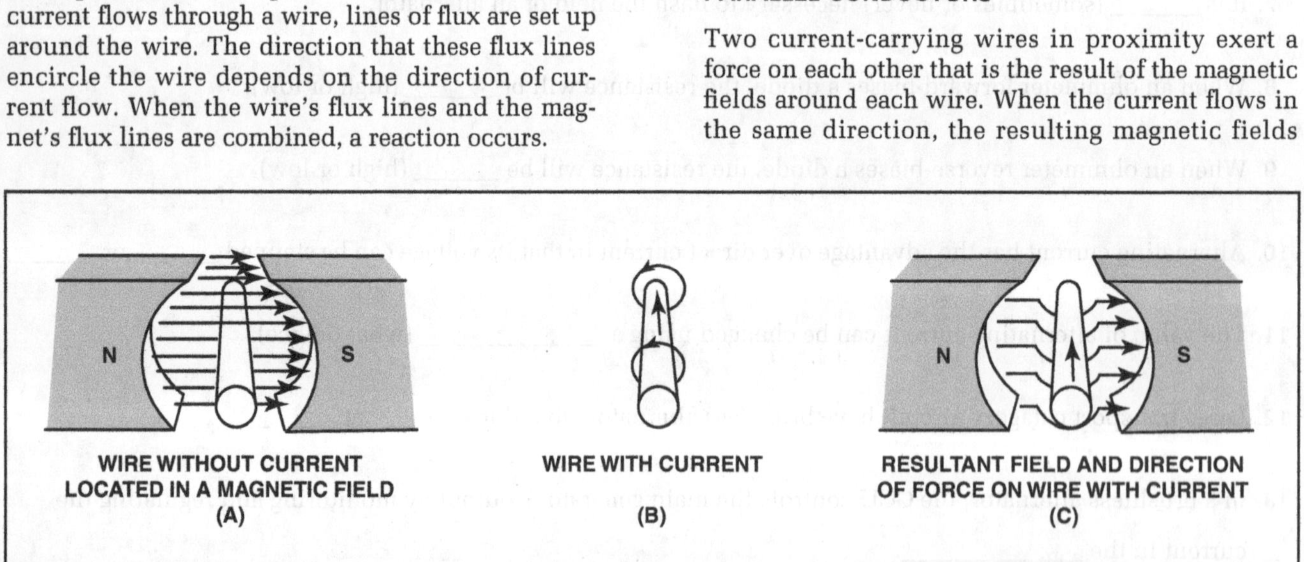


**Figure 8-45. (A) When no current flows through a wire between two magnets, the lines of flux flow undisturbed from north to south. (B) When current flows through a wire, magnetic flux lines encircle it. (C) The flux lines from the magnet and the flux lines that encircle a wire with current react to produce a strong magnetic field below the wire and a weak magnetic field above it.**

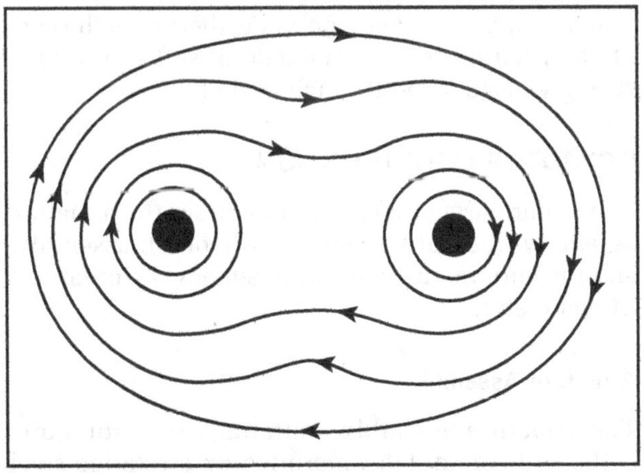

Figure 8-46. When current flows in the same direction through two parallel wires, the magnetic fields merge and circle both wires.

encompass both wires in a clockwise direction. These fields oppose each other and, therefore, cancel each other out. [Figure 8-46]

When the electron flow in the wires is opposite, the magnetic field around one wire radiates outward in a clockwise direction, while the magnetic field around the second wire rotates counterclockwise. These fields combine, or reinforce each other, between the wires. [Figure 8-47]

## DEVELOPING TORQUE

When a current-carrying coil is placed in a magnetic field, the resulting magnetic fields rotate the coil. The force that produces rotation is called torque. [Figure 8-48]

The amount of torque developed in a coil depends on several factors, including the strength of the magnetic field, the number of turns in the coil, and the position of the coil in the field.

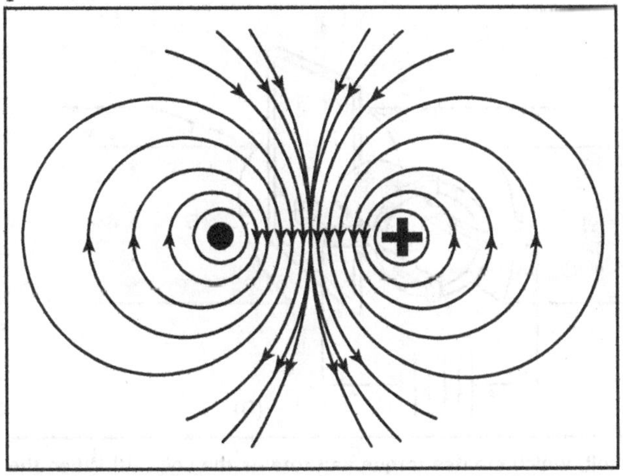

Figure 8-47. When current flows in opposite directions through two parallel wires, the magnetic fields attempt to force the wires apart.

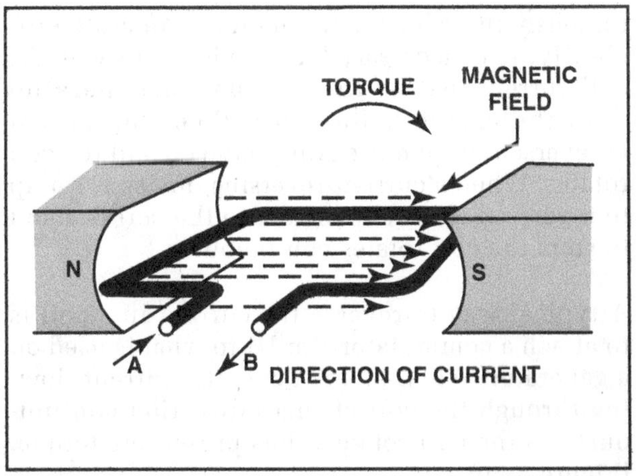


Figure 8-48. This coil has current flowing outward on side A and inward on side B. The magnetic field encircling wire A is counterclockwise, whereas the magnetic field encircling wire B is clockwise. These forces push wire A upward, and wire B downward. The coil rotates until the wires are perpendicular to the magnetic flux lines. The reaction of the magnetic fields around the coil creates torque.

The **right-hand motor rule** is used to determine the direction a current-carrying wire moves in a magnetic field. If the right index finger points in the direction of the magnetic field and the middle finger points in the direction of current flow, the thumb indicates the direction the wire moves. [Figure 8-49]

## BASIC DC MOTOR

The characteristics of torque govern the construction of DC motors. The torque causing a coil to rotate is strongest when it is at a 90-degree angle to the magnetic field produced by two magnets. Therefore, when a coil lines up with the magnetic field, it does not rotate because the torque at that point is zero. Because the coil of a motor must rotate con-

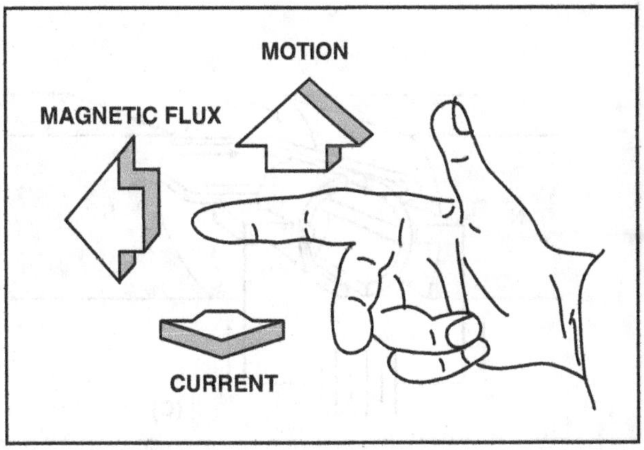


Figure 8-49. According to the right-hand motor rule, the index finger represents the flow direction of the magnetic flux, the middle finger represents the direction of current flow, and the thumb represents the direction a coil rotates.

tinuously in order for the motor to operate efficiently, it is necessary for a device to reverse the coil current just as the coil becomes parallel with the magnet's flux lines. When the current is reversed, torque is again produced and the coil rotates. When a current-reversing device is set up to reverse the current each time the coil is about to stop, the coil rotates continuously.

A typical way to reverse the current in a coil is to attach a commutator similar to what is used on a generator. When this is done, the current flowing through the coil changes direction continuously as the coil rotates, thus preserving torque. [Figure 8-50]

An effective method of ensuring strong, continuous coil torque is to include a large number of coils wound on an armature and spaced so that, for any position of the armature, one of the coils is near the magnet's poles. Although this results in continuous and strong torque, it requires that the commutator contain several segments.

To further increase the amount of torque, the armature is placed between the poles of an electromagnet instead of a permanent magnet. This provides a much stronger magnetic field. Furthermore, the core of an armature is usually made of soft iron that is strongly magnetized through induction.

## DC MOTOR CONSTRUCTION

The major parts in a typical motor are the armature assembly, the field assembly, the brush assembly, and the end frames. This arrangement is similar to a DC generator.

### Armature Assembly

The armature assembly contains a soft-iron core, coils, and commutator mounted on a rotating steel shaft. The core consists of laminated stacks of soft iron that are insulated from each other. Solid iron is not used because it generates excessive heat that uses energy needlessly. The armature windings are made of insulated copper wire that is inserted into slots and protected by a fiber paper, sometimes called fish paper. The ends of the windings are physically connected to the commutator segments with wedges or steel bands. The commutator consists of several copper segments insulated from each other and the armature shaft by pieces of mica. Insulated wedge rings hold the segments in place. [Figure 8-51]

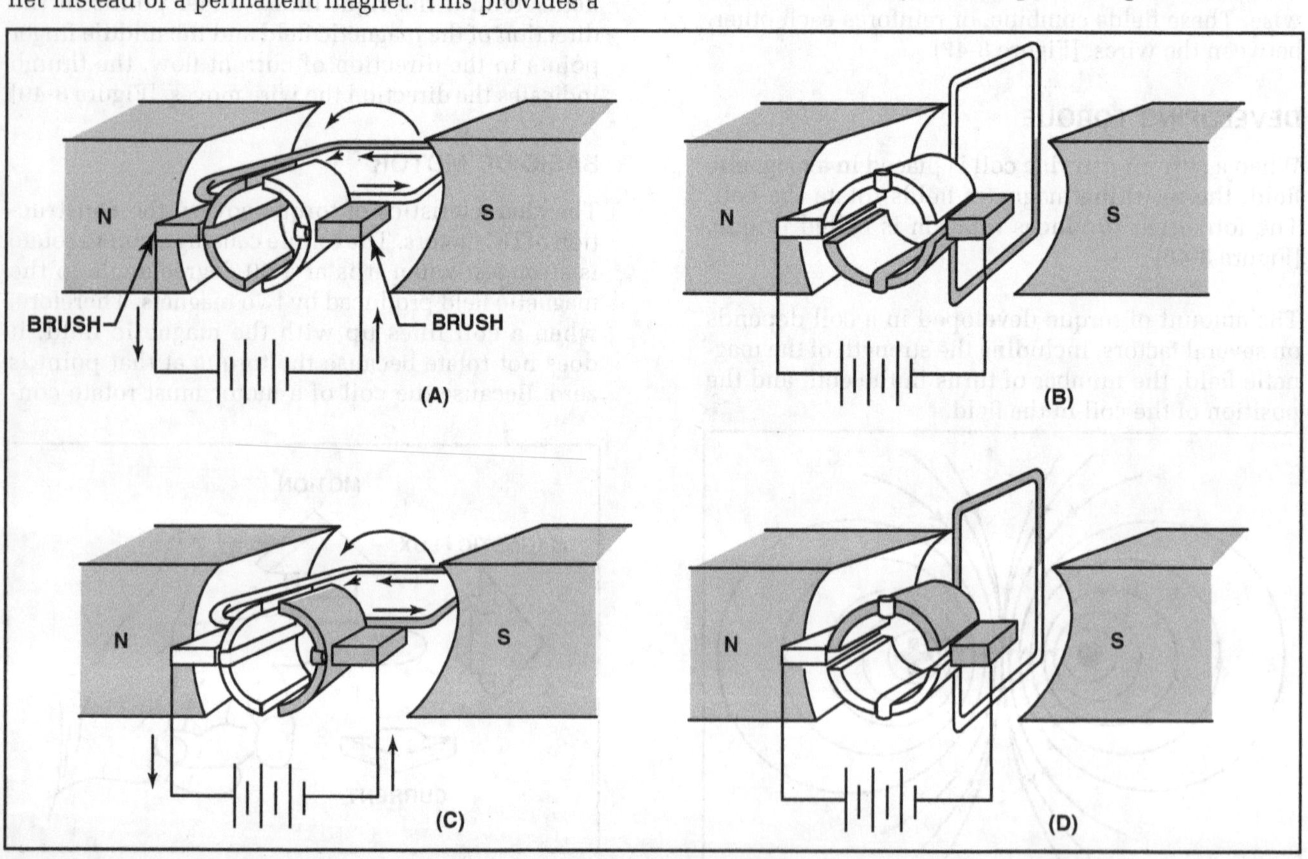


**Figure 8-50. (A) Current flows through brushes to the commutator and coil, which creates torque and rotates the coil. (B) When the coil becomes parallel with the magnetic lines of flux, the brushes switch terminals and the polarity reverses. (C) When the reversed current produces ,torque and rotates the coil. (D) The coil returns to a position parallel with the flux lines and the brushes switch terminals, polarity reverses, and torque rotates the coil.**

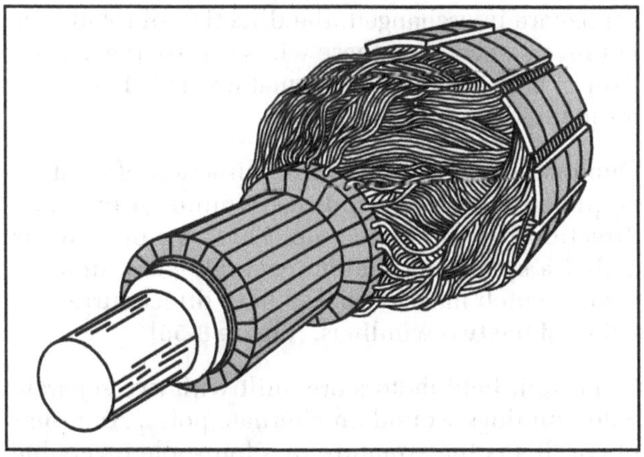

**Figure 8-51. The armature of a DC motor is similar to that of a DC generator.**

### Field Assembly

The field assembly consists of the field frame, a set of pole pieces, and field coils. The field frame is located along the inner wall of the motor housing and contains the laminated steel pole pieces on which the field coils are wound. The field coils consist of several turns of insulated wire that fit over each pole piece. Some motors have as few as two poles, while others have as many as eight.

### Brush Assembly

The brush assembly consists of brushes and their holders. The brushes are usually made of small blocks of graphitic carbon because of its long service life. The brush holders permit the brushes to move somewhat and use a spring to hold them against the commutator. [Figure 8-52]

### End Frame

The end frame is the part of the motor that the armature assembly rotates in. The armature shaft, which rides on bearings, extends through one end frame and is connected to the load. Sometimes the drive end frame is part of the unit or accessory that is driven by the motor.

## MOTOR SPEED, DIRECTION, AND BRAKING

Some applications call for motors whose speed or direction is changeable. Some applications also require a motor to be stopped quickly. For example, a landing gear motor must be able to both retract and extend the gear and stop when the gear has reached a particular position, while a windshield wiper motor must have variable speeds to suit changing weather conditions. A variety of methods and devices have been developed to accommodate these operational requirements.

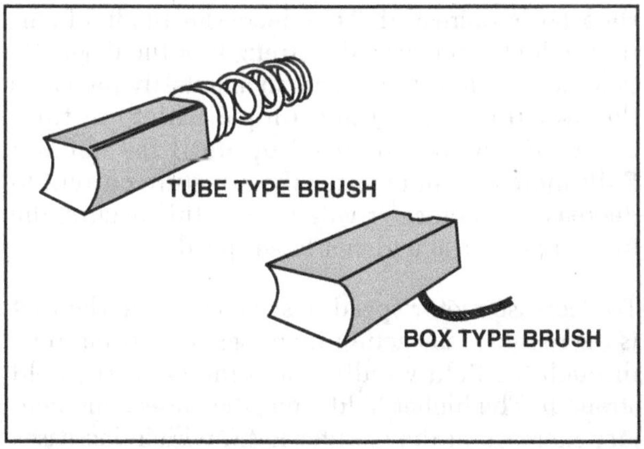


**Figure 8-52. Tube and box brushes are commonly used in DC motors.**

### CHANGING MOTOR SPEED

A motor for which the speed is adjustable is called a **variable speed motor**, and can be either a shunt or series motor. Motor speed is controlled by varying the current in the field windings. For example, when the amount of current flowing through the field windings increases, the field strength increases, causing the armature windings to produce a larger counter electromotive force (EMF) that slows the motor. Conversely, when the field current decreases, the field strength decreases and the motor speeds up because the counter EMF is reduced. [Figure 8-53]

In a shunt motor, speed is controlled by a rheostat that is connected in series with the field winding. Therefore, the speed depends on the amount of current flowing through the rheostat to the field windings. To increase motor speed, the resistance in the

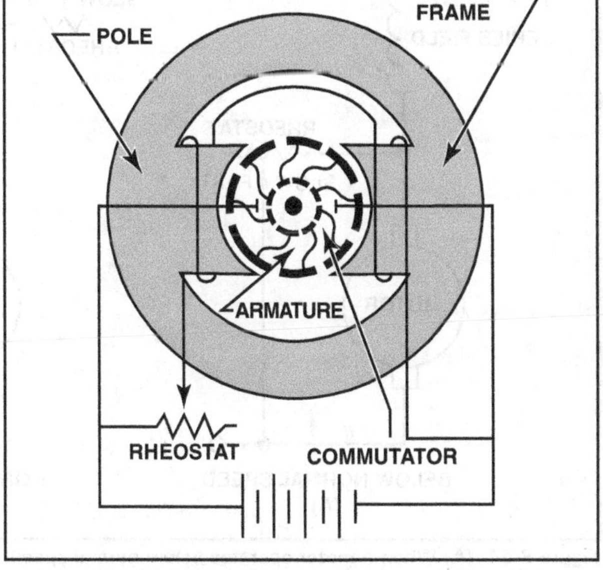


**Figure 8-53. A shunt motor with variable speed control uses a rheostat to control the speed.**

rheostat is increased. This decreases the field current, which decreases the strength of the magnetic field and counter EMF. This momentarily increases the armature current and torque which, in turn, causes the motor to speed up until the counter EMF increases and causes the armature current to decrease to its former value. After this occurs, the motor operates at a higher fixed speed.

To decrease motor speed, resistance in the rheostat is decreased. This action increases the current flow through the field windings and increases the field strength. The higher field strength causes a momentary increase in the counter EMF, which decreases the armature current. As a result, torque decreases and the motor slows until the counter EMF decreases to its former value. After the counter EMF and armature current are balanced, the motor operates at a lower fixed speed than before.

In a series motor, the rheostat speed control is connected in one of three ways: in parallel with the motor field, in series with the motor field, or in parallel with the motor armature. Each method of connection permits operation in a specified speed range. [Figure 8-54]

## REVERSING MOTOR DIRECTION

The direction of a DC motor's rotation is reversed by changing the direction of current flow in either the armature or the field windings. In both cases, this reverses the magnetism of either the armature or the magnetic field within which the armature rotates. If the wires connecting the motor to an external source are interchanged, the direction of rotation is not reversed because these wires reverse the magnetism of both the field and armature. This leaves the torque in the same direction.

One method for reversing the direction of rotation employs two field windings wound in opposite directions on the same pole. This type of motor is called a **split-field motor**. A single-pole, double-throw switch makes it possible to direct current to either of the two windings. [Figure 8-55]

Some split-field motors are built with two separate field windings wound on alternate poles. An example of this is the armature in a four-pole reversible motor. In this configuration, the armature rotates in one direction when current flows through one set of windings, and in the opposite direction when current flows through the other set of windings.

Another method of reversal is called the **switch method**. This type of motor reversal employs a double-pole, double-throw switch that changes the direction of current flow in either the armature or the field. [Figure 8-56]

## MOTOR BRAKING

Many motor-driven devices, such as landing gear, flaps, and retractable landing lights must be stopped at precise positions. These devices are usually very heavy and a lot of inertia is generated when they are being positioned. Brake mechanisms are used to stop the motor and gear train under these circumstances.

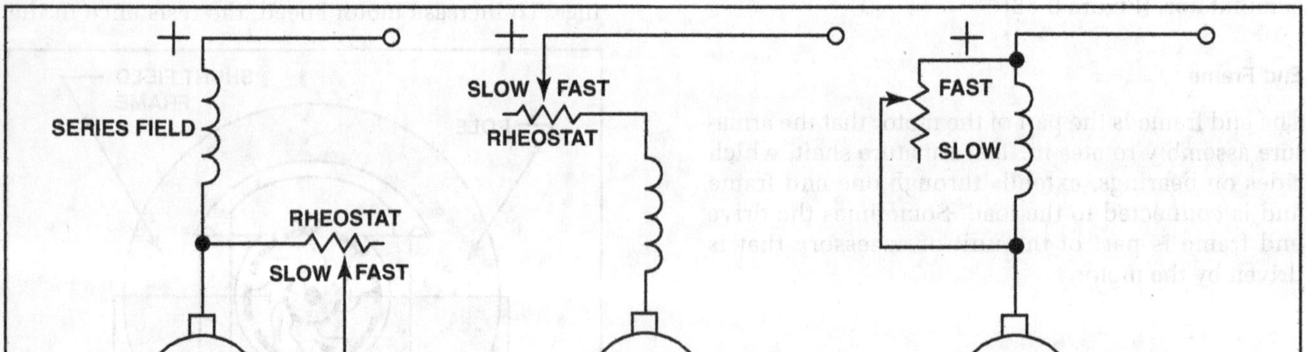


**Figure 8-54. (A) When a motor operates below normal speed, the rheostat is parallel with the armature, decreasing current increases motor speed. (B) When a motor operates in a normal speed range, the rheostat is in series with the motor field, increasing the voltage across the motor increases motor speed. (C) When a motor operates above normal speed, the rheostat is in parallel with the series field. In this configuration, some voltage bypasses the series field, which increases motor speed.**

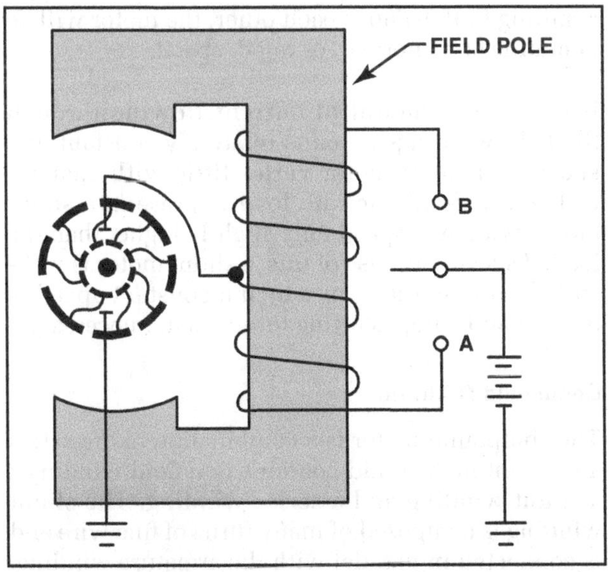


Figure 8-55. When the switch contacts terminal A, current flows through the lower field winding, which creates a north pole at the lower pole piece that causes the armature to rotate. When the switch contacts terminal B, current flows through the upper field winding, which reverses the field magnetism and rotates the armature in the opposite direction.

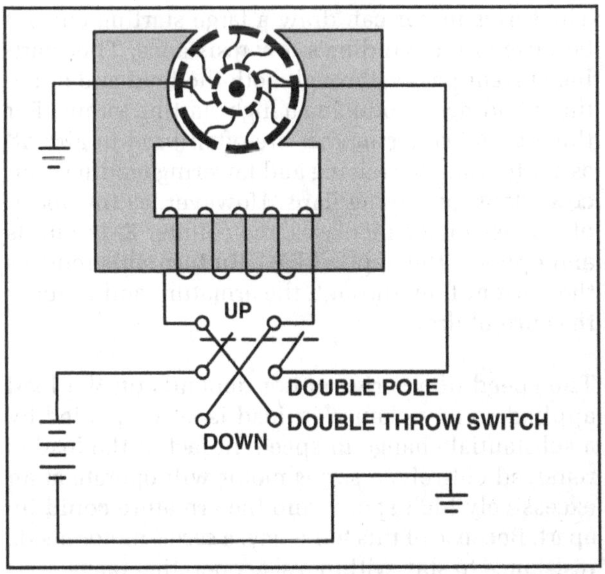


Figure 8-56. A double-pole, double-throw switch can reverse current through a field. When the switch is in the "up" position, current flows through the field windings, a north pole is established on the right side of the motor, and the armature rotates. When the switch is in the "down" position, polarity is reversed and the armature rotates in the opposite direction.

The most common brake mechanism consists of a drum or disc, which is attached to the gear mechanism, and friction pads, or shoes, which are controlled by an electromagnet. When the motor is energized, an electromagnet pulls the friction pad away from the disc or drum. When the motor is turned off, the electromagnet is de-energized and permits a spring to pull the friction material back into contact with the disc or drum.

## TYPES OF DC MOTORS

DC motors are classified by their type of field and armature connection and by the type of duty. For example, there are three basic types of DC field-armature connections: series, shunt, and compound.

### Series DC Motor

In a series motor, the field windings consist of heavy wire with relatively few turns that are connected in series with the armature winding. This means the same amount of current flows through the field windings and the armature windings. In this configuration, an increase in current causes a corresponding increase in the magnetism of both the field and armature. [Figure 8-57]

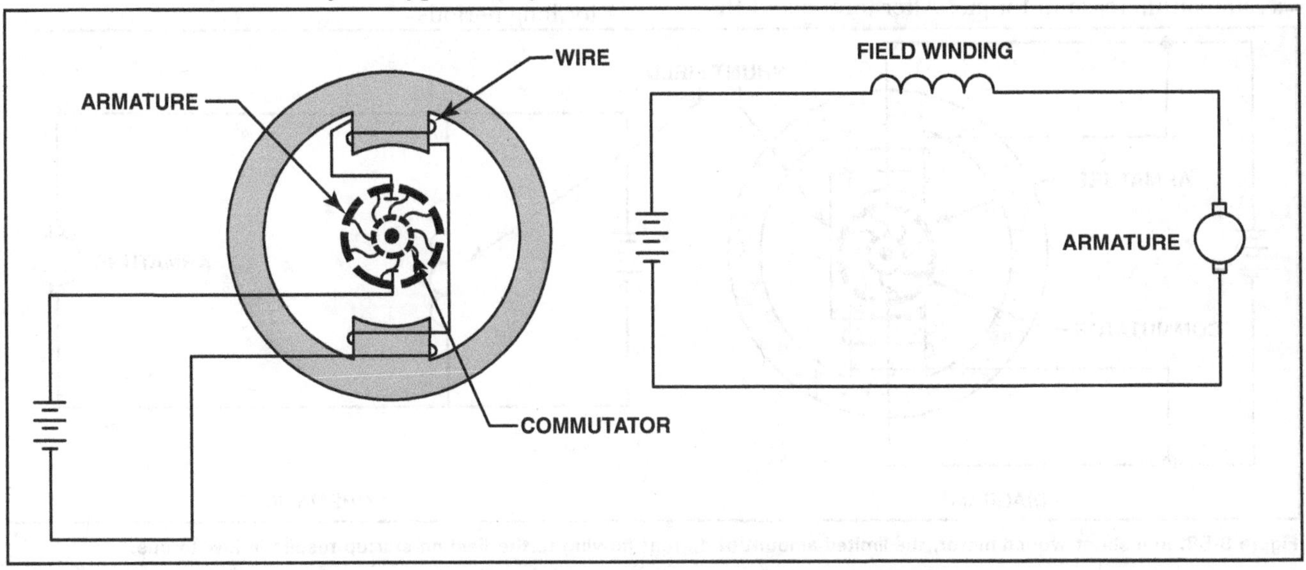


Figure 8-57. In a series motor, an increase of current through the field windings increases the current in the armature.

The series motor can draw a large starting current because of the winding's low resistance. This starting current passes through both the field and armature windings, producing a high starting torque. For this reason, series motors are often used in aircraft as starters and for raising and lowering landing gear, cowl flaps, and wing flaps. However, as the speed of a series motor increases, the counter EMF builds and opposes the applied EMF. In turn, this reduces the current flow through the armature and reduces the current draw.

The speed of a series motor depends on the load applied so any change in load is accompanied by a substantial change in speed. In fact, if the load is removed entirely, a series motor will operate at an excessively high speed, and the armature could fly apart. Because of this tendency, a series motor needs resistance to stay within a safe operating range.

#### Shunt DC Motor

In a shunt motor, the field winding is connected in parallel with the armature winding. To limit the amount of current that passes through the field, the resistance is high in the field winding. In addition, because the field is connected directly across the power supply, the amount of current that passes through the field is constant. In this configuration, when a shunt motor begins to rotate, most of the current flows through the armature, while relatively little current flows to the field. Because of this, shunt motors develop little torque when they are first started. [Figure 8-58]

As a shunt-wound motor picks up speed, the counter EMF in the armature increases, causing a decrease in the amount of current draw in the armature. At the same time, the field current increases slightly, causing an increase in torque. After torque and the resulting EMF balance each other, the motor will be operating at its normal, or rated, speed.

Because the amount of current flowing through the field windings remains relatively constant, the speed of a shunt motor varies little with changes in load. In fact, when no load is present, a shunt motor assumes a speed only slightly higher than the loaded speed. Because of this, a shunt motor is well-suited for operations in which a constant speed is desired and a high starting torque is not necessary.

#### Compound DC Motor

The compound motor is a combination of the series and shunt motors and contains two field windings: a shunt winding and a series winding. The shunt winding is composed of many turns of fine wire and is connected in parallel with the armature winding. The series winding consists of relatively few turns of large wire and is connected in series with the armature winding.

The starting torque is higher in a compound motor than in a shunt motor, but lower than in the series motor. Furthermore, variation of speed with a load is less than in a series-wound motor but greater than in a shunt motor. The compound motor is used whenever the combined characteristics of the series and shunt motors are desired. [Figure 8-59]

### TYPE OF DUTY

Electric motors must operate under various conditions. For example, some motors are used for intermittent operations, while others operate continuously. In most cases, motors built for intermittent duty can be operated for only short periods before they must cool. Conversely, motors built for continuous duty are operable at their rated power for long periods.

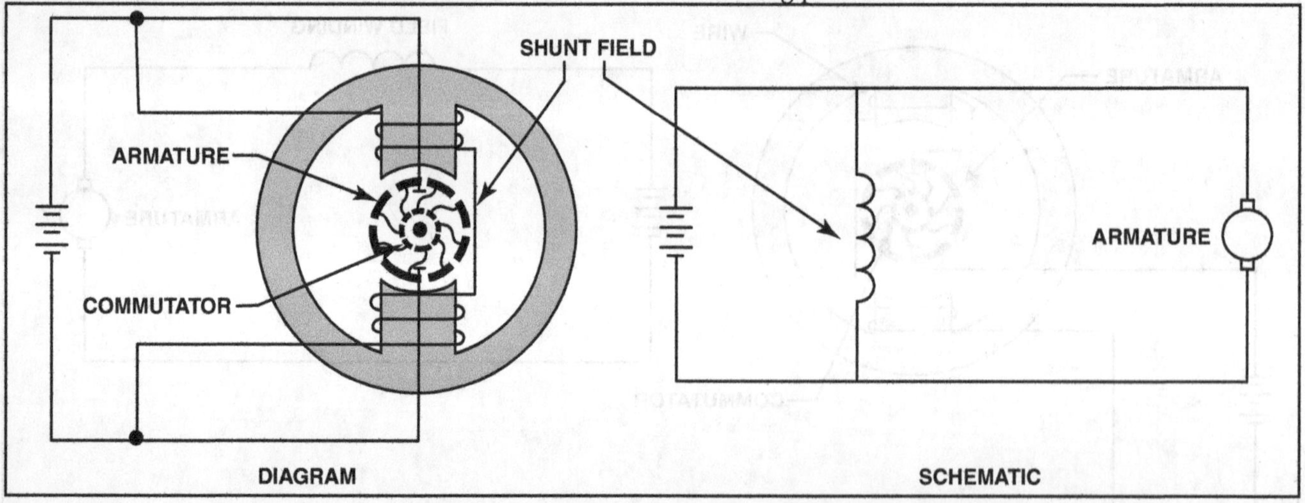


**Figure 8-58. In a shunt-wound motor, the limited amount of current flowing to the field on startup results in low torque.**

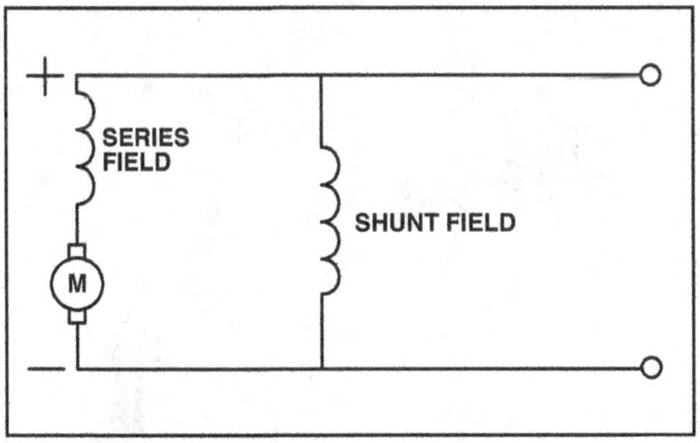


Figure 8-59. In a compound motor, one field winding is connected to the armature in series and the other in parallel.

## ENERGY LOSSES IN MOTORS

When electrical energy is converted to mechanical energy in a motor, some losses occur. Losses also occur when mechanical energy is converted to electrical energy. Thus, for machines to be efficient, both electrical and mechanical losses must be kept to a minimum. **Electrical losses** are classified as either copper losses or iron losses, while **mechanical losses** originate from the friction of various moving parts.

**Copper losses** occur when electrons are forced through the copper armature and field windings. These losses occur because some power is dissipated in the form of heat due to the inherent resistance possessed by copper windings. The amount of loss is proportional to the square of the current, and is calculated with the formula:

$$\text{Copper Loss} = I^2 \times R$$

Iron losses are divided into hysteresis and eddy current losses. **Hysteresis losses** result from the armature revolving in a magnetic field, which causes the current in the armature to alternate, thus magnetizing it in two directions. Because some residual magnetism remains in the armature after its direction is changed, some energy loss occurs. However, because the field magnets are always magnetized in one direction by DC current, they produce no hysteresis losses.

**Eddy current losses** occur because the armature's iron core acts as a conductor revolving in a magnetic field. This sets up an EMF across portions of the core, causing currents to flow within the core. These currents heat the core which, when excessive, can damage the windings. To keep eddy current losses to a minimum, a laminated core made of thin, insulated sheets of iron is used: the thinner the laminations, the greater the reduction in eddy current losses.

## INSPECTION AND MAINTENANCE OF DC MOTORS

The inspection and maintenance of DC motors should be in accordance with the guidelines established by the manufacturer. The following is representative of the types of maintenance checks typically called for:

- Check the unit driven by the motor in accordance with the specific installation instructions.
- Check all wiring, connections, terminals, fuses, and switches for general condition and security.
- Keep motors clean and mounting bolts tight.
- Check the brushes for condition, length, and spring tension. Procedures for replacing brushes, along with their minimum lengths, and correct spring tensions are provided in the applicable manufacturer's instructions. If the spring tension is too weak, the brush could begin to bounce and arc, which causes commutator burning and pitting.
- Inspect the commutator for cleanliness, pitting, scoring, roughness, corrosion, or burning. Check the mica between each of the commutator segments. In some instances, the mica is undercut to prevent it from wearing against the brushes. However, in some newer motor designs, the mica is left flush with the surface of the commutator. Always check the manufacturer's specifications to determine the limitations regarding the depth of the mica between commutator segments before attempting to undercut the mica.
- Clean commutators with the recommended cleaning solvent and a cloth. Polish rough or corroded commutators with fine sandpaper (000 or finer) and blow out remaining particles with compressed air. Never use emery paper or crocus cloth because they contain particles that can cause shorts between the commutator segments. Replace the motor if the commutator is burned, badly pitted, grooved, or worn to the extent that the mica insulation is out of acceptable tolerances.
- Inspect all exposed wiring for evidence of overheating. Replace the motor if the insulation on the leads or windings is burned, cracked, or brittle.
- Lubricate the motor only if called for by the manufacturer's instructions. Most motors in current use do not require lubrication between overhauls.

- Adjust and lubricate the gearbox or drive unit in accordance with the applicable manufacturer's instructions.

Troubleshoot any problems and replace the motor only when the trouble is due to a defect in the motor itself. In most cases, motor failure is caused by a defect in the external electrical circuit or by mechanical failure in the mechanism driven by the motor.

## AC MOTORS

AC motors have several advantages over DC motors. For example, in many instances, AC motors do not use brushes or commutators, and therefore cannot experience arcing. Furthermore, AC motors are well-suited for constant-speed applications, although some are manufactured with variable speed characteristics. Other advantages of some AC motors include their ability to operate on single- or multiple-phase lines as well as at several voltages. In addition, AC motors are generally less expensive than comparable DC motors. Because of these advantages, many aircraft are designed to use AC motors.

Because the electrical systems of large aircraft typically operate on 400 hertz AC, an aircraft AC motor operates at about seven times the speed of a 60-hertz commercial motor with the same number of poles. For example, a 400-hertz induction motor typically operates at speeds ranging from 6,000 to 24,000 r.p.m. This high rotational speed makes AC motors suitable for operating small high-speed rotors. And through the use of reduction gears, AC motors can lift and move heavy loads such as wing flaps and retractable landing gear, as well as produce enough torque to start an engine. The three basic types of AC motors are the universal motor, the induction motor, and the synchronous motor. Each type is a variation on basic AC motor operating principles.

### UNIVERSAL MOTORS

Fractional horsepower (less than one horsepower) AC-series motors are called universal motors. A unique characteristic of universal motors is that they can operate on either alternating or direct current. In fact, universal motors resemble DC motors in that they have brushes and a commutator. Universal motors are used extensively to operate fans and portable tools such as drills, grinders, and saws. [Figure 8-60]

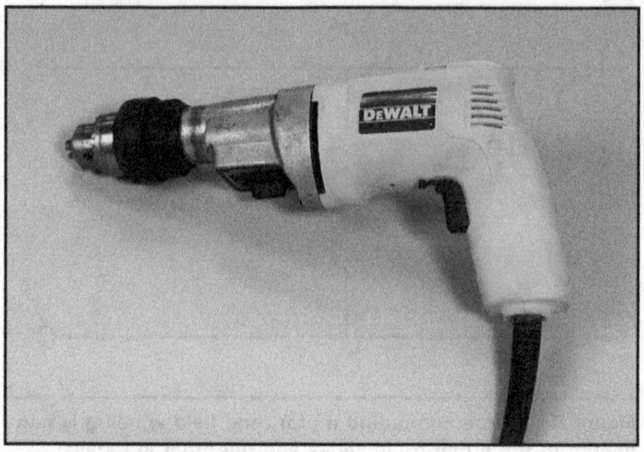


**Figure 8-60. An electric drill uses a universal motor that is similar in construction to a series-wound DC motor.**

### INDUCTION MOTORS

The most popular type of AC motor is the induction motor. Induction motors have no need for an electrical connection between the motor housing and the rotating elements. Therefore, there are no brushes, commutators, or slip rings to service. Induction motors operate at a fixed speed that is determined by their design and the frequency of AC applied. In addition, an induction motor can be operated on either single-phase or three-phase alternating current.

A single-phase induction motor is used to operate devices such as surface locks, intercooler shutters, oil shutoff valves, and other applications for which the power requirements are low. Single-phase induction motors require some form of starting circuit that automatically disconnects after the motor is running. Single-phase induction motors operate well in either rotational direction, with the direction determined by the starting circuit.

Unlike single-phase induction motors, three-phase induction motors are self-starting and are commonly used when high power is needed. Common applications for three-phase induction motors include starting the engines, operating flaps and landing gear, and powering hydraulic pumps.

#### CONSTRUCTION

The two primary parts of an induction motor are the stator and the rotor. The stator is unique because instead of having field poles that extend outward, windings are placed in slots around the stator's periphery. These windings make up a series of electromagnets that produce a magnetic field.

The rotor of an induction motor consists of an iron core made of thin circular laminations of soft steel that are keyed to a shaft. Longitudinal slots are cut into the rotor's circumference and heavy copper or aluminum bars are embedded in them. These bars are welded to a heavy, highly conductive ring on either end. [Figure 8-61]

Figure 8-61. There is no electrical connection between the rotor and the stator of an induction motor.

When AC is applied to the stator, the strength and polarity of the electromagnets change with the excitation current. Furthermore, to give the effect of a rotating magnetic field, each group of poles is attached to a separate phase of voltage.

When the rotor of an induction motor is subjected to the revolving magnetic field produced by the stator windings, a voltage is induced in the longitudinal bars. This induced voltage causes current to flow through the bars, which produces its own magnetic field that combines with the stator's revolving field. As a result, the rotor revolves at nearly a synchronous speed with the stator field. The only difference in the rotational speed between the stator field and the rotor is that which is necessary to induce the proper current into the rotor to overcome mechanical and electrical losses. If a rotor were to turn at the same speed as the rotating field, a resonance would set up. When this happens, the rotor conductors are not cut by any magnetic lines of flux, so no EMF is induced into them. Thus, no current flows in the rotor, resulting in no torque and little rotor rotation. For this reason, there must always be a difference in speed between the rotor and the stator's rotating field.

The difference in rotational speed is called **motor slip**, and is expressed as a percentage of the synchronous speed. For example, if the rotor turns at 1,750 r.p.m. and the synchronous speed is 1,800 r.p.m., the difference in speed is 50 r.p.m. The slip is therefore equal to 50/1,800, or 2.78 percent.

## SINGLE-PHASE INDUCTION MOTOR

A single-phase motor differs from a multiphase motor in that the single-phase motor has only one stator winding. In this configuration, the stator winding generates an expanding and collapsing stator field that induces currents into the rotor. These currents generate a rotor field opposite in polarity to that of the stator.

The field opposition exerts a turning force on the upper and lower parts of the rotor that try to turn it 180 degrees from its original position. Because these forces are exerted in the center of the rotor, the turning force is equal in each direction. As a result, the rotor will not begin turning from a standing stop. However, if the rotor starts turning, it continues to rotate. Furthermore, because the rotor momentum aids the turning force, there is no opposition to rotation.

## SHADED-POLE INDUCTION MOTOR

The first effort to develop a self-starting, single-phase motor was the shaded-pole induction motor. Like the generator, the shaded-pole motor has field poles that extend outward from the motor housing. In addition, a portion of each pole is encircled with a heavy copper ring. [Figure 8-62]

The presence of the copper ring causes the magnetic field through the ringed portion of the pole face to lag appreciably behind that of the other half of the pole. This results in a slight component of rotation in the field that is strong enough to cause rotation of the rotor. Although the torque created by this field is small, it is enough to accelerate the rotor to its rated speed. [Figure 8-63]

## SPLIT-PHASE MOTOR

Another variety of self-starting motor is known as a split-phase motor. Split-phase motors have a winding that is dedicated to starting the rotor. This "start" winding is displaced 90 degrees from the main, or run, winding and has a fairly high resistance that causes the current to be out of phase with the current in the run winding. The out- of-phase condition produces a rotating field that forces the rotor to rotate. After the rotor attains approximately 25 percent of its rated speed, a centrifugal switch automatically disconnects the start winding.

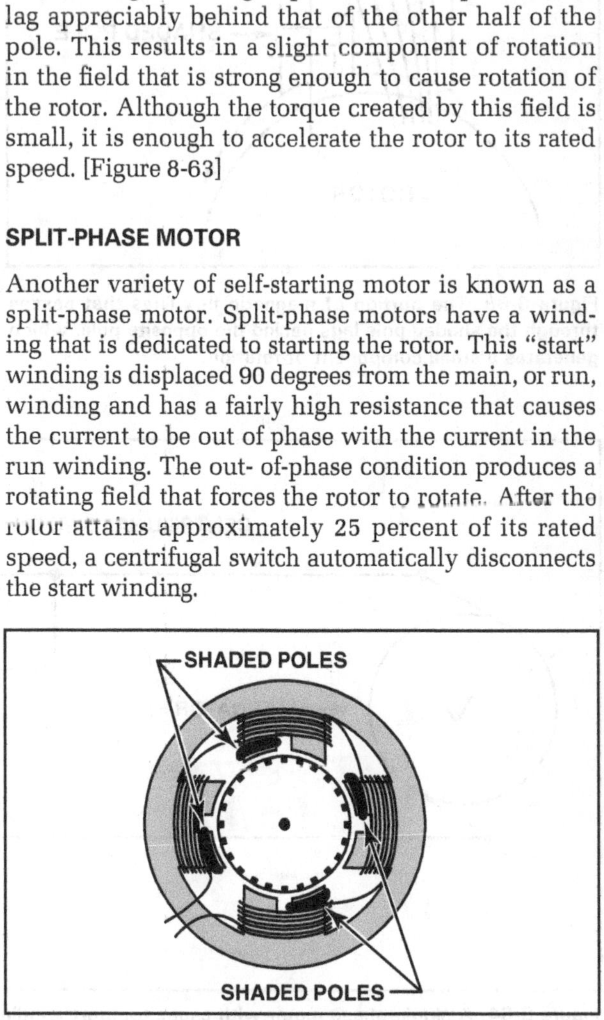


Figure 8-62. In a shaded-pole induction motor, a copper ring encircles a portion of each salient pole.

## CAPACITOR-START MOTOR

The development of high-capacity electrolytic capacitors made a variation of the split-phase motor possible. Motors that use high-capacity electrolytic capacitors are known as capacitor-start motors. Nearly all fractional horsepower motors in use today are of this type.

In a capacitor-start motor, the start and run windings are the same size and have identical resistance values. The phase shift between the two windings is obtained by using capacitors connected in series with the start winding. [Figure 8-64]

Capacitor-start motors have a starting torque comparable to their rated speed torque and are used in applications where the initial load is heavy. Again, a centrifugal switch is required for disconnecting the start winding when the rotor speed is approximately 25 percent of the rated speed.

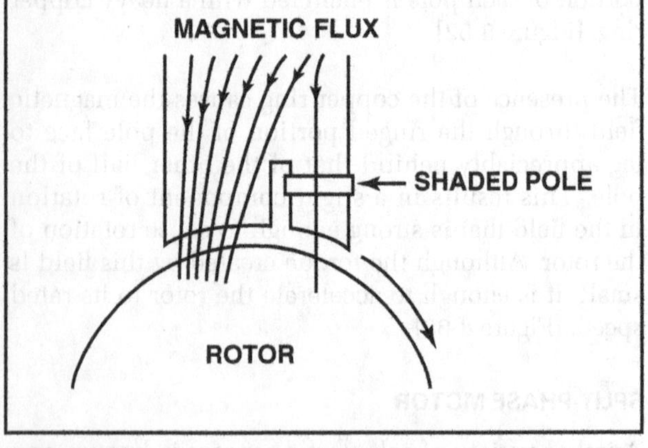


**Figure 8-63. The portion of magnetic flux lines that passes through the shaded pole lags behind the opposite pole, which generates a small component of rotation.**

## DIRECTION OF ROTATION

The direction of rotation for a three-phase induction motor is changed by reversing two of the motor leads. The same effect is obtained in a two-phase motor by reversing the connections on one phase. In a single-phase motor, reversing the connections to the start winding reverses the direction of rotation. Most single-phase motors that are designed for general application enable reversal of the connections to the start winding. A shaded-pole motor cannot be reversed because its rotational direction is determined by the physical location of the copper ring on the shaded pole. One would have to physically alter the position of the shaded poles to affect the motor's rotational direction.

## SYNCHRONOUS MOTORS

Similar to induction motors, synchronous motors use a rotating magnetic field. However, the torque developed by a synchronous motor does not depend on the induction of currents in the rotor. Instead, a synchronous motor starts when a multiphase source of AC is applied to a series of stator windings. When this is done, a rotating magnetic field is produced. At the same time, DC current is applied to the rotor winding, producing a second magnetic field. A synchronous motor is designed so that the rotor is pulled by the stator's rotating magnetic field. The rotor turns at approximately the same speed as the stator's magnetic field. In other words, the rotor and stator are synchronized.

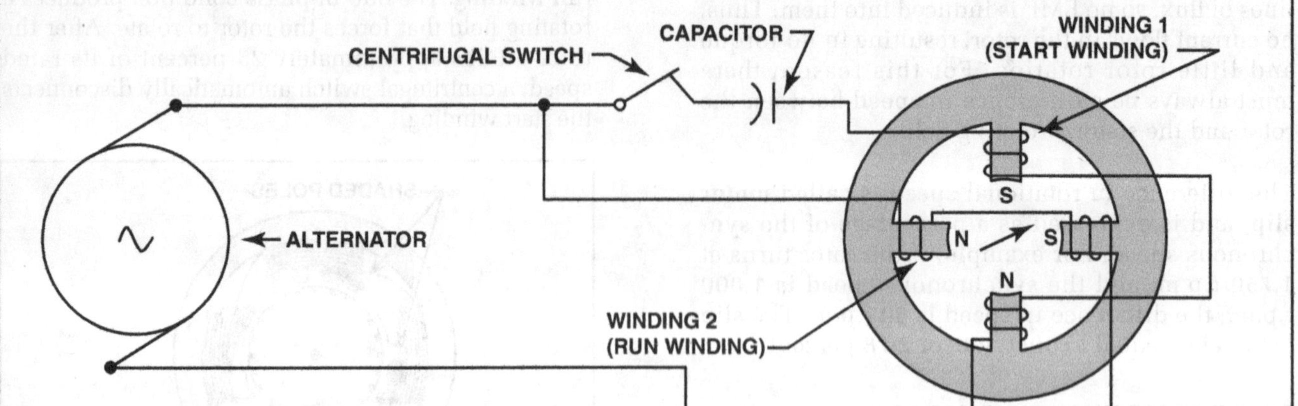


**Figure 8-64. A single-phase motor with capacitor start windings connects a capacitor in series with the alternator and start winding.**

To understand the operation of a synchronous motor, imagine that poles A and B are physically rotated clockwise to produce a rotating magnetic field. These poles would induce the opposite polarity in the soft-iron rotor between them, creating an attraction between the rotating poles and the rotor. This attraction would permit the rotating poles to drag the rotor at the same speed. [Figure 8-65]

When a load is applied to the rotor shaft, its axis momentarily falls behind that of the rotating field. However, the rotor catches up and again rotates with the field at the same speed, as long as the load remains constant. If the load is too large, the rotor pulls out of sync with the rotating poles and is unable to rotate at the same speed. In this situation, the motor is said to be overloaded.

Rotating the poles mechanically is impractical because that would require another motor. Therefore, a rotating magnetic field is produced electrically by using phased AC voltages. In this respect, a synchronous motor is similar to an induction motor.

The synchronous motor consists of a stator field winding that produces a rotating magnetic field. The rotor is either a permanent magnet or an electromagnet. If permanent magnets are used, the rotor's magnetism is stored within the magnet. Conversely, if electromagnets are used, the magnets receive power from a DC power source through slip rings.

Because a synchronous motor has little starting torque, it requires assistance to bring it up to synchronous speed. The most common method for this is to start the motor with no load, let it reach full speed, and then energize the magnetic field. The magnetic field of the rotor then locks with the magnetic field of the stator, and the motor operates at synchronous speed. [Figure 8-66]

The magnitude of the induced rotor poles is so small that sufficient torque cannot be developed for most practical loads. To avoid the limitation on motor operation, a winding is placed on the rotor and energized with direct current. To adjust the motor for varying loads, a rheostat placed in series with the DC source varies the pole's strength.

Synchronous motors are not self-starting. Because rotors are heavy, it is impossible to bring a stationary rotor into magnetic lock with a rotating magnetic field. As a result, all synchronous motors have some kind of starting device. One type of simple starter used is another AC or DC motor that brings the rotor up to approximately 90 percent of its synchronous speed. The starting motor is then disconnected and the rotor locks in with the rotating field.

Another method uses a second winding on the rotor. This induction winding brings the rotor close to synchronous speed before the direct current is disconnected from the rotor windings, after which the rotor is pulled into sync with the field.

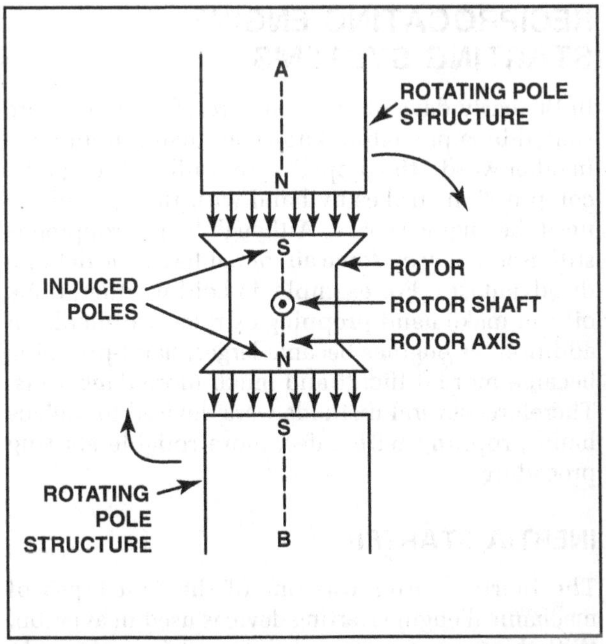


**Figure 8-65. In a synchronous motor, a rotating magnet induces opposing magnetic fields in a soft iron rotor. Under normal loads, the rotor turns at the same speed as the magnet.**

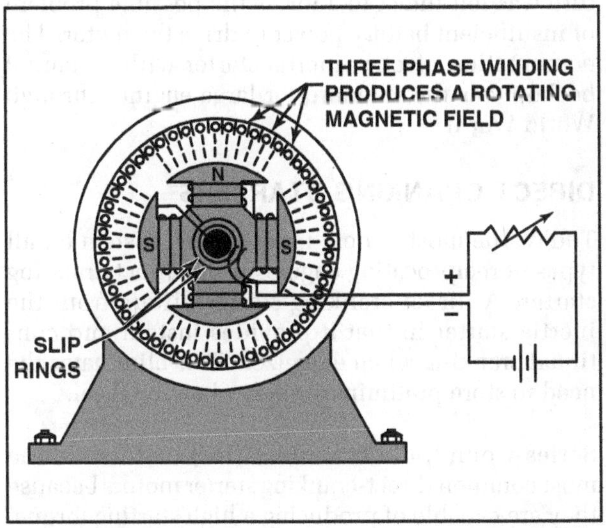


**Figure 8-66. The weak field induced in the rotor poles limits the development of torque. This problem is overcome by applying DC through a rheostat to vary the field strength of the poles.**

## RECIPROCATING ENGINE STARTING SYSTEMS

In the early days of aviation, aircraft engines were started by a procedure known as "hand-propping." In other words, the propeller was pulled through the compression strokes by hand with the ignition on until the engine started. Although hand-propping is still used today on some aircraft, it has some definite disadvantages. For example, in cold weather, thick oil can make hand-propping extremely difficult. In addition, as engines became larger, hand-propping became more difficult and much more dangerous. Therefore, several methods were devised to replace hand-propping with safer, more reliable starting procedures.

### INERTIA STARTER

The inertia starter was one of the first types of mechanical engine starting devices used in aviation. With this type of starter, a hand crank is used to spin up a flywheel through a step-up gear drive assembly. After the flywheel is spinning at a high speed, the hand crank is removed and the starter engage handle is pulled to extend a ratchet-type jaw that meshes with a mating ratchet on the crankshaft. The kinetic energy stored in the mass of the spinning flywheel is then converted to mechanical energy to drive the engine crankshaft. A torque-overload clutch located between the flywheel and ratchet jaws prevents damage to the engine or starter when the starter is first engaged.

To improve the inertia starter, an electric motor was mounted on the starter to spin the flywheel for easier engine starts. However, the hand cranking feature was left intact to address the possible problem of insufficient battery power to drive the motor. The combination electric-inertia starter with a manual backup was the standard for large engines through World War II.

### DIRECT-CRANKING STARTERS

Today, the most widely used starting system on all types of reciprocating engines is the direct-cranking starter. A direct-cranking starter differs from the inertia starter in that it provides instant and continual cranking when energized. This eliminates the need to store preliminary energy in a flywheel.

Series-wound, direct current (DC) motors are the most common direct-cranking starter motors because they are capable of producing a high starting torque. Starter motor characteristics provide a relatively constant voltage throughout a starting cycle while drawing a very high current at the start of motor rotation. The high current draw provides the starting torque needed to crank an engine. However, as engine and starter speed increase, counter electromotive forces build and limit the amount of current that the starter can draw. Typically, starter circuits do not contain fuses or circuit breakers. The reason for this is that initial starter motor current would trip the circuit breaker or blow the fuse each time the engine is started.

### SMALL ENGINE STARTERS

Some small, horizontally opposed engines use a direct-cranking starter comprised of a small series-wound electric motor and a small gear. The small gear meshes with a large gear that is part of an over-running clutch that drives a pinion, or drive gear. This type of starter is typically engaged by either a hand-pulled cable or a solenoid that engages a shift lever. [Figure 8-67]

Typically, the shift lever is attached by a cable or rod to a tee-handle or an electrical switch that activates a solenoid. When the tee-handle is pulled or the switch is closed, the shift lever compresses the meshing spring and forces the pinion gear outward to mesh with the starter gear inside the engine accessory case. When the pinion and the starter gear are fully meshed, further movement of the shift lever closes the starter motor switch, and the starter cranks the engine. When the engine starts, the over-running clutch permits the pinion to spin freely with the engine until the tee-handle or starter switch is released and the return spring pulls the pinion away from the starter gear.

Another type of direct-cranking electric starter also uses a series-wound DC motor, but a Bendix drive similar to that used on automobile engines replaces the over-running clutch. A **Bendix drive** consists of a drive spring, drive pinion, and drive shaft with helical splines. When the starter switch is closed, the starter motor spins the pinion through the Bendix drive spring. The drive pinion fits loosely over the drive shaft and, as the armature spins, the pinion moves forward on the helical splines. As the pinion moves forward, it engages the teeth on the engine's flywheel and the engine turns.

When the engine starts, the spinning flywheel gear begins to spin the Bendix drive pinion faster than the starter motor, which forces the pinion back along the helical splines until it disengages from the flywheel. [Figure 8-68]

Some Teledyne Continental Motors aircraft engines use a starter mounted on the side of the accessory case. This type of starter uses a series-wound electric motor that drives a starter worm gear. The worm gear is permanently meshed with a worm wheel in the engine's accessory case. A clutch spring

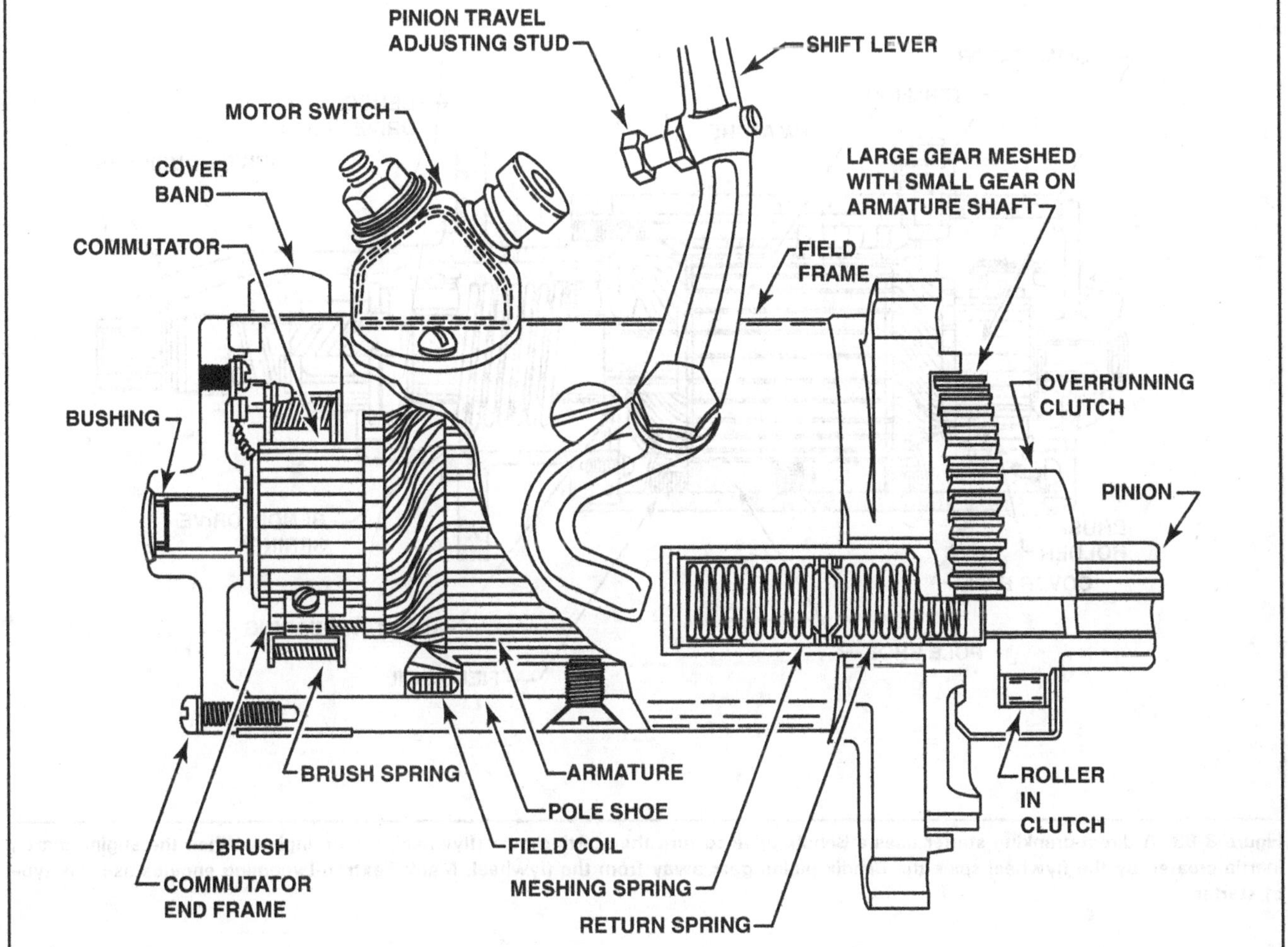


**Figure 8-67. Some small, horizontally opposed aircraft engines use a direct-cranking starter with a small DC motor to drive an over-running clutch. The over-running clutch drives a pinion, or drive gear, that turns the engine.**

is attached to the worm wheel and, as the worm wheel turns, the spring tightens around a knurled drum on the engine's starter shaft. When the spring gets tight enough, the starter shaft begins to rotate at approximately the same speed as the worm wheel and starter motor. Attached to the starter shaft is a starter shaft gear that is permanently meshed with the crankshaft gear in the engine accessory case. Therefore, when the starter motor spins the starter shaft, the starter shaft gear turns the crankshaft. Upon engine start, the crankshaft will spin faster than the starter gear shaft, causing the clutch spring to release the knurled drum on the starter shaft. This allows the engine to accelerate to idle speed without causing damage to the starter or the worm wheel mechanism before the starter is disengaged.

The generator drive pulley is mounted on the end of the starter gear shaft and, with the clutch spring disengaged, serves as the generator drive shaft. [Figure 8-69]

## LARGE ENGINE STARTERS

Because of the increased force required to rotate the crankshaft of a high horsepower engine, a typical direct-cranking electric starter for large, reciprocating engines must employ some sort of reduction gear assembly. The reduction gear assembly, along with the motor assembly and an automatic engaging and disengaging mechanism, are contained in a single starter unit. [Figure 8-70]

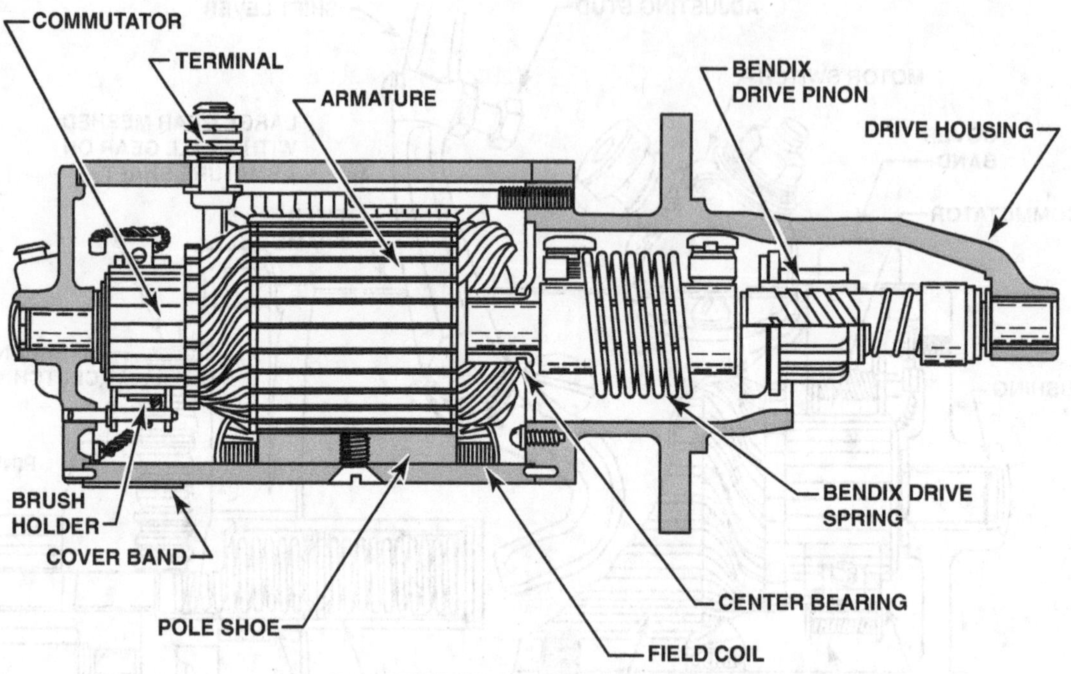


**Figure 8-68. A direct-cranking starter uses a Bendix drive to turn the starting gear (flywheel) on an engine. When the engine starts, inertia created by the flywheel spins the Bendix pinion gear away from the flywheel. Many Textron-Lycoming engines use this type of starter.**

The motor section consists of all the components found in a typical motor and a motor pinion assembly. The starter motor used is typically a non-reversible series interpole motor whose speed varies directly with the applied voltage and inversely with the load.

The starter reduction gear assembly consists of a housing with an integral mounting flange; an integral gear assembly; a planetary gear reduction; a torque-limiting clutch; and a jaw and cone assembly. In this type of assembly, starter motor torque is transmitted to the starter jaw through an internal gear assembly and a reduction gear assembly. [Figure 8-71]

## TURBINE ENGINE STARTING SYSTEMS

Gas turbine engines are generally started by a starter connected to the main gearbox. In this configuration, the starter rotates the compressor through the gearbox. On engines that use a dual axial compressor, the starter rotates the high speed compressor and N1 turbine system only. Likewise, on turboprop and turbo shaft engines using a free-turbine, only the compressor and its associated turbine assembly are rotated by the starter.

Rotating the compressor with a starter provides the engine with sufficient air for combustion and aids the engine in self-acceleration up to idle speed when combustion occurs. Neither the starter nor the turbine wheel has sufficient power on their own to bring an engine from rest to idle r.p.m. However, when used in combination, the process takes place smoothly in approximately 30 seconds on a typical engine.

Many starting systems have a speed sensor device which automatically disengages the starter after self-accelerating speed is reached. At this point, turbine power is sufficient to accelerate the engine to idle r.p.m. If the starter does not get the engine to the correct speed, a hung start may occur. A hung start is what happens when combustion occurs but the engine does not accelerate to idle. If a hung start occurs, the engine must be shut down and the

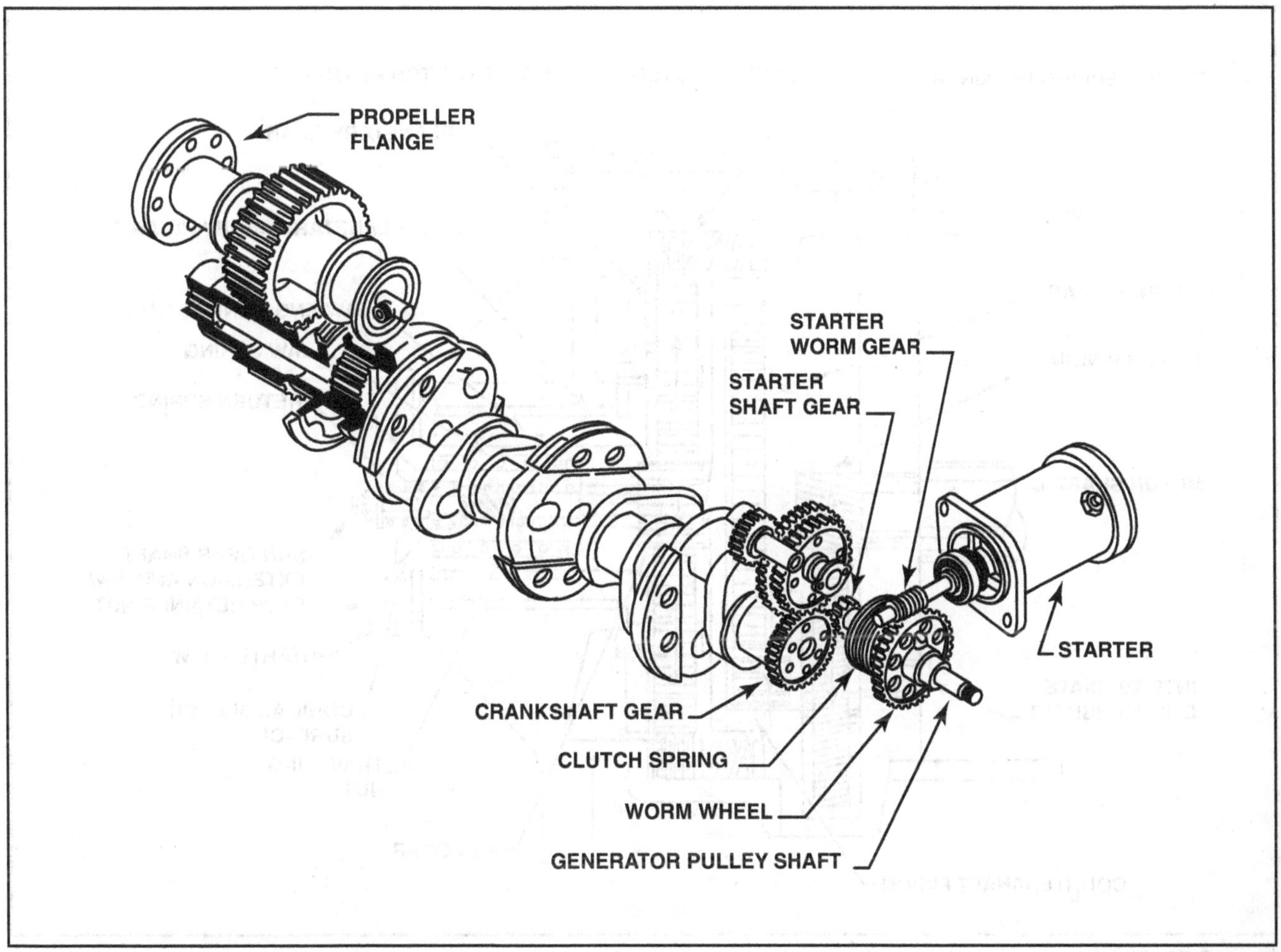


**Figure 8-69. Teledyne Continental Motors aircraft engines commonly use a side-mounted starter with a worm-gear drive assembly. A clutch disengages the starter after the engine starts.**

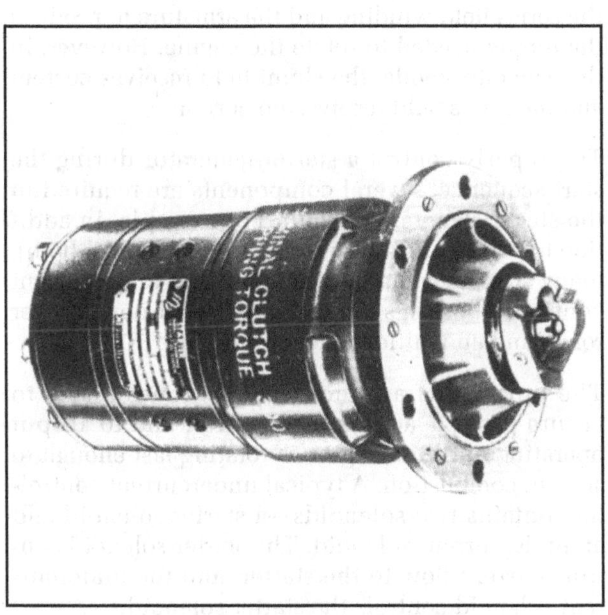

**Figure 8-70. High horsepower engines typically use a starter unit with a starter motor reduction gear assembly and a mechanism for engagement and disengagement.**

cause for insufficient starting speed corrected before another attempt is made. An attempt to accelerate an engine that is hung can lead to a hot start, because the engine is operating with insufficient airflow to combust more fuel.

Starting systems for turboprop and turboshaft engines depend on whether the engine is a fixed shaft or free-turbine design. For example, with a fixed shaft turboprop engine, the starter must rotate the engine and propeller. Therefore, starters used on fixed shaft turboprops engines typically develop more torque. To reduce the load, fixed shaft turboprop engines are started with the propeller in low pitch to reduce drag, allowing more speed and airflow. Free-turbine engines, on the other hand, present very little drag on turbine acceleration because only the gas generator portion of the engine is turned by the starter. This allows the use of lighter weight, less powerful starters. Because the propeller is not turned by the starter, the engine can be started with the propeller blades in any position.

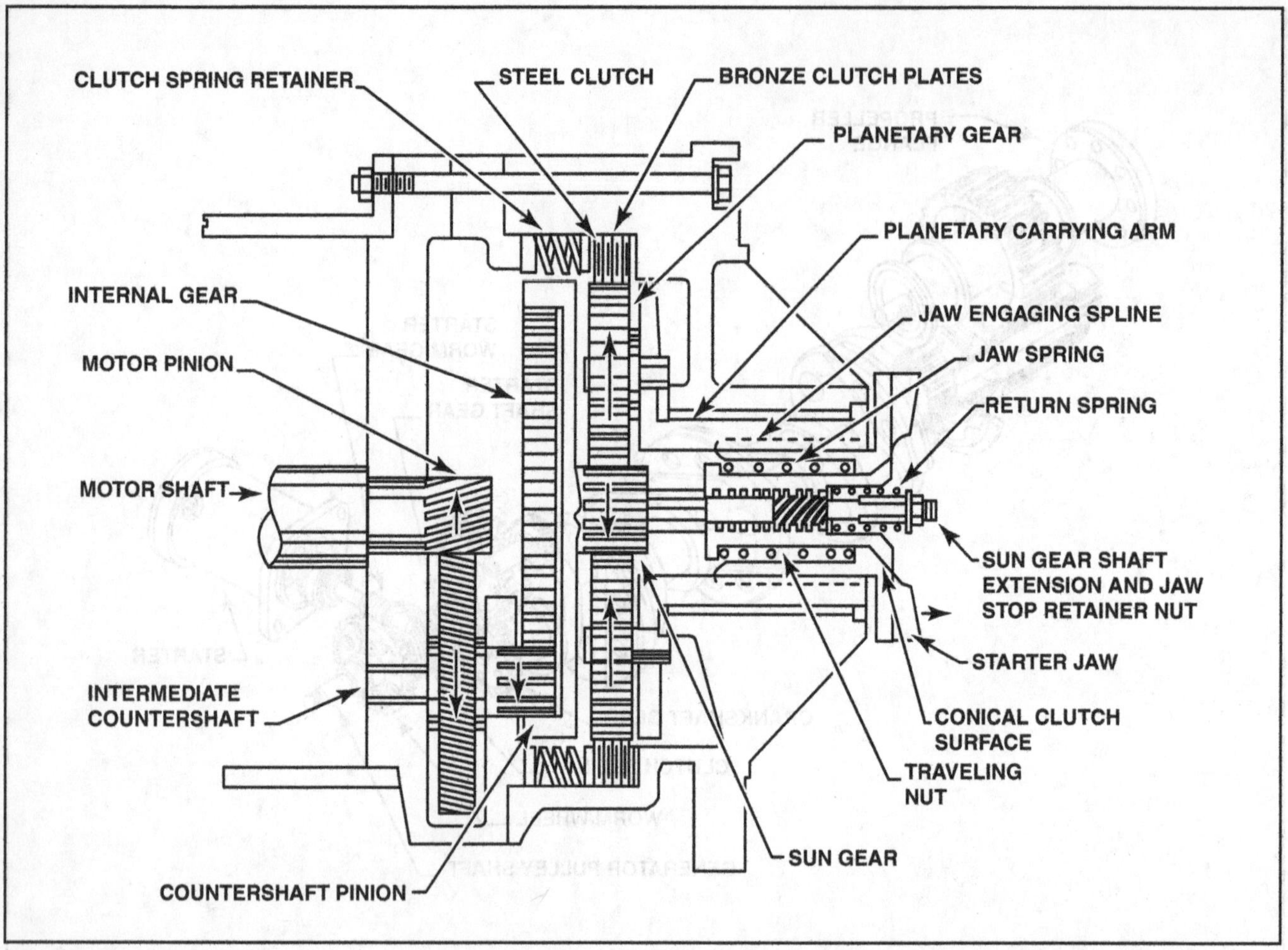


**Figure 8-71. For a large reciprocating engine, the reduction gear train converts the high speed and low torque of a starting motor to the low speed and high torque necessary to start the engine. A pinion gear drives an intermediate countershaft assembly that turns the sun gear in a planetary gear reduction assembly, and the rotation of the planetary gears causes the starter jaw to engage the engine.**

## ELECTRIC STARTERS

Like reciprocating engines, several models of gas turbine engines use an electric starting motor. The two most common types of electric starter motors are the starter-generator and direct-cranking starter.

### STARTER-GENERATORS

Starter-generators provide an efficient means of accomplishing both starting and power generation. Because a starter-generator performs the functions of both a starter and generator, it provides an inherent weight-savings. Because of the efficiency and weight-saving features, starter-generators are widely used on both turboprop and corporate jet aircraft. [Figure 8-72]

Several types of starter-generators are in use today. Most contain two field coils and a common armature winding. One field coil is connected in series with the armature and has a low resistance; the second shunt winding has a comparatively high resistance. When used as a starter, current flows through both the series field winding and the armature to produce the torque needed to rotate the engine. However, in the generator mode, the shunt field receives current and the series field receives no current.

To properly control a starter-generator during the start sequence, several components are required in the starter-generator circuit. For example, in addition to needing a battery and master switch (or both), many starter-generator circuits use an undercurrent controller, a start switch, some sort of power lever relay, and an ignition solenoid. [Figure 8-73]

The purpose of an undercurrent controller is to ensure positive action of the starter and to keep it operating until the engine is rotating fast enough to sustain combustion. A typical undercurrent controller contains two solenoids—a starter solenoid and an undercurrent solenoid. The starter solenoid controls current flow to the starter, and the undercurrent solenoid controls the starter solenoid.

To start an engine equipped with an undercurrent solenoid, you must first close the battery and engine

**Figure 8-72. To save weight and reduce complexity, some gas turbine engines employ a combination starter-generator that starts the engine and then generates electrical power after the engine is running.**

master switches. This completes the circuit from the aircraft's bus to the start switch, fuel valves, and power lever relay. Energizing the power lever relay starts the fuel pumps, which provide the necessary fuel pressure for starting the engine.

As the start switch is turned on, the starter solenoid and the ignition solenoid are closed. The starter solenoid closes the circuit from the power source to the starter motor while the ignition solenoid closes the circuit to the ignition units. As soon as current begins flowing to the motor through the starter solenoid, the undercurrent solenoid closes. In the closed position, the undercurrent solenoid completes a circuit from the bus to the starter solenoid coil and ignition solenoid coil, which permits the start switch to return to its neutral position while the start sequence continues.

As the motor builds up speed, the current draw of the motor decreases. When the current draw falls

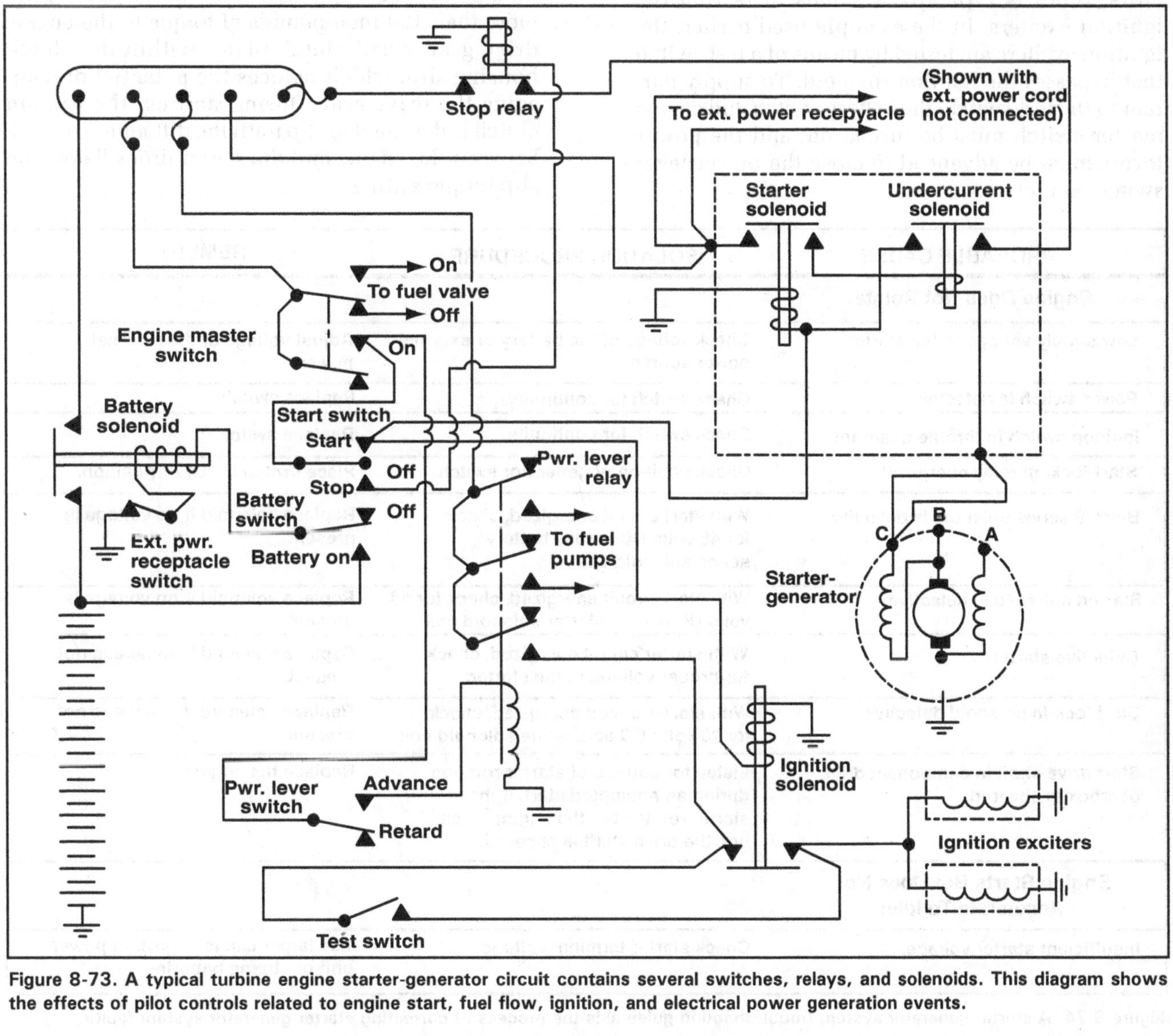


**Figure 8-73. A typical turbine engine starter-generator circuit contains several switches, relays, and solenoids. This diagram shows the effects of pilot controls related to engine start, fuel flow, ignition, and electrical power generation events.**

below approximately 200 amps, the undercurrent solenoid opens. This action breaks the circuit from the bus to the coil of the starter and ignition solenoid, which in turn stops current flow to the starter motor and ignition exciters.

After the start sequence is complete, the engine should be operating efficiently and ignition should be self-sustaining. However, if the engine hangs or fails to reach sufficient speed to halt the starter operation, the start switch should be moved to the stop position to break the circuit from the positive bus to the main contacts of the undercurrent relay.

If the battery has insufficient power to accelerate the engine to starting speed, most starter-generator circuits provide a means to use an external power source. However, when external power is used, a switch must be available in the circuit that prevents the battery from being connected to the bus.

As an added feature in most starter-generator circuits, there is typically a means of testing the ignition exciters. In the example used earlier, the ignition exciters are tested by means of a test switch that bypasses the ignition solenoid. To supply current to the test switch, the battery switch and engine master switch must be turned on, and the power levers must be advanced to close the power lever switch and relay.

When discrepancies are reported, a ground check is typically required to duplicate the condition. When troubleshooting , be sure to reference the manufacturer's troubleshooting guide. [Figure 8-74]

## DIRECT-CRANKING STARTERS

Direct-cranking starters are seldom used on large turbine engines; however, they are used frequently for starting auxiliary and ground power units. A typical direct-cranking electric starter used on a small turbine engine consists of an electric motor, a set of reduction gears, and an automatic engaging and disengaging clutch mechanism. [Figure 8-75]

The automatic clutch assembly performs two functions. First, it prevents the starter from applying excessive torque to the engine accessory drive gearbox. To do this, an adjustable torque setting within the clutch assembly is set at approximately 130 inch-pounds of torque. Whenever the starter applies more than 130 inch-pounds of torque to the engine drive gear, small clutch plates within the clutch housing slip, which reduces the potential of damaging the drive gear. During starting, the friction clutch is designed to slip until the differential torque between the engine and the starter drops below the slip torque setting.

| PROBABLE CAUSE | ISOLATION PROCEDURE | REMEDY |
|---|---|---|
| **Engine Does Not Rotate:** | | |
| Low supply voltage to the starter. | Check voltage of the battery or external power source. | Adjust voltage of the external power. |
| Power switch is defective. | Check switch for continuity. | Replace switch. |
| Ignition switch in throttle quadrant. | Check switch for continuity. | Replace switch. |
| Start-lockout relay energized. | Check position of generator switch. | Place switch in "OFF" position. |
| Battery series solenoid is defective. | With start circuit energized, check for 48 volts DC across battery series solenoid coil. | Replace solenoid if no voltage is present. |
| Started solenoid is defective. | With start circuit energized, check for 48 volts DC across starter solenoid coil. | Replace solenoid if no voltage is present. |
| Defective starter | With starter circuit energized, check for proper voltage at the starter. | Replace solenoid if voltage is not present. |
| Start lock-In solenoid defective. | With starter circuit energized, check for 28 volts DC across the solenoid coil. | Replace solenoid if voltage is not present. |
| Start drive shaft in component drive gearbox is sheared. | Listen for sounds of starter rotation during an attempted start. If the starter rotates but the engine does not, the drive shaft is sheared. | Replace the engine. |
| **Engine Starts But Does Not Accelerate To Idle:** | | |
| Insufficient starter voltage. | Check starter terminal voltage. | Use larger capacity ground power unit or charge batteries. |

Figure 8-74. A starter-generator system troubleshooting guide aids the process of correcting starter-generator system faults.

The second function of the clutch assembly is to act as an over-run clutch. When the starter rotates, centrifugal force causes the pawls to move inward against spring tension to engage the engine drive gear. As the armature drives the clutch housing, the housing bumps the pawls inward until they catch the engine drive gear. This occurs because the pawl cage assembly floats within the pawl clutch housing. After the engine begins to exceed starter speed, the pawls slip out of the tapered slots of the engine drive gear and are disengaged by the retracting springs. This over-running feature prevents the engine from driving the starter to burst speed.

## AIR TURBINE STARTERS

An alternative type of starter is the air turbine, or pneumatic starter. As its name implies, an air turbine starter uses a small turbine wheel to convert the velocity energy of a moving airstream into mechanical energy to turn an engine. A typical air turbine starter consists of a small turbine assembly, reduction gear assembly, and clutch assembly. Because air turbine starters contain so few components, they typically weigh about one-fifth that of a comparable electric starter. This gives air turbine starters a high power-to-weight ratio. Because of this, pneumatic starters are used almost exclusively on commercial jet aircraft. [Figure 8-76]

A pneumatic starter requires a high-volume air source (approximately 40 p.s.i. at 50 to 100 pounds per minute) to start. The air source can be an on-board auxiliary power unit, ground power unit, or an operating engine bleed air source. Air is supplied to the starter inlet where it enters the air turbine assembly.

Two common types of turbine assemblies used on pneumatic starters are the radial inward flow turbine and the axial-flow turbine. As soon as air enters a pneumatic starter, the air passes through a set of turbine nozzle vanes. The vanes convert the low pressure, high volume air to a high velocity airstream that spins the turbine blades at high kinetic energy levels.

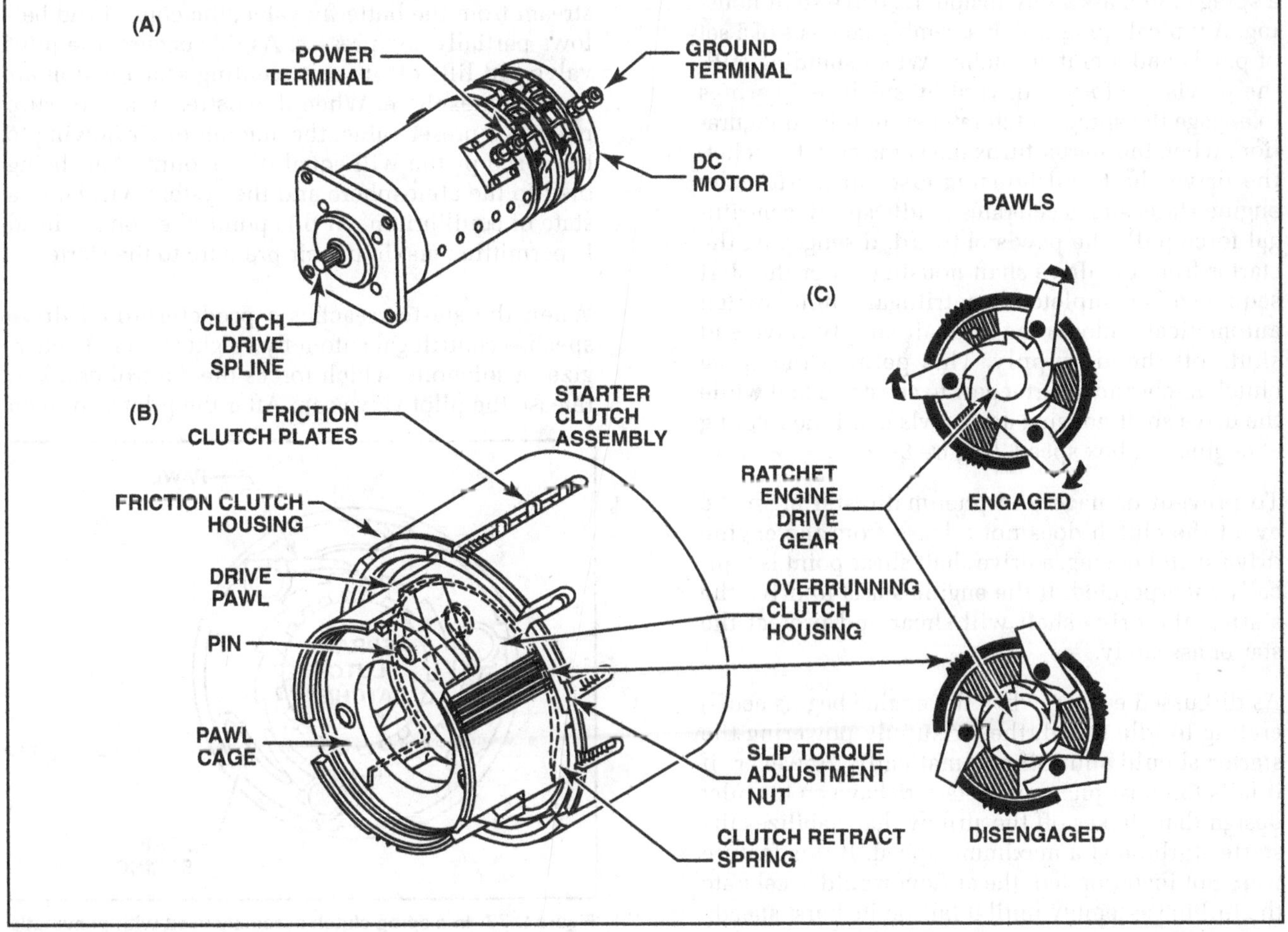


**Figure 8-75. (A) The motors in typical direct-cranking starter for a turbine engine are similar to those used in reciprocating engines. (B) The typical direct-cranking starter for a turbine engine incorporates a clutch assembly. (C) When the starter drive is engaged, pawls in the clutch assembly turn the drive gear and rotate the engine. When the engine starts, the acceleration of the engine drive gear causes disengages the pawls.**

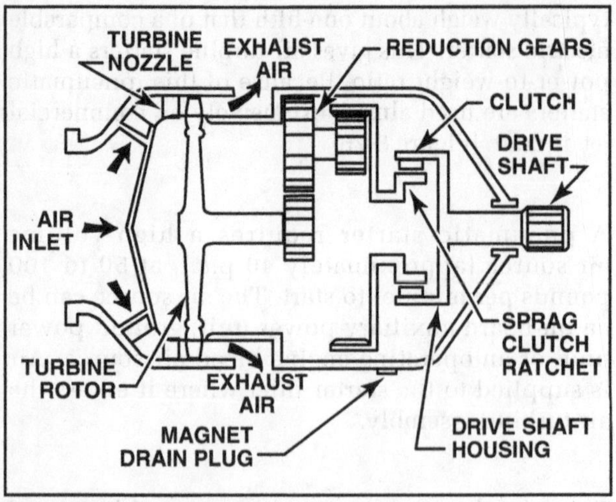


**Figure 8-76. A typical air turbine starter consists of a small turbine assembly, reduction gearing, and a clutch assembly.**

In a typical pneumatic starter, the turbine rotates at 60 to 80 thousand r.p.m. This rotational speed is reduced 20 to 30 times through a reduction gear assembly that is lubricated by an integral oil supply. The output end of the reduction gearing connects to a sprag clutch assembly inside the drive shaft housing. A typical sprag clutch assembly consists of a set of pawls and a clutch ratchet. When standing still, the pawls are forced inward by small leaf springs to engage the sprag clutch ratchet. In this configuration, when the starter turns the sprag clutch ratchet, the drive shaft and housing also turn. After the engine starts and accelerates to idle speed, centrifugal force pulls the pawls outward, disengaging the starter from the drive shaft housing. After the start sequence is complete, a centrifugal cutout switch automatically closes the inlet air supply valve and shuts off the air supply. This permits the sprag clutch ratchet and starter gear to coast to a halt while the drive shaft housing and pawls continue rotating at engine gearbox speed. [Figure 8-77]

To prevent damage to a pneumatic starter in the event the clutch does not release from the engine drive shaft housing, a drive shaft shear point is typically incorporated. If the engine starts to drive the starter, the drive shaft will shear and protect the starter assembly.

As discussed earlier, when the engine begins accelerating to idle speed, the air supply powering the starter should shut off automatically. However, if it fails to, most pneumatic starters have an air inlet design that chokes off the airflow that stabilizes the starter turbine at a maximum speed. If this feature were not incorporated, the airflow would accelerate the turbine assembly until it fails at its burst speed.

On engines that use a pneumatic starter equipped with a sprag clutch, you can sometimes hear a clicking sound after the engine continues to coast after shutdown. This sound is normal and is the result of the spring tension on the pawls overcoming centrifugal force and forcing the pawls to ride on the clutch ratchet.

### AIR SUPPLY VALVE

On aircraft that use a pneumatic starter, an air supply valve is installed in the air inlet line leading to the starter. A typical air supply valve includes a control head and a butterfly valve. In most cases, the control head is actuated by a switch in the cockpit, and the butterfly valve is actuated either pneumatically or manually. [Figure 8-78]

When the control head is actuated, the control crank rotates and pushes the control rod to extend the bellows fully. In addition, the control crank applies pressure to seat the pilot valve rod and displace the pilot valve cap. With the pilot valve cap off of its seat, filtered air flows to the servo piston. As air pressure compresses the servo piston, the butterfly valve opens and air flows to the starter.

As pressure builds in the air supply line downstream from the butterfly valve, the control rod bellows partially compresses. As this occurs, the pilot valve rod lifts off its seat, venting servo piston air to the atmosphere. When downstream air pressure reaches a preset value, the amount of air flowing to the servo piston will equal the amount of air being bled to the atmosphere and the system will be in a state of equilibrium. At this point, the control head is permitting maximum air pressure to the starter.

When the starter reaches a predetermined drive speed, a centrifugal cutout flyweight switch de-energizes a solenoid, which forces the control crank to release the pilot valve cap. After the pilot valve cap

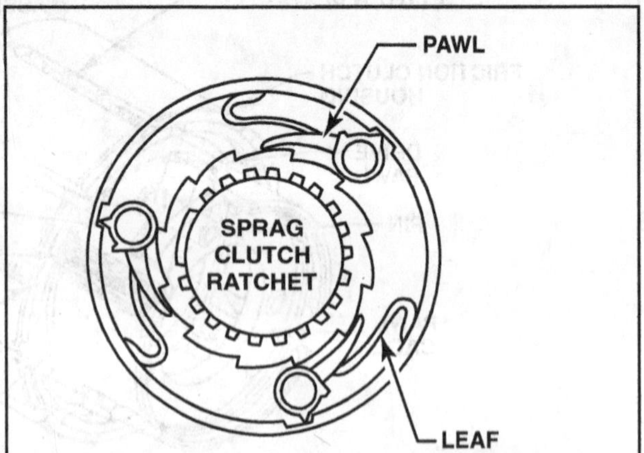


**Figure 8-77. In a sprag clutch assembly used with pneumatic starters, leaf springs force pawls inward to engage the clutch ratchet. When the engine starts and accelerates beyond the starter's speed, centrifugal force pulls the pawls away from the clutch ratchet.**

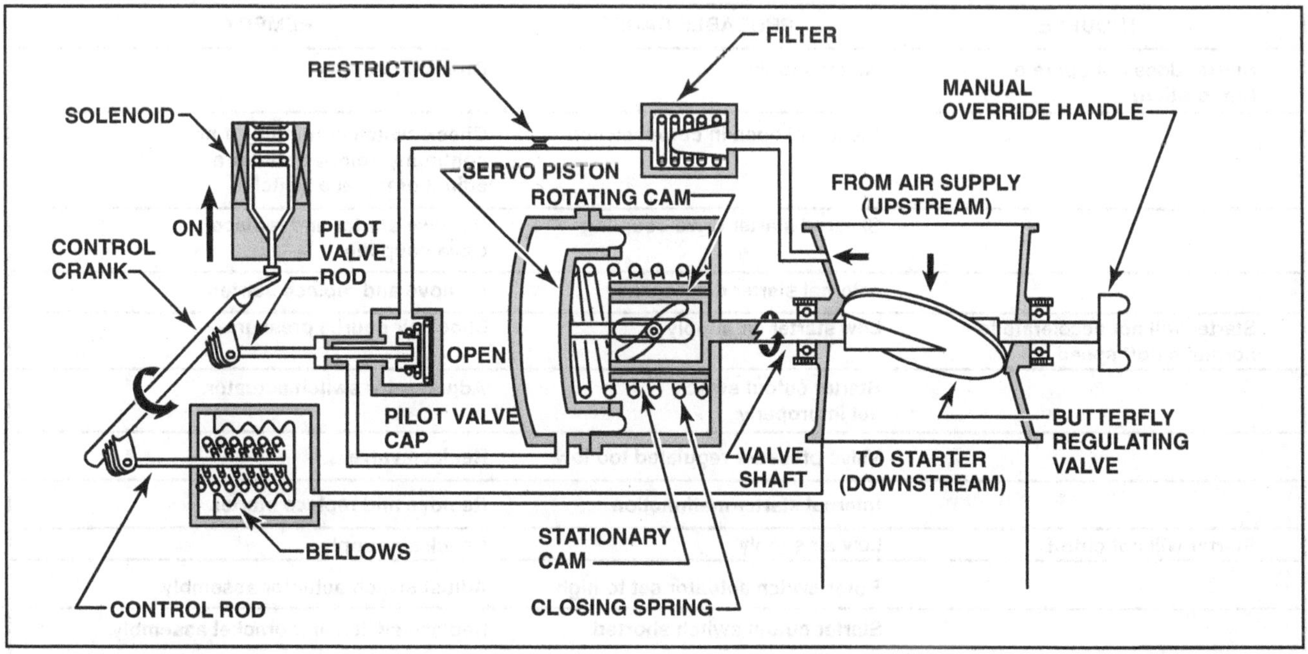


**Figure 8-78. The air supply valve controls the amount of air that flows to a pneumatic starter turbine.**

seats, all air pressure vents to the atmosphere, and the butterfly valve closes.

When the starter air valve cannot be controlled electrically due to a malfunction, a manual override handle can be used to position the butterfly valve. However, when attempting to start an engine using the manual override, make sure you follow the manufacturer's procedures.

## INSPECTION AND MAINTENANCE

Air turbine starters are pneumatic accessories designed to operate at high speed in a high temperature environment. Because of this, adequate lubrication is crucial. Routine inspections of pneumatic starters should include a check of the starter's oil level and examination of the magnetic drain plug. The presence of small particles on the drain plug is considered normal, but particles that feel sandy or gritty are evidence of some sort of internal failure.

In addition to normal maintenance practices, you might occasionally have to troubleshoot a malfunction. To facilitate the troubleshooting process, some manufacturers provide a chart that lists several common malfunctions with the probable causes and remedies. [Figure 8-79]

## COMBUSTION STARTER

A combustion starter is a completely self-contained unit that consists of the same components found in a typical free turbine engine. In other words, a combustion starter has compressor, combustion, turbine, and exhaust sections; as well as its own fuel and oil supply, ignition system, and starting system. The compressor section typically consists of a small centrifugal compressor, and the combustion section generally consists of a reverse flow combustion chamber. The air supply needed to operate a combustion starter is either drawn from the surrounding air or supplied by another high-pressure source.

Operation of a combustion starter is typically automatic. In other words, actuating a single start switch in the cockpit ignites the starter and begins turning the free turbine. As soon as the free turbine begins rotating, a series of reduction gears rotate the main engine. When the main engine starts and reaches its self-sustaining speed, a cutout switch shuts down the combustion starter. [Figure 8-80]

| TROUBLE | PROBABLE CAUSE | REMEDY |
|---|---|---|
| Starter does not operate (no rotation) | No air supply | Check air supply. |
| | Electrical open in cutout switch | Check switch continuity. If no continuity, remove starter and adjust or replace switch. |
| | Skeared starter drive coupling | Remove starter and replace drive coupling. |
| | Internal starter discrepancy | Remove and replace starter. |
| Starter will not accelerate to normal cutoff speed | Low starter air supply | Check air source pressure. |
| | Starter cutout switch set improperly | Adjust rotor switch actuator. |
| | Valve pressure regulated too low | Replace valve. |
| | Internal starter malfunction | Remove and replace starter. |
| Starter will not cutoff | Low air supply | Check air supply. |
| | Rotor switch actuator set to high | Adjust switch actuator assembly. |
| | Starter cutout switch shorted | Replace switch and bracket assembly. |
| External oil leakage | Oil level too high | Drain oil and reservice properly. |
| | Loose vent, oil filler, or magnetic plugs | Tighten magnetic plug to proper torque. Tighten vent and oil filler plugs as necessary and lockwire. |
| | Loose clamp band assembly | Tighten clamp band assembly to higher torque. |
| Starter runs, but engine does not turn over | Sheared drive coupling | Remove starter and replace the drive coupling. If couplings persist in breaking in unusually short periods of time, remove and replace starter. |
| Starter inlet will not line up with supply ducting | Improper installation of starter on engine, or improper indexing of turbine housing on starter | Check installation and/or indexing for conformance with manufacturer's installation instructions and the proper index position of the turbine housing specifed for the aircraft. |
| Metallic particles on magnetic drain plug | Small fuzzy particles indicate noemal wear | No remedial action required. |
| | Partcles coarser than fuzzy, such as chips, slivers, etc., indicate interal difficulty | Remove and replace starter. |
| Broken nozzle vanes | Large foreign particles in air supply | Remove and replace starter and check air supply filler. |
| Oil leakage from vent plug assembly | Improper starter instalation position | Check installed position for levelness of oil plugs and correct as required in accordance with manufacturer's installation instructions. |
| Oil leakage at drive coupling | Leaking rear seal assembly | Remove and replace starter. |

Figure 8-79. A pneumatic starter troubleshooting guide aids in the process of correcting system faults.

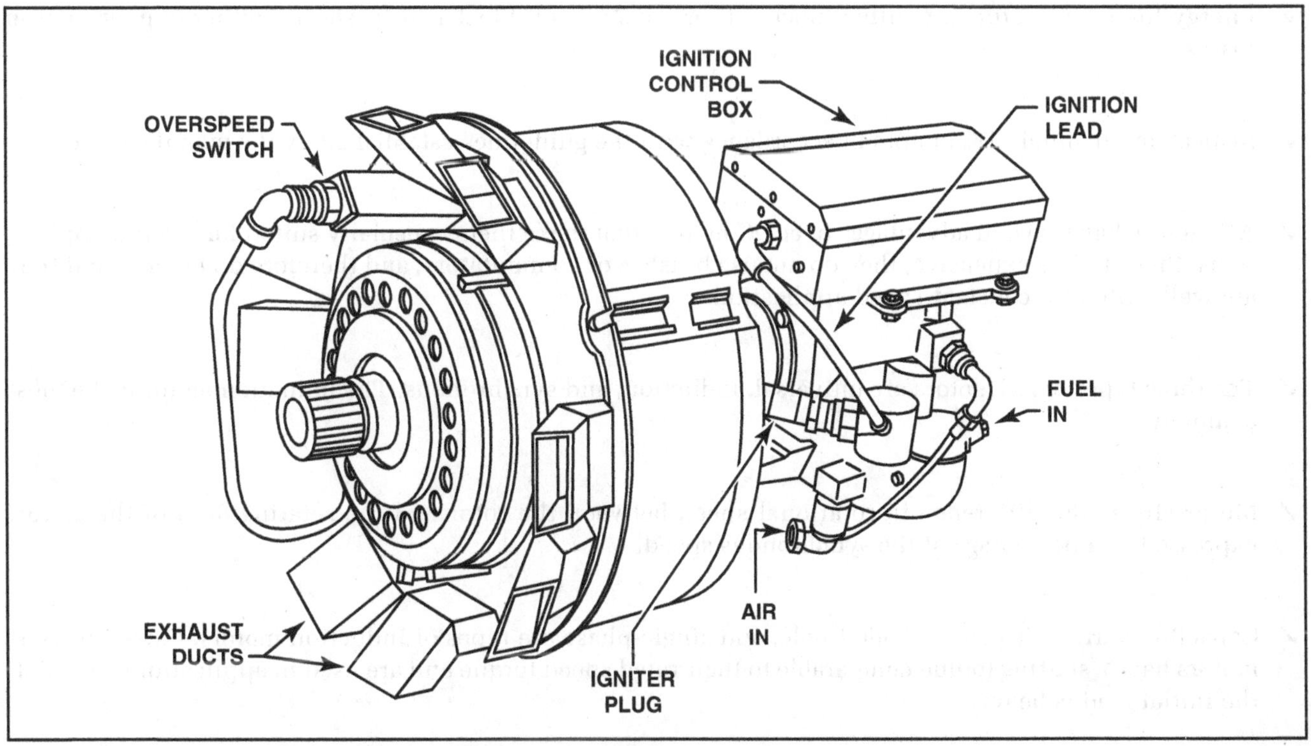


**Figure 8-80. A combustion starter is a gas turbine engine that delivers engine starting power through a high-ratio reduction gear system. Operation of a combustion starter typically consists of actuating a single cockpit switch.**

## SUMMARY CHECKLIST

✓ A DC motor is a rotating machine that transforms direct-current electrical energy into mechanical energy used in many devices on an airplane.

✓ The right-hand motor rule illustrates the direction of rotation of a wire coil in a magnetic field.

✓ A DC motor has an armature assembly, a field assembly, a brush assembly, and end frames.

✓ You can control the speed of variable speed motors by varying the current in the field windings.

✓ You can reverse the rotation of a DC motor by reversing the direction of current flow in either the armature or the field windings.

✓ DC motors are classified by their type of field-armature connection and the duty for which they are designed. The three types of DC field-armature connections are series, shunt, and compound.

✓ Energy losses in motors are either electrical or mechanical. Electrical losses are either copper or iron losses.

✓ Inspect and maintain DC motors in accordance with the guidelines established by the manufacturer.

✓ AC motors have several advantages over DC motors that make them especially suited for aircraft applications: they are less expensive; they do not use brushes or commutators, and therefore do not arc; and they are well-suited for constant-speed applications.

✓ The three types of AC motors are universal, induction, and synchronous. The induction motor is the most common.

✓ Motor slip is the difference in rotational speed between the rotor and the rotating field of the stator, expressed as a percentage of the synchronous speed.

✓ Capacitor start, split-phase, shaded-pole, and single-phase are types of induction motors. Capacitor-start motors have a starting torque comparable to their rated speed torque and are used in applications in which the initial load is heavy.

✓ In a synchronous motor, the rotor turns at the same speed as the stator's magnetic field.

✓ Synchronous motors are not self-starting; they require some sort of starting device—either an AC or DC motor or a second winding on the rotor.

✓ Direct-cranking starters provide a reciprocating engine with instant and continuous cranking. A mechanism is necessary to disengage the starter motor from the engine after the engine starts.

✓ Starters for gas-turbine engines can be powered with electricity, air, or combustion. Electric starters can be direct-cranking or a combination starter-generator.

# KEY TERMS

torque
right-hand motor rule
variable speed motor
split-field motor
switch method
electrical losses
mechanical losses
copper losses
hysteresis losses
eddy current losses
motor slip
Bendix drive

# QUESTIONS

1. The direction of rotation in a DC motor is accomplished by reversing the direction of current flow in either the ______ or the______ ______.

2. A variable speed motor is either a ______ or a ______ motor.

3. The speed of a variable speed motor is controlled by varying the current in the ______ ______.

4. There are three types of AC motors; they are the ____________, ____________, and ____________ types.

5. Inertia starters crank aircraft engines with the energy that is stored in a ____________.

6. The electric motors for direct-cranking starters are of the ______ (series or shunt) type.

7. A Bendix drive uses a drive pinion which moves back and forth on ____________ splines.

8. Some ____________ ____________ (what manufacturer) engines use a right angle worm drive connected to the starter motor.

9. The direct cranking starter used on high-horsepower reciprocating engines consists of these two basic components:

   a. ____________ ______

   b. ____________ ______

10. On a dual spool axial flow compressor gas turbine engine, the starter will rotate only the ______ (high- or low-) speed compressor.

11. Electric starting systems for gas turbine aircraft are of these two general types:

    a. ______ ______

    b. ______ ______

12. Electrically operated starters used for gas turbine engines are usually of the ____________-type.

13. Air turbine starters are used with many gas turbine engines because of their high power-to-______ ratio.

14. An air turbine starter uses ______ (low or high) pressure air.

15. Three sources of compressed air for starting an engine equipped with an air turbine starter are:

    a. ______________

    b. ______________

    c. ______________

16. The ______________ ______________ (what type) starter is very similar to a small gas turbine engine.

# ELECTRICAL SYSTEM COMPONENTS

The satisfactory performance of any modern aircraft depends on the reliability of electrical systems and subsystems. One of the most critical factors for obtaining a high degree of reliability involves the quality of workmanship that technicians use when installing electrical connectors and wiring. Although the concept of assembling and installing wiring might initially seem basic, rigid quality standards require technicians to be highly trained. Improperly or carelessly installed and maintained electrical wiring can be a source of both immediate and potential danger.

## WIRE

When choosing the wire for an electrical system, you must consider several factors. For example, the wire must be large enough to accommodate the required current without producing excessive heat or causing an excessive voltage drop. In addition, the insulation must prevent electrical leakage and be strong enough to resist damage caused by abrasion.

## WIRE TYPES

The majority of aircraft wiring is stranded copper, in most cases coated with tin, silver, or nickel to help prevent oxidation. Prior to the mid-1990s, the wire used most often was manufactured to MIL-W-5086 standards, which is made of annealed copper strands covered with a thin coating of tin. A variety of materials are used for insulation, including polyvinyl chloride (PVC), nylon, and glass cloth braid. Most of these materials are rated to 600 volts. [Figure 8-81]

In the mid-1990s, polyvinyl chloride insulation was discovered to emit toxic fumes when it burns. Therefore, a new group of mil spec wires, MIL-W-22759, was introduced, which consists of stranded copper wire with Teflon® insulation. Today, MIL-W-22759 is used in lieu of MIL-W-5086 in new wiring installations and should be used when replacing original aircraft wiring. However, prior to replacing any aircraft wiring, consult the manufacturer's service manual and service bulletins for specific instructions and information regarding both wire type and size.

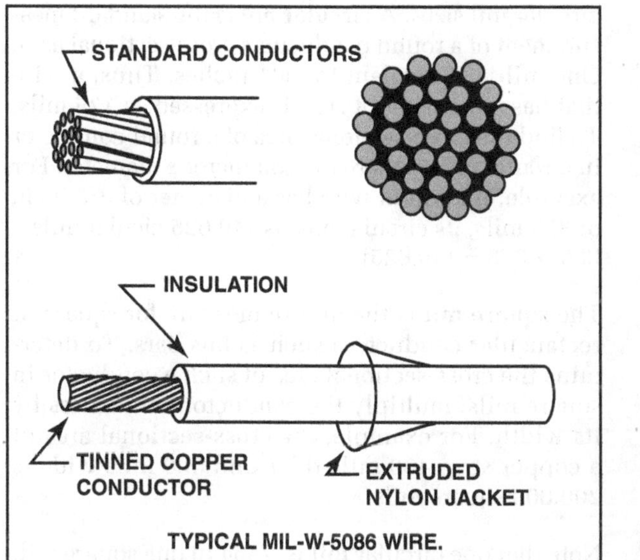


**Figure 8-81. MIL-W-5086 wire consists of stranded copper conductors covered with tin and wrapped with PCV insulation. For added protection, a nylon coating often covers the wire.**

When large amounts of current must be carried for long distances, MIL-W-7072 aluminum wire is often used. This wire is insulated with either fluorinated ethylene propylene (FEP Fluorocarbon), nylon, or with a fiberglass braid. While aluminum wire does save weight, it has some notable disadvantages. For example, it can carry only about two-thirds as much current as the same guage copper wire. In addition, when exposed to vibration, aluminum wire can crystallize and break. In fact, aluminum wire smaller than 8-gauge is not recommended because it is so easily broken by vibration.

In situations where a length of copper wire is to be replaced with aluminum wire, always use aluminum wire that is two wire gauge numbers greater than the copper wire it replaces. For example, use at least a 4-gauge aluminum wire be a piece of 8-gauge copper wire.

## WIRE SIZE

Aircraft wire is measured by the **American Wire Gage (AWG)** system, in which larger numbers represent smaller wires. The smallest size wire normally used in aircraft is 22-gauge wire, which has a diameter of about .025 inch. However, conductors carrying large amounts of current are typically of the 0000, or 4-aught size, and have a diameter of about .52 inch. Each gauge size is related to a specific cross-sectional area of wire.

The amount of current that a wire is capable of carrying is determined by its cross-sectional area. In most cases, a wire's cross-sectional area is expressed in circular mil sizes. A **circular mil** is the standard measurement of a round conductor's cross-sectional area. One mil is equivalent to .001 inches. Thus, a wire that has a diameter of .125 is expressed as 125 mils. To find the cross-sectional area of a round conductor in circular mils, square the conductor's diameter. For example, if a round wire has a diameter of 3/8 inch, or 375 mils, its circular area is 140,625 cicular mils (375 x 375 = 140,625).

The **square mil** is the unit of measure for square or rectangular conductors such as bus bars. To determine the cross-sectional area of such a conductor in square mils, multiply the conductor's thickness by its width. For example, the cross-sectional area of a copper strip 400 mils thick and 500 mils wide is 200,000 square mils.

Note that one circular mil is .7854 of one square mil. Thus, to convert a circular mil area to a square mil area, divide the area in circular mils by .7854 mil. Conversely, to convert a square mil area to a circular mil area, multiply the area in square mils by .7854. [Figure 8-82]

When replacing wire to make a repair, the damaged wire is normally replaced with the same size and type of wire. However, in new installations, you must consider several factors in selecting the proper wire. For example, one of the first things to know is the system operating voltage. You must also know the allowable voltage drop and whether the wiring operates on a continuous or intermittent basis. [Figure 8-83]

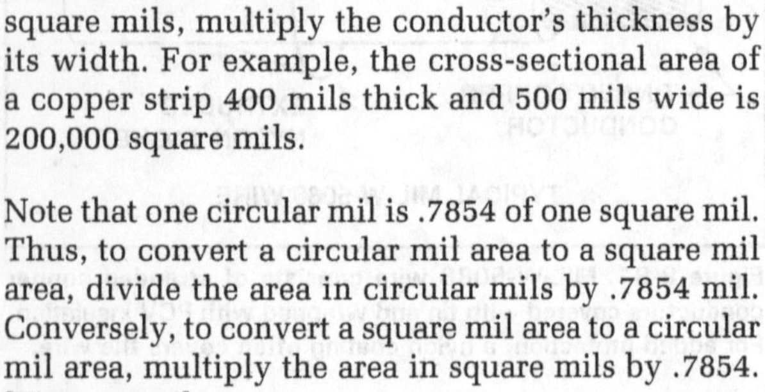


**Figure 8-82. One circular mil is slightly smaller than one square mil. A circular mil is a unit of measure for small, round items, because a measurement in square inches is unnecessarily complex.**

| NOMINAL SYSTEM VOLTAGE | ALLOWABLE VOLTAGE DROP VOLTS | |
|---|---|---|
| | CONTINUOUS OPERATION | INTERMITTENT OPERATION |
| 14 | 0.5 | 1.0 |
| 28 | 1.0 | 2.0 |
| 115 | 4.0 | 8.0 |
| 200 | 7.0 | 14.0 |

**Figure 8-83. Before installing a new component in an aircraft, you must know the system voltage, the allowable voltage drop, and the component duty cycle. These factors are interrelated.**

Assume that you must install a cowl flap motor in a 28-volt system. Because cowl flaps move infrequently during a flight, a cowl flap motor operates on an intermittent basis. By referring to the chart in the previous figure you, determine that the allowable voltage drop for a component installed in a 28-volt system, operated intermittently, is 2 volts. After you know these three factors, use an electric wire chart to determine the wire size needed for installation. [Figure 8-84]

Refer to the chart in figure 7-85 and note that the three curves extend diagonally across the chart from the lower left corner to the right side. These curves represent the ability of a wire to carry the current without overheating. Curve 1 represents the continuous rating of a wire when routed in bundles or conduit. If the intersection of the current and wire length lines is above this curve, the wire can carry the current without generating excessive heat. If the intersection falls between curve 1 and 2, the wire can carry current continuously in free air. If the intersection falls between curves 2 and 3, the wire can carry intermittent current, considered to be two minutes or less.

## WIRE MARKING

The manufacturers of general aviation aircraft have not agreed on a standard wire identification system. However, some form of identification mark is required every 12 to 15 inches along a wire. The identification marking should identify the wire with regard to the type of circuit, location within the circuit, and wire size. Each manufacturer has a code letter to indicate the type of circuit.

For example, wire in flight instrumentation circuits is often identified with the letter F, and the letter N is sometimes identifies the circuit ground. Easy identification of each wire greatly facilitates troubleshooting procedures and saves time. [Figure 8-85]

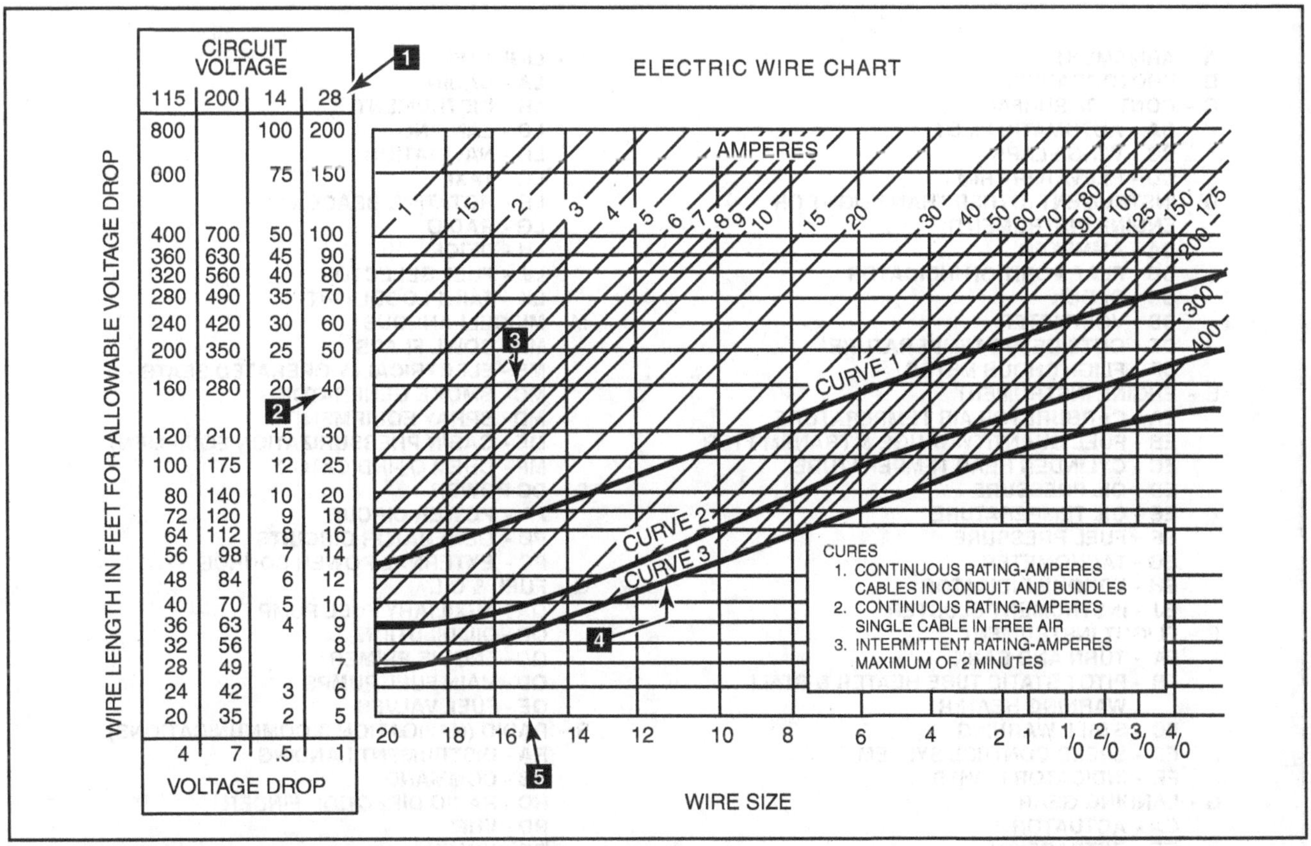


**Figure 8-84. Assume that a 28-volt cowl flap motor draws six amps and you need 40 feet of wire to install it. To determine the correct wire size, locate the appropriate voltage on the left side of the chart (item 1). Move down this column to the required wire length (item 2). Follow the horizontal line to the right to its intersection with the appropriate diagonal amperage line (item 3). Because the wire carries an intermittent current, item 3 must be at or above curve 3 (item 4). From item 3, move to the bottom of the chart to find the correct wire size (item 5). When a chart indication falls between two sizes, select the larger wire. Remember that in wire numbering a smaller number represents a larger wire.**

A typical wire identification code would be F26D-22N. In this case, the letter F indicates that the wire is in the flight instrumentation circuit, while the number 26 identifies the wire as the 26th wire in the circuit. D indicates the fourth segment of the No. 26 wire. 22 is the gauge size of the wire, and the N indicates that the wire goes to ground.

Another wire marking system uses a two-letter identification code. This marking system provides much more detail about the location of a given wire, making it especially helpful in large aircraft that have many systems. [Figure 8-86]

In addition to marking individual wires, wire bundles might have a specific identification number. In this case, pressure-sensitive tape or flexible sleeves are stamped with identification codes and wrapped around a wire bundle. Individual wires within each bundle are usually hot-stamped for easy identification. Typically, wire bundles are marked near the points at which they enter and leave a compartment. [Figure 8-87]

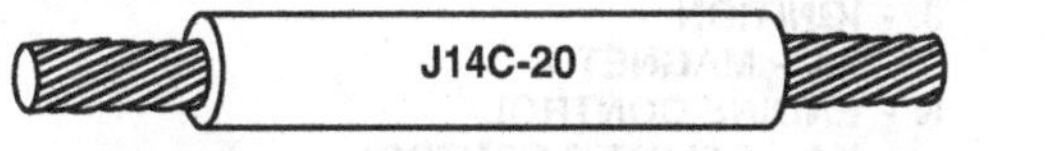


**J – SYSTEM IN WHICH THIS WIRE IS USED**
**14 – INDIVIDUAL WIRE NUMBER**
**C – SECTION OF WIRE FROM POWER SOURCE**
**20 – WIRE SIZE – AWG SIZE**

**CIRCUIT IDENTIFIERS**

| | |
|---|---|
| C – FLIGHT CONTROL SYSTEMS | L – LIGHTING |
| D – ANTI- AND DEICING SYSTEMS | M – MISCELLANEOUS |
| E – ENGINE INSTRUMENTS | N – GROUND NETWORK |
| F – FLIGHT INSTRUMENTS | P – DC POWER SYSTEM |
| H – ENVIRONMENTAL SYSTEMS | Q – FUEL AND OIL |
| J – IGNITION | R – RADIO |
| K – ENGINE CONTROL SYSTEMS | V – INVERTERS |
| | W – WARNING SYSTEMS |
| | X – AC POWER SYSTEMS |

**Figure 8-85. The code J14C-20 indicates that this wire is part of an ignition circuit (J) and is the 14th wire in that circuit (14). In addition, it is the third individual segment of wire No. 14 (C), and it is a 20-gauge wire.**

A - ARMAMENT
B - PHOTOGRAPHIC
C - CONTROL SURFACE
 CA - AUTOMATIC PILOT
 CC - WING FLAPS
 CD - ELEVATOR TRIM
D - INSTRUMENT (OTHER THAN FLIGHT OR ENGINE INSTRUMENT)
 DA - AMMETER
 DB - FLAP POSITION INDICATOR
 DC - CLOCK
 DD - VOLTMETER
 DE - OUTSIDE AIR TEMPERATURE
 DF - FLIGHT HOUR METER
E - ENGINE INSTRUMENT
 EA - CARBURETOR AIR TEMPERATURE
 EB - FUEL QUANTITY GAUGE & TRANSMITTER
 EC - CYLINDER HEAD TEMPERATURE
 ED - OIL PRESSURE
 EE - OIL TEMPERATURE
 EF - FUEL PRESSURE
 EG - TACHOMETER
 EH - TORQUE INDICATOR
 EJ - INSTRUMENT CLUSTER
F - FLIGHT INSTRUMENT
 FA - TURN AND BANK
 FB - PITOT STATIC TUBE HEATER & STALL WARNING HEATER
 FC - STALL WARNING
 FD - SPEED CONTROL SYSTEM
 FE - INDICATOR LIGHTS
G - LANDING GEAR
 GA - ACTUATOR
 GB - RETRACTION
 GC - WARNING DEVICE (HORN)
 GD - LIGHT SWITCHES
 GE - INDICATOR LIGHTS
H - HEATING, VENTILATING, & DEICING
 HA - ANTI-ICING
 HB - CABIN HEATER
 HC - CIGAR LIGHTER
 HD - DEICING
 HE - AIR CONDITIONERS
 HF - CABIN VENTILATION
J - IGNITION
 JA - MAGNETO
K - ENGINE CONTROL
 KA - STARTER CONTROL
 KB - PROPELLER SYNCHRONIZER
L - LIGHTING
 LA - CABIN
 LB - INSTRUMENT
 LC - LANDING
 LD - NAVIGATION
 LE - TAXI
 LF - ROTATING BEACON
 LG - RADIO
 LH - DEICE
 LJ - FUEL SELECTOR
 LK - TAIL FLOODLIGHT
M - MISCELLANEOUS
 MA - COWL FLAPS
 MB - ELECTRICALLY OPERATED SEATS
 MC - SMOKE GENERATOR
 MD - SPRAY EQUIPMENT
 ME - CABIN PRESSURIZATION EQUIPMENT
 MF - CHEM $O_2$-INDICATOR
P - DC POWER
 PA - POWER CIRCUIT
 PB - GENERATOR CIRCUITS
 PC - EXTERNAL POWER SOURCE
Q - FUEL & OIL
 QA - AUXILIARY FUEL PUMP
 QB - OIL DILUTION
 QC - ENGINE PRIMER
 QD - MAIN FUEL PUMPS
 QE - FUEL VALVES
R - RADIO (NAVIGATION & COMMUNICATIONS)
 RA - INSTRUMENT LANDING
 RB - COMMAND
 RC - RADIO DIRECTION FINDER
 RD - VHF
 RE - HOMING
 RF - MARKER BEACON
 RG - NAVIGATION
 RH - HIGH FREQUENCY
 RJ - INTERPHONE
 RK - UHF
 RL - LOW FREQUENCY
 RM - FREQUENCY MODULATION
 RP - AUDIO SYSTEM & AUDIO AMPLIFIER
 RR - DISTANCE MEASURING EQUIPMENT (DME)
 RS - AIRBORNE PUBLIC ADDRESS SYSTEM
S - RADAR
U - MISCELLANEOUS ELECTRONIC
 UA - IDENTIFICATION-FRIEND OR FOE
W - WARNING AND EMERGENCY
 WA - FLARE RELEASE
 WB - CHIP DETECTOR
 WC - FIRE DETECTION SYSTEM
X - AC POWER

**Figure 8-86. A two-letter identification code is used in some wire marking systems to provide more detail about wire function and location.**

## WIRING INSTALLATION

As a general rule, electrical wiring is installed in aircraft either as open wiring or in conduit. With open wiring, individual wires or wire bundles are routed inside the aircraft structure without protective covering. When installed in conduit, electrical wiring is routed inside either rigid or flexible tubing that provides significant protection.

## OPEN WIRING

The most expedient way to install wiring is to install it as open wiring, which provides easy access when troubleshooting or servicing individual circuits.

Electrical wiring is often installed in bundles for a more organized installation. Several methods of assembling wires into bundles may be used, depending on where a bundle is fabricated.

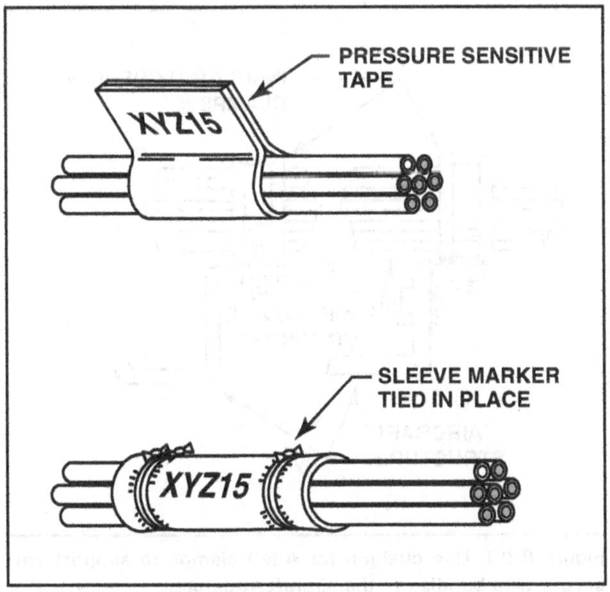


**Figure 8-87. Methods for identifying wire bundles include markings on pressure-sensitive tape or sleeve markers.**

For example, in the shop, wires stamped with identification markings can be lined up parallel to one another on a bench and tied together. However, inside an aircraft, wires might be secured to an existing bundle or tied together to form a new bundle. In some cases, the wires are connected to their destination terminal strip or connector before being secured in a bundle.

Wiring harnesses fabricated at a factory are typically made on a jig board prior to installation in an aircraft. This method enables the manufacturer to preform the wire bundles with the bends needed to fit the bundle into an aircraft. Regardless of the method of bundle assembly, a plastic comb can be used to keep individual wires straight and parallel in a bundle. [Figure 8-88]

When possible, the number of wires in a single bundle is limited. This helps prevent the possibility of a single wire faulting and ultimately damaging an entire bundle. In addition, no single bundle should include wires for both a main and back-up system. This helps prevent the possibility of neutralizing a system if a bundle were damaged. Additionally, it is better to keep ignition wires, shielded wires, and wires not protected by a fuse or circuit breaker separate from all other wiring.

After all wires in a bundle are assembled, the bundle should be tied every three to four inches. Typically, wire bundles that are assembled on a jig are tied

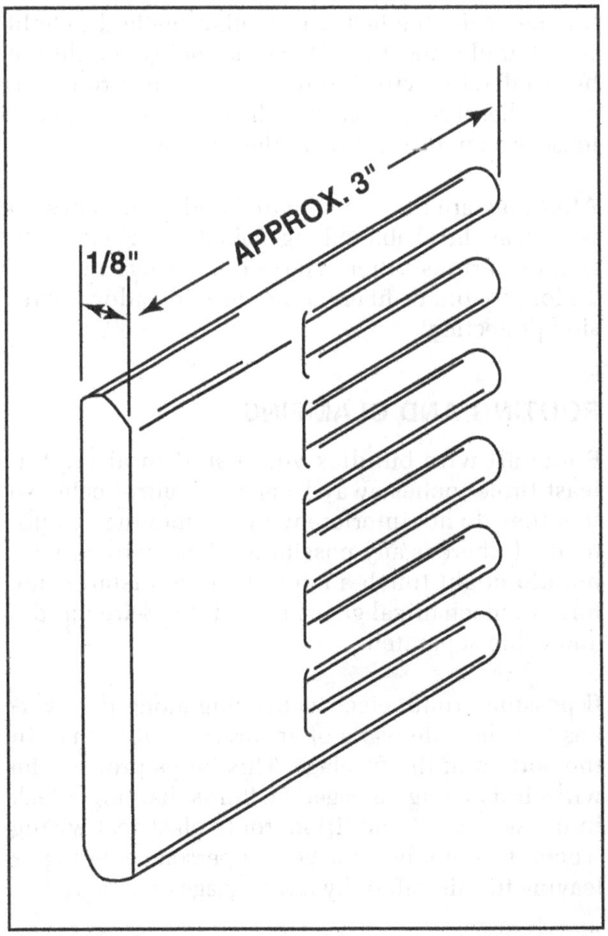


**Figure 8-88. You can use a plastic comb to keep wires straight and parallel when fabricating new wire bundles.**

together with waxed linen or nylon cord using a clove hitch secured with a square knot. [Figure 8-89]

In the field, nylon straps called wire ties are often used to hold wire bundles together. These small nylon straps are wrapped around the wire bundle and one end is passed through a slot in the other end and pulled tight, after which the excess strapping is cut off. When cutting the ends, use flush cutting diagonal pliers or a similar tool to provide a flush cut. Nylon straps can leave sharp edges if they are not cut flush against the locking portion of the strap.

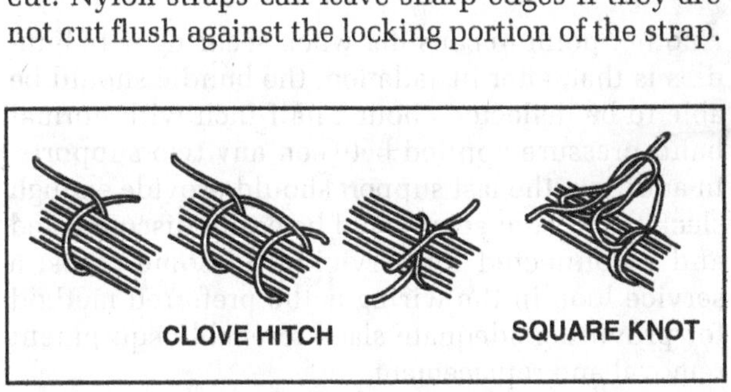


**Figure 8-89. The best knot combination for tying a wire bundle with linen (or nylon) cord is a clove hitch secured by a square knot.**

Single- or double-lacing is another method to hold wire bundles together. However, lacing should not be used with wire bundles installed around an engine because a break anywhere in the lacing cord loosens an entire section of the bundle.

After they are tied, some wire bundles are covered with heat-shrinkable tubing, coiled "spaghetti" tubing, or various other types of coverings made of Teflon, nylon, or fiberglass to provide added abrasion protection.

## ROUTING AND CLAMPING

Route all wire bundles you install in aircraft at least three inches away from any control cable so that they do not interfere with any moving components. If there is any possibility that a wire or wire bundle might touch a control cable, install some form of mechanical guard to keep the wire bundle and cable separated.

If possible, route electrical wiring along the overhead or the side walls of an aircraft rather than in the bottom of the fuselage. This helps prevent the wires from being damaged by fluids that might leak into low areas. In addition, route electrical wiring where it cannot be damaged by persons entering or leaving the aircraft or by any baggage or cargo.

When electrical wires are routed parallel to oxygen or any type of fluid line, the wiring should be at least six inches above the fluid line. However, the distance can be reduced to two inches as long as the wiring is not supported in any way by the fluid line and the proper mechanical protection is provided. Acceptable secondary protection typically includes additional clamps, approved sleeves, and conduit.

Securely clamp wire bundles to the aircraft structure with clamps lined with a non-metallic cushion. In addition, the clamps should be spaced close enough together so the wiring bundle does not sag or vibrate excessively. [Figure 8-90]

Another point to consider when securing wire bundles is that, after installation, the bundle should be able to be deflected about a half-inch with normal hand pressure applied between any two supports. In addition, the last support should provide enough slack that a connector could be easily disconnected and reconnected for servicing. In some cases, a service loop in the wiring is the preferred method for providing adequate slack to enable equipment removal and replacement.

Any bundle that passes through a bulkhead should be clamped to a bracket which centers the bundle

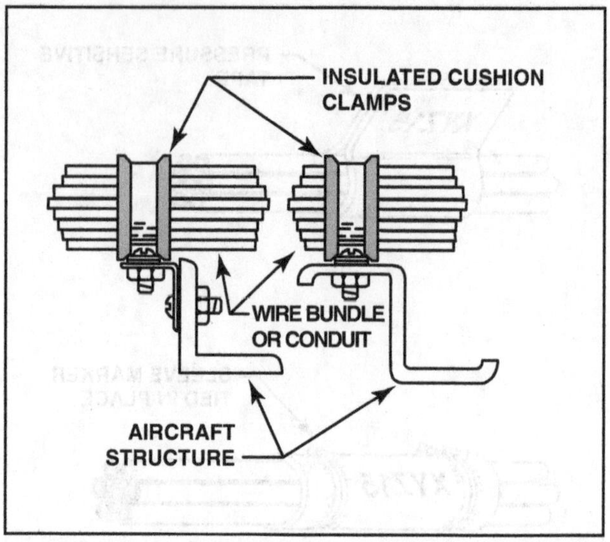


**Figure 8-90. Use cushion (or Adel) clamps to support and secure wire bundles to the aircraft structure.**

in the hole. In addition, if less than 1/4-inch clearance exists between the bundle and the hole, install a protective rubber grommet. The grommet prevents the sharp edges of the metal hole from cutting the wiring if the centering bracket breaks or bends. [Figure 8-91]

Where bundles must make a bend, it is a good practice to use a bend radius approximately 10 times the diameter of the wire bundle so the wires on the inside of the bend do not bunch up.

## CONDUIT

The best mechanical protection for electrical wiring is either a rigid or a flexible metal conduit. This is

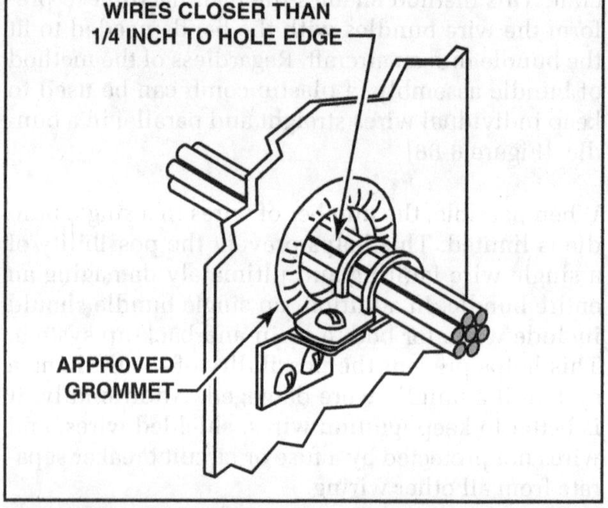


**Figure 8-91. When a wire bundle passes through a bulkhead or frame, a supporting bracket is required. If the clearance is less than 1/4-inch, install a rubber grommet to prevent wiring damage.**

the preferred method of installation in areas such as wheel wells and engine nacelles, where wire bundles are likely to be chafed or crushed.

The inside diameter of the conduit must be 25 percent larger than the maximum diameter of the wire bundle. Note that to determine the conduit size needed, the nominal diameter of the conduit represents its *outside* diameter, so you must subtract twice the wall thickness from the conduit's outside diameter to determine the inside diameter.

When installing a wire bundle inside a conduit, blow some soapstone talc through the tubing first to act as a lubricant between the wiring and conduit wall. This makes it easier to install the wires and to reduce the possibility of damage. You can also attach a long piece of lacing cord to the bundle and blow the lacing through the tubing with compressed air. Then use the lacing cord to help pull the wire bundle through. Flaring the ends of the conduit will also make it easier to insert wiring without damaging the wire. Flaring conduit into a "bell mouth" shape also helps prevent fraying from occurring after installation.

Like open wiring, conduit must be supported by clamps attached to the aircraft structure. In addition, a 1/8-inch drain hole must be made at the lowest point in each run of conduit to provide a means of draining any moisture that condenses inside the conduit.

When you fabricate conduit for electrical wiring requires remove all burrs and sharp edges. In addition, make bends with bends a radius that will not cause the conduit tube to kink, wrinkle, or flatten excessively.

## SHIELDING

Any time that a wire carries electrical current, a magnetic field surrounds the wire. If strong enough, this magnetic field can interfere with some of the aircraft instrumentation. For example, even though the tiny light that illuminates the card of a magnetic compass is powered with low-voltage direct current, the magnetic field produced by the current flow is enough to deflect the compass. To minimize this field, a two-conductor twisted wire is used to carry the current to and from this light. With twisted wire, the magnetic fields cancel each other.

Alternating current or pulsating direct current has an especially bad effect on electronic equipment. To help prevent interference, wires that carry AC or pulsating DC are often shielded. Shielding is a method of intercepting electrical energy and shunting it to electrical ground.

Most shielding consists of a braid of tin-plated or cadmium-plated copper wire that surrounds the insulation of a wire. Typically, the braid is connected to aircraft ground through a crimped-on ring terminal. When a wire is shielded, the braided shielding receives the radiated energy from the conductor and passes it to the aircraft's ground, where it cannot cause interference.

Shielding in aircraft electrical systems is typically grounded at both ends of the wiring run. However, shielding in electronic circuit wiring is usually grounded only at one end to prevent setting up a loop that could cause electromagnetic interference.

## WIRING TERMINALS

Electrical wiring in aircraft is generally terminated with solderless terminals that are staked, or crimped, onto the wire. **Crimping** is a term used to describe the squeezing of a terminal around a wire to secure the wire and provide a high quality electrical connection. Several types of terminals are used in aircraft, including the ring terminal, slotted terminal, and hook terminal. The ring terminal is used most often because it virtually eliminates the possibility of circuit failure due to terminal disconnection.

Typically, solderless terminals used on 10-gauge and smaller wire use color-coded insulated terminals. For example, terminals with red insulation are used on wire gauge sizes 22 through 18, while terminals with blue insulation are used on 16- and 14-gauge wires. Terminals with yellow insulation are used for 12- and 10-gauge wires. [Figure 8-92]

Wires larger than 10-gauge typically use uninsulated terminals. Instead, a piece of vinyl tubing

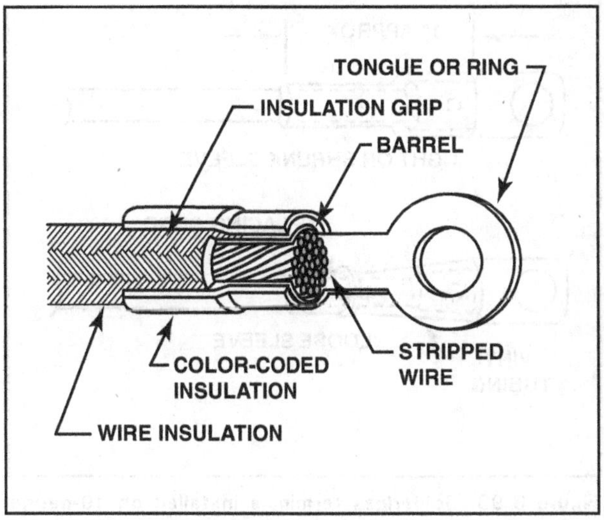


**Figure 8-92. Wire gauge sizes 10 through 22 are typically terminated with preinsulated, solderless terminals that are color-coded to identify size.**

or heat-shrinkable tubing insulates the terminal. However, the insulating material must be slipped over the wire prior to crimping. Then, after the crimping operation, the tubing is pulled over the terminal barrel and secured. [Figure 8-93]

When choosing a solderless terminal, it is important that the materials of the terminal and wire are compatible. This helps eliminate the possibility of dissimilar metal corrosion.

Before you can attach a wire to a terminal, you must remove the protective insulation, typically by cutting the insulation and gently pulling it from the end of the wire. This process is known as stripping the wire. When you strip a wire, expose as little of the conductor as necessary to make the connection and ensure that you do not damage the conductor beyond allowable limits. Aluminum wiring must not be damaged at all because individual strands break easily after being nicked. [Figure 8-94]

The FAA limits the number of nicked or broken strands on any conductor. For example, a 20-gauge copper wire with 19 strands may have two nicks and no broken strands. In general, the larger the number of strands or the larger the conductor, the greater the acceptable number of broken or nicked strands.

Crimping is the process of joining a wire conductor to a contact, in the form of a pin or a socket, by controlled compression and displacement of metal. Because of the environments to which electrical connectors are subjected, precision crimp joints are now the preferred method of contact installation, as opposed to soldered joints.

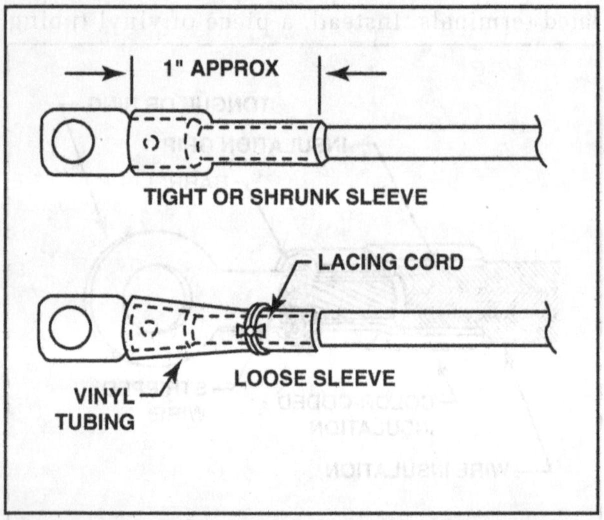


Figure 8-93. Solderless terminals installed on 10-gauge or larger wire require a separate piece of insulation. You can use heat-shrinkable tubing or vinyl tubing secured with lacing cord.

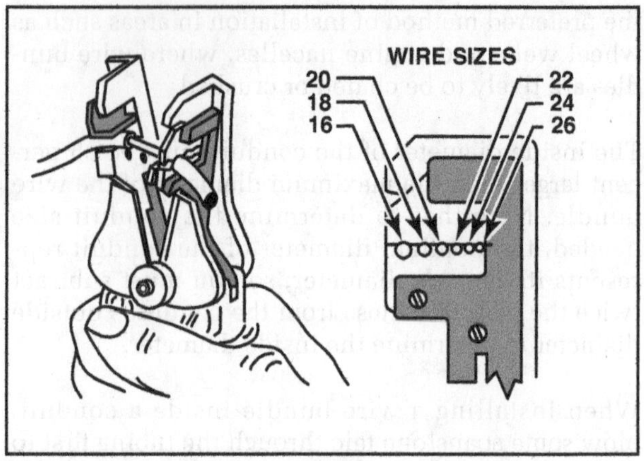


Figure 8-94. When stripping electrical wire, use a quality stripper that is designed for the specific type and size of wire.

Because you can remove pin-and-socket connectors several times, you can modify connector, change circuits, or replace contacts with little difficulty and with the same quality as in the manufacturer's production line assembly. Aircraft avionics systems use connectors for all major systems, and your ability to form good crimped pins and sockets is a skill that you should practice and master. A good crimp joint has uniform indentations on the contact barrel, good mechanical strength between the wire and contact crimp, and good electrical continuity. Inspection holes in each contact enable you to verify that the wire strands are properly positioned before and during placement in the crimp barrel.

The preferred crimping tool is a ratcheting-type crimper that meets military specifications MS22520/1 and /2. This MIL specification defines the four-indenter crimp used on all MS aircraft pins and sockets. The four-indenter crimp provides the most uniform displacement of wire and contact material of all types of indenter crimps. The wire strands and the contact material are joined together with little or no reduction of the mil area of the wire strands while maintaining good mechanical strength.

The Daniels® AF8 and AFM8, or the Astro Tool® 615708 and 615717, are examples of the ratcheting-type crimping installation hand tools. In operation, the handles of these tools will not release until the indenters have moved close enough together to properly compress the pin or socket barrel. Because repeatability of the crimp operation is the most desired characteristic of precision crimping tools, check these tools with a go/no-go gage to insure that proper crimp depths are maintained. Because the ratcheting crimp tool is a precision instrument that wears through use, it is necessary to have the tool periodically calibrated to maintain consistent tolerances and to ensure a proper crimp. [Figure 8-95]

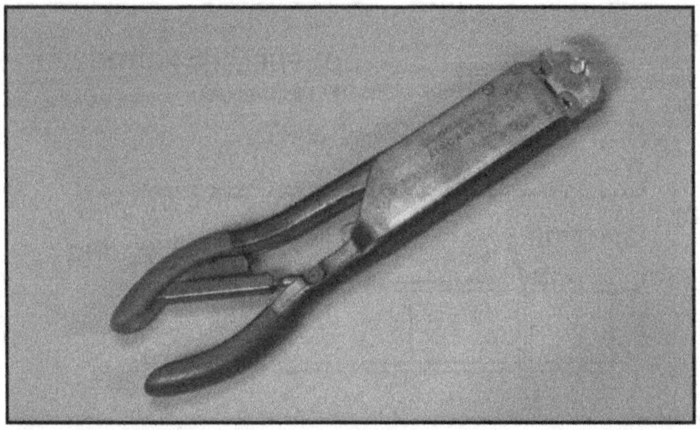

**Figure 8-95. When a pin or socket is inserted into the crimper, insert the wire until it bottoms out before squeezing the handles. The handles will not release until the crimping process is complete. Ratchet-type crimping tools are periodically calibrated to ensure that a quality crimp is provided.**

To perform a proper crimp, locate the correct tool and pin combination in the tool selection charts provided by the tool manufacturer. You can find the correct tool application by searching the pin part number charts. When you identify the pin and select the correct tool, strip the wire and insert the contact into the indenter opening. With the contact in the tool, insert the wire into the contact until it bottoms out and is held in that position. Close the handles until the tool bottoms and the ratchet kicks back. Release the handles and remove the crimped contact. Inspect the crimp through the inspection hole on the contact barrel; you should see wire strands in the hole. If no strands appear in the inspection hole, you must perform the complete crimp process again. [Figure 8-96]

Pneumatic crimping tools are often used on wire gauge sizes 0 through 0000 because of the force required to properly crimp the wire. Like ratchet-type crimpers, pneumatic crimpers must be calibrated periodically.

Aluminum wire presents some special problems when installing terminals. Aluminum wire oxidizes when exposed to air, and the oxides become an electrical insulator. Therefore, to ensure a good quality electrical connection between an aluminum wire and terminal, the inside of a typical aluminum terminal is partially filled with a compound of petroleum jelly and zinc dust. This compound mechanically grinds the oxide film off the wire strands when the terminal is compressed, and then seals the wire from the air, preventing the formation of new oxides. [Figure 8-97]

## CONNECTORS

Mating connectors are usually installed on wiring that is frequently disconnected. For example, the wiring that supplies power to avionic components typically uses multipin connectors that can be easily removed to perform maintenance. The most common styles of connectors used in aircraft electrical circuits are AN (Army-Navy) and MS (Military Specification) connectors available in a variety of sizes and types.

These connectors meet military specifications and have been adapted for use in most aircraft today. Use special moisture-proof connectors in areas that might be exposed to moisture. Mating connectors

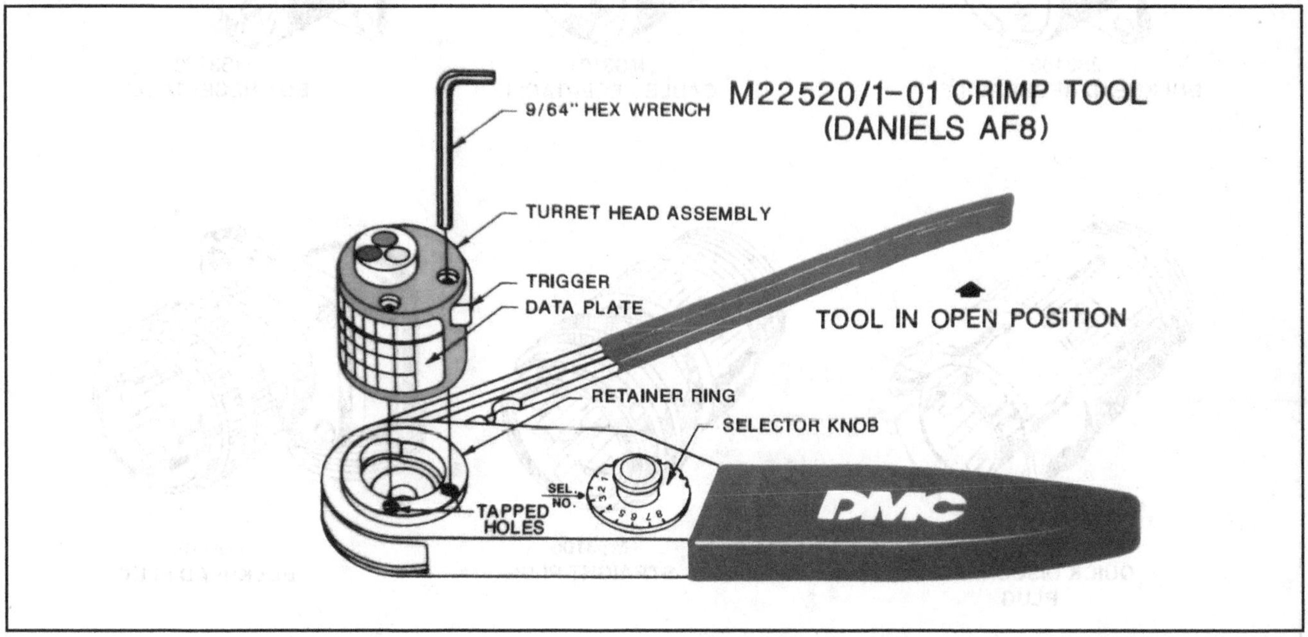


**Figure 8-96. The Daniels® AF8 ratcheting crimp tool requires a positioner turret assembly that accommodates several sizes of contacts.**

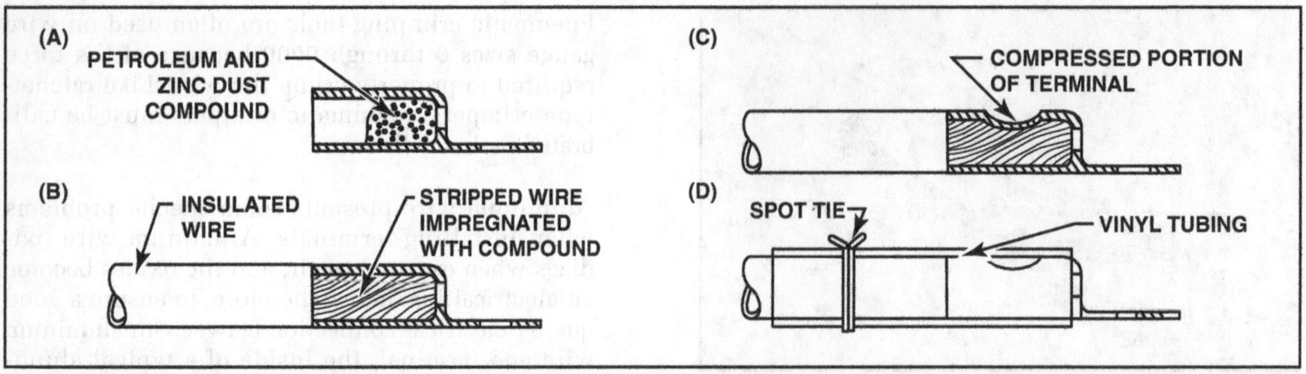


**Figure 8-97. (A) To help prevent oxidation, special terminals filled with a compound of petroleum jelly and zinc dust are used for terminating aluminum wiring. (B) When a stripped wire is inserted into the terminal, the wire strands become impregnated with the compound. (C) As the terminal is crimped, the zinc dust cleans the wire and the petroleum jelly creates an airtight seal. (D) After the terminal is crimped, a piece of vinyl tubing is tied over the terminal end to protect it from moisture.**

consist of one connector with female contacts, or sockets, and another connector with male contacts, or pins. To reduce the chance of an accidental short between the power side of a circuit and any conductive surface when the mating connectors are separated, the ground side of an electrical power conductor is typically connected to a male connector while the power side of the conductor is attached to the female connector. [Figure 8-98]

The wires are typically connected to the contacts in a connector in one of two ways. Newer plugs use tapered pins that are crimped onto the wire end. The pin is then slipped into a tapered hole in the pin or socket end of a connector. A special tool is used to remove or replace the pin if necessary.

Another, less common, type of connector plug requires the wires to be soldered into each end of a connector. To install a typical soldered connector,

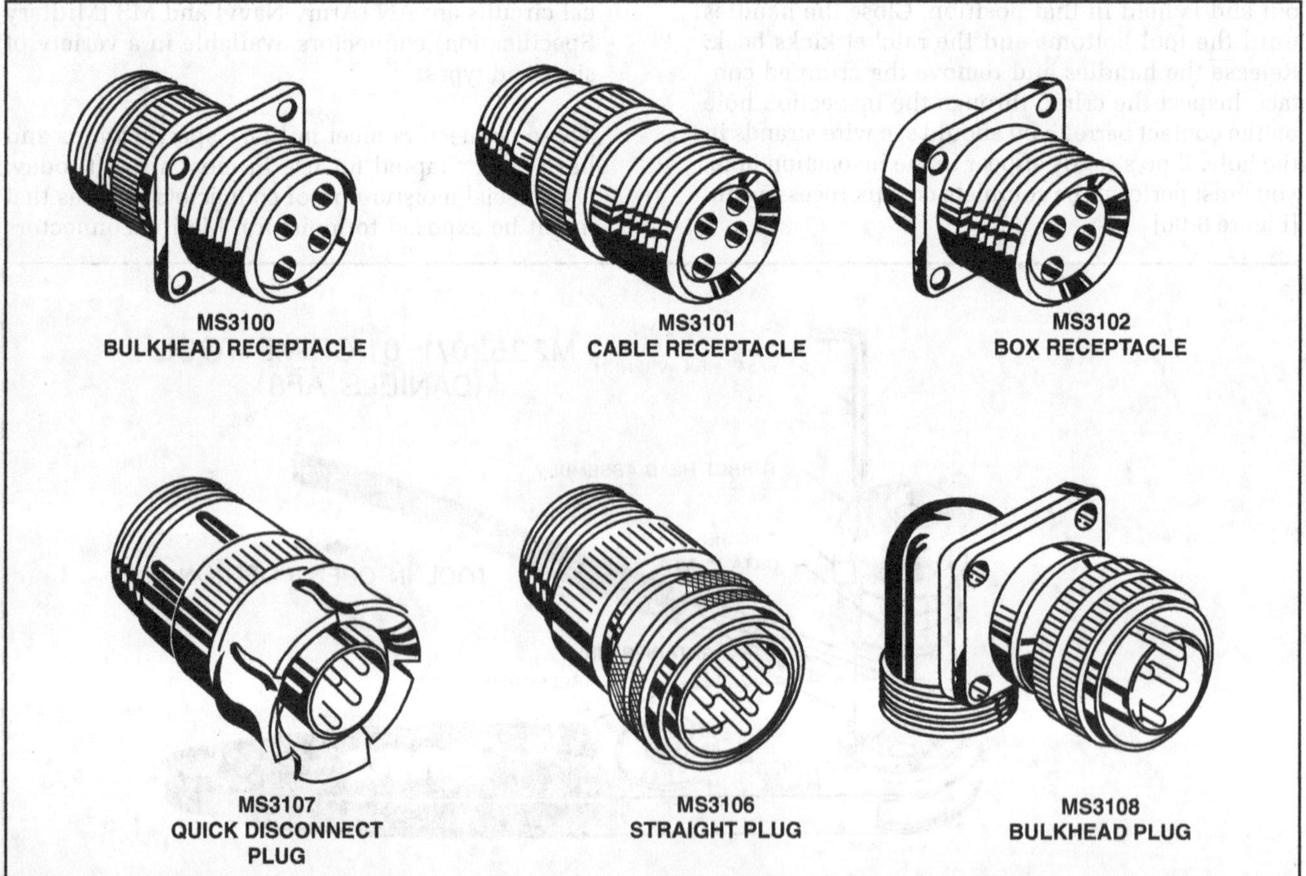


**Figure 8-98. Electrical connectors come in many types and sizes to provide a number of options when attaching electrical wiring to various components.**

begin by stripping enough insulation from the end of each wire to provide approximately 1/32-inch of bare wire between the end of the insulation and the end of a pin when inserted.

Next, slip a specified length of insulated tubing over the end of each wire. Using an appropriate soldering iron, solder, and flux, apply a small amount of solder to the stripped portion of each wire. This is a process known as **tinning** the wires and greatly facilitates their insertion into the connector pins by preventing the strands from unraveling.

After the wires are tinned, fill the end of each pin, or solder pot, with solder. While keeping the solder in a solder pot molten, insert the appropriate wire. Then remove the soldering iron and hold the wire as still as possible until the solder solidifies. If you move the wire before the solder solidifies, the solder will take on a granular appearance and cause excessive electrical resistance. Repeat this process until all pins and wires have been soldered in place. After all of the wires are installed, clean any remaining flux residue from the connector with an approved cleaner. [Figure 8-99]

Inspect the soldered connector before final assembly. If excess solder is bridging two pins, or if some pins do not have enough solder, resolder the connection. The solder in a properly soldered connection should completely fill each pot and have a slightly rounded top. However, the solder must not wick up into the strands of each wire, or the wire may become brittle and break when bent. When the soldered joints are satisfactorily completed, slip the insulation tubing on each wire over its respective solder pot. After all solder pots are covered, spot-tie the bundle just above the insulation tubing to keep it in place.

## SPLICING REPAIRS

In general, keep splices in electrical wire to a minimum and avoid them completely in areas of high vibration. Stagger splices in bundles so there is no more than one splice in any one segment of wire. Never use splices to salvage scrap wire and never install them within 12 inches of a termination device. In certain instances, these rules can be amended if an approved engineer has authorized the splice installation. For example, in some cases, emergency splices have been approved for use in commercial aircraft, with the understanding that the wire will be replaced with a permanent installation within a limited number of flight hours.

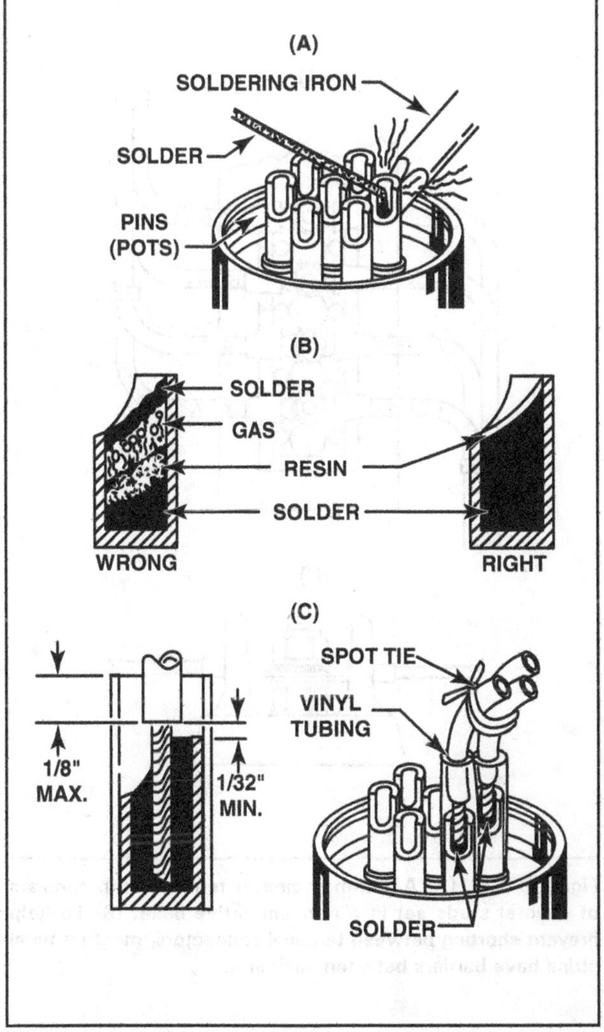


**Figure 8-99. (A) After the wires are tinned, fill a solder pot with solder. (B) Ensure that the pot is sufficiently heated before adding solder. Otherwise, resin could become trapped in the solder, producing a weak connection. (C) After installation, ensure that at least 1/32-inch clearance exists between the wire insulation and the top of the solder joint. Additional insulation, such as vinyl tubing, should be slipped over each connection and secured.**

## TERMINAL STRIPS

A terminal strip consists of a series of threaded studs mounted on a strip of insulating material. A typical terminal strip is made of a plastic or a paper-based phenolic compound that provides high mechanical strength as well as good electrical insulation properties. The terminal studs are typically secured to prevent rotation. Most terminal strips have barriers between adjacent studs to keep the wires properly separated. [Figure 8-100]

The size of the studs on a terminal strip usually ranges from size 6 up to about 1 inch in diameter, with the smaller sizes suitable only for low-current

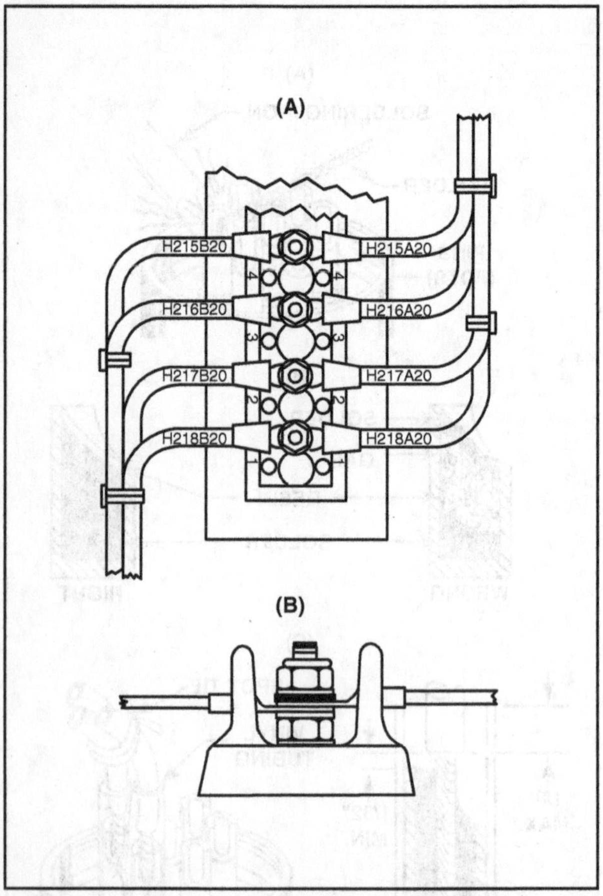


Figure 8-100. (A) A common aircraft terminal strip consists of several studs set in a nonconductive base. (B) To help prevent shorting between terminal connectors, most terminal strips have barriers between each stud.

control circuits. The smallest terminal stud allowed for electrical power systems is number 10.

When attaching the terminal ends of a wire bundle to a terminal strip, fan the wires out from the bundle so the wires align with the terminal studs. In a typical installation, the wires are centered and arranged at right angles to the terminal strip. A short distance from the terminal strip, the wires are then turned 90 degrees to form a wire bundle.

Although regulations permit up to four terminals per stud, ideally, only two wires should be attached to any one stud. When attaching multiple terminals to one stud, angle the wires out from the terminal stud and stack them to avoid damaging the tongue of each terminal. [Figure 8-101]

## JUNCTION BOXES

Junction boxes installed in aircraft powerplant compartments or other high-heat or fire-prone areas are typically made of stainless steel or a heat-resistant aluminum alloy. Aircraft junction boxes must be constructed in a way that no tendency for "oil canning" exists. Oil canning occurs when the metal of a junction box is pushed inward and remains in the bent condition when the pressure is removed. This tendency is considered a shorting hazard.

Junction boxes are mounted in a way that minimizes the possibility of water entering and causing electrical shorts or corrosion. In addition, most junction boxes in powerplant compartments are mounted vertically to help prevent small hardware from becoming lodged between terminals and causing a short circuit or electrical fire.

Junction boxes should be isolated from electrical power when you remove the cover for maintenance. Be cautious when you must apply power to circuits in a junction box. A metal tool carelessly placed across several terminals could cause severe damage to the aircraft electrical system and its components. In addition, remove hand jewelry and wristwatches to avoid accidental shocks or burns while working in the box.

## BONDING

Bonding is a process that electrically grounds all aircraft components to prevent a difference in potential from building to the point that sparks jump from one component to another. For example, all the control surfaces on an aircraft are electrically grounded to the main aircraft structure with braided bonding straps. This helps prevent the inherent resistance in a control surface hinge from insulating the control

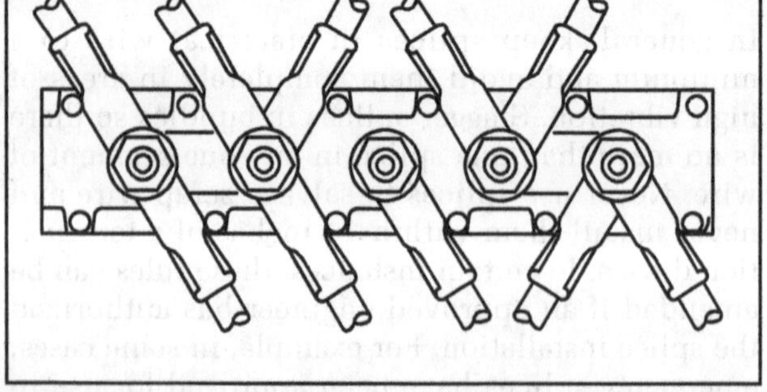


Figure 8-101. (A) Proper stacking of multiple terminals requires terminal tongues to be alternately placed up and down. (B) A typical method of attaching multiple wires to a terminal stud involves both stacking and angled installation.

surface from the main structure. In the powerplant compartment, shock-mounted components are also bonded to the main structure with bonding straps.

Any electrical component that uses the aircraft structure as the return path for its current must be bonded to the structure. When selecting a bonding strap, ensure that it is large enough to handle all the return current flow without producing an unacceptable voltage drop. An adequately bonded structure requires bonding straps that hold resistance readings to a negligible amount.

For example, the resistance between any component and the aircraft structure must be 5 milliohms (.005 ohms) or less, and the resistance of the bonding strap should not exceed 3 milliohms (.003 ohms). A bonding strap must be long enough to permit free movement of a component, but not so long as to increase resistance beyond acceptable limits. Bonding straps should be made from a material that does not produce galvanic corrosion. In addition, you can use appropriate washers to minimize the possibility of corrosion to the aircraft structure itself. For example, installing a sacrificial aluminum washer between a copper strap and an aluminum stringer concentrates all potential galvanic corrosion between the copper and aluminum in the washer rather than the structure.

Aluminum alloy jumpers are recommended for most cases, but copper jumpers should be used to bond together parts made of stainless steel, cadmium-plated steel, copper, brass, and bronze. The bonding strap should have enough mechanical strength to withstand constant flexing and should be easily installed to permit removal of the component being bonded. [Figure 8-102]

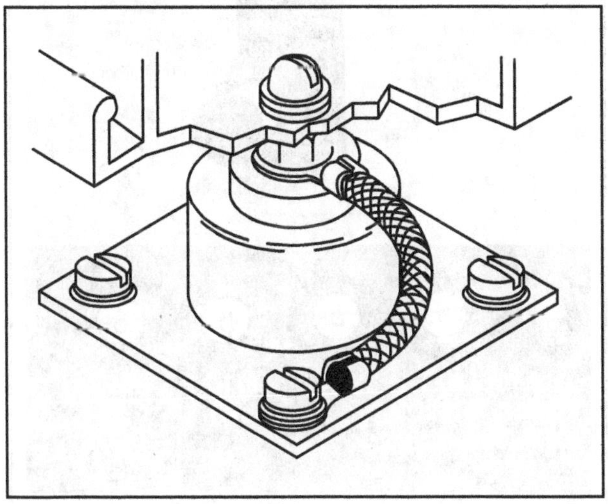

**Figure 8-102. A braided bonding strap of adequate length and capacity provides a current return path for insulated, shock-mounted components.**

The large flow of current from an electrical engine starter requires a heavy bonding strap between the engine and the airframe. This is especially necessary on engines that are mounted in rubber shock mounts that have high electrical insulation properties. If a bonding strap is not installed between the engine and airframe, or if a break or extensive corrosion exists in an installed bonding strap, the risk of fire is greatly increased. This occurs because much of the starter return current will be forced to pass through metal fuel and primer lines to reach ground.

## CURRENT LIMITING DEVICES

Electrical circuit protection devices are installed to protect circuit wiring. To do this adequately, the protection devices should be located as close as possible to the electrical power source bus. The two common types of circuit protection devices used on aircraft are circuit breakers and fuses.

A current limiting device should open an electrical circuit before its conductors become hot enough to emit smoke. To achieve this, circuit breakers or fuses are selected with time and current characteristics that are below that of the associated conductor. Circuit protection should be matched to conductor requirements to obtain maximum use of the equipment operated by the circuit. [Figure 8-103]

### FUSES

A fuse is a piece of low-melting-point alloy encased in a glass tube with metal contacts on each end. It is placed in the circuit, usually at the bus bar, so

| WIRE AND GAUGE COPPER | CIRCUIT BREAKER AMPERAGE | FUSE AMP |
|---|---|---|
| 22 | 5 | 5 |
| 20 | 7.5 | 5 |
| 18 | 10 | 10 |
| 16 | 15 | 10 |
| 14 | 20 | 15 |
| 12 | 30 | 20 |
| 10 | 40 | 30 |
| 8 | 50 | 50 |
| 6 | 80 | 70 |
| 4 | 100 | 70 |
| 2 | 125 | 100 |
| 1 | | 150 |
| 0 | | 150 |

**Figure 8-103. Charts for selecting circuit protection typically apply to specific conditions.**

that all of the current flowing to a circuit must pass through it. If too much current flows, the link melts and opens the circuit. To restore the circuit, the blown fuse must be replaced with a new one.

Two types of fuses are used in aircraft circuits—the regular glass tubular fuse and the slow-blow fuse. Regular fuses have a simple narrow strip of low-melting-point material that melts as soon as excessive current flows through them. Slow-blow fuses have a larger fusible element that is held under tension by a small coil spring inside the glass tube. A slow-blow fuse will enable a momentary surge of high current to pass, such as that when the switch in a lighting circuit is closed, but it will soften under a sustained current flow in excess of its rating. The spring will pull the fusible link in two, opening the circuit. Aircraft fuses are rated according to the maximum continuous amperage they can sustain. [Figure 8-104]

For certification of a normal, utility, acrobatic, or commuter category aircraft, CFR 14 Part 23 requires that a spare fuse of each rating, or 50% of each rating of accessible fuses, whichever is greater, be carried and readily accessible in flight. CFR 14 Part 91 requires the operator of an aircraft, using fuses as protective devices and flying at night, to carry a spare set. The spare set can consist of a complete replacement set of fuses or a quantity of three replacement fuses for each kind required.

Fuses that are accessible to maintenance personnel are found on some aircraft. These fuses, commonly called **current limiters**, are often used to isolate a complete distribution bus in the event of a short to that bus. In the event that the current limiter opens, the pilot can continue the flight without use of the isolated bus, and then have the problem corrected upon landing. [Figure 8-105]

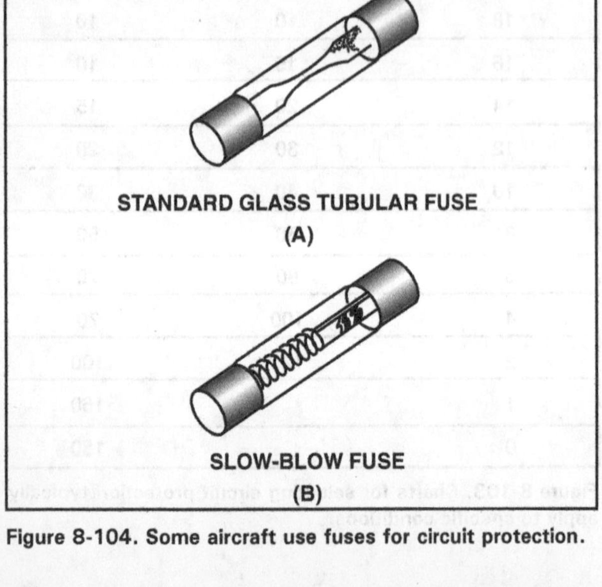


**Figure 8-104. Some aircraft use fuses for circuit protection.**

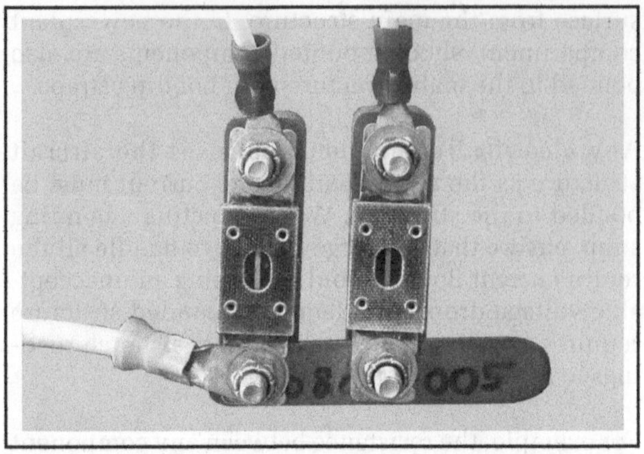

**Figure 8-105. A current limiter operates much like a fuse to protect an entire electrical bus. The center section of the limiter has a clear inspection window to view the condition of the fusible material.**

## CIRCUIT BREAKERS

Circuit breakers are used rather than fuses because of the ease in which a pilot can restore a circuit in flight—by simply resetting the circuit breaker. The two basic types of circuit breakers in aircraft electrical systems are those that open due to excessive heat and those that open by the pull of a magnetic field. Most aircraft breakers, however, open by heat. When current flow exceeds the circuit breaker rating, a bimetallic strip inside the housing warps out of shape and snaps the contacts open, which disconnects the circuit. [Figure 8-106]

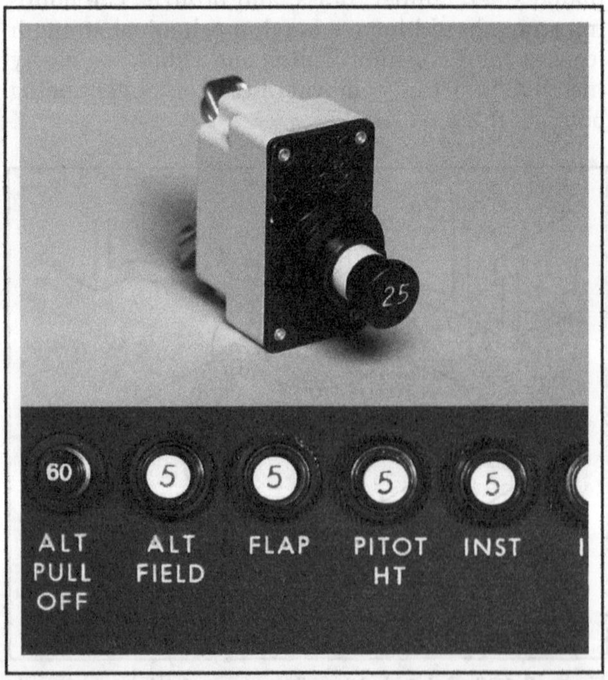


**Figure 8-106. Circuit breakers that can be reset in flight provide most circuit protection in aircraft. Circuit breakers can be push-pull or push-to-reset.**

Aircraft electrical systems use three basic configurations of circuit breaker—the push-to-reset, the push-pull, and the toggle. The button of the push-to-reset circuit breaker is normally in and pops out only when the circuit has been overloaded. Although some types of circuit breakers can be used as switches to isolate a circuit, this type cannot because there is no way to grip the button to trip it manually.

The push-pull circuit breaker has a small lip which can be pulled to open the circuit. Normally these circuit breaker buttons are in, but if a breaker overloads, the button pops out. Many of these circuit breakers have a white band around the button that is visible when the breaker has been tripped. Although this type of circuit breaker can be used as a switch, it should only be used while isolating a circuit for maintenance purposes.

The toggle circuit breaker is normally used as a control switch as well as a circuit breaker. When the toggle is up, the circuit is closed, but if the circuit is overloaded, the breaker will pop partially down. To restore the circuit, the toggle is moved all the way down and then back up.

All aircraft circuit breakers must be trip-free, which means that the breaker contacts will remain open as long as a short circuit exists, regardless of the actuating control position. This prevents the circuit breaker from being closed and manually held closed if a fault exists that could generate enough heat to cause a fire. Circuit breakers that automatically reset are not allowed in aircraft installations.

Any time that a circuit breaker opens a circuit, it should be permitted to cool before being reset. If it tripped due to a transient condition in the electrical system (such as a momentary overload), it will remain closed after reset, and the electrical system should operate normally. If it was opened by an actual fault, it will pop open again and should be left open until you can determine the cause of the excessive current draw.

On many large commercial aircraft, electronic circuit breakers are sometimes used to control overloaded power distribution circuits. The current flowing through a conductor is measured using inductive pickups called current transformers. The inductive pickups generate a signal that is monitored by a control unit computer, and if an overcurrent condition exists, the computer opens the circuit breaker.

## ELECTRICAL CONTROL PLACARDS

When electrical control components such as circuit breakers are installed, ensure that the device is placarded to indicate its function. These placards should be readily visible to the flight crew in day or night conditions.

# SUMMARY CHECKLIST

✓ The wire used in an installation must have sufficient capacity to accommodate the required current without producing excessive heat or voltage drop.

✓ Wire insulation, which must resist abrasion damage, protects the conductor and prevents electrical leakage.

✓ Copper wire with Teflon insulation is commonly used for new and replacement wiring installations. Insulated aluminum wire is used in installations that require large amounts of current to be carried over long distances.

✓ Aircraft wire is measured according to the American wire gauge (AWG) system. The smaller the wire diameter, the larger the number.

✓ The amount of current that a wire can carry is determined by the area of its cross-section, which is expressed in circular mils.

✓ When selecting wire for a new installation, system voltage, permissible voltage drop, and the component duty cycle must be considered.

✓ Wires are typically marked every 12 to 15 inches with the type of circuit, location within the circuit, and wire size. Markings are not standardized among manufacturers.

✓ Wires in an aircraft are either open (in free air) or enclosed in conduit.

✓ Wire installations should be routed at least three inches away from moving control cables or components and above fluid lines.

✓ Wire bundles should be clamped to aircraft structure with cushioned clamps.

✓ Any electrical component that uses the aircraft structure as its current return path must be connected to the structure with a bonding strap.

✓ Current-limiting devices, circuit breakers, and fuses are installed primarily to protect circuit wiring.

✓ Circuit breakers have three basic configurations: push-to-reset, push-pull, and toggle-type.

# KEY TERMS

American Wire Gage
AWG
circular mil
square mil
crimping
tinning
current limiters

# QUESTIONS

1. The wiring between components must be of ______ (stranded or solid) construction.

2. Copper wire use for aircraft electrical system installations must meet MIL-W-______________ specification.

3. Aluminum wire used for aircraft electrical system installations must meet MIL-W-______________ specification.

4. The standard insulation strength for electrical wire used in aircraft installations is ______ volts.

5. The smallest gauge aluminum wire recommended for use in aircraft systems is ______ gauge.

6. A ______ (what number) gauge aluminum wire could be used to replace a 4-guage copper wire.

7. When selecting the wire size to use in an electrical system installation, you must consider the maximum ______ the wire will carry and the maximum ______ ______ allowed.

8. Complete this chart for the maximum voltage drop:

| NOMINAL SYSTEM VOLTAGE | ALLOWABLE VOLTAGE DROP VOLTS | |
|---|---|---|
| | CONTINUOUS OPERATION | INTERMITTANT OPERATION |
| 14 | | |
| 28 | | |
| 115 | | |
| 200 | | |

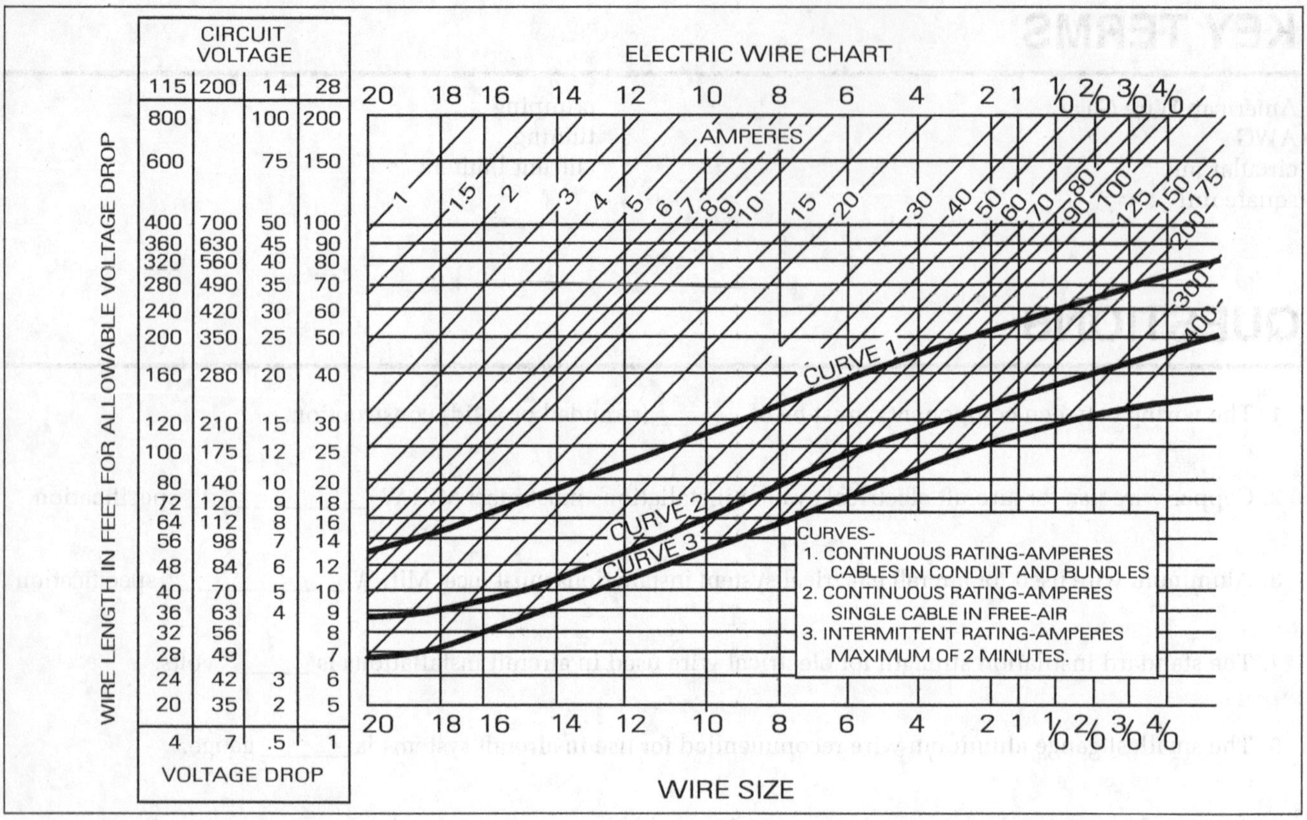


9. Using the wire chart, find the proper size copper wire to use for the following conditions:
   a. 50-amp load, 14-volt system, continuous load, routed in free air, 14 feet of wire. _______-gauge wire
   b. 12-amp load, 28-volt system, continuous load, routed in a bundle, 60 feet of wire. _______-gauge wire
   c. 20-amp load, 28-volt system, continuous load, routed in a bundle, 30 feet of wire. _______-gauge wire
   d. 200-amp load, 28-volt system, intermittent load, routed in free air, 40 feet of wire. _______-gauge wire

10. Two basic types of electrical wiring installations are:
    a. _______ _______
    b. _______ _______

11. If a wire bundle is routed through a compartment parallel to a fuel line, the wire bundle should be _______ (above or below) the fuel line.

12. No wire bundle should be closer than _______ (how many) inches from a control cable.

13. Electrical wire bundles are fastened to the aircraft structure with insulated ___________ clamps.

14. The two basic ways to prevent electromagnetic interference in radio and electronic equipment are:
    a. ______________
    b. ______________

15. The inside diameter of a conduit must be about _______ percent larger than the maximum diameter of the wire bundle it encloses.

16. _______________ (bonding or shielding) is used in an aircraft electrical system to intercept radiated electrical energy.

17. Give the color code for the insulation on a solderless terminal used on each of the following size wires:

    a. 16 gauge = _______

    b. 22 gauge = _______

    c. 10 gauge = _______

    d. 18 gauge = _______

| WIRE SIZE | INSULATION COLOR |
|---|---|
| 16-GAUGE | |
| 22-GAUGE | |
| 10-GAUGE | |
| 18-GAUGE | |

18. When a terminal is properly crimped onto an electrical wire, the joint should be ___________ (what percent) as strong as the wire itself.

19. The smallest terminal stud allowed for electrical power systems is a number _______.

20. There should never be more than _______ (how many) terminals on any one stud.

21. Most junction boxes in the powerplant area are mounted _______________ (vertically or horizontally).

22. _______________ (Bonding or Shielding) consists of connecting all components in the aircraft together so that there will be no insulated components on which electrical charges can build up.

23. A bonding strap that is required to carry return current from a component should not have a resistance of more than _______ milliohms.

24. The circuit breaker or fuse should open before the conductor _______ _______.

25. A circuit breaker that holds the circuit open if a fault is present, regardless of the position of the operating control, is called a _______-_______ circuit breaker.

26. Automatic reset circuit breakers _______ (are or are not) used in aircraft electrical systems.

27. Give the maximum amount of current a switch rated at 35 amps, 24-volts could carry, in the following types of 24-volt circuits.

a. Incandescent lamp _______

b. relay _______

c. DC motor _______

d. Heater _______

28. Two-position "on-off" switches should be mounted so that the "on" position is reached by an _______________ _______________ (upward or downward) movement.

29. The principal difference between a relay and a solenoid is that a relay has a _________ iron core, while a solenoid has a _________ one.

SECTION

E

# RECIPROCATING ENGINE IGNITION SYSTEMS

The ignition system for a gasoline-powered reciprocating engine must deliver a high voltage spark at each plug within each cylinder in all operating conditions. This spark must be consistently created and delivered at a specific moment during the operating cycle. To ensure reliability, 14 CFR Part 33 states that, "...each spark ignition engine must have a dual ignition system with at least two spark plugs for each cylinder and two separate electrical circuits with separate sources of electric energy, or have an ignition system of equivalent in-flight reliability."

Dual ignition systems provide a couple of key advantages. First, by definition, dual systems are redundant, which means that they provide a backup in case of a failure. Second, the use of two spark plugs in each cylinder improves combustion efficiency and engine power output.

## BATTERY IGNITION SYSTEM

Early aircraft engines used a battery as the power source for one or both of the required ignition systems. A typical battery ignition system consists of an ignition switch, a battery, an ignition coil, a set of breaker points, a cam, a capacitor, a distributor, and spark plugs. [Figure 8-107]

The ignition switch controls when the ignition system is active. When the ignition switch is on and the breaker points are closed, battery current flows through the ignition coil's primary circuit. However, when the ignition switch is off, the primary circuit is open and the system is disabled.

In a battery ignition system, the battery supplies current to the primary winding of an ignition coil. The **ignition coil** is a device that steps up the voltage to the level necessary to create a spark in each cylinder. For a coil to step up voltage, current flowing through the primary winding of the coil must pulse. Direct current (DC) from the battery is converted to pulsing DC by the opening and closing of breaker points connected in series with the primary winding. **Breaker points** are mechanical devices that consist of two electrical contacts that control when current flows through the primary winding. When the contacts close, the electrical circuit is complete and current flows through the primary winding. However, when the contacts open, the circuit is interrupted, and the magnetic field surrounding the primary winding collapses. As the magnetic field collapses, current is induced into the secondary winding.

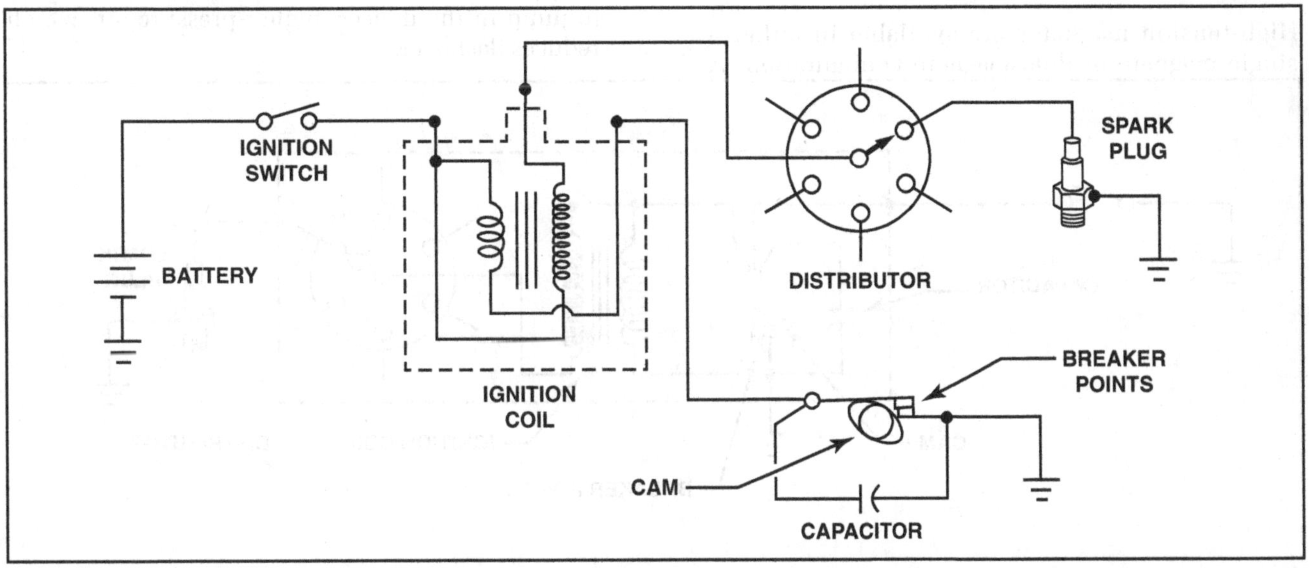


**Figure 8-107. The major components in a battery ignition system include the battery, ignition coil, a set of breaker points, a cam, a capacitor, a distributor, and spark plugs.**

A **capacitor** (or **condenser**), a device that momentarily stores electrical energy, prevents arcing across the points and increases the rate that the magnetic field in the primary winding collapses. A **cam**, a metal disk with two or more raised lobes, opens and closes the points.

When current is induced into the secondary winding, voltage is stepped up to the distributor. The **distributor** directs high voltage current produced by the ignition coil to the spark plugs. The distributor consists of a rotating finger and a distributor block. As it rotates, the finger distributes power from the coil to the contacts mounted in the distributor block. From there, the energy passes through an ignition lead to a spark plug.

## MAGNETO IGNITION SYSTEMS

Most aircraft reciprocating engines use a magneto ignition system. A **magneto** is a permanent-magnet alternating current (AC) generator that uses electromagnetic and induced current to develop a pulse of high voltage electricity to fire a spark plug. Magneto systems are classified as either high-tension or low-tension.

### HIGH-TENSION SYSTEMS

The basic components of a high-tension magneto system include the magneto, a wiring harness, and a set of spark plugs. Unlike a battery ignition system, the magneto in a high-tension system uses a rotating magnet to induce voltage into an ignition, or magneto, coil. The coil steps up voltage just before it reaches the distributor for distribution to a spark plug. This provides a constant voltage from the magneto to the spark plugs. [Figure 8-108]

High-tension magnetos are available in either a single magneto or dual magneto configuration. A single magneto consists of a permanent magnet having two, four, or eight poles fixed to a single rotating shaft. Current is induced as the magnet's flux lines cut across the primary winding of the magneto coil. After the current is induced, it is stepped up and distributed to the spark plugs. To comply with the requirement for dual ignition, two magnetos must be installed on a single engine. [Figure 8-109]

A dual magneto differs from a single magneto in that a single housing contains two independent ignition systems sharing a common rotating magnet. A dual magneto contains two of every part except the housing, drive coupling, rotating magnet, and cam. [Figure 8-110]

The earliest high-tension magneto systems experienced problems with the production and distribution of high voltage pulses to the spark plugs. During high altitude operations, a phenomenon called **flashover** can cause the spark to jump to the wrong electrode. Flashover often leads to **carbon tracking**, which appears as a fine pencil-like carbon trail inside the distributor. Over time, carbon tracks can form a conductive path to ground, which increases the likelihood of flashover.

In an attempt to prevent flashover, some magnetos used enlarged distributors to increase the distance that a spark would have to jump. This solution was only partially effective. The greatest advance in overcoming flashover came from improved materials with better insulating properties. Pressurizing magnetos also improved ignition system performance at high altitudes. With a pressurized magneto, manifold pressure (on a turbocharged engine) or air from a pump is directed into the magneto housing. It is more difficult for the spark to jump in the denser, higher-pressure air, which reduces flashover.

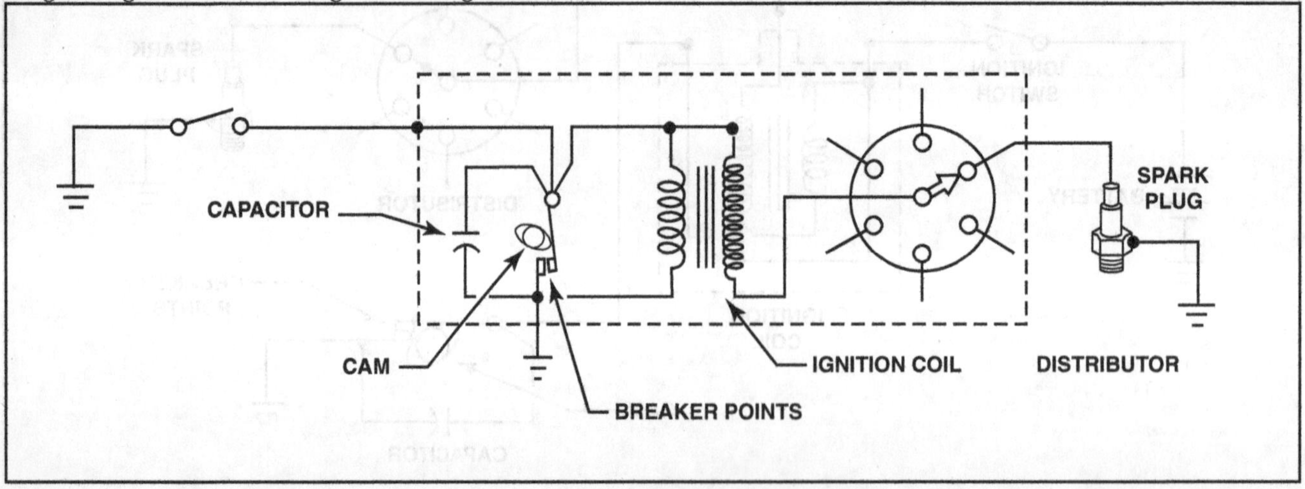


**Figure 8-108. High-tension magneto systems generate high voltage energy by inducing voltage through a coil. High voltage pulses of current are routed to the spark plugs through a distributor block and ignition leads.**

**Figure 8-109. A single magneto uses a multi-pole magnet to induce current in a coil. The voltage pulse of current is stepped up and distributed to the spark plugs.**

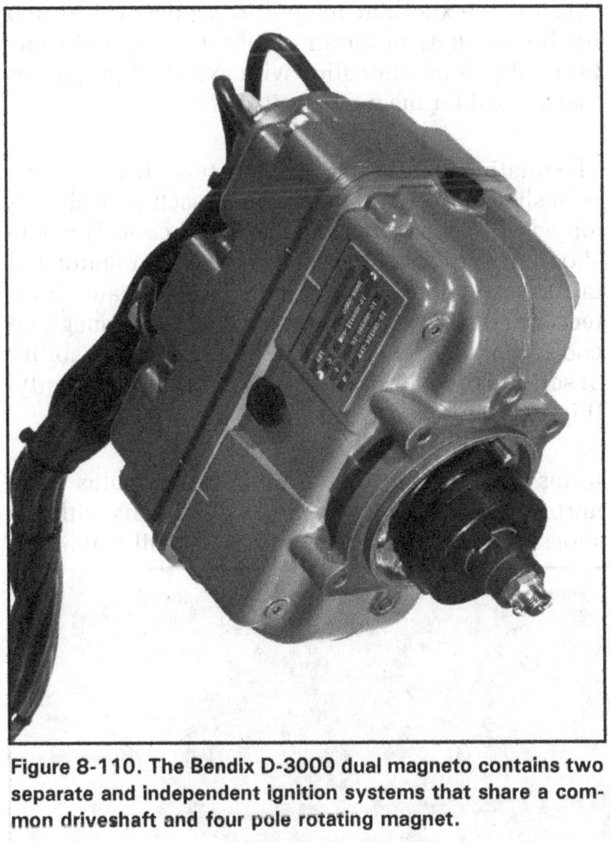

**Figure 8-110. The Bendix D-3000 dual magneto contains two separate and independent ignition systems that share a common driveshaft and four pole rotating magnet.**

### LOW-TENSION SYSTEMS

The low-tension magneto was developed to overcome the problem of flashover in high-tension magnetos. In a low-tension magneto, the coil has a single winding that produces a low-voltage pulse that minimizes flashover. To create the high energy spark needed for ignition, the low-tension system uses a transformer at each cylinder near the spark plug. Each transformer contains a primary coil and a secondary coil to boost the magneto voltage. [Figure 8-111]

Although low-tension magneto circuits overcame some of the problems intrinsic with early high-tension systems, they still had limitations. A low-tension system had more parts than a comparable high-tension system. This was compounded on large radial engines such as those with 18 or 24 cylinders. Low-tension systems are not common.

## MAGNETO OPERATING PRINCIPLES

High- and low-tension magneto systems generate electrical energy on the same principle. However, because low-tension systems are not used in modern aircraft, the following discussion features a typical high-tension magneto. A high-tension magneto consists of a mechanical system and three distinct circuits: magnetic, primary, and secondary. The operation of these circuits is controlled with a cockpit-mounted ignition switch.

### THE MECHANICAL SYSTEM

The mechanical system of a magneto includes the housing, drive shaft, and other nonelectrical components. Most magnetos are encased by an aluminum alloy housing with provisions for mounting to an engine. Aluminum alloy is used because it does not interfere with the magnetic circuit. In addition, aluminum has adequate strength and weight properties.

Magneto-to-engine attachment is accomplished by either a base or flange mount. On early radial engines, base-mounted magnetos were bolted rigidly to a bracket on the accessory case. Flange-mounted magnetos are common on modern reciprocating engines. The mounting flange is cast as an integral part of the magneto housing. The magneto attaches to the engine with mounting hardware that passes through slots or secure L-shaped clamps. [Figure 8-112]

The magneto shaft runs the length of the magneto. The rotating magnet, distributor drive gear, and cam are mounted to the shaft. The shaft is normally supported by ball or needle bearings.

High-tension magnetos use two types of cams: uncompensated and compensated. The **uncompensated cam** is used in most modern reciprocating engines. There is a uniform distance between cam lobes because the number of degrees of crankshaft rotation between the firing of each spark plug is

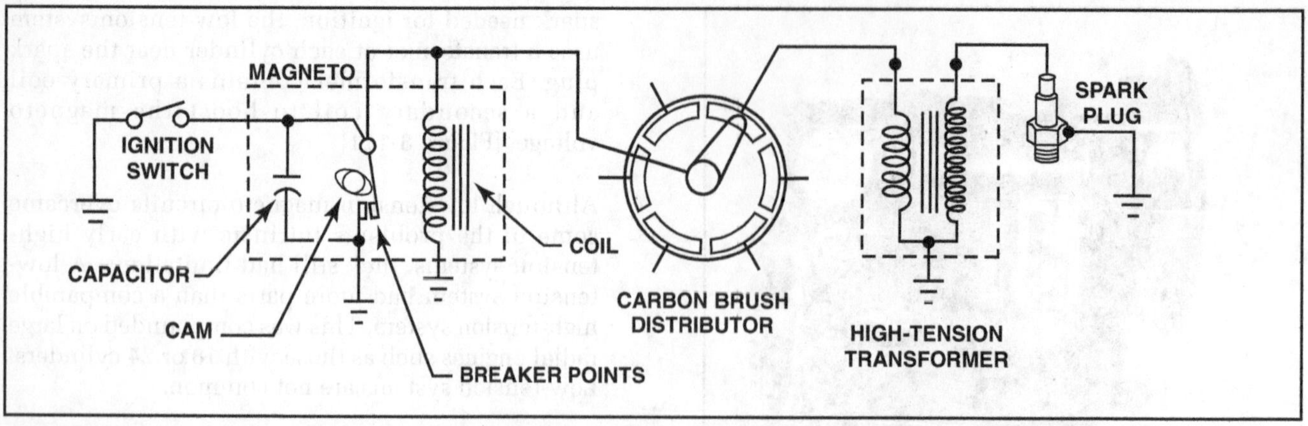


**Figure 8-111. A low-tension magneto uses a magneto coil with only one winding. The magneto produces and distributes a relatively low voltage energy pulse that is stepped up by a high-tension transformer immediately before reaching the spark plugs.**

uniform. The number of lobes on an uncompensated cam is equal to the number of poles on the rotating magnet. This type of cam is normally mounted to the end of the rotating magneto shaft drive.

A **compensated cam** is used in magnetos installed on radial engines. With this type of cam, a separate cam lobe is provided for each cylinder. Due to the elliptical path of the connecting rods, the number of degrees between firing events is not uniform. The spacing between each lobe is designed to fire the spark plugs in each cylinder at the optimal time. Because a compensated cam has one lobe for each cylinder, the cam must complete one revolution for every two revolutions of the crankshaft. Because of this, compensated cams are usually driven by a gear assembly.

## THE MAGNETIC CIRCUIT

The magnetic circuit includes a rotating permanent magnet, pole shoes, pole shoe extensions, and a coil core. A rotating magnet can have two, four, or eight magnetic poles. Magnets with more than two poles are arranged with poles spaced evenly around the shaft, alternating between north and south.

Rotating magnets are often made from **alnico**, an alloy made of aluminum, iron, nickel, and cobalt. Due to its excellent magnetic properties, alnico retains magnetism for an indefinite length of time. **Permalloy** is another alloy with excellent properties that is used for magnet construction.

The rotating magnet in a magneto turns between two pole shoes. To complete a circuit, each pole shoe is joined at one end to the magneto coil core. The pole shoes and coil core are constructed from laminated layers of high-grade soft iron. The laminate architecture reduces eddy currents, keeps the magneto cooler, and boosts efficiency. The high permeability of soft iron enables flux lines to pass through easily. [Figure 8-113]

Lines of magnetic flux flow between poles from north to south. When a pair of poles aligns with the shoes, lines of flux flow through the coil core. This

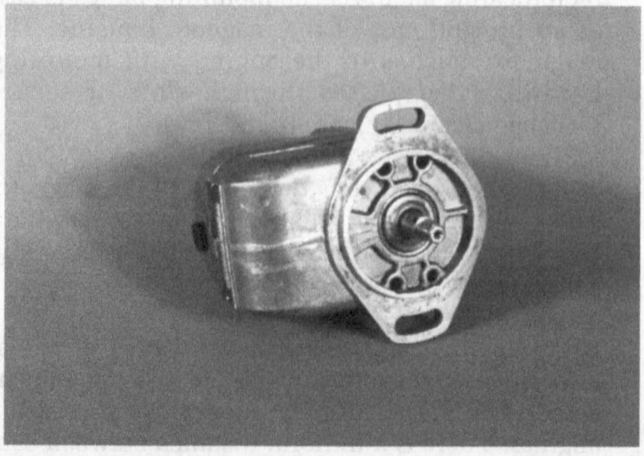

**Figure 8-112. Either type of flange mount on a magneto allows it to be rotated for timing to the engine.**

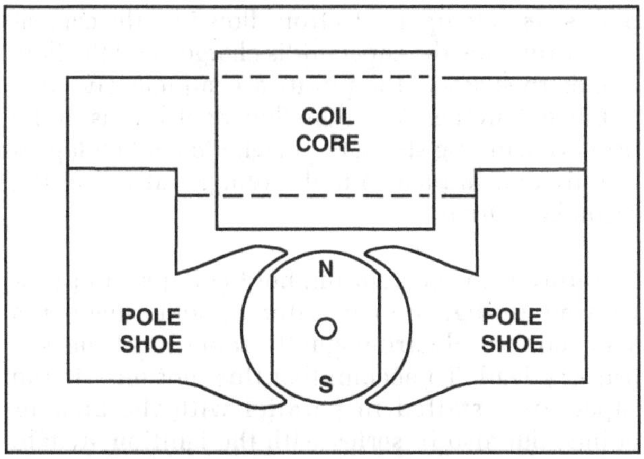


**Figure 8-113. The components of a magnetic circuit include a rotating magnet, a set of pole shoes, and a coil core.**

position is known as the **full register position**; in this position the magnetic field is strongest and the density of flux lines is greatest. As a magnet rotates beyond full register, the magnetic field slowly collapses until no lines of flux pass through the coil core. This position is known as the **neutral position**; in this position the magnetic field is weakest. Continued rotation of the magnet again realigns the poles and shoes in the full register position, but in the opposite direction. [Figure 8-114]

One revolution of a two pole magnet produces results in two positions of maximum flux line concentration and two positions of zero flux flow through the coil core. Additionally, the direction of flux travel reverses twice. As a magnet rotates in a magneto, a magnetic field continuously expands and collapses. This pulsing magnetic field induces current into the primary winding.

Current flowing through a conductor produces a magnetic field. As the magnet rotates, this magnetic field resists changes in current flow. After the magnetic field begins to collapse, the magnetic field resists the collapsing field. The magnetic circuit is designed to hold the flux in the core at the highest possible value until the rotating magnet reaches its neutral position. After the magnet rotates beyond neutral, a magnetic field of opposite polarity begins to build. At this point, the greatest magnetic field stress exists. The specific number of degrees beyond the neutral position is known as the **efficiency gap**, or **E-gap** angle. [Figure 8-115]

## THE PRIMARY CIRCUIT

The primary electrical circuit in a magneto includes the primary winding of an insulated magneto coil, a set of breaker points, and a capacitor. The primary winding in a typical magneto coil consists of 180 to 200 turns of 18-gauge copper wire. The wire is wound directly over the laminated core and coated

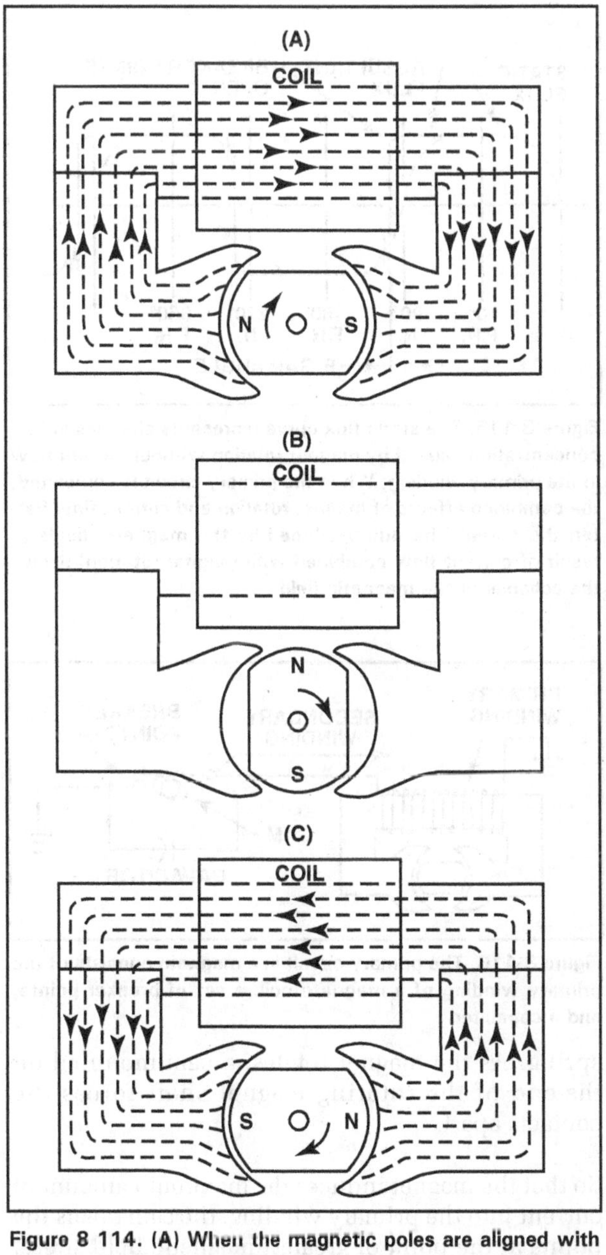


**Figure 8-114. (A) When the magnetic poles are aligned with the pole shoes, the magnet is in the full register position and the maximum number of flux lines flow through the coil core. (B) When the magnetic poles are rotated to the neutral position, no lines of flux pass through the coil core. (C) As the magnet rotates past the neutral position, the number of flux lines passing through the coil's core begin increasing until the magnet reaches the full register position. The magnetic poles switch direction every 180°, reversing the direction of the lines of flux passing through the coil core.**

with enamel insulation. One end of the primary winding is attached to a ground lead and the other end is connected to the secondary winding and the ungrounded (or insulated) side of the breaker points. [Figure 8-116]

The breaker points are normally mounted to the magneto housing and held closed by a leaf-type

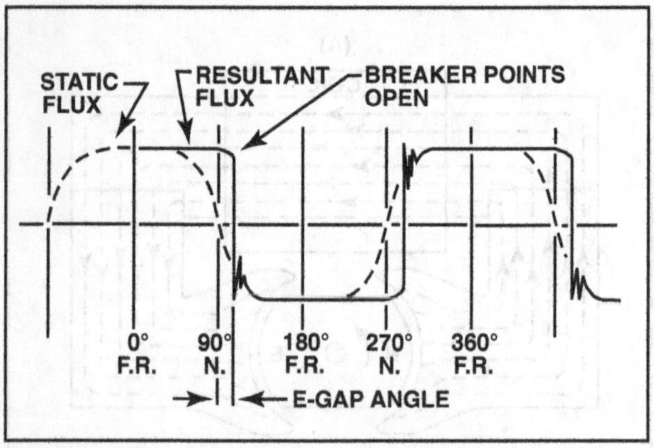


**Figure 8-115. The static flux curve represents changes in flux concentration caused by magnet rotation without current flow in the primary winding. When the primary circuit is completed, the combined effects of magnet rotation and current flow flatten the curve. The flux produced by the magnetic fields (a result of current flow combined with magnet rotation) delays the collapse of the magnetic field.**

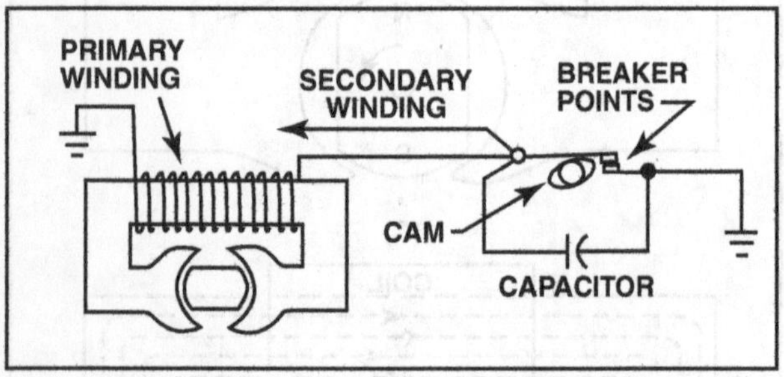


**Figure 8-116. The primary circuit in a magneto consists of the primary winding of a magneto coil, a set of breaker points, and a capacitor.**

spring. As the magnet rotates, a cam mounted on the end of the rotating magnet shaft forces the contacts apart.

So that the magnet induces the maximum amount of current into the primary winding, the cam opens the points at the point of greatest magnetic field stress. At the E-gap position, opening the breaker points interrupts current flow in the primary circuit and induces current into the secondary coil. After the points close, the magnet is near its full register position and the magnetic field in the core experiences a quick reversal.

Opening the contact points interrupts current flow, which produces an arc between the points. As the points begin to separate, the electrical resistance increases and the current flowing through the resistance produces heat. This heat is so extreme that air is ionized and current flows through it. Arcing delays the collapse of the magnetic field in the primary winding and causes metal to transfer from one breaker point to the other. Severe arcing can actually weld the points together. To reduce arcing, a capacitor is installed in parallel with the points. As the points begin to open, electrons flow into the capacitor. By the time the capacitor is charged and the flow of electrons stops, the points are sufficiently open to prevent arcing. When the flow of electrons in the primary winding stops, the magnetic field collapses rapidly and induces a high voltage pulse into the secondary circuit.

In addition to accelerating field collapse and preventing arcing, the capacitor in some magnetos also reduces electromagnetic radiation from the primary lead. To accomplish this, not only is the capacitor installed in parallel with the breaker points, but also in series with the ignition switch. This type of capacitor has a pigtail lead connected to the insulated breaker point and a threaded terminal that connects to the ignition switch lead. When installed, the metal case of the capacitor is grounded to the magneto housing. The energy from any radio frequency induced into the primary lead is carried to ground before it leaves the magneto. This type of component is known as a feed-through (or filter) capacitor. [Figure 8-117]

## THE SECONDARY CIRCUIT

The secondary magneto circuit produces the high-voltage energy required to cause a spark. The components that make up the secondary circuit include the secondary winding in the magneto coil and the distributor.

The amount of current induced into the secondary winding of a magneto coil is directly related to two factors: the rate at which the magnetic field collapses around the primary winding and the ratio of primary to secondary windings. The secondary winding is made from approximately 13,000 turns

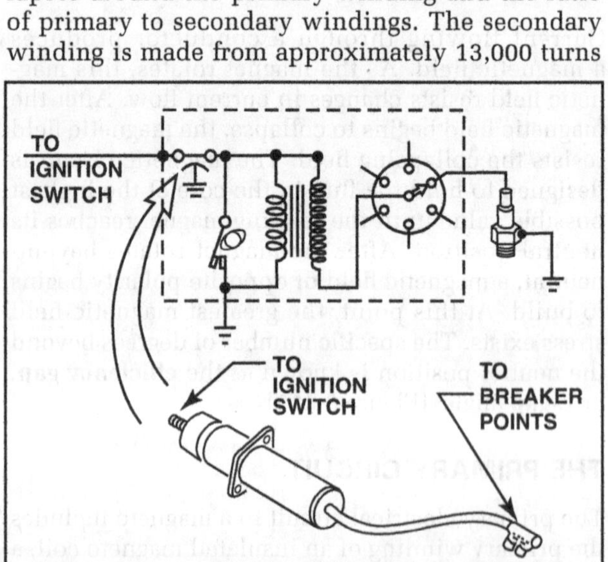


**Figure 8-117. Some magnetos use a special feed-through capacitor to help reduce electrical noise generated by the breaker points. This helps protect electronic equipment from voltage spikes.**

of a very fine-gauge wire. The resulting turn ratio is capable of producing a 20,000 volt pulse. One end of the secondary winding attaches to the primary winding (to provide a path to ground) and the other is attached to a high-voltage contact that protrudes from the body of the magneto coil. [Figure 8-118]

Current flows from the secondary winding to the distributor through a spring-loaded carbon brush mounted in the center of the distributor rotor. High voltage energy passes through the carbon brush into the conductive arm (or finger) of the distributor rotor. A drive gear on the rotor turns the distributor and the conductive arm passes the electrodes for each spark plug in the distributor block. [Figure 8-119]

The gears of the distributor rotor provide a high voltage pulse at specific points during its rotation. For every two revolutions of the crankshaft the distributor rotor must complete one revolution. With this 2:1 ratio, a magneto fires all of its spark plugs once for every 720 degrees that the crankshaft rotates.

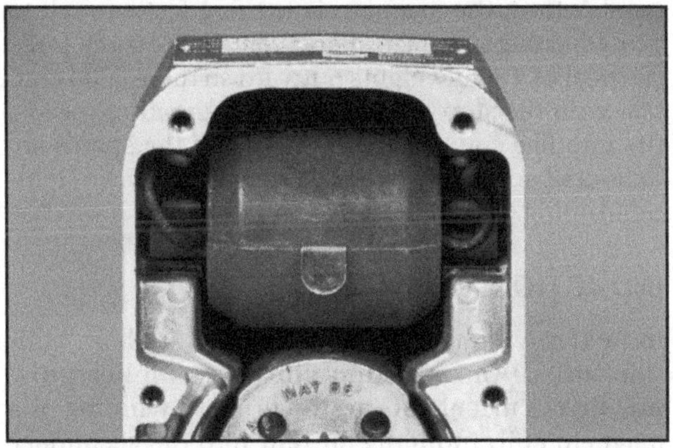

**Figure 8-118. The high-tension terminal for the secondary winding appears as a tab protruding from the magneto coil. To insulate the primary and secondary windings, the entire magneto coil is typically encased in Bakelite™, varnished cambric, or some other type of thermosetting plastic.**

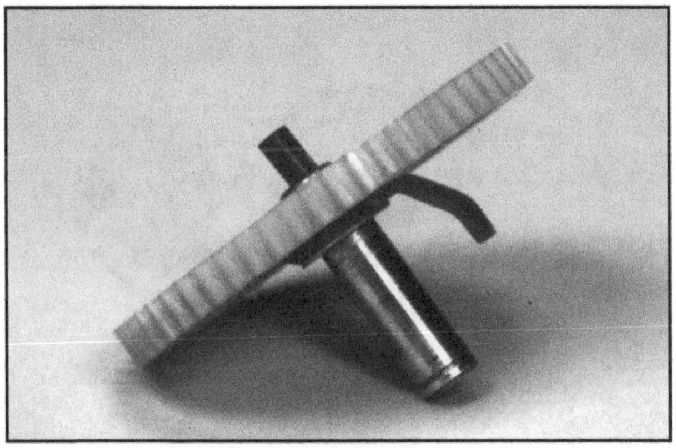

**Figure 8-119. In a typical magneto, a small carbon brush routes current to the distributor rotor. From the distributor rotor, current passes to the distributor block through a distributor finger.**

The distributor block, molded from a lightweight material with excellent insulating properties, is mounted in the magneto housing. Electrodes are on one side of the distributor block and receptacles for receiving the ignition leads are on the other. The electrodes and receptacles are arranged around the circumference of the distributor block. During normal operation, whenever the rotating magnet is in an E-gap position, the distributor finger is aligns with an electrode on the distributor block to deliver a high voltage pulse. [Figure 8-120]

The high voltage pulse travels through the ignition leads to the spark plugs. At each spark plug, the current jumps the air gap between the center and ground electrodes and completes the electrical circuit from the spark plug back to the magneto.

To protect the secondary winding in the magneto coil, some magnetos provide an alternate path for current if an open occurs in the secondary circuit. An alternate path to ground is provided in series with the secondary winding by two electrodes. One electrode is connected to a high-tension brush holder, and the other is connected to a ground plate. This path is used only when the normal path through the spark plug gap becomes interrupted. A **safety gap,** wider than the spark plug gap, is bridged to protect the magneto coil.

## MAGNETO SPEED

The distributor rotor in a magneto always turns at one-half the engine crankshaft speed. Although the rotational speed of the distributor is fixed, the speed of a rotating magnet shaft varies depending on the number of engine cylinders and the number of poles on the rotating magnet. To determine the relation-

**Figure 8-120. The distributor block of a typical magneto is made of an insulating material with electrodes on one side and receptacles for spark plug on the other.**

ship between magneto speed and engine crankshaft speed, use the following formula:

$$\frac{\text{Number of Cylinders}}{2 \times \text{number of poles}}$$

For example, assume a six-cylinder engine uses a magneto with a two-pole magnet. Using the formula above, the magneto speed is 1.5 times the crankshaft speed.

$$\frac{6}{(2\times 2)} = 6/4$$

$$= 3/2$$

$$= 1\,1/2$$

Based on this, when the engine is turning at 2000 r.p.m., the magneto shaft is rotating at 3000 r.p.m.

## AUXILIARY IGNITION SYSTEMS

A significant limitation of a magneto is that the voltage pulse produced at low speeds is insufficient to fire a spark plug. The rotational speed necessary for a magneto to fire a spark plug is known as magneto **coming-in speed**. Although the coming-in speed of different magnetos varies, it is typically between 100 and 200 r.p.m.

During engine start, the starter motor is unable to turn the crankshaft fast enough for a magneto to reach its coming-in speed. Because the ignition event normally occurs before top dead center of the compression stroke, normal ignition timing can cause an engine to kick back during start. To prevent this, some magnetos use a set of **retard breaker points** to delay the spark during engine starting. In most cases, the spark plugs fire after the piston passes top dead center of the compression stroke.

Although retarding the ignition event promotes easier starting, it does not increase the voltage a magneto generates at slow rotational speeds. Almost all magnetos incorporate some form of ignition booster or auxiliary ignition unit. Common forms of ignition boosters include impulse couplings, induction vibrators, shower of sparks ignition systems, and booster magnetos.

### IMPULSE COUPLINGS

Impulse couplings are widely used to augment low speed ignition from magnetos. The spring-loaded impulse coupling is wound up by the magneto drive gear and then released, providing a momentary increase in rotational speed while delaying the spark. The components that make up an impulse coupling include the coupling body, a cam assembly with flyweights, and a coiled spring. [Figure 8-121]

The impulse coupling cam assembly is keyed to the magneto shaft while the coupling body rotates with the engine. When assembled, the coiled spring links the cam assembly and body together. At low speed, when a crankshaft is being rotated by the starter, flyweights on the impulse coupling contact stop pins on the magneto housing. The stop pins stop magneto shaft rotation while the continuing engine rotation winds the impulse coupling spring. Extensions on the impulse coupling body force the flyweights off the stop pins when the piston reaches top dead center. Stored spring force is released and the magneto shaft accelerates to produce a high voltage spark. [Figure 8-122]

An impulse coupling produces a spark for every spark plug during the starting process. However, after the crankshaft is rotating as a result of normal combustion, the magneto is turning fast enough to provide a high-voltage spark; centrifugal force pulls the heel of the flyweights outward so there is no contact with the stop pins. At normal operating speeds, the impulse coupling is disabled and the sparks are delivered according to their normal (advanced) ignition timing.

### INDUCTION VIBRATOR

Induction vibrators are also used as auxiliary ignition units. An **induction vibrator** supplies pulsing direct current (DC) to the primary winding of a magneto coil, inducing current into the secondary winding. The faster that the DC pulses, the greater the amount of current induced into the secondary winding for starting. The frequency of the pulsing DC is controlled by the induction vibrator. A typical induction vibrator operates when the engine start switch is engaged. [Figure 8-123]

**Figure 8-121. The components of an impulse coupling include the housing (or body), a spring, and a set of flyweights mounted to a cam.**

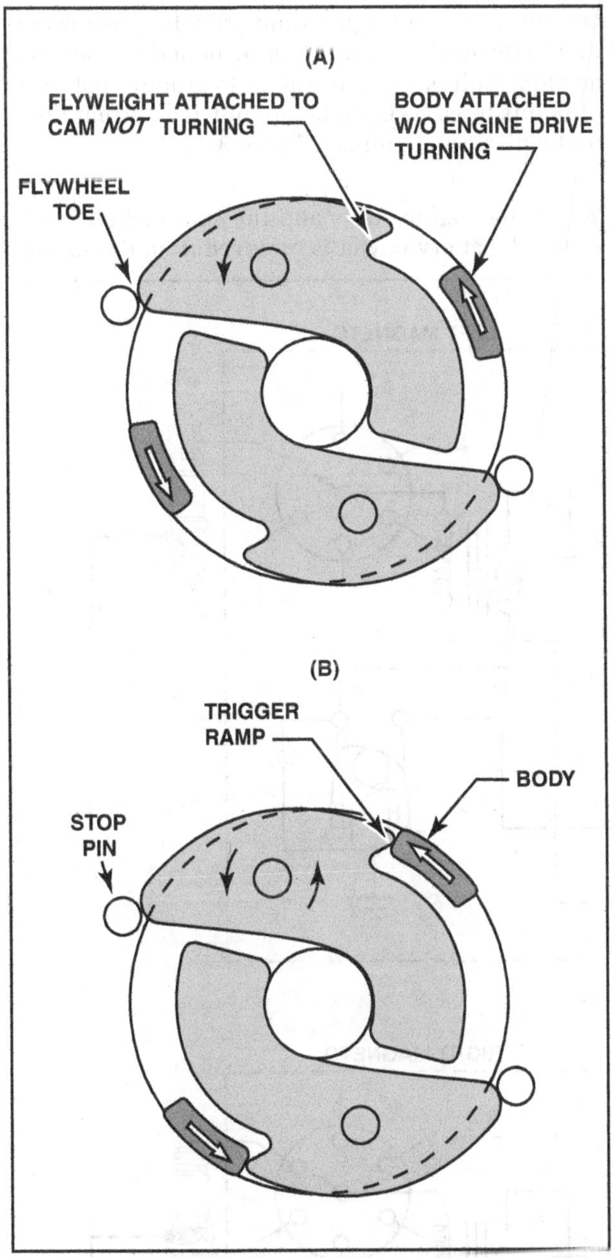


**Figure 8-122. (A) When impulse coupling flyweights contact the stop pins, the magneto stops spinning while the engine continues to rotate the impulse coupling housing. (B) When the body extensions contact the flyweight trigger ramps, the flyweights are pushed off the stop pins and spring tension causes the magnet to at a high speed.**

When the magnoto breaker points are closed, current produced by the vibrator coil flows to ground through the points. When the breaker points open, the pulsing DC flows through the primary winding. The frequency of pulses produced by a vibrator coil enables a single spark plug to produce multiple sparks as long as the points remain open. Current stops flowing to the induction vibrator after the start switch is disengaged.

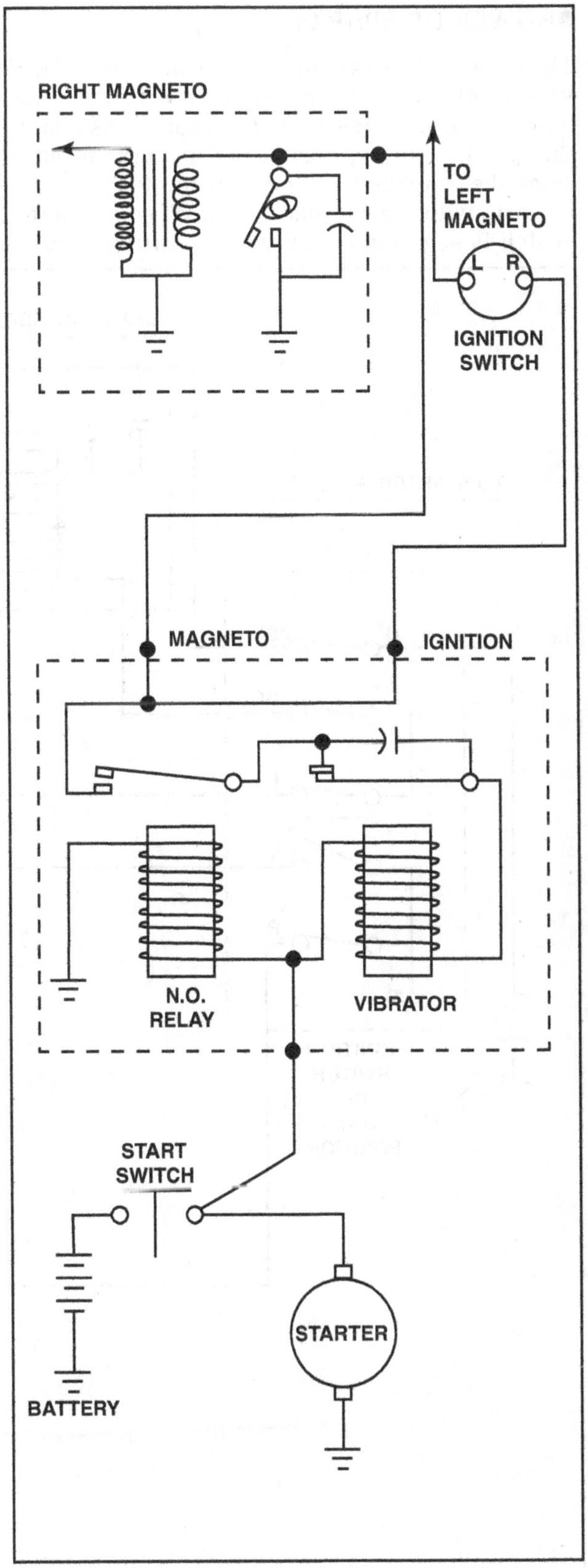


**Figure 8-123. In an ignition system with an induction vibrator, closing the starter switch causes battery current to flow to the induction vibrator. This action closes a normally open relay, and the vibrator coil begins producing pulsing DC to the primary winding of the magneto coil.**

## SHOWER OF SPARKS

The shower of sparks ignition system is an updated version of the induction vibrator with the same functions, except that a set of breaker points retards the ignition timing during engine start. In most cases, the retard breaker points are located in the left magneto with the advance points. When the starter switch is engaged, a relay in the starting vibrator grounds the right magneto and provides pulsing current to the left magneto. Because both the retard and advance points provide a path to ground, both sets of points must be open before pulsing current flows to the primary winding. [Figure 8-124]

When the engine starts and the start switch is disengaged, battery power is removed from the starting

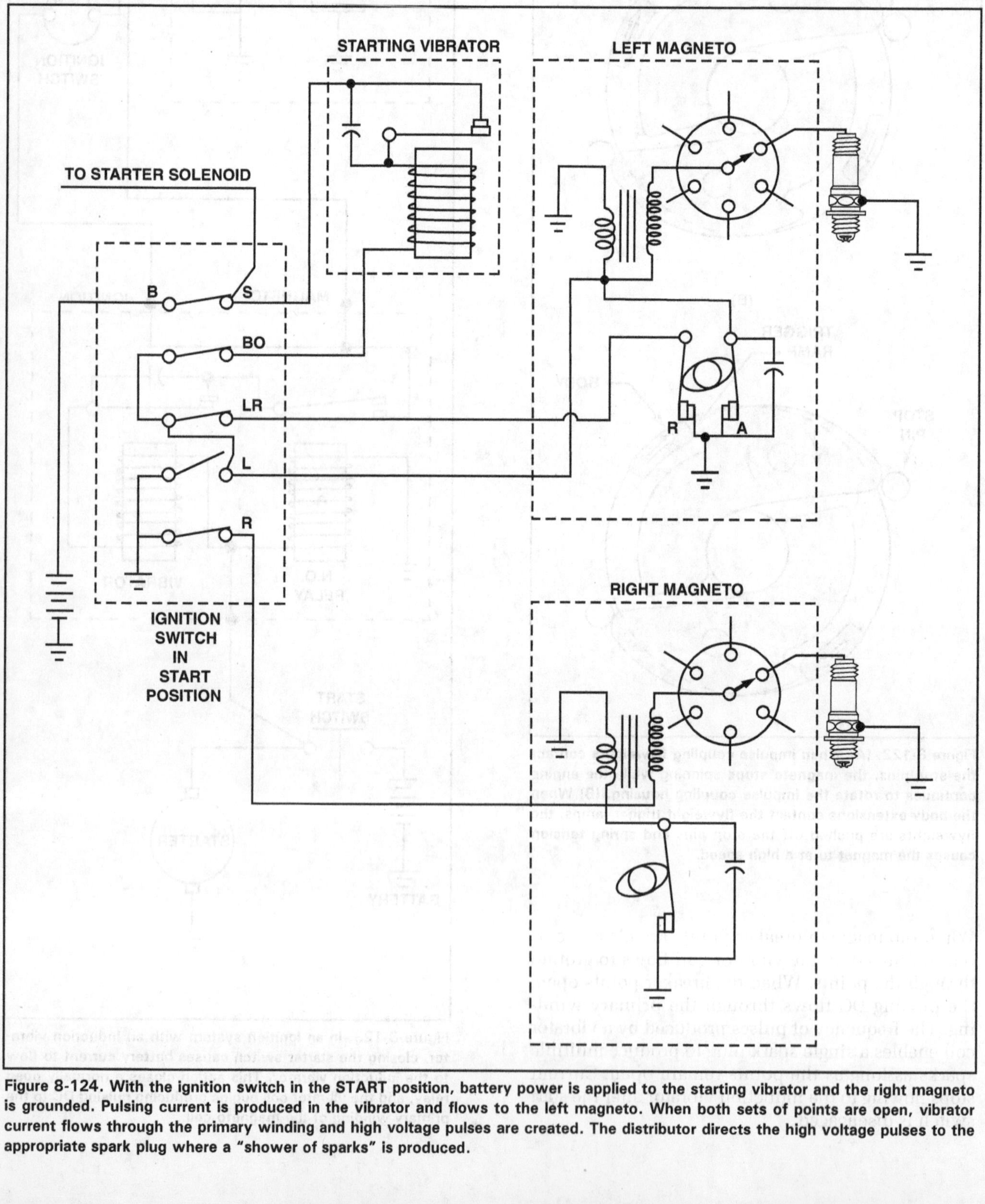


**Figure 8-124. With the ignition switch in the START position, battery power is applied to the starting vibrator and the right magneto is grounded. Pulsing current is produced in the vibrator and flows to the left magneto. When both sets of points are open, vibrator current flows through the primary winding and high voltage pulses are created. The distributor directs the high voltage pulses to the appropriate spark plug where a "shower of sparks" is produced.**

vibrator. This removes the ground path for the right magneto and removes the retard points in the left magneto from the circuit; both magnetos then operate normally and produce advanced spark ignition.

In most installations, the starting vibrator in a shower of sparks system is mounted to the aircraft firewall. Many of the components are solid state and little maintenance activity is allowed beyond removal and replacement. [Figure 8-125]

## BOOSTER MAGNETOS

The booster magneto was an early solution to provide a retarded spark for starting an engine. A typical booster magneto was a cockpit-mounted magneto that was turned by hand. When a booster magneto generated adequate voltage, the output was sent to a special distributor with a trailing finger that directed a spark to the previous cylinder in the firing order. This resulted in ignition occurring when a piston is on its power stroke. For example, consider a nine-cylinder radial engine with a firing order of 1-3-5-7-9-2-4-6-8. A booster magneto sends a spark to cylinder number 1 when the engine-driven magneto is positioned to fire cylinder number 3. Booster systems were widely used until the end of World War II. [Figure 8-126]

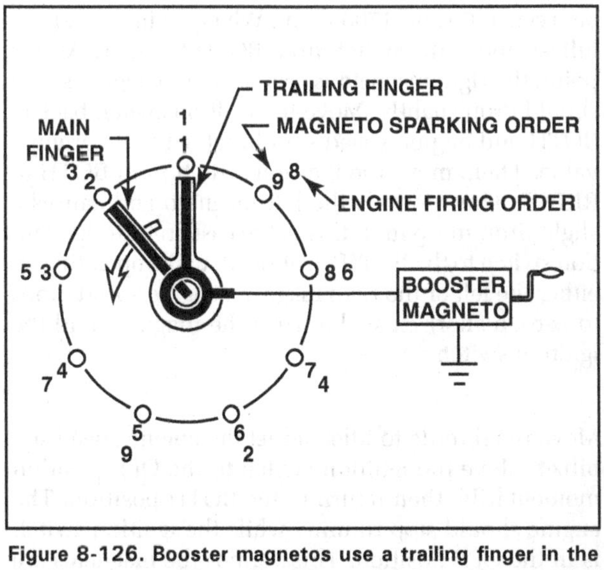


Figure 8-126. Booster magnetos use a trailing finger in the distributor rotor. The trailing finger delivers a hot, retarded spark to each cylinder to promote improved engine starting.

# IGNITION SWITCH

An ignition switch is typically located in the cockpit to provide the pilot direct control over the ignition system. The magneto ignition switch operates differently from most other switches in that when the switch is in the OFF position, switch contacts are closed and the circuit to ground is complete. Conversely, when the ignition switch is in the ON position, switch contacts are open and the circuit is open.

Figure 8-125. The typical vibrator unit consists of several solid state components sealed in a case and mounted to aircraft structure.

Because the ignition switch is wired in parallel with the breaker points, switching it to OFF shorts the breaker points and grounds the primary coil, preventing the magnetic field in the primary winding from collapsing and inducing current into the secondary winding. Conversely, when an ignition switch is in the ON position, the circuit can perform its function.

The wire that connects the switch and primary circuit is called the **P-lead**. The typical P-lead is a shielded copper wire to minimize radio interference.

The typical ignition switch controls both magnetos on an engine and has at least four positions: OFF, LEFT, RIGHT, and BOTH. Some ignition switches also have a START position. When the switch is in the OFF position, the P-leads on both magnetos are grounded. In the LEFT position, the switch operates the left magneto while grounding the right magneto; conversely, in the RIGHT position, the switch operates the right magneto while grounding the left magneto. When the switch is set to BOTH, the left and right magnetos operate simultaneously.

Any time you perform maintenance on an ignition system, you should perform an operational check of the switch. Operate the engine at normal temperatures between 1500 and 1700 r.p.m. When engine speed stabilizes, move the switch from BOTH to LEFT. At this point, the right magneto is grounded and engine speed should drop slightly. Move the ignition switch back to BOTH and engine speed should return to its original value. Then, move the ignition switch from BOTH to RIGHT. This grounds the left magneto and causes a slight drop in r.p.m. If this is the case, return the ignition switch to the BOTH position. If, while operating on either the left or the right magneto, engine speed drops to zero, a short exists between the magneto and the ignition switch.

Move the throttle to idle and let the engine speed stabilize. Move the ignition switch to the OFF position momentarily, then return to the BOTH position. The engine should stop running while the ignition switch is in the OFF position. This verifies the magnetos are grounded and that the switch operates properly. If the engine continues running with the switch OFF, a P-lead might be open or the switch could be faulty. Perform this check quickly with the engine running at the slowest possible speed. While the ignition switch is turned off, fuel is still being drawn into the cylinders. If excessive quantities of fuel accumulate before you move the switch back to BOTH, the engine could backfire.

## MAGNETO OVERHAUL

Magnetos typically operate reliably during the service life of an engine because the materials used to build the components are extremely durable.

Magnetos are typically sent to the manufacturer or a certified repair station for overhaul. However, an aviation maintenance technician can overhaul a magneto; the following discussion describes some general procedures for magneto overhaul.

### DISASSEMBLY AND CLEANING

Always follow the procedures outlined in the manufacturer's maintenance manual. Handle components carefully to avoid accidental damage. To retain magnetism in the rotating magnet, place **soft iron keepers** across the poles. A keeper links the poles of a magnet and provides a highly permeable path for the lines of flux to flow.

Clean magneto components only with approved methods and solvents. Most manufacturers specify the use of acetone for cleaning grease and carbon tracks from capacitors and coils. An unapproved cleaning solvent can damage the enamel insulation on the coil windings or the finish on the distributor block or rotor.

### INSPECTION

At overhaul, manufacturers typically require the replacement of several magneto components. Inspect these parts for evidence of a malfunction and excessive wear before you discard them. Typically replaced components include the breaker point assembly, capacitor, distributor block, rotor, and bearings. Much of the hardware is considered consumable and must be replaced at overhaul. For example, you always replace lock washers, gaskets, cotter pins, self-locking nuts or screws, and oil seals.

Inspect the remaining components according to the manufacturer's overhaul manual. Inspection often requires precision measuring tools and specialized electrical testing equipment.

#### MAGNETO CASE

At overhaul, carefully inspect the magneto case for cracks. If cracking exists, the case must be replaced. Areas prone to cracking include the mounting flange, bearing surfaces, areas around threaded holes, and near mating surfaces.

Inspect the bearing races and case interior for pitting or corrosion. You can often remove light corrosion but excessive corrosion requires replacement of the case.

To help prevent corrosion, most magneto cases have one or more drains and at least one vent. The drain prevents condensation moisture from pooling inside the magneto case and the vent permits corrosive gases (produced by normal arcing) to escape. Magneto ventilation contributes to magneto cooling and helps evaporate light condensation.

#### ROTATING MAGNET

Visually inspect the magnet and magneto shaft for physical damage and wear. Manufacturers often require you to perform a dimensional inspection of the magneto shaft to determine its serviceability.

Use a **magnetometer** (or **gauss meter**) to check the strength of a magnet. If the magnetic field is weak, it can be remagnetized with special equipment.

#### GEAR ASSEMBLIES AND BEARINGS

Clean the distributor drive gear assemblies and inspect for excessive wear, cracks, and broken teeth. Excessive backlash or play in a distributor drive gear is cause for rejection of the gear assembly.

In most cases, you must replace magneto shaft bearings and races when you overhaul a magneto. Some manufacturers do allow reuse of a bearing and its associated race. In this case, inspect and service the bearing as prescribed by the manufacturer.

### MAGNETO COIL

Carefully check the insulating material of a magneto coil for cracks and burn marks. Visually inspect the coil leads for general condition and security. Most manufacturers require a check for continuity and resistance in each winding. Use an ohmmeter or multimeter to perform these checks.

### BREAKER ASSEMBLY

The breaker point assembly is subjected to the most intense wear of any component in a magneto. Always install a new set of points during magneto overhaul. Before you discard the old points, inspect them for clues than can indicate problems with other ignition system components. For example, a set of points that are badly pitted may indicate that the capacitor is faulty.

### DISTRIBUTOR

When a manufacturer permits reuse of a distributor assembly, you must inspect the distributor block and rotor for cracks, carbon tracks, soot, and other evidence of arcing. If no evidence of cracking or arcing is present on the distributor block, test it for electrical shorts or leakage with a high-tension harness tester. Check for excessive play between the distributor rotor gear teeth by inserting a specific size drill between each of the gear teeth. If the drill fits snugly, the gear is within tolerances. [Figure 8-127]

On the distributor rotor, measure the distance between the rotor shaft and the end of the rotor finger. This provides an indirect indication of the gap between the rotor finger and the electrodes in the distributor block. If the distance between the rotor shaft and finger is too small, the gap between the rotor finger and distributor block is too large.

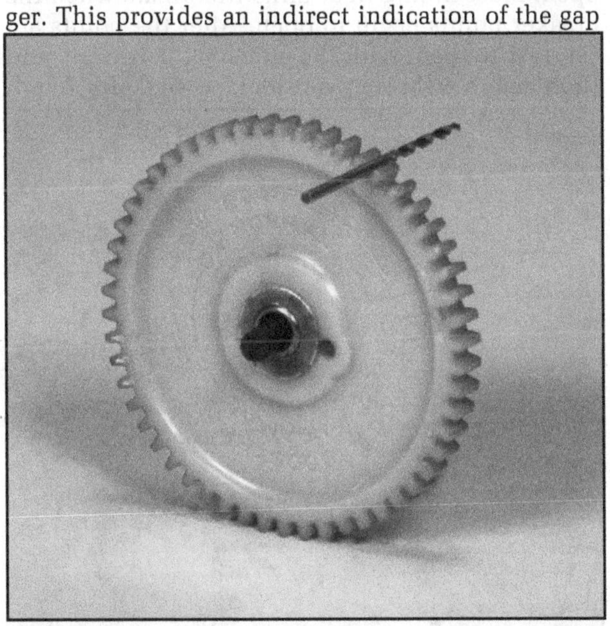

**Figure 8-127. To check for excessive wear between distributor gear teeth, insert a specific size drill bit between the teeth. If the bit fits snugly, the gear is within specifications.**

If replacement is not required and the distributor components are serviceable, you should prepare them for reassembly. Be careful to follow the manufacturer's instructions.

### CAM

The cam of a magneto is normally constructed from a solid piece of metal or a phenolic compound. If the cam is made of metal and the manufacturer permits it to be reused, perform a dimensional inspection. However, you must discard and replace a phenolic cam.

## ASSEMBLY AND INTERNAL TIMING

Reassemble the magneto in accordance with the manufacturer's instructions. In most cases, you begin by pressing new bearing races into the case halves and new bearings onto the magneto shaft. Sealed bearings do not usually require lubrication; otherwise, lubricate the bearings and races as prescribed.

After you install the bearings and races install the magneto coil. Magneto coils are held in place by a set of retaining clamps or a pair of wedges driven between the coil ends and the magneto case. Next, install the distributor block and rotor assembly, breaker points, and capacitor.

Setting internal timing is the final step in magneto reassembly. The procedures for doing so differ by manufacturer: Bendix and Slick magnetos are the two most common.

### BENDIX MAGNETOS

When aligning the drive and distributor gears in a Bendix magneto, place the rotating magnet in its neutral position. Rotate the magnet shaft by hand until you feel the magnet pull into alignment. When the magnet pulls into alignment, it might feel as though it has slipped into a detent. In this position (the magnet's *neutral* position), the magnet resists movement in either direction.

Align the timing marks on the distributor gear and drive gear and mesh them together. In most cases, the distributor gear is marked for use in both clockwise "CW" and counterclockwise "CCW" rotating magnetos. This gear has directional markings and a timing mark for each direction. Gears are usually marked with a "CW" and "CCW", or "RH" and "LH" indicating right hand and left hand rotation. A distributor gear can also be marked with a painted, chamfered tooth for visibility through an inspection port in the magneto case. [Figure 8-128]

With the gears properly aligned, carefully slide the magneto case halves together. Avoid using excessive pressure to prevent damage to the distributor gear. In addition, avoid turning the case halves to prevent damage to the carbon brush on the high-voltage tab protruding from the magneto coil. Ensure that the case halves are evenly mated before screwing them together.

After you assemble the case halves, complete the internal timing procedure by adjusting the points to open at the E-gap position. Starting with the magnet in the neutral position, verify that the distributor is ready to fire on the number 1 cylinder (the painted, chamfered tooth on the distributor gear will be visible through the inspection port). Attach a timing scale to the magneto housing and a pointer to the cam attaching screw on the magneto drive shaft. Set the pointer to zero, and then rotate the magneto shaft in its normal direction of rotation to the specified angle for E-gap. [Figure 8-129]

Lock the magnet in the E-gap position with one of two different tools. With one type, you thread the tool into the inspection port to lock the distributor gear and prevent rotation. The other type clamps directly to the magneto shaft and secures the magnet by applying friction against the case via a thumbscrew. [Figure 8-130]

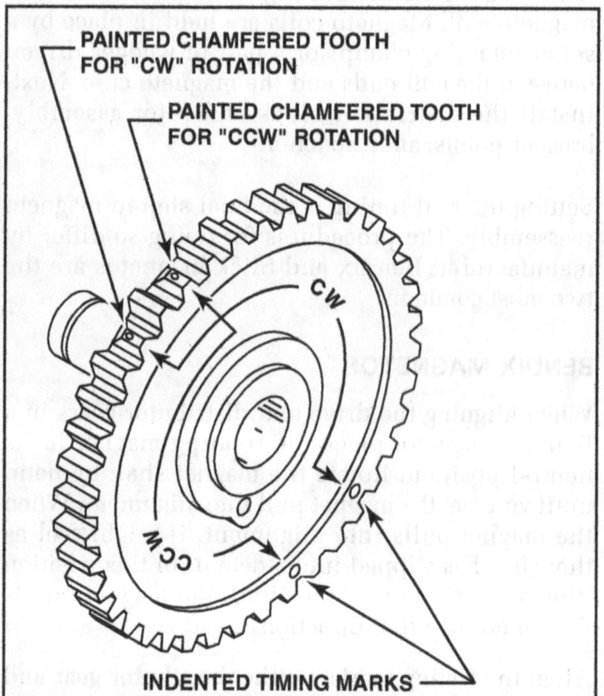


Figure 8-128. In most magnetos, the same distributor gear can be used for a clockwise rotating magneto or a counterclockwise rotating magneto. This distributor gear has an indented timing mark for alignment with the drive gear. The drive gear has alignment marks for use in either direction. A painted, chamfered tooth visible through an inspection port corresponds with the timing marks.

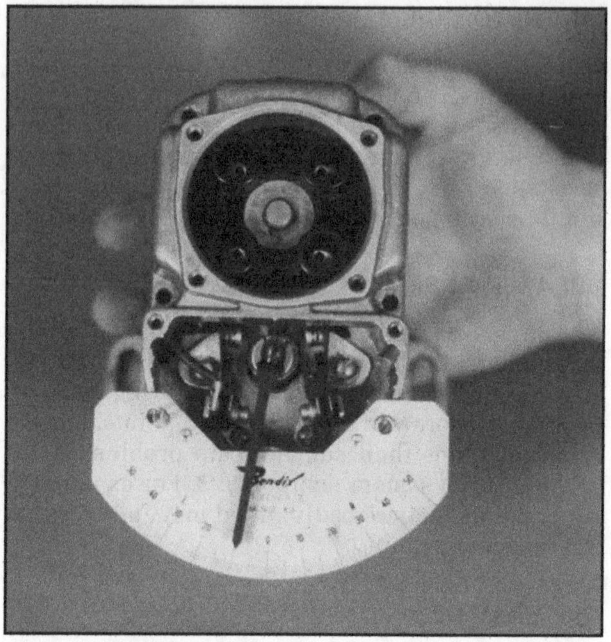

Figure 8-129. Adjusting the points in a Bendix magneto requires a Bendix timing kit with a pointer and a scale marked in degrees. These tools allow you to identify when the magnet is in its E-gap position.

With the magnet locked in position, connect a magneto timing light across the breaker points. Using the timing light to indicate the moment, adjust the position of the breaker points so they just begin to open. Most timing light units illuminate when the breaker points begin to open. After the points are set, secure them with the attaching hardware, and then remove the magnet-locking tool. By hand,

Figure 8-130. A Bendix magneto holding tool holds the magnet at the correct E-gap angle.

rotate the magnet backwards to the neutral position (the indicator needle should read zero). Now, slowly rotate the magnet forward to the E-gap angle. The points should begin to open (as indicated by the timing light) just as the pointer reaches the E-gap angle. If this does not occur, repeat the procedure to readjust the points.

In some Bendix magnetos, a timing (or index) mark is cast in the case and a second mark is stamped on the cam. When the timing marks on the case and cam align, the magnet is in the E-gap position.

On magnetos equipped with retard points, these must be adjusted to open after the main points. The exact number of degrees that the points are retarded is in the manufacturer's manual but might also be stamped on the case. To set the retard points with the indicator needle, you must add the degrees of retard to the specified E-gap angle. For example, if the main breaker points open at 10 degrees, and the retard is supposed to be at 35 degrees, then the magnet must be rotated until the timing needle indicates 45 degrees. With the timing needle indicating 45 degrees, lock the magnet with a holding tool to adjust the retard points so they just begin to open.

After you adjust the points, rotate the magneto drive shaft to position the cam in its highest position (where the points are spread to the widest gap). Use a thickness gauge to measure the gap and compare it with the clearance specified in the maintenance manual. If the gap is outside of specified limits, readjust the points and recheck the timing with the timing light.

## SLICK MAGNETOS

The primary difference in the internal timing procedure of a typical Slick magneto from that of a Bendix magneto is that you must adjust and set the points before you join the case halves. The magnet is locked in its E-gap position with a timing pin or a special E-gap gauge. The procedure for setting the points is similar to that for Bendix magnetos. [Figure 8-131]

When joining the case halves, align the timing marks on the drive and distributor gears and gently slide the case halves together. As with Bendix magnetos, be careful joining the case halves together to prevent damage to the distributor rotor.

## BENCH TESTING

After a magneto is reassembled and internally timed, you must bench test it. This procedure requires a magneto test stand. Several types of magneto test stands are available, but they typically include a variable-speed drive motor, a tachometer, and a spark rack.

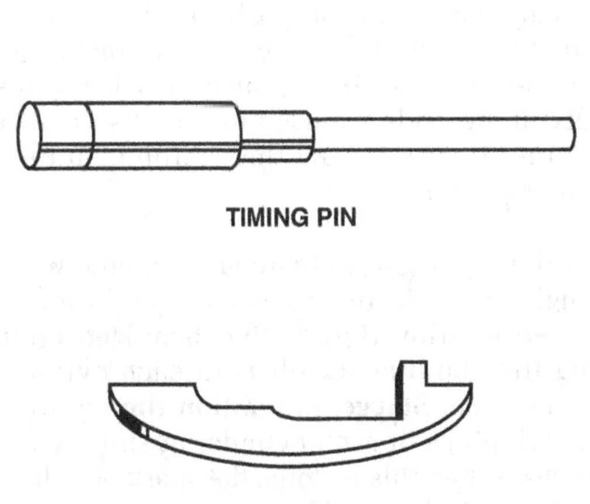


**Figure 8-131. To adjust the breaker points on a Slick magneto, set the magnet to the E-gap position with a special E-gap tool or a timing pin.**

To test a magneto, mount the magneto on the stand. Set the proper gap for the points on the spark rack as specified in the overhaul manual. The gap on the spark rack will be greater than the gap between spark plug electrodes; a spark will jump farther in free air than in a pressurized cylinder. However, if the gap is too wide, excessive voltage can build in the magneto's secondary circuit and sparks may discharge internally. If this occurs, the magneto coil or distributor might become damaged.

Connect the high-tension leads between the magneto and the spark rack. Because the motors on most test stands can drive a magneto in either direction, you should verify the direction of rotation before engaging the motor. Slowly increase the speed of the motor until the magneto reaches operating speed. As the magneto approaches its coming-in speed, you should begin to see sparks on the spark rack. If the actual coming-in speed is higher than the specified speed, stop the test and identify the cause of the discrepancy. Possible causes include improper internal timing, a weak capacitor, or a weak magnet.

In addition to verifying the operation of a magneto, you can also check the strength of the rotating magnet. Hold the breaker points open and check the output of the primary coil with an AC ammeter as the magneto rotates at a specified speed. Compare the readings with values specified in the overhaul manual. After running the magneto at its maximum design speed and checking its performance, slowly decrease speed until the unit stops.

## MAGNETO-TO-ENGINE TIMING

If a magneto performs properly on a test stand, you can install it on an engine. During installation, magneto-to-engine timing must be set. Because a variety of methods are used to establish magneto-to-engine timing, follow the engine manufacturer's instructions.

When timing magnetos to an engine, note whether the engine manufacturer specifies synchronized or staggered ignition timing. **Synchronized ignition timing** fires both spark plugs in each cylinder at the same time. **Staggered ignition timing** fires the two spark plugs in each cylinder at slightly different times. When this is done, the spark plug located nearest a cylinder's exhaust port is typically fired first. In some engines, because the fuel/air mixture near the exhaust port is diluted by exhaust gases, it burns more slowly than the mixture in the rest of the cylinder. To compensate for this, the mixture in this area is ignited slightly before the mixture in the rest of the cylinder.

Flange- and base-mounted magnetos are timed with different procedures. Because flange-mounted magnetos are more common, the following discussion describes magneto-to-engine timing with this type of magneto.

### FLANGE -MOUNTED MAGNETO

Before you install a magneto on an engine, position the crankshaft with the number 1 piston in the firing position. Ignition typically occurs on the compression stroke between 15 and 30 degrees before top dead center. The specific position for an engine is indicated on the engine data tag, engine type certificate data sheet, and engine maintenance manual. To identify this position, remove the top spark plug from each cylinder. Turn the propeller in the normal direction of rotation until the number 1 piston is on its compression stroke. With your finger placed above the number 1 spark plug hole, you will feel air flow past your finger when the piston is on the compression stroke. Continue rotating the propeller until the number 1 piston reaches top dead center between its compression and power strokes.

To accurately identify piston position, use a timing plug and a propeller protractor. With a piston plug threaded into cylinder number 1, you can accurately calculate the piston position after measuring degrees of rotation between where the piston contacts the plug when rotating the propeller forward and backward.

An alternate, but accurate, method to indicate number 1 piston position is the Time-Rite™ indicator. This instrument mounts to the cylinder and measures piston movement. After it is calibrated, it indicates the location of a piston, in number of degrees, from top dead center. [Figure 8-132]

On some engines, timing reference marks are stamped on engine parts. On Lycoming engines, these marks are typically on the front side of the flywheel. On Teledyne Continental Motors engines, the reference marks are on the propeller mounting flange or on an internal gear. The exact location of these marks is specified in the engine maintenance manual. These marks are best used for reference only. Before using these marks, you should confirm their accuracy with a timing plug and propeller protractor.

After you identify top dead center (TDC), rotate the propeller opposite its normal direction of rotation until passing a few degrees before the ignition point. Rotate the propeller in its normal direction to the firing position. Moving the piston backward beyond the ignition timing mark and then forward to the firing position ensures that you have compensated for any backlash in the gear train.

With the engine positioned to fire cylinder number 1 and internal magneto timing set, you are now ready to install the magnetos. When installing a magneto with an impulse coupling, be sure the impulse coupling is disengaged before mounting the magneto to the engine. Some magnetos use a rubber, anti-vibration coupling between the accessory drive gear and the magneto. As you slip the magneto drive gear into the accessory case, you might have to rotate the magneto somewhat to get the accessory gear and magneto

**Figure 8-132. You can accurately measure piston position within a cylinder with a Time-Rite indicator**

drive gear to mesh. If the two gears do not mesh right away, do not try to force the magneto into the accessory case. [Figure 8-133]

With the magneto in place, insert the mounting hardware and tighten it enough to support the magneto but loose enough that you are able to rotate the magneto. After you install the magneto, remove the magneto locking device. Forgetting to do so can result in substantial damage when the propeller is moved.

Attach the timing light to each magneto, and then rotate each magneto until its respective light first illuminates. At that point, tighten the magneto mounting bolts. If the propeller was not moved during magneto installation, the magneto should be timed correctly. Always verify magneto-to-engine timing by rotating the propeller opposite the direction of normal rotation until both timing lights are extinguished. Then, rotate the propeller forward in its normal direction until the timing lights illuminate. Verify that the lights illuminate within the tolerances required by the engine manufacturer.

## BASE-MOUNT MAGNETOS

Base-mounted magnetos are typically found on radial engines and are connected to the engine accessory drive with a vernier coupling. A vernier coupling is a special coupling with a slotted rubber disk sandwiched between two gears with different numbers of teeth. Adjust magneto-to-engine timing by disconnecting the coupling and rotating the rubber disk the necessary number of slots. The rubber disk is slotted to fit between the two gears in an almost infinite number of positions.

## OPERATIONAL CHECK

After reinstalling a magneto on an engine, reinstall the P-leads and the ignition harness before performing an operational check. However, before the operational check, verify that you have correctly hooked up the P-leads and installed properly all of the spark plug leads. When installing the spark plug leads, be aware that the numbers on the distributor represent the firing order of the magneto, not the engine cylinders. Therefore, match the firing order of the magneto to the firing order of the engine. For example, if a four-cylinder engine has a firing order of 1-3-2-4, you must attach the ignition lead for cylinder number 1 to distributor electrode number 1. The ignition lead for cylinder number 3 must be attached to distributor electrode number 2. The ignition lead for cylinder number 2 plug attaches to distributor electrode number 3 and the ignition lead for cylinder 4 plug attaches to distributor electrode number 4.

After you have installed the ignition system completely, proceed with the operational check. Always start the engine using the manufacturer's normal starting procedures. When the engine starts and the engine speed stabilizes at idle, look at the tachometer and listen to the engine for indications of smooth operation. If engine operation is normal, advance the throttle to increase engine speed as specified in the checklist. After engine speed stabilizes, turn the magneto switch from BOTH to LEFT and let the engine speed stabilize. Note the drop in engine r.p.m., and then turn the magneto switch back to BOTH. The engine speed should return to its earlier setting. Then, turn the magneto switch from BOTH

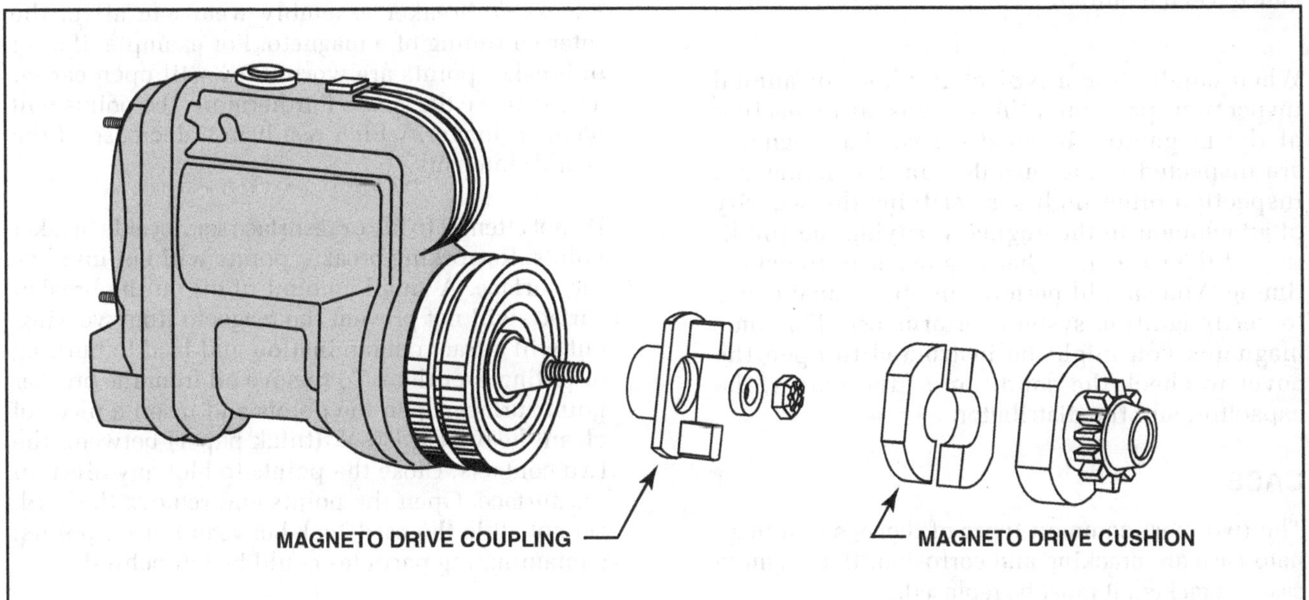


**Figure 8-133. Some magnetos are connected to the engine with an anti-vibration coupling. The engine drives the magneto through a rubber cushion housed by a steel retainer attached to the magneto drive gear. The cushion reduces the amount of vibration transferred to the magneto.**

to RIGHT and let the engine speed stabilize. Note the drop in engine r.p.m., and then return the magneto switch to BOTH. The proper operation of magnetos will result in a slight drop in engine speed (25 to 100 r.p.m) when the ignition switch is in either the RIGHT or LEFT positions.

If an excessive drop in engine speed occurs while operating on the left or right magneto, or, if the difference between the drops in r.p.m. exceeds allowable limits (50 r.p.m.); troubleshoot the ignition system. If a rapid drop in speed occurs when switching to a single magneto, faulty or fouled spark plugs are a likely cause. On the other hand, a slow drop in engine speed more likely indicates incorrect ignition timing.

To complete the operational check, return the engine to idle speed and let it stabilize. Momentarily turn the magneto switch to the OFF position and then back to the BOTH position. The engine should stop operating while the ignition switch is in the OFF position. This verifies that the magnetos are grounded and that the ignition switch is operating properly.

## MAGNETO MAINTENANCE

Maintenance to magnetos is somewhat limited. Often the only maintenance you may perform is an adjustment of magneto-to-engine timing. On some engines, you may also be able to perform more detailed inspections and some corrective maintenance when required.

When conducting a typical 100-hour or annual inspection, perform a through visual inspection of the magnetos. In most cases, the magnetos are inspected while installed on the engine. An inspection often includes verifying the security of attachment to the engine, verifying the condition of the case, and checking magneto-to-engine timing. You should perform an operational check to verify ignition system performance. For some magnetos you might be instructed to open the cover to check the condition of the points, the capacitor, and the distributor.

### CASE

The two most common types of damage to a magneto case are cracking and corrosion. If a magneto case is cracked, it must be replaced.

Although not as common as cracking, magnetos exposed to a salt-air environment can corrode. This is especially true for magneto cases made from a magnesium alloy. Minor corrosion can typically be removed and the case painted to prevent further corrosion. However, if corrosion with severe pitting occurs, you should replace the magneto case.

Clogged vents in a magneto case or a plugged orifice in a pressurized magneto case can also lead to corrosion because trapped moisture and unvented gases from arcing create a corrosive atmosphere. Unvented, nitric acid in the magneto will cause corrosion. Verify that any vents and drains are open or, for a pressurized magneto, that the pressurization orifice is not plugged.

### BREAKER ASSEMBLY

When a magneto's breaker assembly is accessible, it should be inspected. To access the points, you muse disconnect the P-lead. When the P-lead is disconnected, the magneto is on regardless of the ignition switch position; inadvertent movement of the propeller could start the engine.

The points of a new breaker assembly have a smooth, flat surface with a dull gray frosted appearance. After a few hours of operation, the point surfaces appear because of from metal transfer between the two points. Some transfer of material is normal; however, pitted or coarse-grained points indicate excessive transfer and you must replace the points. Severe pitting is apparent by a substantial protrusion on one contact with a corresponding pit on the other contact. [Figure 8-134]

Excessive breaker assembly wear can affect the internal timing of a magneto. For example, if a set of breaker points are worn, they will open earlier and advance the spark. Furthermore, the points will be open longer, which result in a decrease of the spark's intensity.

Do not attempt to file or resurface serviceable breaker points. Reworking breaker points will not improve the surface. A small amount of oil on the breaker surface will not prevent the magneto from working, but will attract contamination and lead to burning or pitting over time. To remove oil from the breaker point surface, open the points and insert a piece of clean, heavy cardstock (thick paper) between the two contacts. Close the points to blot any oil from the surface. Open the points and remove the card. Do not slide the cardstock between closed points; contaminating particles could be left behind.

After inspecting the surface of the breaker points, you should check the spring tension exerted on the points. Attach a small spring scale to the movable arm of the breaker assembly and carefully pull

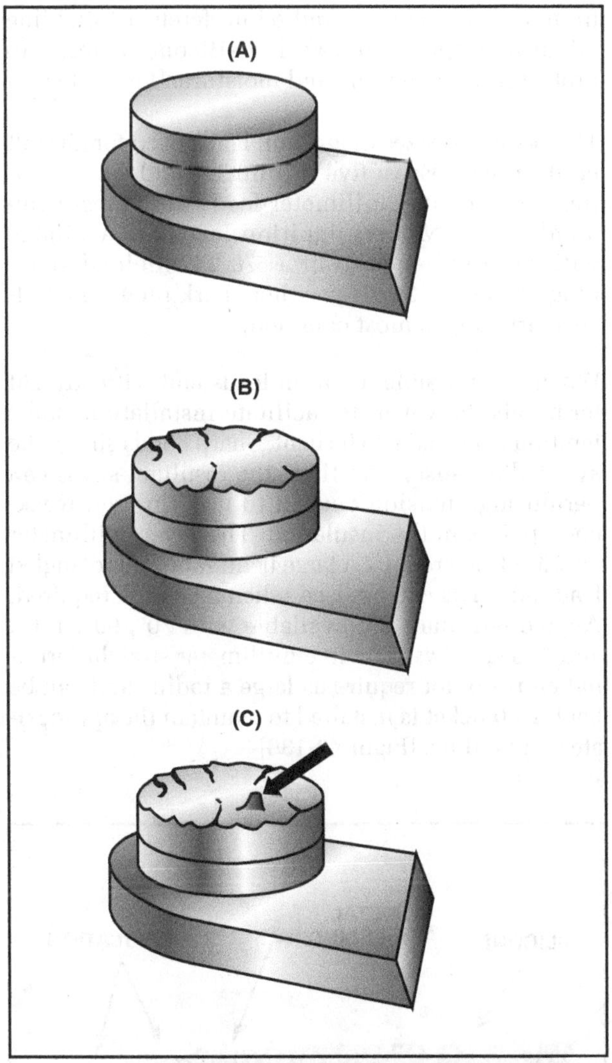


**Figure 8-134. (A) A new set of points have a smooth and frosty appearance. (B) After a few hours of operation, metal begins to transfer between the points, leaving a slightly wavy appearance. (C) A mound extending above the surrounding surface on a contact indicates excessive wear requiring breaker assembly replacement.**

the contact points apart. Do not open the points more than one-sixteenth of an inch or damage to the spring can occur. If spring tension readings are below acceptable levels, replace the points to prevent point float (or bounce) at high speeds—a condition that reduces spark energy.

Visually inspect the breaker cam for pitting or distortion and perform a dimensional inspection to check for wear. The cam surface must be smooth and within limits or it must be replaced. Excessive wear could be a result of a dry lubrication pad on the breaker assembly. If a cam is excessively worn, the points will open late and the spark will be retarded. Because a worn cam holds the points open for a shorter time, the intensity of the spark decreases.

## CAPACITOR

Excessive breaker point wear is typically caused by a defective capacitor. Check the condition of the capacitor with a capacitance test device (or **condenser tester**). These testers use AC voltage to check capacity and DC voltage to check for electrical leakage. If the capacitance value of a capacitor becomes too low, the breaker points are likely to become burned and pitted.

## DISTRIBUTOR

Inspect the distributor block and rotor for cracks, carbon tracks, soot, and other signs of arcing. A cracked distributor block or rotor provides a low resistance path to ground for secondary voltage, so you must a component that has even a small crack.

## SEALS

The presence of engine oil in a magneto generally indicates failure of an oil seal. Because oil is conductive, any time that you find oil in a magneto, you should remove the magneto from the engine, disassemble, clean, and inspect it.

## TIMING

As part of a 100-hour and annual inspection, you must check magneto-to-engine timing. To do this, attach a timing light to each magneto P-lead. In some installations, you need to remove the P-lead from the magneto and insert a special tool to open the ground circuit. For other magnetos you might be able to simply move the ignition switch to the ON or BOTH position with the primary lead still attached. Before opening the ground circuit, remove all of the ignition leads from the spark plugs to prevent inadvertent spark plug firing when the propeller is moved.

With the timing light attached to both magnetos, rotate the crankshaft until the number 1 piston is in the firing position. Then, rotate the propeller opposite the direction of normal rotation until the timing lights indicate the points are closed. *Bear in mind that for some timing lights, closed points might be indicated by the lights going out, while in others closed points are indicated by the lights coming on.* After the points close, rotate the propeller a few degrees further before reversing direction to slowly move the propeller in its normal direction of rotation. Stop moving the crankshaft the moment that the timing light indicates that the points have opened. Note the position that the points open for each magneto and compare it with engine manufacturer's requirements. Most engines are timed to fire both magnetos simultaneously, although some have slightly staggered timing.

Be aware that when you time magnetos with impulse couplings, you will likely need to rotate the propeller past the normal firing position to allow the impulse coupling to disengage. If the impulse coupling is engaged, you cannot accurately adjust magneto-to-engine timing. You should hear a distinct snap when the coupling releases. When adjusting magnetos equipped with retard breaker points, be sure that you connect the timing light to the primary points and not to the retard breaker.

If a magneto performs unsatisfactorily during an operational check, but the magneto-to-engine timing is correct, you might have to adjust the magneto's internal timing. Internal timing can be adjusted only by removing the magneto from the engine. After removal, adjust the internal timing using the manufacturer's procedures. Any time that you remove the breaker assembly in a magneto for cleaning or replacement, you must readjust the internal timing. Furthermore, any time that you adjust internal magneto timing, you must reset magneto-to-engine timing.

Cylinder head temperature (CHT) gauges and exhaust gas temperature (EGT) gauges can be used as indirect indicators of ignition system efficiency. Along with the fuel/air mixture ratio, ignition timing affects the amount of heat generated during combustion. Digital CHT and EGT systems that monitor the temperature of each cylinder are particularly useful when diagnosing ignition system faults related to a single cylinder. For example, if one spark plug in a cylinder is not firing, combustion will be incomplete and the cylinder will not reach the same operating temperature as the others. Chapter 14B of this book contains a more in-depth discussion of troubleshooting with a digital CHT and EGT system.

## IGNITION HARNESS

For an ignition system to be efficient, the high-energy voltage produced by a magneto must be delivered to the spark plugs with minimal loss. A typical ignition harness consists of 4, 6, or 8 individual ignition leads. One end of each ignition lead attaches to a receptacle on a magneto distributor block while the other end attaches to a spark plug.

### CONSTRUCTION

The conductor in a modern spark plug lead is made of either stranded wire or a single coiled conductor. The conductor is typically encased in one or two layers of rubber (or silicone) insulation, covered by a braided metal shield. The insulation prevents current leakage while the shielding collects and grounds high-frequency electromagnetic waves emanating from the lead to reduce radio interference. Shielding might be impregnated with a silicone material to protect it from chaffing and moisture. [Figure 8-135]

There are two sizes of ignition leads used for aircraft ignition harnesses: five millimeter and seven millimeter. The five-millimeter lead is the most commonly used. Modern ignition leads are available with terminal ends to fit a 5/8-24 shielded spark plug or the 3/4-20 all-weather spark plug. The 3/4-20 spark plug is most common.

Whenever possible, ignition leads end with straight terminals; however, to facilitate installation, some ignition leads have to be bent. Sharp bends should be avoided because, over time, the resultant stress can permit high-tension current to leak through weakened points in the insulation. The seven-millimeter ignition leads require a large bend radius, and angled lead terminals can be used when a bend is required. Angled terminals are available with 70°, 90°, 110°, and 135° elbows. The five-millimeter straight terminal ends do not require as large a radius and can be bent if a bracket is installed to maintain the appropriate bend radius. [Figure 8-136]

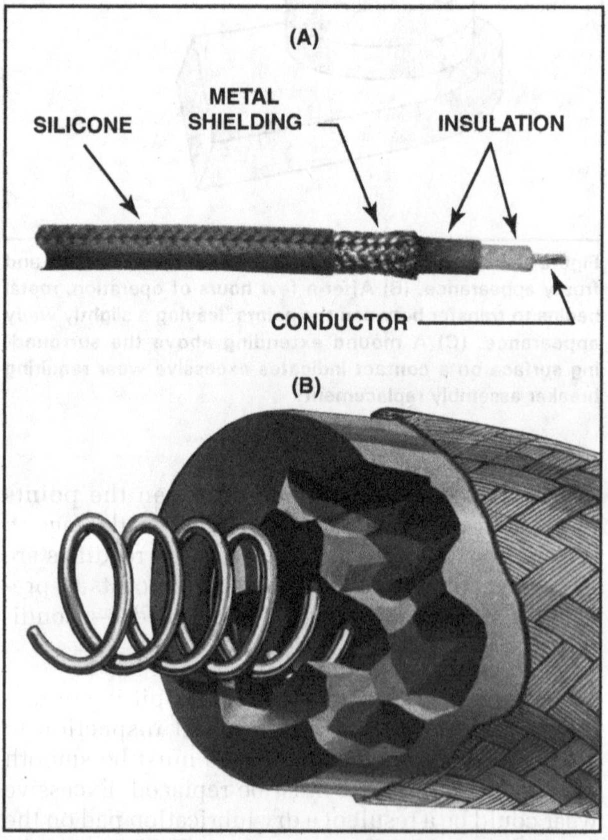


**Figure 8-135. (A) A typical ignition lead consists of a center conductor, one or more layers of insulation, and a silicone-impregnated layer of metal shielding. (B) Instead of using stranded wire, some ignition leads use a single wire shaped in a continuous spiral.**

The terminal ends used on modern ignition leads are a silicone rubber nose and coiled wire that fit inside the body of a spark plug. This type of terminal is referred to as "all-weather" because the silicone forms a water-tight seal at the top of the spark plug. These terminals are crimped onto an ignition lead and the coiled wire screws over the end of the terminal so they are repairable if damage occurs. [Figure 8-137]

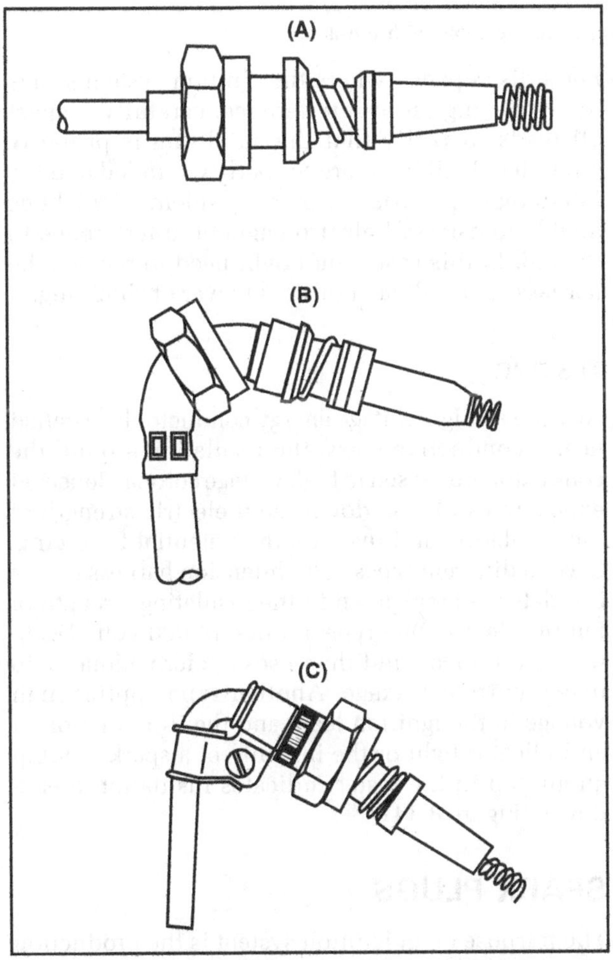


**Figure 8-136. (A) Ignition wiring is normally terminated with straight terminals. (B) Some installations require bent leads for access, and angled terminals are available. (C) In some situations, a bracket may be used to support the bend in a lead with a straight terminal.**

Older aircraft used terminals designed with a phenolic or ceramic insulator tube (often referred to as a cigarette). This type of terminal contains a coiled spring extending beyond the end of the insulator tube to provide positive electrical contact between the lead and spark plug. [Figure 8-138]

Like the spark plug end, the magneto ends of modern ignitions lead also use crimp-on-type connectors. However, different types of magnetos use different types of connectors. [Figure 8-139]

In older aircraft, some ignition leads were attached to the distributor block with cable-piercing screws. With this type of installation, the ignition lead conductor is cut even with the insulation. The lead is inserted into the distributor block where it is held in place with a cable-piercing screw; the screw forms threads in the conductor.

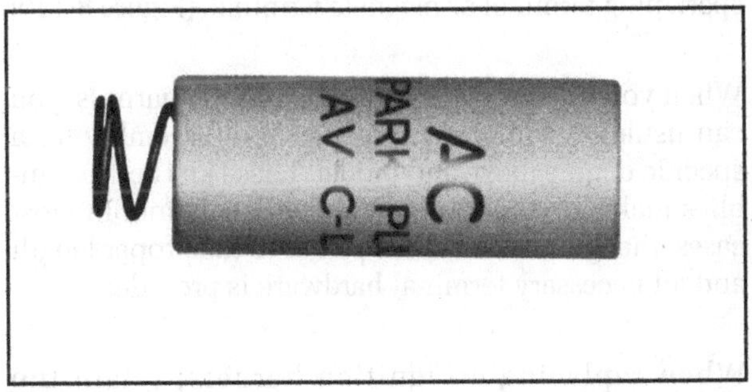

**Figure 8-138. Older-style ignition harnesses use a phenolic or ceramic insulator tube in the ignition lead terminal.**

When installing terminals on an ignition lead, the braided shield must be securely attached to the terminal at both ends. If not, radio interference can occur whenever the engine is running. With crimped-on terminals, the shielding is grounded through the attachment nut.

## MAINTENANCE

Ignition harnesses typically operate trouble-free; however, at times, maintenance might be required. Typical maintenance consists of the repair or

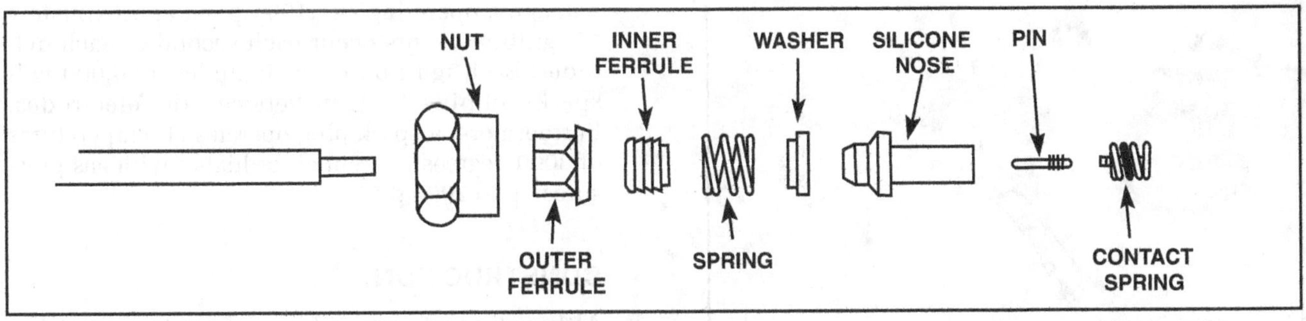


**Figure 8-137. On an all-weather terminal, the terminal is crimped onto an ignition lead. The ignition shielding is held tightly between the inner and outer ferrule and provides a durable ground connection.**

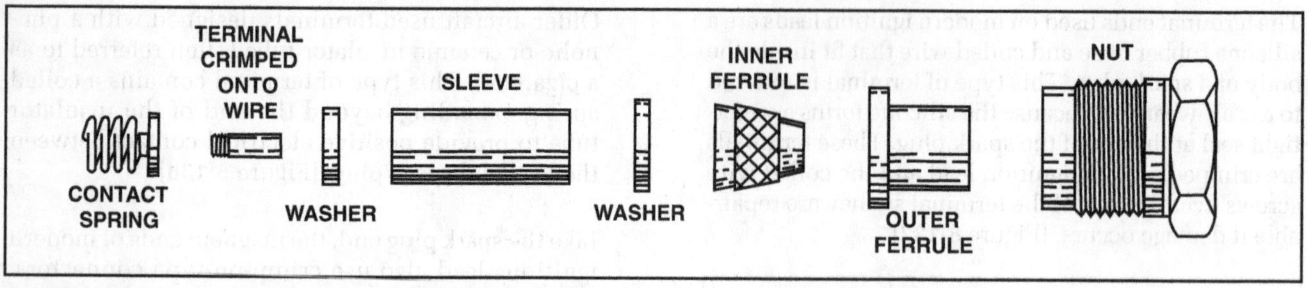


**Figure 8-139. The magneto end terminal of a typical ignition lead is crimped to the cable with ferrules.**

replacement of a terminal end or replacement of a chaffed lead. In most cases, you can replace a single damaged ignition lead without replacing the entire harness. When the manufacturer of an ignition harness supplies individual replacement components, they typically provide detailed replacement procedures. Use the approved methods and tools prescribed by the manufacturer to install a new lead on a spark plug terminal or magneto terminal. [Figure 8-140]

When you must replace an entire ignition harness, you can usually acquire a complete kit or assembly for a specific engine make and model. These kits and assemblies make for a relatively simple installation. In most cases, the ignition wires are precut to the proper length and all necessary terminal hardware is provided.

When replacing an ignition harness, retain the serviceable hardware and clamps used for routing the leads from the old harness. Pay close attention to wire markings that indicate the distributor terminal-to-spark plug destinations for each lead. A typical marking is "1T," which indicates the lead is intended for the top spark plug in cylinder number 1.

Install the new harness on the magneto and route the leads to their respective cylinders. Ensure that leads are routed around and away from hot exhaust components and that they not interfere with movement of the engine controls. Secure the harness with the clamps and hardware provided in the kit or the hardware from the old harness.

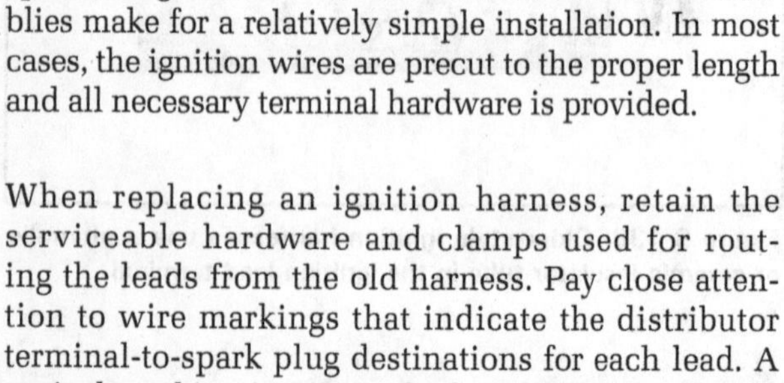


**Figure 8-140. Special terminal installation tools are required for an ignition harness repair.**

For a discrepancy where the ignition system seems to be causing radio interference, carefully inspect all leads to verify that the shielding is properly grounded. If all leads are properly grounded and the interference persists, the existing shielding might be unable to carry all electromagnetic interference to ground. In this case, you might need to replace the harness or install an additional layer of shielding.

### TESTING

Any time a high-voltage energy conductor is installed near a conductive mass, the insulation around the conductor is exposed to high voltage corona. Repeated exposure can break down the dielectric strength of the insulation and increase the potential for arcing. Several different types of high-tension harness testers can detect a breakdown in the insulating strength of ignition leads. One type applies 15,000 volts DC to the ignition lead and then uses a micro-ammeter to detect current leakage. Another type applies high voltage to the ignition lead, and the illumination of an indicator light or the inability of a spark to jump an air gap in the tester indicates insulation breakdown. [Figure 8-141]

## SPARK PLUGS

The purpose of an ignition system is the production of a spark to ignite the fuel/air mixture in a cylinder. The spark plugs transmit the high voltage current from the ignition harness into the combustion chamber. The construction and operation of a spark plug is simple, but the performance and reliability requirements are substantial. Remember that, in an engine operating at 2,100 r.p.m., approximately 17 ignition events occur each second in each cylinder. Each ignition event includes a 20,000-volt spark jumping the gap between the electrodes. Furthermore, a spark plug operates at temperatures of 3000 degrees Fahrenheit or higher with gas pressures up to 2000 p.s.i.

### CONSTRUCTION

Although most spark plugs appear to be similar, differences exist among different spark plug types. Because of this, engine manufacturers specify

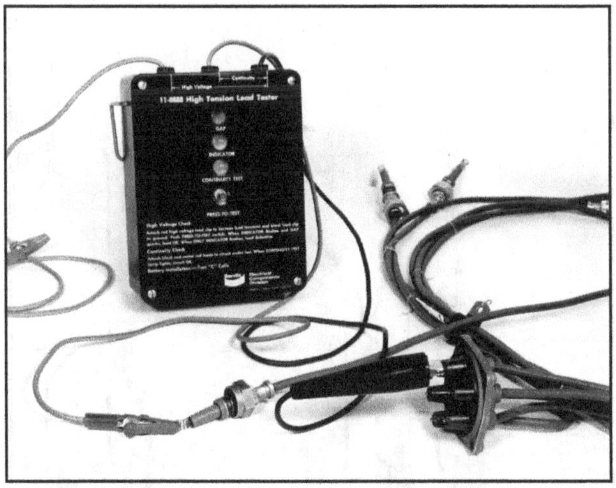

**Figure 8-141. Ignition harness testers can detect defects that cause intermittent ignition harness problems.**

the type of spark plugs that must be used in their engines. A typical spark plug consists of three major parts: a durable metal shell, a ceramic insulator, and an electrode assembly. [Figure 8-142]

The metal shell supports the internal components and provides an electrical ground path for the braided shielding of the ignition lead. All shielded spark plug shells are threaded at both ends. On the terminal end, the ignition lead to is attached to the spark plug. The threads on the opposite end enable the spark plug to be installed in a cylinder. To enable installation and removal, part of the metal shell is cast in a hexagonal shape to accommodate a socket wrench.

A ceramic insulator prevents the high-voltage current flowing through a plug from arcing to ground. In most cases, the insulator consists of two sections. One section insulates between the tip of the center electrode and the terminal contact. The other section overlaps with the first and extends toward the top of the spark plug barrel. Nickel gaskets between the spark plug shell and the insulator prevent the escape of high-pressure combustion gases from the cylinder assembly.

The electrode assembly consists of a terminal contact, resistor, glass seal, and inner and outer electrodes. The terminal contact is the point where the ignition lead contacts the spark plug. A small resistor is included to prevent capacitance afterfiring. **Capacitance afterfiring** is the undesirable process whereby electrical energy is induced into the ignition shielding during normal current flows through the ignition lead. Eventually the electrical potential stored in the shielding is released in a surge across the air gap. This increases the duration of the normal spark and accelerates wear of the electrodes. The resistor, typically 1,500 ohms, dissipates this energy.

The electrode materials vary depending on the style of electrode. On massive-electrode spark plugs, the outer or ground electrodes are typically made of a nickel alloy while the center electrode is nickel-clad copper. On fine-wire electrode spark plugs, the ground electrode is typically made from platinum or iridium while the center electrode is made of silver. [Figure 8-143]

An air gap separates the inner and outer electrodes on all spark plugs. The size of the air gap determines the amount of resistance the spark must overcome before it can jump the gap. If an air gap is not adjusted to the manufacturer's specifications; the intensity of the spark produced will be incorrect.

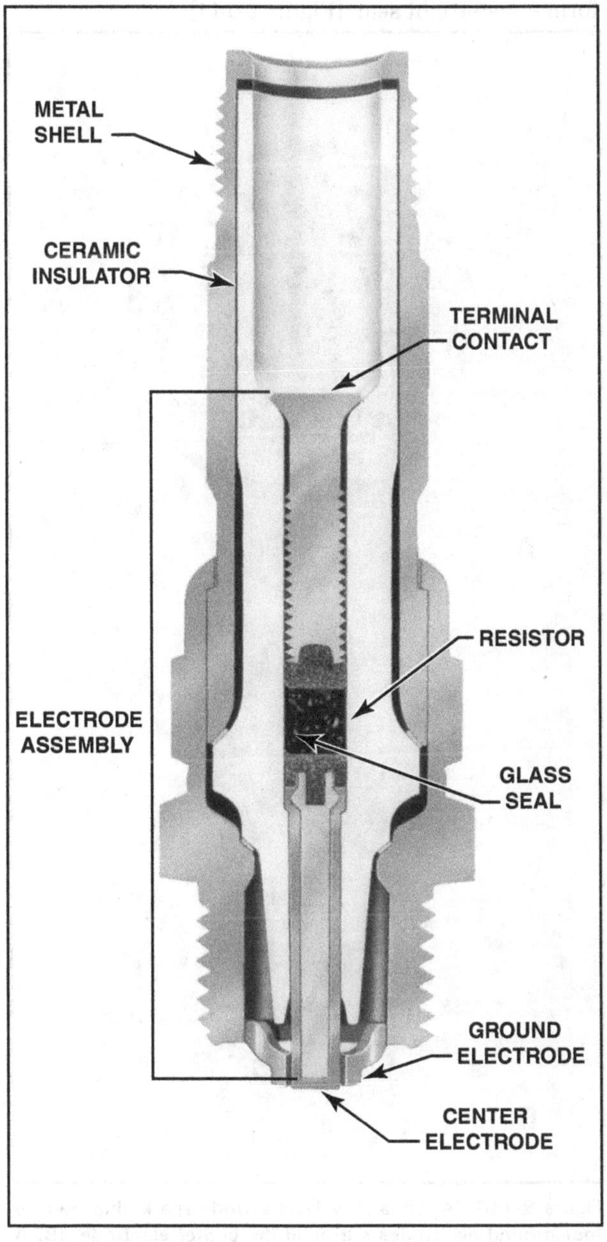


**Figure 8-142. The three basic components of a spark plug are the metal shell, a ceramic insulator, and an electrode assembly.**

## SPARK PLUG THREADS

One method for classifying spark plugs is by the size of the threads that screw into the cylinder assembly. In aviation, spark plug threads are either 14 or 18 millimeter. Nearly all modern aircraft engines use 18mm spark plugs.

The terminal end threads also come in two sizes: either 5/8 inch?24 thread or 3/4 inch?20 thread. Both sizes are in use; however, the 3/4 inch?20 thread is most common. The 3/4 inch?20 thread is referred to as an all-weather spark plug. In an all-weather spark plug, the ceramic insulator does not extend to the top of the plug shell. Instead, there is room to accommodate a silicone grommet on the spark plug lead to form a watertight seal. [Figure 8-144]

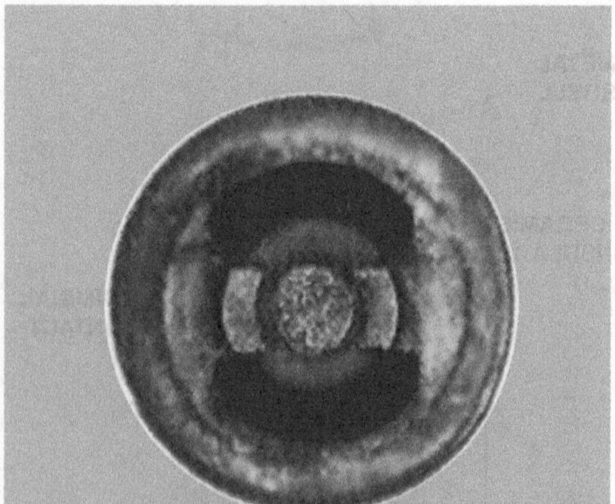


Figure 8-143. (A) On a massive-electrode spark plug, two to four ground electrodes surround the center electrode. (B) A fine-wire electrode spark plug has two square ground electrodes and one round center electrode.

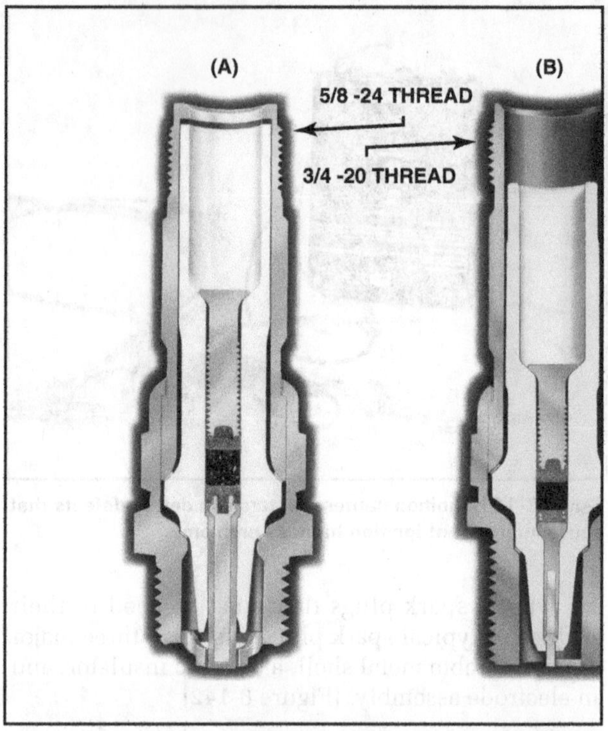


Figure 8-144. (A) The 5/8-24 thread is often used on older massive-electrode spark plugs. (B) The 3/4-20 thread is most often used with all-weather spark plugs. With all-weather spark plugs, the ceramic insulator is recessed in top of the shell with room for a resilient grommet on the ignition lead to form a watertight seal.

## SPARK PLUG REACH

The reach of a spark plug is defined as the linear distance from the shell gasket seat to the end of the shell threads, or shell skirt. Spark plugs are available with either long or short reach to account for the differences in cylinder head construction from engine to engine. When you install the recommended spark plug, the end of the threads should be flush with the inside wall of the cylinder head. If you install a spark plug with the wrong reach, the electrodes might extend into the combustion chamber or recess in the cylinder head. [Figure 8-145]

## HEAT RANGE

The ability of a spark plug to conduct heat from the tip to the cylinder head is referred to as its heat range classification. Spark plugs are generally classified as "hot," "normal," or "cold." Hot plugs dissipate less heat than cold plugs. [Figure 8-146]

Each engine manufacturer determines what type and heat range of spark plugs should be used in its engines. As a general rule, because a high-compression engine operates at higher temperatures, it uses cold spark plugs. Lower compression engines

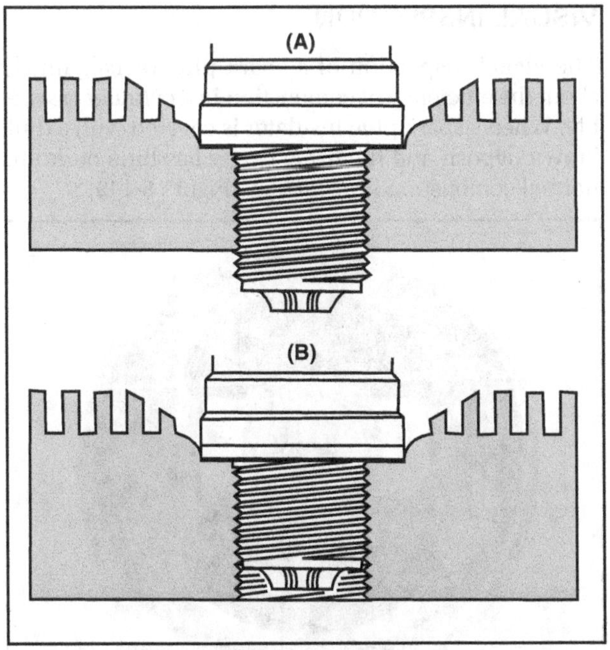


**Figure 8-145. (A) If a long reach plug is installed in a cylinder head requiring a short reach plug, the plug will extend into the cylinder head. This exposes the spark plug threads to the heat and corrosive gases produced during the combustion process. (B) If a short reach plug is installed in place of a long reach plug, the spark plug will be recessed in the cylinder head. This decreases combustion efficiency and exposes the threads in the cylinder head to carbon buildup.**

typically operate at relatively low temperatures and use hot spark plugs. If you install a hot spark plug in an engine that requires a cold spark plug, the hotter operating temperature of the plug could lead to preignition or engine run-on. Likewise, installing a cold spark plug in a cold-running engine could result in a plug fouled with unburned carbon and lead deposits.

Some circumstances call for installation of a spark plug that is not in the recommended heat range. For example, some small, horizontally opposed engines were originally designed to run on 80-octane avgas. However, when 100LL is burned, a hotter spark plug might be required. Because 100LL contains four to eight times more tetraethyl lead than 80-octane avgas, retaining the heat is useful to prevent lead fouling.

## SERVICING

Manufacturers recommend the removal of spark plugs for inspection and servicing at regular intervals. Removal, inspection, and cleaning of spark plugs is a 100-hour inspection item. If a spark plug is defective or becomes fouled, earlier service is necessary.

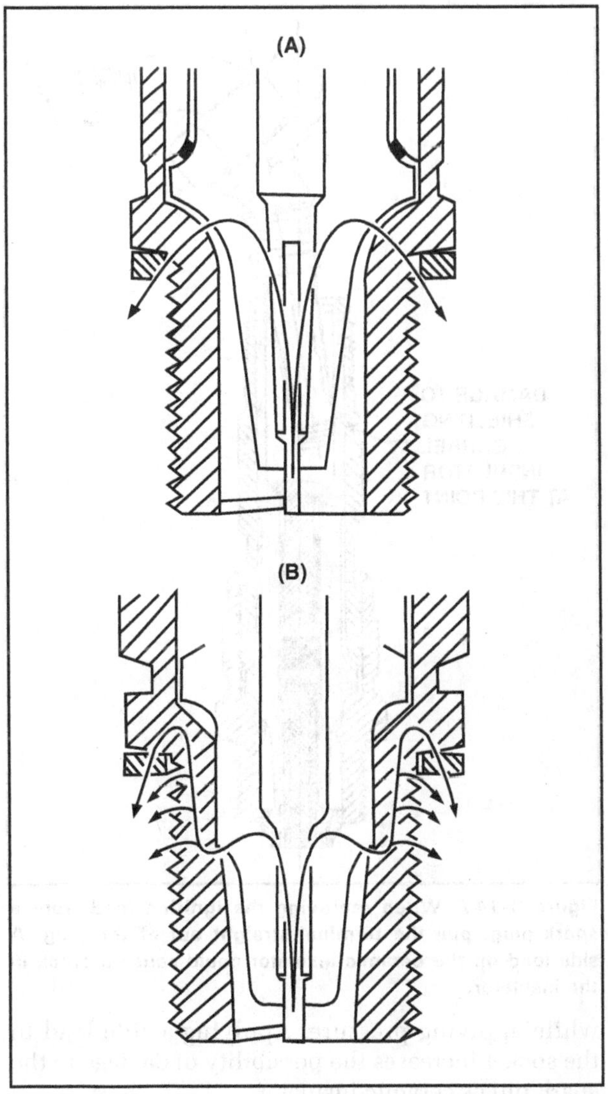


**Figure 8-146. (A) Hot spark plugs have long nose cores that provide relatively little contact area between the insulator and shell. The small amount of contact area slows the rate at which heat can be conducted away from the plug tip. (B) Cold plugs, on the other hand, have a shorter nose core that permits a large contact area for dissipating heat.**

## REMOVAL

Before you can remove a set of spark plugs, you must remove the terminal ends of the ignition leads. When removing an ignition lead, you should hold it with one hand (or an open-end wrench) and loosen the terminal nut with an open-end wrench. After the terminal nut is completely backed off, pull the terminal end straight out of the spark plug. [Figure 8-147]

After the ignition lead off, loosen the spark plug from the cylinder with a six-point deep-well socket. Several tool manufacturers make special sockets for removing aviation spark plugs. Place the socket squarely over the spark plug hex and keep it square

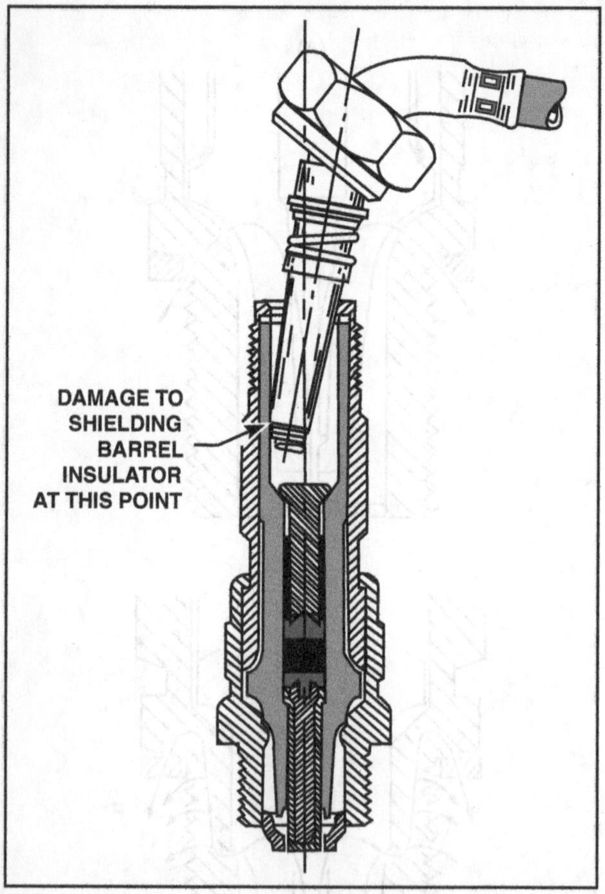


Figure 8-147. When removing the ignition lead from a spark plug, pull the terminal straight out of the plug. A side load on the ceramic insulator could cause a crack in the insulator.

while applying pressure. Applying a side load to the socket increases the possibility of damage to the spark plug's ceramic insulator.

After you remove a spark plug, place it in a tray that holds each plug securely, preventing it from rolling around or striking another plug. Additionally, the tray should identify the original position of each plug (cylinder number and position). [Figure 8-148]

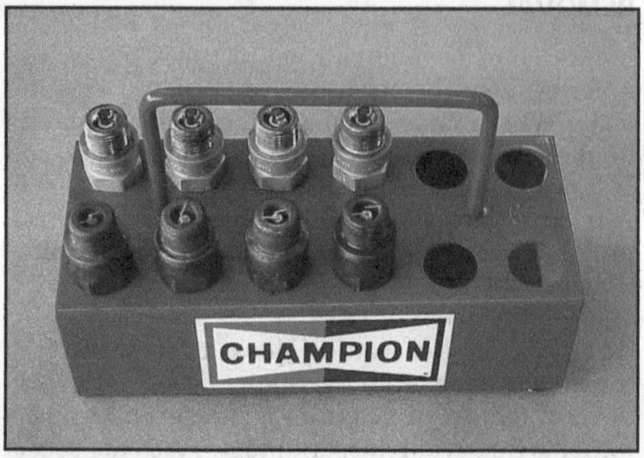


Figure 8-148. Spark plug trays provide a secure, organized place to store spark plugs when you remove them for service.

## VISUAL INSPECTION

The visual inspection of a spark plug reveals much about the efficiency of combustion in a cylinder assembly. When a spark plug insulator is covered with a dull brown deposit and the firing cavity has little buildup, normal combustion is occurring. [Figure 8-149]

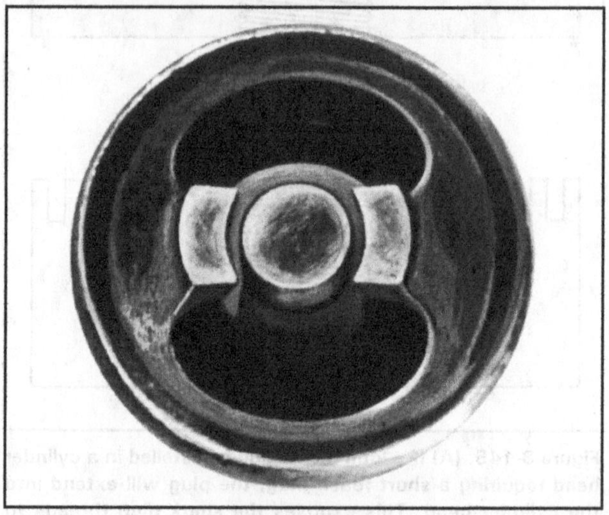

Figure 8-149. A light deposit of dull brown material on a spark plug insulator indicates normal combustion is occurring in the cylinder.

However, if the firing cavity is filled with hard, bead-like deposits, excessive lead fouling has occurred. In addition to cleaning the spark plug, you must investigate and correct the reason for the fouling. Typical causes of lead fouling include improper fuel vaporization, low cylinder head temperatures, or spark plugs with an improper heat range. If all spark plugs in an engine show signs of severe lead fouling, you might recommend installing spark plugs with a hotter heat range. [Figure 8-150]

Spark plugs covered with a soft, black, sooty deposit on all surfaces indicate carbon fouling. This condition could be caused by operation with an excessively rich mixture or by a leaking primer. Similar deposits in the exhaust stack also point to operation with an excessively rich mixture. [Figure 8-151]

Oil fouling also affects spark plugs. Oil fouling typically appears as a slippery, black coating on the electrodes. Oil fouling often indicates a serious condition that must be resolved; this could include broken or worn piston rings and worn valve guides. Severe oil fouling might require you to remove the engine from service until repairs are completed.

A hard glaze on an insulator nose can indicate that sand was ingested into the engine. If sand enters a combustion chamber, the silicates in the sand melt with the heat of combustion. As the molten silicates

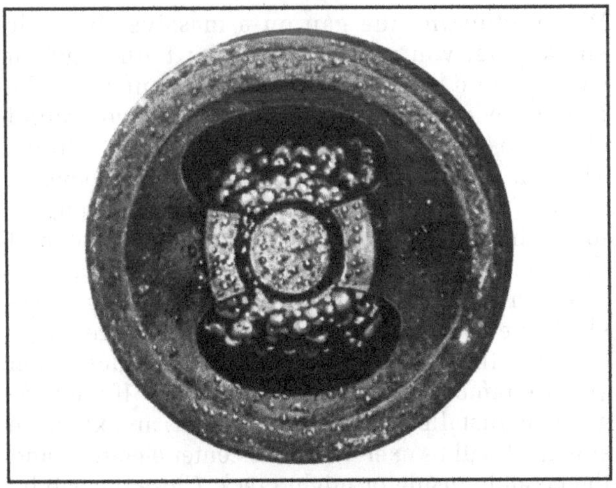

Figure 8-150. Excessive lead deposits appear as hard, bead-like deposits in the firing cavity of a spark plug.

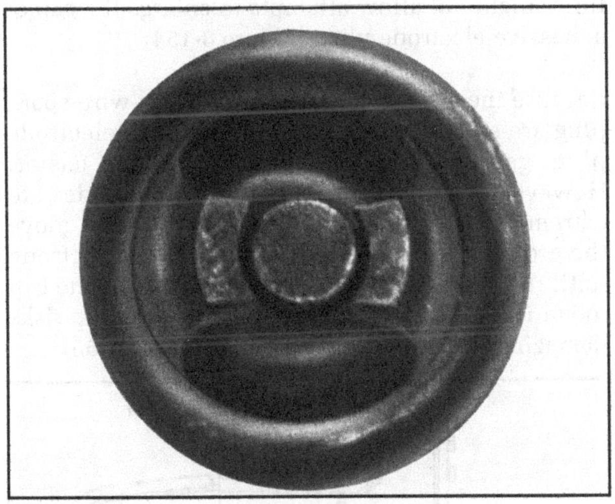

Figure 8-151. Soft, black, sooty deposits indicate severe carbon fouling often related to engine operation with an excessively rich mixture.

cool, they form a glass-like coating on the surfaces of the spark plug. This silicon glaze is nonconductive at low temperatures; however, at high temperatures the glaze becomes conductive and the spark plug may misfire. Sand ingestion typically occurs as the result of an induction system leak or a worn air filter.

When the electrodes on a spark plug are worn to approximately half their original size, the spark plug should be replaced. In some cases, excessive wear distorts the shape of both the center and ground electrodes. [Figure 8-152]

Abnormal wear on the electrodes of a spark plug can indicate fuel metering problems. For example, when the engine is operated with an excessively lean mixture, the increase in combustion temperatures can promote electrode wear. An induction air leak can cause a lean mixture in a carbureted engine while a partially clogged fuel nozzle can cause a lean mixture in a fuel-injected engine.

In addition to inspecting a spark plug for wear, you should examine both ends of the ceramic insulator for cracks. If any sign of cracking exists, you must discard and replace the spark plug. In addition, if you drop a spark plug you should automatically discard it as a safety precaution; the ceramic insulator might be cracked in an area that is not visible.

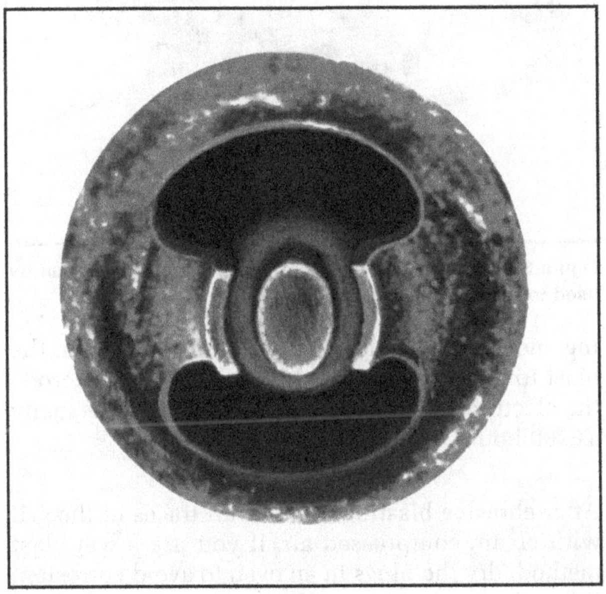

Figure 8-152. If either the center or ground electrodes are worn up to 50% or severely distorted, the spark plug should be replaced.

## CLEANING

Begin cleaning spark plugs by degreasing them with an approved safety solvent. This removes oil, grease, and other soft deposits from the interior cavities and exterior of a spark plug. Dry the spark plugs with compressed air.

Lead and carbon deposits are typically removed with a vibrating tool. When you use this type of tool, use the proper cutting blade and hold the spark plug directly over the blades. Otherwise, damage to the ceramic insulator and electrodes might occur. Use a slight back and forth motion over the vibrating blades to chip away the lead deposits. [Figure 8-153]

After removing the lead deposits, you can use an abrasive grit blasting cleaner unit to complete the cleaning. These units clean with either dry or wet media. Follow the manufacturer's instructions concerning the type of grit and air pressure settings. In most cases, a silica (sand) abrasive is not recommended because it can contribute to silica fouling.

When using a grit blasting cleaner, press the firing end of the spark plug into the proper size adapter hole. To help prevent excessive erosion while clean-

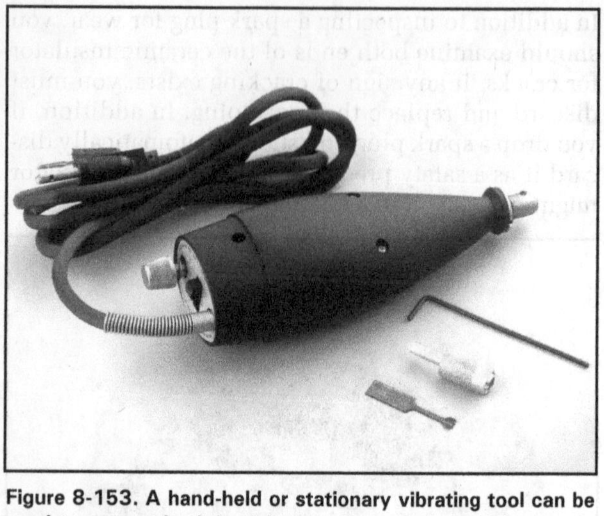

Figure 8-153. A hand-held or stationary vibrating tool can be used to remove lead deposits.

ing, move the plug in a circular motion and limit the blast to a few seconds. Otherwise, you could erode the electrodes and reduce operating life by as many as 300 hours.

After abrasive blasting, remove all traces of the grit with clean, compressed air. If you use a wet-blast method, dry the plugs in an oven to avoid corrosion. When the spark plugs are clean and dry, inspect them with a light and a magnifying glass. Verify that the insulator and electrodes are within serviceable limits and that all traces of the grit have been removed.

If necessary, clean the terminal end of a spark plug with the appropriate cleaning tool and approved cleaning compound. Then remove any remaining carbon or corrosion from the threads at both ends of the spark plug with a steel brush or a wire wheel with soft bristles.

## GAPPING

After a plug is inspected and determined to be serviceable, check and adjust the electrode gap as necessary. Use a round wire gauge to check the gap in a spark plug. In most cases, these gauges have two wires to measure both the minimum and maximum gap. For example, if a plug is supposed to have a gap of .016-inch, an appropriate wire gauge would have a .015-inch and a .019-inch wire. In this case, the smaller diameter wire must pass through the gap while the larger wire should be too big to pass through the gap.

If a gap is too large, the ground electrode can be forced inward. To do so, you must have the proper tools and follow the manufacturer's instructions closely. Improper gapping procedures increase the chance of damaging the spark plug or reducing its service life.

When adjusting the gap on a massive-electrode spark plug, you must ensure that both edges of each ground electrode are equidistant from the center electrode and that each of the two ground electrodes is equidistant from the center electrode. This can be accomplished only by using a special gapping tool. With most massive-electrode gapping tools, the spark plug is clamped into the tool, and the ground electrode is moved inward using a movable arm or adjusting ram. When you gap a massive-electrode spark plug, do not leave the wire gauge between the center and ground electrodes when you are removing the ground electrode. If the wire gauge is installed during adjustment, an excessive side load will be exerted on the center electrode and the ceramic insulator might crack. Close the gap by slowly moving the ground electrode, being careful to avoid closing the gap too much. The manufacturer might not allow attempts to enlarge the gap of a massive-electrode plug. [Figure 8-154]

Because the ground electrodes on a fine-wire spark plug are smaller than those of a massive-electrode plug, gapping a fine-wire spark plug is easier. However, the platinum and iridium electrodes are extremely brittle. Using a special gapping tool, move the ground electrodes toward the center electrode until the specified gap exists. Avoid closing the gap too much because an attempt to widen the gap risks damaging the ground electrodes. [Figure 8-155]

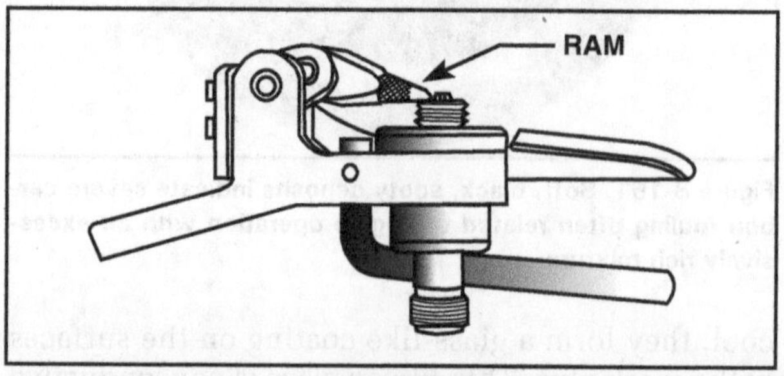


Figure 8-154. A special gapping tool is required for adjusting the gap of a massive-electrode spark plug.

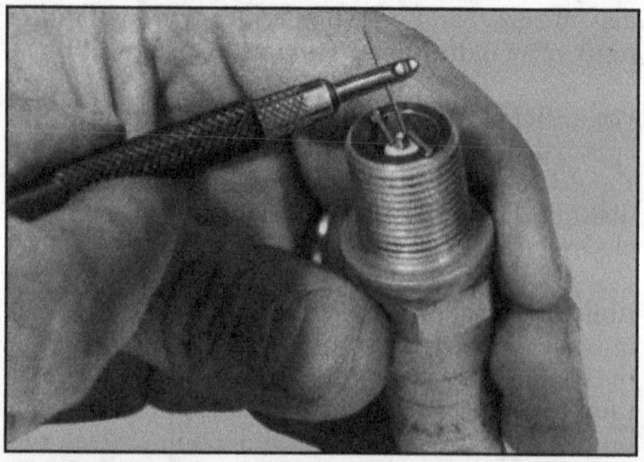

Figure 8-155. The gapping tool for a fine-wire spark plug allows adjustment of the ground electrodes with a minimal risk of damage.

## TESTING

After you have cleaned and gapped a spark plug, you should test fire it on special bench testing equipment. The testing unit pressurizes the firing end of a spark and provides the voltage necessary to fire the plug in rapid succession. A window enables you to inspect the quality of the sparks. [Figure 8-156]

## INSTALLATION

When you reinstall a set of spark plugs, you should always rotate their positions. Spark plug rotation promotes even electrode wear and extends service life. Every time the rotating magnet in a magneto passes the neutral position, the **polarity** of the current changes. As a result, the polarity of sparks produced by a magneto alternate. For any engine with an even number of cylinders, each spark plug fires with the same polarity every time. When the polarity of sparks on a spark plug does not change, one electrode loses metal relative to the other electrode. When a plug fires positively, the ground electrode wears more than the center electrode. Likewise, when a plug fires negatively, the center electrode wears more than the ground electrode. Spark plug rotation enables each plug to fire with opposite polarity for its next period in service. Rotation increases the service life of spark plugs by balancing electrode wear.

In addition to changing the firing polarity of a set of spark plugs, changing plug positions between top and bottom also extends spark plug life. This is because lead and other impurities produced during combustion tend to collect on the lower plugs, which causes increased wear. Changing positions helps equalize plug wear. [Figure 8-157]

**Figure 8-156. A combination spark plug cleaner and tester is widely used in maintenance shops.**

Before installing spark plugs, apply a small amount of antiseize compound to the shell threads. Antiseize compound of the correct type is typically available from the spark plug manufacturers. Apply the compound sparingly to the second thread from the firing end. Never apply the compound to the firing end, where it could run down over the electrodes. [Figure 8-158]

Most manufacturers recommend installing a new solid copper gasket whenever you reinstall a spark plug. Gaskets tend to work-harden over time and lose their ability to create a seal.

Some cylinder head temperature gauges use a gasket thermocouple pickup under one of the spark plugs. You should install a gasket thermocouple pickup on the hottest operating cylinder. In addition, do not install an additional gasket between the spark plug and cylinder head when using this type of pickup.

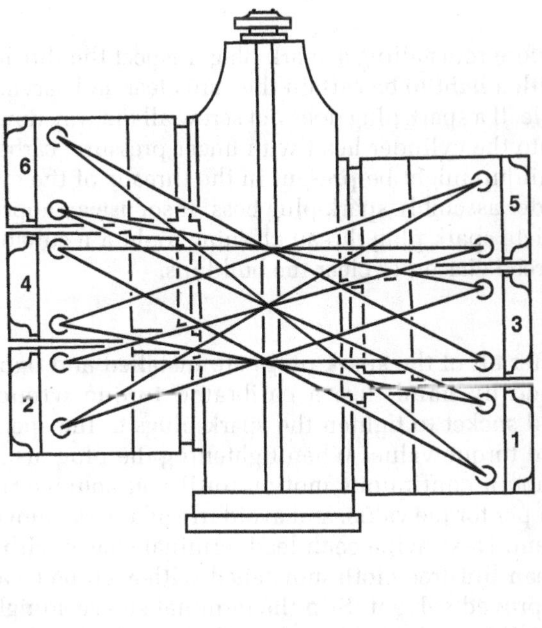


FIRING ORDER 1-6-3-2-5-4

| | | | | | | | | | | | | |
|---|---|---|---|---|---|---|---|---|---|---|---|---|
| REMOVE PLUG FROM | 1T | 6B | 3T | 2B | 5T | 4B | 1B | 6T | 3B | 2T | 5B | 4T |
| REPLACE PLUG IN | 6B | 3T | 2B | 5T | 4B | 1T | 6T | 3B | 2T | 5B | 4T | 1B |

**Figure 8-157. Rotating spark plugs extends their service life. As a general rule, a spark plug should be moved to the next cylinder in the firing order and position switched (top to bottom or bottom to top).**

**Figure 8-158. Sparingly apply antiseize compound to the second thread of each spark plug before installation.**

Before reinstalling a spark plug, inspect the threads with a light to be certain they are clear and serviceable. If a spark plug does not screw all the way down onto the cylinder head with finger pressure, carbon buildup might be present in the threads of the cylinder assembly spark plug boss. If so, use an appropriate spark plug thread cleaning tool (or a suitable thread chaser) to clear the buildups.

After all of the spark plugs are installed and tightened by hand, use a calibrated torque wrench and socket to tighten the spark plugs to the specified torque value. When tightening the plug, use a smooth continuous motion until you achieve the proper torque value, and avoid irregular jerky movement. Next, wipe each lead terminal sleeve with a clean lint-free cloth moistened with acetone or an approved solvent. Slip the terminal sleeve straight into the spark plug barrel and finger-tighten the terminal retainer nut. After you have installed all of the lead terminals, tighten the terminal nuts approximately one-eighth inch with an open-end wrench.

## ELECTRONICALLY CONTROLLED IGNITION

The use of electronically controlled ignition systems (often referred to as Full Authority Digital Engine Control, or FADEC) is increasing in reciprocating engines fueled by gasoline. *FADEC reciprocating engines powered by JetA (diesel) do not include an ignition system.* The ignition system is computer-controlled for ideal operation. Engine sensors provide data to a computer, which determines and controls every ignition event in each cylinder.

Ignition timing is adjusted continuously so that each cylinder always operates at peak performance and efficiency. Manufacturers of these systems anticipate the possibility of running on alternative fuels.

Electronically-controlled ignition systems typically include a data-logging feature, which stores data about engine performance. A trained aircraft maintenance technician with the appropriate equipment can download and analyze this data to monitor aircraft performance over time and diagnose discrepancies. Installation of these systems on legacy aircraft might be possible with the development of supplemental type certificates.

Following are descriptions of two engines with electronically controlled ignition:

### TELEDYNE CONTINENTAL MOTORS – POWERLINK™

The TCM PowerLink FADEC system controls ignition with microprocessor circuit boards in the base of the electronic control units (ECU). Spark plug towers replace magnetos and provide the ignition spark. The TCM PowerLink FADEC system is powered by the aircraft power supply. To ensure continuous operation of this system in the event of an electrical system failure, a second power supply (typically a backup battery) is required. [Figure 8-159]

### LYCOMING - iE$^2$

The Lycoming - iE$^2$ FADEC system features self-contained, independent power generation. The system computers can control either normally aspirated or turbocharged engines. The system does not have to rely on the aircraft electrical system; it can be equipped to generate its own power.

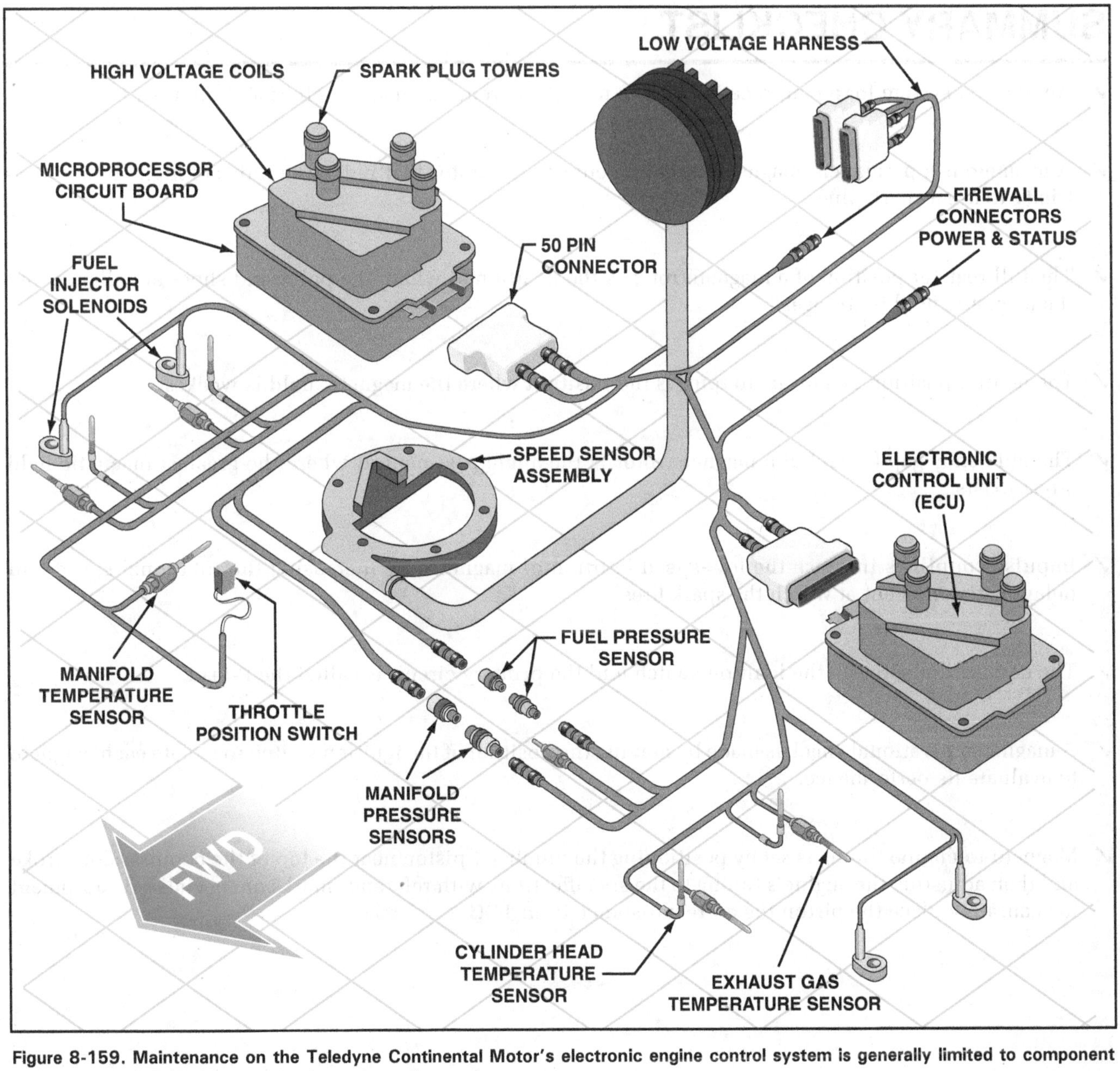


**Figure 8-159. Maintenance on the Teledyne Continental Motor's electronic engine control system is generally limited to component replacements identified by means of computer diagnostics.**

# SUMMARY CHECKLIST

- ✓ An ignition system for a reciprocating engine must have redundant spark plugs and circuits.
- ✓ A magneto is a permanent-magnet alternating current generator that induces a pulse of high voltage electricity to fire a spark plug.
- ✓ The full register position of a magneto rotor is the position at which the poles and shoes are aligned and the magnetic field is strongest.
- ✓ The neutral position of a magneto rotor is the position where the magnetic field is weakest.
- ✓ The efficiency gap (E-gap) of a magneto rotor is the angle past neutral where the greatest magnetic field stress exists.
- ✓ Impulse couplings increase the low-speed ignition of magnetos by increasing the rotational speed and delaying the moment at which the spark fires.
- ✓ The connection between the ignition switch and the primary circuit is called the P-lead.
- ✓ A magneto operational check is made by moving the position of the ignition switch to isolate each magneto to evaluate its performance.
- ✓ Magneto-to-engine timing is set by positioning the number 1 piston near the top of the compression stroke and then adjusting the engine's timing to the specifications with reference marks or specialized equipment to accurately place the piston the correct distance from TDC.

# KEY TERMS

ignition coil
breaker points
capacitor
condenser
cam
distributor
magneto
flashover
carbon tracking
uncompensated cam
compensated cam
alnico
Permalloy
full register position
neutral position
efficiency gap
E-gap
safety gap
coming-in speed
retard breaker points
induction vibrator
P-lead
soft iron keepers
magnetometer
gauss meter
synchronized ignition timing
staggered ignition timing
condenser tester
capacitance afterfiring
polarity

# QUESTIONS

1. Aircraft engines are required to have dual ignition. (true or false) ______

2. A magneto is actually a self-contained ______________ (alternating or direct) current generator.

3. Currently manufactured, certificated, reciprocating engines will use the __________ (high- or low-) tension magneto ignition.

4. What kind of magneto ignition system was developed to prevent high voltage breakdown in the distributor when the aircraft is flying at high altitudes? ___________-______________

5. Dual magnetos contain two separate and independent systems but share the following components:

   a. ____________

   b. ____________

   c. ____________

6. The four basic systems in a rotating-magnet magneto are:

   a. ____________

   b. ____________

   c. ____________

   d. ____________

7. An 18-cylinder radial engine using a low-tension magneto ignition system will have ______ (how many) high-tension transformers.

8. Two methods of mounting a magneto to an aircraft engine are by:

   a. ____________

   b. ____________

9. The pole shoes in a magneto are made of ______________ ______.

10. When the magnet is in its full-register position, the ______ (maximum or minimum) number of lines of magnetic flux are passing through the coil core.

11. The greatest change in the number of lines of magnetic flux in the coil core takes place when the magnet is in its ______________ (neutral or full-register) position.

12. The magnetic field produced by current flowing in the primary coil ______ (opposes or aids) the magnetic field that caused it to flow.

13. Because of the magnetic field produced by the primary current, the greatest change in the total magnetic flux occurs _________ (before or after) the magnet passes its neutral position.

14. The breaker points in a magneto are closed when the rotating magnet is in its __________ (neutral or full-register) position.

15. The point at which the breaker points open is called the ________ angle.

16. Two functions of a capacitor in a modern magneto are:

    a. To minimize ______________. For this function the capacitor is in parallel with the breaker points.

    b. To minimize ______________ ______________. For this function the capacitor is in series between the brake points and the ignition switch.

17. The high-tension magneto uses a ________________ (built-in or separate) distributor.

18. Which winding in a magneto coil has the greater number of turns, the primary or the secondary winding? ________________

19. The distributor in a magneto is in the ________________ (primary or secondary) electrical circuit.

20. The vast majority of four- and six-cylinder horizontally opposed engines use a/an ______________ (what system) to produce a hot and late spark for starting.

21. Magnetos have the problem of not producing a hot enough spark when they turn too ________ (fast or slow).

22. Four methods of providing a hot spark for starting an aircraft engine are:

    a. ______________

    b. ______________

    c. ______________

    d. ______________

23. The Bendix ________________ (what system) is a modern version of the induction vibrator.

24. The extra set of breaker points used with the "shower of sparks" system are referred to as the ______ points.

25. On an engine equipped with the "shower of sparks" system, the ______ (left or right) magneto is of standard construction.

26. An engine equipped with the "shower of sparks" system will use only the ______ (left or right) magneto for starting.

27. The "shower of sparks" will jump across the spark plug only as long as which conditions exist? (A, B, or C)

    A. The retard points are open.

    B. The advance points are open.

    C. Both sets of points are open.

28. The rotating magnet in a Slick Electro magneto is in its __________ (neutral, full-register, or E-gap) position when the timing pin can slip through the hole in the housing and the hole in the rotating magnet shaft.

29. You can be sure that the breaker points will close at the correct position of the rotating magnet if their _______ _______ is correct.

30. Magneto-to-engine timing is accomplished using the firing position of cylinder number ______ (which cylinder) as the reference.

31. The impulse coupling _______ (should or should not) be engaged when timing the magneto to the engine.

32. A __________ __________ (what kind of equipment) is used to show exactly the time at which the breaker points open.

33. Close timing of a base-mounted magneto to an aircraft engine is permitted by using a ________ __________.

34. Wear of the breaker points will cause the timing of a magneto to drift ________ (early or late).

35. The engine analyzer is an adaptation of the laboratory _______________ (what instrument).

36. Ignition leads are usually made of ________ _________ or ________ _________ wire, enclosed in a rubber or silicone insulation.

37. Modern ignition harnesses are available with terminal ends to fit either the standard _________ (what size) shielded spark plug or the _________ (what size) all-weather spark plug.

38. The ______________ (capacitance or inductance) caused by shielding of the ignition leads causes excessive electrode erosion around the ignition leads.

39. The ______________ (what component) in a spark plug is installed to minimize electrode erosion caused by using shielded ignition leads.

40. The length of the shell threads on a spark plug is called the __________ of the spark plug.

41. A short reach spark plug has ________-inch of threads on its shell, and a long reach plug has ________-inch of threads.

42. A spark plug that has a long nose core insulator (heat path) is a ______ (hot or cold) spark plug.

43. A ______ (hot or cold) spark plug should be used in a high-compression engine.

44. An engine operating with a too ______ (rich or lean) idle mixture will cause the spark plugs to have black sooty deposits in their firing end cavity.

45. Hard bead-like deposits found in the firing end of the spark plug indicate that the plug has been subject to _______ _______.

46. Lead fouling may occur on a spark plug that is too ______ (hot or cold) for the engine operating conditions.

47. Two sources of oil that can cause spark plug fouling are:

a. ______________

b. ______________

48. A spark plug should not be allowed to wear away more than ________(what fraction) of its electrode dimension before it is discarded.

49. Severe erosion of both the center electrode and the ground electrode may indicate ______ ______________ ______________ problems.

50. Lead deposits in the firing-end cavity of a spark plug should be removed with a ______________ (what type) cleaning tool.

51. It _______ (is or is not) recommended that the spark plug gap be widened if it has been inadvertently closed too much.

52. The spark plug that is removed from cylinder number one, bottom, should be replaced in cylinder number _______ (what number), _______ (top or bottom), if the firing order of the engine is 1-6-3-2-5-4.

53. Thread lubricant should be placed on the _______ (first or second) thread from the end of the shell when installing a spark plug in an engine.

54. The lead terminal of a spark plug harness should be wiped with a cloth dampend with ______________ or ______________ before it is installed in the spark plug.

SECTION

F

# TURBINE ENGINE IGNITION SYSTEMS

The primary function of a turbine engine ignition system is to ignite the fuel in the combustion chamber during an engine start. After ignition, combustion is self-sustaining and an ignition source is no longer required. Therefore, most turbine engine ignition systems are normally operated only for brief periods.

A secondary function of the ignition system is to provide standby protection against an in-flight flameout. Most turbine engine ignition systems have continuous or automatic relight settings that can be selected in flight. Engines equipped with a continuous setting contain a separate low-tension, continuous-duty circuit. The pilot can select continuous ignition for one or both igniter plugs. On engines equipped with an automatic relight setting, the system provides ignition only when a monitored parameter falls below a particular operational value. A common method of system activation is a pressure sensor installed at the compressor discharge; a drop in discharge pressure automatically activates the ignition system.

## CAPACITOR-DISCHARGE

The majority of turbine engines use a **capacitor-discharge** ignition system. A capacitor-discharge ignition system delivers a high-voltage, high-amperage spark with high heat intensity (unlike a reciprocating-engine ignition system, which produces high-voltage, low-amperage sparks). This high-energy spark is necessary to ignite the fuel/air mixture in low temperatures and at high altitudes.

The two common types of capacitor-discharge systems are the high-tension system and the low-tension system. Both systems contain two identical sets of components (for redundancy), including transformers (or exciter units), high-tension leads, and igniter units. The exciter box generates the energy to operate the igniters. Most exciters are sealed units containing electronic circuitry potted in an epoxy resin. In some instances, both exciters are housed together as a single unit. In such instances, the two exciter circuits are often considered as a single unit. [Figure 8-160]

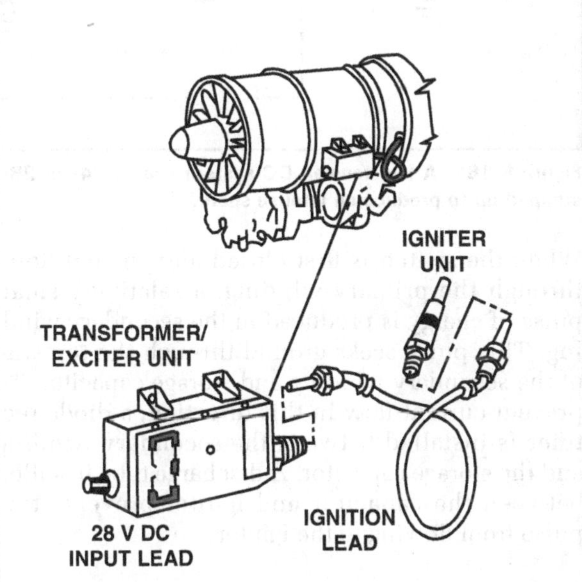


**Figure 8-160. A turbine engine ignition system typically consists of two separate ignition circuits, each with a transformer (or exciter), an ignition lead, and an igniter unit.**

## LOW-TENSION SYSTEM

In a low-tension system, 28 volts DC is supplied to each exciter. Voltage is stepped up in a coil to produce the high voltage pulses necessary to fire the igniter unit. The DC input current must be modified to pulse in the coil's primary winding. Many low-tension systems accomplish this with a vibrator circuit. [Figure 8-161]

When the switch for a low-tension system is open, a permanent magnet holds the points in the vibrator circuit closed. However, when the cockpit switch is closed, current flows from ground, through the primary winding, across the points, and to the battery's positive terminal. As electromagnetic force builds in the primary winding and overcomes the force of the permanent magnet, the points open and current flow stops. This action repeats approximately 200 times per second to produce pulsating DC voltage. To prevent arcing at the points, a capacitor is installed in parallel with the points.

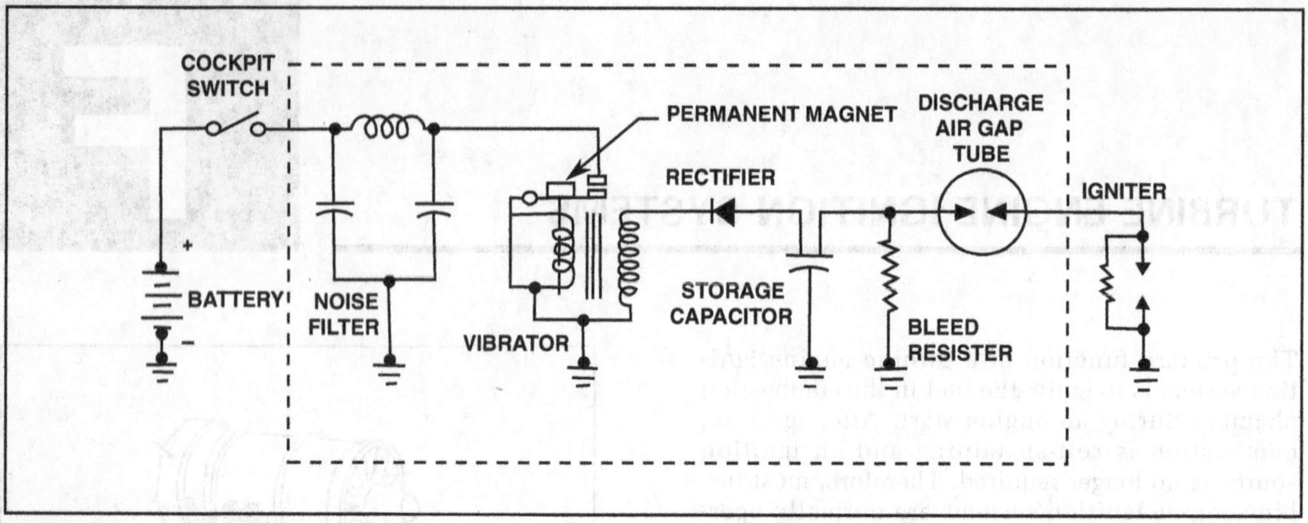


**Figure 8-161. A low-tension DC system uses a 24- to 28-volt DC input and vibrator circuit to produce pulsing DC current that is stepped up to produce an intense spark.**

When the switch is first closed and current flows through the primary winding, a relatively small pulse of energy is produced in the secondary winding. This pulse seeks ground through the top side of the secondary winding and storage capacitor. To prevent current flow in this direction, a diode rectifier is installed between the secondary winding and the storage capacitor. A discharge tube installed between the capacitor and igniter prevents this pulse from flowing to the igniter.

When the points open, the electromagnetic field surrounding the primary winding collapses and a strong pulse is induced into the seconding winding. Secondary current flows from the top of the secondary winding, through the rectifier, and into the storage capacitor. As electrons accumulate on the top plate of the storage capacitor, a negative charge develops and free electrons flow from the bottom plate of the capacitor to ground.

After a number of cycles, the storage capacitor develops a charge capable of jumping the gap in the discharge tube. The initial current surge ionizes the air gap, making it conductive, which enables the capacitor to discharge fully through the igniter.

The igniter in a low-tension system is referred to as a **self-ionizing** or **shunted-gap** igniter. The firing end of the igniter is made of a semiconductor material that bridges the gap between the center and ground electrodes. When current enters the igniter, it flows through the center electrode, semiconductor, outer casing, and back to the capacitor. Current flow through the semiconductor causes it to heat up, which increases its resistance. Simultaneously, the air gap is heated and ionized, which decreases its resistance. When the resistance across the air gap becomes less than the resistance across the semiconductor, the capacitor fully discharges across the air gap to create a high-energy capacitive-discharge spark.

To prevent accidental electrical shock, many ignition systems have a bleed resistor. The bleed resistor permits the capacitor to slowly discharge after the system is de-energized. Additionally it protects the circuit from overheating if the ignition system is energized without an igniter plug installed.

## HIGH-TENSION SYSTEM

In a high-tension ignition system, 115 volt, 400 Hz alternating current (AC) is applied to the transformer/exciter unit. Using AC eliminates the need for a vibrator circuit and its associated operational issues. [Figure 8-162]

When 115 volts AC is applied to a high-tension circuit, during the first half-cycle, the primary winding of the power transformer induces approximately 2,000 volts into the secondary winding. Current flows from the negative side of the winding to ground. Then current flows from ground at rectifier tube A, through resistor R1 and the doubler capacitor, to the positive side of the secondary winding. This charges the left side of the doubler capacitor to 2,000 volts. Rectifier tube B blocks any other current path during this half-cycle.

During the second half-cycle, the primary winding induces another 2,000 volts into the secondary winding. Current flows from the positive side of the coil and charges the right side of the doubler capacitor to 2,000 volts. The charge of the doubler capacitor is now approximately 4,000 volts, and current flows through resistor R2, the rectifier tube B, and the storage capacitor to ground. The circuit is com-

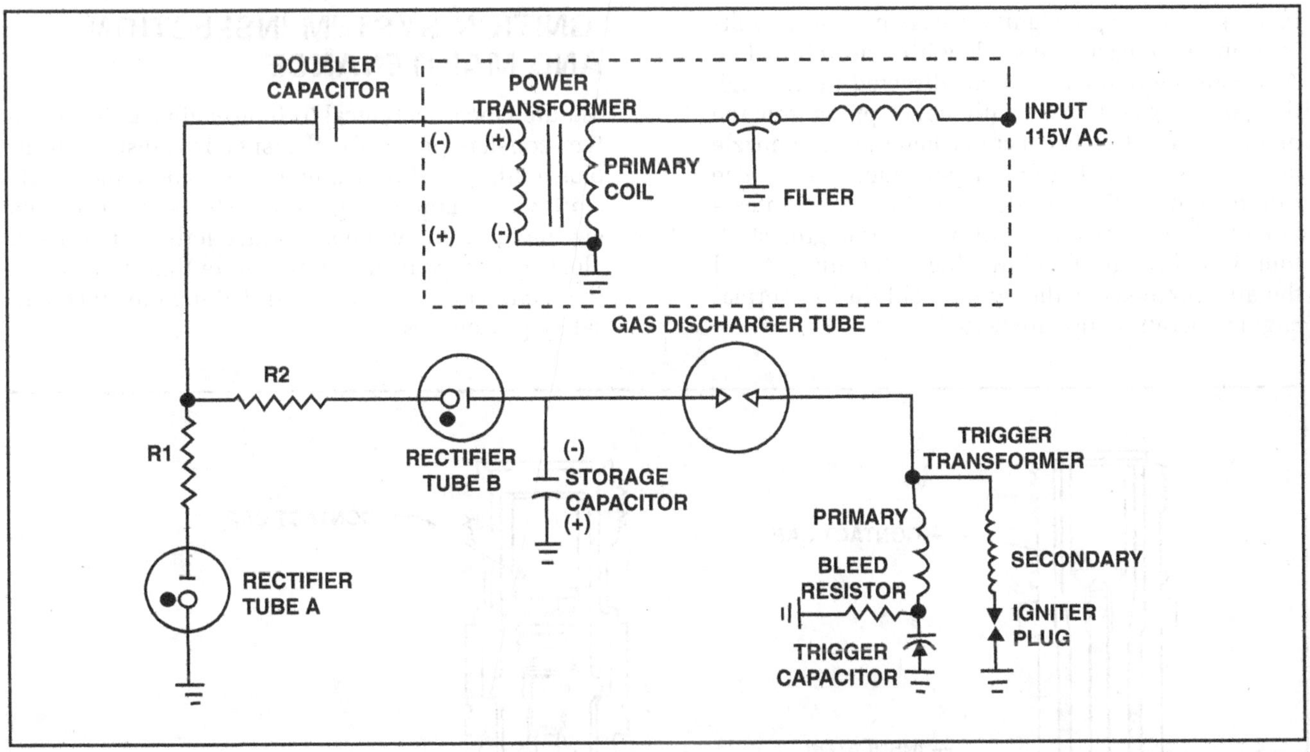


**Figure 8-162. A high-tension AC input system uses 115 volt, 400 Hz alternating current to induce high voltage and produce an intense spark.**

pleted after current passes through ground to the negative side of the secondary coil. During this half-cycle, rectifier tube A prevents current flow from the doubler capacitor and R1 to ground to ensure current flow to the storage capacitor.

Repeated pulses charge the storage capacitor to a point where the air gap in the discharge tube is ionized. Then, current flows across the air gap to the trigger transformer. At the trigger transformer, current flows through the primary winding and trigger capacitor to ground. The storage capacitor discharges through the primary winding of the trigger transformer, which induces a 20,000 volt pulse in the secondary winding. This 20,000 volt pulse ionizes the igniter plug air gap, which creates a low resistance path and permits both the trigger and storage capacitors to fully discharge through the igniter plug. The high-tension spark vaporizes and ignites atomized fuel around the igniter electrodes.

## IGNITERS

Igniters for gas turbine engines are considerably different from the spark plugs used on reciprocating engines. For example, the air gap on an igniter is much wider than a spark plug and the electrode is designed to develop a much more intense spark. Because of the high energy spark, an igniter plug is much less susceptible to fouling. Because igniters do not operate continuously, they generally have a long service life.

The construction of igniters also differs from spark plugs. One material difference is that the outer shell of most igniters is made of a high quality, nickel-chromium alloy. This material is corrosion resistant and its coefficient of heat expansion is low.

### TYPES OF IGNITERS

Due to the many varieties of igniter plugs, procedures regarding the service and maintenance of igniters vary. Engine manufacturers always specify the approved igniters for a given engine and this choice determines the service instructions. [Figure 8-163]

When installed in an engine, the igniter tip typically extends approximately 0.1 inch into the combustion chamber. The exception is a **constrained-gap** igniter, in which the center electrode is recessed in the body of the plug. With a constrained-gap igniter, the high intensity spark jumps out away from the plug's tip, which enables the igniter to operate at cooler temperatures.

### GLOW PLUGS

Some small turbine and turboprop engines ignite fuel with a glow plug type igniter instead of a spark. In the strictest definition, a glow plug is not an igniter, but they serve the same purpose. A glow plug is a resistance coil that generates a very high heat value capable of igniting a fuel/air mixture even at extremely low temperatures.

In a typical glow plug ignition system, 24 to 28 volts is supplied to each coil so they become yellow hot. At operating temperature, air directed up through the glow plug coil mixes with fuel dripping from the main fuel nozzle. This occurs when the main nozzle is not fully atomizing fuel during engine start. The influence of airflow on the dripping fuel creates a hot streak or torch-like ignition. After engine start, fuel flow through the glow plug is terminated and the air source keeps the igniter cool during normal engine operation. [Figure 8-164]

## IGNITION SYSTEM INSPECTION AND MAINTENANCE

Maintenance of a typical turbine engine ignition system consists primarily of inspecting, testing, troubleshooting, and replacing various components. Be alert when maintaining these systems; most turbine engine ignition systems produce lethal amounts of electrical current. It is imperative that you follow the manufacturer's recommended maintenance and safety procedures.

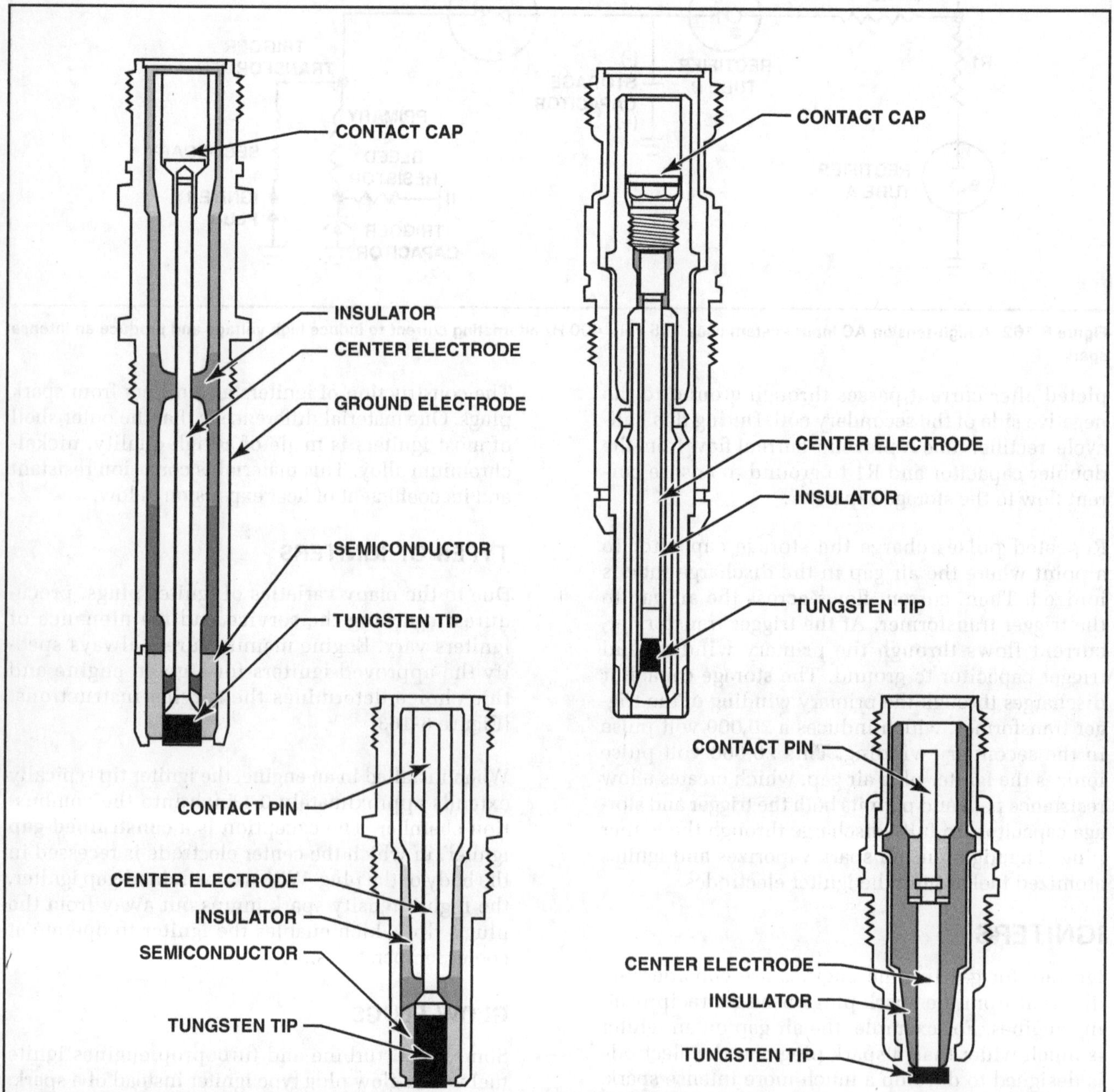


**Figure 8-163. Several types of igniters are used in turbine engines. The two igniters on the left are typical of a low-tension system while the two igniters on the right are typical of a high-tension system.**

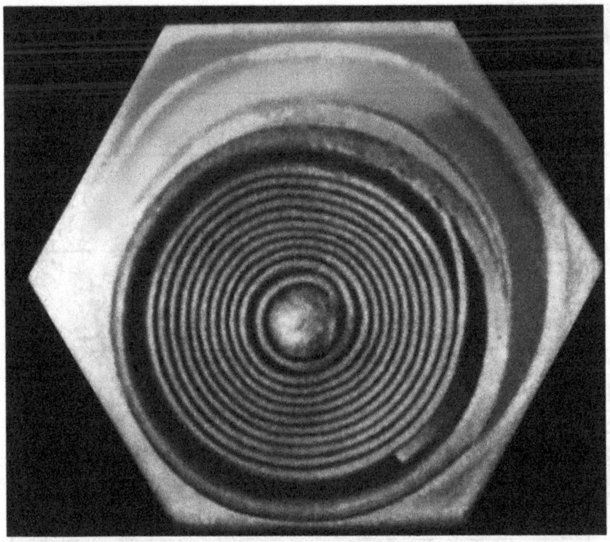

**Figure 8-164. Some small turbine engines use glow plugs.**

For example, before you perform any maintenance on an ignition system ensure that the ignition switch is off. Furthermore, manufacturers typically define a waiting period for capacitor discharge after the ignition system is turned off before disassembling any system connections. To remove an igniter plug, disconnect the transformer input lead and wait the time prescribed by the manufacturer. Then, disconnect the igniter lead and ground the center electrode to the engine. These steps protect you from lethal electrical discharges during removal.

Transformer removal and handling also require extra caution. Some older transformers contain small amounts of radioactive material. The radioactive material calibrates the discharge for a preset voltage.

## CLEANING AND SERVICING IGNITERS

The outer case of high voltage igniter plugs can be cleaned with a soft brush and an approved solvent. Typically, ceramic insulators and electrode tips are cleaned with solvent and a felt swab. After cleaning, blow off any remaining solvent with dry compressed air.

The self-ionizing, or shunted-gap igniters used with low-tension systems are generally cleaned only on their outer casing. The semiconductor material at the firing end is easily damaged, and manufacturers seldom permit any type of cleaning, even if carbon buildup is present.

If glow plug heater coils have carbon buildup (which appears to fuse the coils), you can immerse the coil in carbon remover to soften the deposit, after which you can use a soft nylon or fiber brush to remove any build-up. Finally, rinse the coil in warm water and blow it dry with compressed air.

High voltage igniter plugs or glow plugs are generally inspected visually and dimensionally. You should use a technician's scale or suitable depth micrometer to carry out the dimensional inspection. Self-ionizing igniters used in low-tension systems are visually inspected but do not require dimensional checks. The delicate nature of the semiconductor material makes tool contact risky. The semiconductor material often is little more than a very thin coating over a ceramic base.

If an igniter is faulty, follow the manufacturer's disposal procedures. Because of the materials used, some igniters require special handling.

After you have completed a visual and dimensional inspection, reinstall serviceable igniters (or glow plugs) and prepare the engine for an operational check. Be sure that no fuel is in any of the combustors before carrying out the operational test of the ignition system. A combustor wet with fuel might erupt in fire when you test the igniters. The operational check should follow the guidelines established by the engine manufacturer, using the appropriate aircraft ground run-up checklist.

Igniters produce a snapping sound when fired. The sound emanates from the high intensity spark jumping the air gap between the igniter electrodes. As a rule, the more intense the spark, the louder the noise. To conduct an operational test, one person stands near the engine to listen for the snapping while someone in the cockpit activates the ignition switch.

## TROUBLESHOOTING

Apply logical troubleshooting procedures when you investigate an ignition system problem. To aid in this process, many engine manufacturers provide troubleshooting charts for diagnosing and repairing commonly encountered problems. [Figure 8-165]

As a safety precaution, never energize a turbine engine ignition system for troubleshooting with the igniter plugs removed. Doing so can cause serious overheating or damage to the exciter box.

| 1. NO IGNITER SPARK WITH THE SYSTEM TURNED ON | | |
|---|---|---|
| **Possible Cause** | **Check For** | **Remedy** |
| A. Ignition Relay | Correct Power Input to Transformer Unit | Correct Relay Problems, Refer to Starter-Generator Circuit |
| B. Transformer Unit | Correct Power Output, Observing Ignition System Cautions | Replace Transformer<br>Replace Lead |
| C. High Tension Lead | Continuity or High Resistance Shorts With Ohmmeter and Megger-Check Unit | Replace Plug |
| D. Igniter Plug | 1. Cracked Insulator or Damaged Semiconductor | |
| | 2. Hot Electrode Erosion | Replace Plug |
| **2. LONG INTERVAL BETWEEN SPARKS** | | |
| **Possible Cause** | **Check For** | **Remedy** |
| Power Supply | Weak Battery | Recharge Battery |
| **3. WEAK SPARK** | | |
| **Possible Cause** | **Check For** | **Remedy** |
| Igniter Plug | Cracked Ceramic Insulation | Replace Plug |

**Figure 8-165. Manufacturers provide troubleshooting charts to provide guidance on commonly encountered problems.**

# SUMMARY CHECKLIST

✓ The majority of gas turbine engines use a capacitor-discharge system that delivers a high-voltage, high-amperage spark with high heat intensity.

✓ The high-energy spark delivered by a gas turbine igniter makes it less susceptible to fouling. Because igniters do not operate continuously, they have a long service life.

✓ Some small gas turbine engines use a glow plug as the fuel ignition source.

# KEY TERMS

capacitor-discharge ignition
self-ionizing igniter
shunted-gap igniter
constrained-gap igniter

# QUESTIONS

1. Turbine engine ignition systems operate all of the time the engine is running. This statement is _______ (true or false).

2. Turbine engine ignition systems are rated in _______ (what unit).

3. The current in a typical capacitance-discharge ignition system may be as high as 20 joules and _______ amps.

4. There are usually _______ (how many) igniter plugs in a turbine engine.

5. The two common classifications of turbine engine ignition systems are:

   a. _______________

   b. _______________

6. A low tension system is typically a _______ (28 volt DC or a 115 volt AC) system.

7. A shunted-gap igniter plug is normally used with a _______ (low or high) tension ignition system.

8. The use of alternating current in high tension exciters eliminates the need for a _______ circuit.

9. The gap on a turbine engine igniter plug is _____________ (wider or narrower) than that on a reciprocating engine spark plug.

10. Some smaller turbine engines may incorporate a _________ plug-type igniter rather than a spark type.

11. A glow plug is designed to ignite ___________ rather than atomized fuel mixtures.

12. An igniter plug _______ (should or should not) be removed immediately after the ignition switch is turned off.

13. Igniter plugs ________ (are or are not) cleaned in the same manner as spark plugs.

14. A troubleshooting test of the igniter plug is to listen for the ________ ________ made when the plug fires.

CHAPTER 9

# ENGINE LUBRICATION

## INTRODUCTION

The primary purpose of a lubricant is to reduce friction between moving parts. An engine lubricant also functions in engine cooling, sealing and cushioning moving parts, cleaning the engine interior, and protecting against corrosion. Because engines require a lubricant that can circulate freely, liquid lubricants (such as oils) are most widely used in aircraft engines.

# SECTION A

## ENGINE LUBRICATING OILS

The properties and characteristics of lubricating oils vary with oil type. You must always use oil with the correct specifications in each engine, or damage to or failure of engine components can result. The following discussion focuses on the properties of various types of oil, typical uses for different oil types, and the methods used to grade aircraft engine oil.

### FUNCTIONS OF LUBRICATING OIL

An engine will not operate without lubricating oil. Friction between moving parts would cause an engine to wear rapidly. In addition to reducing friction, lubricating oil removes a great deal of engine heat. In fact, if a reciprocating engine is not lubricated with an adequate supply of engine oil, it could overheat. Lubricating oils also create a seal between moving parts, cushion impact forces created by combustion, clean the internal components of the engine, and protect against corrosion.

#### REDUCES FRICTION

Many of the metal parts inside an aircraft engine have surfaces that appear smooth to the unaided eye, but if you examine them with a microscope, you will see rough surfaces consisting of many peaks and valleys. Without a film of lubricating oil between these parts, the resulting friction when they rub against one another would wear away the metal. Oil wets the surfaces, fills in the valleys, and holds the metal surfaces apart as long as the oil film remains unbroken. Friction is reduced and part wear is minimized as engine parts slide over each other on the film of oil rather than grinding together. [Figure 9-1]

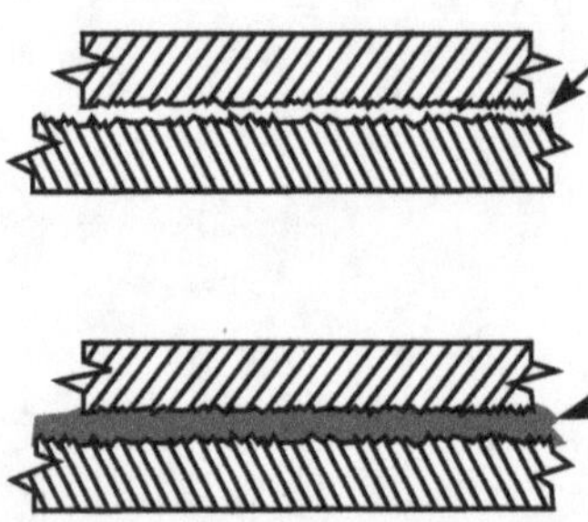


Figure 9-1. Engine parts that appear smooth to the unaided eye reveal rough surfaces under a microscope. Lubricating oil separates these surfaces and minimizes wear.

The amount of clearance between moving parts is a determining factor when choosing the proper type and grade of oil. Oil must adhere to a part sufficiently and be thick enough to provide an adequate protective film that will not break down and permit metal-to-metal contact.

#### ABSORBS HEAT

In addition to reducing friction and wear, as oil circulates through the engine, it absorbs some of the heat produced by combustion. The pistons and cylinder walls, which absorb the greatest amount of heat in an engine, are especially dependent on lubricating oil for cooling. However, after the oil heats up, the oil itself must be cooled, so many engine lubrication systems contain an oil cooler. An **oil cooler** is a heat exchanger (similar to an automotive radiator) that transfers heat from the oil to the outside air.

#### SEALS

Oil has excellent wetting characteristics; the oil film has an ability to evenly coat metal surfaces. This makes it a good sealing agent between moving parts. For example, the oil film on cylinder walls forms an effective seal with the piston rings in a cylinder that helps prevent gas leakage during the combustion process.

#### CUSHIONS

The same characteristic of oil that makes it a good sealing agent also provides a cushioning effect between metal parts. For example, the thin film of oil between a rocker arm and its bushing absorbs some of the hammering shock from the valve action. The cushioning action also helps reduce some of the impact force between a crankshaft and the connecting rods.

### CLEANS

The oil in a lubrication system reduces engine wear by serving as a cleaning agent. As the oil circulates, it picks up foreign particles such as dirt, dust, carbon, and small amounts of water. These particles are held in suspension by the oil and carried to a filter that traps and removes them.

### PROTECTS AGAINST CORROSION

Metal engine parts that are exposed to moist air and various chemicals tend to rust or form other kinds of surface corrosion. This is especially true for cylinder walls and crankshafts which have been hardened by nitriding. The oil film that coats internal engine parts acts as a barrier to prevent oxygen and moisture from causing corrosion on metal surfaces.

## OIL CONSUMPTION

As the lubricating oil performs all of these functions, a portion of the oil is consumed. The amount of oil consumed during combustion depends on factors such as engine speed, temperature, operating clearances, and lubricant characteristics. Generally, higher speeds and temperatures, larger clearances, and lower viscosity correspond to higher consumption rates. Larger clearances, usually caused by wear over time, are one reason why reciprocating engines typically consume more oil than turbine engines.

## OIL PROPERTIES

Theoretically, the perfect engine oil is thin enough to circulate freely, yet viscous enough to maintain reasonable film strength. In practice, the best oil for a given engine is a compromise of those characteristics. Several factors determine the proper grade of oil for use in a particular engine. Some of these factors are engine operating loads, rotational speeds of bearings, and operating temperatures. To determine the proper grade of oil to use, engineers must consider a variety of properties.

### VISCOSITY

One of the most important properties of oil is viscosity, which is a measure of oil's resistance to flow. Oil that flows slowly is said to have a high viscosity. Conversely, oil that flows freely has a low viscosity.

Oil viscosity is measured using an instrument known as the **Saybolt Universal Viscosimeter**. To measure viscosity, a specific quantity of oil is heated to a predetermined temperature. Then, the number of seconds required for 60 cubic centimeters of heated oil to flow through a calibrated orifice is recorded as a measure of the oil's viscosity. The recorded time is known as the **Saybolt Universal Seconds** viscosity or **SUS**. Typical aviation oils have an SUS of 80, 100, or 120 when heated to 210 degrees Fahrenheit.

Of all the factors that affect oil viscosity, temperature has the greatest effect. In fact, some high viscosity oils become almost semisolid in cold weather. When this happens, component drag increases and oil circulation decreases. Conversely, low viscosity oils can become so thin at high temperatures that the oil cannot maintain a solid film. This causes rapid wear and lower than normal oil pressure. For these reasons, lower viscosity oils are used in cold climates and higher viscosity oils are used in warm climates.

Oils used in reciprocating engines typically have a relatively high viscosity for several reasons. Most reciprocating engines have large operational clearances and high operating temperatures. High viscosity oil ensures an adequate oil film between the moving parts. Because most reciprocating engines operate at relatively high temperatures, high viscosity oil is needed to keep the oil from becoming too thin at operating temperatures. Furthermore, high bearing pressures in reciprocating engines require the cushion that higher viscosity oils provide.

### VISCOSITY INDEX

In addition to having a viscosity rating, many oils are assigned a **viscosity index**, or **VI** number. The viscosity index is a standard used to identify the rate of change in viscosity for a given change in temperature. The index itself is based on a comparative analysis of the temperature-induced viscosity changes of two reference oils, arbitrarily chosen by the **American Society of Testing and Materials,** or **ASTM.** One oil is assigned a viscosity index rating of 100, and the other is rated at zero. The smaller the change in the viscosity for a given temperature change, the higher the viscosity index number.

### SPECIFIC GRAVITY

The specific gravity of oil is a comparison of its weight to the weight of an equal volume of distilled water at a specified temperature. For example, water weighs approximately 8 pounds per gallon. Therefore, oil with a specific gravity of 0.9 weighs 7.2 pounds per gallon ($0.9 \times 8 = 7.2$).

The **American Petroleum Institute,** or **API,** has formulated a measurement for the specific gravity of oils that is an expansion of the regular specific gravity scale. The API scale is a more accurate measure of oil gravity because it provides more detail on the portion of the specific gravity range where lubricating oils occur. In most cases, an oil's API number can be converted to a specific gravity number using a conversion chart.

## COLOR

Oil color is determined by the amount of light that passes through an oil sample in a glass container when placed in front of a light of known intensity. The color test is conducted with a device known as an **ASTM union colorimeter**. The color is then compared to an ASTM color chart. A color reference number of 1.00 on the chart is pure white, and a reference number of 8.00 is darker than claret red.

Oils that are darker than number 8.00 are diluted with kerosene to form a mixture 85 percent kerosene and 15 percent oil by volume. The mixture is then given a color rating in the same manner as other oils.

If a color test performed with indirect or reflected light, the oil color is referred to as a **bloom** and can be used to determine the origin of the oil.

## CLOUD POINT

Another property of lubricating oil is known as cloud point. The cloud point is the temperature at which paraffin wax and other solids normally held in a solution of oil begin to solidify and separate into tiny crystals. At this temperature, the oil begins to lose clarity and appears cloudy or hazy.

## POUR POINT

The pour point of oil represents the lowest temperature at which it can flow or be poured. As a rule, the pour point should be within five degrees Fahrenheit of the average ambient starting temperature to ensure oil circulation.

## FLASH POINT AND FIRE POINT

Flash point is the temperature at which oil begins to emit ignitable vapors. As temperature increases beyond the flash point, the oil reaches its fire point when sufficient it emits sufficient vapor to support a flame. Typical lubricating oil has a fire point approximately 50 to 60 degrees Fahrenheit higher than the flash point. Oil must be able to withstand the high temperatures encountered in an engine without creating a fire hazard. Both temperature ratings are important when selecting the proper oil for an engine.

## CARBON RESIDUE TEST

In the carbon residue test, a given amount of oil is placed in a stainless steel receptacle and heated at a controlled temperature until it evaporates. The container is weighed before and after the test. The difference in weight is then divided by the weight of the original oil sample to obtain the percentage of carbon, by weight, in the oil.

## ASH TEST

An ash test is an extension of a carbon residue test in that it requires the carbon residue to be burned until only ash remains. The amount of remaining ash is then expressed as a percentage by weight of the carbon residue. New oil leaves almost no ash and is considered to be pure. On the other hand, the ash left by used oil can be analyzed for iron and lead content. The amount of iron and lead in the remaining ash provides clues to the amount of internal engine wear.

# ENGINE OIL GRADING SYSTEM

Most commercial aviation oils are assigned numerical designations such as 80, 100, or 120 that approximate the oil's viscosity. This practice has proven to be much more workable than using actual Saybolt values to designate viscosity because oil viscosity varies enough among commonly used oils to produce several hundred grades when using Saybolt values.

A system designed by the **Society of Automotive Engineers (SAE)** further simplifies the oil grading process. The SAE system scale divides all oils into seven groups, ranging from SAE 10 to SAE 70. The groupings are based on viscosity at either 130°F or 210°F. In addition, an SAE rating with the letter "W," such as 20W indicates the oil is acceptable for use in cold, or winter, climates.

Although SAE ratings are used with most oils, there are still some oils that carry commercial aviation or military designations. It is important to note that SAE ratings are arbitrary and bear no direct relationship to any other ratings. [Figure 9-2]

The SAE system scale has eliminated a lot of confusion in the designation of lubricating oils. However, do not assume that an SAE designation covers all important viscosity requirements. An SAE number indicates only the relative viscosity of the oil, not quality or other essential characteristics. Both high-quality oils and inferior low-quality oils can have the same viscosity at a given temperature and the same SAE number. Always bear in mind that an SAE rating on an oil container is not an endorsement or recommendation of that particular oil by the Society of Automotive Engineers. The only way to be sure that an oil meets the requirements of a particular engine is to be familiar with the individual characteristics of the oil. [Figure 9-3]

| SAE No. | COMMERCIAL AVIATION No. | AN SPECIFICATION (MILITARY) |
|---|---|---|
| SAE 30 | GRADE 65 | AN 1065 |
| SAE 40 | GRADE 80 | AN 1080 |
| SAE 50 | GRADE 100 | AN 1100 |
| SAE 60 | GRADE 120 | AN 1120 |
| SAE 70 | GRADE 140 | |

**Figure 9-2. This chart illustrates how a similar oil can have an SAE rating, a commercial aviation rating, and a Military rating.**

## TYPES OF OIL

Oils from a variety of sources have been used in aircraft. For example, the earliest aircraft engines used castor oil as a lubricant, which is a pure vegetable oil derived from castor beans. However, vegetable-based lubricants have poor chemical stability and tend to oxidize when used in reciprocating engines. Because of this, vegetable-based oils were soon replaced with mineral-based oils. Mineral-based oils tend to be more chemically stable than vegetable-based lubricants and are still widely used in reciprocating engines. Synthetic oils are also used in reciprocating and turbine aircraft engines. A blend of mineral and synthetic oils is called a semi-synthetic.

### STRAIGHT MINERAL OIL

For many years MIL-L-6082E, a straight mineral oil with no additives, was the principle type of oil used in aircraft engines. Although straight mineral oil is an effective lubricant, it has some limitations. For example, when exposed to elevated temperatures in an aerated condition, straight mineral oil has a tendency to oxidize. In addition, if straight mineral oil becomes overly contaminated, sludge can form that can clog filters and passages and score engine components. Because of this, the use of straight mineral oil is generally limited to new or newly overhauled engines during their break-in period.

### ASHLESS-DISPERSANT OILS

The most commonly used oil in reciprocating engines is **ashless-dispersant** (AD) oil that conforms to MIL-L-22851D. It does not have the carbon forming restrictions of straight mineral oil nor does it form ash deposits like detergent oils. This oil contains a **dispersant** that causes sludge-forming materials to repel each other and remain in suspension until trapped by the oil filter. This characteristic helps oil passages and ring grooves remain free of harmful deposits.

In addition to a dispersant, several ashless-dispersant oils contain an anti-wear, anti-foam additive that does not leave metallic ash deposits in an engine. Ash deposits are undesirable because they can lead to preignition and spark plug fouling.

Because ashless-dispersant oils are such an effective lubricant, engine manufacturers typically do not recommend their use during an engine's break-in period because there must be some component wear. Before a set of piston rings can effectively seal against a cylinder wall, the two surfaces must wear against each other to produce a sealable junction. Without sufficient wear, the engine will consume excessive amounts of oil throughout its operating life. Therefore, to promote some degree of wear,

| | SAE 30 AVIATION 65 AN 1065 | SAE 40 AVIATION 80 AN 1080 | SAE 50 AVIATION 100 AN 1100 | SAE 60 AVIATION 120 AN 1120 |
|---|---|---|---|---|
| VISCOSITY | | | | |
| SUS @ 100°F | 443.0 | 676.0 | 1,124.0 | 1,530.0 |
| SUS @ 130°F | 215.0 | 310.0 | 480.0 | 630.0 |
| SUS @ 210°F | 65.4 | 79.2 | 103.0 | 123.2 |
| VISCOSITY INDEX | 116.0 | 112.0 | 108.0 | 107.0 |
| GRAVITY API | 29.0 | 27.5 | 27.4 | 27.1 |
| COLOR ASTM | 1.5 | 4.5 | 4.5 | 5.5 |
| POUR POINT °F | -20.0 | -15.0 | -10.0 | -10.0 |
| POUR POINT DILUTED °F | -70.0 | -70.0 | -70.0 | -50.0 |
| FLASH POINT °F | 450.0 | 465.0 | 515.0 | 520.0 |
| CARBON RESIDUE %W | 0.11 | 0.23 | 0.23 | 0.40 |

**Figure 9-3. This chart illustrates the characteristics of various oils. Note that a given SAE rating indicates only specific viscosity and does not guarantee any other characteristic.**

most manufacturers recommend that new and newly overhauled engines be operated on straight mineral oil for the first 10 to 50 hours of operation or until oil consumption stabilizes. After this, you should drain the straight mineral oil and replace it with a quality ashless-dispersant oil for the remaining life of the engine.

## MULTIVISCOSITY OILS

Multiviscosity oils were developed to help address some of the drawbacks of single viscosity oils. For example, in a warm climate an SAE 10 oil will get too hot and lose its ability to maintain an adequate film on moving parts while, in a cold climate, SAE 30 oil will not circulate properly, especially when an engine is first started.

Unlike single viscosity oils, multiviscosity oils provide adequate lubrication over a wider temperature range. Multiviscosity oils flow more quickly in cold weather and keep from thinning in hot weather. A typical multiviscosity oil, such as SAE 15W50, can generally be used over the combined temperature range of both an SAE 15 and an SAE 50 oil.

## SYNTHETIC OILS

The chemical composition of synthetic oils provides them with multiviscosity properties similar to automotive grades SAE-5 to SAE-20. They contain a blend of chemical additives and certain **diesters,** which are synthesized extracts of mineral, vegetable, and animal oils. Stated another way, synthetic oils are made by synthesizing raw materials into a base stock rather than refining base stock from crude oil.

Because of their chemical make up, synthetic oils have extremely low internal friction. In addition, they have a high resistance to thermal breakdown and oxidation. Because of this, synthetic oils are ideal for use in turbine engines and can typically go longer between oil changes. In addition, the wear characteristics of synthetic oil appear to be about the same as ashless-dispersant oil and superior to straight mineral oil.

One problem with synthetic oils is that they do not disperse and suspend contaminants as well as ashless-dispersant oils. Therefore, synthetic oils tend to cause sludge build-up in reciprocating engines, especially in engines that are infrequently operated. Another problem with synthetic oil is that, in some cases, it can soften rubber products and resins in the engine. Because of this, one manufacturer requires more frequent replacement of the inter-cylinder drain lines when synthetic oil is used. In addition, pleated paper oil filters must be examined more closely to be sure that the oil does not dissolve the resins, which would cause the filter to collapse.

As a general rule, synthetic oils are not compatible with, and cannot be mixed with, mineral-based oils. In addition, most manufacturers recommend against mixing different brands or types of synthetic oils. If manufacturers permit mixing at all, the guidelines for doing so are strict. For example, you typically are not permitted to mix different types of synthetics. In addition, you are not permitted to mix different brands unless they have been identified as compatible.

Another negative characteristic of synthetic oil is its tendency to blister or remove paint. If a spill occurs, wipe it up immediately with a petroleum solvent. When servicing an engine filled with synthetic oil, avoid excessive or prolonged exposure to your skin. Synthetic lubricants contain highly toxic additives that are readily absorbed through the skin.

Instead of an SAE rating, synthetic oils are given a **Kinematic Viscosity Rating** in **centistokes (cSt)**. Some synthetic lubricant container labels are marked with the centistoke value, or metric viscosity measurement. For example, a synthetic oil with a 5 centistoke rating has a viscosity approximately equal to an SAE 5W10 multi-viscosity mineral-based oil. Likewise, a 7 centistoke oil has a viscosity approximately equal to an SAE 5W20 multi-viscosity oil rating.

## EXTREME PRESSURE LUBRICANTS

Extreme pressure (EP) lubricants, also known as **hypoid lubricants,** are specially formulated to provide protection under high loads. A hypoid lubricant contains additives that bond to metal surfaces to reduce friction under high pressures or high rubbing velocities. A typical hypoid lubricant consists of a mineral-based oil containing loosely held sulfur or chlorine molecules. The spur-type gears in a propeller reduction case operate under high tooth pressures and often require EP lubricants to prevent gear failure.

# SUMMARY CHECKLIST

✓ Oil lubricates internal engine components and removes heat.

✓ Viscosity is the measure of oil's resistance to flow.

✓ In a reciprocating engine, straight mineral oil is typically used to break in new and newly overhauled engines.

✓ Multiviscosity oils are typically used for most of the service life of reciprocating engines.

# KEY TERMS

oil cooler
Saybolt Universal Viscosimeter
Saybolt Universal Seconds
SUS
viscosity index
American Society of Testing and Materials
ASTM
American Petroleum Institute
API
ASTM union colorimeter
bloom
Society of Automotive Engineers
SAE
ashless-dispersant oil
AD
dispersant
diesters
Kinematic Viscosity Rating
centistokes
cSt
hypoid lubricants

# QUESTIONS

1. Five functions of the oil in an engine lubrication system are:

   a. ____________

   b. ____________

   c. ____________

   d. ____________

   e. ____________

2. The resistance of an oil to flow is known as its ____________.

3. Oil that flows freely has a ________ (high or low) viscosity.

4. The oil used in reciprocating engines has a relatively ________ (high or low) viscosity.

5. The measure of the change in viscosity of oil with a given change in temperature is known as the ____________ ________.

6. An engine lubricating oil whose viscosity changes very little for a given change in temperature has a ______ (high or low) viscosity index.

7. The point at which a liquid will begin to give off ignitable vapors is known as the ______ (flash or fire) point.

8. Aviation 80 engine oil has the same viscosity as SAE ______.

9. The use of straight mineral oil in aircraft reciprocating engines is associated with what conditions?

   a. ____________

   b. ____________

10. The lubricating properties of straight mineral oil ____________ (are or are not) as good as those of ashless dispersant oil.

11. Synthetic lubricating oils are ________ (multi- or single-) viscosity oils.

12. If incompatible oil has been added to a turbine engine, it is often necessary to ________ and ________ the oil system before refilling with the proper oil.

13. Turbine engine oils ________ (do or do not) use a standard identification system.

14. SAE numbers ________ (are or are not) used to identify turbine oils.

# SECTION B

# RECIPROCATING ENGINES

## OIL DISTRIBUTION

The primary purpose of a lubrication system is to deliver oil to the internal engine components. The most common ways of distributing oil are pressure, splash, and spray lubrication. To ensure adequate lubrication, reciprocating engines rely on a combination of pressure and splash lubrication. However, on larger engines, adequate oil circulation can be accomplished only through the use of pressure, splash, and spray lubrication. [Figure 9-4]

### PRESSURE LUBRICATION

Reciprocating engines primarily use pressure lubrication. In most cases, a positive displacement, engine-driven pump supplies pressurized oil to critical engine parts. The term **positive displacement** indicates that the pump moves a specific amount of fluid for each revolution or cycle of the pump mechanism. After oil passes through an oil pump, it passes through several passages for distribution to various engine components. The components that are typically lubricated by pressurized oil include all plain bearings, crankshaft and camshaft main bearings, lower connecting rod bearings, and valve assemblies.

### SPLASH LUBRICATION

In addition to pressure lubrication, many reciprocating engines also use splash lubrication. Splash lubrication is produced by the movement of internal components that splash oil around the crankcase. This method of lubrication is very effective in engines where oil is stored in the crankcase. As the crankshaft rotates, each crank throw becomes partially submerged in oil. As it emerges from the reservoir, it splashes oil onto nearby components, including cylinder walls, camshaft lobes, upper bearings of connecting rods, piston pins, and accessory gears.

### SPRAY LUBRICATION

Some large reciprocating engines are too big for splash lubrication to be effective. In this case, some form of spray lubrication is typically used. Spray lubrication uses the same pressurized oil from the pressure lubrication system; however, instead of routing the oil to a component through an oil passage, the oil is sprayed on to a component through a nozzle. Engine components that are lubricated by sprayed engine oil include some cylinder walls and camshaft lobes.

## SYSTEM CLASSIFICATION

Reciprocating engine lubrication systems are generally classified as wet-sump or dry-sump. In a **wet-sump** system, all the oil is stored in the engine crankcase, similar to the engines in most automobiles, and a pump distributes it throughout the engine. After the oil has circulated, it returns to the sump to be recirculated. Some advantages of wet-sump systems include their relative simplicity and light weight. However, two disadvantages of wet-sump systems are that the sump size limits their oil capacity and they are more difficult to cool because the oil is contained in the hot engine.

In **dry-sump** systems, the oil is stored in an oil reservoir separate from the engine, which typically enables them to carry a larger quantity of oil. Dry-sump systems were used mostly on large radial engines, but also on some horizontally opposed engines. In a dry-sump system, an oil pump pulls the oil from the oil reservoir and circulates it throughout the engine. The oil then accumulates in the bottom of the crankcase where a **scavenge pump** transports it back to the tank. If the oil reservoir is installed so that it is higher than the engine oil inlet, check valves must be installed to prevent oil from draining back into the engine crankcase.

## LUBRICATING SYSTEM COMPONENTS

A typical pressure lubrication system consists of an oil reservoir, oil pump, oil pressure relief valve, oil filter, oil cooler, vent lines, and all of the necessary piping and connections. In addition, on engines with a dry-sump, a scavenge pump transports the oil back to the oil reservoir. To enable the operator to monitor the operation of the lubrication system, most systems include gauges to monitor oil temperature and oil pressure. [Figure 9-5]

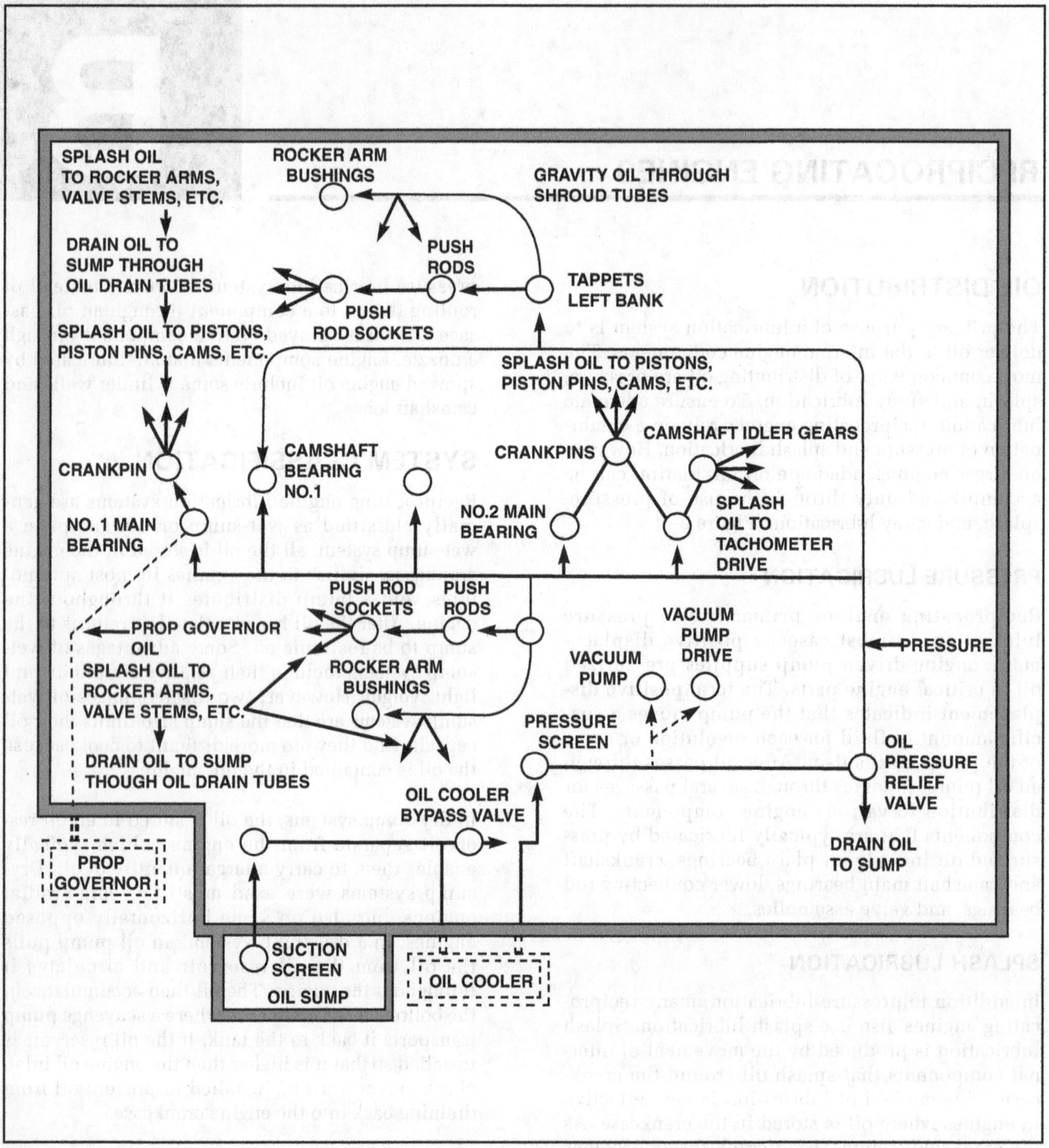


**Figure 9-4. This figure shows how a typical wet-sump system uses a combination of lubrication methods.**

## OIL RESERVOIR

The oil reservoir must be large enough to hold an adequate supply of oil to lubricate the engine, based on the maximum endurance of the airplane and the maximum acceptable oil consumption rate plus a margin to ensure adequate circulation, lubrication, and cooling. In the absence of a valid determination of aircraft range, several ratios of fuel-to-oil quantity may be used. For example, an aircraft without an oil reserve or transfer system must have a fuel-to-oil ratio of at least 30:1. However, if an aircraft has a transfer system, a ratio of 40:1 is adequate.

As discussed earlier, the oil reservoir on a wet-sump engine is part of the engine crankcase. Wet-sump oil reservoirs are often constructed of cast aluminum

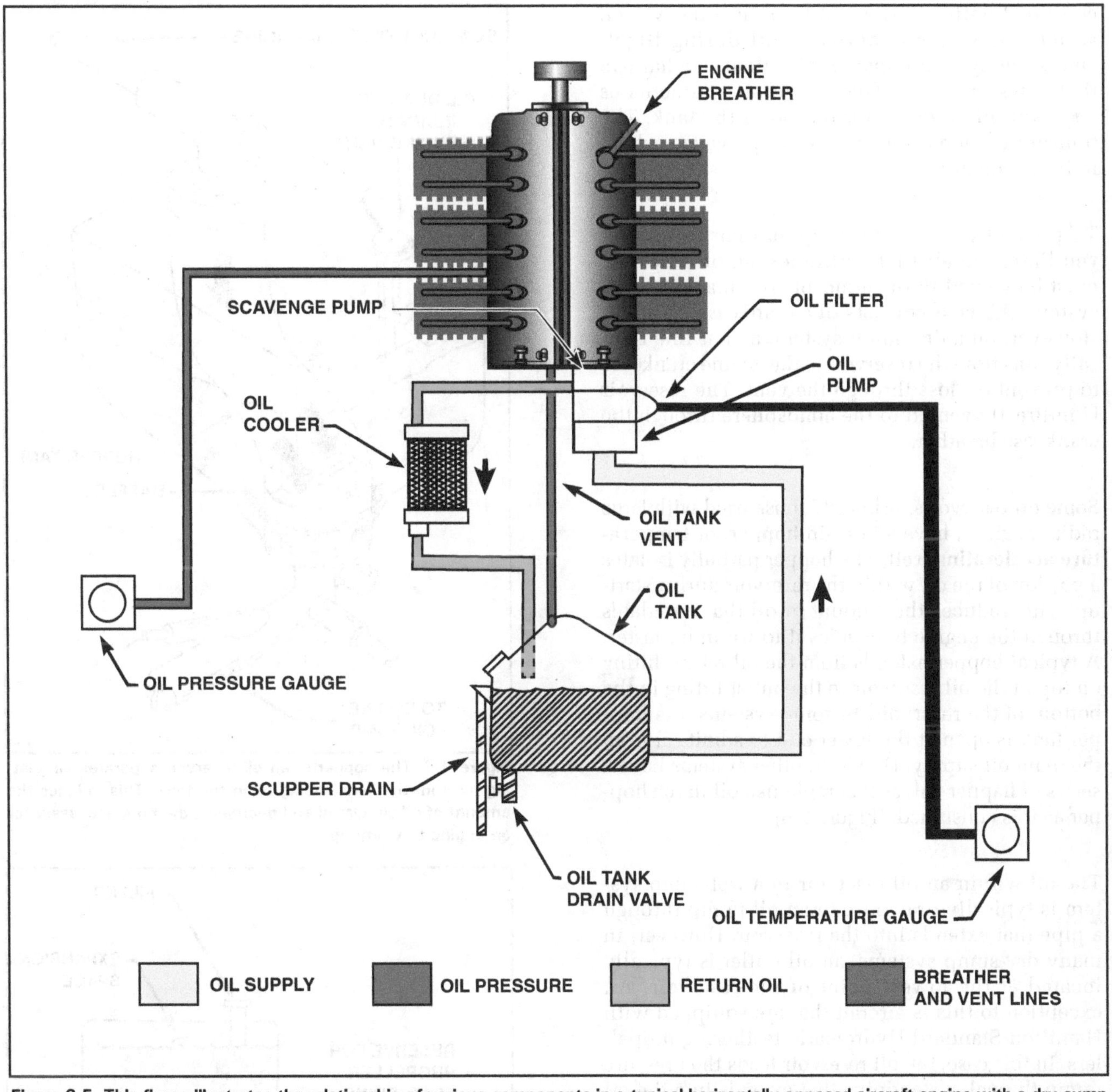


**Figure 9-5. This figure illustrates the relationship of various components in a typical horizontally opposed aircraft engine with a dry-sump lubrication system.**

alloy. Oil reservoirs used in dry-sump systems are also constructed from an aluminum alloy. The location of a dry-sump reservoir is typically close to the engine, but higher than the oil pump inlet to ensure reliable gravity feed.

Regulations require that every oil reservoir have an expansion space at least 10 percent greater than the tank capacity or 0.5 gallon, whichever is greater. The expansion space provides room for oil expansion and the accumulation of foam. Another regulatory requirement is that all oil filler caps or covers be marked with the word "OIL" and the permissible oil designations, or reference to the Airplane Flight Manual for permissible oil designations. As an added feature, the oil reservoirs installed in some dry-sump systems include a scupper drain. A **scupper drain** is a drain built into the filler cap well that catches overflow oil and directs it overboard when the reservoir is serviced.

Most aircraft oil systems are equipped with a dipstick-type quantity gauge, sometimes referred to as a **bayonet gauge**. Some large aircraft might be equipped with an oil quantity indicating system, which shows the quantity of oil during flight. One such system consists of a float mechanism that rides on the surface of the oil and actuates an electronic transmitter on top of the tank. The transmitter sends a signal to a cockpit gauge, which indicates quantity.

To prevent pressure buildup and ensure proper ventilation in all flight attitudes, an oil reservoir must be vented to the atmosphere. In a wet-sump system, the vent consists of a crankcase breather. However, on a dry-sump system, a vent line typically runs from the reservoir to the engine crankcase to prevent oil loss through the vent. The reservoir is indirectly vented to the atmosphere through the crankcase breather.

Some oil reservoirs, primarily those used with large radial engines, have a built-in **hopper**, or **temperature accelerating well**. The hopper partially isolates a portion of the oil within the reservoir during start-up. This reduces the amount of oil that circulates through the engine to enables it to warm up faster. A typical hopper extends from the oil return fitting on top of the oil reservoir to the outlet fitting in the bottom of the reservoir. In some systems, the hopper tank is open at the lower end to admit oil from the main oil supply. However, other systems have a series of flapper valves that replenish oil in the hopper as it is consumed. [Figure 9-6]

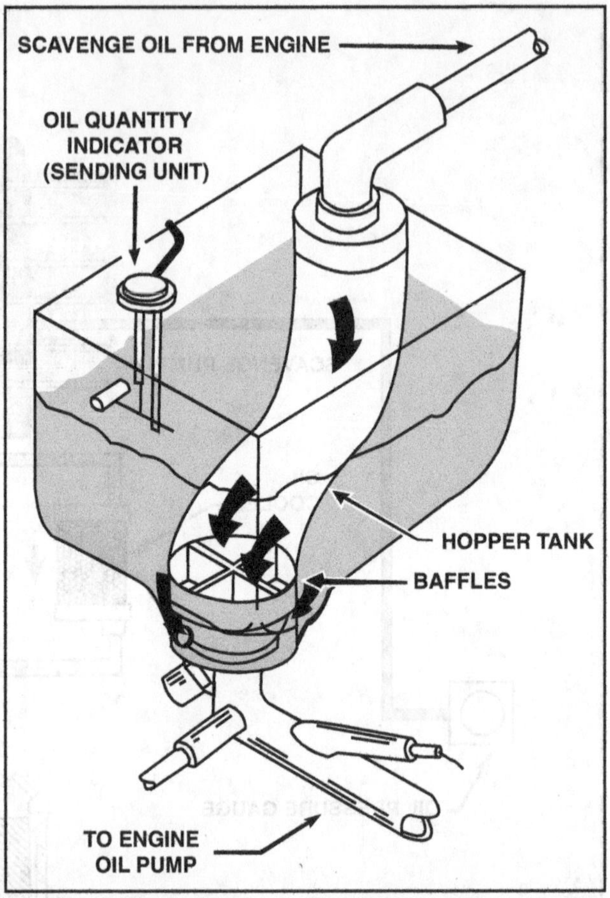


**Figure 9-6. The hopper in an oil reservoir separates circulating oil from the surrounding oil in the tank. This reduces the amount of oil circulated and decreases the time necessary for an engine to warm-up.**

The oil within an oil reservoir in a wet-sump system is typically drawn up to an oil pump through a pipe that extends into the reservoir. However, in many dry-sump systems, an oil outlet is typically located at the lowest point of the reservoir. An exception to this is aircraft that are equipped with Hamilton-Standard Hydromatic feathering propellers. In this case, the oil reservoir feeds the pressure pump through a standpipe that extends into the oil tank while the supply line for propeller feathering is installed at the bottom of the reservoir. This arrangement ensures that enough oil will remain in the reservoir to feather the propeller if an oil line breaks and all of the engine oil is pumped overboard. [Figure 9-7]

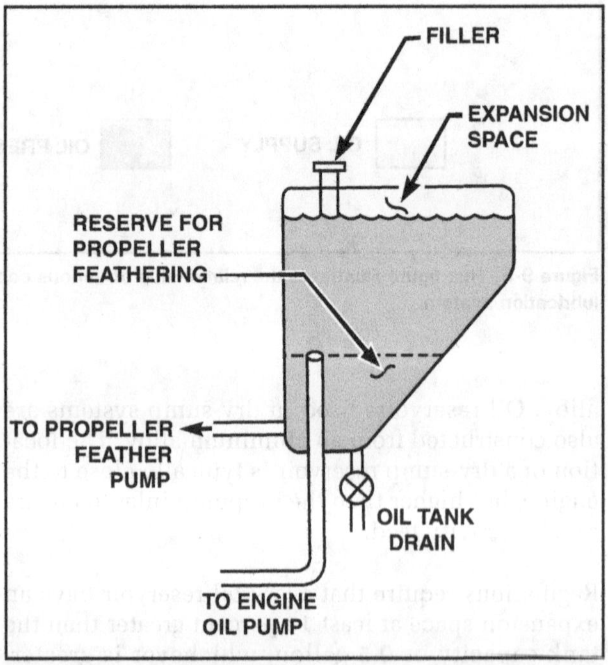


**Figure 9-7. The oil reservoir used with a Hamilton-Standard Hydromatic feathering propeller has two oil outlets. Engine oil is supplied through a standpipe while propeller-feathering oil is drawn from the bottom of the tank; a reserve of oil is always available for propeller feathering.**

## OIL PUMPS

As mentioned earlier, all lubrication systems use constant displacement pumps. Recall that a constant displacement pump moves a fixed volume of fluid per pump revolution or cycle. The two types of constant displacement pumps in reciprocating engine lubrication systems are the gear and gerotor pump.

## GEAR PUMP

The gear oil pump is the most common type of oil pump used in reciprocating engines. A typical gear pump consists of two meshed gears that rotate inside a housing. The gears and housing are precisely machined to tight clearances. The gears pick up oil at the pump inlet, and trap it between the teeth and the housing. As the gears rotate, they deliver the oil to the pump outlet. [Figure 9-8]

## GEROTOR PUMP

Another type of constant-displacement pump is the gerotor-type pump. A typical gerotor pump consists of an engine-driven spur gear that rotates within a free spinning rotor housing. The rotor and drive gear ride inside a housing with two oblong ports—an inlet and outlet. [Figure 9-9]

## SCAVENGE PUMP

In addition to a pressure pump, most dry-sump systems use a scavenge pump to return oil to the reservoir. A scavenge pump can be either a gear or gerotor pump that is driven by the engine. As a rule, the capacity of a scavenge pump is greater than a pressure pump. As oil flows through an engine, its volume increases due to foaming and thermal expansion. The larger capacity of the scavenge pump ensures that oil does not collect in the engine sump.

## PRESSURE RELIEF VALVE

To ensure adequate engine lubrication, oil pressure must be maintained within a particular range at all times. For an engine-driven oil pump to maintain system pressure at low engine speeds, it must produce excessive pressure at high engine speeds. A pressure relief valve prevents this excessive pressure from damaging the engine. A typical pressure relief valve is spring-loaded in the closed position. When oil pressure rises above a preset value, the valve opens and excess oil is returned to the reservoir or oil pump inlet. In a typical system, the relief valve is installed between the main supply pump and the internal oil system. [Figure 9-10]

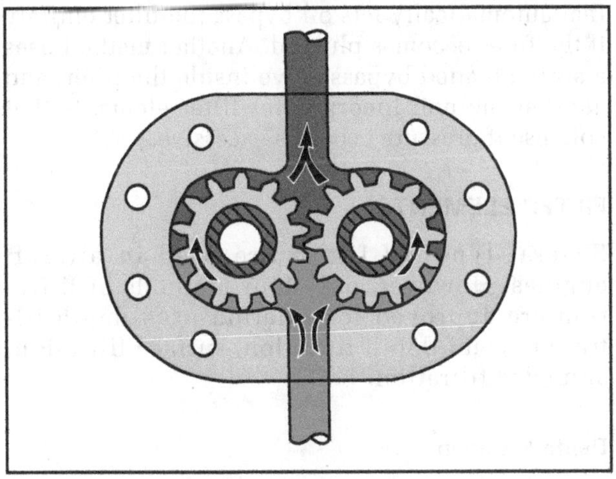

**Figure 9-8. In a gear oil pump, two spur gears rotate inside a housing to pump oil through an engine.**

Relief valves are typically set at a lower pressure than the output pressure of the pressure pump, so a small amount of oil constantly flows through the relief valve at cruise speed. The amount of oil that the valve permits to bypass the internal oil system depends on the clearances between an engine's moving parts. For example, as the clearances between engine parts increase from normal wear, the pump continues to supply a constant volume of oil but the relief valve permits less oil to bypass back to the sump.

Most relief valves can be adjusted by turning a screw to increase or decrease spring pressure. The greater the spring pressure, the higher the resulting oil pressure. On the simplest relief valves, you adjust spring tension by either changing the spring or changing the number of washers behind the spring. However, whenever an oil pressure reading is low, you should first determine why before you adjust to the relief valve. For example, if a light-viscosity oil is used or if some foreign material becomes lodged between the relief valve and its seat, oil pressure will indicate lower then normal. If this is the case, the cause for the low pressure reading should be corrected; any adjustment to the relief valve would be inappropriate.

To help ensure adequate circulation during start up when oil is cold, some engines use a compensated oil pressure relief valve. A **compensated oil pressure relief valve** maintains a higher system pressure when the oil is cold; then, after the oil warms, the valve automatically lowers pressure to the normal operating range. This is accomplished through the use of two springs and a thermostatic valve. When the oil is cold, both springs hold the valve on its seat, which, in turn, permits a higher oil pressure. However, after the oil warms, the thermostatic valve opens a passage and permits oil to flow beneath a piston in the pressure relief valve. As the piston moves upward, it removes the pressure exerted by the high-pressure spring. Normal operating pressure is maintained by the force of the low-pressure spring alone. [Figure 9-11]

## OIL FILTERS

After oil is discharged from an oil pressure pump, it flows to an oil filter that removes solid particles suspended in the oil. This filtration is required to protect the engine's moving parts from solid contaminants.

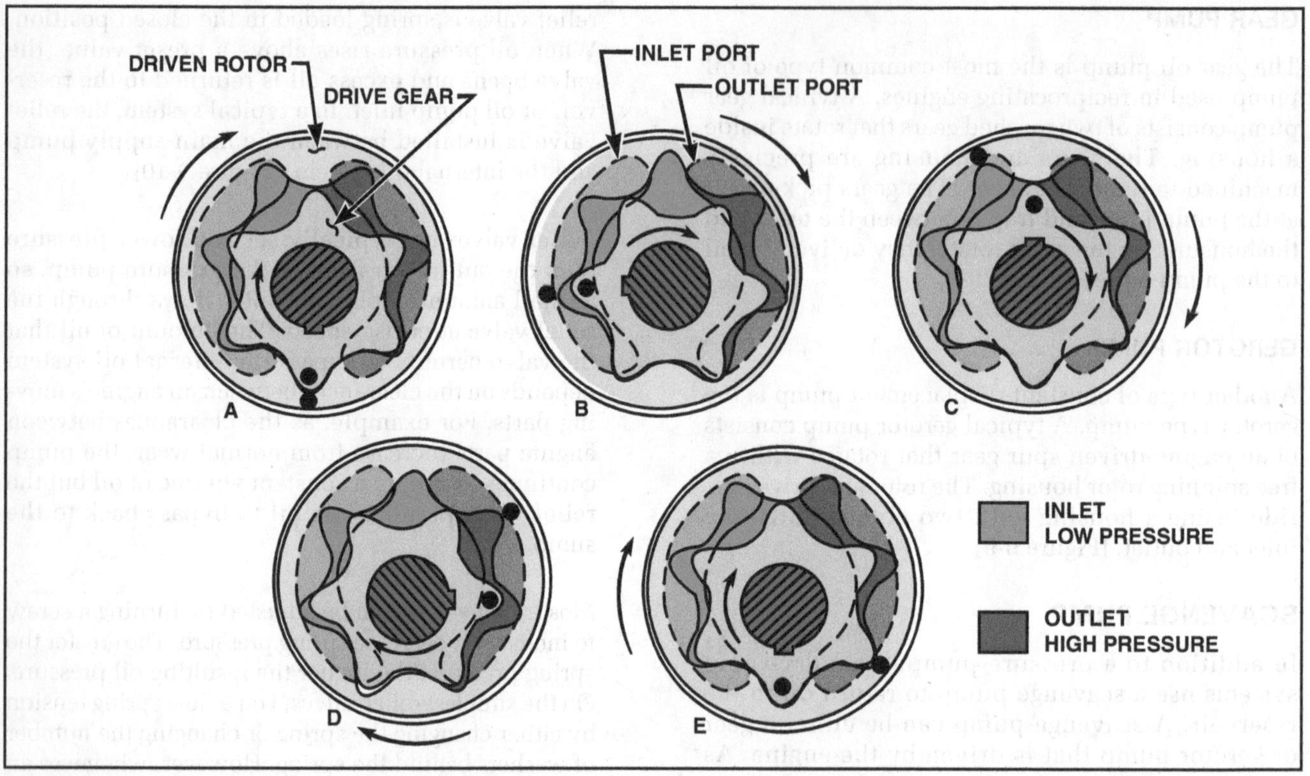


**Figure 9-9. As a gerotor pump rotates, the space between the drive gear teeth and rotor housing alternately increases and decreases. When the space increases at the oil inlet (A, B, and C), oil is drawn into the pump. However, as the space decreases at the outlet (D and E), oil is forced out of the pump.**

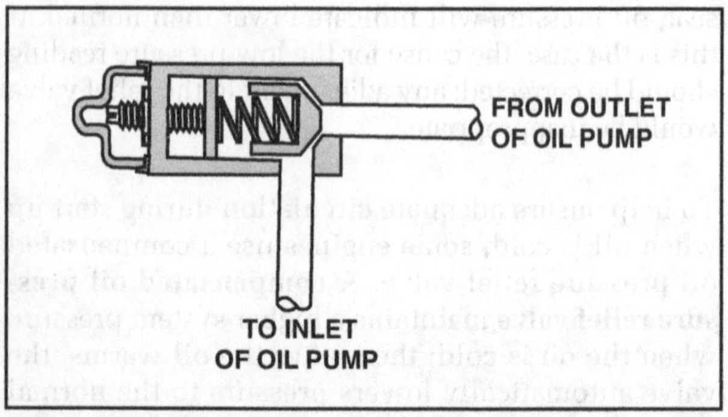


**Figure 9-10. On all pressure lubrication systems, a pressure relief valve is needed to maintain proper system pressure.**

Currently, the two types of filtration systems installed in aircraft engines are the full-flow system and the bypass system. In a **full-flow** filter system, all of the engine oil passes through a filter each time it circulates through an engine. To accomplish this, the filter is in series with the oil pump, between the pump and the engine bearings. [Figure 9-12]

Although not as common, some older engines use a bypass filtration system. With a **bypass**, or **partial flow system**, the filter is parallel with passages to the engine bearings. In this type of system, only about 10 percent of the oil is filtered each time the oil circulates through the system. However, over time, the entire oil supply passes through the filter. [Figure 9-13]

Federal aviation regulations dictate that all oil filters be constructed and installed in a way that permits full oil flow even if the filter becomes completely blocked. Bypass oil filter systems easily accommodate this requirement because most of the oil already bypasses the filter. However, a full-flow filter system must have some means of bypassing the filter. One method is to incorporate an **oil bypass valve** that automatically lets oil bypass the filter entirely if the filter becomes plugged. Another method uses a spring-loaded bypass valve inside the filter; and another method incorporates filter elements that collapse if pressure becomes excessive.

## FILTER ELEMENTS

Several types of filters are used in aircraft engines. However, only four methods of filtration are approved for aviation use—depth filtration, semi-depth filtration, surface filtration, and edge filtration.

### Depth Filtration

Depth filters consist of a matrix of fibers that are closely packed to a depth of about one inch. Oil

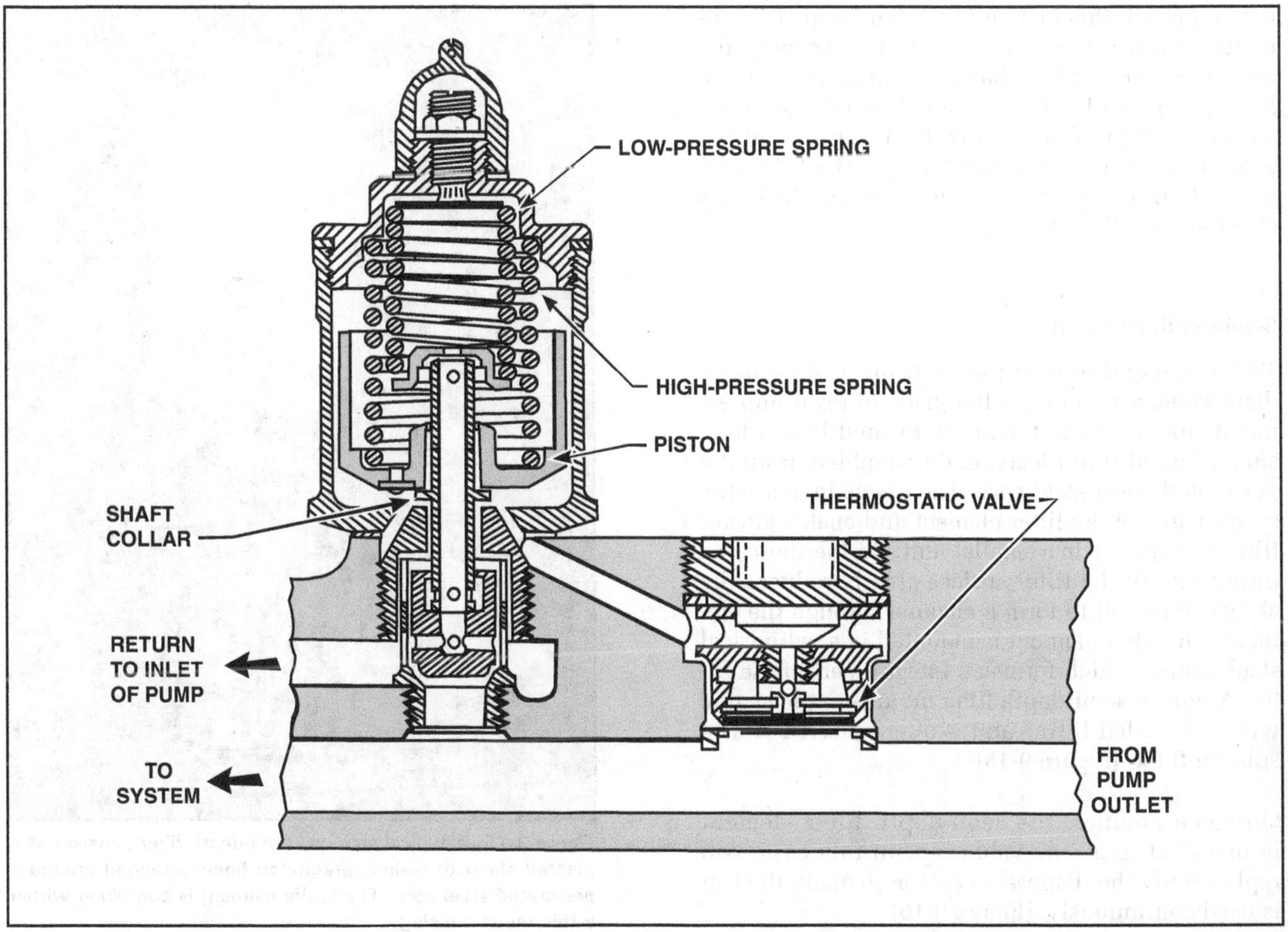


**Figure 9-11. In a compensated oil pressure relief valve, when the oil is cold, the high- and low-pressure springs hold the relief valve closed to maintain an elevated system pressure. However, after the oil has warmed, the thermostatic valve lets pressurized oil enter the relief valve and overcomes high-pressure spring pressure in the relief valve.**

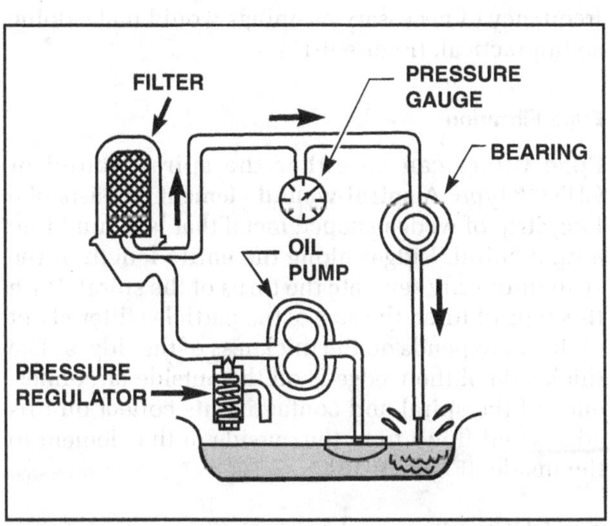


**Figure 9-12. In a full-flow filtration system, all of the engine oil is filtered each time it circulates in an engine.**

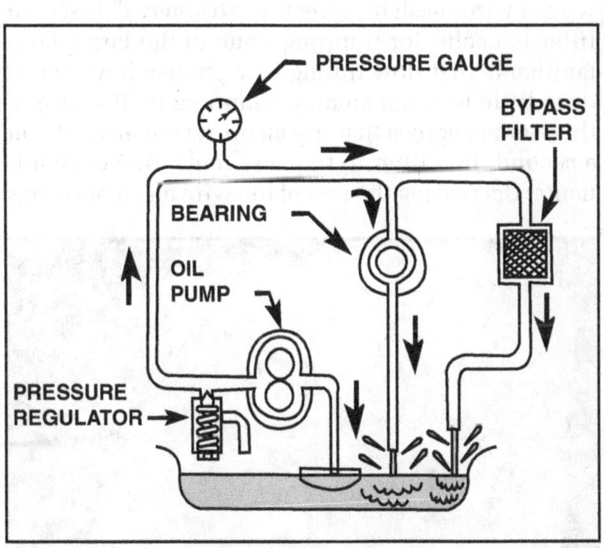


**Figure 9-13. In a bypass filtration system, approximately 10 percent of the oil passes through the filter each time it circulates through the engine. This type of system is typically found on older engines.**

flows through this mat and the fibers trap contaminants. Depth filters are very effective because the large number of fibers have the capacity to trap a large quantity of contaminants. However, a disadvantage of depth filters is that high-pressure oil can sometimes form a channel through the filter element. If this occurs, the filter loses a great deal of its effectiveness. [Figure 9-14]

**Semi-Depth Filtration**

Today, general aviation aircraft most often use a disposable, semi-depth filter made of resin-impregnated fibers. These fibers are formed into a long sheet, folded into pleats, and assembled around a perforated sheet steel core. The pleats increase the surface area of the filter element and enable greater filtering capacity in a smaller unit. Furthermore, the uniformity of the filter surface greatly reduces the ability of the oil to form a channel through the element. The filter element is mounted in a cylindrical steel casing, which forms an integral part of the filter. A typical semi-depth filter mounts to the engine with a threaded fitting and is often referred to as a spin-on filter. [Figure 9-15]

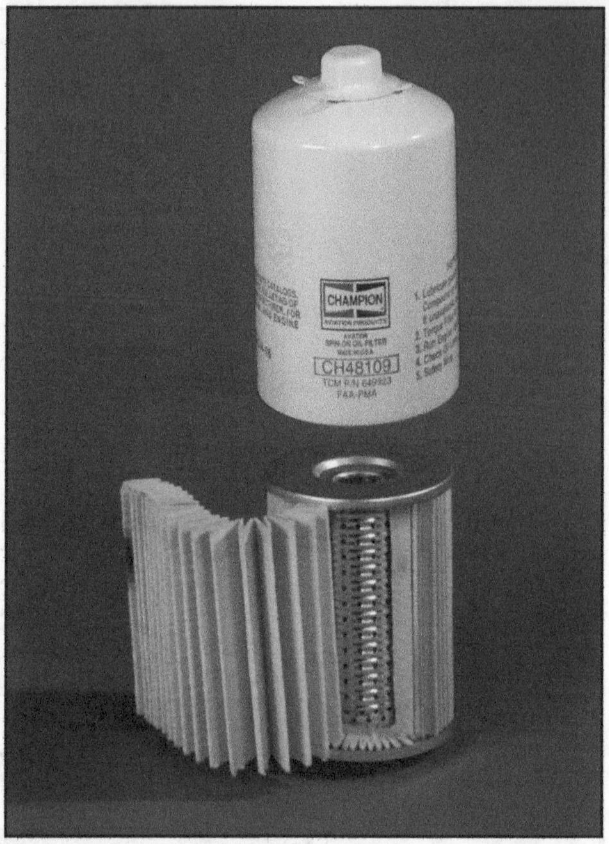


**Figure 9-15. A typical spin-on, semi-depth filter consists of a pleated sheet of resin-impregnated fibers arranged around a perforated steel core. The entire element is contained within a thin metal housing.**

On some engines, the semi-depth filter element is installed in a removable can. In this case, you replace only the disposable center element; the can is used continuously. [Figure 9-16]

**Surface Filtration**

Some aircraft engines are equipped with a standard woven wire-mesh **oil screen**, or **strainer**. This screen filter is useful for trapping some of the larger contaminants that flow through the engine; however, it does little to catch small contaminants. Because of this, some engines that use an oil screen also rely on a second, fine filter to trap any remaining contaminants. Decreasing the size of the wire mesh openings for better filtration is not recommended because the frequency of necessary cleanings would make doing so impractical. [Figure 9-17]

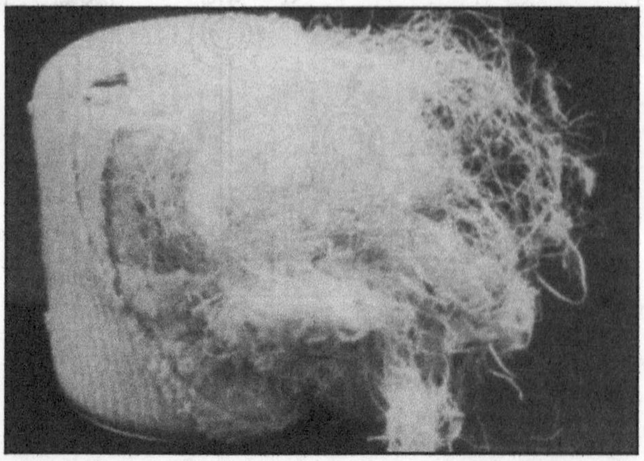

**Figure 9-14. A depth filter consists of a closely-packed fiber matrix element.**

**Edge Filtration**

Edge filters can be either the spiral-wound or CUNO® type. A **spiral-wound element** consists of a long strip of wedge-shaped metal that is wound into a tight spiral. Ridges along the entire length of the strip uniformly separate the turns of the spiral. With this type of filter, the size of the particles filtered out of the oil depends on the thickness of the ridges. The thick side of the wedge is on the outside circumference of the spiral and contaminants collect on this edge as oil flows from the outside of the element to the inside. [Figure 9-18]

The **CUNO filter** consists of a large number of thin metal disks that are stacked on a center shaft. Thin spacers attached to the filter housing separate the disks so that oil can pass between the disks. As with the spiral-wound edge filter, oil flows from the outside of the filter to the inside, leaving contaminants on the outside edge. The spacer thickness

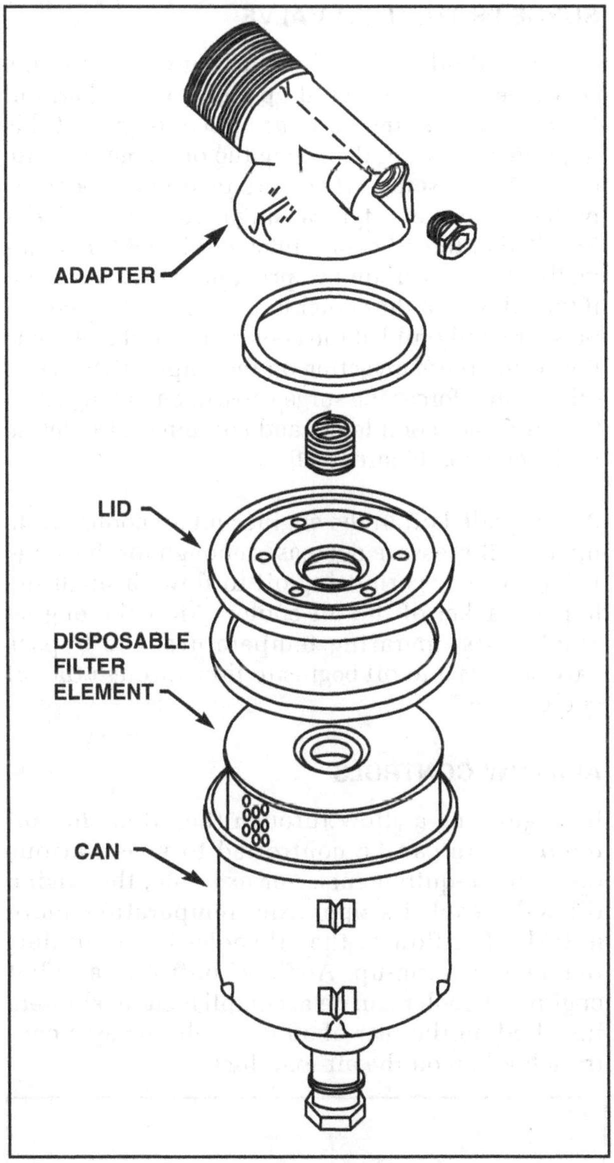


Figure 9-16. On some engines, the filter housing is reused while its disposable filter element is replaced as necessary.

Figure 9-17. Many aircraft engines use a screen surface filtration oil strainer. An oil strainer filters out large particles and helps prevent other filtering elements from becoming clogged.

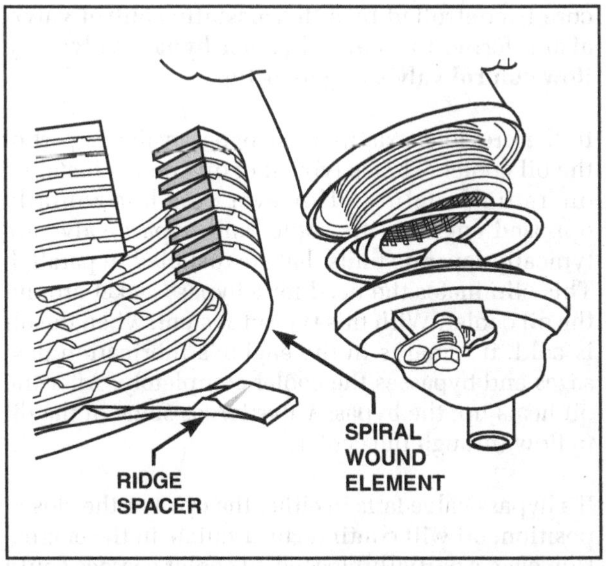


Figure 9-18. A long piece of wedge-shaped metal is wound into a spiral-wound edge filter. Spacers installed on every turn of the element permit oil to pass through the spiral. In this configuration, contaminants collect on the outside of the spiral.

determines the size of the particle contaminants that are filtered out of the oil. Periodically, contaminants must be scraped from the outside edge of the disks. To do this, a handle is attached to the center shaft and used to rotate the disks. Because the spacers are fixed rigidly to the filter housing, they remain stationary and act as scrapers. Contaminants scraped from the disks accumulate in the bottom of the filter housing and are cleaned out during maintenance inspections. CUNO filters were commonly used on many large radial reciprocating engines but are seldom found on aircraft operating today.

## OIL COOLER

Recall that one function of oil is to cool the engine; to do this effectively; heat absorbed by the oil must be removed. In most cases, the excess heat is removed by an oil cooler, or **oil temperature regulator**. An oil cooler is simply an oil-to-air heat exchanger. When installed in a dry-sump system, the oil cooler is typically located in the return line between the scavenge pump outlet and storage reservoir. However, in a wet-sump system, the oil cooler is attached to the engine in the best location as determined by the manufacturer.

One type of oil cooler consists of a core with several copper or aluminum tubes enclosed in a double-walled **annular** shell. When the oil is cold, it flows between the two walls, or **bypass jacket** of the cooler, and bypasses the core completely. However, after the oil heats up, it is routed through the core for cooling. The amount of oil that flows through the core is controlled by a **thermostatic control valve**, also referred to as an oil cooler **bypass valve** or a **flow control valve**. [Figure 9-19]

In the previous example, the bypass valve is part of the oil cooler. This is typical of oil coolers installed on radial engines. However, on horizontally opposed engines, the cooler and bypass valve are typically separate units that are installed in parallel. This eliminates the need for a bypass jacket around the oil cooler. With this type of system, when the oil is cold, it remains in the engine's lubrication passages and bypasses the cooler completely. After the oil heats up, the bypass valve forces some of the oil to flow through the cooler.

If a bypass valve fails in either the open or the closed position, oil will continue to circulate in the engine. However, a partially clogged oil cooler passage could reduce oil flow. For example, if an oil cooler passage becomes partially clogged, less oil will flow through the core and oil temperatures will rise. However, as the oil temperature rises, the bypass valve closes even further to direct more oil through the partially restricted core. This, in turn, limits the amount of oil that circulates through the engine.

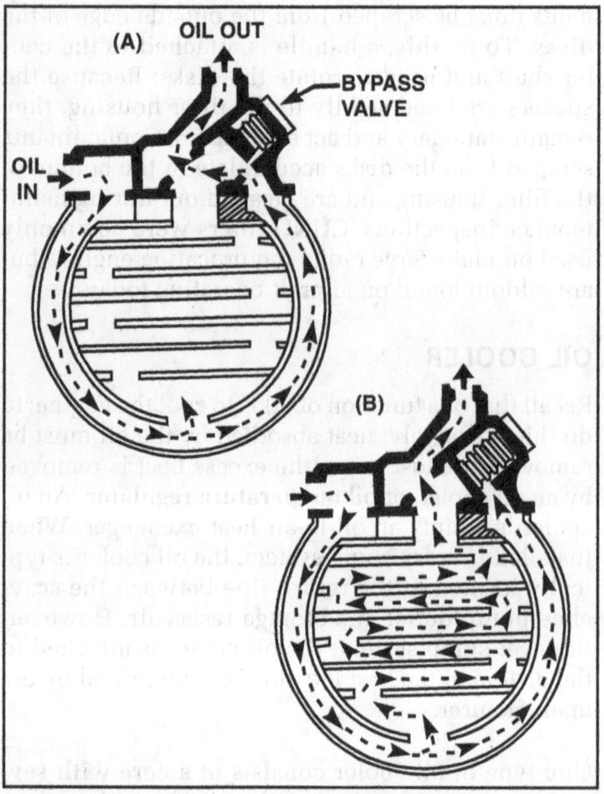


**Figure 9-19. (A) When engine oil is cold, the bypass valve opens and lets the oil bypass the oil cooler core. (B) After the oil warms up, the bypass valve closes and oil is routed through the core, where it transfers its heat to the passing airstream.**

## SURGE PROTECTION VALVE

When cold oil congeals in a dry-sump system, the scavenge pump can build up a potentially harmful high pressure in the oil return line. To prevent this high pressure from damaging the oil cooler or hose connections, some oil coolers incorporate a surge protection valve. A typical surge protection valve is installed at the oil cooler inlet and is held in a normally closed position by spring pressure. However, if the oil within the cooler is severely congealed, oil pressure will build at the cooler inlet and overcome the spring pressure acting on the surge valve. When oil pressure forces the surge valve open, oil bypasses the oil cooler completely and continues circulating in the engine. [Figure 9-20]

As congealed oil in the engine and oil cooler heats up, the oil pressure decreases enough for the surge valve to seat, permitting oil to flow through the bypass jacket of the oil cooler. After the engine reaches its operating temperature, the bypass valve closes and oil begins to flow through the oil cooler core.

## AIRFLOW CONTROLS

By regulating airflow through the oil cooler, oil temperature can be controlled to meet various operating requirements. For example, the engine oil will reach its operating temperature more quickly if airflow to the oil cooler is cut off during engine warm-up. Airflow control to a radial engine oil cooler can be accomplished by shutters installed on the rear of an oil cooler or by a controllable flap on the air-exit duct.

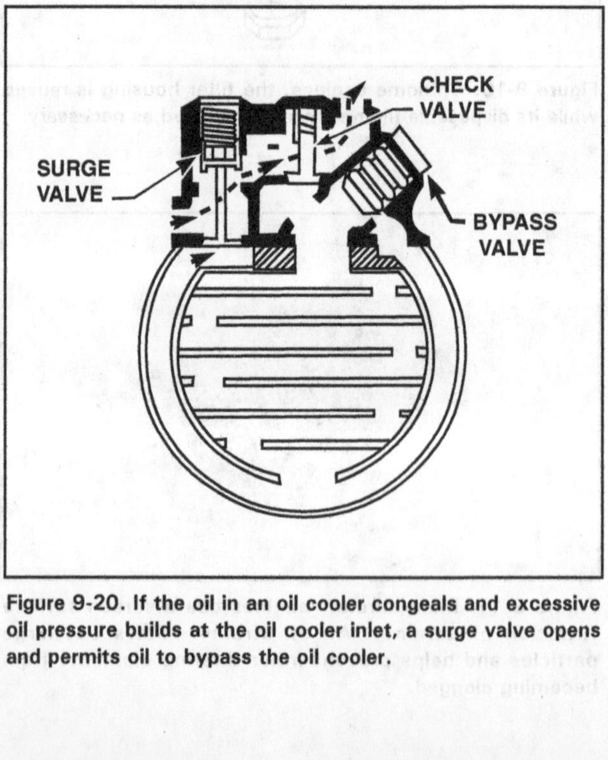


**Figure 9-20. If the oil in an oil cooler congeals and excessive oil pressure builds at the oil cooler inlet, a surge valve opens and permits oil to bypass the oil cooler.**

An oil cooler air exit can be opened and closed automatically or by a control in the cockpit. To provide automatic control, a **floating control thermostat** operates an electrical actuator. In this type of system, a thermostat inserted in the oil line between the cooler and the oil supply reservoir senses the oil temperature and sends electrical impulses that automatically control the actuator.

On horizontally opposed engines, an oil cooler bypass valve is generally sufficient to control oil temperatures. However, when an aircraft regularly flies in an extremely cold climate, an airflow restrictor can be installed to limit the amount of airflow into the oil cooler. An airflow restrictor typically consists of a metal plate that is installed either directly over the face of the oil cooler or in front of a blast tube hole in the rear engine baffling.

## OIL SEPARATOR

On engines that use a wet vacuum pump, engine oil lubricates and seals the vacuum pump. However, as oil circulates through this type of pump, air bubbles become trapped in the oil. To eliminate this entrapped air, an oil separator is installed on the outlet side of the vacuum pump. A typical oil separator consists of several baffle plates that cause the vacuum pump outlet air to swirl. As the air swirls, centrifugal force pulls the oil out of the air and deposits it on the baffle plates. From the baffle plates, the oil drains back to the engine through an oil outlet in the separator. Separating the air and oil accomplishes two things: it prevents oil from flowing into the air system and damaging components such as de-icing boots, and it prevents excess air from being introduced into the oil system.

## OIL DILUTION

On some large reciprocating engines that are operated in extremely cold temperatures, an oil dilution system can be installed. The purpose of such a system is to dilute the oil with fuel to prevent the oil from congealing at extremely cold temperatures. A typical oil dilution system injects gasoline into the oil pump before engine shutdown. This distributes diluted oil throughout the lubrication system. This way, when the engine is started later, the diluted oil flows freely through the engine, ensuring adequate lubrication. After the engine and oil warm up, the gasoline evaporates out of the oil and exits the engine through the crankcase breather.

A typical oil dilution system consists of a cockpit-controlled oil dilution solenoid, an oil dilution valve, and the necessary plumbing. As a rule, the line that injects fuel into the oil is never installed between the pressure pump and the engine pressure system. This prevents pressurized oil from flowing into the fuel supply and contaminating the fuel.

On aircraft with an oil dilution system, engine oil pressure is an indirect indication of how the system is operating. For example, when starting an engine that has diluted oil, the oil pressure will be lower than normal. Similarly, if too much fuel is introduced into the oil or if the oil dilution valve is leaking, the oil pressure will be excessively low and oil temperature will be high.

## OIL PRESSURE GAUGE

The engine lubrication system supplies oil under pressure to the moving parts of the engine. To monitor the effectiveness of the lubrication system, each aircraft engine is equipped with a calibrated oil pressure gauge. Because inadequate oil pressure can lead to oil starvation in engine bearings, and because excessive pressure can rupture gaskets and seals, the oil pressure in most reciprocating engines is limited to a fairly narrow operating range.

Some oil pressure gauges use a Bourdon tube; this design enables a gauge to measure relatively high fluid pressures. The gauge is connected by a metal tube directly to a point immediately downstream from the engine oil pump. The oil pressure gauge measures the oil pressure being delivered to the engine. To protect the gauge from occasional pressure surges, most gauges have a small restriction at their inlet. In addition, most fittings that attach the oil line to the engine also have a small restriction to limit oil loss in the event the oil sense line breaks.

A disadvantage of this type of oil pressure indicating system is that it does not work well in cold weather because the oil in the sense line tends to congeal. The congealed oil then causes false readings of either low or no oil pressure. This error is minimized by filling the oil line with a low-viscosity oil.

In larger and more modern aircraft, electric transmitters measure oil pressure. This system does away with long oil-filled lines between engines and instruments in favor of lightweight wire. In addition to saving weight, electrical transmitters provide greater accuracy. Pressurized oil enters the inlet port of the transmitter and interacts with a diaphragm assembly. As oil pressure increases or decreases, the diaphragm expands and contracts. The diaphragm motion is amplified by a lever and gear arrangement that varies resistance in a circuit by adjusting a potentiometer. The position of the potentiometer is then displayed on the cockpit indicator.

Oil pressure instrument readings provide a critical indicator of engine operation and should be monitored frequently, especially during engine starts. For example, during startup, many aircraft manuals instruct you to shut down an engine after 30 seconds in warm weather (or one minute in extremely cold weather) if no sign of oil pressure is present. Engine shutdown is a precaution to prevent engine damage until the reason for the lack of oil pressure is determined and remedied. A different discrepancy, excessive pointer oscillation, typically indicates that air is trapped in the sense line or that some unit in the oil system is functioning improperly. Furthermore, low oil pressure or fluctuations from zero to normal can be a sign of low oil quantity.

## OIL TEMPERATURE GAUGE

The oil temperature gauge enables a pilot to monitor the temperature of oil entering the engine. Temperature is important because oil circulation cools the engine while it lubricates moving parts. Most oil temperature gauges are calibrated in degrees Fahrenheit and sense oil temperature at the engine's oil inlet.

Most modern oil temperature systems are electrically operated and use either a Wheatstone bridge circuit or a ratiometer circuit. A **Wheatstone bridge** circuit consists of three fixed resistors and one variable resistor whose resistance varies with temperature. When power is applied to a Wheatstone bridge circuit and all four resistances are equal, there is no difference in potential between the bridge junctions. However, when the variable resistor is exposed to heat, its resistance increases and more current flows through the fixed resistor R3 than the variable resistor. This imbalance in current flow produces a voltage differential between the bridge junctions, which causes current flows through the galvanometer indicator. The greater the voltage differential, the greater the current flow through the indicator and the greater the needle deflection. Because indicator current flow is directly proportional to the oil temperature, an indicator calibrated in degrees provides an accurate means of registering oil temperature. [Figure 9-21]

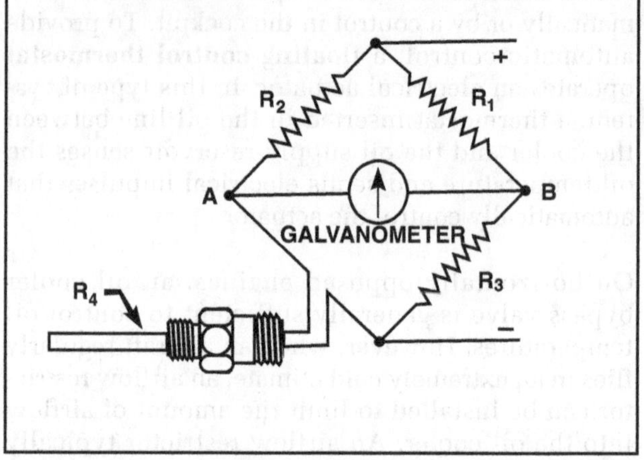


Figure 9-21. A typical Wheatstone bridge has three fixed resistors and one variable resistor. The temperature probe contains a variable resistor. The bridge in the circuit is a galvanometer calibrated in degrees to indicate temperature.

A **ratiometer** circuit measures a current ratio and is more reliable than a Wheatstone bridge, especially when the supply voltage varies. Typically, a simple ratiometer circuit consists of two parallel branches powered by the aircraft electrical system. Two coils are wound on a rotor that pivots between the poles of a permanent magnet, forming a meter movement in the gauge. One branch uses a fixed resistor and coil, and the other uses a variable resistor and coil. [Figure 9-22]

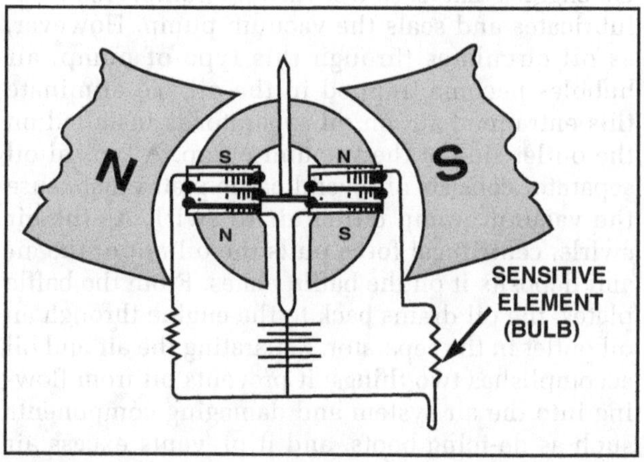


Figure 9-22. A ratiometer temperature measuring system operates with two circuit branches that balance electromagnetic forces.

The shape of the permanent magnet provides a larger air gap between the magnet and coils at the bottom than at the top. Therefore, flux density, or the magnetic field, is progressively stronger from the bottom of the air gap to the top. Current flow through each coil creates an electromagnet that reacts with the polarity of the permanent magnet; torque repositions the rotor until the magnetic forces are balanced. If the resistances of the temperature probe and fixed resistor are equal, current flow through each coil is the same, and the indicator pointer remains in the center position. However, when the probe temperature increases, its resistance increases, causing a decrease in current through the temperature-sensing branch. Consequently, the electromagnetic force on the temperature-sensing branch decreases; the resulting imbalance causes the rotor to rotate until each coil reaches a null, or balance. The pointer attached to the rotor then indicates the oil temperature.

Ratiometer temperature measuring systems are useful for applications in which accuracy is critical or large variations of supply voltages are encountered. Therefore, aircraft and engine manufacturers generally prefer the ratiometer oil temperature sensing system more than Wheatstone bridge circuits.

Some early oil temperature gauges used **vapor pressure**, or a Bourdon tube instrument. With this type of instrument, a Bourdon tube is connected by a capillary tube to a liquid-filled temperature-sensing bulb. The bulb is in the engine's oil inlet line where oil heats the volatile liquid in the bulb. As the liquid in the sensing bulb heats up, the capillary and Bourdon tubes also heat up. This causes the vapor pressure within the capillary and Bourdon tubes to increase, which straightens the Bourdon tube. A mechanical linkage transmits the motion of the Bourdon tube to an indicator.

## SYSTEM MAINTENANCE

The maintenance practices discussed in this section are typical of those used on a horizontally opposed aircraft engine but they are by no means all-inclusive. Before you conduct any maintenance on an aircraft's lubrication system, always consult the appropriate manufacturer's maintenance manuals and service bulletins. [Figure 9-23]

### OIL CHANGE AND SERVICING

In routine service, oil is exposed to many substances that reduce its ability to protect moving parts. Combustion by-products that escape past the piston rings and oil carbonizing are the primary sources of oil contamination in a reciprocating engine. Additional contaminants that can be

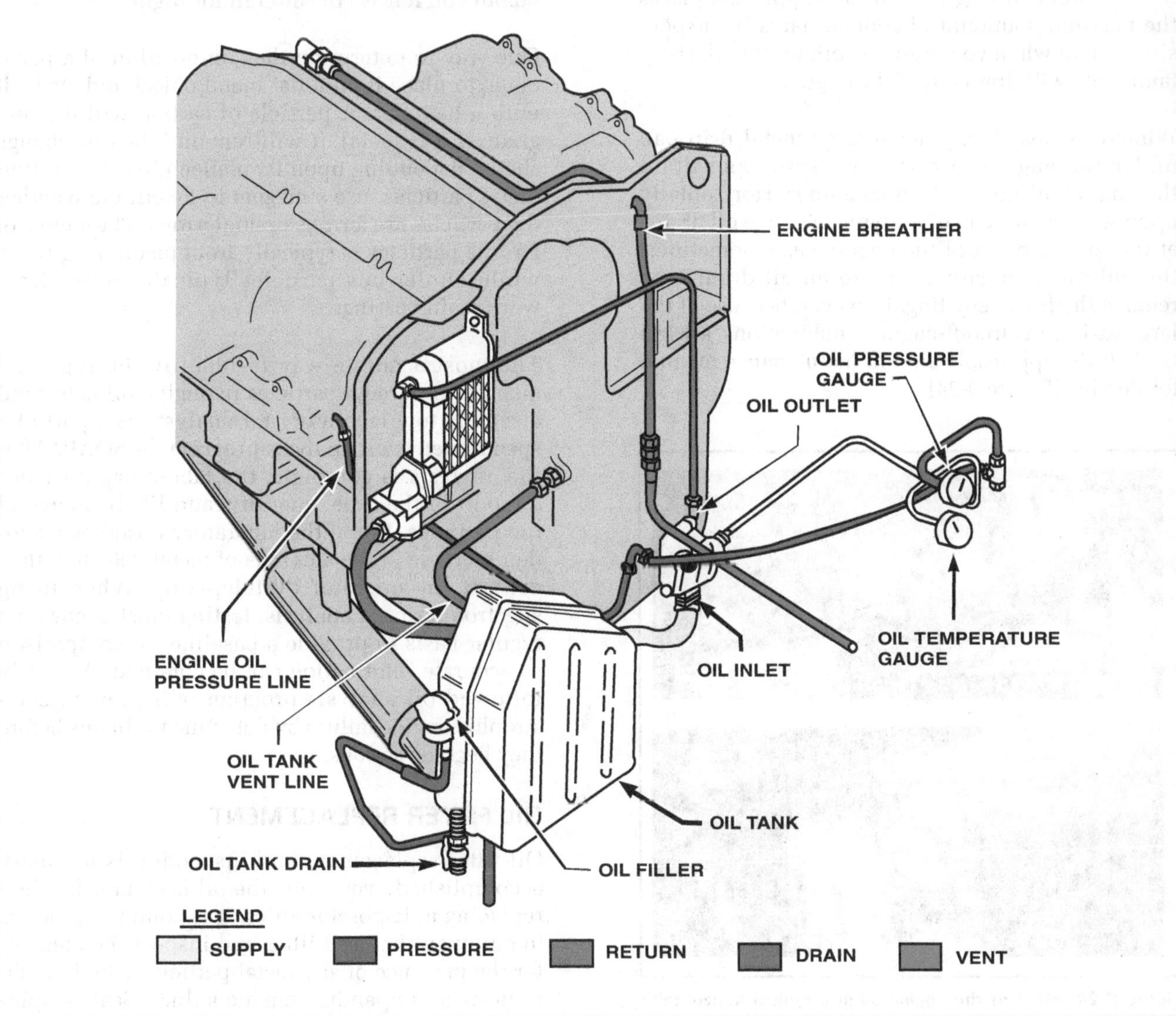


Figure 9-23. This figure illustrates the location of service items on a typical dry-sump system in a horizontally opposed engine.

trapped in lubricating oils include gasoline, moisture, acids, dirt, carbon, and metal particles. If these contaminants accumulate over a period of time they can cause excessive wear on internal engine components. Certain clues that indicate internal engine wear include excessive oil consumption with no evidence of oil leakage. In this case, excessive oil consumption is typically caused by oil leaking past worn piston rings and being consumed in the combustion chambers. To prevent this type of engine damage, the entire lubrication system is drained at regular intervals and refilled with clean, fresh, oil. The recommended interval between oil changes is typically based on the manufacturer's recommendations.

Prior to draining engine oil, you should run up the engine. In addition to warming the engine oil, a pre-inspection runup enables you to verify that the oil temperature and pressure are within acceptable limits. The runup also agitates the oil supply and places the maximum amount of contaminants in suspension so that when you drain the oil, most of the contaminants will drain out of the engine.

Whenever possible, place a large metal drip pan under the engine to catch any spills and drain the engine oil into a clean container. Horizontally opposed wet-sump engines typically have oil drains at the lowest point of the engine case. Sometimes the only way to gain access to an oil drain is to remove the lower cowling. However, because of the large variety of aircraft-engine combinations, always consult the applicable aircraft maintenance manual for details. [Figure 9-24]

**Figure 9-24. Most of the engine oil in a typical horizontally opposed engine is drained by removing one or more oil drain plugs or by opening a drain valve.**

Before opening an oil drain, check the maintenance manual for instructions regarding aircraft position. This step is important because the normal ground attitude of some aircraft can prevent the tank from draining completely. On aircraft that use a dry-sump engine, if you are unable to position the aircraft as necessary, the amount of undrained oil can be excessive; however, you can usually loosen and tilt the oil reservoir completely drain the oil.

The presence of an excessive number of metal particles in the oil itself generally indicates an internal failure in the engine. Be aware, that due to the construction of aircraft oil systems, it is possible for metal particles to remain in the sludge from a previous engine component failure. Furthermore, carbon buildup can break loose from an engine's interior and can be mistaken for metal particles. In any case, you must identify the source of any foreign particles in engine oil and make the appropriate corrections before you release the aircraft for flight.

One way to determine the composition of a particle is to place it on a flat metal object and strike it with a hammer. A particle of carbon will disintegrate; if it is metal, it will remain intact or change shape, depending upon its malleability. If you find metal particles, use a magnet to determine whether the particles are ferrous or nonferrous. The source of ferrous particles is typically from piston ring wear, while nonferrous particles typically result from worn main bearings.

The most accurate way to identify the type and quantity of foreign particles in engine oil is to send a sample to a laboratory for analysis as a part of a **spectrometric oil analysis program**, or **SOAP.** After the analysis is complete, the laboratory provides a report of the type, quantity, and likely source of the particles. When the laboratory observes a sudden increase in the amounts of metal detected, they contact the operator by telephone. When using spectrometric oil analysis, testing must occur on a regular basis to provide a baseline for comparison so accurate information can be obtained. A closely followed oil analysis program will prevent catastrophic engine failure by detecting problems before they become serious.

## OIL FILTER REPLACEMENT

Oil filter replacement and inspection is normally accomplished every time the oil is changed. When replacing a disposable filter, it is common practice to cut open the used filter and inspect the element for the presence of any metal particles which might indicate an impending engine failure. Sealed, spin-on type filters are opened with a special roller can cutter. The cutter removes the top of the container without introducing metal particles that could provide false indications of impending engine problems. [Figure 9-25]

When servicing an engine equipped with an oil screen, remove, inspect, and clean the screen. When removing an oil screen, place a clean, suitable container under the housing to collect the oil that will drain from the engine. The container must be clean to avoid contaminating the collected oil. Otherwise, contaminants in the container might falsely indicate imminent engine failure.

After you remove the oil screen, inspect it for contamination and the presence of metal particles. Metal particles large enough to be trapped by the screen could indicate impending internal engine failure. After you have completed your inspection, clean the screen with an approved solvent prior to reinstalling it in the engine. [Figure 9-26]

After you have completely drained the oil and inspected the screen or filter, replace the drain plug or close the drain valve. If the filter is disposable, install and secure a new one. For aircraft uses an oil screen, clean, reinstall, and secure it. After you have secured all filters and screens, be sure to refill the oil reservoir with the recommended quantity and grade of oil.

After you refill the reservoir, operate the engine long enough to warm the oil. After engine shutdown, wait a few minutes for the oil to settle, and then check the oil level. If necessary, add oil to bring the level up to the prescribed quantity. In addition, inspect the areas around the oil drain plug, oil filter, and oil screen fitting for leaks.

## OIL RESERVOIR

In some instances, you must remove the oil reservoir in a dry-sump system for cleaning or repair. To do this, drain all of the oil and disconnect the oil inlet and vent lines. Then, remove the scupper drain hose and bonding wire. Remove the safety wire and loosen the clamps of the tank-securing straps; then lift the tank out of the aircraft. Reverse this sequence to reinstall the tank.

## OIL COOLER

Oil coolers are normally removed and cleaned during engine overhaul. However, an oil cooler that loses a portion of its cooling effectiveness might have accumulations of sludge that block internal portions of the cooler. If this is the case, you must remove and clean the cooler and then visually inspect it for cracks and other damage. Pay particular attention to all welded or soldered seams because excessive oil pressure can damage them. After you complete the cleaning and repairs, pressure-test the cooler according to the manufacturer's instructions. [Figure 9-27]

## RELIEF VALVE ADJUSTMENT

During routine maintenance, you might be required to adjust the oil pressure relief valve. Oil pressure specifications typically vary between 35 and 90 p.s.i., depending on the engine model. The oil pressure must be high enough to ensure adequate lubrication of the engine and accessories at high speeds and powers, but not so excessive that leakage and damage to the oil system result.

Initial adjustment of an oil pressure relief valve is made at the overhaul shop on a newly overhauled engine prior to the initial test run. However, after an engine is installed on an aircraft, the relief valve pressure setting might require a slight adjustment. In addition, over time, the spring in a relief valve can weaken and require minor adjustment.

To adjust an oil pressure relief valve, remove the cover nut, loosen the locknut, and turn the adjusting screw either clockwise to increase the pressure or counterclockwise to decrease the pressure. After

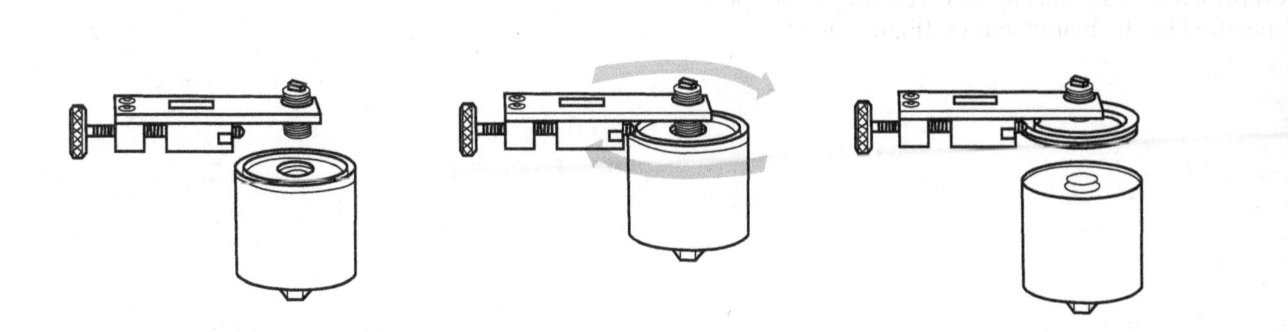

**Figure 9-25. When replacing a disposable oil filter, the standard practice is to cut open the old filter with a special filter cutter and inspect the element for metal particles.**

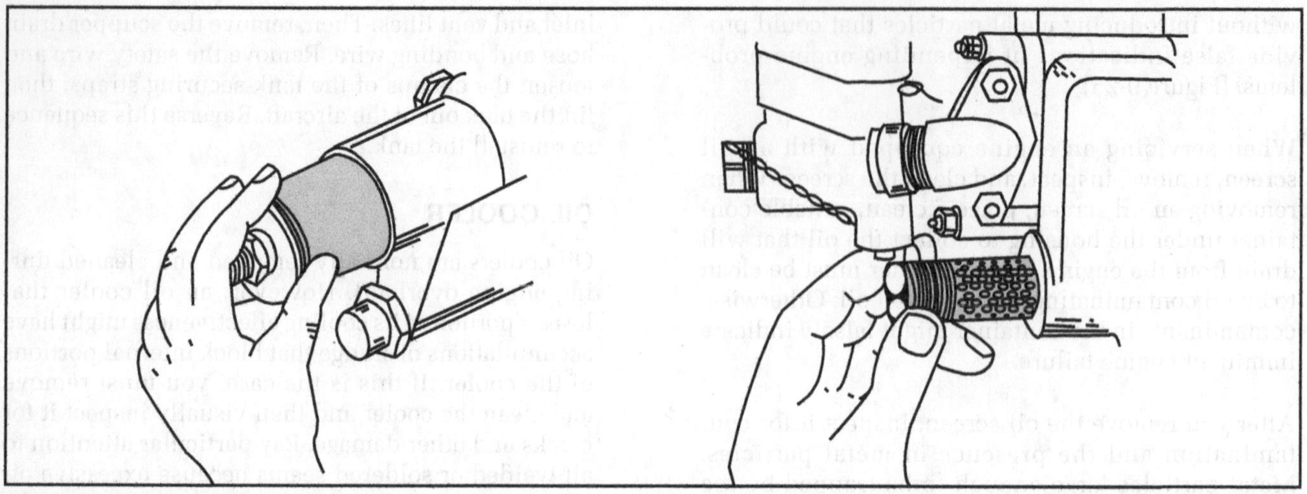

**Figure 9-26. Some reciprocating engines use reusable metal screens to trap sludge and large contaminants. These screens might be installed in both the pressure and scavenge systems.**

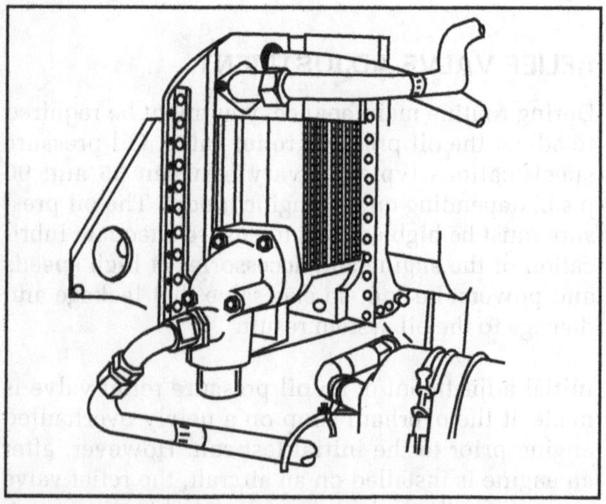

**Figure 9-27. When inspecting an oil cooler, note any sign of leakage, which can indicate a crack in the cooler's core. If you suspect a crack or if the cooler is no longer effectively cooling the oil, you should remove, inspect, and pressure-test the cooler.**

each pressure adjustment, tighten the adjustment screw locknut and operate the engine to check the oil pressure while the engine is running at the speed specified by the manufacturer. [Figure 9-28]

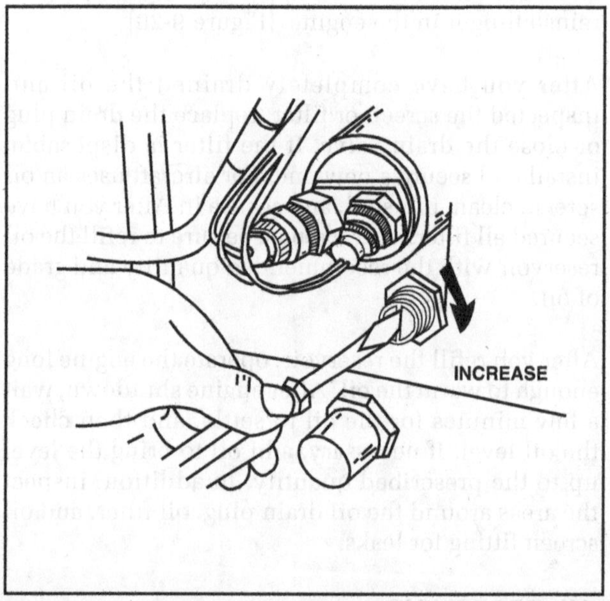


**Figure 9-28. An oil pressure relief valve occasionally requires adjustment. On a typical relief valve, turning the adjusting screw clockwise increases the maximum system pressure and turning it counterclockwise decreases system pressure.**

# SUMMARY CHECKLIST

✓ The oil system of a reciprocating engine can be classified as wet- or dry-sump. In a wet-sump system, oil is stored in the crankcase. In a dry-sump system, the oil is stored in a separate reservoir.

✓ Relief valves prevent the oil system from creating too much pressure.

✓ Oil filters remove solid particles that are suspended in oil. Full-flow filters typically include an oil-bypass valve to enable continued flow if the filter becomes clogged.

✓ An oil cooler is a heat exchanger that uses air flowing through a nacelle to remove heat from engine oil, which flows through tubes that are shrouded by cooling fins.

✓ Oil pressure and temperature are sensed at the engine and displayed in the cockpit to provide the pilot with indications of engine performance.

# KEY TERMS

positive displacement
wet-sump
dry-sump
scavenge pump
scupper drain
bayonet gauge
hopper
temperature accelerating well
compensated oil pressure relief valve
full-flow filter system
bypass system
partial flow system
oil bypass valve
oil screen
strainer
spiral-wound element
CUNO filter
oil temperature regulator
annular
bypass jacket
thermostatic control valve
bypass valve
flow control valve
floating control thermostat
Wheatstone bridge
ratiometer circuit
vapor pressure
spectrometric oil analysis program
SOAP

# QUESTIONS

1. Two types of lubricating systems for reciprocating aircraft engines are:

   a. ______________

   b. ______________

2. The lubrication is distributed to the parts of a reciprocating engine by these three methods:

   a. ______________

   b. ______________

   c. ______________

3. The main disadvantages of a wet-sump engine are:

   a. ______________

   b. ______________

   c. ______________

4. What two markings must be on the oil filler cap?

   a. ______________

   b. ______________

5. Oil tanks used on engines equipped with Hydromatic propellers will feed the pressure pump from a standpipe, leaving a reserve of oil for ______________ ______________.

6. A gear-type oil pump is a ______________ (constant or variable) displacement pump.

7. Constant-displacement oil pumps ______ (do or do not) require a relief valve to control their output pressure.

8. The two types of oil filter systems are:

   a. ______ ______

   b. ______________

9. In the ______ (full-flow or by-pass) filter system, only a portion of the oil is filtered each time it circulates.

10. The most popular filter in common use for general aviation aircraft is the disposable ________ (surface or semi-depth) filter.

11. The CUNO filter is an ________ (edge- or depth-) filtration type oil filter.

12. The ________ ________ (flow control or surge protection) valve determines which of the two possible paths the oil will take through a cooler.

13. When the oil is cold, it flows ______________ (through or around) the core of the oil cooler.

14. ________ ______________ is a system installed on some reciprocating engines to aid in cold weather starting by introducing fuel into the oil system prior to shutdown.

15. Oil pressure is measured at the ___________ (inlet or outlet) of the engine driven oil pump.

16. The main contaminants found in used engine oil are:

   a. ______________

   b. ______________

   c. ______________

   d. ______________

   e. ______________

   f. ______________

17. Oil coolers are normally removed and thoroughly cleaned and inspected at ________ ________ (what event).

18. The oil pressure on engines using an adjustable oil pressure relief may be increased by turning the adjustment screw ______________ (clockwise or counter-clockwise).

# SECTION C

## TURBINE ENGINES

The lubrication system of a turbine engine supplies oil to the internal moving parts to reduce friction and heating. In most cases, pressure is used to lubricate all the necessary components within a turbine engine. Unlike reciprocating engines, whose moving parts can splash oil around the engine, the moving parts of a turbine engine simply rotate on bearings. Because turbine engines operate at much higher temperatures than their reciprocating counterparts, the lubrication system must carry a greater amount of heat away from the components that it lubricates. To do this, oil typically circulates through a turbine engine at a high flow rate.

In a turbine engine, the oil never comes into contact with combustion gases. As a result, the engine consumes very little oil. The oil reservoir of a turbine engine is smaller than one for a comparably sized reciprocating engine. The oil reservoir on a small turbine engine on a business jet typically holds between three and five quarts of oil. Because the oil is separated from combustion gases, the oil remains cleaner and oil changes are less frequent.

### LUBRICATING OILS

Turbine engines have extremely tight tolerances and their ball and roller bearings are subject to relatively low pressures. Because of this, low viscosity oils are used in turbine engines.

The oil used in turbine engines must provide adequate lubrication over a wide temperature range, typically from –60°F to +400°F. With such a wide temperature range, conventional mineral-based oil would congeal at the low temperature extremes and break down at the upper extremes. Furthermore, mineral-based oils tend to leave lacquer and carbon, or **coke**, deposits when exposed to extremely high temperatures. Because of this, turbine engines almost exclusively use synthetic oils.

Synthetic oils have a low volatility, which prevents evaporation at high altitudes. Most synthetic oils also contain an additive to reduce foaming, which ensures positive lubrication. Synthetic oils also possess a high viscosity index, high flash point, low pour point, and excellent cohesion and adhesion properties. Cohesion is the characteristic of an oil molecule that causes it to stick to other molecules under compression loads. Adhesion allows oil to adhere to surfaces under centrifugal loads.

Two types of synthetic oils are currently used in turbine engines: Type I (MIL-L-7808) and Type II (MIL-L-23699). Type I synthetic oil is an alkyl diester oil with a 3 centistoke rating. This type of synthetic oil has very low viscosity and was used primarily in early turbine engines. Type II synthetic oil is a polyester lubricant that has a 5 centistoke rating and is used in most modern turbine engines.

As discussed in Section A, different types of synthetic oil should not be mixed. Furthermore, because different brands of synthetic oil have different, often proprietary, additives, different brands of the same type of oil should not be mixed.

### SYSTEM CLASSIFICATION

Like reciprocating engines, turbine engines can have a wet- or dry-sump lubrication system. Currently, wet-sump lubrication systems are primarily used on some auxiliary power units; however, they were used extensively on early turbine engines. In a typical wet-sump system, oil is stored in an engine sump or accessory gearbox. From here, oil is pressurized and routed through multiple filters before reaching the main rotor bearings and couplings. After oil lubricates the main bearings, it drains to low-lying areas where a scavenge pump sends it back to the sump or gearbox. Because the oil in a wet-sump system is generally stored in the accessory gearbox, the bearings and drive gears within the accessory gearbox can receive oil through splash lubrication. [Figure 9-29]

Today, the majority of turbine engines use a dry-sump lubrication system with pressure, scavenge, and breather subsystems. In this type of system, an oil pump draws oil from the oil reservoir and provides pressure and spray lubrication throughout the engine. After the oil circulates, it accumulates in low-lying areas, and the scavenge pump sends it back to the reservoir.

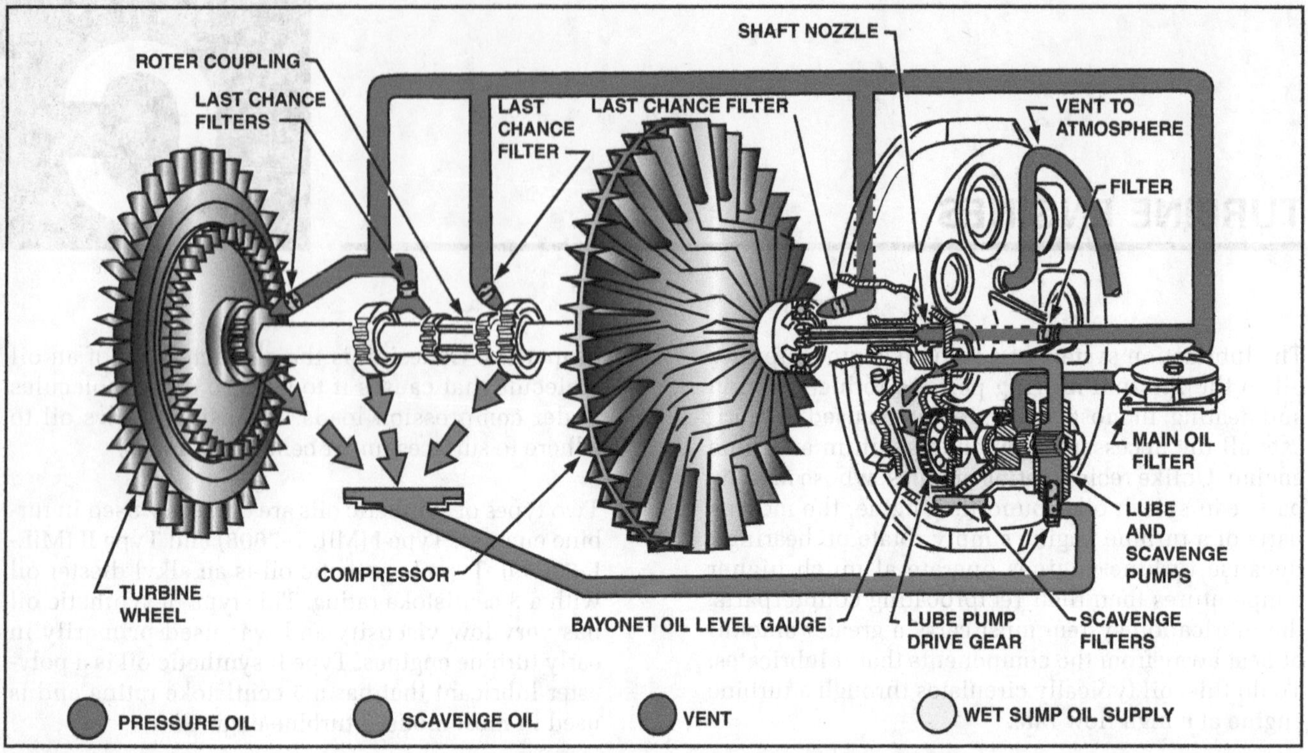


**Figure 9-29. In this wet-sump lubrication system, pressurized oil flows from the oil pump through several filters to the main rotor bearings and coupling. After the oil circulates through the bearings, one or more scavenge pumps return the oil to the accessory case.**

A typical pressure lubrication system consists of an oil reservoir, pressure and scavenge pumps, a pressure relief valve, several oil filters, oil jets, an oil cooler, and vent lines. Usually an integrated oil temperature and oil pressure gauge monitors system performance.

## OIL RESERVOIR

The oil reservoir of a dry-sump system is typically constructed of formed sheet aluminum or stainless steel, and furnishes a constant supply of oil to the engine during all approved flight maneuvers. As mentioned earlier, in a dry-sump system, the oil reservoir can be mounted externally or internally. When mounted externally, the reservoir might be attached to the engine case or mounted inside the aircraft structure. When mounted internally, the oil reservoir is formed by an internal space, or cavity, within the engine structure. Common locations for internal oil reservoirs include cavities between major case sections and propeller reduction gear boxes.

The oil supply for a wet-sump system is typically located in the main gearbox at the lowest point in the engine. This position permits splash lubrication of accessory gears and bearings.

To ensure a positive flow of oil to the oil pump inlet, most oil reservoirs are pressurized. Pressurizing the reservoir suppresses oil foaming, which helps to prevent pump cavitation. In most cases, an adjustable relief valve pressurizes the oil reservoir vent line. Reservoir pressure builds until the relief valve opens to evacuate excess pressure. A typical relief valve is adjusted to maintain a reservoir pressure between approximately three and six p.s.i.

As mentioned in the previous section, regulations require that all oil reservoirs have an expansion space of at least 10 percent of the reservoir capacity, or 0.5 gallon, whichever is greater. The expansion space provides sufficient room for oil to expand as it heats and to accommodate the accumulation of foam. In addition, all oil filler caps or covers must be marked with the word "OIL" along with designations regarding the permissible oil. Most of the oil reservoirs installed in dry-sump systems include a scupper drain.

As an engine's moving parts agitate lubricating oil, air typically becomes entrained in the oil. To counteract this, many oil reservoirs contain some form of **deaerator**, or **air-oil separator**. In some engines, a separator is installed in the accessory gearbox; other systems use on a separator in the oil reservoir. One type of deaerator swirls the air/oil mixture, relying on centrifugal force to separate the oil from the air. The oil then drains to the reservoir while the air is vented overboard. Another type of deaerator uses a tray in the top of the reservoir to disperse the oil when it returns to the reservoir. As the oil spreads in a thin layer, the trapped air bubbles escapes from the oil. A similar method is used by oil reservoirs with a dwell chamber. In this system, the oil/air mixture enters the dwell chamber at the bottom of the oil reservoir. Scavenge pump pressure then forces the oil upward through the dwell chamber and spreads it into a thin film from which the entrained air is released. [Figure 9-30]

The most common method for checking the oil level in a reservoir is with a dipstick. In addition to a dipstick, some oil reservoirs use a sight gauge to satisfy the regulatory requirements for a visual means to check oil level. However, after prolonged use glass indicators tend to cloud over and then operators must rely on the dipstick method. [Figure 9-31]

## OIL PUMPS

Like reciprocating engines, all turbine engine pressure lubrication systems use a constant displacement pump. Recall that a constant displacement pump moves a fixed volume of fluid per revolution or cycle. The three types of constant displacement pumps that turbine engines use are gear, vane, and gerotor pumps.

### GEAR PUMP

The gear pump is the most common type of oil pump used on turbine engines. A typical gear pump consists of two meshed gears that rotate inside a housing. The gears and housing are precisely machined to maintain tight clearances. Oil is picked up by the gears at the pump inlet and trapped between the teeth and the housing. As the gears rotate, the trapped oil is delivered to the pump outlet.

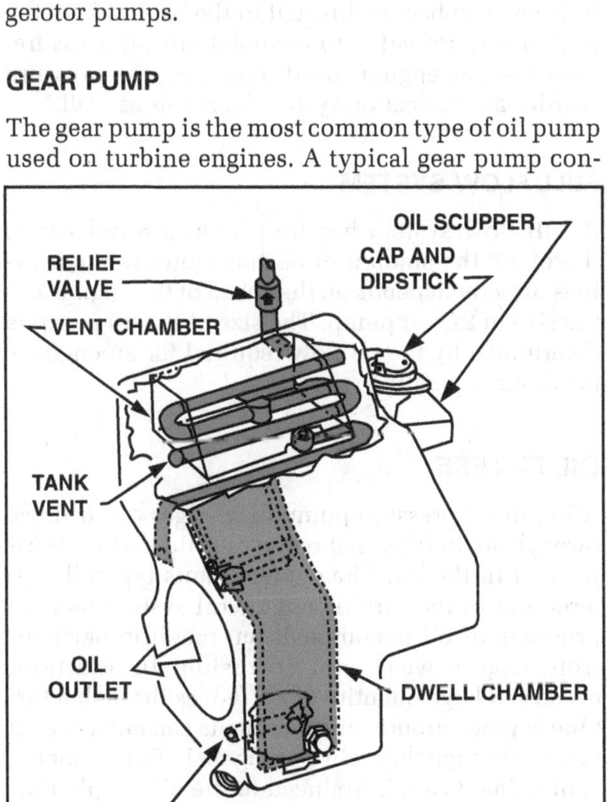


**Figure 9-30. In an oil reservoir with a dwell chamber, oil enters the bottom of the oil reservoir. Oil passes through the dwell chamber and is spread into a thin film to release entrained air.**

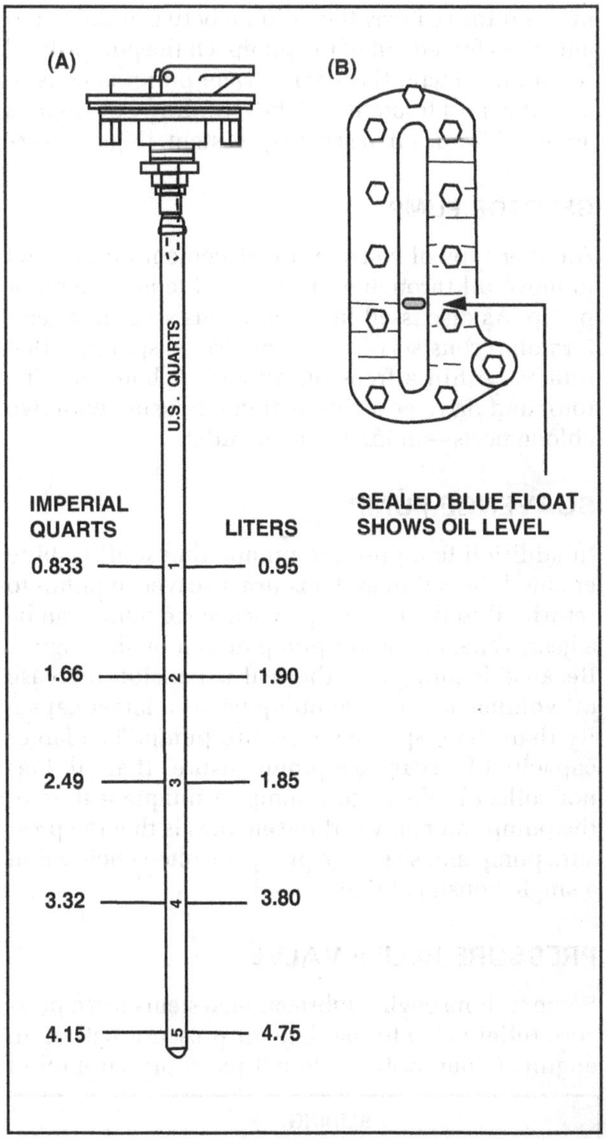


**Figure 9-31. (A) Many turbine engines use a conventional dipstick to indicate oil level in the main reservoir. (B) Some reservoirs are equipped with a sight gauge to provide a visual method for checking oil level.**

### VANE PUMP

A vane pump uses sliding vanes in an eccentric rotor to move fluid. The rotor drive shaft and eccentric rotor form a single rotating part, driving the vanes, which form the pump chambers. The sliding vanes move in and out of the eccentric rotor, increasing the chamber volume when approaching the oil inlet. As a chamber rotates past the inlet, the eccentric shape of the rotor reduces the volume between the vanes and oil is forced out of the pump. Of the pumps used in an oil system, the sliding vane pump is considered the most tolerant of debris. Sliding vane pumps are ideal for use in a scavenge system. [Figure 9-32]

## GEROTOR PUMP

Another type of constant-displacement pump used to move oil through a turbine engine is the gerotor pump. As discussed in the previous section, a gerotor pump consists of an engine-driven spur gear that rotates within a free-spinning rotor housing. The rotor and drive gear ride within a housing with two oblong ports—an inlet and an outlet.

## SCAVENGE PUMP

In addition to a pressure pump, almost all turbine engine lubrication systems use a scavenge pump to return oil to the reservoir. A scavenge pump can be a gear, vane, or gerotor pump driven by the engine. Because foaming and thermal expansion increase oil volume, a scavenge pump needs a larger capacity than the respective pressure pump. The larger capacity of a scavenge pump ensures that oil does not collect in the engine sump. A unique feature of the pumps on many turbine engines is that the pressure pump and scavenge pump are often enclosed in a single housing. [Figure 9-33]

## PRESSURE RELIEF VALVE

Some turbine engine lubrication systems use a pressure relief valve to regulate oil pressure within an engine. Other systems do not use a pressure relief

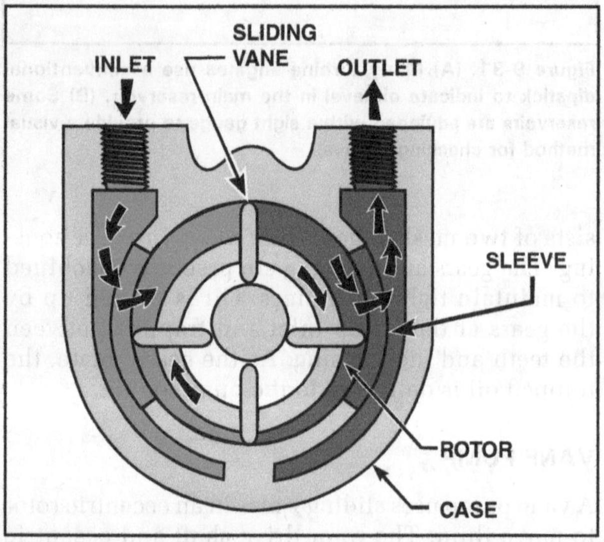


**Figure 9-32. In a vane pump, a set of vanes slide in and out of the rotor as it rotates in the pump housing. Because the rotor is offset in the housing, the volume between each set of vanes increases and decreases, causing the pump to pull fluid in one side and force it out the other.**

valve, but instead permit full pump pressure to circulate in the engine. Lubrication systems with a relief valve are often referred to as pressure relief valve systems, while systems without are called full-flow systems.

## PRESSURE RELIEF VALVE SYSTEM

In a pressure relief valve system, a spring-loaded, normally closed relief valve regulates oil flow to the bearing chambers. When the oil pressure rises above a preset value, the valve opens and returns excess oil to the reservoir or oil pump inlet. The pressure required to open the valve typically corresponds to the oil pump's output capability when the engine is running at idle speed. This guarantees adequate oil pressure throughout the engine's operating range.

In a turbine engine, the pressure within the bearing chambers increases dramatically with increases in engine speed. As the pressure within the bearing chambers increases, the pressure differential between the bearing chambers and the lubrication system decreases. Therefore, as the pressure within the bearing chambers increases, less oil flows to the bearings. To maintain adequate oil pressure to the bearings, some of the pressurized air within the bearing chambers is directed to the back side of the pressure relief valve to augment spring pressure. This way, as engine speed increases, the pressure within the lubrication system increases as well.

## FULL-FLOW SYSTEM

A full-flow system has no pressure relief valve; therefore, the amount of oil that flows to the bearings directly depends on the speed of the engine and the size of the oil pump. The size of the oil pump is determined by the oil flow required for an engine's maximum operating speed.

## OIL FILTERS

After an oil pressure pump discharges oil, it flows through an oil filter that removes solid particles suspended in the oil. The contaminants typically filtered out of the turbine engine oil system include products of oil decomposition, metallic particles from engine wear, and corrosion. In addition, because a large quantity of air moves through a turbine engine, airborne contaminants can enter the oil system through the main bearing seals. Occasionally, contaminants are introduced to the oil supply during servicing.

All turbine engines include an oil filter downstream from the oil pump. Additionally, most engines force the oil through another filter just prior to enter-

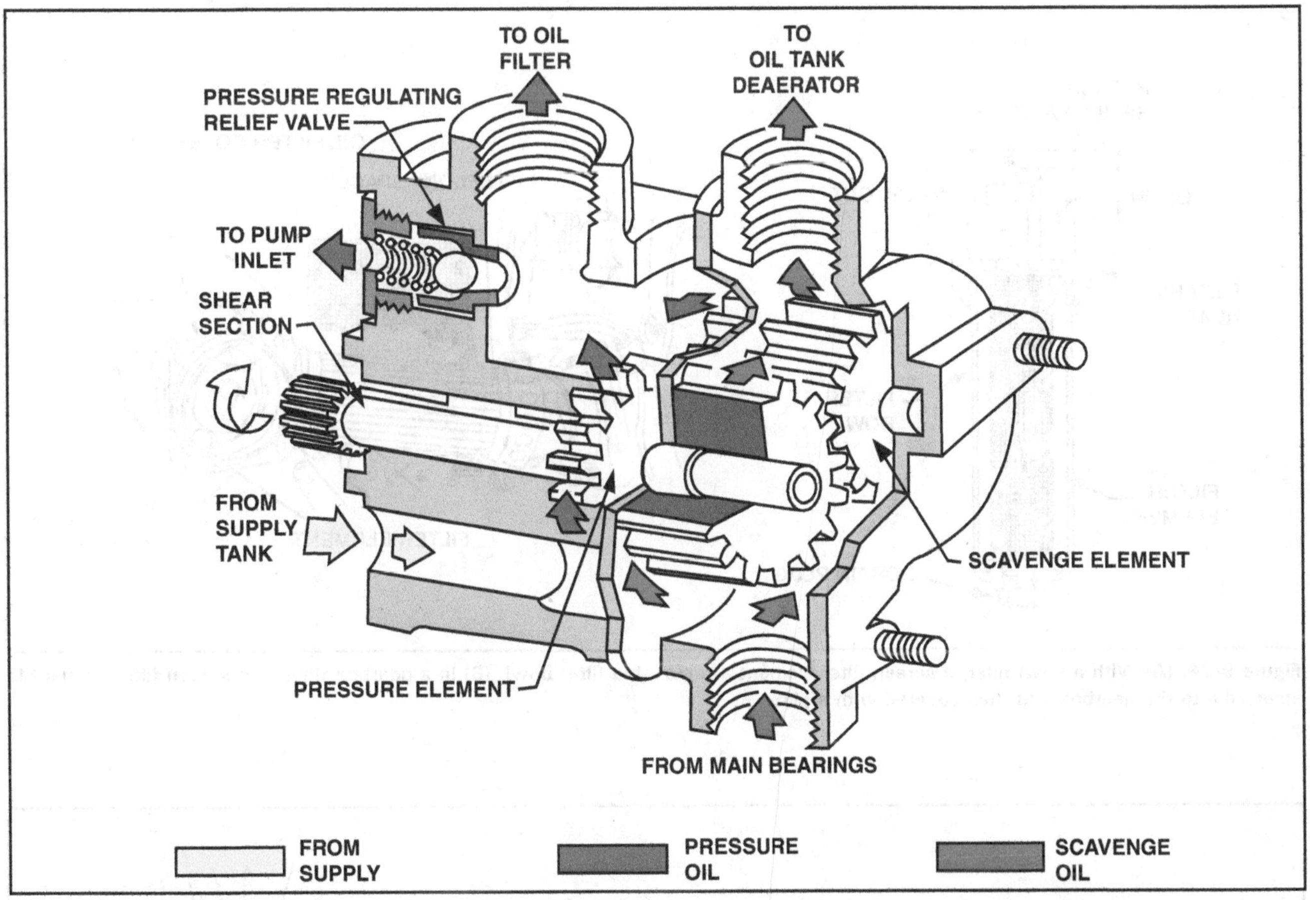


**Figure 9-33. Many turbine engines use a single pump unit that houses both the pressure and scavenge pumps.**

ing the bearing chambers. This filter is commonly referred to as a **last chance filter** because it represents the final opportunity to filter oil before it enters the bearing chamber. Because last chance filters are installed deep within an engine, they are cleaned only when an engine is disassembled for overhaul.

On some engines, filtration is also provided in the scavenge subsystem. In this type of system, the oil is filtered prior to its return to the reservoir; contaminants flushed out of the bearing chambers are not mixed with the clean oil in the reservoir.

The effectiveness of a turbine engine oil filter is measured in microns. One micron represents a size or distance equal to one millionth of a meter, or approximately .000039 inch. To put micron measurements in perspective, consider that objects must be approximately 40 microns or larger to be distinguishable by the human eye.

The three types of filters used in turbine engines are the wire-mesh oil screen, the screen disk, and the pleated-fiber filter. A typical wire-mesh filter is rated at 20 to 40 microns. Particles larger than 40 microns in size are filtered from the oil supply, but smaller particles can pass through. To create a larger surface area for filtration, many oil screens are pleated. Typically installations that use screen filters include bowl filters, in-line filters and gearbox filters. [Figure 9-34]

The screen-disk filter is more common to Pratt & Whitney engines and consists of a series of wafer-thin screens separated by spacers. The screens are stacked on a perforated metal core and oil is filtered as it passes from the outer edge to the core. A typical rating on a screen disk filter is approximately 20 microns. The construction of this filter permits disassembly for cleaning. This type of filter is often used in the pressurized portion of an oil system and fits into an annulus in the main accessory gearbox. [Figure 9-35]

Pleated-fiber filters are typically rated at about 15 microns and are similar to the filters used in reciprocating engines. A typical pleated-fiber filter element consists of millions of resin-impregnated fibers,

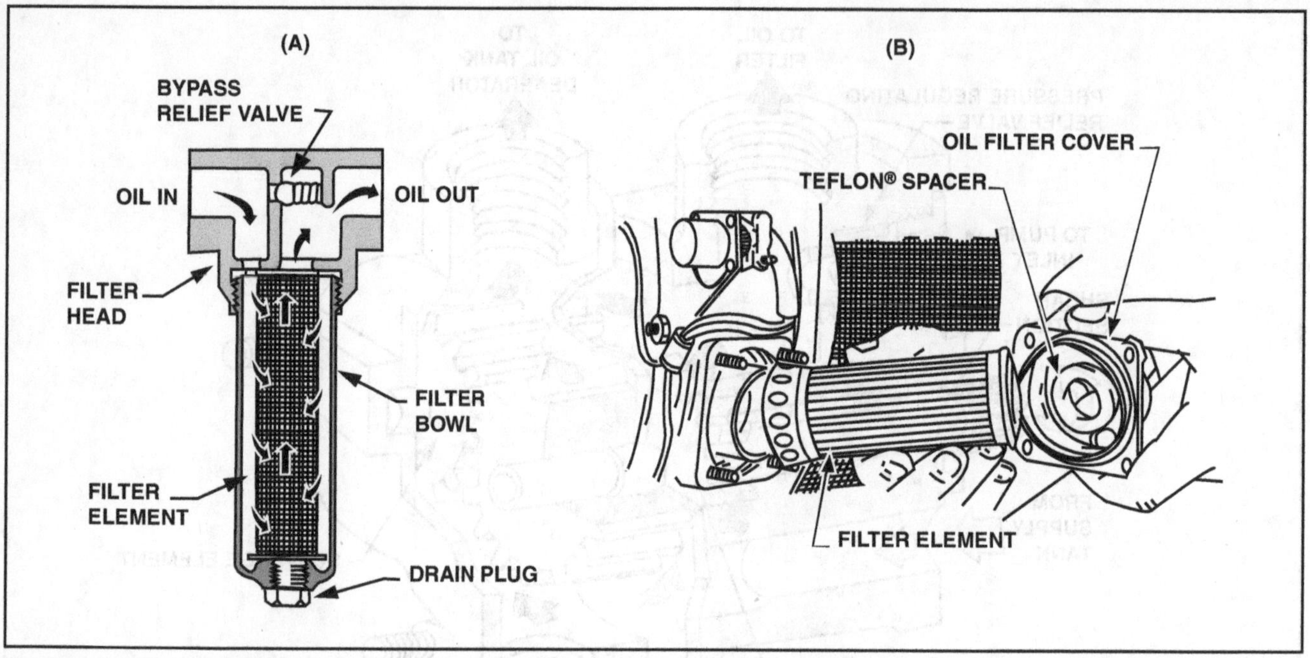


**Figure 9-34. (A) With a bowl filter, a screen filter element a removable filter bowl. (B) In a gearbox filter, the screen filter element is inserted into the gearbox and then covered with a plate.**

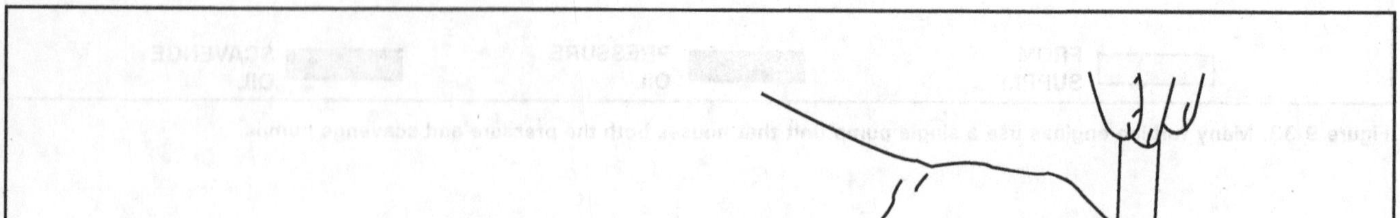


**Figure 9-35. (A) A typical screen-disk filter consists of several wafer-thin screens separated by spacers. (B) This configuration allows easy disassembly and cleaning.**

formed into a long sheet, folded into pleats, and assembled around a perforated steel core. Pleated-fiber filters are generally replaced at specific time intervals.

Regulations require that oil must be able to flow fully even if a filter becomes completely blocked. Therefore, a means for bypassing the filter is necessary. The most common way to meet this requirement is to incorporate an **oil bypass valve.** The use of unfiltered oil to lubricate main bearings can cause extensive damage, so most turbine-powered aircraft include a warning light to alert the pilot that the filter is being bypassed.

## OIL JETS

An oil jet is a fixed nozzle that provides a relatively constant oil flow to the main bearings at all engine speeds. Oil jets are located in the pressure lines adjacent to, or within, the bearing compartments and rotor shaft couplings. Due to the high speed at which main rotor bearings operate and the high loading placed on them, a constant oil flow to the bearings is vital. This is especially true for the turbine bearings because they are subjected to the most heat.

Oil jets can deliver lubrication oil as a solid oil spray or an air-oil mist. While an air-oil mist is considered adequate for some types of bearings, a solid oil spray typically provides better lubrication. In fact, a solid oil spray is required in engines that use oil dampened bearings to reduce rotor vibrations and compensate for slight rotor misalignments.

The small nozzle orifices in the tips of oil jets clog easily, but because they are located deep within an engine, they are accessible for cleaning only during engine overhaul. Therefore, the oil must be free of particle contaminants. As discussed earlier, last chance filters are placed in the oil line upstream from the oil jets to help prevent nozzle clogs. Should the last chance filter become clogged, bearing failure is imminent.

## VENT SYSTEM

In many turbine engines, the bearing chambers and accessory gearbox are vented to the oil reservoir. The vents keep excessive pressure from developing, maintain the appropriate pressure differential in the bearing chambers, and ensure that oil jets maintain the proper spray pattern. In addition, the pressurized air within the bearing chambers and accessory gearbox provides a source of pressurization for the oil reservoir. Turbine engine oil reservoirs are pressurized to help ensure a positive flow of oil to the pump and to minimize foaming. To regulate the amount of pressurization, the oil reservoir is vented to the atmosphere through a check relief valve that maintains a reservoir pressure of three to six p.s.i.

## CHECK VALVES

A check valve is sometimes installed in the oil supply line of dry-sump oil systems. The check valve prevents supply oil from seeping through the oil pump elements and high-pressure lines after shutdown. Without the check valve, oil could accumulate in the accessory gearbox, compressor rear housing, and combustion chamber. Such accumulations could cause excessive loading on the accessory drive gears during the next engine start, contamination of the cabin pressurization air, or an internal oil fire. Check valves are usually spring-loaded, ball-and-socket valves constructed to permit the free flow of pressurized oil in one direction. The oil pressure required to open a check valve varies, but typically ranges from two to five p.s.i.

## OIL COOLER

One function of oil is to cool the engine; however, to accomplish this, the heat absorbed by the oil must be removed. In most cases, an oil cooler removes excess heat. The oil cooler in a turbine engine can be located in either the pressure subsystem or the scavenge subsystem. When installed in the pressure subsystem, the lubrication system is sometimes referred to as a **hot tank system** because the scavenge oil is not cooled before entering the reservoir. When the oil cooler is located in a scavenge subsystem, the lubrication system is often referred to as a **cold tank system** because the oil is cooled immediately before entering the reservoir.

The oil coolers on some early turbine engines were simple oil-to-air heat exchangers similar to the oil coolers on reciprocating engines. Although this type of oil cooler is effective, the cooler must be installed near the front of the engine for exposure to ram air. Modern oil coolers use fuel to cool the oil. Oil-to-fuel heat exchangers achieve two important functions simultaneously: they cool the oil to an acceptable operating temperature and preheated the fuel to improve combustion. In addition, because an oil-to-fuel heat exchanger does not have to be exposed to ram air, its placement and installation is simplified.

In a typical oil-to-fuel heat exchanger, consisting of a series of joined tubes with an inlet and outlet port, fuel flows through the cooler continuously while a thermostatic bypass valve controls the amount of oil that flows to the oil cooler. When the oil is cold, the bypass valve permits the oil to bypass the cooler. When the oil heats up, the bypass valve forces the oil to flow through the cooler. [Figure 9-36]

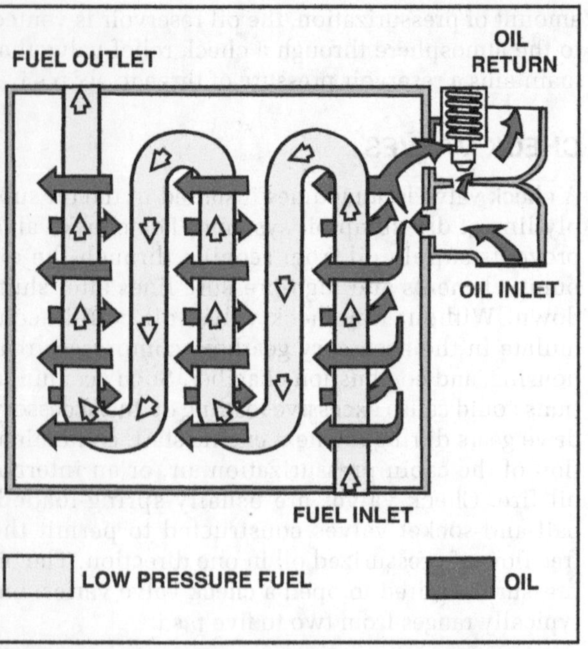


**Figure 9-36. An oil-to-fuel heat exchanger transfers heat from the engine oil to the fuel. This cools the hot oil before it re-enters the engine and warms the fuel to prevent the formation of ice crystals.**

## CHIP DETECTORS

Many scavenge subsystems contain permanent magnet chip detectors to attract and retain ferrous metal particles. These chip detectors serve two functions. First, the magnet prevents metal particles attracted to the detector from circulating in the engine and causing additional wear. Second, metal particles collected on a chip detector provide valuable information when troubleshooting an engine problem.

As a rule, the presence of small fuzzy particles or grey metallic paste demonstrates normal engine wear and is not a cause for concern. However, the presence of metallic chips or flakes indicates serious internal wear that must be investigated further and remedied. [Figure 9-37]

Some chip detectors incorporate an electric circuit to control a cockpit indicator light. An **indicating chip detector** has a positive electrode in the center of the detector and a negative, or ground electrode incorporated in the shell. When a metal chip bridges the gap, it completes the indicator circuit, and the warning light illuminates. The flight crew must respond to the warning to take the necessary precautions to limit engine damage while ensuring flight safety. The appropriate response is usually based, in part, on the indications of several engine instruments and on what happens after the indicator is reset. [Figure 9-38]

A modern type of chip detector is the **electric pulsed chip detector**. This type of detector can discriminate between small particles associated with normal wear and larger particles, which can indicate impending component failure.

Pulsed detectors are designed to operate in a manual mode or a combination manual and automatic mode. In the manual mode, the warning light illuminates each time the gap is bridged, regardless of particle size. The engine operator can activate an electrical pulse to burn off small debris. If the warning light is extinguished and remains off, the warning indication is due to a non-failure-related cause. However, if the warning light remains illuminated or repeatedly comes on after being cleared, maintenance should be scheduled to troubleshoot the cause.

In the automatic mode, a time-delay relay is activated in the warning circuit. This relay prevents the warning light from illuminating immediately when the electrode gap is bridged. This way, if the gap is bridged by small debris, a pulse of electrical energy has time to automatically discharge across the gap before the warning light illuminates. If the resulting burn-off opens the gap, the light does not illuminate;

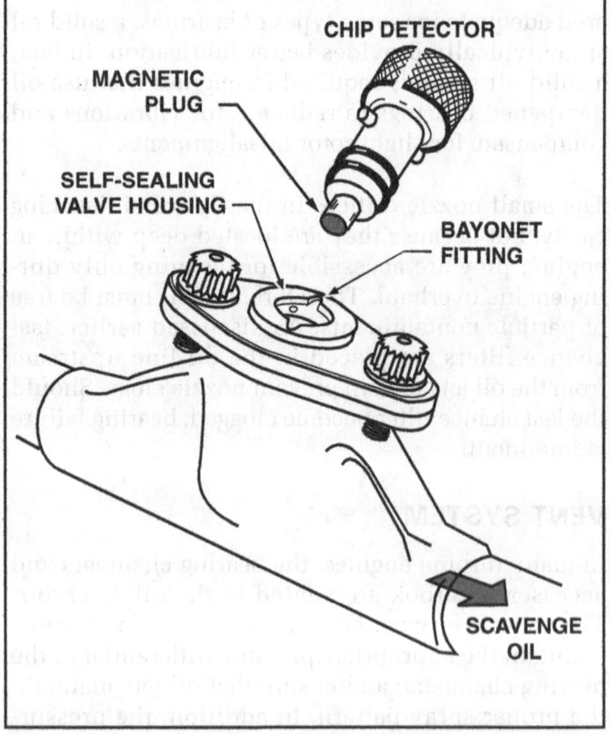


**Figure 9-37. A magnetic chip detector, typically located in the oil return line, collects ferrous particles suspended in the engine oil. During scheduled engine maintenance, the chip detector is removed and visually inspected.**

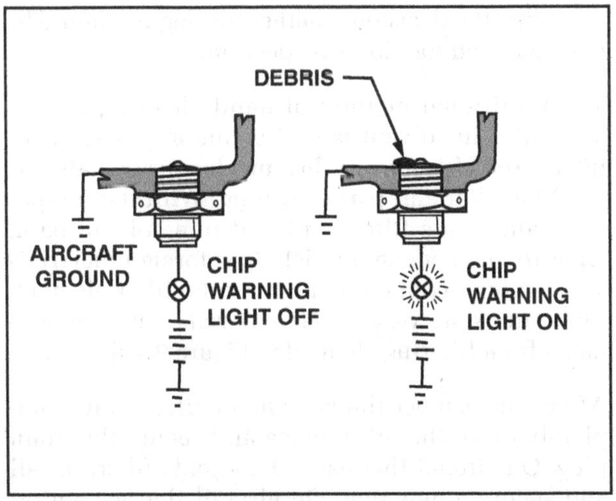


**Figure 9-38. With a chip detector that incorporates a warning light, ferrous debris collecting on the magnet bridges the gap between the positive and ground electrodes and completes the indicating circuit.**

however, large debris will remain in place after the burn-off cycle and the warning light will illuminate when the time-delay relay closes. [Figure 9-39]

## OIL PRESSURE GAUGE

To monitor the effectiveness of the lubrication system, all aircraft engines are equipped with a calibrated oil pressure gauge. The sensor location for a turbine engine pressure gauge is typically down-

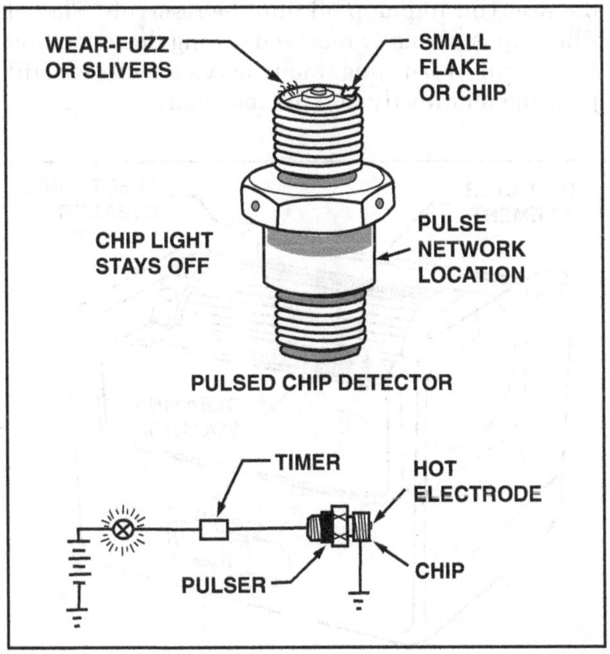


**Figure 9-39. With an electric pulse chip detector, the engine operator can fire an electrical pulse across the detector gap to burn off insignificant debris. In addition, incorporating a timer reduces false warnings.**

stream of the main oil filter. This location ensures an accurate indication of the pressure being delivered to the engine. As an additional feature, some oil pressure systems incorporate a low-pressure warning light. When aircraft electrical power is turned on and the engine is not operating, the low oil pressure light illuminates. After the engine is started, the warning light should extinguish when oil pressure surpasses the low limit.

## OIL TEMPERATURE GAUGE

The oil temperature gauge indicates the cooling effectiveness of the oil as it lubricates the moving parts. The location of the oil temperature sensor in a turbine engine lubrication system can either be in the pressure subsystem or the scavenge subsystem. Because of the lubrication system's high flow rate (typically two to five times reservoir capacity every minute), the temperature of oil throughout the entire system is very consistent.

# SYSTEM MAINTENANCE

The following discussion of maintenance practices is typical for turbine engines but not all-inclusive. Before performing any maintenance on an aircraft engine, consult the appropriate manufacturer's maintenance manuals and service bulletins.

Maintenance of a turbine engine lubrication system usually includes adjusting, removing, cleaning, and replacing various components. For example, oil filters are periodically cleaned or replaced, and pressure relief valves require occasional adjustment.

## OIL CHANGE

In routine service, oil is constantly exposed to substances that reduce its ability to protect moving parts. The primary contaminants in turbine engines include gasoline, moisture, acids, dirt, carbon, and metal particles. If contaminants accumulate over a period of time, they would cause excessive wear on internal engine components.

The recommended interval between oil changes is typically based on the manufacturer's recommendations. Because the oil in turbine engines is sealed from combustion gases, there is a longer interval between oil changes than with reciprocating engines. For example, a typical oil change interval for many business jets is between 300 and 400 hours or 6 months, whichever comes first. On larger turbine engines that consume more than 0.2 quarts per hour, some operators rely on oil replenishment as an effective method of changing oil. The logic behind this is that normal replenishment automatically changes all of the oil every 50 to 100 hours.

When changing engine oil, drain the engine as soon as possible after engine shutdown. At this point the maximum amount of oil is in the reservoir, and the contaminants are in suspension. As a result, the majority of contaminants will be removed from the engine with the oil.

The oil in turbine engines is typically drained from the oil reservoir, the accessory gearbox sump, the main oil filter, and other low points in the system. Some manufacturers recommend that the lubrication system be flushed periodically. Flushing procedures usually consist of filling the engine with the proper oil or cleaning agent and motoring the engine with the starter. Then the oil or cleaning agent is drained from the engine.

When draining oil, inspect it closely for signs of contamination. For example, if the engine oil is dark brown or blackish, but little or no contaminants are present, the engine may have overheated. This discoloration is a result of a chemical reaction that indicates oil decomposition. The cause of overheating could be low oil quantity or an engine malfunction such as a clogged oil jet or disintegrating bearing. Consult the engine logs for evidence of excessive oil consumption and thoroughly analyze other clues in accordance with the appropriate troubleshooting guides in the maintenance manual.

A spectrometric oil analysis program (SOAP) is extremely valuable for turbine engines. As with reciprocating engines, you must be analyze a series of samples before you can develop an accurate trend forecast. On engines that do not receive regular oil changes, regular oil analysis is still recommended. To do this, samples must be drawn from the oil reservoir. In this case, oil samples should be drawn from the center of the oil reservoir within 15 minutes after engine shutdown to ensure that the wear materials and contaminants remain suspended in the sample.

## OIL FILTER REPLACEMENT

You should remove the oil filter at every regular inspection. The type of filter element determines whether you clean or replace it. If the filter is reusable, disassemble, inspect, clean the element, and then reinstall it. Inspect disposable filters for metallic particles and replace them.

Any contaminants that are large enough to be seen in filter bowls or on a filter screen are a matter of concern. Always follow the manufacturer's instructions to determine the source of the contaminants. If a spectrometric oil analysis program has been followed, you can compare a read-out of the various metals present in the latest oil sample to earlier test results. These results provide important information regarding the decision whether the engine should be disassembled for closer inspection.

The traditional method of hand cleaning a reusable filter in solvent is still common practice. An **ultrasonic cleaner** or **vibrator cleaner** can also be used for filter and parts cleaning. With these types of cleaners, the filter is placed in a solvent bath. High frequency energy dislodges foreign materials and removes contaminants from the filter element. These units are very effective at removing contaminants from filtering elements. [Figure 9-40]

After you inspect the screens or filters and completely drain the oil, replace and secure the drain plug. On aircraft that use a disposable filter, install and secure a new one. On aircraft that use an oil screen, clean and reinstall the screen, and secure the original unit. After all filters and screens are secure, refill the oil reservoir with the recommended grade of oil.

There is no standard oil identification system in use. In fact, some oil products do not include a type number or MIL Specification on their labels. In some cases, you can find these specifications only in oil company's literature.

Synthetic oils for turbine engines are usually supplied in one-quart containers to minimize the opportunities for contaminants to enter the lubrication system. However, many oil reservoirs are equipped with pressure remote filling capability. To use this feature, an oil pumping cart is attached to the reservoir to pump oil into the reservoir. The oil filler cap is normally removed during this operation to prevent over-filling. Many service facilities still pour the oil directly into the reservoir.

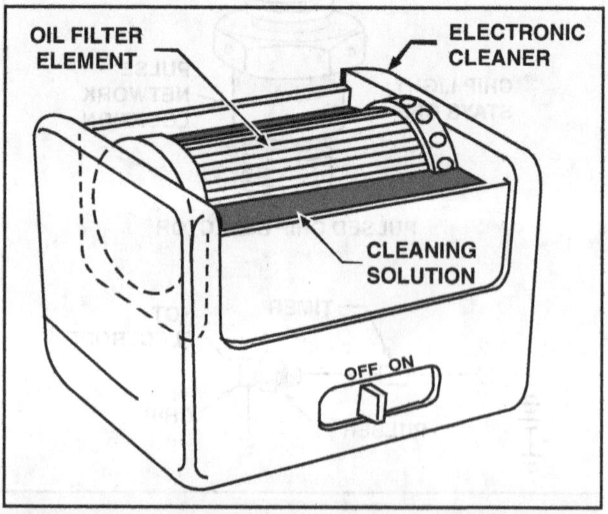


**Figure 9-40. If approved by the engine manufacturer, you can thoroughly clean reusable oil filter elements by immersing them in a cleaning solution in an ultrasonic cleaning device.**

Ground servicing personnel should ensure cleanliness during servicing to avoid inadvertently contaminating the oil supply. When adding oil that is supplied in cans with metal tops, use a clean oil spout to penetrate the metal can top. Avoid using a regular can opener tool because it can deposit metal slivers in the oil. If you use bulk oil, you should filter it with a filter rated at 10-microns or smaller while being poured into the reservoir.

If incompatible lubricants are mixed when filling an engine, many manufacturers require the oil system to be drained and flushed. Furthermore, when changing from one approved oil to another, you must drain and flush the system if the oils are incompatible. Whenever an engine is filled with a new approved brand or type of oil, check the oil placard near the filler opening. If the new oil is not identified, change the placard or stencil it accordingly.

After you fill the reservoir, operate the engine long enough to warm the oil. After engine shutdown, let the oil settle a few minutes, and then check the oil level. If necessary, add oil to bring the level up to the prescribed quantity. In addition, inspect the areas around the oil drain plug, oil filter, and oil screen fitting for leaks.

## OIL SERVICING

Turbine engines do consume some oil; therefore, periodic oil servicing is required. When servicing the oil system, ensure that servicing is accomplished shortly after shutdown. Manufacturers normally require this in order to prevent overservicing. **Overservicing** means filling the engine with too much oil. This can occur on engines when some of the oil in the storage reservoir seeps into lower portions of the engine after periods of inactivity. After engine runup, the oil supply is thoroughly agitated and areas of pooled oil are circulated in the system. This way, after the new oil is added, it is easier to establish the proper oil level in the oil reservoir.

Whenever you add oil to a turbine engine, make a note in the aircraft logbook regarding the amount of oil added. A record of oil consumption provides a valuable trend analysis of engine wear at main bearing and seal locations.

When servicing the lubrication system, be careful to avoid accidental oil contamination caused by silicone-based grease. Greases might be used at some point in the servicing process to hold O-rings in place during assembly; however, unapproved greases or excess grease can contaminate a lubrication system with silicone. Silicone contamination can cause engine oil to foam, resulting in oil loss through the reservoir vents. If severe enough, oil loss can cause oil pump cavitation and result in eventual engine damage.

## OIL RESERVOIR

In some instances, you must remove the oil reservoir installed in a dry-sump for cleaning or repair. Any repairs made to an oil reservoir must restore it to its original specifications. Therefore, after you make a repair, you must pressure-test the reservoir to its maximum operating pressure, plus five p.s.i. You can reinstall a lubrication system component only after you have successfully tested it.

## OIL PRESSURE ADJUSTMENTS

Oil pressure is normally adjusted with a screwdriver at the oil pressure relief valve. The first step in adjusting a pressure relief valve is to remove the adjusting screw cap. Then, loosen the locknut and turn the adjusting screw clockwise to increase pressure or counterclockwise to decrease pressure. Oil pressure adjustments must adhere to the specifications of the engine manufacturer. The adjustment is usually made while the engine is idling, and the setting is then confirmed with the engine operating at approximately 75 percent of normal rated thrust. Several adjustments are typically required before the oil pressure stabilizes at the desired pressure. After you have achieved the correct pressure setting, tighten the adjusting screw locknut and install and secure the cap. [Figure 9-41]

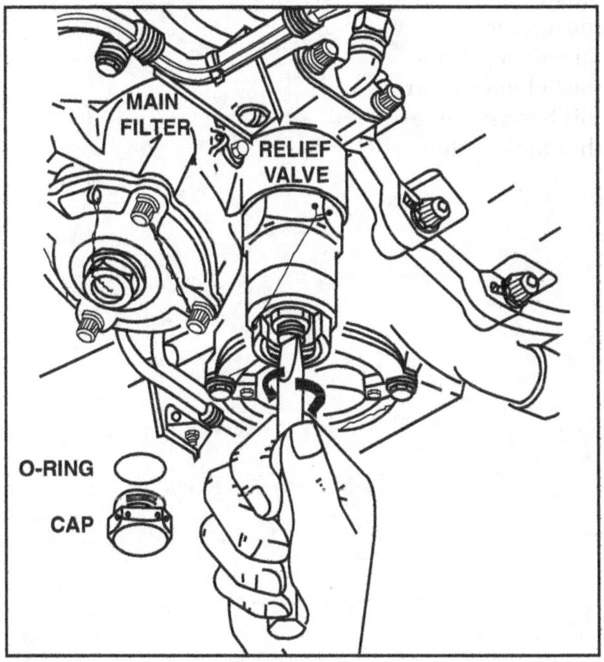


**Figure 9-41. An oil pressure relief valve occasionally requires adjustment. With the engine operating at idle speed, turn the adjusting screw clockwise to increase oil pressure and counterclockwise to decrease oil pressure.**

# SUMMARY CHECKLIST

- ✓ Gas turbine engines use low viscosity oil because of close tolerances and low internal pressures.
- ✓ With few exceptions, gas turbine engines use synthetic oils.
- ✓ Like those of reciprocating engines, oil systems for gas turbine engines are either wet- or dry-sump.
- ✓ Most oil heat exchangers in gas turbine engines use fuel to cool the oil; heating the fuel is a beneficial side effect.
- ✓ Chip detectors collect metal particles suspended in the oil.
- ✓ A spectrometric oil analysis program (SOAP) provides valuable data about engine wear and can identify the development of some problems before they become detrimental.

# KEY TERMS

coke
deaerator
air-oil separator
last chance filter
oil bypass valve
hot tank system
cold tank system
indicating chip detector
electric pulsed chip detector
ultrasonic cleaner
vibrator cleaner
overservicing

# QUESTIONS

1. Oil consumption in turbine engines is _______ (lower or higher) than that in reciprocating engines.

2. Most turbine engines use _______________ (what type) lubricating oil.

3. Most gas turbine engines for aircraft use a _______ (wet- or dry-) sump oil system.

4. Turbine engine oil tanks must have an expansion space of _______% or 0.5 gallon, whichever is greater.

5. Two methods of determining the amount of oil in a dry-sump system oil tank are:

   a. _______________

   b. _______________

6. Three types of oil pumps used with turbine engines are:

   a. _______________

   b. _______________

   c. _______________

7. The gerotor pump is considered a _______________ (positive or variable) displacement pump.

8. One micron = ____________________ inch.

9. Three types of main system oil filters used with turbine engines are:

   a. ____________________

   b. ____________________

   c. ____________________

10. Fine mesh screens called ___________ ___________ filters strain the oil just before it is sprayed onto the bearing surfaces of a turbine engine.

11. Check valves in the oil supply lines prevent accumulations of oil in the _______________ _______________ (what area) of the engine while the engine is not operating.

12. The cockpit oil pressure gauge measures the pressure _______________ (upstream or downstream) of the main oil filter.

13. The location of the oil temperature sensor in a turbine engine _______ (does or does not) make a significant difference in readings.

14. If the oil cooler is located in the pressure subsystem of a gas turbine engine, the engine uses a _______ (hot or cold) tank lubrication system.

15. Two types of oil coolers used with aircraft gas turbine engines are:

    a. ____________

    b. ____________

16. If turbine oil is observed to be dark brown or blackish with little or no contaminants present, it is probably caused by a chemical reaction to ____________.

17. Oil pressure adjustments on turbine engines are usually made while the engine is ________ (idling or at 75% rated thrust).

18. The scavenge subsystem will have a __________ (greater or less) capacity than the pressure subsystem.

19. Magnetic chip detectors are usually found in the ________________ (pressure or scavenge) subsystem of a gas turbine engine.

20. The Electric Pulsed Chip Detector ____________ (can or cannot) discriminate between small wear particles and larger particles.

CHAPTER 10

# COOLING SYSTEMS

## INTRODUCTION

Aircraft engines convert heat energy into mechanical energy. However, in doing this, only about one-third of the heat produced is used for thrust. The remaining two-thirds is wasted and must be removed from an engine. Therefore, cooling systems are designed to remove the unused heat energy produced by combustion to enable an engine to operate at peak efficiency.

# SECTION A

## RECIPROCATING ENGINES

Of the heat that is generated in an internal combustion engine, approximately 30 percent is converted to useful work while 40 to 45 percent is expelled through the exhaust. The remaining 25 to 30 percent is absorbed by the oil and metal mass of the engine. It is this heat that is removed by an aircraft's cooling system. Without cooling, engine performance suffers as volumetric efficiency decreases. Additionally, excessive heat shortens the life of engine parts and reduces the lubricating properties of the oil. The two most common methods for cooling an engine are direct air cooling and liquid cooling.

## AIR COOLING

Most modern aircraft engines are cooled by air. For effective air cooling, an engine must have a large surface area to transfer heat. To accomplish this, air-cooled engines use cast or machined **cooling fins** on the exterior surfaces of the cylinder barrels and heads. The fins increase surface area to transfer heat to the surrounding airflow. Additional cooling is sometimes provided by fins that are cast into the underside of pistons. These fins provide additional surface area to transfer heat to the engine oil.

The cylinder fins on early engines were thick and shallow and provided little additional surface area for cooling. However, as techniques of casting and machining improved, fins became thinner with deeper grooves. Today, aircraft engines use steel cylinder barrels that have fins machined directly onto their surface. These barrels are screwed into aluminum cylinder heads with cast fins. Because the area around the exhaust valve is typically the hottest part of a cylinder, more fin area is provided. The intake portion of a cylinder head has few cooling fins because the fuel/air mixture provides adequate cooling.

### COWLINGS

A downside of air cooling is the effect of increased drag. Early aircraft cruised at speeds where drag was of minimal consequence; however, above airspeeds of 120 miles per hour, the problem of drag had to be addressed.

### RADIAL ENGINE COWLING

To reduce drag on aircraft equipped with radial engines, the **Townend ring**, or **speed ring** was developed. A Townend ring is an airfoil shaped ring installed around the circumference of a radial engine. The airfoil shape produces an aerodynamic force that smoothes airflow around the engine and improves the air flowing around each cylinder. When installed properly, a Townend ring can reduce drag by as much as 11 percent on some aircraft. [Figure 10-1]

As new aircraft and engine designs resulted in higher cruising speeds, the need increased for more efficient cooling systems with less drag. In the early 1930's an engine cowling known as the **NACA cowling** was developed. This streamlined cowling completely covered all portions of a radial engine and extended all the way back to the fuselage. In addition, NACA cowlings are designed with an airfoil shape that produces thrust by converting the incoming air into a solid jet blast as it leaves the cowling. [Figure 10-2]

### OPPOSED ENGINE COWLING

The cylinders on early horizontally opposed engines stuck out into the airstream to receive cooling air. However, because the forward-most cylinders received the bulk of air from the airstream, leaving

**Figure 10-1. A Townend ring, or speed ring, reduces the drag caused by air flowing over the cylinders of radial engines.**

Figure 10-2. Radial engines enclosed in NACA cowlings produce less drag and have improved engine cooling.

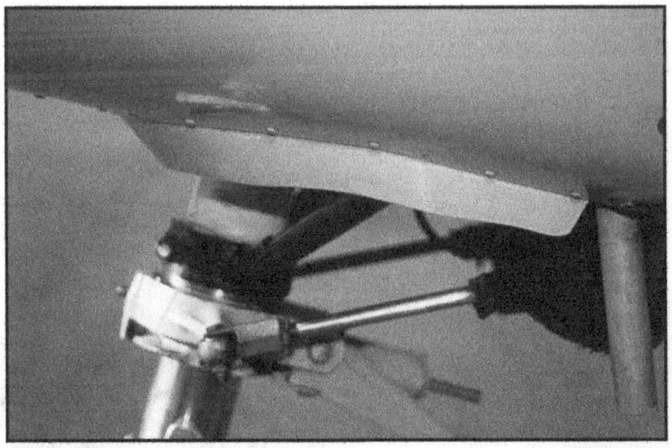

Figure 10-4. The flared portion of a lower cowl helps produce a low-pressure area at the cowling exit, which draws inlet air down through the cylinders.

the rearward cylinders starved of air, a thin sheet metal hood was installed on each side of the engine to force air down between the cylinder fins. [Figure 10-3]

The cowling surrounding a modern reciprocating engine encloses the entire engine. Cooling air enters the cowling through forward facing openings and exits from one or more openings in the bottom rear of the cowl. All of the other areas where the cowling meets the fuselage are sealed with fabric or rubberized strips to prevent excessive air leakage. Because of ram effect, cooling air enters the cowling at a pressure above ambient. This produces **pressure cooling**.

To facilitate pressure cooling, the outlet on most lower cowls is flared to create an area of low pressure at the bottom of the cowling. This low-pressure area draws inlet air down through the cylinders and into the lower cowl before exiting the cowling. [Figure 10-4]

Figure 10-3. The cowling on early horizontally opposed engines consisted of a thin sheet metal hood that forced cooling air through the cylinder fins.

## BAFFLES AND DEFLECTORS

Only 15 to 30 percent of the total ram airflow approaching an airborne engine cowling actually enters the cowling to provide engine cooling. Therefore, baffles and deflectors are installed to maximize effectiveness of the airflow. Baffles and deflectors block and redirect airflow to provide effective cooling. Baffles and deflectors are installed between the cowling and engine, as well as between the engine cylinders. The baffles installed between the engine and cowling effectively divide the cowling into two separate compartments. This way, when air enters the upper cowl, it has no choice but to flow around the cylinders and into the lower cowl. The primary purpose of the baffles installed between cylinders is to force cooling air to pass over all parts of a cylinder. These baffles are sometimes referred to as **inter-cylinder baffles** or **pressure baffles.** [Figure 10-5]

## COWL FLAPS

On some aircraft, the amount of cooling air that flows into the cowling is controlled with cowl flaps. Cowl flaps are hinged doors at the bottom rear of the cowling where the cooling air exits. Open cowl flaps create a stronger low pressure area in the lower cowl and pull more air through the cylinders. When the cowl flaps are closed, the low pressure area is weaker and less cooling air is drawn between the cylinders. The position of the cowl flaps is controlled from the cockpit and, depending on design, can be operated manually, electrically, or hydraulically. [Figure 10-6]

During ground operations, cowl flaps are typically in their full open position for maximum cooling. After the aircraft is established in level flight, the

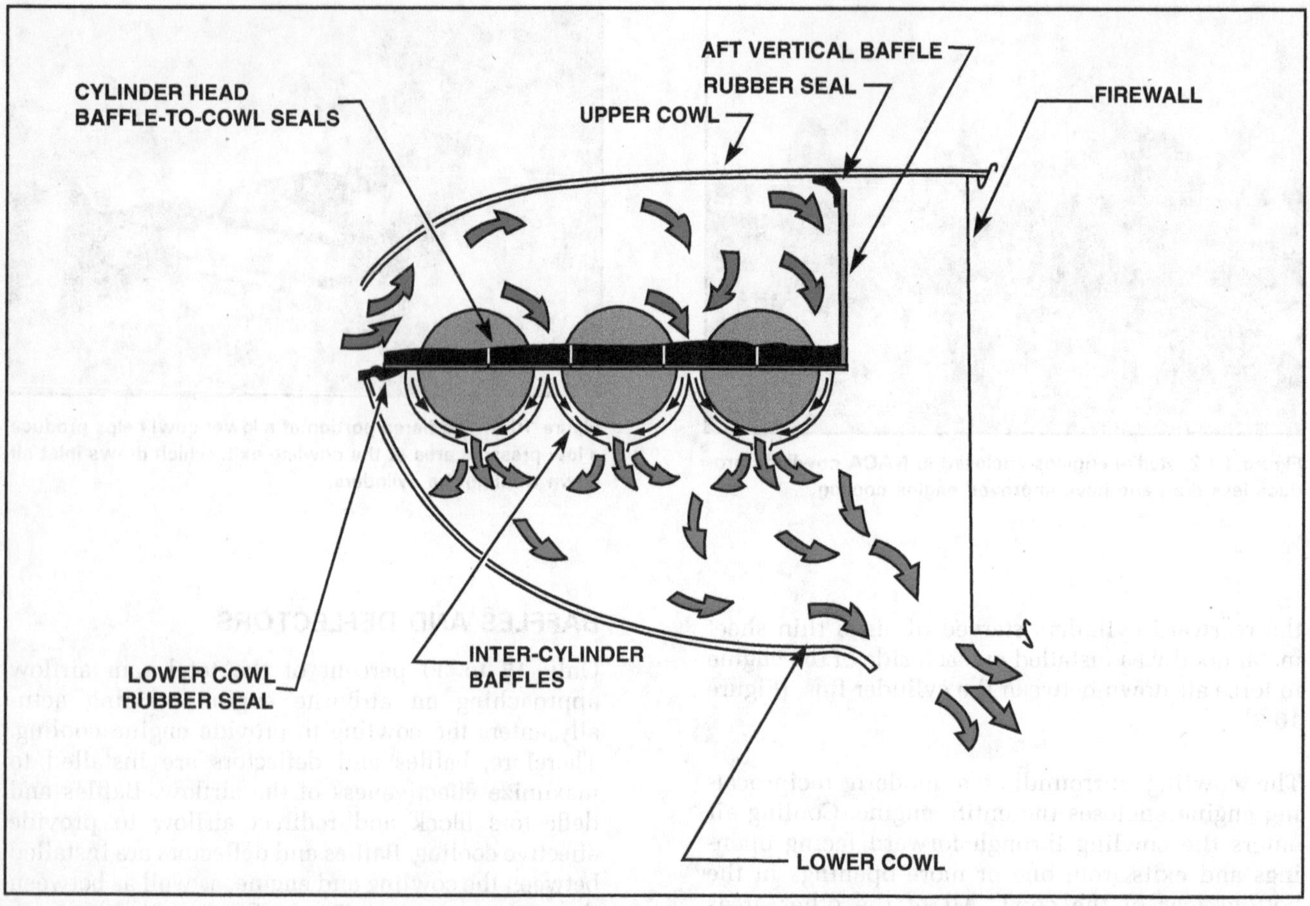


**Figure 10-5. A series of baffles and seals directs cooling air between the cylinders of a horizontally opposed aircraft engine.**

cowl flaps are normally closed to reduce drag and prevent the engine from operating below its ideal temperature.

## AUGMENTER SYSTEMS

Some aircraft use augmenter tubes to increase airflow through the cylinders. Like cowl flaps, augmenter tubes create a low pressure area at the lower rear of the cowling that increases the airflow through the cylinder cooling fins. [Figure 10-7]

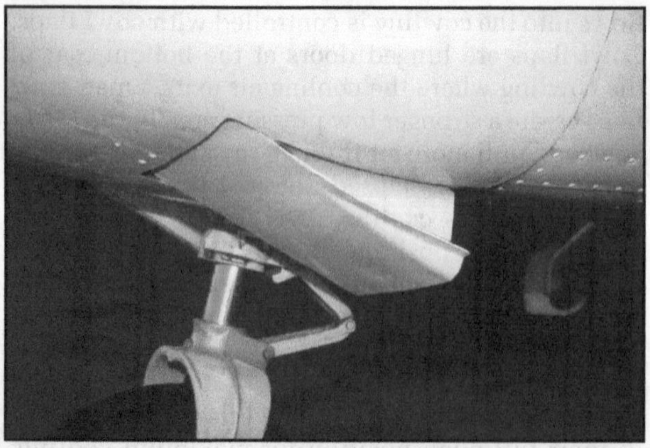

**Figure 10-6. By adjusting cowl flap position on an aircraft, the operator can control the amount of air that flows through the cowling.**

An augmenter system routes the exhaust gases from the engine into a collector that discharges them into the inlet of a stainless steel augmenter tube. The flow of high-velocity exhaust gases creates an area of low pressure at the inlet of the augmenter tube and draws air from above the engine through the cylinder fins. The combination of exhaust gases and cooling air exits at the rear of the augmenter tube.

## BLAST TUBES

Many engine installations use blast tubes to direct cooling air onto components in an engine compartment that are outside of the cowling airflow. A blast tube is a small pipe, or duct, that channels air from the main cooling airstream onto heat-sensitive components and accessories such as magnetos, alternators, and generators. Blast tubes, where used, are typically built into the baffles and are an integral part of the baffle structure.

## HELICOPTER COOLING SYSTEMS

Because helicopter engines generally operate at a high speed for prolonged periods and produce more heat, they present unique challenges for cooling an engine. Furthermore, helicopters typically fly at

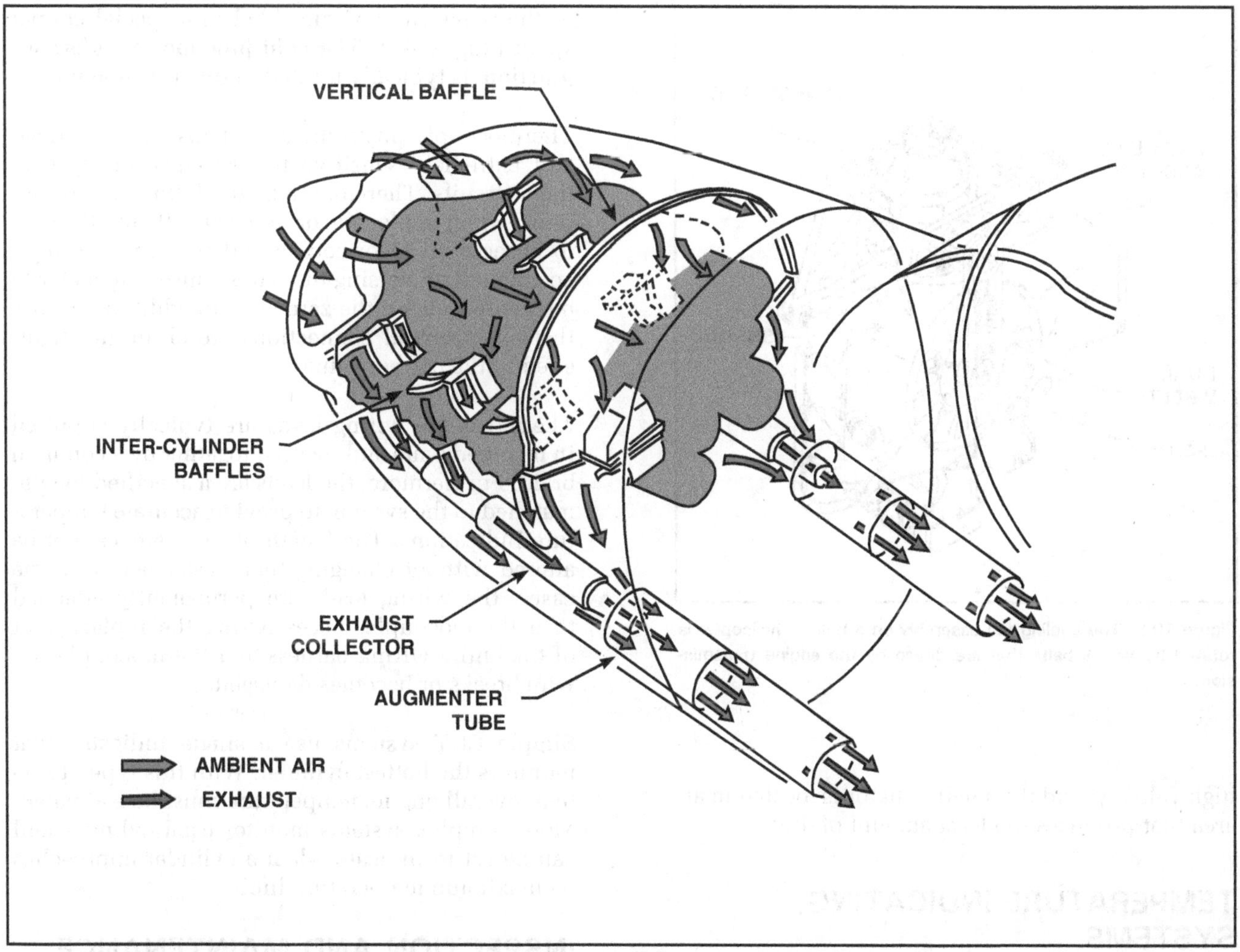


**Figure 10-7. Some reciprocating engines use augmenter tubes to improve engine cooling. As exhaust gas flows into an augmenter tube, an area of low pressure is created, which draws additional cooling air over the engine cylinders.**

slower airspeeds than fixed-wing aircraft and receive less ram airflow. Because the downwash from the main rotor is insufficient to cool an engine, an alternate method of engine cooling is required. The most commonly used auxiliary engine cooling system in helicopters is a large belt-driven cooling fan.

The Bell 47 is an example of a helicopter that uses a cooling fan assembly. The cooling fan is mounted on the front side of the engine and is driven by the transmission fan quill assembly through two matched V-belts. The 1.2:1 quill gear ratio turns the fan at a higher speed than the engine to distribute an adequate supply of cooling air to the engine. [Figure 10-8]

## LIQUID-COOLING

The cylinders of liquid-cooled aircraft engines are surrounded by metal water jackets. As coolant circulates in the **water jacket**, heat passes from the cylinder walls into the coolant. A coolant pump circulates the coolant in a pressurized loop from the water jacket to a radiator, where heat is transferred from the coolant to the air.

Liquid-cooled engines have limited use in aviation because the radiator, water jacket, coolant, and other associated hoses and lines add a substantial amount of weight. Additionally, air-cooled engines are not hampered by cold-weather operations as severely as liquid-cooled engines.

In spite of the disadvantages, liquid-cooled engines were used with great success in some American- and British-built WWII fighter aircraft. Two such aircraft were the P-38 Lightning and the P-51 Mustang, which flew with liquid-cooled V-12 engines. A recently produced liquid-cooled engine, the Teledyne Continental Motors Voyager, uses a mixture of 60 percent ethylene glycol and 40 percent water as a coolant. The coolant is circulated at a

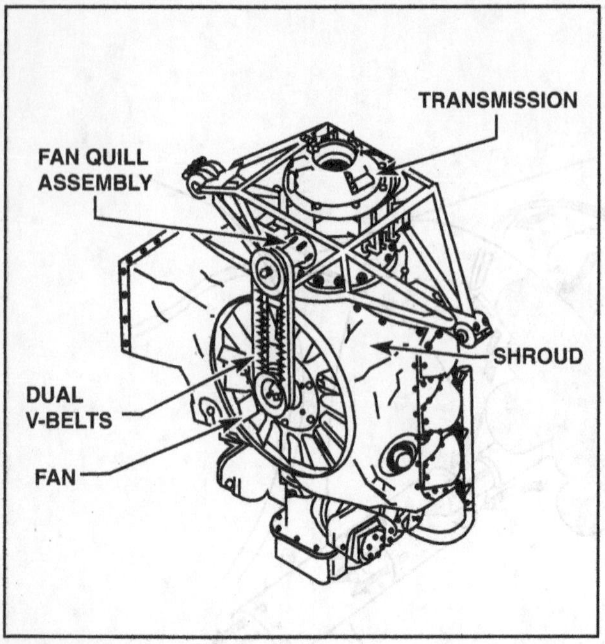


Figure 10-8. The cooling fan assembly on a Bell 47 helicopter is rotated by two V-belts that are driven by the engine transmission.

high velocity, and the small radiator is located in an area that produces the least amount of drag.

## TEMPERATURE INDICATING SYSTEMS

Engine temperature has a dramatic effect on engine performance. Therefore, most aircraft powered by reciprocating engines are equipped with a cylinder head temperature (CHT) gauge to enable the pilot to monitor engine temperatures.

Most CHT gauges are galvanometer-type meters that display temperature in degrees Fahrenheit. A galvanometer measures the amount of electrical current produced by a thermocouple. A **thermocouple** is a circuit consisting of two dissimilar metal wires connected together at two junctions to form a loop. Anytime a temperature difference exists between the two junctions, an electrical current is generated proportional to the temperature difference. This difference is measured and indicated by the galvanometer.

The two junctions of a thermocouple circuit are commonly referred to as a hot junction and a cold junction. The **hot junction** is installed in the cylinder head in one of two ways—the two dissimilar wires can be joined inside a bayonet probe that is then inserted into a special well in the top or rear of the hottest cylinder (or sometime in all cylinders) or the wires can be embedded in a special copper spark plug gasket. The **cold junction**, or **reference junction**, is typically located in the instrument case.

Thermocouple instrument systems are polarized and extremely sensitive to resistance changes in their circuits. Therefore, take the following precautions when replacing or repairing them. Be sure to observe all color-coding and polarity markings; accidentally reversing the wires causes the meter to move off-scale on the zero side. In addition, ensure that all electrical connections are clean and tightened to the correct value.

Thermocouple wiring leads are typically supplied in matched pairs and secured together by a common braid. Furthermore, the leads are a specified length, matched to the system, to provide accurate temperature indications. The length of the leads cannot be altered without changing their resistance. In some cases, the wiring leads are permanently attached to a thermocouple, necessitating the replacement of the entire wiring harness and thermocouple if a wire breaks or becomes damaged.

Simple CHT systems use a single indicator that monitors the hottest cylinder. With this type of system, overall engine temperature must be estimated. More complex systems monitor each cylinder and can be set to indicate when a cylinder approaches its maximum temperature limit.

## INSPECTION AND MAINTENANCE

All cooling system components are inspected during a 100-hour or annual inspection. After a thorough visual inspection is complete, it should be followed with all necessary repairs or replacements. Some of the components typically inspected include the cowling, cylinder cooling fins, baffling, and cowl flaps.

### COWLING

Recall that only 15 to 30 percent of the total ram airflow enters the cowling. Therefore, the aerodynamic shape of a cowling must be clean and smooth to reduce drag and energy loss. You must consider this smoothness when repairing a cowling or adjusting the alignment of cowl panels and access doors.

Inspect cowl panels for dents, tears, and cracks that can weaken the panel structure and increases drag by disrupting the airflow. An accumulation of dents and tears can lead to cracking and contribute to corrosion. Closely examine the internal construction of cowl panels to ensure that the reinforcing ribs are not cracked and that the air seal is not damaged.

Inspect the cowl panel latches for missing rivets and loose or damaged handles. Check the safety locks for damaged rivets and the condition of the safety spring. Examine all support brackets carefully to verify the security of mounting, and repair any cracks found in accordance with the manufacturer's instructions. Early detection of breaks and cracks provides an opportunity to limit the damage and extend the service life of a cowling.

## CYLINDER COOLING FINS

The condition of a cooling fin has a significant impact on its effectiveness, so you must check cooling fins during each regular inspection. The cooling fins on an engine are designed with a specific surface area to dissipate a certain amount of heat. When cooling fins are broken off of a cylinder, less fin area is available for cooling. An engine's **fin area** is the total area (both sides of the fin) exposed to the air. Any time an excessive amount of fin area is missing, hot spots can form on the cylinder.

The manufacturer establishes the amount of permissible fin damage on a given cylinder based on a percentage of total fin area. Therefore, when you perform a repair to a cylinder cooling fin, be sure to consult the engine manufacturer's service or overhaul manual to ensure that the repair is within limits.

Generally, you can repair a crack in cooling fins that does not extend into the cylinder head. A typical repair requires you to remove the damaged portion of the fin with a die grinder and rotary file. After you remove the damage, file the edges to a smooth contour. The percentage of total fin area that you remove must not exceed the manufacturer's limits. [Figure 10-9]

A crack at the edge of a fin can be filed or stop-drilled to prevent it from lengthening. Additionally, you can file any rough or sharp edges produced by broken fins to a smooth contour if the damage does not exceed the repair limits. If a cooling fin is inadvertently bent on an aluminum cylinder head and no crack forms, the fin should be left alone; aluminum cooling fins are brittle and any attempt to straighten one could cause it to crack or break.

## BAFFLES AND DEFLECTORS

If an inspection reveals defects in cylinder baffles and deflectors, you must repair them to prevent a loss of cooling efficiency. Because baffles are subject to constant vibration, work-hardening of the metal occurs considerably faster than on other components. Work-hardening can make engine baffles extremely brittle, which increases the likelihood of fatigue cracking.

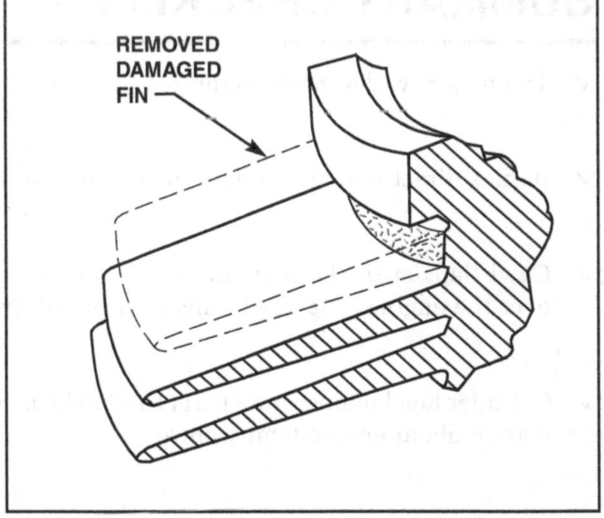


**Figure 10-9. When repairing a damaged fin on a cylinder, do not remove any of the primary cylinder casting. In addition, fin loss near spark plug openings or exhaust ports can cause dangerous hot spots.**

Using an inspection mirror and light, examine the baffles, deflectors, and shrouds for cracks, bent sections, dents, and loose attachment hardware. Stop-drill small cracks that are just beginning to form, and straighten bent baffles.

When installing a cowling, take care to avoid damaging the baffle air seals. These seals are typically made from plastic, rubber, or leather strips and must be oriented as directed in the manufacturer's service manual. Damaged air seals and improperly installed or loose baffles can develop cylinder hot spots. Burned paint found on a cylinder during the inspection could be evidence of a hot spot.

## COWL FLAPS

Visually inspect the cowl flaps for security of mounting and signs of cracking. In addition, operate the cowl flaps to verify the condition of the hinges and operating mechanism.

If the cowl flaps were removed for maintenance, check their adjustment after reinstallation. Proper adjustment helps ensure the correct rigging for the open and closed positions. Establishing the correct rigging in both positions is important for maintaining correct cylinder head temperatures. For example, cowl flaps that are opened too far permit too much cooling air through the cowling, which results in insufficient engine temperatures. However, cowl flaps that do not open far enough can cause cylinder head temperatures to exceed specified limits.

# SUMMARY CHECKLIST

✓ The majority of aircraft reciprocating engines use airflow for primary cooling.

✓ Baffles direct ram air through the cowling and around cylinders to promote even cooling.

✓ Cowl flaps at the bottom, aft area of a cowling are pilot-adjustable to change the amount of air flowing over the engine. The cowl flaps change the strength of the area of low pressure in the lower cowl.

✓ Cylinder head temperature (CHT) and exhaust gas temperature (EGT) indicators provide pilots with information about engine temperature.

# KEY TERMS

cooling fins
Townend ring
speed ring
NACA cowling
pressure cooling
inter-cylinder baffles
pressure baffles
water jacket
thermocouple
hot junction
cold junction
reference junction
fin area

# QUESTIONS

1. A reciprocating engine converts only about ______ (what percent) of the heat energy of the burning fuel into mechanical energy.

2. The radial engine cowling that encloses the engine and provides for pressure cooling is called a/an

   ________________ cowling.

3. ________________ ________________ (what devices) are used between the cylinders of an air cooled engine to force the cooling air to flow between the cooling fins on the cylinders.

4. Cowl flaps on an air-cooled engine are located in such a way that they produce a ________ (low or high) pressure area to increase the airflow through the cylinder fins.

5. Cowl flaps on an air-cooled engine should be __________ (open or closed) during ground runup.

6. The velocity of the exhaust gases creates a ______ (high or low) pressure at the inlet of the augmentor tubes.

7. Accessories and local hot spots are typically cooled with additional air from ______ tubes directed at them.

8. Helicopter engines are typically cooled by a __________ system that provides cooling airflow.

9. The thermocouples used to monitor cylinder heat temperature may be either of these designs:

   a. __________

   b. __________

10. If a cylinder head thermocouple lead is too long, you should ________ (cut off or coil and tie) the excess.

11. Cracks in cylinder head fins can sometimes be __________ __________ to prevent further cracking.

12. Dents or bends in cylinder head fins should be ________________ (repaired or left alone) if there is no danger of cracking.

# SECTION B

## TURBINE ENGINES

Like reciprocating engines, turbine engines convert heat energy into work. However, the continuous combustion process in a turbine engine produces more heat, so most of the cooling air passes through the inside of the turbine engine. Otherwise, internal engine temperatures could rise above 4,000 degrees Fahrenheit. In practice, a typical turbine engine uses approximately 25 percent of the total inlet air flow to support combustion. This airflow is referred to as the engine's **primary airflow**. The remaining 75 percent is used for cooling, and is referred to as **secondary airflow**.

When the proper amount of air flows through a turbine engine, the temperature of the outer case is typically between ambient and 1,000 degrees Fahrenheit. The temperature depends on the section of the engine. For example, at the compressor inlet, the outer case temperature will remain at, or slightly above, the ambient air temperature, but at the front of the turbine section, where internal temperatures are greatest, outer case temperatures can easily reach 1,000 degrees Fahrenheit. [Figure 10-10]

### COOLING REQUIREMENTS

To properly cool each section, all turbine engines are constructed with an intricate internal air system that must route ram and bleed air to internal components deep within the engine. In most engines, the compressor, combustion, and turbine sections all use some amount of cooling air.

### NACELLE AND COMPRESSOR

For the most part, ram air cools an engine's nacelle and compressor as it enters the engine. Cooling air is typically directed between the engine case and nacelle. To direct the cooling air, a typical engine compartment is divided into a forward section and an aft section. The forward section is constructed around the engine inlet duct and the aft section encircles the engine. A seal separates the two sections and forms a barrier that prevents combustible fumes in the front section from passing into the aft section and igniting from the heat of the engine case.

In flight, ram air provides ample cooling for both compartments. However, on the ground, airflow is provided by the reduced pressure at the rear of the nacelle caused by exhaust gases exiting the exhaust nozzle. The lower the pressure at the rear of the nozzle, the more air is drawn through the forward section. [Figure 10-11]

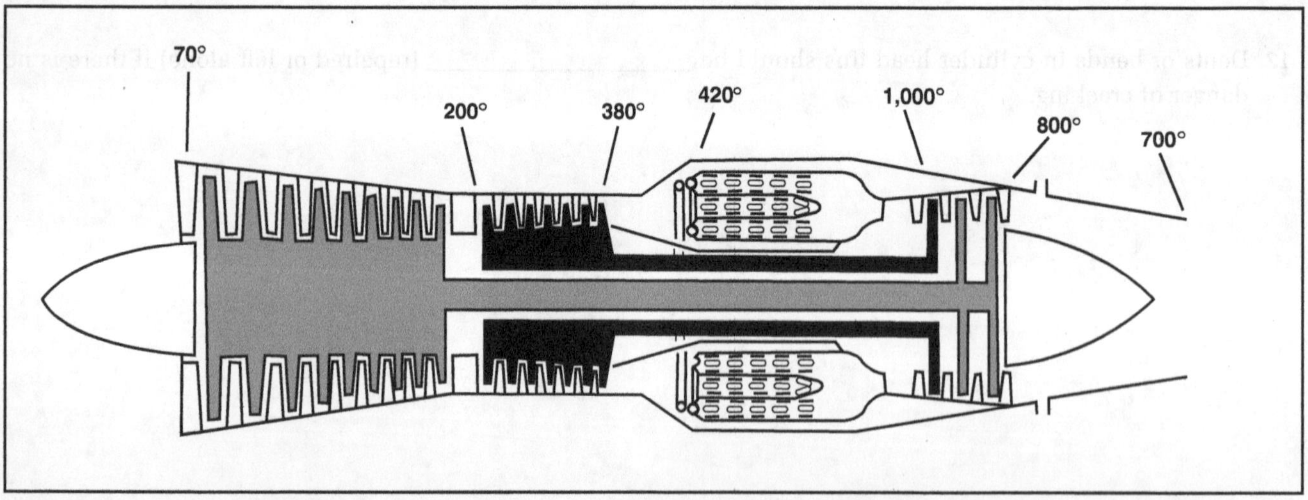


**Figure 10-10. A properly cooled, two-spool turbojet engine has outer-case temperatures that range from 70 to 1000 degrees Fahrenheit. Effective cooling airflow keeps these temperatures far below internal engine temperatures.**

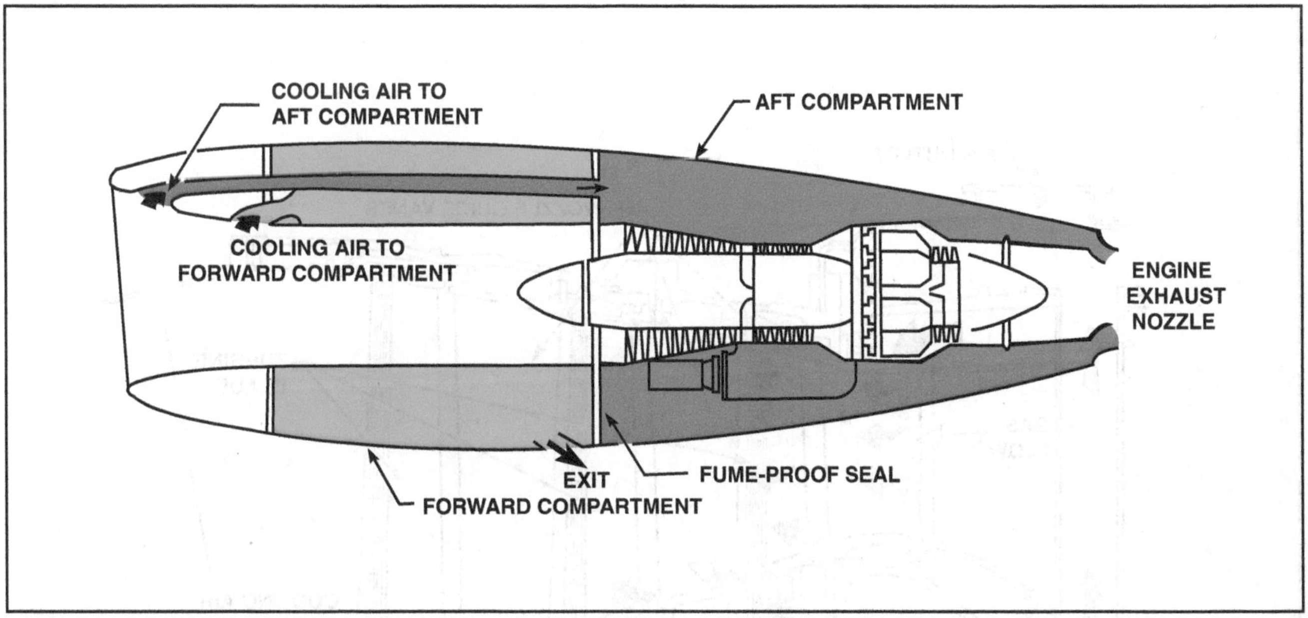


**Figure 10-11. Nacelle cooling is typically accomplished by ram air that enters the nacelle at the inlet duct.**

As inlet air is compressed, its temperature increases. The heat produced by compression is transferred to components within the compressor section. This heat, along with the heat produced by mechanical friction on the bearings, is taken from bleed air at an early compressor stage and directed over, or through, the bearing compartment.

## COMBUSTION SECTION

The fuel and air mix and burn in the combustion section. A typical combustor consists of an outer casing with a perforated inner liner. The various sizes and shapes of perforations have a specific effect on flame propagation and cooling.

The airflow through the combustor is divided into primary and secondary paths to properly mix the incoming fuel and air and to cool the combustion gases. Approximately 25 percent of the incoming air is designated as primary while 75 percent becomes secondary. As primary, or **combustion air,** enters the liner at the front end of the combustor, it passes through a set of **swirl vanes** that impart a radial motion to the air and slow its axial velocity.

The secondary airflow in the combustion section moves around the combustor's periphery at a velocity of several hundred feet per second. This airflow forms a cooling blanket on both sides of the liner and centers the combustion flames to prevent contact. Some secondary air is slowed and metered into the combustor through the perforations in the liner to ensure combustion of any remaining unburned fuel. Finally, secondary air mixes with burned gases and cools the air to provide an even distribution of energy to the turbine nozzle at a temperature that the turbine section can withstand.

## TURBINE SECTION

Temperature is an important consideration in the design of the turbine section. In fact, the most critical limiting factor in running a gas turbine engine is the temperature of the turbine section. However, the higher an engine raises the temperature of the incoming air, the more thrust it can produce. Therefore, the effectiveness of a turbine engine's cooling system is important to engine performance. Due to effective cooling systems, some turbine vane and blade components operate in a thermal environment 600 to 800 degrees Fahrenheit above the temperature limits of their metal alloys.

Engine bleed air is one of the most common ways of cooling the components in the turbine section. For example, turbine disks absorb heat from hot gases passing near their rims and from the blades through conduction. Because of this, disk rim temperatures are normally well above the temperature of the disk portion nearest the shaft. To limit the effect of these temperature variations, cooling air is directed over each side of the disk. [Figure 10-12]

To sufficiently cool turbine nozzle vanes and turbine blades, compressor bleed air is typically directed through hollow blades and out holes in the tip, leading edge, and trailing edge. This type

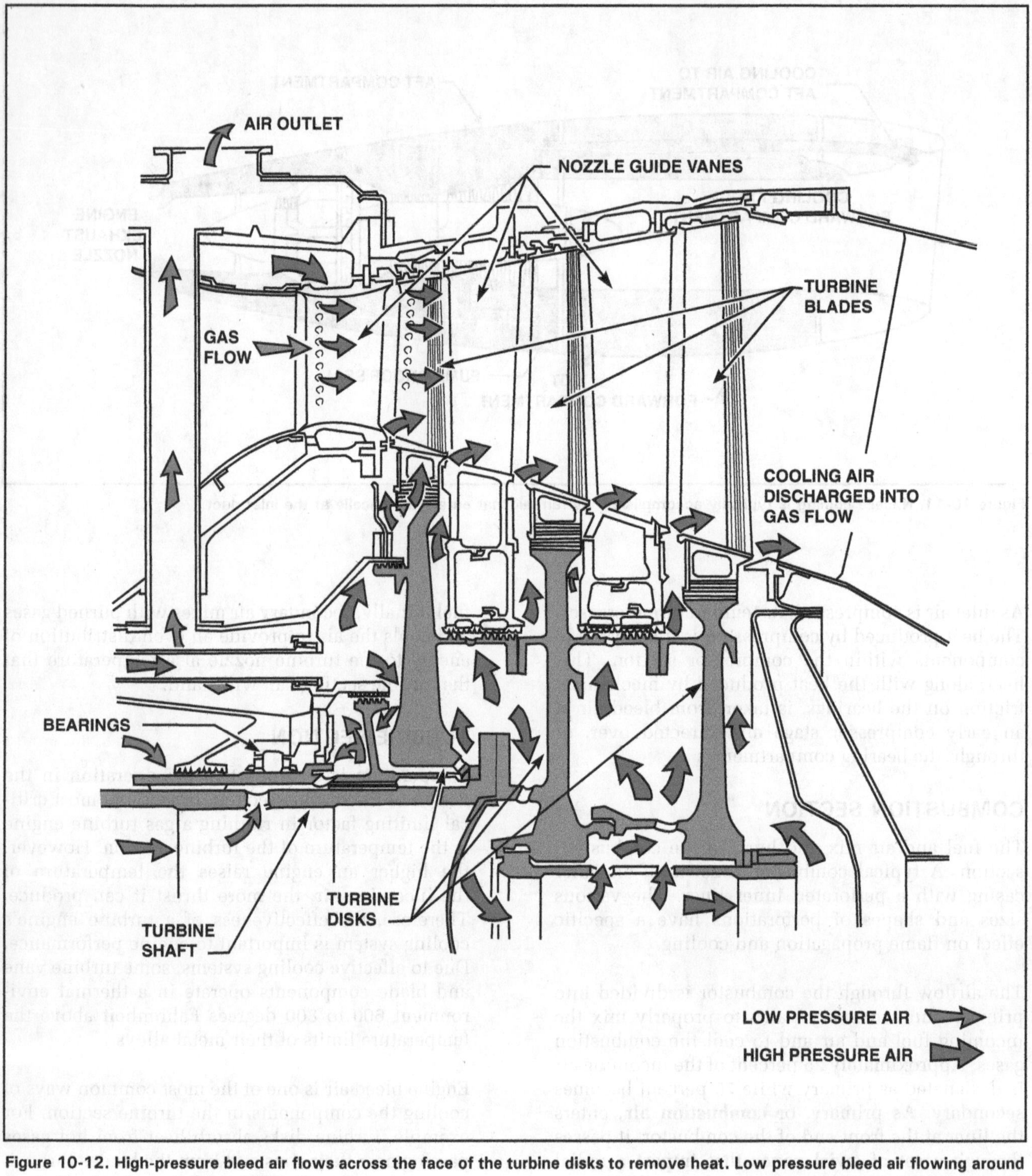


**Figure 10-12. High-pressure bleed air flows across the face of the turbine disks to remove heat. Low pressure bleed air flowing around the turbine bearings provides additional cooling.**

of cooling is known as **convection cooling** or **film cooling.** [Figure 10-13]

In addition to having holes drilled in turbine vanes or blades, some nozzle vanes are constructed of a porous, high-temperature material. In this case, bleed air is ducted into the vanes and exits through the porous material. This type of cooling is known as **transpiration cooling** and is used only on stationary nozzle vanes.

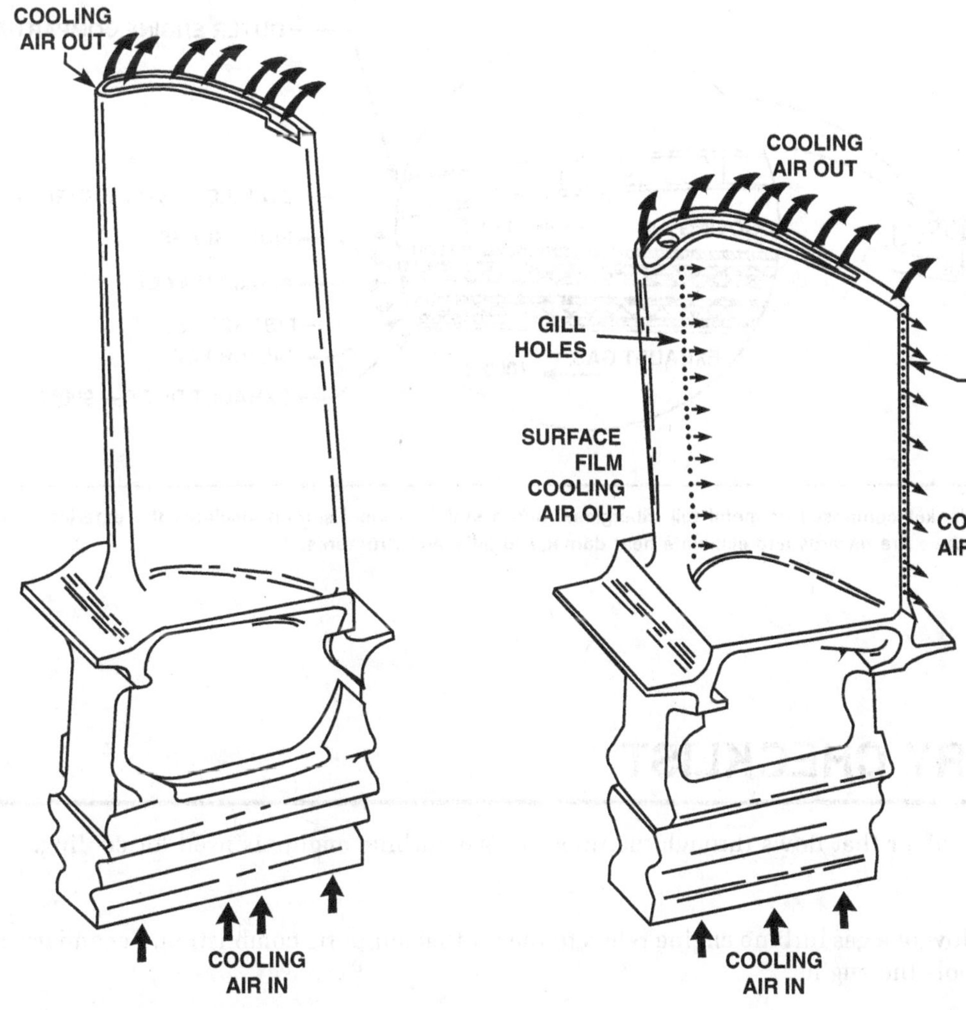


**Figure 10-13. An internally cooled blade receives cooling air at its root and expels the air at the tip or through holes in the leading and trailing edges.**

Modern engine designs incorporate many combinations of air cooling methods using low and high pressure air for both internal and surface cooling of turbine vanes and blades. However, to provide additional cooling, the turbine vane shrouds can also be perforated with cooling holes.

Some high-bypass turbofan engines use electronic engine controls that feature **active tip clearance control** or **ACC**. ACC controls the thermal expansion rate of the turbine case by regulating the flow of cooling air around it. This provides optimum turbine blade tip clearance and increases engine efficiency.

## ENGINE INSULATION BLANKETS

On early turbine engines, insulation blankets were used to shield portions of an aircraft's structure from the intense heat radiated by the exhaust duct. The blankets reduce the possibility of leaking fuel or oil coming in contact with hot engine parts and accidentally igniting. Common places where insulation blankets are used include the combustion, turbine, and exhaust sections.

Aluminum, glass fiber, and stainless steel are among the materials used to manufacture engine insulation blankets. Several layers of fiberglass, aluminum foil, and silver foil are covered with a stainless steel shroud to form a typical blanket. The fiberglass is a low-conductance material and the layers of metal foil act as radiation shields. Each blanket is manufactured with a suitable covering that prevents it from becoming oil-soaked. [Figure 10-14]

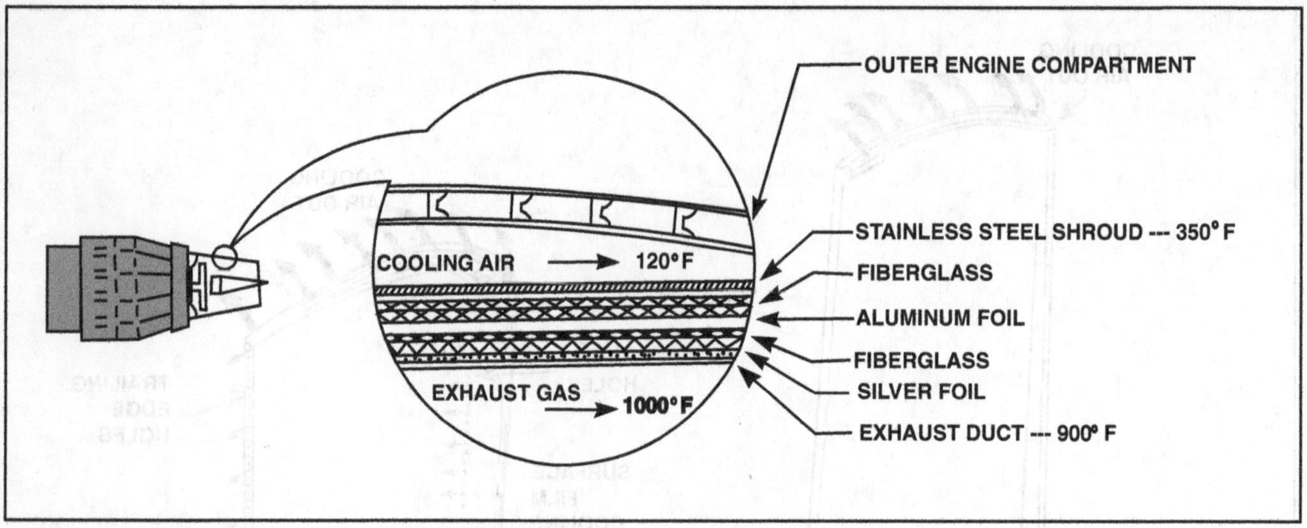


**Figure 10-14. A blanket composed of metal foil, fiberglass, and a stainless steel shroud insulates the exterior of a turbine engine exhaust duct to reduce fire hazards and eliminate heat damage to adjacent structures.**

# SUMMARY CHECKLIST

✓ The majority of air that flows through the inlet of a gas turbine engine is used for cooling.

✓ Primary airflow of a gas turbine engine refers to the air that supports combustion. Secondary airflow refers to air that cools the engine.

✓ Bleed air cools the internal components of a gas turbine engine.

# KEY TERMS

primary airflow
secondary airflow
combustion air
swirl vanes
convection cooling
film cooling
transpiration cooling
active tip clearance control
ACC

# QUESTIONS

1. Nearly all of the cooling air for a turbine engine must be passed _________ (through or around) the engine.

2. The 25% of the airflow through a turbine engine that is used to support combustion is called ______ airflow.

3. Cooling airflow is called _______________ airflow.

4. The coolest point within a gas turbine engine is at the _______________ _________.

5. The engine exterior and the engine nacelle may be cooled by passing _____________ between the case and the shell of the nacelle.

6. The thin walls of the combustors of a gas turbine engine are protected from heat by a flow of __________.

7. The hottest point within a gas turbine engine is in the ________ section.

8. Cooling hollow vanes and blades with bleed air is known as ______________ cooling or _______ cooling.

9. Cooling air passing through porous high temperature material is known as _______________ cooling.

10. What may be used to reduce the temperature of the structure in the vicinity of the exhaust duct?

    _____________ _____________

# CHAPTER 11

# ENGINE FIRE PROTECTION

## INTRODUCTION

An aircraft powerplant and its related systems constitute an obvious fire hazard. Consider that flammable materials such as fuel and oil are present in large quantities and are frequently pressurized. Additionally, an engine's exhaust system encloses high-temperature gases (and sometimes flames) that could ignite fuel vapors. Because of these hazards, many aircraft are equipped with a fire protection system to detect and extinguish fires in the engine compartment. As an aircraft maintenance technician, you must be familiar with the operating principles, maintenance practices, and repair of fire protection systems.

# SECTION A

# FIRE DETECTION SYSTEMS

Fire protection systems perform two separate functions: fire detection and extinguishment. The primary purpose of a **fire detection system** is to activate a warning device in the event of a fire. An ideal fire detection system should:

1. Not cause a false warning.
2. Provide a rapid indication and accurate location of a fire.
3. Provide a continuous indication when a fire exists.
4. Provide an accurate indication that a fire is extinguished.
5. Provide an accurate indication that an extinguished fire has reignited.
6. Provide a means to test the system from the aircraft cockpit.
7. Have detectors that resist exposure to oil, fuel, hydraulic fluid, water, vibration, extreme temperatures, and maintenance handling.
8. Have detectors that are lightweight and easily mounted.
9. Use detector circuitry powered by the aircraft electrical system without the use of an inverter.
10. Require minimal electrical current when armed.
11. Activate both a cockpit light and an audible alarm.
12. Provide a separate detection system for each engine.

Several types of fire detection systems are used in aviation today. Most systems consist of one or more detectors that activate an alarm when the air surrounding the detector reaches a predetermined temperature. Because of this, fire detectors are sometimes referred to as overheat detectors.

## ENGINE FIRE DETECTION SYSTEMS

There are two categories of engine fire detection systems: spot-detection systems and continuous-loop systems. In a **spot-detection system,** individual fire detectors, or switches, detect a fire. In this type of system, a fire warning sounds only when a fire exists in the same location as the detector, so fire detectors are located in the where a fire is most likely to occur. A **continuous-loop system** works according to the same basic principle as a spot-detection system except that it uses a single switch, in the form of a long tube, to detect a fire. Because the small diameter tube is routed completely around an engine nacelle or tail cone, it provides more complete coverage than a spot-type detection system. The following paragraphs provide information on the most common types of fire detection systems found in modern aircraft.

### THERMAL SWITCH DETECTOR

A thermal switch fire detection system is a spot detection system that uses a number of thermally activated switches. Each switch, or sensor, consists of a **bimetallic thermal switch** that closes when heated to a predetermined temperature. [Figure 11-1]

There are two basic types of thermal switch systems, the single-loop and the double-loop. In the Fenwal **single-loop** system, all of the switches are wired in

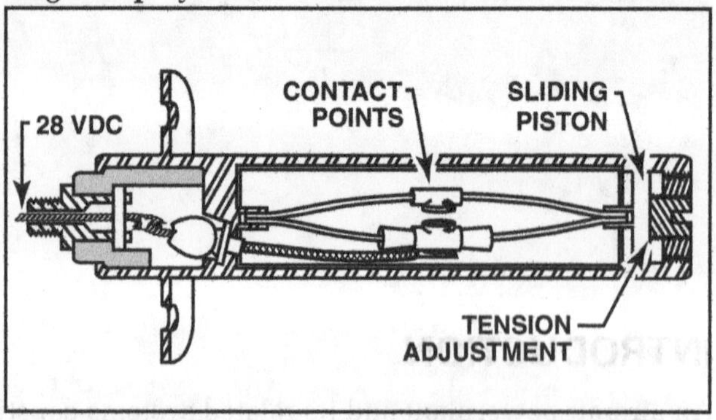


**Figure 11-1. The sensor on a thermal switch detector is mounted inside a stainless steel housing. In a fire, the housing heats up and becomes elongated, which causes the contact points to close. To adjust a thermal switch, heat the housing to the specified temperature and adjust the tension screw until the contacts just close.**

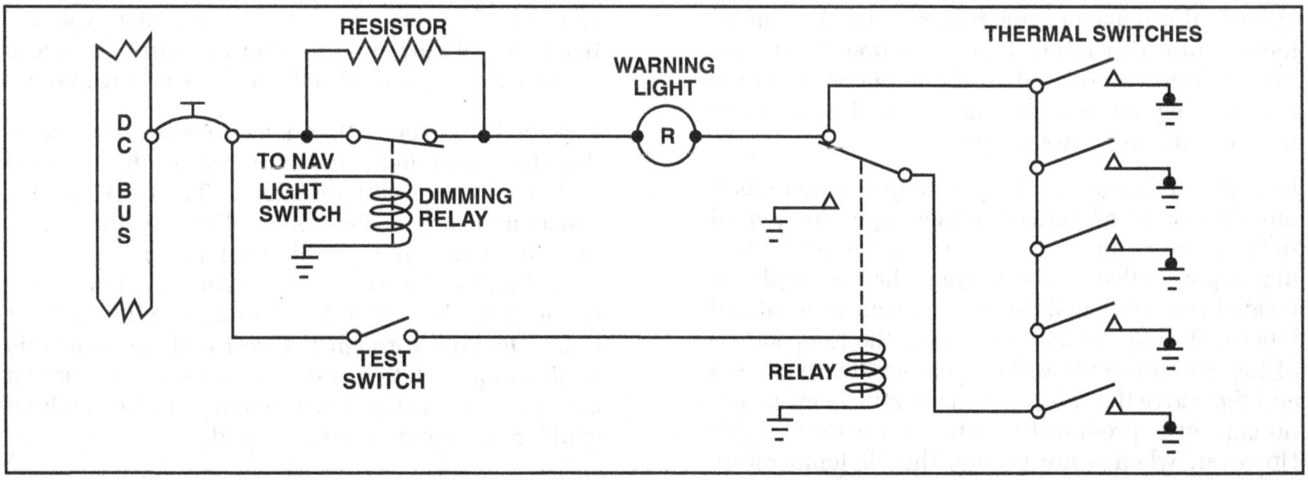


**Figure 11-2. Fire detection systems using multiple thermal switches are wired with the switches in parallel with each other and the entire group of switches in series with the indicator light. When one switch closes, a ground is provided for the circuit and the warning light illuminates.**

parallel, and the entire group of switches is connected in series with an indicator light. In this arrangement, if a switch closes, the circuit is completed and power flows to the warning light. [Figure 11-2]

When circuit test switch in the cockpit is depressed, power flows to a relay that provides a ground to the warning light, simulating a closed thermal switch. After it is grounded, the warning light illuminates only if no break occurs in the warning circuit. In addition to the test feature, most fire detection circuits include a dimming feature for night operations that works by increasing the circuit resistance. The increased resistance reduces the amount of current flowing to the light.

In a **double-loop** system, all of the sensors are connected in parallel between two complete loops of wiring. The system is wired so that one branch of the circuit supplies current to the sensors and the other serves as a path to ground. With a double-loop arrangement, the detection circuit can withstand one fault, either an open or a short circuit, without indicating a false warning. For example, if a ground loop developed a short, a false fire warning does not occur because the loop is already grounded. However, if the powered loop shorts, the rapid increase in current flow triggers a relay, which then causes the powered loop to become the ground and the grounded loop to become powered. [Figure 11-3]

## THERMOCOUPLE DETECTOR

A thermocouple, **Edison** fire detector system is similar to a thermal switch system in that it is also a spot detection system. However, in a thermocouple

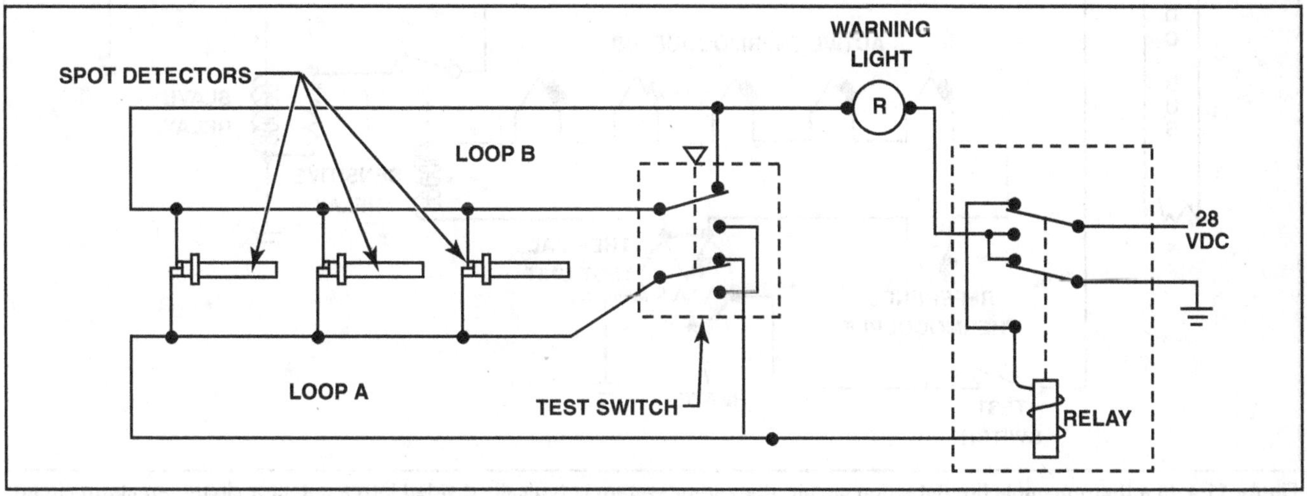


**Figure 11-3. In a double-loop thermal switch system, loop A is positive and loop B is negative. However, if an open or short develops in loop A, the sudden rush of current activates a relay to reverse the polarity of the loops.**

system, the detectors are triggered by the rate of temperature rise rather than by a preset temperature. In other words, when the temperature of the surrounding air rises too rapidly, a thermocouple detector initiates a fire warning.

In a typical thermocouple system, one or more thermocouples, called **active thermocouples** are placed in fire zones around an engine while a separate thermocouple, called the **reference thermocouple**, is located in a space of dead air between two insulated blocks. During normal operations, the temperature of the air surrounding the reference thermocouple and the active thermocouples is relatively even, and no current is produced to activate a warning light. However, when a fire occurs, the air temperature around the active thermocouples rises much faster than the air temperature around the reference thermocouple. The temperature differential produces a current in the thermocouple circuit and activates a warning light and horn. [Figure 11-4]

In most thermocouple systems, a sensitive relay, slave relay, and a thermal test unit are contained in a **relay box**. A typical relay box can contain up to eight identical circuits, one for each potential fire zone. The thermocouples control relay operation and the relays control the warning lights. The test circuit uses a **test thermocouple** wired into the detector circuit and a small electric heater. When the test switch is closed, current flows through the heater to activate the test thermocouple. The temperature difference between the test thermocouple and the reference thermocouple produces current flow that closes the sensitive and slave relays and activates the warning circuit. Approximately 4 milliamperes of current is all that is required to close the sensitive relay and activate the warning system.

The total number of thermocouples in a particular detector circuit depends on the size of the fire zone and the total circuit resistance. Typically, circuit resistance is less than five ohms. Additionally, most thermocouple circuits contain a resistor connected across the slave relay terminals. This resistor absorbs the self-induced voltage when current ceases to flow through the coil and the magnetic field collapses. If this voltage is not absorbed, arcing can occur across the sensitive relay contacts, which could cause them to burn or weld.

## FENWAL SYSTEM

In addition to a thermal switch detection system, Fenwal also produces a continuous-loop type system that consists of a single fire detection element, or **overheat sensing element**, that varies in length from 1 to 15 feet, depending on the size of the fire zone. The sensing element in a continuous-loop fire detection system is a flexible, small diameter Inconel® tube with a single wire electrode. The pure nickel electrode is surrounded by ceramic beads to insulate the electrode and conductor. The beads in this system are wetted with a **eutectic salt,** which has an electrical resistance that varies with temperature. [Figure 11-5]

The center conductor protrudes from each end of the Inconel tube where an electric terminal is affixed to the electrode. Current is then applied to

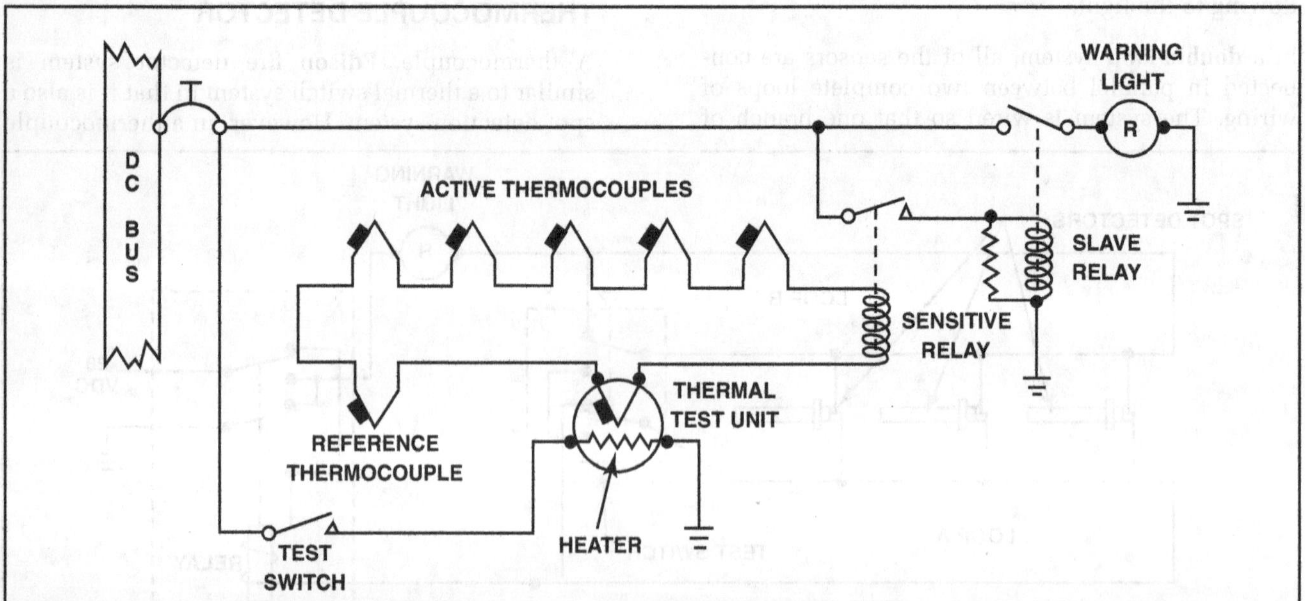


**Figure 11-4. In a thermocouple fire detection circuit, the wiring system is typically divided into a detector circuit, an alarm circuit, and a test circuit. When a temperature difference exists between an active thermocouple and the reference thermocouple, current flows through the sensitive relay coil. When the sensitive relay closes, it triggers the slave relay, which permits current to flow to the warning light.**

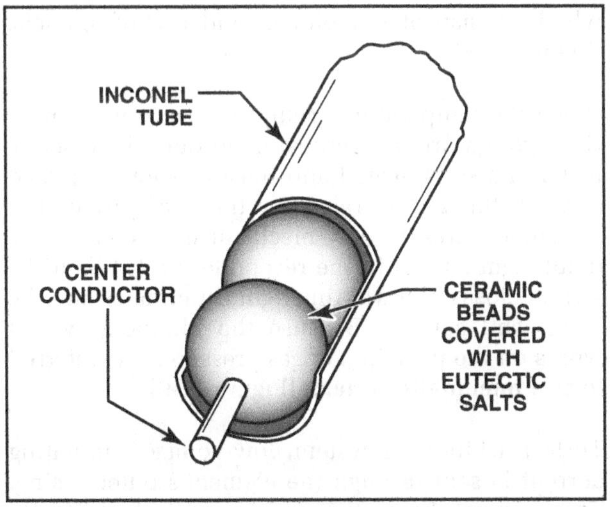


**Figure 11-5. A Fenwal continuous-loop sensing element consists of a sealed Inconel tube containing a eutectic salt and a single center conductor.**

the conductor while the outer tube is grounded to the aircraft structure. At normal temperatures, the eutectic salt core material prevents electrical current from flowing between the center conductor and the tube. However, when a fire or overheat condition occurs, the core resistance drops and current flows between the center conductor and ground, which energizes the alarm circuit.

The Fenwal system uses a magnetic amplifier control unit. The controller supplies power to the sensing element and sounds an alarm when the circuit to ground is completed through the tube. [Figure 11-6]

## KIDDE SYSTEM

The Kidde system is another continuous-loop system consisting of a single overheat sensing element; the length of the sensor varies based on the size of the fire zone. The sensing element is a rigid, preshaped Inconel tube with two wire conductors. The conductors are embedded in a **thermistor**, or **thermal resistor material**, to insulate the two electrodes from each other and the exterior casing. Like the eutectic salt in the Fenwal system, the electrical resistance of the thermistor material decreases as the temperature increases. [Figure 11-7]

One wire functions as an internal ground; it is electrically grounded to the outer tube at each end. The second wire is a positive lead. When a fire or overheat occurs, the resistance of the thermistor material drops, which permits current to flow between the two wires and activate the alarm.

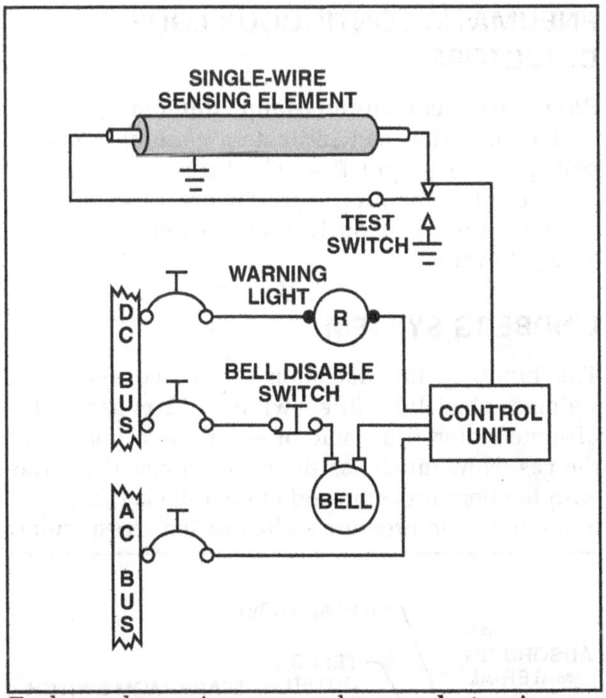


**Figure 11-6. In a Fenwal continuous-loop fire detection system, AC voltage is applied to the sensing element through the control unit. When the air surrounding the sensing element reaches a predetermined temperature, the resistance of the eutectic salt in the element decreases and permits current to flow to ground. The control unit senses the flow of AC current and closes a relay to ground the warning circuit and illuminate the warning light.**

Each conductor is connected to an **electronic control unit** mounted on separate circuit cards. In addition to constantly measuring the total resistance of the full sensing loop, the dual control unit provides redundancy if one side fails. In fact, both the Fenwal and Kidde systems will detect a fire when a sensing element is inoperative, even though the press-to-test circuit does not function.

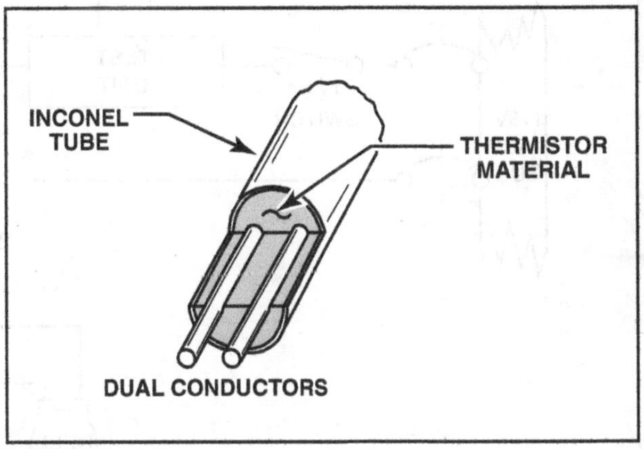


**Figure 11-7. A Kidde sensing element is a sealed Inconel tube containing two conductors embedded in a thermistor material.**

## PNEUMATIC CONTINUOUS-LOOP DETECTORS

**Pneumatic continuous-loop detectors** use a sealed tube that can indicate a general overheat condition or a spot fire. The three primary systems used on modern aircraft are the Lindberg system, the Systron-Donner system, and the Meggitt system.

## LINDBERG SYSTEM

The Lindberg fire detection system consists of a stainless steel tube filled with an inert gas and a discrete material capable of absorbing a portion of the gas. How much gas the material absorbs varies with temperature. One end of the tube is connected to a pneumatic pressure switch called a **responder**, which consists of a diaphragm and a set of contacts. [Figure 11-8]

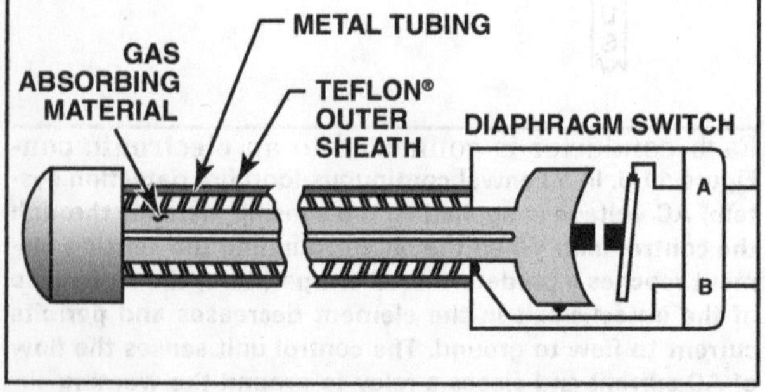


**Figure 11-8. The sensing element in a Lindberg continuous-loop system is a stainless steel tube filled with an inert gas and a gas-absorbing material. One end of the tube is sealed while the other end is connected to a diaphragm switch.**

When the temperature around the sensing element rises from a fire or overheat condition, the discrete material also is heated and releases some absorbed gas. As the gas is released, the pressure within the tube increases and mechanically actuates the diaphragm switch in the responder unit. When the switch closes, the warning light illuminates and the alarm bell sounds. Because the Lindberg system works on the principle of gas pressure, it is referred to as a **pneumatic system**. [Figure 11-9]

To test a Lindberg system, low-voltage alternating current is sent through the element's outer casing. This current heats the casing until the discrete material releases enough gas to close the contacts in the diaphragm switch and initiate a fire warning. After the test switch is released, the sensing element cools and the discrete material reabsorbs the gas. After the gas is reabsorbed, the contacts in the diaphragm switch open and the fire warning stops.

## SYSTRON-DONNER SYSTEM

The helium-filled, stainless steel tube in a Systron-Donner system uses a titanium wire running through its center as a sensing element. The wire is a gas absorbing material that contains a quantity of hydrogen. For protection, the wire is typically wrapped with an inert metal tape or inserted in an inert metal tube. One end of the sensor tube is connected to the responder assembly with a diaphragm

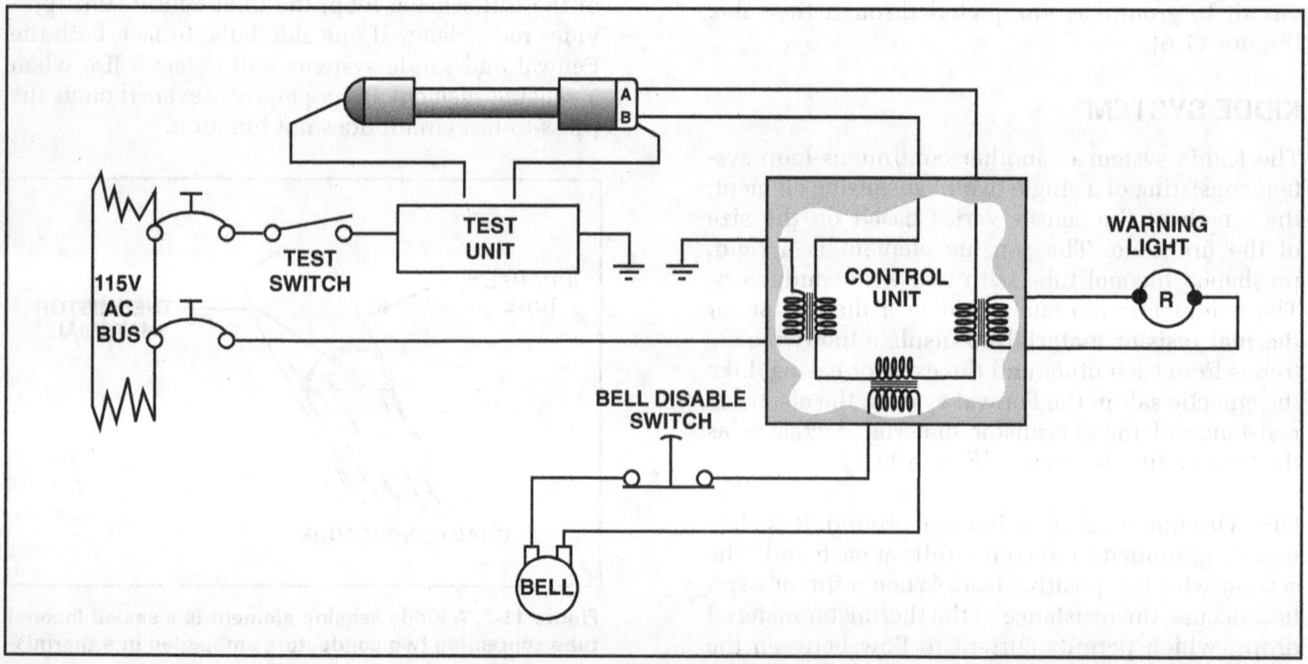


**Figure 11-9. An AC bus supplies power to both the control unit and test unit of a Lindberg fire detection system. When a fire or overheat condition exists, the diaphragm switch closes, which completes the circuit for both the warning light and the bell.**

switch that closes to provide a warning for both an overheat condition and a fire.

Like the Lindberg system, the Systron-Donner system operates by changes in gas pressure. The helium gas provides a systems **averaging**, or **overheat**, **function**. At normal temperatures, the helium pressure in the tube exerts an insufficient amount of force to close the overheat switch. However, when the average temperature along the length of the tube reaches an overheat level, the gas pressure increases and closes the diaphragm switch to activate the alarm. After the overheat source is removed, the helium gas pressure drops and the diaphragm switch opens.

The system's fire detection function, or **discrete function**, is provided by the gas-charged titanium wire. When exposed to a localized high temperature, such as a fire or a bleed air leak, the titanium wire releases hydrogen gas. This increases the sensor's total gas pressure, which closes the diaphragm switch to activate the fire alarm. A typical Systron-Donner system sensor activates a fire alarm when exposed to a 2000 degree Fahrenheit flame for five seconds. After a fire is extinguished, the sensor core material reabsorbs the hydrogen gas and the responder automatically resets the system. [Figure 11-10]

To check system integrity, the responder unit of a Systron-Donner system contains an **integrity switch** that is held closed by the normal gas pressure of the helium. When the integrity switch is closed, depressing the test switch results in a fire warning. However, if the sensing element becomes cut or severely chafed, the helium gas can escape, in which case the integrity switch would remain open. In this situation, depressing the test switch provides a "no test" indication.

Systron-Donner sensor elements are quite durable and can be flattened, twisted, kinked, and dented without losing overheat and fire detection properties. A typical sensing system uses two separate sensing loops for redundancy. Both loops are required to sense a fire or overheat before an alarm will sound. If one loop fails, system logic will isolate the defective loop and reconfigure to single-loop operation. [Figure 11-11]

## MEGGITT SYSTEM

The Meggitt system is a result of the merger of the Lindberg Company with the Systron-Donner Company. The Meggitt pneumatic continuous-loop detector is similar to the Systron-Donner system covered above. The primary difference is in the test circuit. The Meggitt system uses a normally closed integrity switch that is held open by the helium gas in the system. If the system is breached, the loss of gas permits the switch to close and illuminate a fault indication that the system is no longer functional.

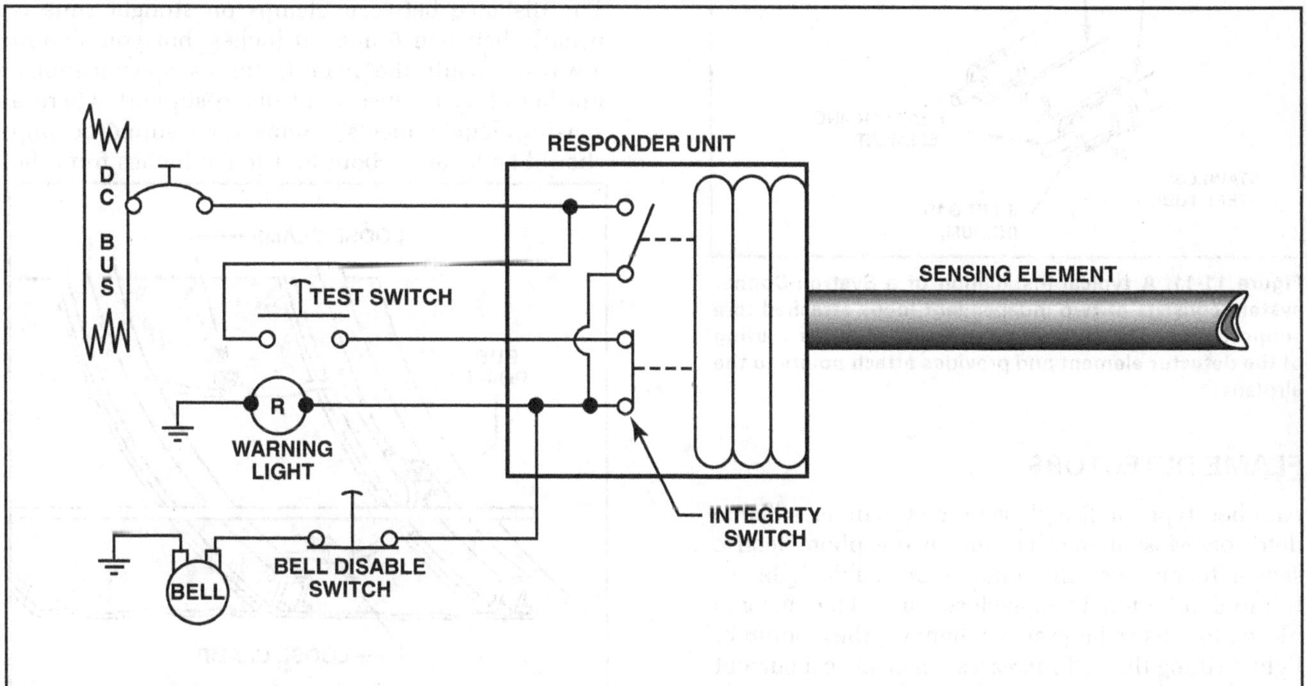


**Figure 11-10. The Systron-Donner fire detection and overheat system consists of a helium-filled sensor tube surrounding a hydrogen-charged core. With this system, excessive temperatures increase the gas pressure to force a diaphragm switch closed, after which power flows to the warning light and bell.**

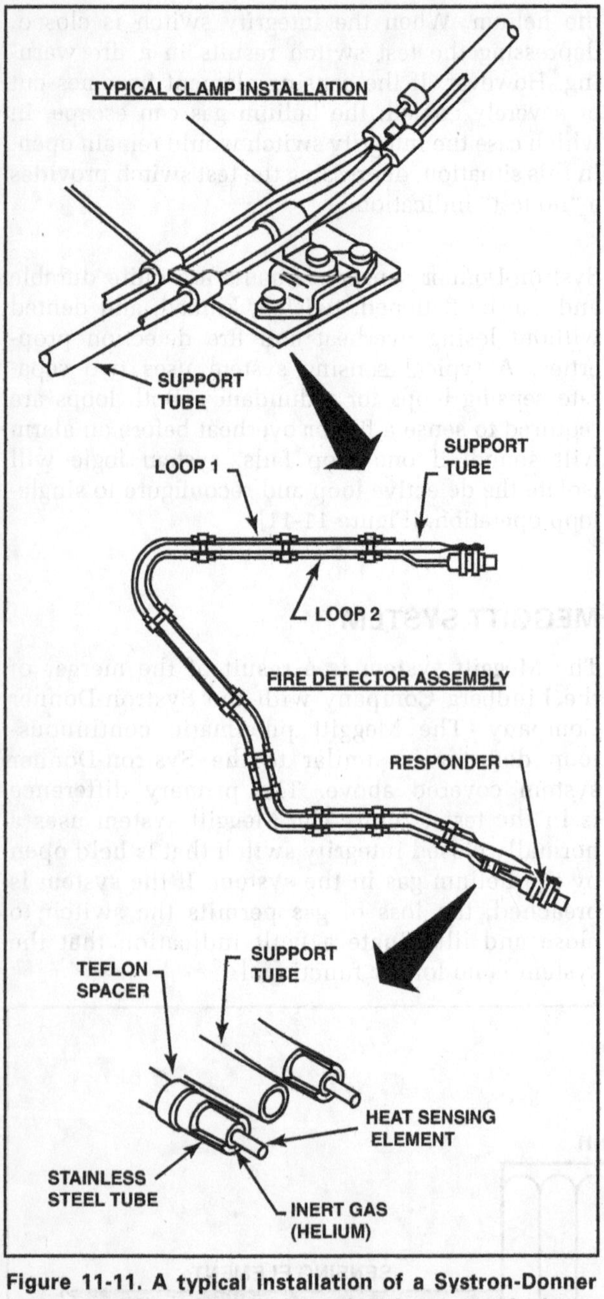


**Figure 11-11. A typical installation of a Systron-Donner system consists of two independent loops attached to a support tube. The support tube establishes the routing of the detector element and provides attach points to the airplane.**

## FLAME DETECTORS

Another type of fire detection system is a flame detector. Most flame detectors use a photoelectric sensor to measure the amount of visible light, or infrared radiation, in an enclosed area. The sensor is placed to sense a large area; whenever the amount of light striking the cell increases, an electrical current is produced. When a sufficient amount of current is produced and channeled through an amplifier, a fire warning is initiated.

## SMOKE AND TOXIC GAS DETECTION SYSTEMS

In addition to engine fire detection systems, you should be aware of a number of related airframe detection systems. The most common types of detectors used in aircraft cabin areas and cargo pits are flame detectors, smoke detectors, and carbon monoxide detectors. Each of these is discussed in detail in the *A&P Technician Airframe Textbook.* However, note that smoke detectors and carbon monoxide detectors are not used to detect fires in powerplant areas because air turbulence around an engine dissipates smoke and gas too rapidly for a detector to recognize a fire.

## INSPECTION AND TESTING

Although the engine cowl provides some protection for the sensing elements of a fire detection system, damage can still result from engine vibration and handling during inspections and maintenance. This, combined with the relatively small size of the sensing elements, emphasizes the need for a regular inspection program. The following general procedures are examples of some periodic inspection practices for a typical fire detection system. However, you should always follow the specific manufacturer's maintenance instructions.

You must regularly inspect the routing and security of sensing elements. Long, unsupported sections can vibrate excessively and damage an element. The distance between clamps on straight runs is usually between 8 and 10 inches, but you should always consult the manufacturer's specifications. Furthermore, to ensure adequate support where a sensing element meets a connector, a support clamp should be located about four to six inches from the

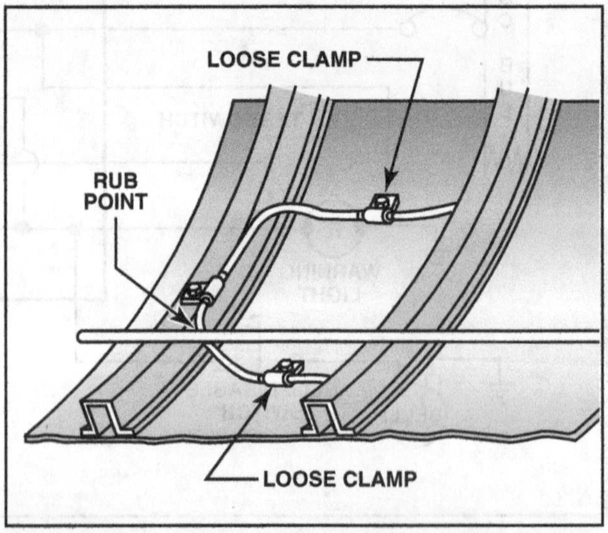


**Figure 11-12. A loose clamp can result in damage to a sensing element.**

connector fitting. On elements routed around components, a straight run of one inch is typically maintained from all connectors before the start of a bend. The optimum bend radius for continuous-loop type sensing elements is typically three inches. Common locations of cracked or broken elements are near inspection plates, cowl panels, engine components, and cowl supports. [Figure 11-12]

The clamps that support continuous-loop sensing elements often consist of a small piece of hinged aluminum that is bolted to the aircraft structure. To absorb some of the engine vibration, most support clamps wrap a rubber grommet around the sensing element. These grommets can soften through exposure to oils and hydraulic fluid, or they can become hardened from excessive heat. Therefore, you should inspect grommets should on a regular basis and replaced them as necessary. [Figure 11-13]

In addition to checking for security, you should check a continuous-loop sensing element for dents, kinks, and crushed areas. Each manufacturer establishes limits for acceptable damage and the minimum acceptable diameter of a sensing element. For a dent or kink that falls within the manufacturer's limits, no attempt should be made to straighten it. The stresses developed while attempting to straighten a sensing element can cause the tubing to fail. [Figure 11-14]

Be sure to inspect shielded flexible leads for fraying. The braided sheath is made up of many fine metal strands woven into a protective covering that surround the inner insulated wire. Continuous bending or rough treatment can break the wire strands, especially those near the connectors, which can result in a short circuit.

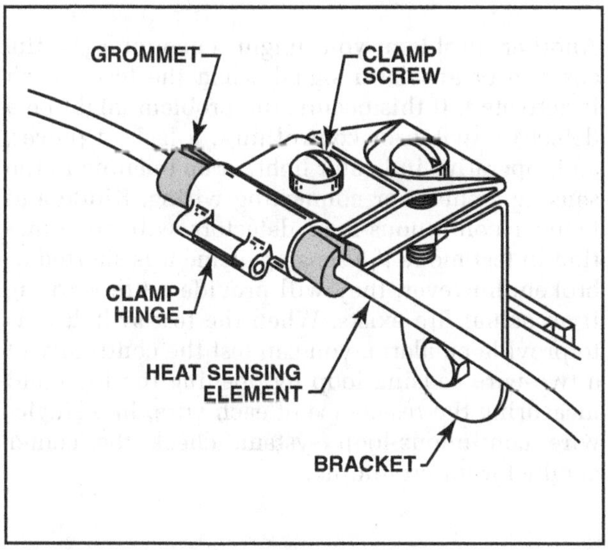


**Figure 11-13. Grommets should be installed on a sensing element centered in a clamp. The split end of the grommet should face the outside of the nearest bend. Clamps and grommets should fit the element snugly.**

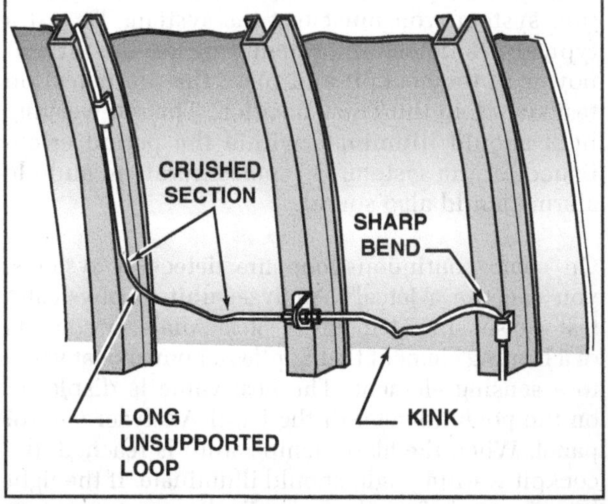


**Figure 11-14. Fire sensing elements are located in exposed areas and are subject to impact and abrasion. When inspecting fire elements, look for sharp bends, kinks, and crushed sections.**

Inspect the nuts at the end of a sensing element for tightness and proper security. Tighten any loose nuts to the torque value specified by the manufacturer. Some connection joints require the use of copper crush gaskets. If this type of gasket is used, replace it each time the connection is separated. Additional items to look for include stray pieces of safety wire or other metal particles that might short the sensing element. [Figure 11-15]

Thermocouple detector mounting brackets should be repaired or replaced if cracked, corroded, or damaged. When replacing a thermocouple detector, note which wire is connected to the positive terminal of the defective unit and connect the replacement detector in the same way.

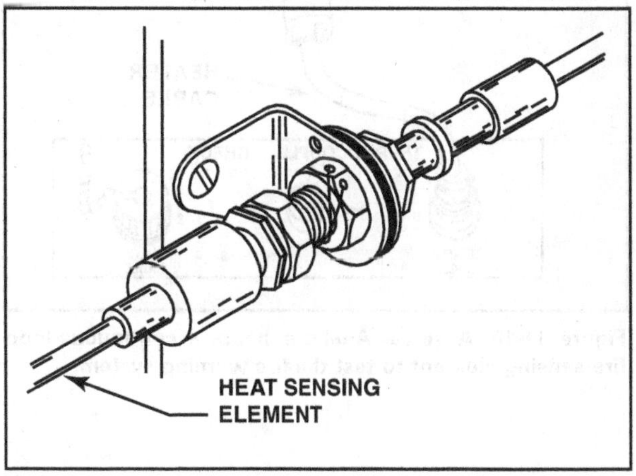


**Figure 11-15. When inspecting an electrical connector joint, verify that the retaining nut is properly tightened and that the safety wire is secure.**

After you inspect the components of a fire detection system, you must test the system. To test a typical fire detection system, turn on the aircraft power in the cockpit and place the fire detection test switch in the TEST position. The red warning light should illuminate within the period established for the system. On some aircraft an audible alarm should also sound.

On some continuous-loop fire detection systems, you can use a Jetcal® Analyzer unit to physically test the sensing element. A Jetcal Analyzer consists of a heating element that applies a known heat value to a sensing element. The heat value is displayed on the potentiometer of the Jetcal Analyzer control panel. When the alarm temperature is reached, the cockpit warning light should illuminate. If the light illuminates before the prescribed temperature setting, the entire loop should be inspected for dents, kinks, or other damage that could reduce the normal spacing between the power lead and ground potential of the loop. [Figure 11-16]

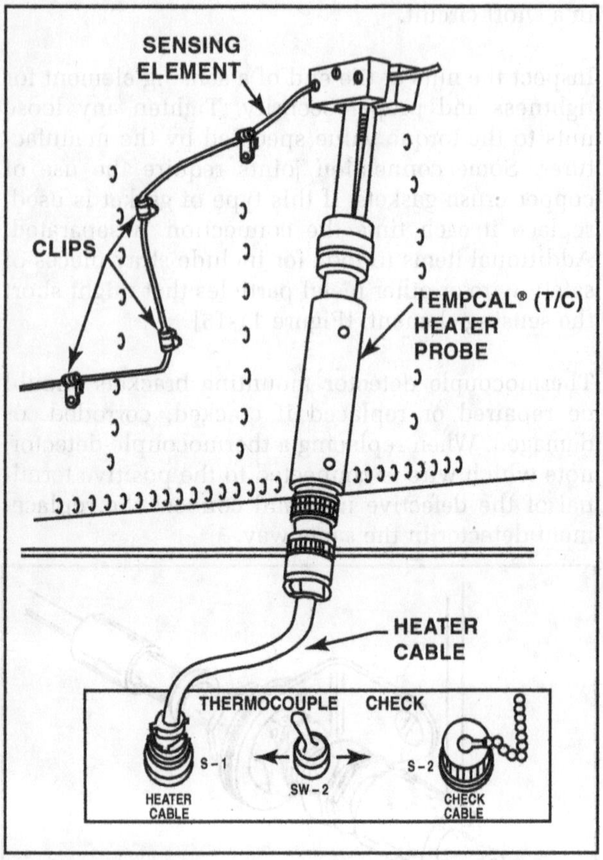


**Figure 11-16. A Jetcal Analyzer heats a continuous-loop fire-sensing element to test the fire warning system.**

## TROUBLESHOOTING

Intermittent or false alarms are the most common discrepancies associated with fire detection systems. Most intermittent alarms are caused by a short circuit in the detector system wiring. Electrical shorts are often caused by a loose wire that occasionally touches a nearby terminal, a frayed wire that brushes against a structure, or a sensing element that rubs against a structural member and wears through the insulation. Intermittent faults can sometimes be located by applying power to the system and moving wires to reestablish the short.

False alarms can typically be located by disconnecting the engine sensing loop from the aircraft wiring. If the false alarm continues, a short must exist between the loop connections and the control unit. However, if the false alarm ceases when the engine sensing loop is disconnected, the fault is in the disconnected sensing loop. Examine the loop to verify that no portion of the sensing element is touching the hot engine. If you cannot locate a contact point, locate the shorted section by isolating and disconnecting elements consecutively around the entire loop. Kinks and sharp bends in the sensing element can cause an internal wire to short intermittently to the outer tubing. The fault can often be located by checking the sensing element with a megohmmeter, while tapping the element in a suspected area to produce the short.

Moisture in a detection system seldom causes a false fire alarm. However, if moisture does cause a false alarm, the warning will persist until the contamination either is removed or boils away and the loop resistance returns to its normal value.

Another problem you might encounter is the absence of an alarm signal when the test switch is activated. If this occurs, the problem might be a defective switch or control unit, a lack of power, an inoperative indicator light, or an opening in the sensing element or connecting wiring. Kidde and Fenwal continuous-loop detectors will not function in test mode if a sensing element is shorted or broken; however, they will provide a fire warning if an actual fire exists. When the test switch fails to provide an alarm, you can test the continuity of a two-wire sensing loop by opening the loop and measuring the resistance of each wire. In a single-wire continuous-loop system, check the center conductor for grounding.

# SUMMARY CHECKLIST

✓ Engine fire detections systems are classified as spot-detection and continuous-loop systems.

✓ Thermally activated sensors indicate elevated temperatures in an engine compartment that might indicate a fire.

# KEY TERMS

fire detection system
spot-detection system
continuous-loop system
bimetallic thermal switch
single loop system
double loop system
Edison system
active thermocouples
reference thermocouple
relay box
test thermocouple
overheat sensing element
eutectic salt
thermistor
thermal resistor material
electronic control unit
pneumatic continuous-loop detectors
responder
pneumatic system
averaging function
overheat function
discrete function
integrity switch

# QUESTIONS

1. The ____________ (spot detector or thermocouple) sensors operate using a bimetallic thermal switch that closes when heated to a preset temperature.

2. The ____________ (thermal switch or thermocouple) type of fire detection system operates on a rate-of-rise principle.

3. The thermocouple in an Edison system that is located where it is relatively protected from the initial flame is known as the ____________ thermocouple.

4. The two relays used in the warning circuit of a thermocouple-type system are:

   a. ____________

   b. ____________

5. The continuous loop detection system works on the same basic principle as the ____________ (spot detector or thermocouple) fire warning system.

6. Continuous loop fire detectors are ____________ (overheat or rate-of-rise) systems.

7. The two types of continuous loop systems widely used are:

   a. ____________

   b. ____________

8. The ________ (Kidde or Fenwall) has two wires inside the Inconel tube.

9. The two types of pressure-type sensor responder fire detection systems are:

   a. ____________

   b. ____________

10. Carbon monoxide detectors are generally located in aircraft cabins or ________ areas.

11. The ____________ ____________ (what unit) may be used to test certain continuous loop detection systems.

12. Intermittent alarms are most often caused by an intermittent ________ (short or open) in the detector system wiring.

# FIRE EXTINGUISHING SYSTEMS

To understand how fires are extinguished, you must know what makes a fire burn. Simply put, a fire is a chemical reaction that occurs when oxygen combines with a fuel and produces heat and, in most cases, light. Three components must be present for a fire to occur: a combustible fuel, a supply of oxygen, and heat. If you remove any one of these elements, combustion is not sustainable.

The easiest components for a fire extinguishing agent to remove are the oxygen supply and heat. Therefore, fire extinguishing systems are designed to either dilute oxygen levels or reduce the temperature below the fuel's ignition point.

## CLASSIFICATION OF FIRES

All fires are classified by the National Fire Protection Association (NFPA) according to the type of fuel involved. **Class A fires** consume solid combustible materials such as wood, paper, or cloth. An aircraft cabin fire is a good example of a Class A fire.

**Class B fires** consume liquids such as gasoline, oil, turbine fuel, hydraulic fluid, and many of the solvents used in aviation maintenance. Class B fires are the most common type of fire encountered in an engine nacelle.

**Class C fires** involve energized electrical equipment. Special care must be exercised when extinguishing a Class C fire because of the dangers of the fire and the electricity.

**Class D fires** involve burning metal, such as magnesium. Because Class D fires burn so hot, the use of water or other liquids on Class D fires results in more violent reactions or explosions.

### ENGINE FIRE ZONES

The powerplant area is divided into fire zones based on the volume and smoothness of the airflow through the engine compartment. These classifications enable manufacturers to match the type of detection and extinguishing system to the fire conditions. This system uses some of the same letters as NFPA, but be aware that these zones are different from the letter designations for types of fires.

**Class A fire zones** have large volumes of air flowing past obstructions of similar shape. The power section of a reciprocating engine, where air flows over the cylinders, is an example of a Class A fire zone.

**Class B fire zones** have large volumes of air flowing past aerodynamically clean obstructions. Heat exchanger ducts and exhaust manifold shrouds constitute Class B fire zones. Additional Class B fire zones include cowlings or tight, smooth enclosures free of pockets and drained to prevent puddles of flammable liquids. Turbine engine surfaces are sometimes considered Class B fire zones if engine surfaces are aerodynamically clean and all airframe structural formers are covered by a fireproof liner to produce a smooth enclosure.

**Class C fire zones** have relatively small volumes of air flowing through them. The compartment behind the firewall is considered to be a Class C fire zone.

**Class D fire zones** are areas with little or no airflow. Wheel wells and the inside of a wing structure are typical Class D fire zones.

**Class X fires zones** have large volumes of air flowing through them at an irregular rate. Because of the sporadic airflow, Class X fire zones are the most difficult to protect from fire. In fact, the amount of extinguishing agent required to adequately protect a Class X fire zone is normally twice that required for other zones. Class X fire zones are common in engine nacelles.

## FIRE EXTINGUISHING AGENTS

The fixed fire extinguisher systems used in most engine fire protection systems are designed to displace the oxygen with an inert agent that does not support combustion. The most common types of extinguishing agents are carbon dioxide and halogenated hydrocarbons.

### CARBON DIOXIDE

Carbon dioxide ($CO_2$) is a colorless, odorless gas that is about one and one-half times heavier than air. To be used as an extinguishing agent, carbon dioxide must be compressed and cooled for storage as a liquid in a steel cylinder. When released into the atmosphere, carbon dioxide expands and cools to a temperature of about –110 degrees Fahrenheit. When it cools, it becomes a white solid that smothers the fire. After the fire is extinguished, the remaining carbon dioxide slowly changes from a solid directly to a gas; almost no residue is left behind.

Carbon dioxide is effective on both Class B and Class C fires. Because little residue remains, $CO_2$ is well-suited for engine intake and carburetor fires. Furthermore, $CO_2$ is nontoxic and noncorrosive. However, if used improperly, carbon dioxide can cause physiological problems such as mental confusion and suffocation. Because its vapor pressure varies with temperature, $CO_2$ must be stored in containers that are stronger than those required for most other extinguishing agents.

## HALOGENATED HYDROCARBONS

A **halogen** element is one of a group that contains chlorine, fluorine, bromine, or iodine. Some hydrocarbons combine with halogens to produce very effective fire extinguishing agents that extinguish fires by excluding oxygen from the fire source and chemically disrupting the combustion process. Halogenated hydrocarbon fire extinguishing agents are most effective on Class B and Class C fires, but can also be used on Class A and Class D fires. However, its effectiveness on Class A and Class D fires is somewhat limited.

Halogenated hydrocarbons are numbered with five-digit Halon numbers to identify the chemical makeup of the agent according to their chemical formulas. The first digit represents the number of carbon atoms in the compound molecule; the second digit, the number of fluorine atoms; the third digit, the number of chlorine atoms; the fourth digit, the number of bromine atoms; and the fifth digit, the number of iodine atoms, if any. If no iodine is present, the fifth digit does not appear. For example, bromotrifluoromethane CBrF3 is referred to as **Halon 1301**, or sometimes by the trade name **Freon® 13**.

Halon 1301 is extremely effective for extinguishing fires in engine compartments of piston- and turbine-powered aircraft. In engine compartment installations, the Halon 1301 container is pressurized by compressed nitrogen and is discharged through spray nozzles. [Figure 11-17]

A number of halogenated hydrocarbon agents have been used in the past, but are no longer in production. Some early Halon extinguishing agents produced toxic or corrosive gases when

**Figure 11-17. Halogenated hydrocarbon fire extinguishing agents provide effective fire suppression in aircraft engine compartments.**

exposed to fire. For example, carbon tetrachloride (Halon 104) was very good around electrical hazards, but, when exposed to heat, its vapors formed a deadly phosgene gas. Another agent no longer in use is methyl bromide (Halon 1001). Methyl bromide is toxic to people and animals and corrosive to aluminum, magnesium, and zinc alloys. Of all the halogenated hydrocarbon extinguishing agents, Halon 1301 is the safest to use with regard to toxicity and corrosion hazards.

Because of changing regulations and research about environmental impact, you should keep abreast of current developments regarding the use of halogenated hydrocarbons as fire extinguishing agents. For example, several studies indicate that chlorofluorocarbons (CFCs) such as Halon damage the ozone layer in the stratosphere, causing higher levels of ultraviolet radiation to reach the earth. To limit future damage to the ozone layer, the United States Environmental Protection Agency banned the production of CFCs after December 31, 1995. However, existing stock of CFCs were permitted to be used after this date. Several alternatives to CFCs are likely to find application as aviation fire extinguishing agents. For example, DuPont FE-25™ has proven to be an acceptable substitute for Halon 1301 as an extinguishing agent that does not harm earth's ozone layer.

You should become familiar with EPA and FAA regulations governing the use and disposal of CFCs. Improper handling or disposal of halogenated hydrocarbons can lead to civil and criminal penalties.

## FIRE EXTINGUISHING SYSTEMS

The two basic categories of fire extinguishing systems are conventional systems and high-rate discharge (HRD) systems. Both systems use one or more containers of extinguishing agent and a distribution system to release the extinguishing agent through perforated tubing or discharge nozzles. As a general rule, the type of system installed can be identified by the type of extinguishing agent used. Conventional systems usually employ carbon dioxide as the extinguishing agent while HRD systems typically use halogenated hydrocarbons.

## CONVENTIONAL SYSTEMS

The fire extinguishing installations used in many older aircraft are referred to as conventional systems. Many of these systems are still in use and function satisfactorily. A **conventional fire extinguisher system** consists of a cylinder that stores carbon dioxide under pressure and a remotely controlled valve assembly that distributes the extinguishing agent to the engines.

Carbon dioxide cylinders are made of stainless steel and are typically wrapped with steel wire to make them shatterproof. These cylinders are available in different sizes and store gas at between 700 and 1000 p.s.i. Because of the low freezing point of carbon dioxide, a storage cylinder does not require protection against cold weather; however, cylinders can discharge prematurely in hot climates. To prevent this, manufacturers sometimes charge a cylinder with about 200 p.s.i. of dry nitrogen before filling the cylinder with carbon dioxide. This protects most $CO_2$ cylinders against premature discharge up to 160 degrees Fahrenheit. The nitrogen also provides additional pressure to discharge the extinguishing agent.

Carbon dioxide cylinders are equipped internally with a **siphon tube**. The cylinders used in aircraft typically use a straight-rigid or a short-flexible siphon tube. The type of siphon tube depends on whether the cylinder is mounted vertically or horizontally. [Figure 11-18]

Carbon dioxide is distributed through tubing from the cylinder valve to the control valve in the cockpit. From the control valve, $CO_2$ proceeds to the engines through solid tubing installed in the aircraft structure. Inside the engine compartment, the tubing is perforated to discharge the $CO_2$. [Figure 11-19]

To operate a conventional fire extinguisher system, a selector valve in the cockpit is manually set to the engine compartment with the fire. Then, a T-shaped handle next to the selector valve is pulled upward to actuate the release lever in the $CO_2$ cylinder valve. After release, the compressed carbon dioxide flows in a rapid burst to the outlets in the distribution line of the selected engine compartment. Contact with the air converts the liquid $CO_2$ into a solid that smothers the flames. Some $CO_2$ systems have multiple bottles that enable the pilot to deliver extinguishing agent to any engine compartment twice.

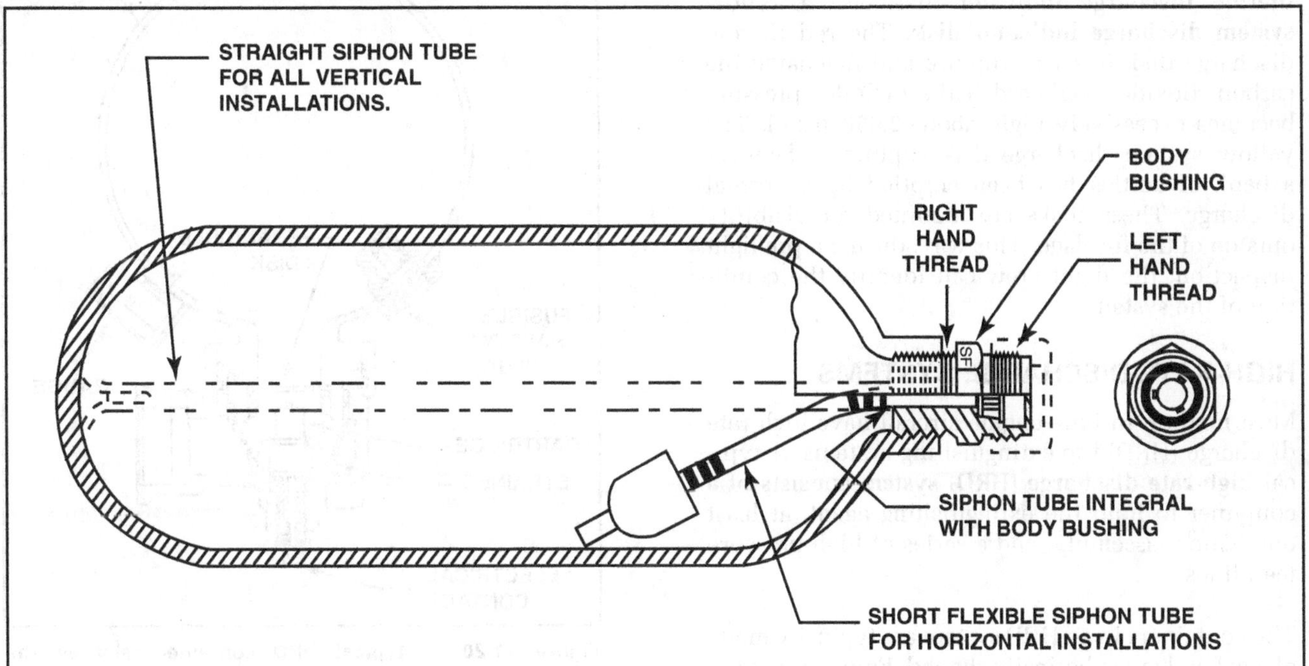


**Figure 11-18. A vertically mounted $CO_2$ cylinder uses a straight-siphon tube. A horizontally mounted cylinder uses a short-flexible siphon tube. A code stamped on the body bushing indicates the type of siphon tube: SF indicates a short-flexible siphon and "S" indicates a straight siphon tube. Some manufacturers stamp or stencil the type of siphon used on the cylinder body.**

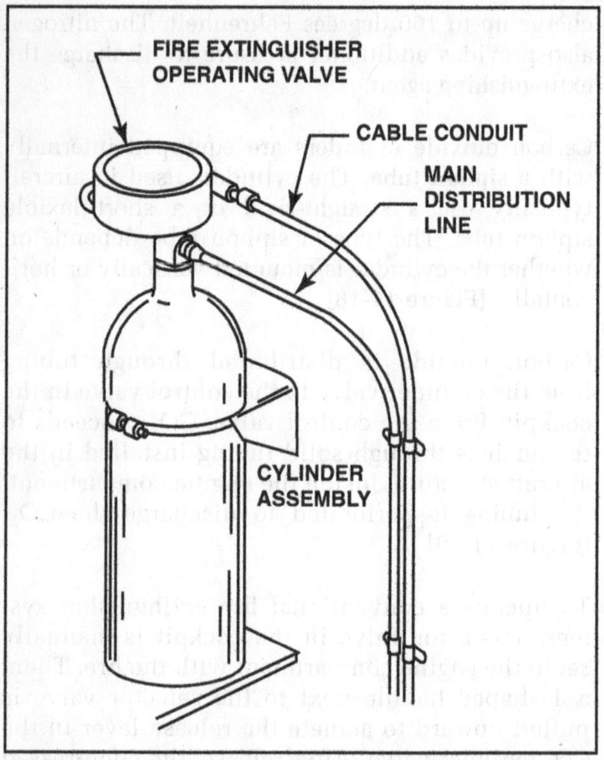


**Figure 11-19. A fire extinguishing system that uses carbon dioxide as the extinguishing agent has a sturdy cylinder assembly mounted to the airframe and connected to a distribution line. A cockpit-controlled operating valve releases the carbon dioxide from the cylinder.**

Each bank of $CO_2$ bottles is equipped with a red **thermo discharge indicator disk** and a yellow **system discharge indicator disk**. The red thermo discharge disk is set to rupture and discharge the carbon dioxide overboard if the cylinder pressure becomes excessively high (about 2,650 p.s.i.). The yellow system discharge disk ruptures whenever a bank of bottles has been emptied by a normal discharge. These disks are mounted for visibility outside of the fuselage. This way, during a preflight inspection, the flight crew can identify the condition of the system.

## HIGH-RATE DISCHARGE SYSTEMS

Most modern turbine-engine aircraft have high-rate discharge (HRD) fire extinguishing systems. A typical **high-rate discharge (HRD) system** consists of a container to hold the extinguishing agent, at least one bonnet assembly, and a series of high-pressure feed lines.

The containers in an HRD system are typically made of steel and are spherically shaped. Four sizes are in common use today, ranging from 224 cubic inches to 945 cubic inches. The smaller containers typically have two openings, one for the bonnet assembly, or **operating head**, and the other for a fusible safety plug. The larger containers usually have two bonnet assemblies.

Each container is partially filled with an extinguishing agent, such as Halon 1301, sealed with a frangible disk, and pressurized with dry nitrogen. A container pressure gauge is provided for quick reference of the container pressure. The **bonnet assembly** contains an electrically ignited discharge cartridge, or **squib**, which fires a projectile into the **frangible disk**. When the disk breaks, the pressurized nitrogen forces the extinguishing agent out of the sphere. To prevent the broken disk fragments from entering the distribution lines, the bonnet assembly also has a strainer. [Figure 11-20]

As a safety feature, each extinguishing container has a thermal fuse, or **fusible safety plug**, that melts and releases the extinguishing agent if the bottle is subjected to high temperatures. If a bottle empties this way, the extinguishing agent blows out a red indicator disk as it vents to the atmosphere. If the bottle discharges normally, it blows out a yellow indicator disk. Like a conventional system, the indicator disks are visible from the outside of the fuselage for easy reference.

When installed on a smaller multiengine aircraft, the fire-extinguishing agent containers are typically

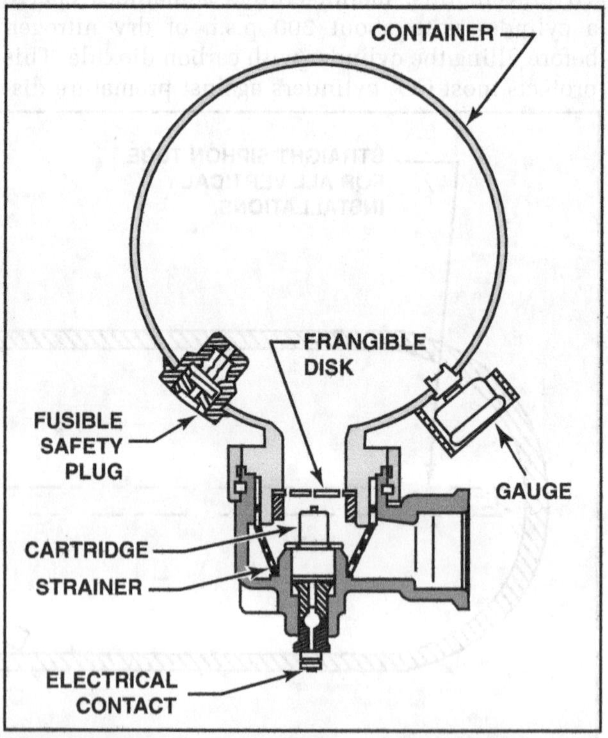


**Figure 11-20. A typical HRD container releases the extinguishing agent within one to two seconds after an electrically actuated explosive cartridge ruptures a frangible disk. A strainer collects the disk fragments to keep them apart from the extinguishing agent, which is directed to the engine nacelle.**

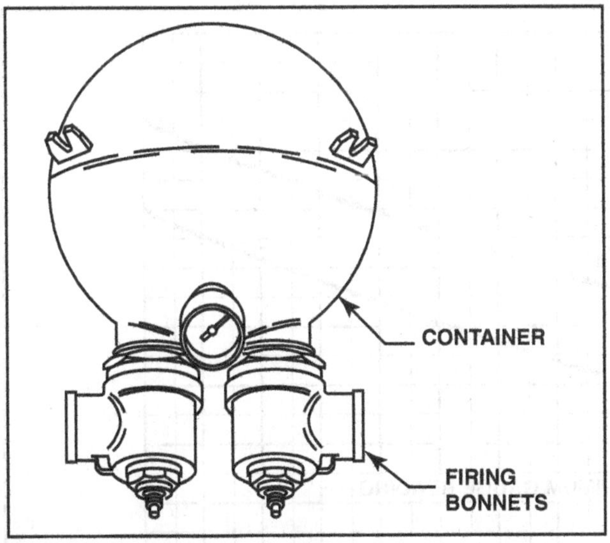


**Figure 11-21. A typical extinguishing agent container on a multiengine aircraft has two firing bonnets.**

equipped with two bonnet assemblies so that one container can serve two engines. [Figure 11-21]

On large multiengine aircraft, typically have two extinguishing agent containers, each with two firing bonnets. This arrangement provides twin-engine aircraft with a dedicated container for each engine. The two discharge ports on each bottle provide redundancy so that both containers can discharge into either engine compartment. [Figure 11-22]

## INSPECTION AND SERVICING

Regular maintenance of fire extinguishing systems includes inspection and service of the fire extinguisher bottles, removing and reinstalling discharge cartridges, testing the discharge tubing for leaks, and testing electrical wiring for continuity. The following discussion describes some common maintenance procedures to provide an understanding of the operations involved. However, maintenance procedures vary depending on the design and construction of the particular unit being serviced; therefore, you should always follow the detailed procedures outlined by the airframe or system manufacturer whenever you perform maintenance.

### CONTAINER PRESSURE CHECK

Periodically conduct a pressure check of fire extinguisher containers to determine that the pressure is within the manufacturer's minimum and maximum limits. Aircraft service manuals contain pressure charts that provide the permissible gauge readings, with corrections for temperature. If the pressure is not within the prescribed limits, remove and replace the container with a properly charged container. [Figure 11-23]

After you have determined that a bottle is properly charged, ascertain that the glass on the pressure gauge is not broken. Then verify that the bottle is securely mounted to the airframe.

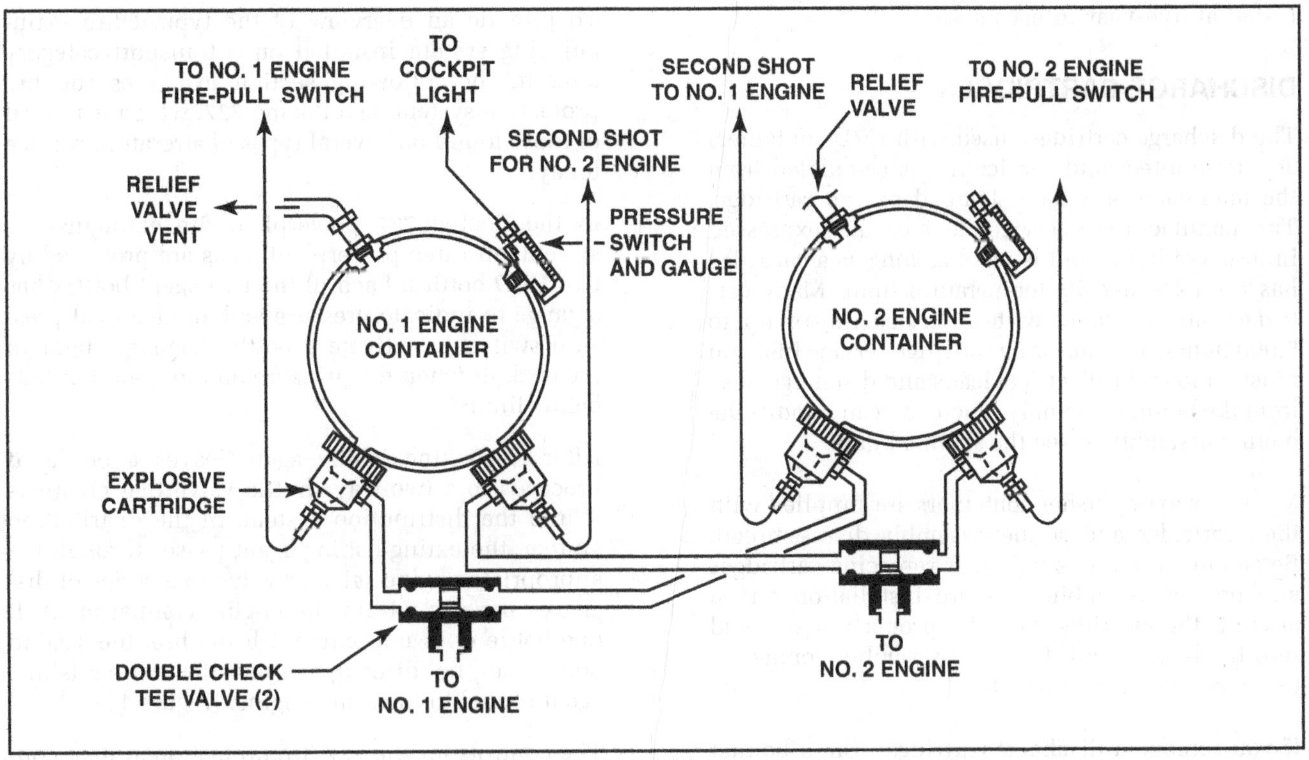


**Figure 11-22. A typical high-rate discharge extinguishing system on a large multiengine aircraft uses two agent containers, each with two discharge ports. This permits two applications of extinguishing agent to any one engine.**

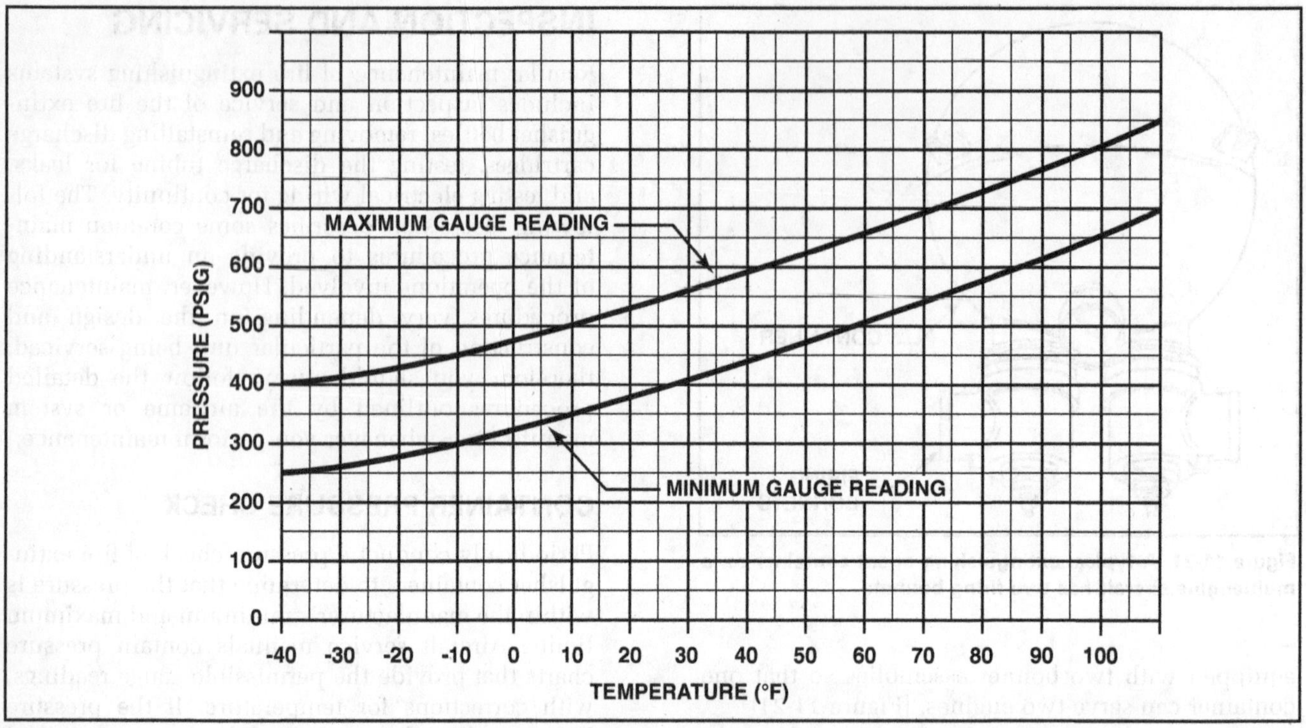


**Figure 11-23. A pressure/temperature chart helps you to determine if a specific fire extinguishing bottle is properly charged.**

The only way to determine whether an appropriate amount of extinguishing agent is in a container is to weigh the container. Therefore, most fire extinguishing containers require a weight check at frequent intervals. Additionally, fire extinguisher containers must be hydrostatically tested at five-year intervals.

## DISCHARGE CARTRIDGES

The discharge cartridges used with HRD containers are life-limited, and service life is calculated from the manufacturer's date stamped on the cartridge. The manufacturer's service life is usually expressed in terms of hours and is valid as long as a cartridge has not exceeded its temperature limit. Many cartridges are available with a service life of up to 5,000 hours. To determine cartridge service life, you must remove the electrical leads and discharge hose from the bonnet assembly. Then you can remove the bonnet assembly to see the stamped date.

Most new extinguisher containers are supplied with their cartridge and bonnet assembly disassembled. Be careful when assembling or replacing cartridges and bonnet assemblies. Before installation on an aircraft, the cartridge must be properly assembled into the bonnet and the entire assembly connected to the container. [Figure 11-24]

If you remove a discharge cartridge from a bonnet assembly, do not us it in another bonnet assembly. Furthermore, because discharge cartridges are fired electrically, they should be properly grounded or shorted to prevent accidental firing.

## BOEING 727 FIRE PROTECTION SYSTEM

To provide an overview of the typical fire extinguishing system installed on a transport category aircraft, the following section examines the fire protection system on a Boeing 727, which is typical of those found on several types of aircraft in service today.

In the Boeing 727 powerplant fire extinguishing system, all three powerplant areas are protected by two HRD bottles. Each of the two agent bottles has a gauge to indicate pressure and an electrical pressure switch to activate a bottle discharge light in the cockpit when the pressure on the agent bottle is below limits.

After the extinguishing agent leaves a bottle, it proceeds to a two-way shuttle valve that channels it into the distribution system. In the distribution system, the extinguishing agent passes through the appropriate engine selector valve to a series of discharge nozzles within the engine compartment. If one bottle does not extinguish the fire, the second bottle can be discharged and the extinguishing agent routed to the same engine. [Figure 11-25]

The controls for the 727 fire protection system consist of three engine fire warning lights, one wheel well fire warning light, a bottle transfer switch, a

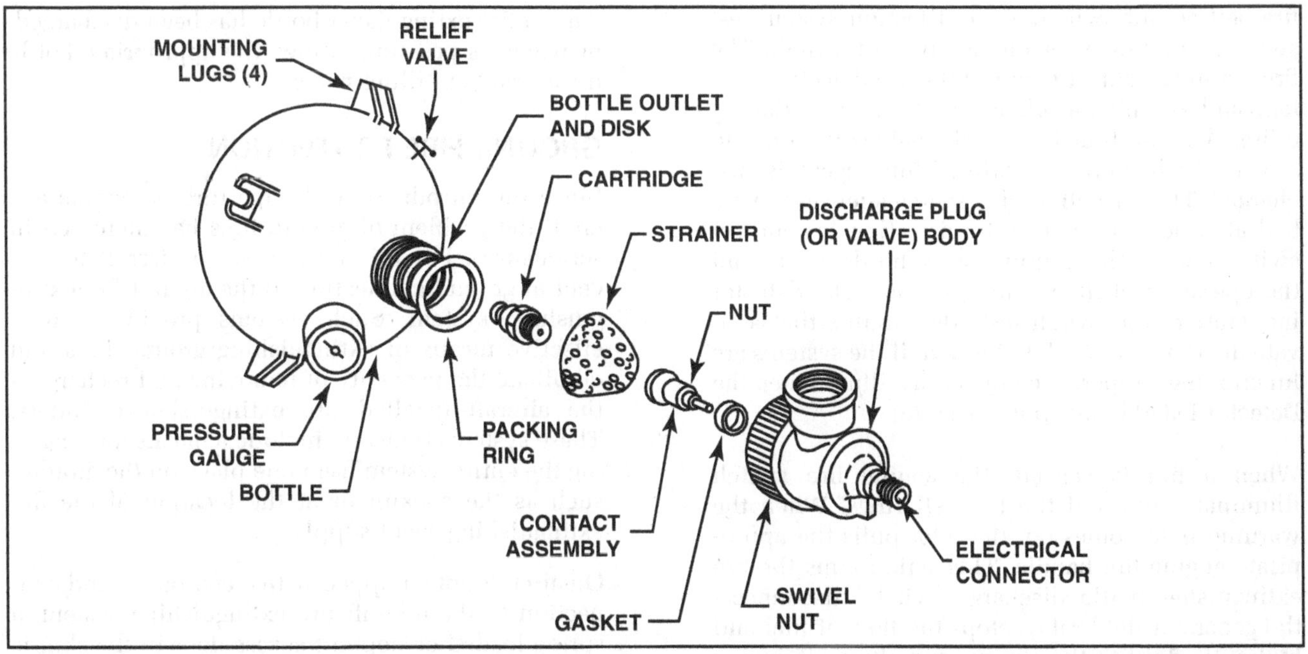


**Figure 11-24. An exploded view drawing is useful when assembling a discharge cartridge into a bonnet assembly. After reassembly, the entire bonnet assembly is attached to the container with a swivel nut that tightens against a packing ring gasket.**

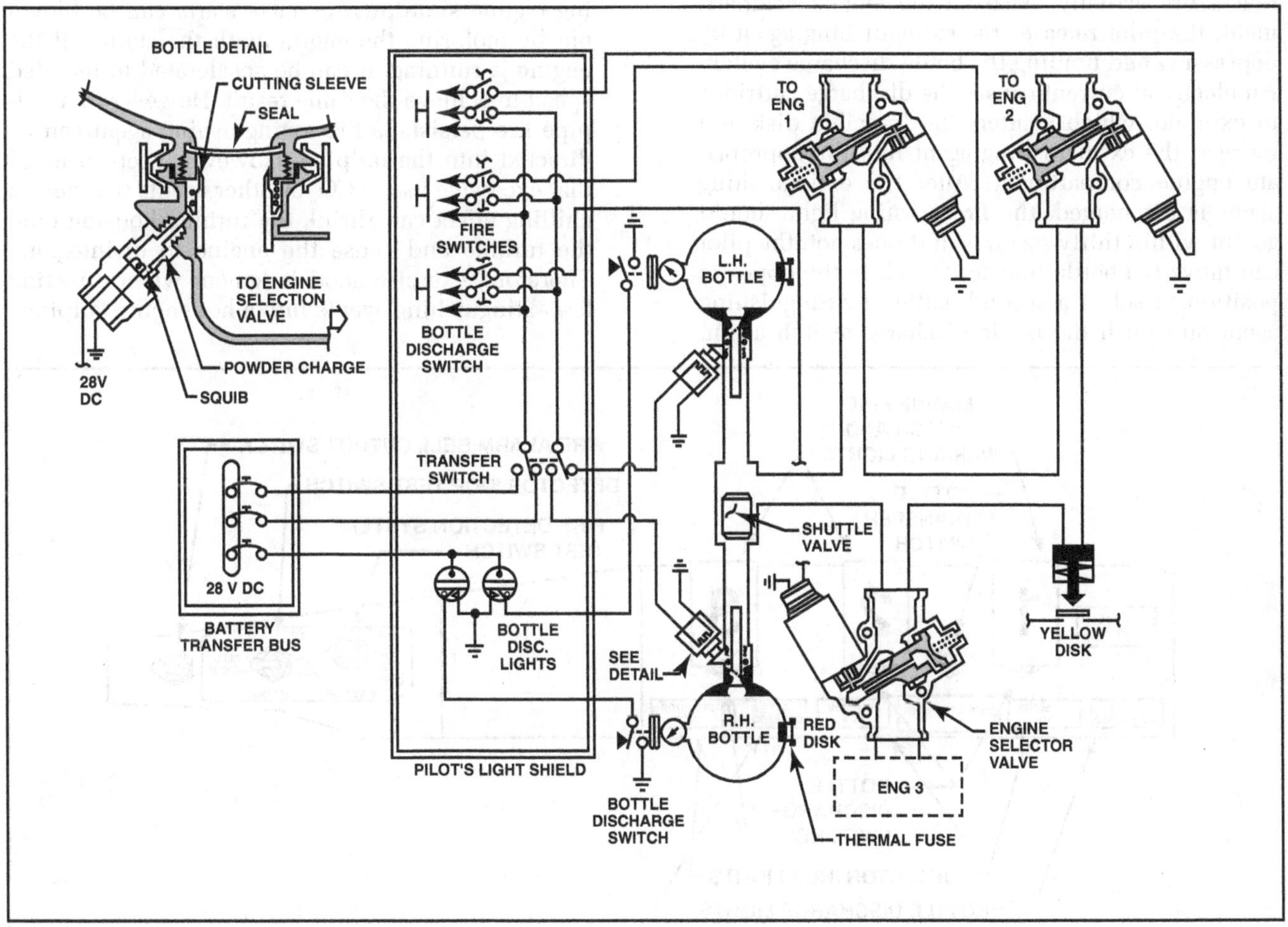


**Figure 11-25. The Boeing 727 aircraft use two fire bottles and three selector valves to provide fire suppression for all three engines. With this arrangement, the cockpit crew can discharge both bottles to a single engine.**

fire bell cutout switch, a fire detection system test switch, and a detector inoperative test switch. The fire warning lights are part of the fire detection system and illuminate whenever the system detects a fire. A bottle transfer switch enables the pilot to select which bottle of extinguishing agent is discharged. The fire bell disable switch silences the fire bell after activation. The fire detection system test switch checks the continuity of the detectors and the operation of the warning system. The detector inoperative test switch tests the circuits that activate the Detector INOP lights and, if the systems are functioning properly, momentarily illuminates the Detector INOP lights. [Figure 11-26]

When a fire is sensed, the engine fire switch illuminates red and the fire bell rings. When the warning light comes on, the pilot pulls the appropriate engine fire handle. This action arms the fire extinguisher bottle discharge switch, disconnects the generator field relay, stops the flow of fuel and hydraulic fluid to the engine, and shuts off engine bleed air. It also deactivates the engine-driven hydraulic pump low-pressure lights and uncovers the bottle discharge switch. If the pilot determines that a fire actually exists in the engine compartment, the pilot releases the extinguishing agent by depressing and holding the bottle discharge switch. An electrical current causes the discharge cartridge to explode, which shatters the frangible disk and releases the extinguishing agent into the appropriate engine compartment. After the extinguishing agent is discharged, the fire warning light should go out within thirty seconds. If it does not, the pilot can move the bottle transfer switch to the opposite position to select a second bottle of extinguishing agent and push the bottle discharge switch again. After a fire extinguisher bottle has been discharged, or when its pressure is low, the appropriate bottle discharge light illuminates.

## GROUND FIRE PROTECTION

Since the introduction of large turbine engine aircraft, the problem of ground fires has increased in seriousness. For this reason, some aircraft have a central ground connection to the aircraft fire extinguishing system. Such systems provide a more effective means of extinguishing ground fires and eliminate the necessity of removing and recharging the aircraft-installed fire extinguisher cylinders. These systems typically include a means for operating the entire system from one place on the ground, such as the cockpit or at the location of the fire extinguishing agent supply.

On aircraft not equipped with a central ground connection to the aircraft fire extinguishing system, a spring-loaded or pop-out access door in the skin is usually provided for rapid access to the compressor, tailpipe, or burner compartments.

Internal engine tailpipe fires that take place during engine shutdown or false starts can be blown out by motoring the engine with the starter. If the engine is running, it can be accelerated to its rated speed to achieve the same result. However, if a tailpipe fire persists, a fire extinguishing agent can be directed into the tailpipe. However, keep in mind that excessive use of $CO_2$ or other agents that have a chilling effect can shrink the turbine housing onto the turbine and cause the engine to disintegrate. Therefore, exercise good judgment when directing fire extinguishing agents into a hot engine tailpipe.

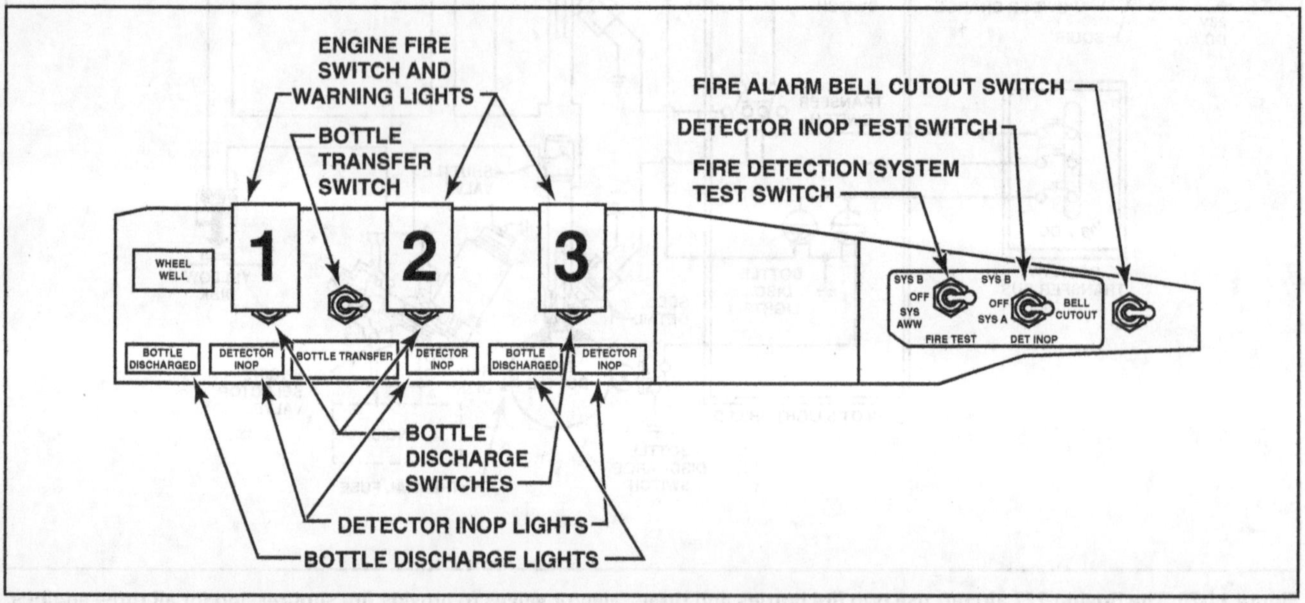


**Figure 11-26. A typical Boeing 727 fire control panel provides an indication of wheel well or engine compartment fires, controls fire bottle discharge, and permits testing of the fire detector system.**

# SUMMARY CHECKLIST

✓ Classes of fires and engine fire zones are both indicated by letters; both systems use the same letters, but with different meanings.

✓ Early fire extinguishing systems for gas turbine engines used carbon dioxide as the extinguishing agent.

✓ Modern fire extinguishing systems for gas turbine engines use a high-rate discharge system that is activated by an electrically ignited squib.

✓ Fire extinguishing systems typically use colored disks to indicate whether a system has been discharged.

# KEY TERMS

Class A fires
Class B fires
Class C fires
Class D fires
Class A fire zones
Class B fire zones
Class C fire zones
Class D fire zones
Class X fires zones
halogen
Halon 1301
Freon 13
conventional fire extinguisher system
high-rate-of-discharge systems
HRD
siphon tube
thermo discharge indicator disk
system discharge indicator disk
operating head
bonnet assembly
squib
frangible disk
fusible safety plug

# QUESTIONS

1. The three requirements for a fire are:

   a. ______________

   b. ______________

   c. ______________

2. Identify the class of each fire described below, using the NFPA classification system.

   a. A brake fire on a system using magnesium wheels. ______

   b. A electrical subpanel. ______

   c. A trash can fire. ______

   d. Spilled solvent ignited by a cigarette. ______

   e. An aircraft cabin fire. ______

3. Halogenated hydrocarbon extinguishing agents are identified using a system of ______ numbers.

4. Name the two basic categories into which extinguishing systems are installed:

   a. ______________

   b. ______________

5. Conventional systems are usually associated with the use of ______________ ______________ as the extinguishing agent.

6. The fire extinguishing agent used in most turbine engine HRD fire extinguishing systems are ______________ ______________.

7. A blown-out ______ (yellow or red) indicator disk tells the technician that the system has been discharged by an overheat condition at the bottle location.

8. A blown-out ______ (yellow or red) indicator disk tells the technician that the system has been discharged by normal operation of the system.

9. If a cartridge is removed from a discharge valve, it ______ (may or may not) be used in another discharge valve assembly.

10. Fire extinguisher containers are re-weighed at frequent intervals to determine the ______ of ______.

11. Four things that happen when the pilot pulls the fire switch on a Boeing 727 airplane are:

    a. ______________________________

    b. ______________________________

    c. ______________________________

    d. ______________________________

12. Care should be exercised when using $CO_2$ to extinguish a tailpipe fire because of ______________ caused by the chilling effect of the agent.

# CHAPTER 12

# PROPELLERS

## INTRODUCTION

Since the first powered flight, propellers have been used to convert aircraft engine power into thrust. Although most modern transport category aircraft are powered by turbojet or turbofan engines, many of the aircraft in use today are propelled by one or more propellers driven by either a turbine or reciprocating engine. Regardless of engine type, the propeller converts engine power to aircraft thrust. As an aircraft maintenance technician, you must have a thorough understanding of the basic principles, maintenance, and repair of propeller systems.

# SECTION A

## PROPELLER PRINCIPLES

Almost all early aircraft designs used propellers to create thrust. At the end of the 19th century, many unusual and innovative propeller designs were tried on flying machines. Early propeller designs included simple fabric-covered wooden paddles and elaborate multiblade wire-braced designs. As aeronautical science developed, propeller designs evolved from flat boards that pushed air backward to airfoils that produced lift to pull aircraft forward.

Propeller design developed with new materials that made possible thinner airfoil sections with greater strength. Because of structural strength, aluminum alloys have been used widely as a structural material in the majority of aircraft propellers. However, several varieties of propellers in still in service that are constructed of wood.

Propeller designs continue to improve through the use of new airfoil shapes, composite materials, and multi-blade configurations. Recent improvements include the use of composite materials to produce laminar flow symmetrical airfoils and scimitar propeller blade designs.

### NOMENCLATURE

Familiarity with some basic terms and component names is critical to understand the principles of how a propeller produces thrust. All modern propellers consist of at least two blades connected to a central **hub**. The portion of a propeller blade that is nearest the hub is referred to as the **blade shank,** and the portion furthest from the hub is called the **blade tip**. The propeller hub, or hub assembly, is machined to permit mounting onto an engine crankshaft or a reduction gear assembly. [Figure 12-1]

Each blade of a propeller functions as a rotating wing that produces lift to move an aircraft through the air. As such, propeller blades share much of the same nomenclature as an aircraft wing. All propeller blades have a **leading edge**, a **trailing edge**, and a chord line. A **chord line** is an imaginary line drawn through an airfoil from the leading edge to the trailing edge. Some terms, however, are unique to propellers. The curved, or cambered, side of a propeller blade is called the **blade back** and the flat side is called the **blade face**. A propeller's **blade angle** is the acute angle formed by a propeller's plane of rotation and the blade's chord line. A propeller's plane of rotation is always perpendicular to the engine crankshaft. [Figure 12-2]

Propellers with adjustable blade angles use removable blades that are secured to a hub assembly by a set of **clamping rings**. Each **blade root** has a flanged butt, or shoulder, which mates with grooves in the hub assembly. The blade shank on this type of blade is typically round and extends to at least the end of the hub assembly; however, in some cases, the shank can extend beyond the hub assembly and into the airstream. When this is the case, blade cuffs might be installed to improve air flow around the blade shank. A **blade cuff** is an airfoil-shaped attachment made of thin sheets of metal, plastic, or composite material. Blade cuffs increase the flow of cooling air to the engine nacelle. Mechanical clamping devices and adhesive bonding agents attach the cuffs to the blades. [Figure 12-3]

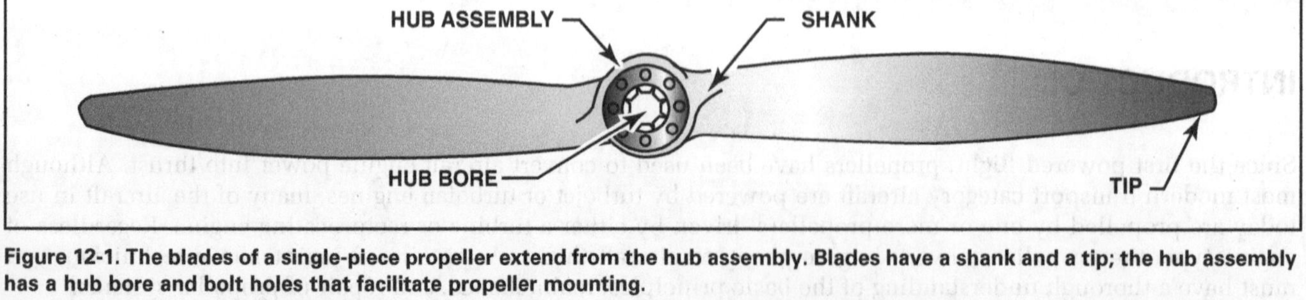


**Figure 12-1. The blades of a single-piece propeller extend from the hub assembly. Blades have a shank and a tip; the hub assembly has a hub bore and bolt holes that facilitate propeller mounting.**

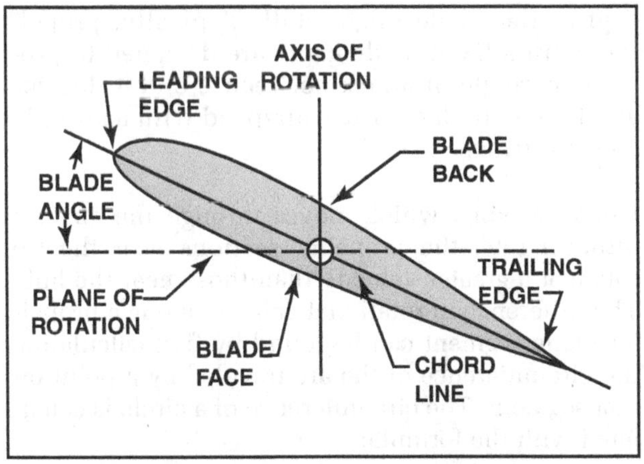


**Figure 12-2. All propeller blades have a leading edge, a trailing edge, and a chord line. Additionally, propeller blades are set at a specific angle defined by the acute angle formed by a propeller's plane of rotation and the chord line.**

To aid in identifying specific points along the length of a propeller blade, most blades have several defined blade stations. A **blade station** is a reference position on a propeller blade that is measured from the center of the hub.

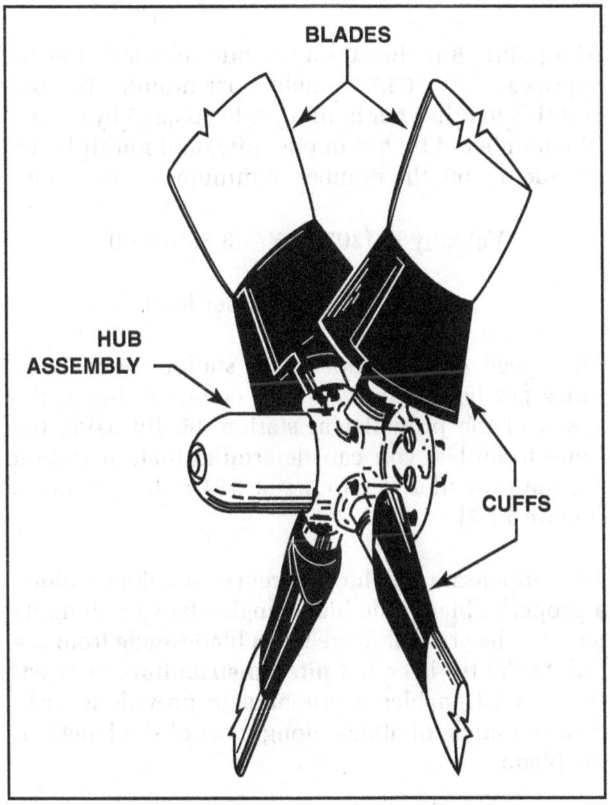


**Figure 12-3. Some large turboprop propeller blades are fitted with blade cuffs to improve the airflow around the blade shanks.**

## PROPELLER THEORY

A propeller rotating through the air creates an area of low pressure in front of the blade. This low-pressure area, combined with an area of high pressure behind the blade, enables a propeller to produce thrust. The amount of thrust produced depends on several factors including the propeller blade's angle of attack, speed, and airfoil shape. The **angle of attack** of a propeller blade is the angle formed by the chord line of the blade and the relative wind. The direction of the **relative wind** is determined by the speed that aircraft moves through the air and the rotational motion of the propeller. For example, when a propeller rotates on a stationary aircraft, the direction of the relative wind is exactly opposite to the rotational movement of the propeller. In this case, the angle of attack is the same as the propeller blade angle. [Figure 12-4]

When the aircraft begins moving forward, the relative wind direction shifts because, in addition to rotating, the propeller now has forward motion. The result is that the relative wind is much closer to the angle of attack. In this case, the angle of attack will always be less than the blade angle. [Figure 12-5]

Based on the effect that forward motion has on the relative wind of a propeller blade, the faster an aircraft moves through the air, the smaller the angle of attack on the propeller blade. However, if propeller speed increases, the trailing edge of the propeller blade travels a greater distance for the same amount of forward movement. As propeller speed increases, the relative wind strikes the propeller blade at a greater angle and the angle of attack increases. [Figure 12-6]

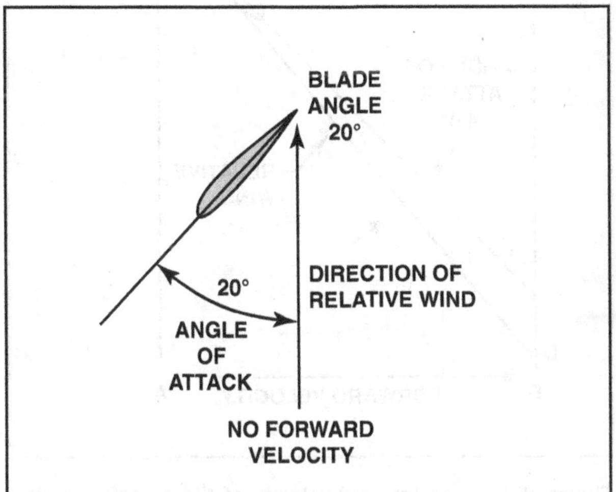


**Figure 12-4. With no forward velocity, the relative wind is directly opposite the movement of a propeller blade. In this condition, a propeller's angle of attack is the same as its blade angle.**

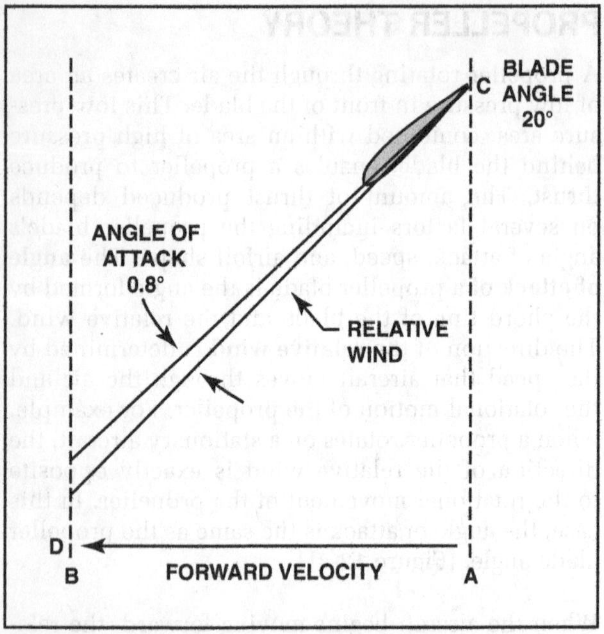


**Figure 12-5. In forward flight, as an airplane moves from point A to B, the propeller moves from point C to D. In this case, a propeller's trailing edge follows the path from C to D, which represents the resultant relative wind. This results in an angle of attack less than the blade angle.**

The most effective angle of attack for a propeller blade is between 2 and 4 degrees. Any angle of attack exceeding 15 degrees is ineffective because

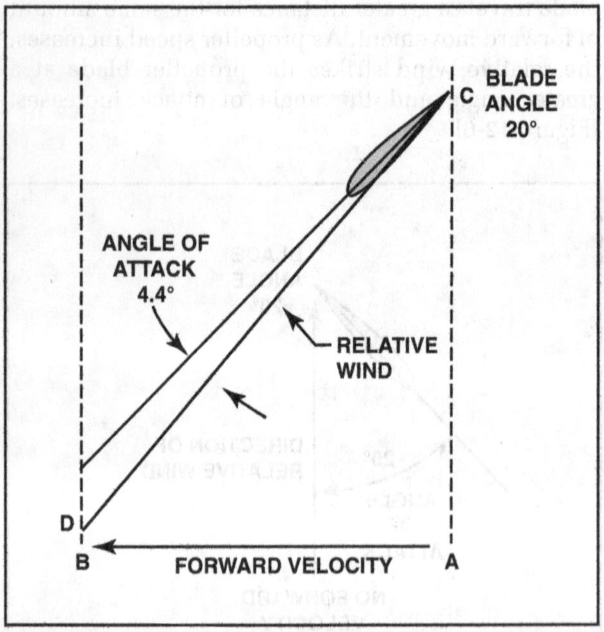


**Figure 12-6. If the forward velocity of the aircraft remains constant, but a propeller's rotational speed increases, the propeller's trailing edge moves a greater distance for the same amount of forward movement. This increases the angle at which the relative wind strikes the propeller blade, which increases the angle of attack.**

a propeller blade might stall. Typically, propellers with a fixed blade angle are designed to produce an angle of attack between 2 and 4 degrees at either a climb or cruise airspeed with a specific speed setting.

Unlike a wing, which moves through the air at a uniform rate, the propeller sections near the tip rotate at a greater velocity than those near the hub. The difference in rotational velocity along a propeller blade segment can be found by first calculating the circumference of the arc traveled by a point on that segment. The circumference of a circle is calculated with the formula:

$$2\pi r$$

The circumference is then multiplied by engine speed in r.p.m. to find rotational velocity. For example, to determine blade velocity at a point 18 inches from the hub that is rotating at 1800 r.p.m., use the following formula:

$$\text{Velocity} = 2\pi r \times \text{r.p.m.}$$

$$= 2 \times \pi \times 18 \times 1800$$

$$= 203{,}575$$

At a point 18 inches from the hub the blade travels approximately 203,575 inches per minute. To convert this to miles per hour, divide 203,575 by 63,360 (the number of inches in one mile) and multiply the product by 60, the number of minutes in one hour.

$$\text{Velocity} = (203{,}575 / 63{,}360) \times 60$$

$$= 192.7 \text{ miles per hour}$$

The speed of the propeller at station 18 is 192.7 miles per hour. You can now compare this to the speed of the propeller at station 48. By using the same formulas, you can determine that, at station 48, the propeller is moving at 514 miles per hour. [Figure 12-7]

To compensate for the difference in velocity along a propeller blade, the blade angle changes along its length. The gradual decrease in blade angle from the hub to the tip is called **pitch distribution**, or **twist**. Blade twist enables a propeller to provide a fairly constant angle of attack along most of the length of the blade.

In addition to blade twist, most propellers have a thicker, low speed airfoil near the blade hub and a thinner, high speed airfoil near the tip. This, along

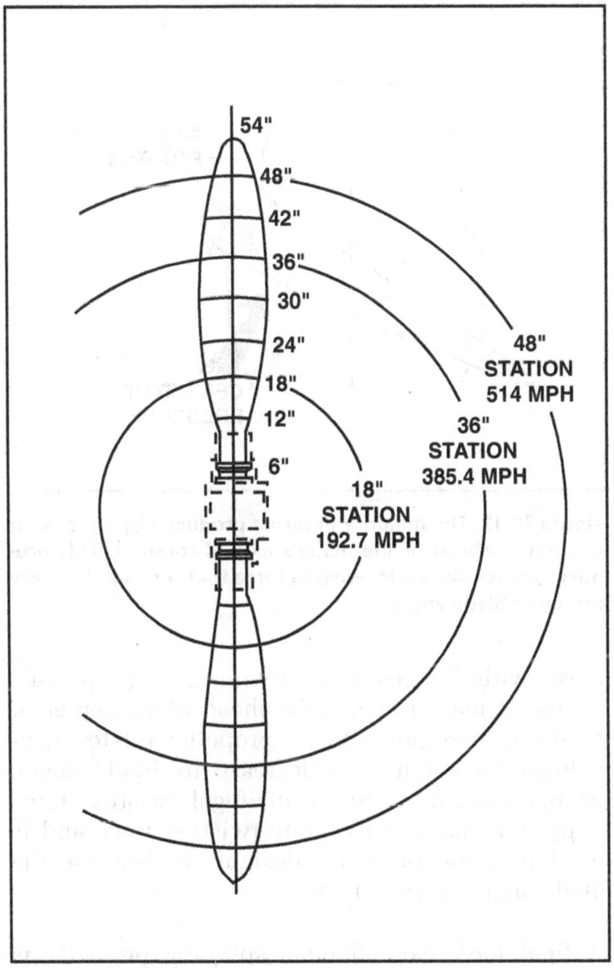


**Figure 12-7. As a propeller blade rotates at a fixed rotational speed, each blade segment moves through the air at a different velocity.**

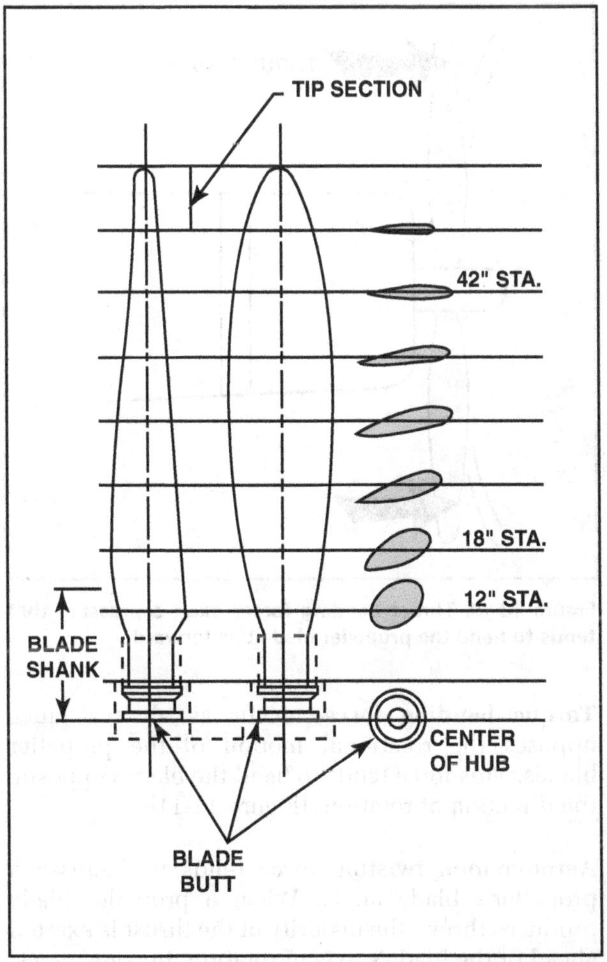


**Figure 12-8. The variation in airfoil shape and blade angle along the length of a propeller blade compensates for differences in rotational speed and provides a relatively even distribution of thrust along the blade.**

with blade twist, enables the propeller to produce a relatively constant amount of thrust along the entire length of a propeller blade. [Figure 12-8]

## FORCES ACTING ON A PROPELLER

A rotating propeller is subjected to many forces that cause tension, twisting, and bending stresses. Of all the forces acting on a propeller, centrifugal force causes the greatest stress. **Centrifugal force** can be described as the force tending to pull the blades out of the hub. The amount of stress created by centrifugal force can be more than 7,500 times the weight of the propeller blade. [Figure 12-9]

**Thrust bending force** tends to bend the propeller blades forward at the tips. Because propeller blades are typically thinner near the tip, thrust produced at the tip tends to flex the blade forward. Thrust bending force opposes centrifugal force to some degree. [Figure 12-10]

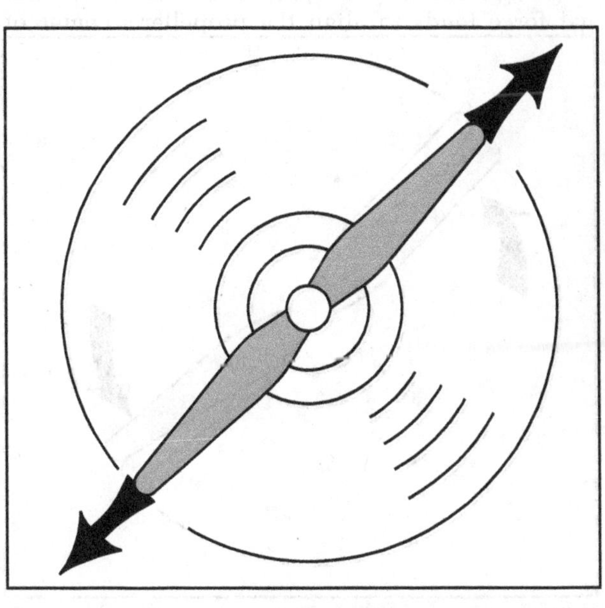

**Figure 12-9. When a propeller rotates, centrifugal force tends to pull propeller blades away from the hub.**

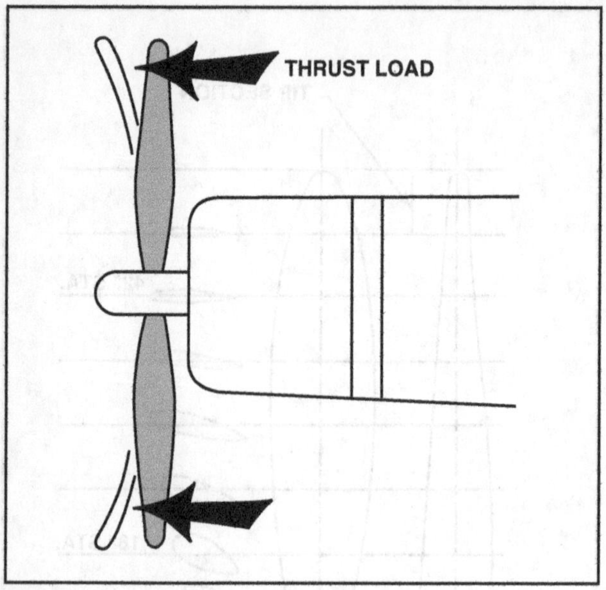


**Figure 12-10. Thrust bending forces exert a pressure that tends to bend the propeller blade tips forward.**

**Torque bending forces** occur as air resistance opposes the rotational motion of the propeller blades. This force tends to bend the blades opposite the direction of rotation. [Figure 12-11]

**Aerodynamic twisting force** tends to increase a propeller's blade angle. When a propeller blade produces thrust, the majority of the thrust is exerted ahead of the blade's axis of rotation. In some cases, aerodynamic twisting force is used to help change the blade angle on a propeller. [Figure 12-12]

**Centrifugal twisting force** opposes aerodynamic twisting force. When a propeller rotates, centrifugal force tends to align the propeller's center of

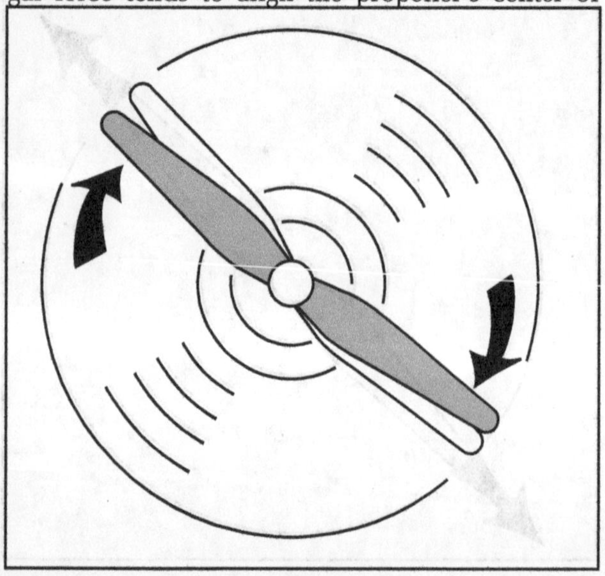

**Figure 12-11. Torque bending forces exert a pressure that tends to bend the blades opposite the direction of rotation.**

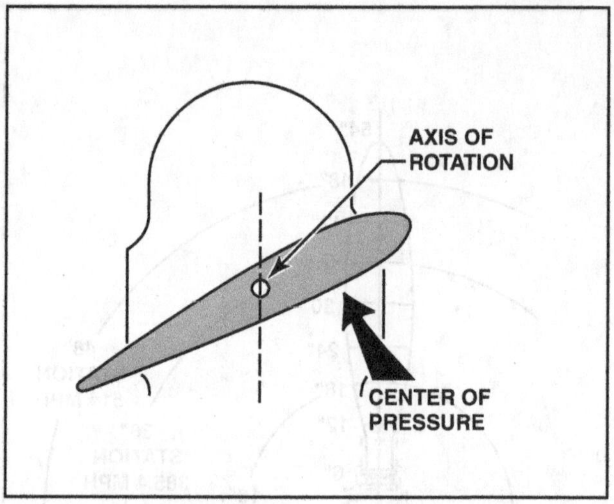


**Figure 12-12. The majority of thrust produced by a propeller is exerted ahead of the blade's axis of rotation. This produces an aerodynamic twisting force that tends to increase propeller blade angle.**

mass with its center of rotation. A propeller's center of mass is typically ahead of its center of rotation; therefore, when a propeller rotates, centrifugal force tends to decrease its blade angle. At operational speeds, centrifugal twisting force is greater than aerodynamic twisting force and is used in some propeller designs to decrease the blade angle. [Figure 12-13]

A final force exerted on a spinning propeller is **blade vibration.** When a propeller produces thrust, blade vibration occurs due to the aerodynamic and mechanical forces. These include aerodynamic forces that tend to bend the propeller blades forward at the tips as well as the mechanical power pulses in a reciprocating engine. Of the two, mechanical

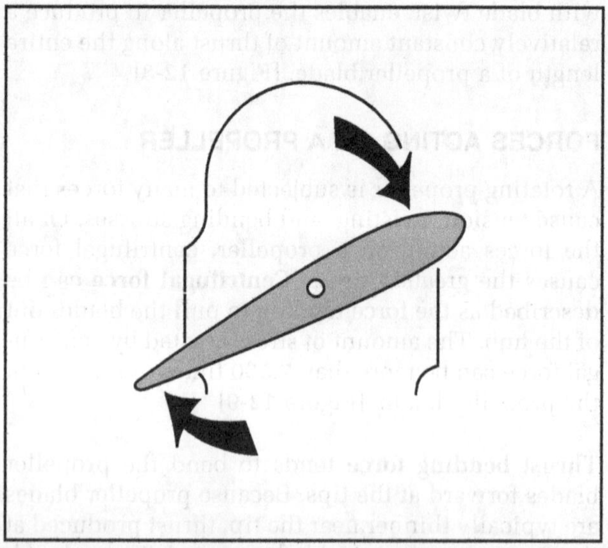

**Figure 12-13. Centrifugal twisting force attempts to decrease blade angle by aligning a propeller blade's center of mass with its center of rotation.**

vibrations are considered to be more destructive than aerodynamic vibrations. The reason for this is that engine power pulses tend to create standing wave patterns in a propeller blade that can lead to material fatigue and structural failure.

The location and number of stress points in a blade depend on the characteristics of the individual combination of propeller and engine. Although concentrations of vibrational stress are detrimental at any point on a blade, the most critical location is the outboard six inches to the blade tips.

The design of most airframe-engine-propeller combinations has eliminated the detrimental effects of vibrational stresses. Nevertheless, some engine and propeller combinations do have a **critical range** in which severe propeller vibration can occur. In this case, the critical range is indicated on the tachometer by a red arc. Engine operation in the critical range should be limited to a brief passage from one speed setting to another. Engine operation in the critical range for extended periods can lead to structural failure of the propeller or aircraft.

Propeller design typically accommodates some degree of vibrational stress. However, in situations in which a propeller has been improperly altered, vibration can cause excessive flexing and work hardening of the metal. In severe instances, the damage can cause sections of a propeller blade to break off in flight.

## PROPELLER PITCH

In the strictest sense, **propeller pitch** is the theoretical distance a propeller advances longitudinally in one revolution. Although pitch and blade angle describe two different concepts, they are closely related, and the two terms are often used interchangeably. For example, when a propeller is said to have a fixed pitch, what is actually meant is that the blades on the propeller are set at a fixed blade angle.

A propeller's **geometric pitch** is defined as the distance, in inches, that a propeller would move forward in one revolution if it were moving through a solid medium and did not encounter any loss of efficiency. Measurement of geometric pitch is based on the propeller blade angle at a point equal to 75 percent of the blade length from the propeller hub.

When traveling through air, inefficiencies prevent a propeller from moving forward at a rate equal to its geometric pitch. Therefore, **effective pitch** is the actual amount a propeller moves forward in one revolution. Effective pitch varies from zero when the aircraft is stationary on the ground to about 90 percent of the geometric pitch in the most efficient flight conditions. The difference between geometric pitch and effective pitch is called **slip**. Propeller slip represents the total losses caused by inefficiencies. [Figure 12-14]

If a propeller has a geometric pitch of 50 inches, in theory it should move forward 50 inches in one revolution. However, if the aircraft actually moves forward only 35 inches in one revolution, the effective pitch is 35 inches and the propeller is 70 percent efficient. In this case, slip represents 15 inches or a 30 percent loss of efficiency. In practice, most propellers are 75 to 85 percent efficient.

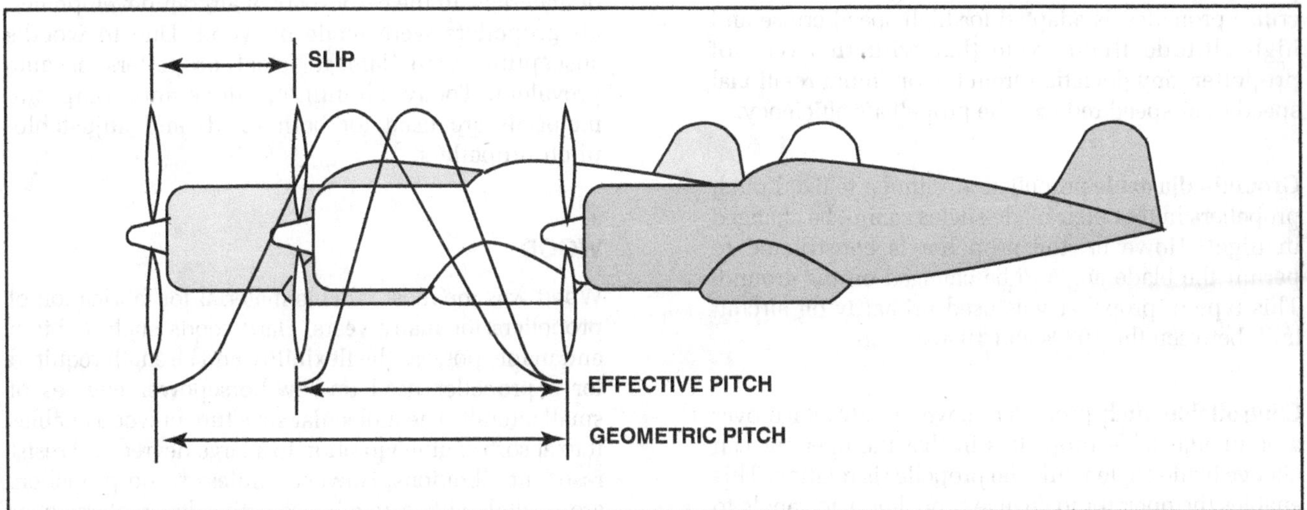


**Figure 12-14. Geometric pitch is the theoretical distance a propeller would move forward if it were 100% efficient. Effective pitch is the actual distance a propeller moves forward in one revolution. Slip is the difference between geometric and effective pitch.**

# PROPELLER CLASSIFICATIONS

Propellers are typically classified according to their position on the aircraft. For example, **tractor propellers** are on the front of an engine and pull an aircraft through the air. **Pusher propellers** are on the aft end of an engine and push an airplane through the air. Most aircraft are equipped with tractor-type propellers; however, several seaplanes and a few other aircraft are equipped with pusher propellers. A major advantage of the tractor-type propeller is that it experiences lower stresses because it rotates in relatively undisturbed air.

Both tractor and pusher propellers can effectively propel an aircraft through the air. Aircraft designers choose which type of propeller is best suited for a given airplane. For example, on land planes that have little propeller-to-ground clearance, pusher propellers are subject to more damage than tractor propellers. The reason for this is that rocks, gravel, and small objects that are dislodged by wheels are frequently thrown or drawn into a pusher propeller. On the other hand, to maintain adequate clearance between the water and a propeller makes it impractical to install a tractor propeller on some seaplanes.

Propellers are commonly classified by the method used to establish pitch. Typical classifications include fixed-pitch, ground-adjustable, controllable-pitch, constant-speed, reversible, and feathering.

The simplest type of propeller is a fixed-pitch propeller. **Fixed-pitch** propellers enable an aircraft to produce optimum efficiency at a specific rotational and forward speed. A fixed-pitch propeller with a low blade angle, often called a climb propeller, provides the best performance for takeoff and climb. A fixed-pitch propeller with a high blade angle, often called a cruise propeller, is adapted for high speed cruise and high altitude flight. Note that with this type of propeller, any deviation from the optimum rotational speed or airspeed reduces the propeller's efficiency.

**Ground-adjustable** propellers are similar to fixed-pitch propellers in that their blade angles cannot be changed in flight. However, the propeller is constructed to permit the blade angle to be changed on the ground. This type of propeller was used primarily on aircraft built between the 1920s and 1940s.

**Controllable-pitch** propellers have an advantage over ground-adjustable propellers in that the operator can change blade angle while the propeller is rotating. This enables the operator to change propeller blade angle to achieve improved performance for a particular flight condition. Depending on design, the number of pitch positions might be limited (as with a two-position controllable propeller) or the pitch might be adjustable to any angle between a minimum and maximum pitch setting.

**Constant-speed** propellers, sometimes referred to as **automatic propellers**, maintain the rotational speed selected by the pilot. Pitch control is provided by a device known as a **governor**. A typical governor uses oil pressure to control blade pitch. Constant speed propeller systems provide maximum efficiency by letting the pilot set the ideal propeller blade angle for most flight conditions.

**Reversible-pitch** propellers are a further development of the constant-speed propeller. On aircraft equipped with a reversible propeller, the propeller blades can be rotated to a negative angle to produce reverse thrust. This forces air forward instead of backward and permits a shorter landing roll and improved ground maneuvering.

Most multi-engine aircraft are equipped with a propeller that can **feather**. A feathering propeller is a type of constant-speed propeller that has the ability to rotate the propeller blades so that the leading edge of each blade is pointed straight forward into the wind. The only time a pilot would select the feather position is if an engine fails. Placing the blades in the feather position eliminates much of the drag associated with a windmilling propeller.

# PROPELLER CONSTRUCTION

Almost all propellers produced are made of wood, steel, aluminum, composite materials or a combination of materials. In the early years of aircraft development, all propellers were made of wood. Due to wood's susceptibility to damage, steel propellers became prevalent. Today, aluminum alloys and composite materials are used for both fixed- and adjustable-pitch propellers.

## WOOD

Wood was the most reliable material for fabrication of propellers for many years. Hardwoods such as birch and maple possess the flexibility and strength required for a propeller used on low-horsepower engines of small aircraft. The molecular structure of wood enables it to absorb engine vibration to a large degree and resist resonant vibrations. However, unless wood propellers are coated with a tough protective layer of resin or other material, they are susceptible to damage from gravel and debris during ground operations.

### STEEL

Steel propellers and propeller blades are still in use on antique and older-generation transport aircraft. Because steel is a heavy metal, the blades are normally hollow steel sheets attached to a rib structure. The hollow interior is filled with a foam material to absorb vibration and maintain a rigid structure.

### ALUMINUM ALLOY

The majority of propellers in use are constructed of an aluminum alloy. Aluminum permits thinner, more efficient airfoils to be constructed without sacrificing structural strength. Advanced machining techniques enable aluminum propeller blades to be produced in complex shapes. Aluminum propeller blades typically require less maintenance than wood propellers, resulting in reduced operating costs. Because airfoil sections can extend inward, closer to the hub, aluminum propellers provide better engine cooling airflow than wood propellers.

### COMPOSITE

The use of composite propeller blades is increasing. Composite propeller blades are lightweight, durable, and can be formed into complex shapes. In addition, composite materials absorb vibration and are resistant to corrosion.

## SUMMARY CHECKLIST

- ✓ Propellers convert rotational engine power to thrust in both reciprocating and with turboshaft engines.
- ✓ Propeller pitch is the theoretical distance that a propeller advances forward in a single revolution.
- ✓ A tractor propeller is located on the front end of an engine and pulls an aircraft forward.
- ✓ A pusher propeller is located on the aft end of an engine and pushes an aircraft forward.
- ✓ Fixed-pitch propellers are designed with a particular performance characteristic. Based on desired aircraft operations and performance, a pilot can choose either a climb or a cruise propeller.
- ✓ Constant-speed propellers change blade angle to maintain an engine speed selected by the pilot and controlled by a governor.
- ✓ Feathering propellers rotate the blades straight into the wind. If the engine stops turning during flight, this position reduces drag and enables the aircraft to glide farther.
- ✓ Reversible-pitch propellers enable an aircraft to reduce its landing roll; in addition, reversible-pitch propellers enable an aircraft to back up during taxi.

# KEY TERMS

hub
blade shank
blade tip
leading edge
trailing edge
chord line
blade back
blade face
blade angle
clamping rings
blade root
blade cuff
blade station
angle of attack
relative wind
pitch distribution
twist
centrifugal force
thrust bending force
torque bending force
aerodynamic twisting force
centrifugal twisting force
blade vibration
critical range
propeller pitch
geometric pitch
effective pitch
slip
tractor propeller
pusher propeller
fixed-pitch propeller
ground-adjustable propeller
controllable-pitch propeller
constant-speed propeller
automatic propeller
governor
reversible-pitch propeller
feather

# QUESTIONS

1. The basic function of a propeller on an airplane is to convert engine torque into ________________.
2. Propeller blade angle is the angle between the chord of the propeller blade and the ______________ of ______________.
3. The flat surface of a propeller blade is called the _______ (face or back) of the blade.
4. Propeller blade stations are measured, in inches, from the ________ of the ________.
5. A ____________ (what unit) is designed primarily to increase the flow of cooling air to the engine nacelle.
6. The gradual twist in the propeller blade from shank to tip is known as _______ _________.
7. On a given propeller blade, the blade angle nearest the hub will be the ______ (highest or lowest).
8. The six forces that act on rotating propeller are:
   a. ______________
   b. ______________
   c. ______________
   d. ______________
   e. ______________
   f. ______________
9. Thrust bending force tries to bend the tip of a propeller blade ______________ (forward or rearward).
10. Torque bending force tries to bend the propeller blades in the ______________ (same or opposite) direction of their rotation.

11. Aerodynamic twisting moment tries to move the propeller blades toward a _______ (low or high) pitch angle.

12. Centrifugal twisting moment tries to move the propeller blades toward a _______ (low or high) pitch angle.

13. "Normally, aerodynamic twisting moment is greater than centrifugal twisting moment." This statement is _______ (true or false).

14. Because of vibration problems encountered with certain engine/propeller combinations, the critical range is indicated on the tachometer by a _______ _______.

15. The _______________ (geometric or effective) pitch is the distance, in inches, that a propeller would move forward in a medium that allowed no slip.

16. The _______________ (geometric or effective ) pitch is the distance, in inches, that the aircraft actually moves forward in one revolution of the propeller.

17. The difference between geometric pitch and effective pitch is called _______________.

18. _______________ (tractor or pusher) propellers are those mounted on the upstream end of a drive shaft in front of the supporting structure.

19. Automatic propellers are usually termed _______________ _______________ propellers.

# SECTION B

# FIXED-PITCH PROPELLERS

The simplest type of propeller is a fixed-pitch propeller. As its name implies, the blade angle on a fixed-pitch propeller cannot be changed. Because of this, fixed-pitch propellers achieve their optimum efficiency at a specific rotational and forward speed.

## FIXED-PITCH CLASSIFICATIONS

A typical fixed-pitch propeller installed on a light aircraft has a diameter between 67 and 76 inches and a pitch between 53 and 68 inches. The aircraft manufacturer specifies the exact diameter and pitch required for a specific airplane. In some cases, manufacturers authorize multiple propellers, each with a different pitch. For example, a propeller with the lower blade angle provides the best performance for takeoff and climb; this is often called a **climb propeller**. A low blade angle lets the engine develop its maximum speed at the slower airspeeds associated with climbout. However, after the aircraft reaches its cruising altitude and begins to accelerate, the low blade angle is less efficient.

A fixed-pitch propeller with a slightly higher blade angle is called a **cruise propeller**. A cruise propeller is designed to be efficient at cruising speed and high altitude flight. However, because of the higher pitch, cruise propellers are less efficient during takeoff and climbout.

A **standard propeller** is generally a compromise between a climb propeller and cruise propeller. Each aircraft manufacturer typically designates a standard propeller designed to provide the best overall performance under normal circumstances.

When an aircraft and engine combination is certificated with a specific combination of standard, climb, and cruise propellers, aircraft operators can choose which propeller performs best for their specific operations. For example, an aircraft frequently operating from short runways or high field elevations generally performs better with a climb propeller. Conversely, aircraft that normally operate at sea level from airports with long runways might perform better if equipped with a cruise propeller.

## PROPELLER CONSTRUCTION

Fixed-pitch propellers are typically made of wood, aluminum, or composite materials. Aluminum is the most common, especially on production aircraft. However, new wood propellers are still being made and the use of composite materials for fixed-pitch propellers is increasing.

### WOOD PROPELLERS

Wood propellers are still in limited use on small utility aircraft. Hardwoods such as ash and birch are typically used to build a wood propeller. However, mahogany, maple, cherry, oak, and black walnut have all been used. Whatever wood a propeller it is made from must be free of grain irregularities, knots, pitch pockets, and insect damage.

A wood propeller is constructed from at least five laminations of kiln-dried wood bonded together with waterproof resin adhesive. Each lamination is normally the same thickness and type of wood; however, types can be alternated between laminations. Laminated wood is used instead of a solid block of wood because the orientation of the grain makes it less likely to warp. After the laminations are bonded together, they form a **propeller blank**.

During fabrication, a blank is rough-cut to shape and permitted to season. This waiting period enables the moisture in the wood to disperse equally through all of the laminations. The rough-shaped blank is finished to the exact airfoil and pitch dimensions. In addition, the center bore and bolt holes are drilled and a metal hub assembly is inserted through the hub bore to accommodate the face plate and mounting bolts.

After a propeller blank is finished and sanded smooth, a cotton fabric is sometimes glued to the last 12 to 15 inches of the propeller blade to reinforce the thin tip sections. After application, the fabric is doped to prevent deterioration caused by weather and ultraviolet radiation. Then the entire propeller is finished with a clear varnish to protect the wood surface. In some cases, wood propellers might be finished with a black or gray plastic coating to provide additional protection against chipping. In this case, a propeller is said to be **armor coated**. [Figure 12-15]

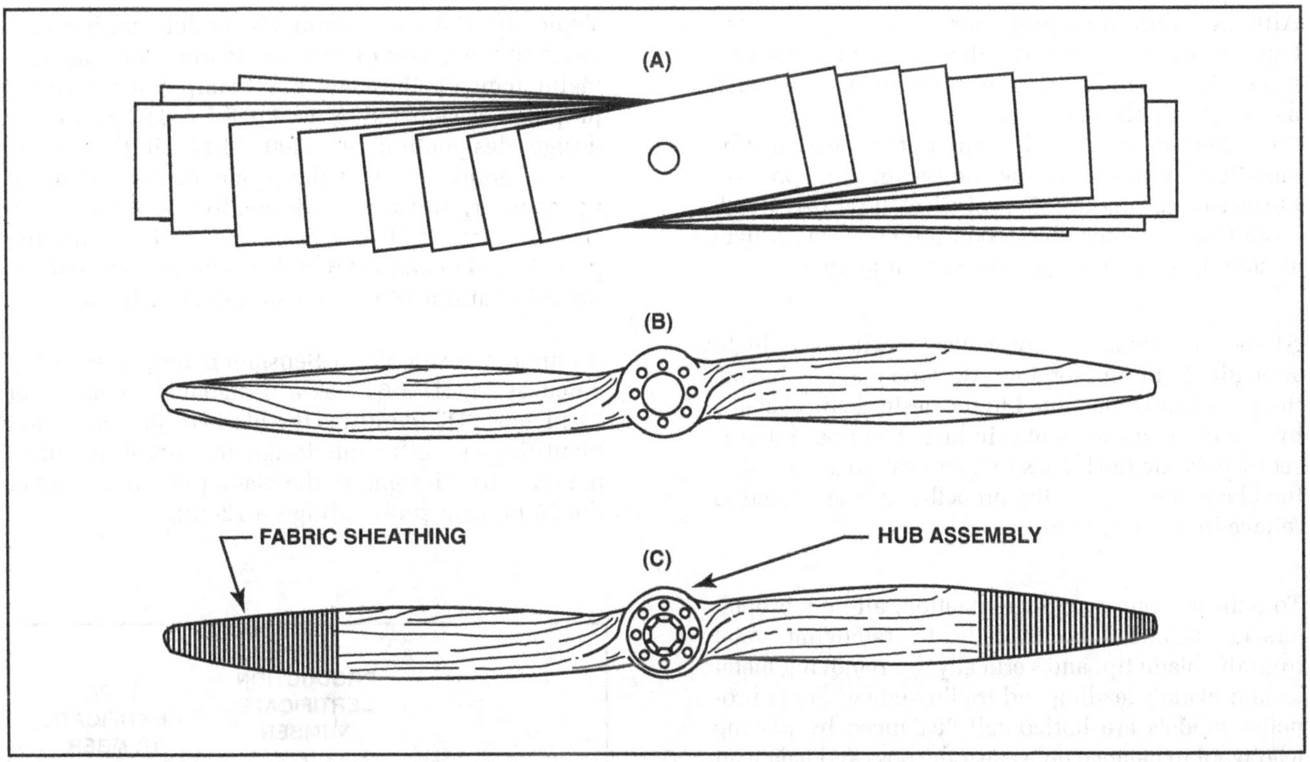


**Figure 12-15. (A) The first step in the manufacture of a wood propeller is to laminate planks to form a propeller blank. (B) The propeller blank is shaped and its hub is drilled. (C) After the propeller is sanded smooth, a fabric sheathing and varnish coating are applied for reinforcement and protection.**

Monel, brass, or stainless steel tipping is applied to the leading edge and tip of most wooden propellers to prevent damage from small stones. To permit the metal edging to conform to the contour of the leading edge, the metal is notched. To attach the edging to the blade, countersunk screws are used in the thick blade sections while copper rivets are used in the thin sections near the tip. After the screws and rivets are in place, they are secured with solder. Using a number 60 drill, three small holes are then drilled 3/16 inch deep into the tip of each blade. These holes let moisture drain from behind the metal tipping and permit the wood to breathe. [Figure 12-16]

## ALUMINUM ALLOY PROPELLERS

Most fixed-pitch propellers are fabricated from aluminum. The use of aluminum rather than wood enables blades to be made thinner and more efficient without compromising structural strength. Aluminum has the strength and flexibility to accommodate the high horsepower engines available in modern small aircraft.

A great advantage of aluminum propellers is their low susceptibility to damage from gravel and debris often encountered during ground operations. Aluminum blades are easier to repair than wooden blades. Minor damage, such as small nicks, is easily dressed out with special files. Additionally, a certified propeller repair station can repitch fixed-pitch aluminum propellers to an approved blade angle.

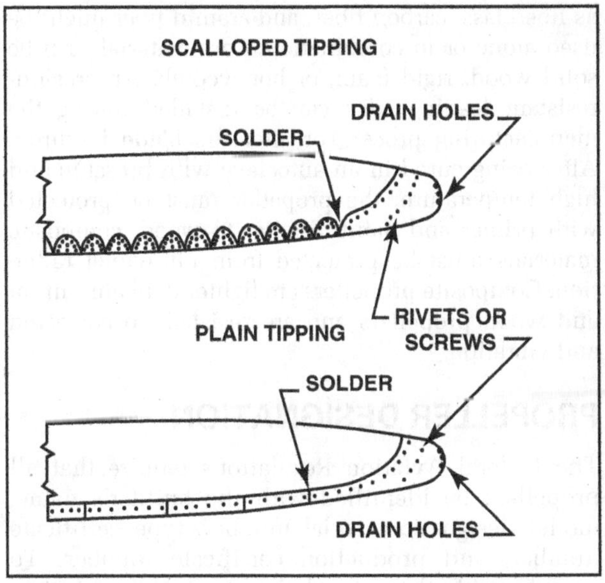


**Figure 12-16. Metal tipping is applied to propeller blade tips and leading edges to prevent erosion damage. Three small holes drilled in the tip of each blade release moisture and let the wood breathe.**

Although aluminum propellers offer several advantages over wood propellers, there are some disadvantages. For example, aluminum propellers are much more susceptible to damage caused by resonant vibrations. Because of this, aluminum propellers must be vibrationally tested during the certification process. Furthermore, aluminum propellers typically weigh more than a comparable wood propeller. On a light aircraft, this difference can be several pounds.

Almost all aluminum propellers begin as a high-strength aluminum forging. After the blank is forged, the propeller is machined to the desired airfoil shape by machine and manual grinding. The final pitch is set by twisting the blades to their desired angle. After the blade angle is set, the propeller is heat-treated to relieve internal stresses.

To help prevent excessive vibration, all new propellers are balanced horizontally, by removing metal from the blade tip, and vertically, by removing metal from a blade's leading and trailing edges. Some propeller models are horizontally balanced by placing lead wool in balance holes near the boss and balanced vertically by attaching balance weights to the side of the propeller hub. After the propeller is balanced, the surfaces are finished by anodizing and painting.

### COMPOSITE PROPELLERS

Composite propellers are fabricated in a mold by laminating layers of composite materials, core material, and a reinforcing shank with a thermosetting resin. Various advanced composite materials, such as fiberglass, carbon fiber, and aramid fiber might be used alone or in combination. Core materials can be solid wood, rigid foam, or honeycomb. An erosion-resistant leading edge can be installed during the manufacturing process or after the blade is cured. After being cured in an autoclave with pressure and high temperature, the propeller must be protected with primer and paint. Similar to wood, composite materials must be protected from ultraviolet radiation. Composite propellers are lighter than aluminum and wood propellers and are resistant to corrosion and vibration.

## PROPELLER DESIGNATION

The Federal Aviation Regulations require that all propellers be identified with the builder's name, model designation, serial number, type certificate number, and production certificate number. To comply with these regulations, most manufacturers of fixed-pitch propellers mark or stamp all of the required information on the propeller hub. [Figure 12-17]

Typically, the manufacturer's model number provides the majority of the information relevant to a maintenance technician. For example, a McCauley propeller designated as 1A90/DM 7651 has a basic design designation of 1A90. "DM" indicates the type of crankshaft that the propeller fits, the blade tip contour, and other information pertaining to a specific aircraft installation. "7651" indicates the propeller diameter is 76 inches, and the pitch of the propeller at the 75 percent station is 51 inches.

As another example, a Sensenich propeller designated as M74DM-61 has a designated diameter of 74 inches. "D" identifies the blade design, and "M" identifies a specific hub design and mounting information. "61" designates the blade pitch in inches at the 75 percent station. [Figure 12-18]

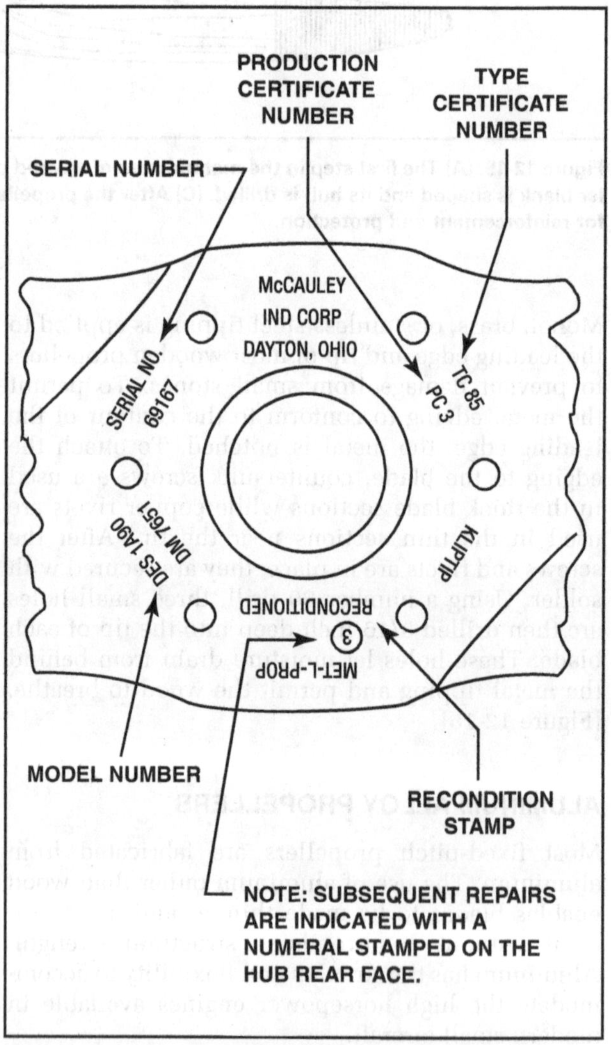


**Figure 12-17. On McCauley fixed-pitch propellers, the builder's name, model designation, serial number, type certificate number, and production certificate number are stamped around the propeller hub.**

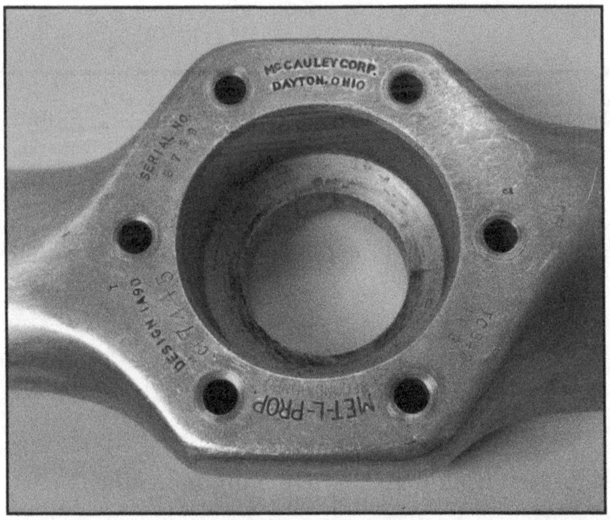


**Figure 12-18. An aluminum propeller has information stamped on the hub to identify hub design, blade design, blade length, and pitch. The number 1 stamped on the blade root identifies installation position.**

# SUMMARY CHECKLIST

✓ Propeller blades are constructed from laminated wood, aluminum alloys, or composite materials.

✓ Propeller designations often contain coded information about propeller characteristics and performance.

# KEY TERMS

climb propeller
cruise propeller
standard propeller
propeller blank
armor coated

# QUESTIONS

1. An aircraft manufacturer may specify two models of a propeller for the same installation, a ____________ and a ______________ propeller.

2. ______________-pitch propellers are simple propellers whose blade angle cannot be changed in normal operation.

3. Most wooden propellers are now made of _______________ or _______________(what types of wood).

4. Aluminum propeller blanks are _______________ (forged or cast) from high strength aluminum alloy.

5. A McCauley propeller designated as 1B90/CM7448 has a diameter of _________ inches and a pitch of inches at the 75% station.

# ADJUSTABLE-PITCH PROPELLERS

The design and construction of an adjustable pitch propeller permits the operator to change the propeller blade angle to achieve the best performance from a particular propeller and engine combination. Although some older adjustable pitch propellers could be adjusted only on the ground by a maintenance technician, most adjustable pitch propellers permit a pilot to change the propeller pitch in flight. Early pitch propeller systems offered two pitch settings—a low pitch setting and a high pitch setting. Today, however, almost all adjustable pitch propeller systems are automatic over the full range of pitch settings.

## GROUND-ADJUSTABLE PROPELLERS

As mentioned in Section A, ground-adjustable propellers permit the blade angle to be changed when the aircraft is on the ground and the engine is not operating. This type of propeller is seldom used anymore and is usually found on older aircraft equipped with radial engines.

The hub of a ground-adjustable propeller consists of two aluminum or steel halves that are machined to form a matched pair. The interior of each piece is machined with grooves to receive the shoulders on the shank of the propeller blades. When wooden blades are used, the shoulders are cast or machined into a metal sleeve that is fastened to the blade shank by lag screws. [Figure 12-19]

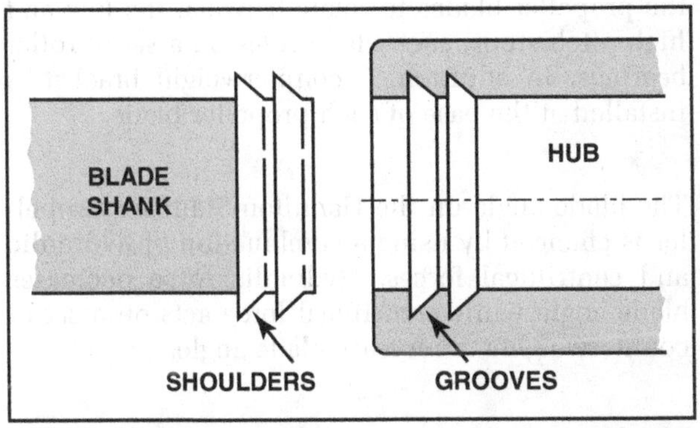


**Figure 12-19. To ensure that centrifugal force does not pull the propeller blades out of the hub on a ground-adjustable propeller, shoulders are machined into the base of each blade shank. These shoulders fit into grooves machined into each hub half.**

When steel blades are used, bolts typically secure the hub halves. However, when wood or aluminum alloy blades are used, either bolts or clamp rings might be used to hold the hub halves together. [Figure 12-20]

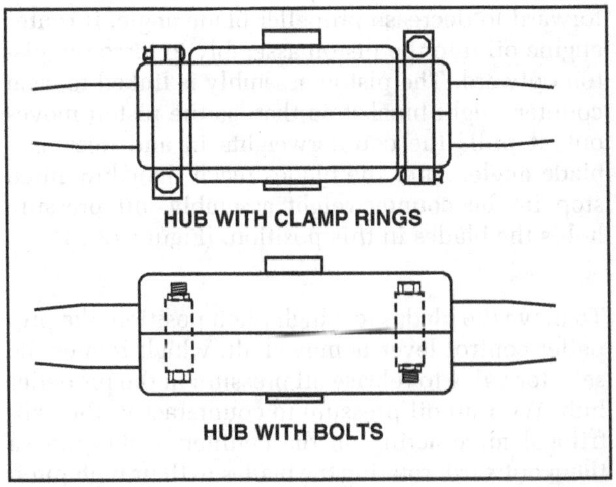


**Figure 12-20. Ground-adjustable propellers use clamp rings or bolts to secure the hub halves and hold the blades in place.**

## CONTROLLABLE-PITCH PROPELLERS

With a controllable-pitch propeller, a cockpit control changes the blade angle while the propeller is rotating. This enables the pilot to select the blade angle that provides the best performance for a particular flight condition. The number of pitch positions might be limited, as with a two-position controllable propeller, or automatic and unlimited between the minimum and maximum pitch settings.

### TWO-POSITION PROPELLERS

One of the first controllable-pitch propellers to see widespread use was the Hamilton-Standard counterweight propeller. This propeller, developed in the 1930's, permitted a pilot to select low pitch or high pitch. The low pitch setting was used during takeoff and climb, so the engine operated at its maximum speed and developed its full rated horsepower. The high pitch setting was used to gain more efficient operation and improved fuel economy during cruise flight.

Similar to a ground-adjustable propeller, the Hamilton-Standard propeller uses a two piece hub to hold the propeller blades in place. To enable the propeller blades to rotate between the low and high pitch stops, each blade rides on a set of roller bearings. In addition, a counterweight bracket is installed at the base of each propeller blade.

The blade angle on the Hamilton-Standard propeller is changed by using a combination of hydraulic and centrifugal forces. Hydraulic force decreases blade angle while centrifugal force acts on a set of counterweights to increase blade angle.

The hydraulic force that decreases blade angle is derived from engine oil that flows out of the crankshaft and acts on a piston assembly on the front of the propeller hub. The flow of engine oil into the piston assembly is controlled by a three-way selector valve that is mounted in the engine and controlled from the cockpit. When this valve moves forward to decrease propeller blade angle, it routes engine oil into the piston assembly to force the piston outward. The piston assembly is linked to each counterweight bracket so that, as the piston moves out, it pulls the counterweights in and decreases blade angle. After the blades reach their low pitch stop in the counterweight assembly, oil pressure holds the blades in this position. [Figure 12-21]

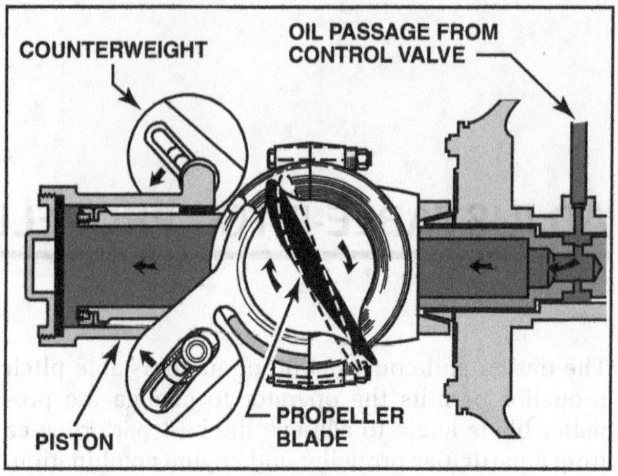


**Figure 12-21. When low pitch is selected, engine oil pressure forces the cylinder forward. This motion moves the counterweights and blades to the low pitch position.**

To move the blades to a high pitch position, the propeller control lever is moved aft, which rotates the selector valve to release oil pressure in the propeller hub. With no oil pressure to counteract it, the centrifugal force acting on the counterweights moves them outward, rotating the blades to their high pitch position. As the blades rotate, oil is forced out of the propeller cylinder and returned to the engine sump. The blades stop rotating when they contact their high pitch stops located in the counterweight assembly. [Figure 12-22]

In most cases, the pitch stops of a two-position propeller can be adjusted. This adjustment can be made only when the engine is not operating. To do this, rotate a pitch stop adjusting nut until the desired blade angle is obtained.

The operation of a two-position propeller is straightforward. Prior to engine shutdown, the propeller should be placed in its high pitch position. Doing so retracts the piston assembly, protecting it from corrosion and accumulation of dirt. Furthermore, most of the oil is forced from the piston, where it could otherwise congeal in cold weather.

## MULTIPLE-POSITION PROPELLERS

As technology advanced, the two-position propeller improvements enabled pilots to select any blade angle between the high and low pitch stops and achieve the optimum engine and propeller efficiency over the full range of power settings and airspeeds. For example, during takeoff, the propeller blade angle is set at its lowest blade angle, so the engine can generate its maximum power output. When the aircraft is established in a climb, the blade angle can be increased slightly to provide the best climb performance. In cruise flight, the blade angle is further increased to obtain the best cruise performance.

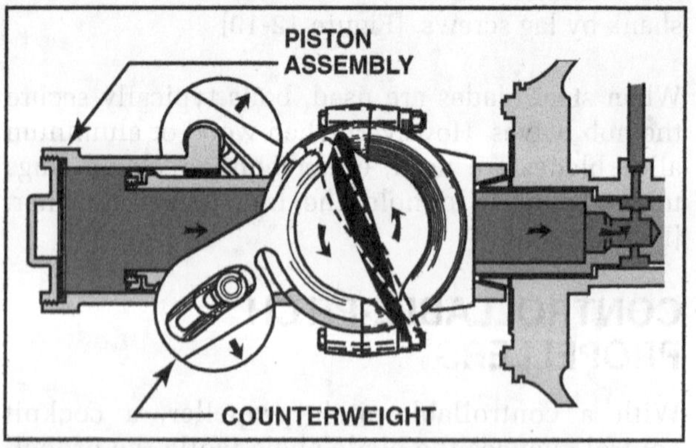


**Figure 12-22. When high pitch is selected, engine oil pressure is removed from the piston assembly, which permits centrifugal force to move the counterweights outward. This rotates the blades to the high pitch position.**

## CONSTANT-SPEED PROPELLERS

A constant-speed propeller, often called a variable-pitch or controllable-pitch propeller, is the adjustable-pitch propeller used on the majority of aircraft. The main advantage of a constant-speed propeller is that it converts a high percentage of the engine's power into thrust over a wide range of engine speed and airspeed combinations. The primary reason why a constant-speed propeller is more efficient than other propellers is because it enables the operator to select the most efficient engine speed for the given conditions. After a specific engine speed is selected, a device called a governor automatically adjusts the propeller blade angle to maintain the engine speed. For example, after selecting an engine speed during cruising flight, an increase in airspeed or decrease in propeller load causes the propeller blade angle to increase as necessary to maintain the selected engine speed Likewise, a reduction in airspeed or increase in propeller load will decrease the propeller blade angle.

The range of possible blade angles for a constant-speed propeller is called the propeller's **constant-speed range** and is defined by the high and low pitch stops. As long as the propeller blade angle is within the constant-speed range and not against either pitch stop, a constant engine speed will be maintained. However, if the propeller blades contact a pitch stop, the engine speed will increase or decrease as appropriate, with changes in airspeed and propeller load.

On aircraft that are equipped with a constant-speed propeller, engine power output is controlled by the throttle and indicated by a manifold pressure gauge. The propeller blade angle, on the other hand, is controlled by a propeller control lever; the resulting change in engine speed caused by a change in blade angle is indicated on the tachometer. By providing the operator with the means to control both engine power output and propeller angle, the most efficient combination of blade angle and engine power output can be maintained for a variety of flight conditions.

An important point that you must keep in mind when operating a constant-speed propeller is that, for a given r.p.m. setting, there is a maximum allowable manifold pressure. Operating above this level can cause internal engine stress and possibly detonation. As a general rule, avoid high manifold pressure with low r.p.m. settings. If you observe a high manifold pressure, adjust the propeller control to obtain a lower engine speed or throttle to reduce manifold pressure.

### OPERATING PRINCIPLES

Most constant-speed, nonfeathering propellers rely on a combination of hydraulic and centrifugal forces to change the propeller blade angle. They use high-pressure oil to increase propeller blade angle and the centrifugal twisting force inherent in a spinning propeller to decrease the blade angle. Conversely, most feathering propellers use counterweights and centrifugal force to pull the blades to high pitch and oil pressure to force the blades to low pitch. The following discussion describes the operation of a typical nonfeathering, noncounterweighted propeller assembly.

The device that is responsible for regulating the flow of high-pressure oil to the propeller is called the governor. The typical governor does three things: it boosts the pressure of the engine oil it delivers to the propeller hub, it controls the amount of oil that flows to the propeller, and it senses the rotational speed of the engine. A propeller governor is typically mounted on the front of an engine near the propeller or on the engine accessory case. All governors consist of three basic components; a gear boost pump, a pilot valve, and a speed-sensitive flyweight assembly. [Figure 12-23]

A typical governor boost pump increases oil pressure to between 180 and 300 p.s.i., depending on system requirements. The boost pump is driven by an engine drive gear. Because most boost pumps are

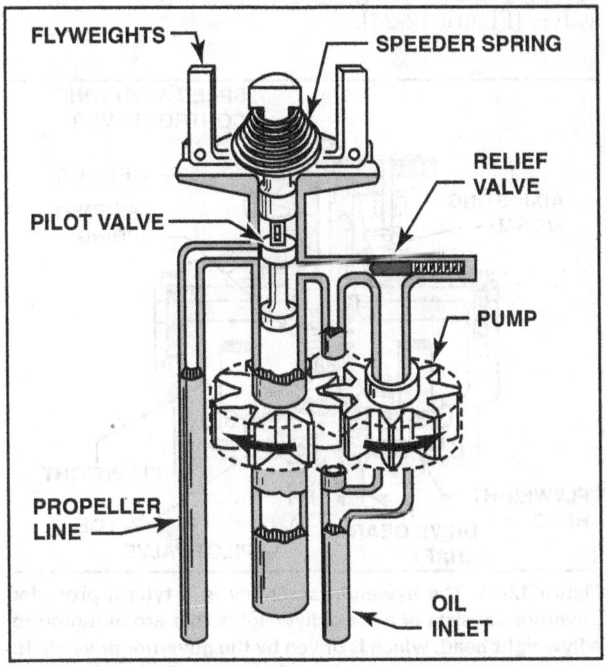


**Figure 12-23. A typical propeller governor consists of a gear boost pump that increases oil pressure before it enters the propeller hub, a pilot valve that controls the amount of oil flowing into and out of the propeller hub, and a flyweight assembly that senses engine speed and positions the pilot valve to maintain a constant speed.**

constant-displacement pumps, they produce excessive oil pressure at high engine speeds; therefore, they are equipped with a spring-loaded relief valve to prevent damage to seals and other components. This way, when the oil pressure increases enough to overcome the spring pressure acting on the relief valve, the valve opens and routes the excess oil back to the inlet side of the boost pump. In some cases, the drive shaft is hollow to provide a passage for oil to return to the engine.

The valve that controls oil in and out of the propeller hub is called the pilot valve. Although their design varies between manufacturers, all pilot valves perform the same basic function. A typical pilot valve is a shuttle-type that alternately covers and uncovers oil passages to direct flow.

For a governor to adjust the propeller blade angle to maintain a constant speed, it must be able to sense engine speed. The **flyweight assembly** is the portion of a governor that senses engine speed. A typical flyweight assembly consists of a set of **flyweights** mounted on a flyweight head that is driven by the same drive shaft as the boost pump. The pilot valve is located inside the drive shaft and extends into the flyweight assembly where it rests on the toe of each flyweight. As the flyweights tilt in and out, the pilot valve is moved up or down. To enable an operator to select, or set, a desired blade angle, a control lever adjusts the tension on a **speeder spring** to apply pressure against the flyweights and pilot valve. [Figure 12-24]

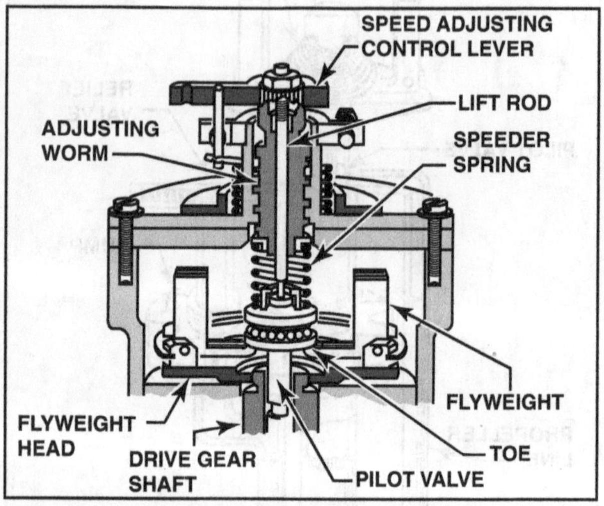


**Figure 12-24. The flyweight assembly in a typical propeller governor consists of a set of flyweights that are mounted to a flyweight head, which is driven by the governor drive shaft. The pilot valve extends up through the drive shaft and rests on the toe of each flyweight so that when the flyweights move, the pilot valve also moves. To enable the operator to select a blade angle, a speeder spring adjusts the amount of force acting on the flyweights and pilot valve.**

When the engine is operating, the governor drive shaft drives the governor boost pump and flyweight assembly. When the propeller control in the cockpit is in its full-forward, low pitch position, the speeder spring is fully compressed, holding the pilot valve down and permitting no oil into the propeller hub. With no oil pressure acting on the pitch change mechanism in the propeller hub, centrifugal twisting force holds the blades in their low pitch position. This propeller setting is typically used during takeoff when the engine's maximum power output is needed.

When the propeller control in the cockpit is moved aft, speeder spring pressure decreases, and centrifugal force tilts the flyweights outward. As the flyweights move outward, the pilot valve is pulled up and governor oil is directed to the propeller hub to increase propeller blade angle. As the blade angle increases, engine speed decreases, which reduces the amount of centrifugal force acting on the flyweights. The flyweights tilt inward and lower the pilot valve until oil flow to the propeller hub is cut off. At this point, speeder spring pressure and the centrifugal force acting on the flyweights balance, and the governor is said to be on speed.

When the propeller governor is on speed, the governor automatically adjusts propeller pitch to maintain a selected speed. Any change in airspeed or load on the propeller results in a change in blade pitch. For example, if a climb is initiated from level flight, aircraft speed decreases and the load on the propeller blades increases. As this occurs, engine speed slows causing a decrease in centrifugal force on the flyweights. Speeder spring pressure forces the flyweights to tilt inward. When this happens, the governor is said to be in an underspeed condition. The position of the flyweights move the pilot valve downward and oil from the propeller hub is returned to the engine. As oil leaves the propeller hub, centrifugal twisting force moves the blades to a lower pitch. The lower pitch reduces the load on the propeller and permits the engine to accelerate. As the engine speed increases, centrifugal force on the flyweights also increases and causes the flyweights to tilt outward and return the governor to an on-speed condition. [Figure 12-25]

A similar process occurs when airspeed increases or the load on the propeller decreases. In these situations, engine speed increases, which causes the centrifugal force acting on the flyweights to increase. When this occurs, the flyweights tilt outward, which results in an overspeed condition. As the flyweights move outward, the pilot valve moves up and directs boost pump oil to the propeller hub to increase blade pitch. The increased pitch increases the load on the propeller and slows the engine. As

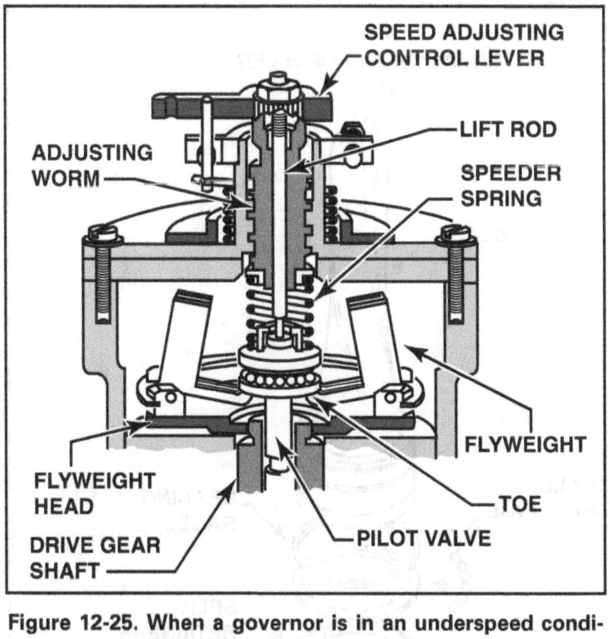


**Figure 12-25. When a governor is in an underspeed condition, speeder spring pressure is greater than the centrifugal force and the flyweights tilt inward.**

the engine speed decreases, the centrifugal force acting on the flyweights also decreases and causes them to tilt inward and return the governor to an on-speed condition. [Figure 12-26]

Similar to changes in airspeed and propeller load, changes in throttle settings also affect the governor. For example, advancing the throttle increases power output, which, in turn, increases engine speed. To maintain the selected engine speed, the governor must increase the propeller blade pitch. Conversely, pulling the throttle back decreases

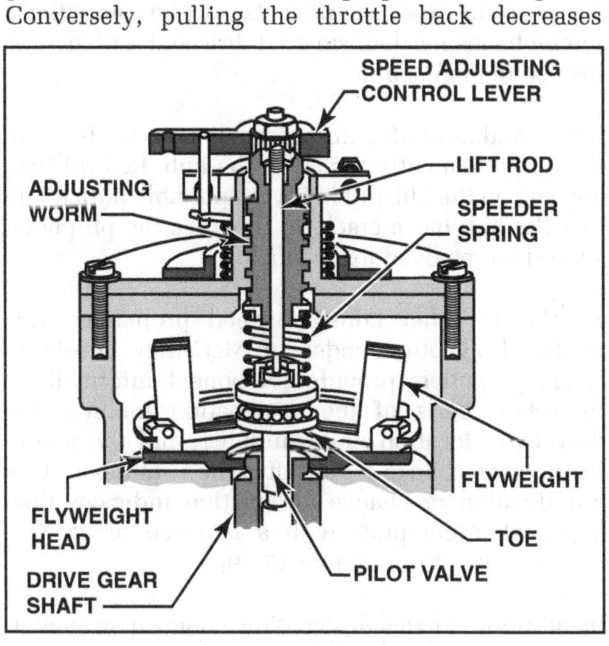


**Figure 12-26. When a governor is in an overspeed condition, the centrifugal force acting on the flyweights overcomes the force of the speeder spring to tilt the flyweights outward.**

power output and causes engine speed to decrease. Therefore, in an attempt to maintain the original r.p.m. setting, the governor must decrease the blade angle to unload the engine and propeller. Keep in mind that after the propeller blades reach the low pitch stop, engine speed will decrease with any further power decrease.

As a safety feature, to protect the engine from overspeeding, governors incorporate an adjustable stop to limit the minimum blade pitch. In addition, some governors incorporate a balance spring above the speeder spring that automatically sets the governor to produce a cruise engine speed if the propeller control cable breaks.

## McCAULEY CONSTANT-SPEED PROPELLERS

The McCauley constant-speed propeller system is a popular system used on light and medium size general aviation aircraft. McCauley provides two types of constant-speed propeller—the threaded series and the threadless series. Both use the same pitch change mechanism in the propeller hub; however, the method of attaching the propeller blades to the hub differs. In a threaded series propeller, a retention nut threads onto the propeller hub and holds the blades in the hub. This differs from the threadless-type blades, which use a split retainer ring to hold each blade in the hub. [Figure 12-27]

Both series of McCauley propellers are nonfeathering and noncounterweighted. Oil pressure is used to increase propeller blade angle; and centrifugal twisting force combines with an internal spring to rotate the blades to low pitch. With this type of system, when a higher blade pitch is selected, high pressure oil is routed to the propeller hub to push against the piston. After the pressure builds enough to oppose the spring inside the hub and the centrifugal force exerted on the blades, the piston slides back toward the hub. This movement is transmitted to the propeller blades through blade actuating links to actuating pins located on each blade butt. [Figure 12-28]

The propeller blades, hub, and piston are made from an aluminum alloy. The propeller cylinder, blade actuating pins, piston rod, and spring are manufactured from either chrome or cadmium-plated steel. To help prevent metal particles from wearing off the blade actuating links and becoming trapped inside the propeller hub, most actuating links are made of a phenolic material.

O-ring seals are installed between the piston and the cylinder, the piston and the piston rod, and the piston rod and the hub prevent propeller pitch control oil from leaking out of the propeller hub.

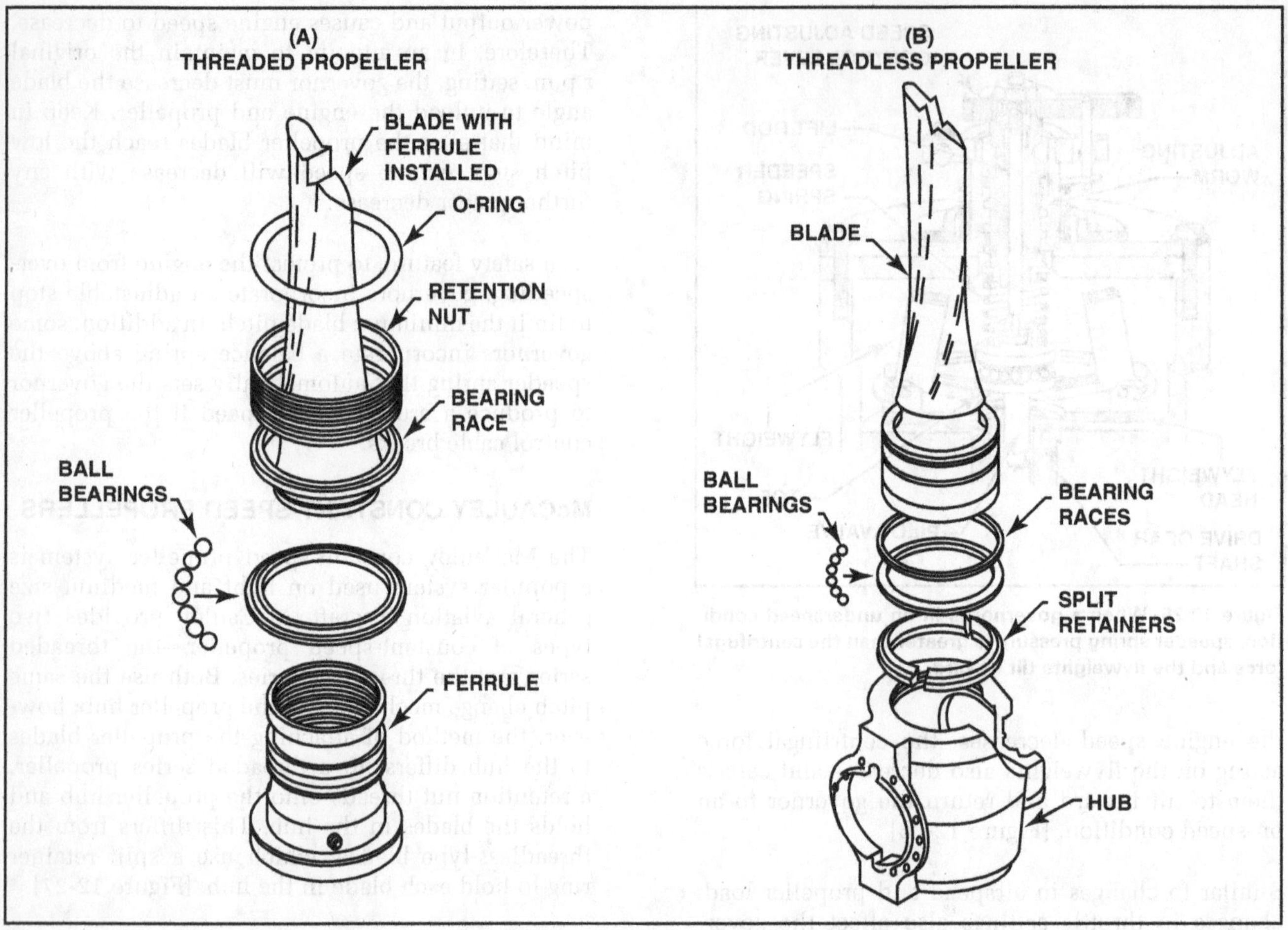


Figure 12-27. (A) McCauley threaded blades use retention nuts and threaded ferrules to secure the propeller blades to the hub. (B) The modern McCauley design incorporates a split retainer ring to hold each propeller blade in place.

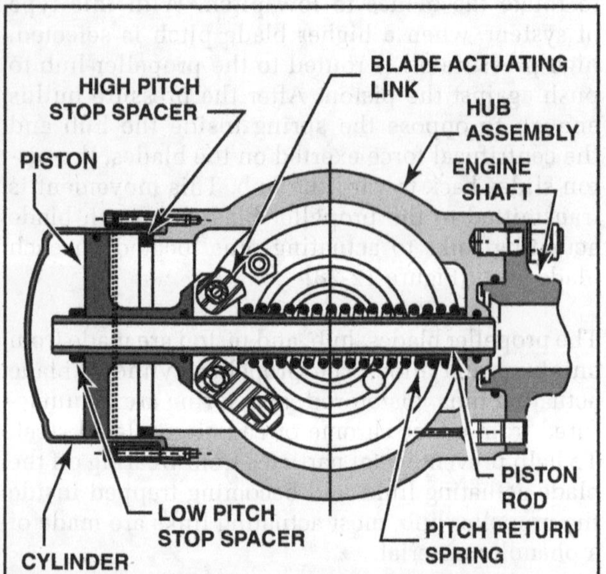


Figure 12-28. McCauley constant-speed propellers use oil pressure to increase blade angle and a combination of centrifugal twisting force and spring pressure to decrease blade angle.

As a result, the components of the propeller's pitch-change mechanism are lubricated with grease instead of engine oil.

Some models of McCauley propellers use a dyed oil that is permanently sealed in the hub. Red oil that appears on the hub or blades is a possible indication that the hub has a crack. In this case the propeller should be removed for repair.

Similar to other constant-speed propellers, the model designation codes of McCauley constant-speed propellers provide component information. Important parts of the designation include the dowel pin location, the C-number, and the modification, or change letter, after the C-number. The modification or change designation indicates that a propeller complies with a required or recommended alteration. [Figure 12-29]

In addition to the designation code on propeller blades, propeller hubs have their own designation code. In most cases, the code includes two groupings of numbers that indicate the year of

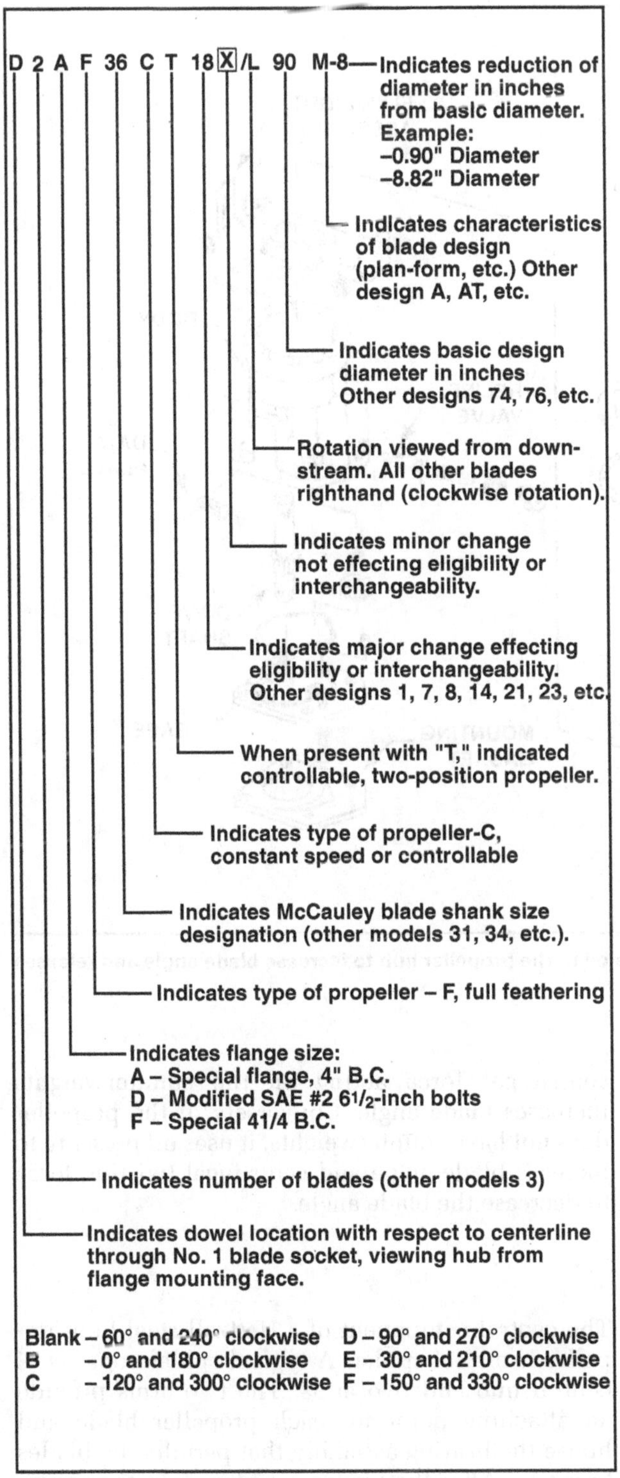


**Figure 12-29. The McCauley designation system provides important information to help determine whether a propeller is compatible with a specific aircraft.**

manufacture and the number of hubs that were manufactured in that year. For example, a designation code of 72 1126 indicates that the hub was manufactured in 1972 and that a total of 1,126 hubs were manufactured in that year.

## McCAULEY GOVERNORS

McCauley governors use the same basic operating principles as those discussed earlier. The governor directs high pressure oil to the propeller hub to increase the propeller blade angle. Most McCauley governors use a control arm to adjust the speeder spring pressure that acts on the flyweights and pilot valve. The end of the control arm typically has a number of holes that permit either a rigid control shaft or a flexible control cable, or a combination of the two, to be connected to the arm. [Figure 12-30]

For safety purposes, the governor control lever is spring-loaded to the high speed setting. This way, if the propeller control cable breaks, the propeller blades automatically return to low pitch, which permits the engine to develop its maximum power output. As another safety feature, all McCauley governors incorporate a high-speed stop to prevent the engine and propeller from overspeeding. In some cases, a McCauley governor might also have an adjustable low-speed stop. Both the high- and low-speed stops are adjusted with a setscrew on the governor head. Depending on the engine and governor combination, one turn of the screw changes the speed between 17 and 25 r.p.m. [Figure 12-31]

As with other governor manufacturers, McCauley governors have a unique designation system. Some of the information provided in the designation code includes the specific features of a given model, modifications that have been accomplished, and ability to interchange the governor with another. For a full explanation of a given designation, consult a McCauley propeller maintenance manual. [Figure 12-32]

## HARTZELL® CONSTANT-SPEED PROPELLERS

Hartzell constant-speed propeller systems are widely used on modern general aviation airplanes. Currently, Hartzell produces two types of constant-speed propellers, a steel hub propeller and a compact model. The Hartzell steel hub propeller is similar to a Hamilton-Standard constant-speed propeller in that the pitch change mechanism is exposed. However, the pitch change mechanism on a Hartzell compact propeller is housed inside the propeller head. [Figure 12-33]

Regardless of the type of hub used, Hartzell typically stamps a model designation code on both the propeller hub and the propeller blades. A typical designation system identifies the specific hub or blade model, any modifications that have been made, the mounting type, and any specific features. [Figure 12-34]

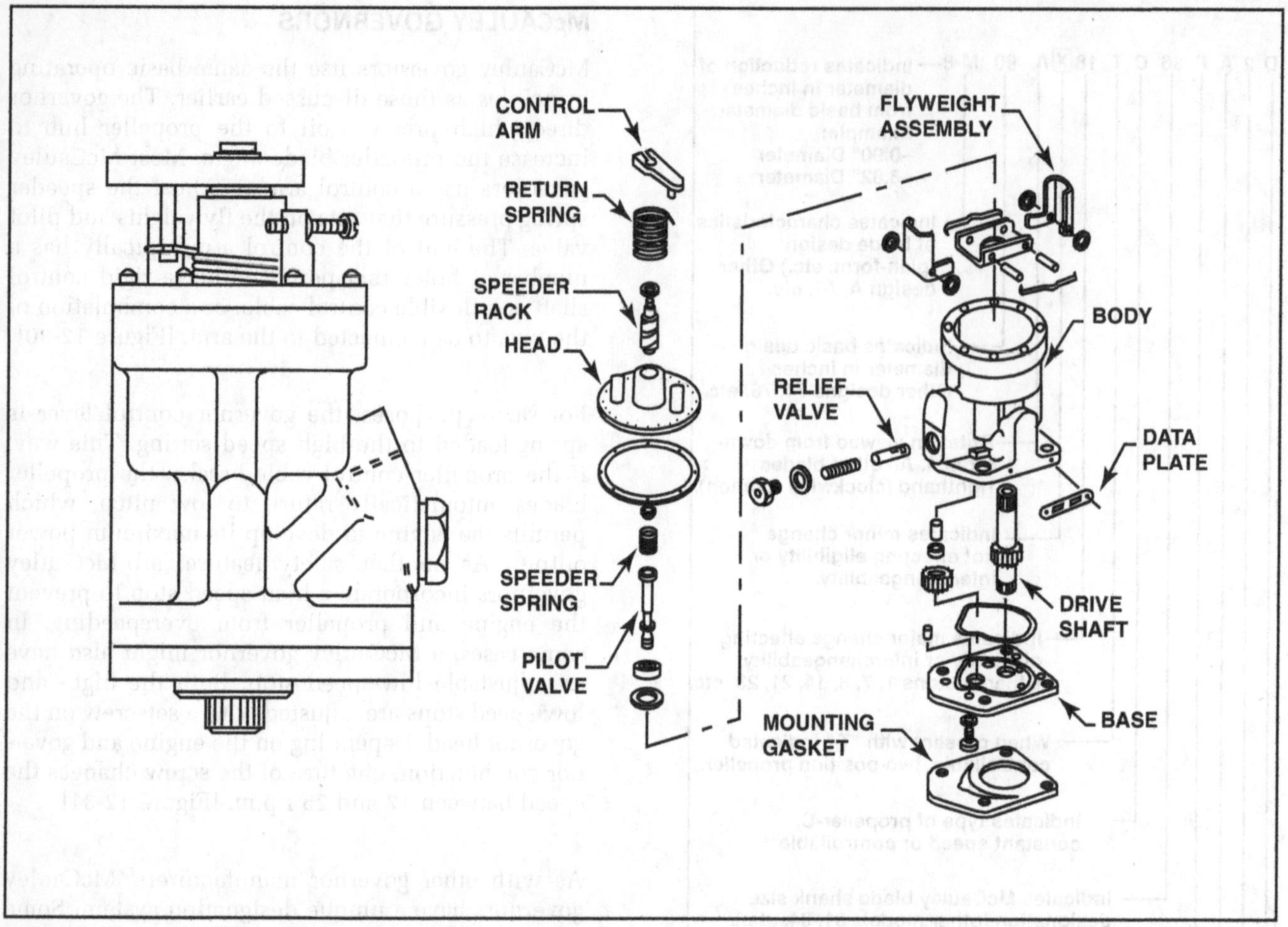


**Figure 12-30. A McCauley nonfeathering governor ports high pressure oil to the propeller hub to increase blade angle and releases the oil pressure to decrease blade angle.**

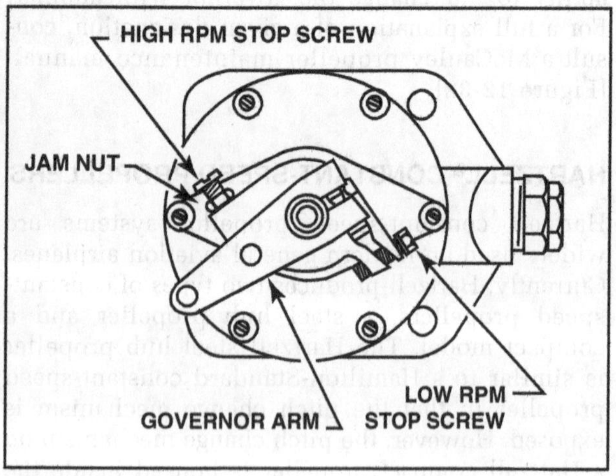


**Figure 12-31. Some McCauley governors incorporate both a high- and a low-speed stop.**

## STEEL HUB PROPELLERS

Hartzell steel hub propellers might or might not be counterweighed. If the propeller has counterweights, oil pressure decreases blade angle and centrifugal force acting on the counterweights increases blade angle. Conversely, if the propeller does not have counterweights, it uses oil pressure to increase blade angle and centrifugal twisting force to decrease the blade angle.

The central component of a Hartzell steel hub propeller is a steel spider. A typical spider consists of central hub and two arms. The two arms provide an attaching point for each propeller blade and house the bearing assembly that permits the blades to rotate. After the blades are placed on the spider arms, they are secured by two-piece steel clamps. To provide a means of changing pitch, a steel cylinder is threaded onto the front of the spider and an aluminum piston is placed over the cylinder. The piston is connected to blade clamps on each blade with a sliding rod and fork system. This way, as oil is directed in and out of the propeller hub, the piston moves, causing the propeller blades to rotate. [Figure 12-35]

**D C F U S 290 D1 -X/ TX**

- **TX** — TYPE NUMBER: DETERMINES CHANGEABLE FEATURES, SUCH AS CONTROL COVER POSITION, SPEEDER SPRING, ETC.
- **-X** — MINOR DESIGN CHANGE NOT EFFECTING ELIGIBILITY OR INTERCHANGEABILITY.
- **D1** — MAJOR DESIGN CHANGE EFFECTING ELIGIBILITY OR INTERCHANGEABILITY.
- **290** — NOMINAL SETTING OF PRESSURE RELIEF VALVE.
- **S** — WHEN PRESENT, INDICATES SYNCHRONIZING FEATURE.
- **U** — WHEN PRESENT, INDICATES UNFEATHERING FEATURE.
- **F** — WHEN PRESENT, INDICATES FULL FEATHERING FEATURE.
- **C** — INDICATES CONSTANT SPEED TYPE GOVERNOR.
- **D** — WHEN PRESENT, INDICATES DAMPENED HEAD FEATURE.

**Figure 12-32. The model, modifications, interchangeability, and specific features of a McCauley governor are identified in the McCauley designation code.**

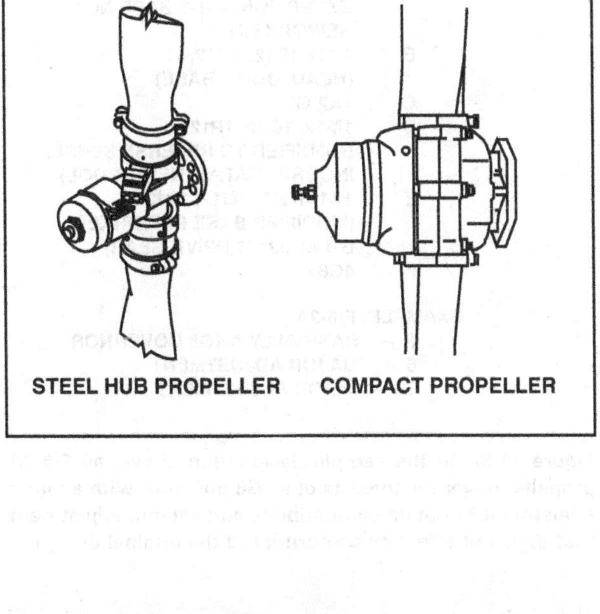


### HUB MODEL

**B HC-82XF-1D**

- **D** — MINOR MODIFICATION
- **1** — DENOTES SPECIFIC DESIGN FEATURES, AS:
  - –1, Non-feathering counterweights
  - –4, 6, 8, Non-feathering, no ctwts.
  - –2, Feathering
  - –3, 5, 7, Feathering and reversing
- **F** — SHAFT MOUNTING
  - F, Flange, 4 in. bolt circle
  - L, Flange, SAE No. 2, $^{7}/_{16}$ bolts
  - K, R, Flange, SAE No. 2, $^{1}/_{2}$ bolts
  - 20, Spline, SAE 20, 21 British
  - 30, Spline, SAE 30, 31 French
  - N, Flange, $4^{1}/_{4}$ B.C. eight $^{9}/_{16}$ bolts
- **X** — BLADE SHANK SIZE
  - X, double shoulder; V, needle bearings
  - Z, single shoulder; W, needle bearings, P, R
  - T, single shoulder with 2 needle bearings
- **2** — NUMBER OF BLADES
- **8** — BASIC DESIGN DESIGNATION
  - 8, 9, A, B
- **HC** — HARTZELL CONTROLLABLE PITCH
- **B** — MOUNTING DOWEL PIN LOCATION
  - B, P, E, Also Blank

### BLADE MODEL

**V L-9333 C H-3**

- **3** — Diameter reduced 3 inches
- **H** — Hard alloy, 7076
- **C** — C modified blade; B anti-icing boots
- **33** — Design basic number
- **93** — Basic diameter before reduction
- **L** — Left Hand
- **V** — Shank configuration

**Figure 12-34. Hartzell constant-speed propellers carry two model designations numbers—one for the propeller hub and the other for the propeller blades.**

## COMPACT PROPELLERS

Hartzell compact propellers are of a newer style that incorporates several features to make them smaller, lighter, and more dependable. A typical compact propeller hub is forged out of an aluminum alloy as two separate halves. Each half is machined to contain the shanks of propeller blades and the entire pitch change mechanism. Bolts hold the halves together. [Figure 12-36]

Hartzell constant-speed propeller systems can use several makes and models of governors. Like other manufacturers, Hartzell uses a unique designation system to identify the governors in its propellers. A typical Hartzell designation uses a three-character code that designates the governor's basic body style and major modifications, any major adjustments that were made to make it compatible with a specific system, and any minor adjustments that do not affect its conformity to the original design. [Figure 12-37]

## HAMILTON-STANDARD CONSTANT-SPEED PROPELLERS

Early in the development of constant-speed propellers, the two-position, Hamilton-Standard counterweight propeller system was transformed into a constant-speed propeller system. To accomplish this, a flyweight governor was developed to replace the selector valve.

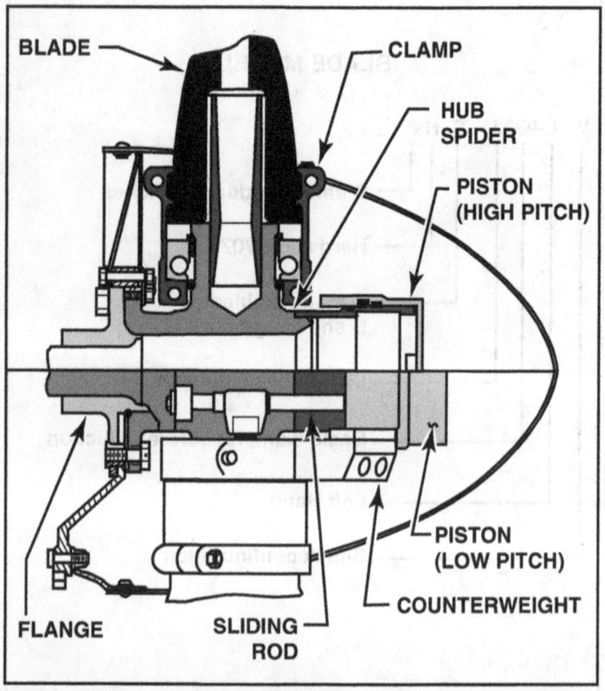


**Figure 12-35. In a Hartzell constant-speed, counterweighted steel hub propeller, oil pressure forces an aluminum piston forward. This motion is then transmitted to the propeller blades through a sliding rod and fork system.**

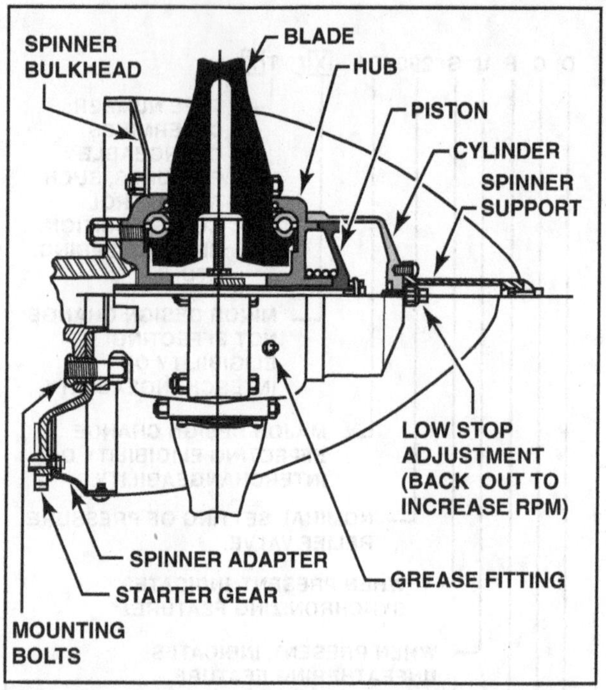


**Figure 12-36. The aluminum hub of a compact propeller houses the entire pitch-change mechanism. Depending on the model, governor oil pressure can be used either to increase or to decrease blade angle.**

**HARTZELL GOVERNOR MODEL**

**X -X -X**

**MINOR ADJUSTMENT NOT EFFECTING ELIGIBILITY.**

**MAJOR ADJUSTMENT TO OBTAIN ENGINE-PROPELLER-GOVERNOR COMPATABILITY.**

**BASIC BODY AND MAJOR PARTS MODIFICATION**

| | |
|---|---|
| A | 1A1, 1Q12, 1M12, 1P12, MODIFIED (BASE REWORKED-B-149 EXCEPTION: A-1-1-BASE NOT REWORKED) |
| B | 1Q12,1P12, 1M12, (HEAD, BODY, BASE) |
| C | 1A2-G5 |
| D | 1M12, 1Q12, 1P12 (MODIFIED TO REVERSE SENSE, INCORPORATING NEW SPOOL) |
| E | 1A1, 1Q12, 1M12, 1P12 (MODIFIED BASE REWORKED B-149, 52141 DRIVE GEAR) |
| F | 4G8 |

**EXAMPLE: F-6-3A**

**F – BASICALLY A 4G8 GOVERNOR**
**6 – MAJOR ADJUSTMENT**
**3A – MINOR ADJUSTMENT**

**Figure 12-37. In the sample designation above, an F-6-3A propeller governor consists of a 4G8 governor with a major adjustment to obtain compatibility and a minor adjustment that does not affect its conformity to the original design.**

The propeller used with the Hamilton-Standard constant-speed system is essentially the same counterweight propeller used as the two-position propeller discussed earlier. However, because a counterweight propeller is used, oil pressure provides the force required to decrease blade angle while centrifugal force acting on the counterweights is used to increase the blade angle.

In most cases, a Hamilton-Standard governor has a designation code stamped on the body. The designation system indicates the design of the head, body, and base. For example, a governor with a designation code of 1A3-B2H identifies head design 1, body design A, and base 3. In addition, the "B2H" indicates the modifications made to the head, body, and base respectively.

## FEATHERING PROPELLERS

When an engine fails in flight, a propeller continues to **windmill**, or turn, slowly as air flows over the blades. This creates a considerable amount of drag that adversely affects an aircraft's glide characteristics. To help eliminate the drag created by a windmilling propeller, engineers developed a way to rotate the propeller blades to a 90 degree angle. This is known as **feathering** and eliminates the drag of a windmilling propeller by presenting the smallest blade profile to the oncoming airstream. Today, all modern multiengine, propeller-driven aircraft are equipped with feathering propellers. [Figure 12-38]

The operating principles discussed previously for constant-speed propellers also apply to feathering propeller systems. However, the propeller control lever in the cockpit typically incorporates an additional position to rotate the propeller blades to a feathered position. In most cases, the propeller control is pulled all the way aft to feather the blades. If a propeller is feathered from a low blade angle, the blades will move from a low angle through a high angle before reaching the feather position.

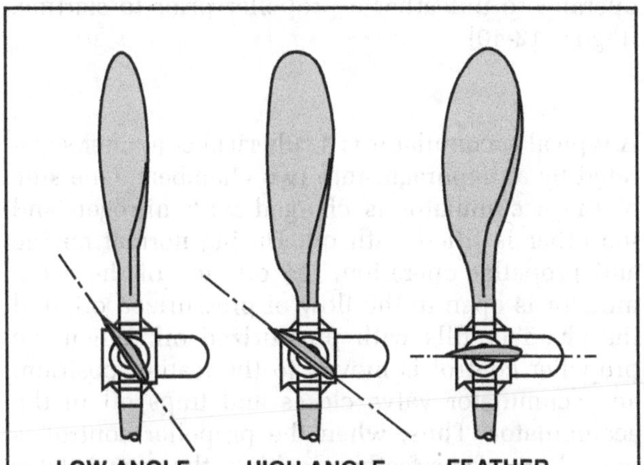


**Figure 12-38. When a propeller is feathered, the blades are rotated beyond their normal high angle to an angle that is approximately 90 degrees to the plane of propeller rotation. This presents the smallest possible blade profile to the airstream and decreases aerodynamic drag.**

On most aircraft, feathering functions are independent of constant-speed operation. In other words, the operator can override a constant-speed system to feather the propeller at any time.

Most manufacturers of constant-speed propellers also build feathering propellers. However, to help simplify this discussion, only the Hartzell compact feathering propeller and the Hamilton-Standard hydromatic propeller will be discussed in detail.

### HARTZELL COMPACT FEATHERING PROPELLERS

The constant-speed operation of a Hartzell compact feathering propeller is the same as the constant-speed model with one difference; the feathering propeller uses both governor oil pressure and centrifugal twisting force to rotate the blades to low pitch while some combination of a high-pressure nitrogen charge, an internal spring, or counterweights is used to increase blade angle. The nitrogen charge is stored in a cylinder head in the propeller hub. One type of Hartzell compact feathering propeller uses a high-pressure nitrogen charge and a mechanical spring to increase blade angle and feather the blades.

Another model of Hartzell compact propeller uses a combination of air pressure and centrifugal force acting on counterweights to increase the angle of the propeller blades and to feather. With this type of propeller, the high-pressure nitrogen charge is stored in the propeller hub, and a counterweight is mounted to the base of each propeller blade. [Figure 12-39]

Both of these designs include a safety feature that automatically moves the propeller to the feathered position if governor oil pressure drops to zero for any reason. This feature helps prevent further damage to the engine from a windmilling propeller and lowers aerodynamic drag on the aircraft.

To prevent a propeller from feathering when the engine is shut down on the ground, most Hartzell compact propellers use a latch mechanism called an **automatic high pitch stop**. The latch mechanism consists of spring-loaded latches, fastened to the stationary hub that engage high-pitch stop-plates

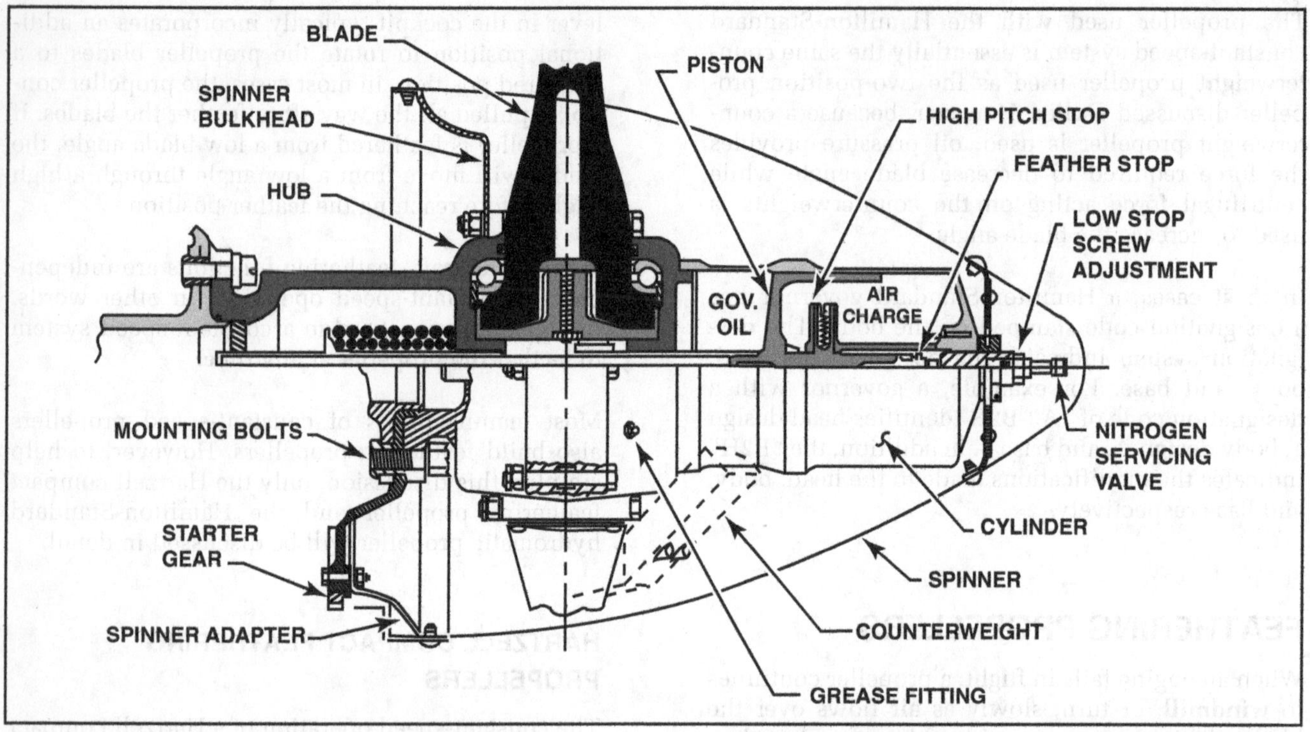


**Figure 12-39. The Hartzell compact feathering propeller depicted here relies on governor oil pressure to decrease blade angle and a combination of blade-mounted counterweights and compressed nitrogen in the propeller cylinder to increase blade angle.**

bolted to the movable blade clamps. As long as the propeller rotates faster than 800 r.p.m., centrifugal force permits the pins to overcome spring pressure, leaving the propeller free to feather. However, when the propeller rotates below 800 r.p.m., the latches engage with the high-pitch stops and prevent the propeller blade angle from increasing to feather.

To feather a Hartzell compact feathering propeller, the operator places the propeller control in the feather position. This action dumps all oil pressure from the hub so that the nitrogen charge and either spring pressure or centrifugal force can rotate the blades to the feather position. The speed at which the blades rotate to the feather position depends on how rapidly the oil drains from the propeller hub and on the amount of force exerted by the nitrogen charge and either spring pressure or centrifugal force. The typical Hartzell propeller takes between 3 and 10 seconds to feather.

Unfeathering is accomplished by repositioning the propeller control to the normal flight range and restarting the engine. As soon as the engine begins to turn over, the governor delivers the oil pressure necessary to unfeather the blades. After the propeller is partially unfeathered, it starts to windmill, which cause the unfeathering to accelerate. To facilitate engine cranking with the blades feathered, the feathering blade angle is set between 80 and 85 degrees at the 3/4 point on the blade. This setting lets the oncoming air assist the engine starter. Typically, an engine with a feathered propeller restarts within a few seconds.

On aircraft in which engine starting might be difficult, the propeller system might incorporate an accumulator. The **accumulator** stores a quantity of oil under pressure until it is needed to unfeather a propeller. In some cases, an accumulator enables an operator to unfeather a propeller prior to starting. [Figure 12-40]

A typical accumulator is a spherical container separated by a diaphragm into two chambers. One side of the accumulator is charged with nitrogen and the other is filled with oil. During normal engine and propeller operation, the oil side of the accumulator is open to the flow of pressurized oil, and the chamber fills with pressurized oil. When the propeller control is moved to the feather position, an accumulator valve closes and traps oil in the accumulator. Thus, when the propeller control is moved out of the feather position, the accumulator valve opens and permits the pressurized oil within the accumulator to flow to the propeller hub. When the oil reaches the hub, it pushes the piston enough to begin moving the propeller blades out of the feathered position.

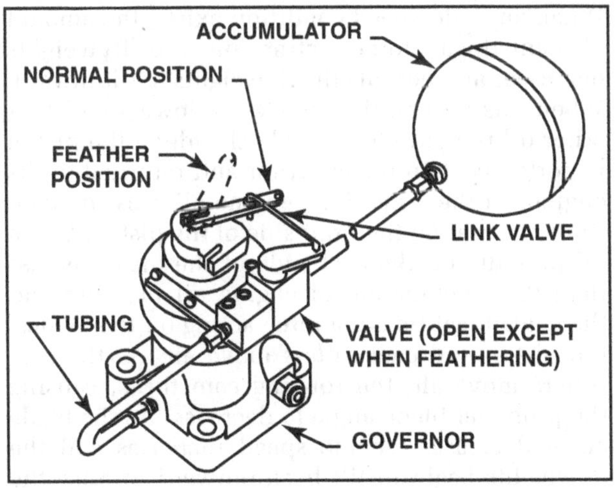


## HAMILTON-STANDARD HYDROMATIC PROPELLER

The second type of feathering propeller to be discussed in detail is the Hamilton-Standard Hydromatic propeller. This type of propeller was common on medium and large radial engine transport aircraft built during the WWII era.

A typical nonreversing, full-feathering, Hamilton-Standard Hydromatic propeller is made up of three major assemblies: the hub (or barrel) assembly, the dome assembly, and the distributor valve. All three assemblies work together to permit constant-speed operation of the propeller. [Figure 12-41]

The hub assembly consists of two halves that support the spider and the propeller blades. Hydromatic propeller blades differ from other constant-speed propellers in that the butt of each blade consists of a sector gear that meshes with the pitch-changing gear in the dome assembly. Each blade slips onto an arm on the spider; then the spider/blade assembly is placed between the two hub halves. To permit each blade to rotate freely within the hub, as well as to hold the blades in place, a combination of bearings and spacers is installed between the blade butt and the hub.

The dome assembly houses the primary components of the pitch-change mechanism including a piston, a rotating cam, and a fixed cam. When the dome assembly is threaded into the propeller hub, oil pressure acts on the piston to move it fore and aft within the dome. As the piston moves, a set of cam rollers mounted to the piston engage the rotating cam, which causes it to turn within the fixed cam. A beveled gear attached to the rear of the rotating cam engages each of the propeller blades to change blade pitch.

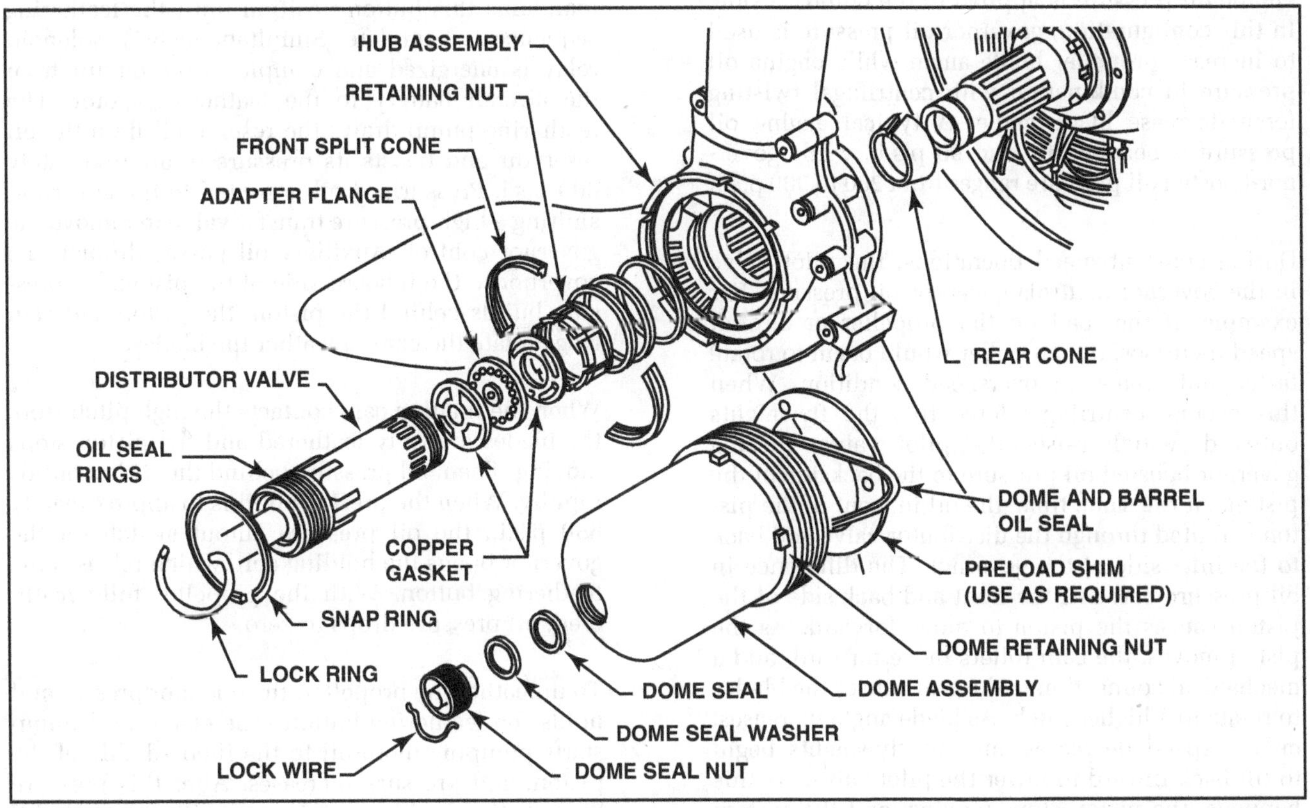


**Figure 12-41. A Hamilton Standard Hydromatic propeller is made up of three major assemblies: the hub assembly, the dome assembly, and the distributor valve.**

The distributor valve acts as an extension to the engine's crankshaft and is installed in the center of the dome assembly. The purpose of the distributor valve is to direct both governor oil and engine oil into and out of the dome assembly.

## GOVERNORS

In addition to the governor parts described in other models, a Hydromatic governor also includes a high-pressure transfer valve that disables the governor constant-speed functions when the propeller is feathered or unfeathered. Additionally, an electric pressure cutout switch is located on the side of the governor. The cutout switch automatically stops oil pressure delivery when the blades reach their fully feathered position.

## OPERATING PRINCIPLES

The Hydromatic propeller uses no springs or counterweights to change blade angle. Instead, engine oil pressure acts on one side of the piston while governor oil pressure acts on the opposite side. Depending on the propeller model, governor oil pressure can be directed to either the inboard or outboard side of the piston. For the purposes of this discussion, assume that governor oil pressure is applied to the inboard side of the piston while engine oil pressure is applied to the outboard side. In this configuration, governor oil pressure is used to increase propeller blade angle while engine oil pressure in combination with centrifugal twisting force decrease blade angle. A typical engine oil pressure is between 60 and 90 p.s.i., while governor-boosted oil pressure ranges from 200 to 300 p.s.i.

During constant-speed operations, the pilot valve in the governor controls governor oil pressure. For example, if the load on the propeller or aircraft speed increases, the propeller would begin to rotate faster and create an overspeed condition. When this occurs, centrifugal force tilts the flyweights outward, which raises the pilot valve, routing governor-boosted oil pressure to the backside of the piston. At the same time, the oil in front of the piston is routed through the distributor valve and back to the inlet side of the governor. The difference in oil pressure between the front and back side of the piston causes the piston to move forward. As the piston moves, the cam rollers move forward, and a mechanical connection to the gear causes the blades to rotate to a higher pitch. As blade angle increases, engine speed decreases and the flyweights begin to tilt back inward to lower the pilot valve. As this happens, the piston stops moving, and the system returns to an on-speed condition. [Figure 12-42]

When an underspeed condition exists, the amount of centrifugal force acting on the flyweights decreases and permits the flyweights to tilt inward. When this occurs, the pilot valve lowers and governor oil pressure from the back side of the piston is ported back to the governor and returned to the engine. At the same time, engine oil pressure continues to bear on the front side of the piston. When oil pressure on the back side of the piston is less than the combination of engine oil pressure and the centrifugal twisting force acting on the blades, the piston and cam rollers move aft. As the cam rollers move aft, the rotating cam turns, causing the propeller blade angle to decrease. As the blade angle decreases, engine speed increases and the flyweights begin to tilt back outward to raise the pilot valve. As this happens, the piston stops moving and the system returns to an on-speed condition. [Figure 12-43]

## FEATHERING

The Hydromatic propeller uses high-pressure oil to feather the blades. To ensure an adequate supply of oil and a means to pressurize it, an oil reservoir and separate electric oil pump are installed in the propeller system.

To feather this propeller, the operator depresses a feathering button in the cockpit. A holding coil maintains this button position until the feathering sequence is complete. Simultaneously, a solenoid relay is energized and completes the circuit from the aircraft battery to the feathering motor. The feathering pump draws the reserve oil from the oil reservoir and boosts its pressure to approximately 600 p.s.i. Pressurized oil is routed to the governor, shifting a high-pressure transfer valve to remove the governor control. Auxiliary oil passes through the governor to the inboard side of the piston. As pressure builds behind the piston, the piston and cam rings rotate the cam to feather the blades.

When the rotating cam contacts the high pitch stop, the blades are fully feathered and the piston stops moving. Then, oil pressure behind the piston builds rapidly. When the pressure builds to approximately 650 p.s.i., the oil pressure cutout switch on the governor opens the holding coil, which releases the feathering button. With the propeller fully feathered, oil pressure drops to zero.

To unfeather the propeller, the operator presses and holds the feathering button. The electric oil pump starts pumping more oil to the inboard side of the piston, and pressure increases. After this pressure exceeds the combined spring and oil pressure holding the distributor valve in place, the distributor

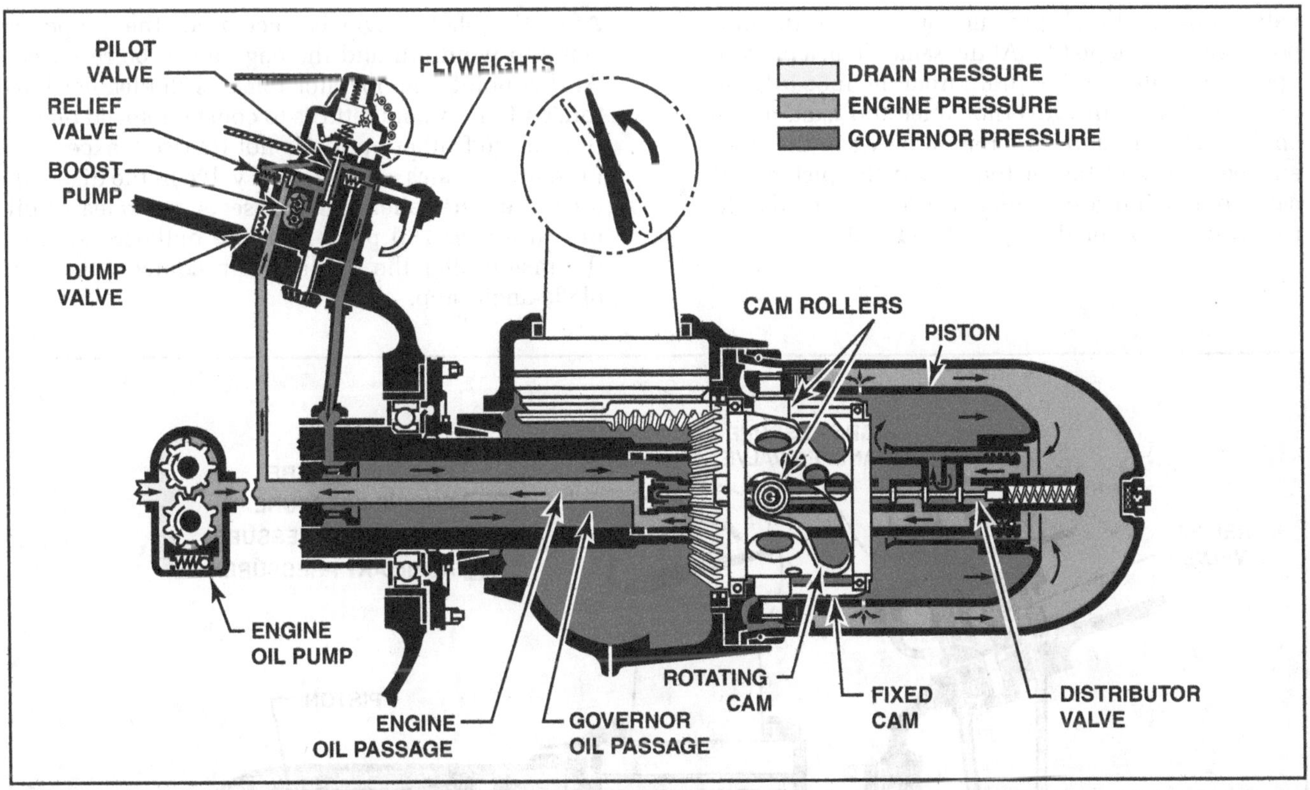


**Figure 12-42.** In an overspeed condition, governor oil pressure forces the piston in the dome assembly forward. As a result, the cam rollers move forward and rotate the cam. As it rotates, the beveled gear attached to the back of the cam engages the propeller blade sector gears and rotates the blades to a higher angle.

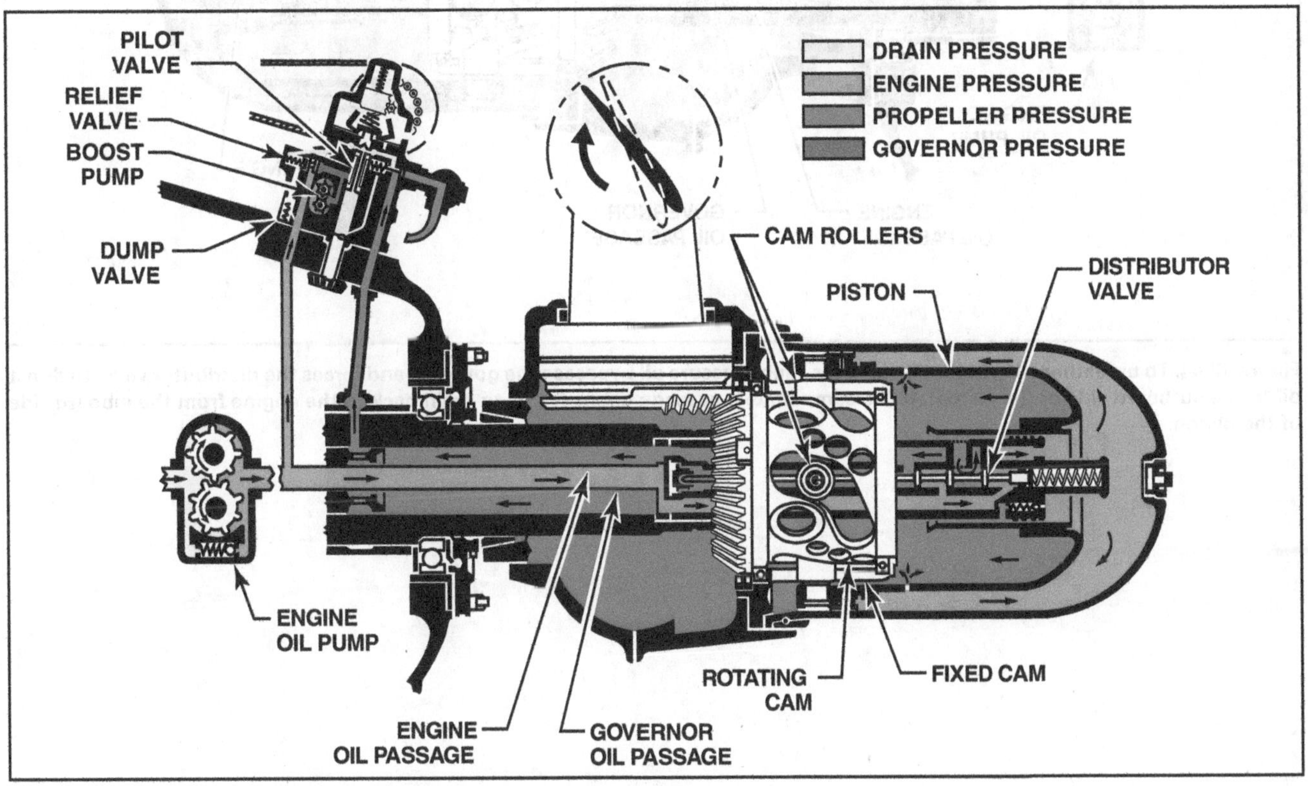


**Figure 12-43.** In an underspeed condition, governor oil pressure is returned to the engine through the governor. When the pressure behind the piston decreases below the engine oil pressure, the piston moves aft. The aft movement rotates the cam, which in turn drives the propeller blades to a lower blade angle.

valve shifts and high pressure oil flows to the outboard side of the piston. At the same time, a passage opens, permitting oil to drain from the inboard side of the piston to the governor inlet and back to the engine. The pressure differential between the front and back side of the piston moves the piston and cam rollers inboard, which causes the blades to rotate to a lower blade angle. [Figure 12-44]

After the blade angle is decreased, the propeller starts to windmill and the engine can be restarted. At this point, the operator releases the feather button, and the system returns to constant-speed operation. If the feather button is not released, excess oil pressure actuates a dome relief valve in the distributor valve. The relief valve off-seats and releases oil pressure over 750 p.s.i. from the outboard side of the piston after the rotating cam contacts the low blade-angle stop.

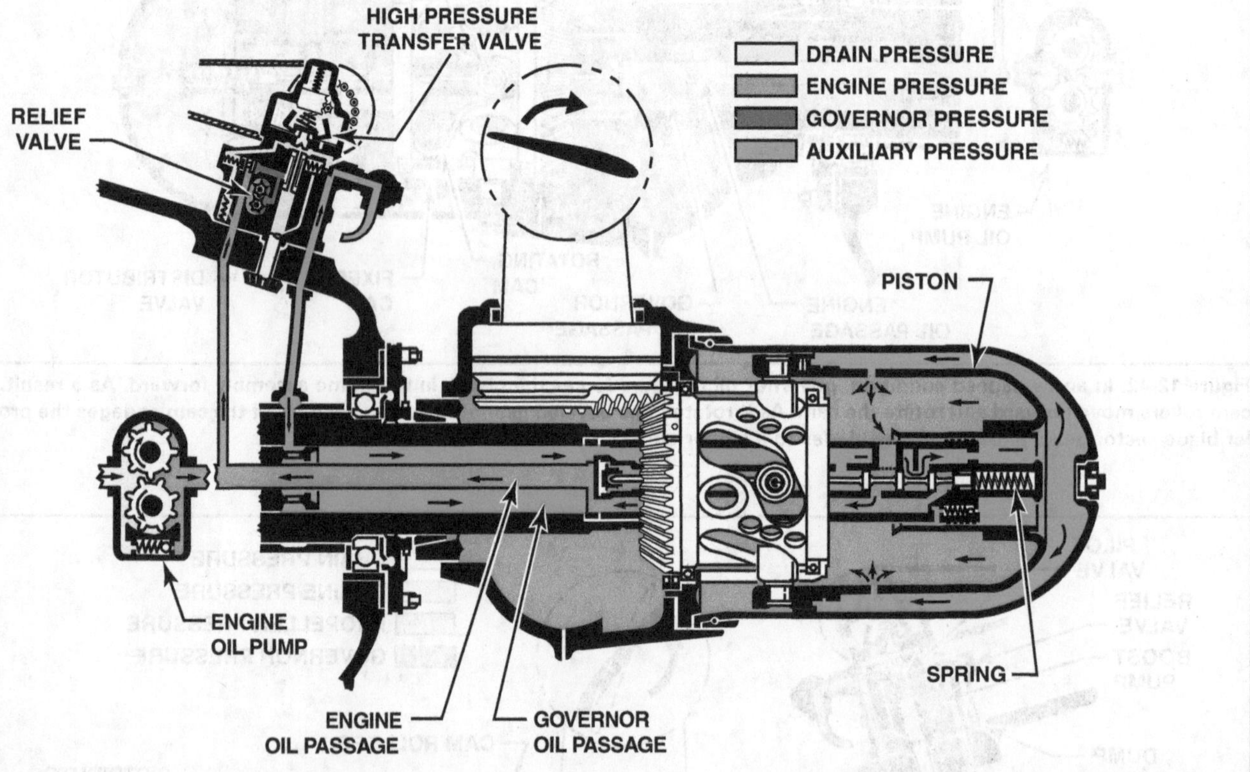


**Figure 12-44. To unfeather a Hydromatic propeller, high pressure oil bypasses the governor and forces the distributor valve to direct oil to the outboard side of the piston. At the same time, a passage opens for oil to drain back to the engine from the inboard side of the piston.**

## SUMMARY CHECKLIST

- ✓ Nonfeathering, constant-speed propellers typically change pitch by balancing centrifugal and hydraulic pressures.
- ✓ Feathering, constant-speed propellers operate similarly to nonfeathering models, but a high-pressure, nitrogen-charged cylinder is typically used to remove the blades from their feathered position.

## KEY TERMS

constant-speed range
flyweight assembly
flyweights
speeder spring
windmill
feathering
automatic high pitch stop
accumulator

# QUESTIONS

1. The propeller governor is an _______ (what variable) sensing device.

2. An aircraft with a constant-speed propeller system will use the _______________ (what instrument) gauge to indicate the throttle setting, and the _______________ (what instrument) to indicate the propeller setting.

3. The _______ valve directs oil through ports in the drive shaft to or from the propeller to vary the blade angle.

4. The position of the pilot valve is determined by the action of the _______________ (what unit).

5. When the flyweights in a governor tilt outward they _______ (raise or lower) the pilot valve.

6. The action of the flyweights is opposed by a _______________ spring.

7. When the flyweights are tilted outward, the governor is said to be in an _______________ (overspeed or underspeed) condition.

8. If the governor senses an overspeed condition, the pilot valve will direct oil so that the propeller blade angle _______________ (increases or decreases).

9. The two series of McCauley constant-speed propellers are:

   a. _______________

   b. _______________

10. McCauley constant-speed propellers use oil pressure to _______________ (increase or decrease) the blade angle.

11. Hartzell produces two styles of constant-speed propellers, they are:

    a. _______________

    b. _______________

12. The Hamilton-Standard propeller governor is divided into these three parts:

    a. _______________

    b. _______________

    c. _______________

13. The ______________ (compact or steel hub) propeller may be identified by their exposed pitch changing mechanism.

14. Hartzell propeller systems may use either Hartzell or ______________ (what make) propeller governors.

15. The primary purpose of a ______________ (what type) propeller is to eliminate the drag created by a windmilling propeller when an engine fails.

16. The engine ______________ (does or does not) have to be developing power for the propeller to feather.

17. Most multi-engine aircraft are equipped with ______________ (what type) propellers.

18. A feathered propeller has an extremely ______________ (high or low) blade angle.

19. Hartzell compact feathering propellers use _______ ______________ (what force) to move the propeller blades into feather.

20. The feathering function ______________ (can or cannot) override the constant-speed operation at any time.

21. The accumulator used with Hartzell or McCauley feathering propellers is used to assist the propeller ______________ (feathering or unfeathering) in flight.

22. Medium and large reciprocating engine powered transport type aircraft may use the ______ ______ (what make) Hydromatic propeller system.

23. The Hydromatic propeller is made up of three major assemblies, they are:

   a. ______________

   b. ______________

   c. ______________

24. The Hydromatic propeller operates by using ______________ oil pressure on one side of the propeller piston, and ______________ oil pressure on the other side of the piston.

25. An ______________ operated feathering pump is used to supply oil under high pressure to the Hydromatic propeller when the feathering system is actuated.

26. The feathering system of a Hydromatic propeller is actuated by depressing the ______________ button in the cockpit.

# SECTION D

# TURBOPROP PROPELLERS

## OPERATING PRINCIPLES

A wide assortment of turboprop propeller designs are in use today from those found in relatively small, single-engine utility airplanes, to those used in large multi-engine transport category airplanes. This section discusses the basic design and operational characteristics common to all turboprop propellers and contains a detailed description of the turboprop propeller systems for two different turboprop engines. By understanding how these propeller systems operate, you should understand the basic operating principles of most types of turboprop propeller systems.

## PROPELLER SPEED REDUCTION

Turboprop engine propeller systems are similar to those for reciprocating engines, but with a few distinct operational differences. Because turboprop engines turn at much higher speeds than reciprocating engines, they need a reduction gear assembly to convert the high speed, low torque of the engine to a low speed with high torque. For example, a turboprop engine can operate at rotational speeds in excess of 40,000 r.p.m. Propellers cannot safely operate at these speeds. The typical reciprocating engine typically operates below 2500 r.p.m.

## POWER SECTIONS

The combination of a turboprop engine's reduction gear assembly and propeller is often referred to as the power section. Two designs are used for driving a turboprop's power section. In one design, the power section is driven directly through a fixed shaft of the integral turbine. In the other design, the power section is driven by a separate **free turbine** (or **power turbine**), which is not mechanically attached to the compressor turbine in the engine. In this design, the term *power section* generally refers to the power turbine, the reduction gearbox, and the propeller. [Figure 12-45]

## PROPELLER GOVERNING

All turboprop engines use constant-speed, feathering propellers controlled by one or more governors. Generally, turboprop engines use the same governing principles to control propeller pitch and maintain a constant speed. Because a turboprop engine requires more time to react to fuel flow and

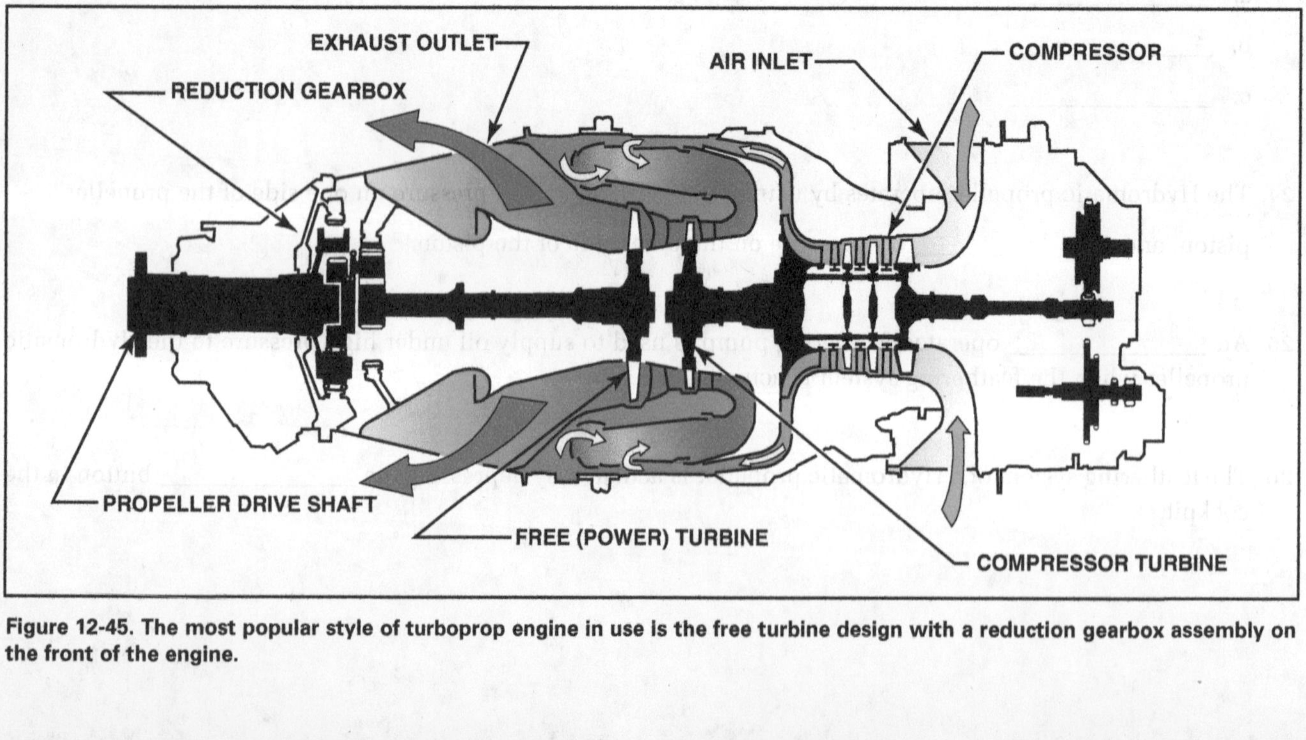


**Figure 12-45. The most popular style of turboprop engine in use is the free turbine design with a reduction gearbox assembly on the front of the engine.**

power changes, thrust changes in turboprop engines are accomplished by changes in propeller pitch. As a result, turboprop aircraft cannot use varying engine speed to effectively control the aircraft on the ground. Therefore, to facilitate ground handling characteristics, the gas generator speed is held relatively constant while propeller pitch is varied as necessary to produce the desired amount of thrust.

## REVERSIBLE-PITCH PROPELLERS

Most turboprop propellers are reversible. A reversing propeller is essentially a variable pitch, constant-speed propeller that is capable of operating with the propeller blades at a negative blade angle so that the propeller's thrust is directed forward instead of aft. This is useful in decreasing an aircraft's landing distance by producing reverse thrust similar to a thrust reverser on a turbojet or turbofan engine. A reversing propeller also enables the operator to control taxi speeds and move the aircraft in reverse.

When a reversible-pitch propeller is operated in the standard, constant-speed mode, it is said to be operating in its **Alpha mode**. However, when the blades are rotated to produce zero or negative thrust, the propeller is said to be operating in its **Beta mode**. On some aircraft, Beta is divided into two ranges: a **Beta for taxi range** and a **Beta plus power range**. The Beta for taxi range includes the blade angles that occur between the bottom of the Alpha mode to a blade angle that produces zero thrust. This range of blade angles is used primarily for taxiing and enables the gas generator to operate at a high speed while limiting the thrust produced by the propeller. This enables the aircraft operator to better control the aircraft's speed on the ground with minimal braking. On most engines with a Beta for taxi range, the power lever must be moved back past a detent below the flight idle position.

The Beta plus power range represents the range of negative thrust. This range is primarily used when an aircraft must be landed in a short distance. When operating in this range, power lever movement also controls the amount of fuel that flows to the engine; the farther aft the power lever is moved, the greater the engine power output and reverse thrust produced. On most aircraft, the Beta plus power range is obtained by pulling the power lever back beyond the Beta for taxi range. To identify the reversing range, the power lever quadrant is striped or labeled with a placard.

When operating an aircraft with reversible propellers, several precautions must be taken. For example, because a reversible propeller tends to stir up debris in front of the aircraft, rocks and other foreign objects can be ingested into the engine or can damage the propeller blades. To circumvent these hazards, propeller reversing should be carried out only on smooth, clean surfaces. In fact, some aircraft manufacturers might limit propeller reversing to a minimum forward speed. When reverse thrust is used to back an aircraft up, keep in mind that rearward visibility is sometimes impossible. Also, if an aircraft is moving backward rapidly and the brakes are applied, the aircraft's nose can inadvertently rise and cause the tail to contact the ground.

Mechanically, a reversible propeller is similar to a typical constant-speed propeller. Depending on the make and model of propeller, oil pressure is used to increase or decrease blade angle. Opposing the oil pressure can be a combination of spring pressure, centrifugal force acting on counterweights, and compressed nitrogen. The only significant difference between a reversing and a nonreversing propeller is the absence of permanently fixed low- pitch stops. The appropriate low-pitch blade angle is achieved and maintained by creating a hydraulic lock with the propeller governor. In other words, after a desired blade angle is achieved, the amount of oil pressure in the hub balances the sum of the other forces acting on the propeller blades. Therefore, if the quantity of oil in the hub is not changed, or locked, at this point, the propeller blade angle will remain set.

As a backup to the primary pitch lock mechanism, some reversible propellers incorporate a secondary method for locking the blade pitch. This way, if the primary pitch lock should fail, the secondary pitch lock will prevent the blades from rotating to reverse pitch.

## TURBOPROP FUEL CONTROL

In most cases, the fuel control on a turboprop engine works in conjunction with the propeller governor to control the propeller blade angle. For example, at speeds above flight idle, both the fuel flow and propeller blade angle are controlled by the power lever position according to a predetermined schedule. As more fuel is metered into the engine, the blade angle is automatically increased for optimum efficiency. On the other hand, at speeds below flight idle, propeller blade angle is controlled almost exclusively by the power lever; when a turboprop engine is running below flight idle speed, governor control over propeller blade angle is incapable of handling the engine efficiently.

## HARTZELL REVERSING PROPELLER SYSTEMS

The following discussion focuses on the Hartzell reversing propellers used with AlliedSignal® TPE-331 and Pratt & Whitney PT6 engines. Many operational characteristics of Hartzell propellers are typical of propellers for turboprop engines produced by other manufacturers; therefore, studying these propeller systems provides an overview of the operation of most turboprop propeller systems.

### ALLIEDSIGNAL TPE-331

Hartzell propeller systems are used on many aircraft equipped with TPE-331 model engines including the Mitsubishi® MU-2, the Fairchild® Merlin®, and the Aero Commander 690 aircraft. The TPE-331 is a fixed-shaft turbine that, depending on the model, produces between 665 and 1,100 shaft horsepower when the gas generator operates at approximately 42,000 r.p.m. The TPE-331 is sometimes referred to as a constant-speed engine. This means that the engine operates at or near 100 percent r.p.m. through an entire operational cycle.

### REDUCTION GEARING

The propeller reduction gearing for the TPE-331 engine is housed on the front of the engine with a fixed shaft coupled directly to the third stage axial turbine. The reduction gearing produces a propeller shaft rotational speed of approximately 2,200 r.p.m., which is a reduction ratio of approximately 14:1. Depending on the airframe manufacturer's requirements, the reduction gearing can be situated either above or below the engine's centerline. [Figure 12-46]

To prevent the propeller from driving the turbine and compressor sections of a fixed-shaft turbine engine, the reduction gear portion of the engine incorporates a **negative-torque-sense (NTS) system** that automatically increases propeller pitch whenever negative torque exists. This condition can occur if the engine power is rapidly decelerated and the propeller's pitch configuration causes the prop to windmill due to slipstreaming. In this situation, the NTS changes the propeller's pitch enough to prevent the propeller from driving the engine. Another benefit of the NTS is that, if the engine fails, NTS will sense the loss of engine torque and automatically rotate the blades to a high-pitch position. Some engines incorporate a separate **thrust sensitive signal (TSS)** to automatically feather the propeller in the event of an engine failure.

### PROPELLER

The propeller commonly used on a TPE-331 engine is a flange-mounted three- or four-bladed Hartzell steel hub, feathering and reversing propeller. With this type of propeller, governor oil pressure moves the blades to low pitch and reverse pitch. To move the blades to high pitch and feather position, the

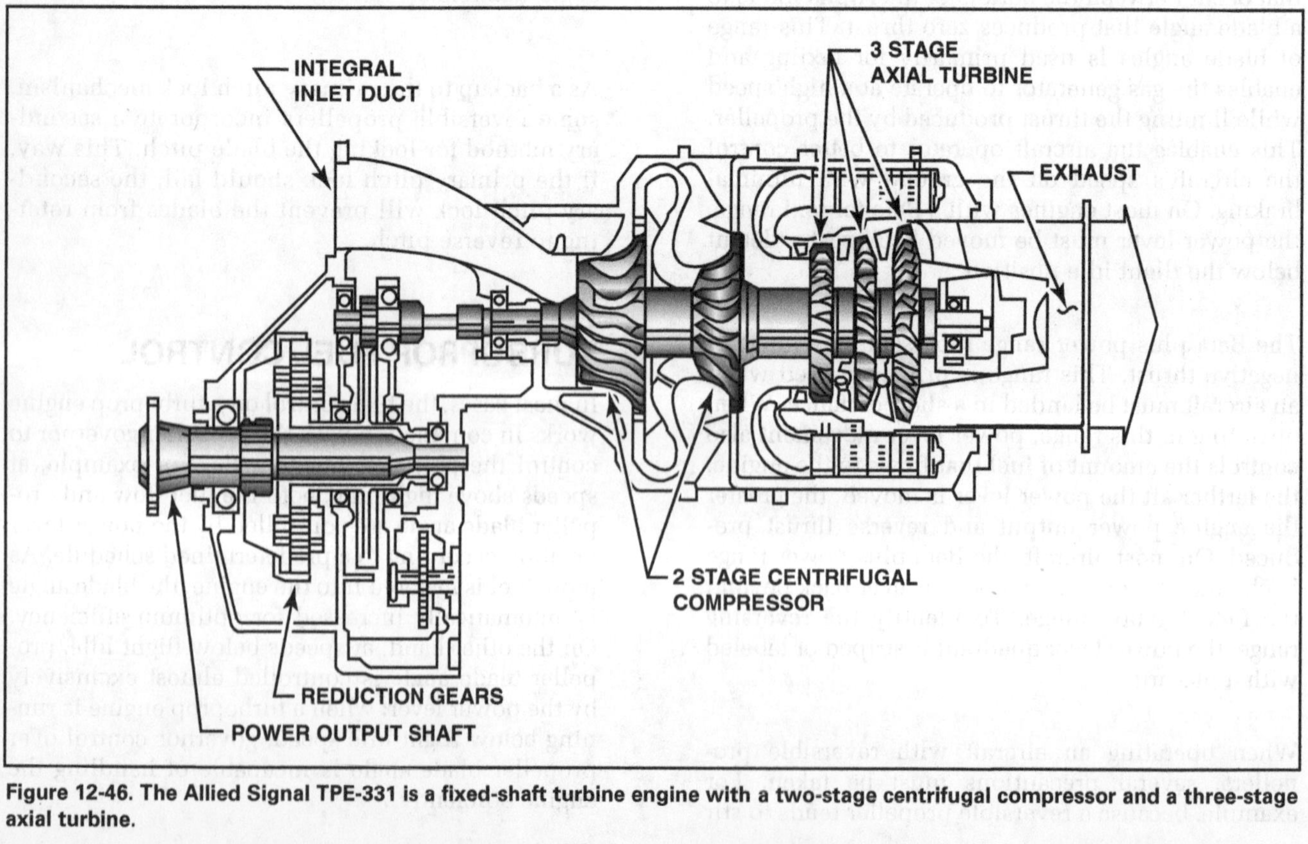


**Figure 12-46. The Allied Signal TPE-331 is a fixed-shaft turbine engine with a two-stage centrifugal compressor and a three-stage axial turbine.**

system uses a combination of spring pressure and centrifugal force acting on blade counterweights. A set of retractable pitch stops is incorporated to prevent the blades from rotating into the feather position during shutdown. This is typical of fixed-shaft turboprop engines to minimize the air load on the propeller during the subsequent engine start. [Figure 12-47]

The Hartzell propeller's construction is similar to that of the feathering steel hub design installed on a reciprocating engine. However, instead of a low pitch stop, this propeller uses a **spacer** or **Beta tube**, which serves as a reverse pitch stop. The Beta tube also transfers oil between the propeller pitch control unit and the propeller dome.

## PROPELLER CONTROL

In flight, engine power output is controlled by the fuel control unit while propeller blade angle is controlled by a propeller governor. The governor permits the operator to set a desired engine speed and then directs oil into and out of the propeller hub to change the blade angle as engine load or power output changes.

During ground operations (Beta mode), a conventional fuel control and governor cannot properly regulate engine power output and propeller blade angle. Therefore, a separate **underspeed governor** controls fuel flow to the engine while a **propeller pitch control** mechanism is used to meter oil in and out of the propeller hub to control the blade angle. As a speed-sensing device, the underspeed governor controls fuel flow to the engine to maintain a specific power output. The propeller pitch control is necessary because the governor does not have the ability to select a reverse blade angle.

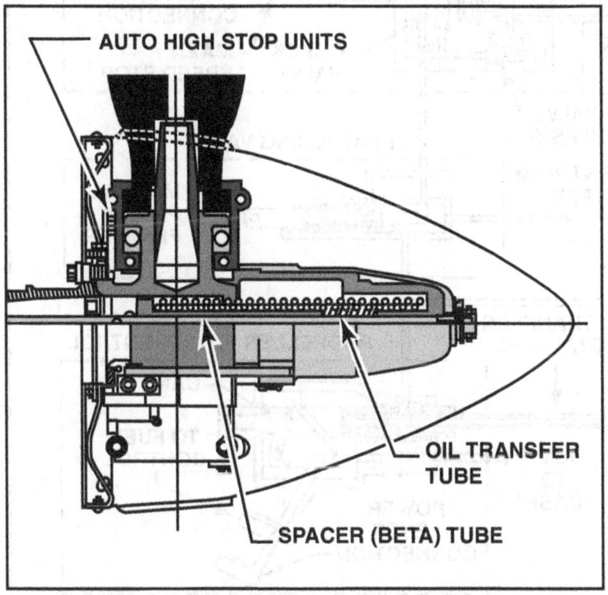


**Figure 12-47. A Hartzell HC-B3TN-5 three-bladed propeller is often used on TPE-331 engines. This propeller relies on high-pressure oil to move the blades to low and reverse pitch, while spring pressure and centrifugal force act on counterweights to increase propeller blade angle.**

## COCKPIT CONTROLS

The controls for a typical TPE-331 turboprop installation are similar regardless of the aircraft. A typical installation consists of two engine controls; a **power lever** and a **speed lever**, or **condition lever**. [Figure 12-48]

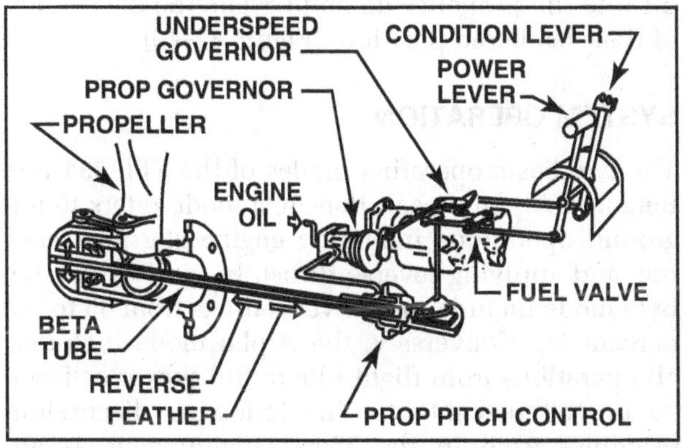


**Figure 12-48. TPE-331 turboprop controls include a power lever and a condition lever.**

The power lever is mechanically connected to both the propeller pitch control and the fuel control so that fuel flow and propeller pitch can be coordinated for fuel scheduling. In most cases, the power lever has four positions: REVERSE, GROUND IDLE, FLIGHT IDLE, and MAXIMUM. During flight, the power lever functions to directly adjust the fuel control unit. However, during ground operations, the power lever bypasses the propeller governor and directly controls propeller blade angle through the propeller pitch control unit.

The condition lever is connected to the primary and underspeed governor through a mechanical linkage. The primary function of the condition lever is to control engine speed and, in some installations, to manually shut off the fuel and feather the propeller. In most cases, the condition lever has three positions: CUTOFF, LOW RPM, and HIGH RPM. On installations in which the feather valve is connected to the condition lever, propeller feathering is accomplished by moving the condition lever fully aft. However, if the condition lever is not mechanically linked to the feather valve, a separate feather handle is provided.

During flight, the condition lever controls the propeller governor, causing it to vary the blade angle to maintain engine speed. During ground operation in the Beta range, the condition lever adjusts the underspeed governor on the fuel control unit. This action varies the fuel flow to maintain a fixed engine speed in spite of blade angle changes caused by power lever adjustments.

In addition to the engine controls, most TPE-331 installations include an unfeathering switch, or button. As its name implies, this switch unfeathers the propeller during an engine restart attempt. When the unfeathering switch is activated, current energizes an electric unfeathering pump, which forces oil into the propeller dome to rotate the blades out of their feathered position. [Figure 12-49]

## SYSTEM OPERATION

The two basic operating modes of the TPE-331 are Beta and Alpha. Recall that Beta mode refers to all ground operations including engine starting, taxiing, and applying reverse thrust. In most cases, the Beta mode includes all power settings from 65 to 95 percent $N_1$. Conversely, the Alpha mode includes all operations from flight idle to full power or from 95 to 100 percent $N_1$. The following discussion examines each in the TPE-331component as an engine is started and operated through both the Beta and Alpha modes.

To begin, assume that a TPE-331 is at rest on an aircraft and the propeller blades are resting against the pitch stops. To start the engine, the power lever is placed in its GROUND IDLE position and the condition lever is placed in its LOW RPM position. After the engine starts, the propeller latches are retracted by easing the power lever toward the reverse position. In turn, the mechanical linkage that connects the power lever and the propeller pitch control (PPC) slides the follower sleeve in the PPC forward. A port in the oil transfer tube (or Beta tube) opens to port high-pressure governor oil to the propeller hub. [Figure 12-50]

When the high-pressure oil from the governor reaches the propeller hub, it overcomes both spring pressure and the centrifugal force acting on the counterweights to force the propeller piston outward. The propeller blades move to a shallower pitch; this removes the force of the blades from the pitch stops, which then retract due to centrifugal force.

The Beta tube is attached to the propeller piston; therefore, when the propeller piston moves, the Beta tube also moves. The propeller blade angle stops changing when the port in the Beta tube is blocked by the follower sleeve. This is referred to

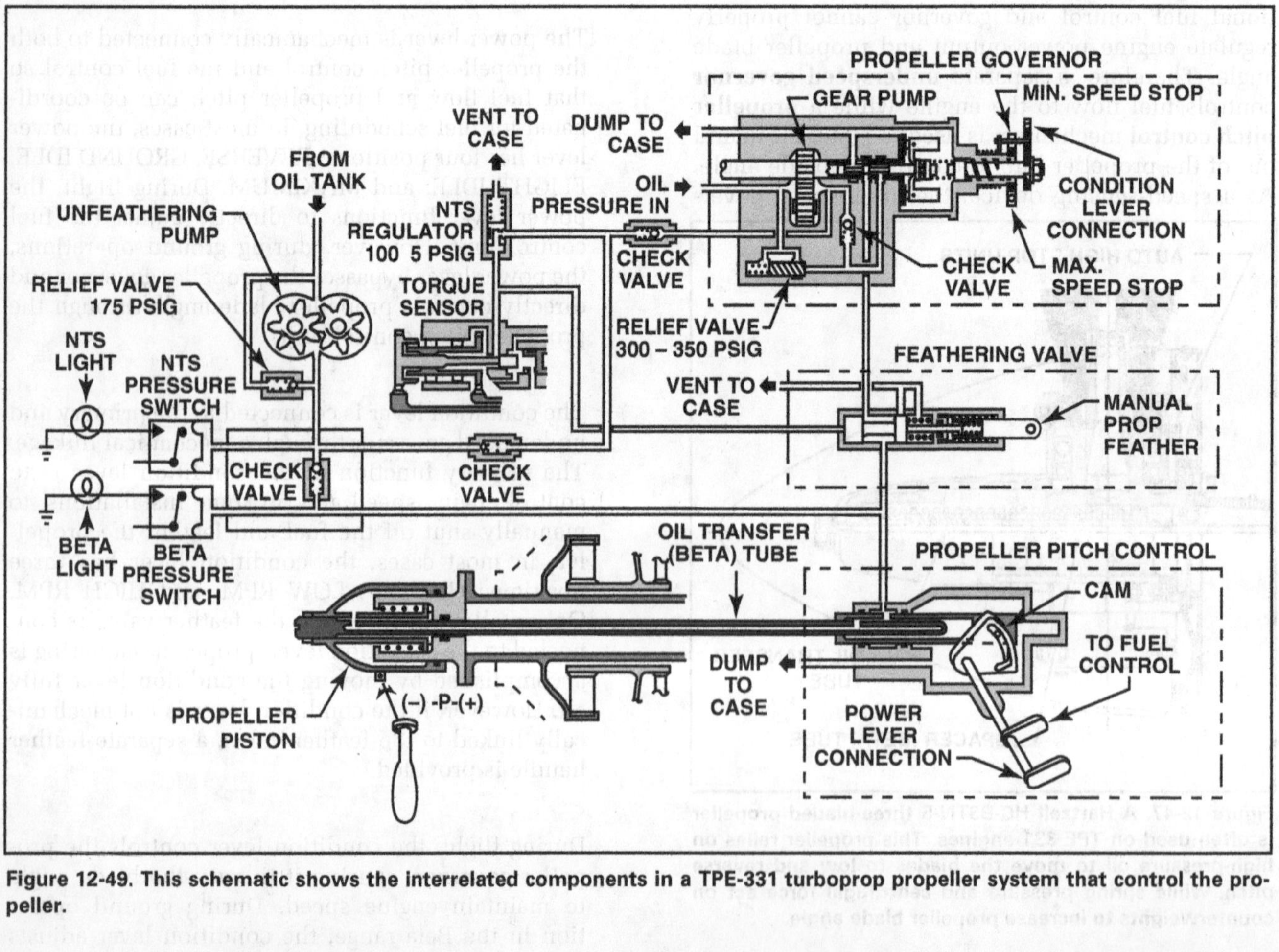


**Figure 12-49. This schematic shows the interrelated components in a TPE-331 turboprop propeller system that control the propeller.**

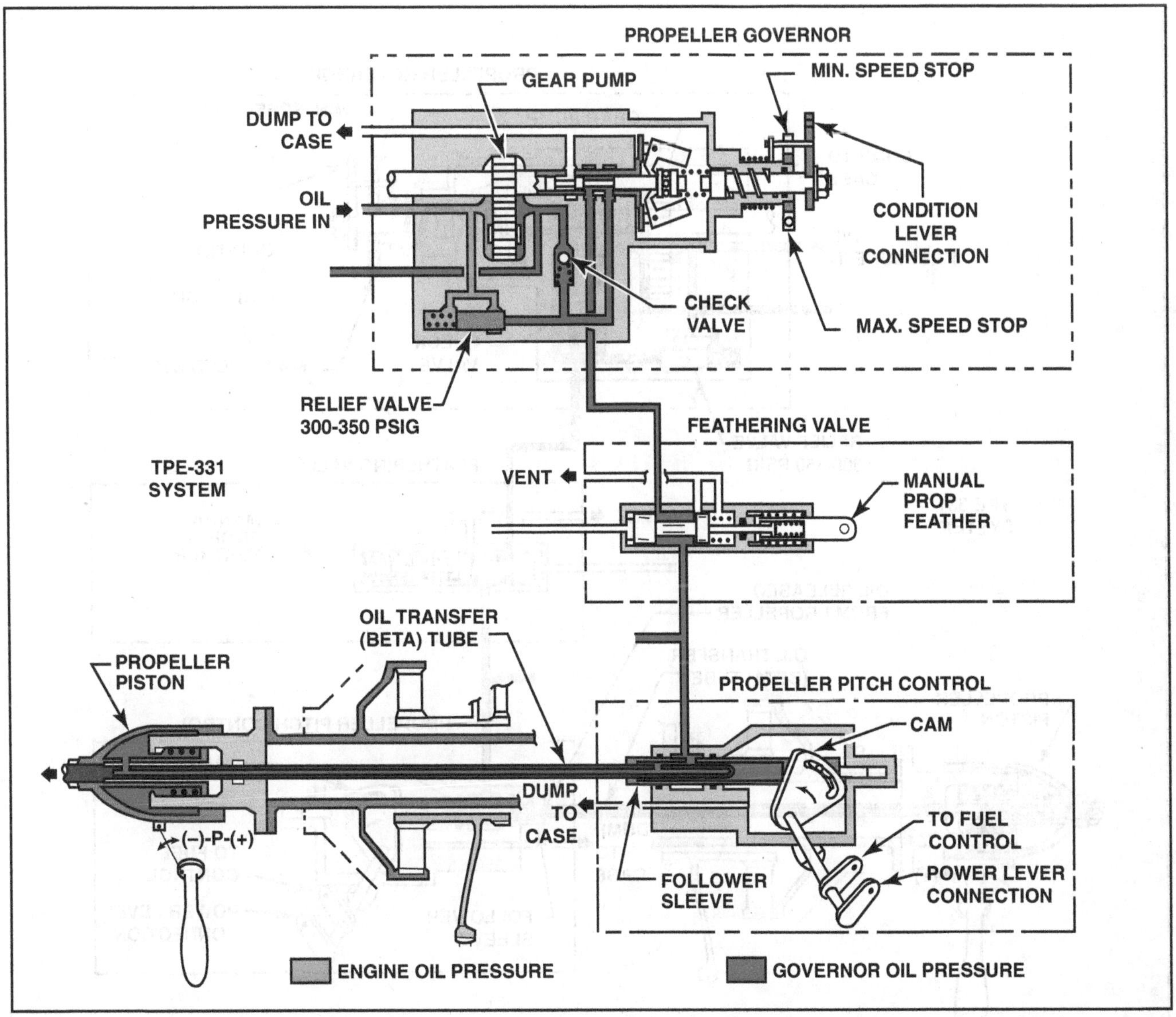


**Figure 12-50. When the power lever is moved toward the REVERSE position, the follower sleeve in the propeller pitch control moves and exposes an oil port in the oil transfer (Beta) tube. This enables high pressure governor oil to flow to the propeller hub and decrease the propeller blade angle.**

as the neutral position and represents the point at which oil pressure within the propeller hub achieves equilibrium with the spring pressure and centrifugal force acting on the counterweights. [Figure 12-51]

After the propeller moves to a lower pitch and the pitch stops retract, the power lever is moved forward to increase blade pitch. A mechanical linkage pulls the follower sleeve in the propeller pitch control aft and unports the Beta tube. With the Beta tube oil port open, oil flows freely into the gear reduction case. This permits the combination of spring tension and centrifugal force acting on the counterweights to force oil out of the propeller hub, thus increasing the blade angle. As the blade angle increases, the propeller piston and Beta tube move aft until the Beta tube returns to its neutral position. The result is a change in blade angle proportional to power lever movement. [Figure 12-52]

When the aircraft is positioned for takeoff, the condition lever is moved to the HIGH RPM setting and the power lever is moved to the FLIGHT IDLE position. With the condition lever in this position, the underspeed governor is open and no longer controls fuel flow. Furthermore, when the power lever is moved forward to the FLIGHT IDLE position, the follower sleeve in the propeller pitch control can no longer cover the port in the Beta tube. This eliminates the ability of the propeller pitch control to change propeller pitch; at this point, the propeller governor has full control over propeller blade angle. In this mode, the power lever controls fuel flow through the engine's fuel control unit and does not affect propeller pitch.

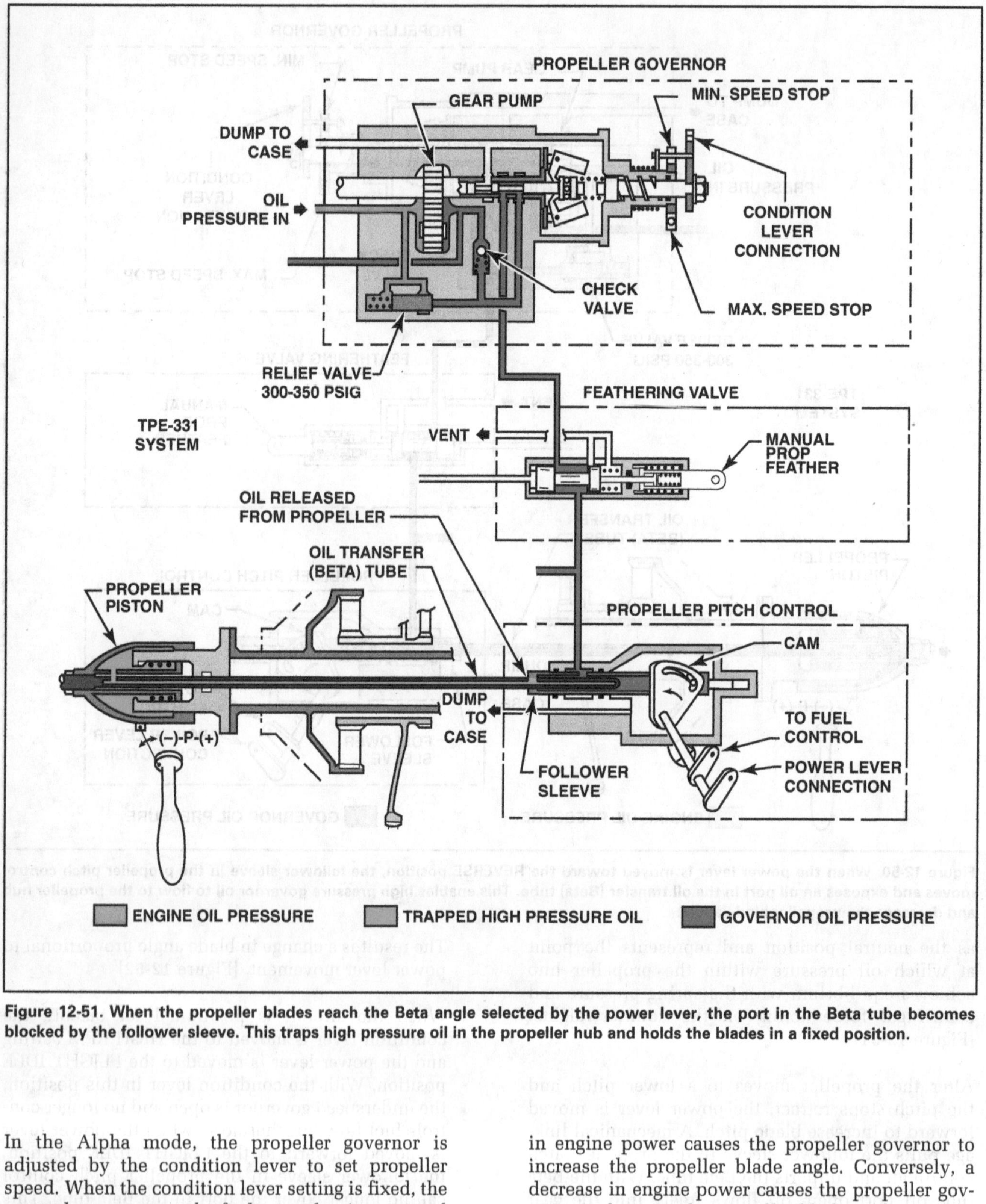


**Figure 12-51. When the propeller blades reach the Beta angle selected by the power lever, the port in the Beta tube becomes blocked by the follower sleeve. This traps high pressure oil in the propeller hub and holds the blades in a fixed position.**

In the Alpha mode, the propeller governor is adjusted by the condition lever to set propeller speed. When the condition lever setting is fixed, the power lever operates the fuel control unit to control the amount of fuel delivered to the engine. Moving the power lever forward increases fuel flow and increases engine power. With the governor attempting to maintain a constant engine speed, an increase in engine power causes the propeller governor to increase the propeller blade angle. Conversely, a decrease in engine power causes the propeller governor to decrease the propeller blade angle.

To feather the propeller on a TPE-331 engine, the condition lever must be moved fully aft or, if so equipped, the feather handle must be pulled. Either of these actions shifts the feather valve and permits the oil in the propeller hub to return to the engine. With no counteracting oil pressure in the propeller hub, spring tension and centrifugal force acting on the counterweights rotates the propeller blades to the feather position. [Figure 12-53]

To unfeather a propeller installed on a TPE-331 engine, an electric unfeathering pump is used. A toggle switch in the cockpit is the typical way to activate the pump. After the pump is activated, it pumps oil to the propeller hub and forces the propeller piston forward. As the piston moves forward, the blades rotate out of a feathered position and into high pitch. As soon as the blades unfeather, the propeller begins to windmill, which can assist in an air start attempt. In some cases, the unfeathering pump can be used on the ground if the engine was shut down with a feathered propeller.

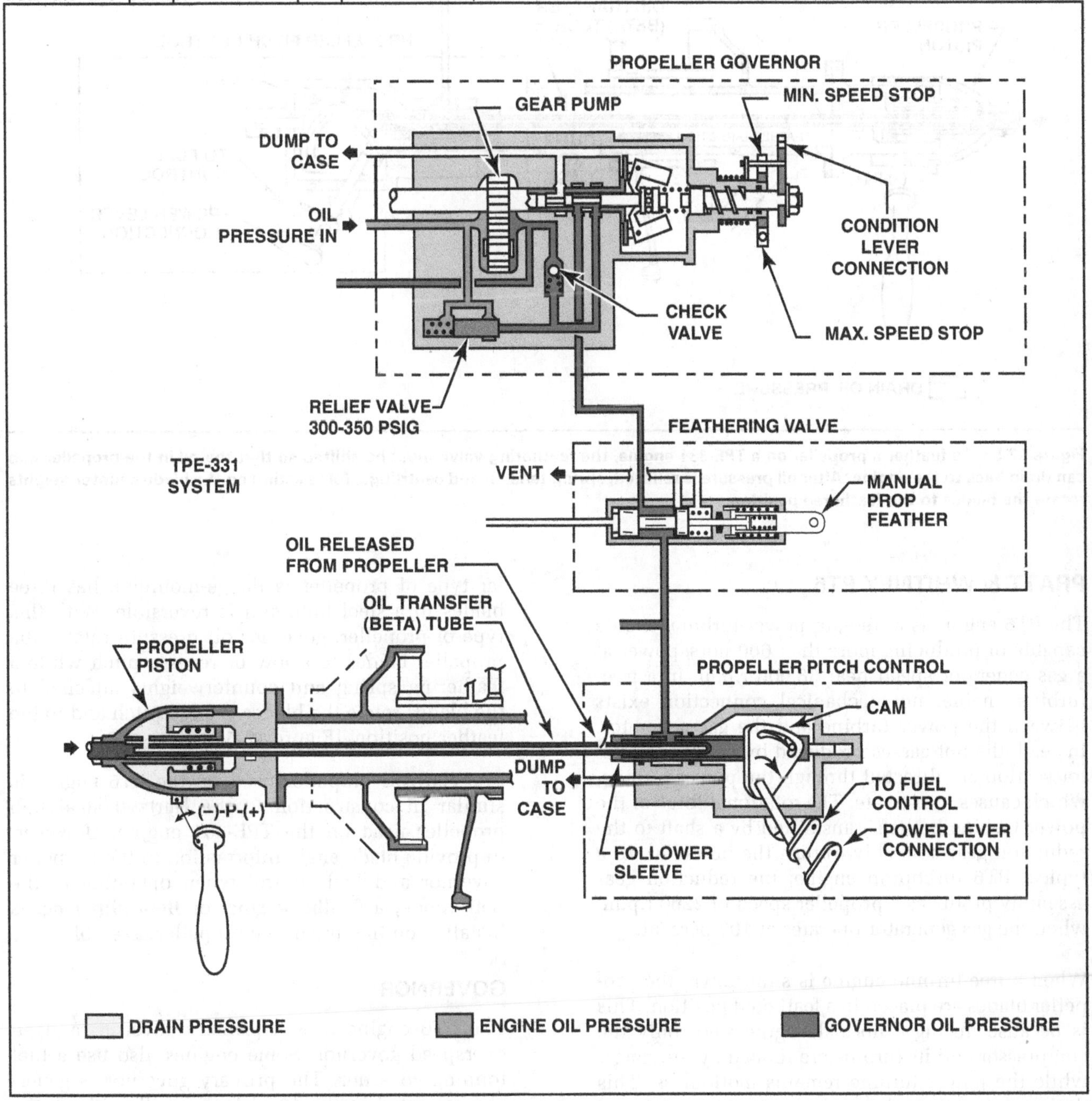


**Figure 12-52. When the power lever is moved forward in the Beta mode, the follower sleeve in the propeller pitch control opening the port of the Beta tube, permitting oil to flow out of the propeller hub. The loss of oil pressure in the hub permits the combination of spring tension and centrifugal force acting on the counterweights to rotate the blades to a higher pitch.**

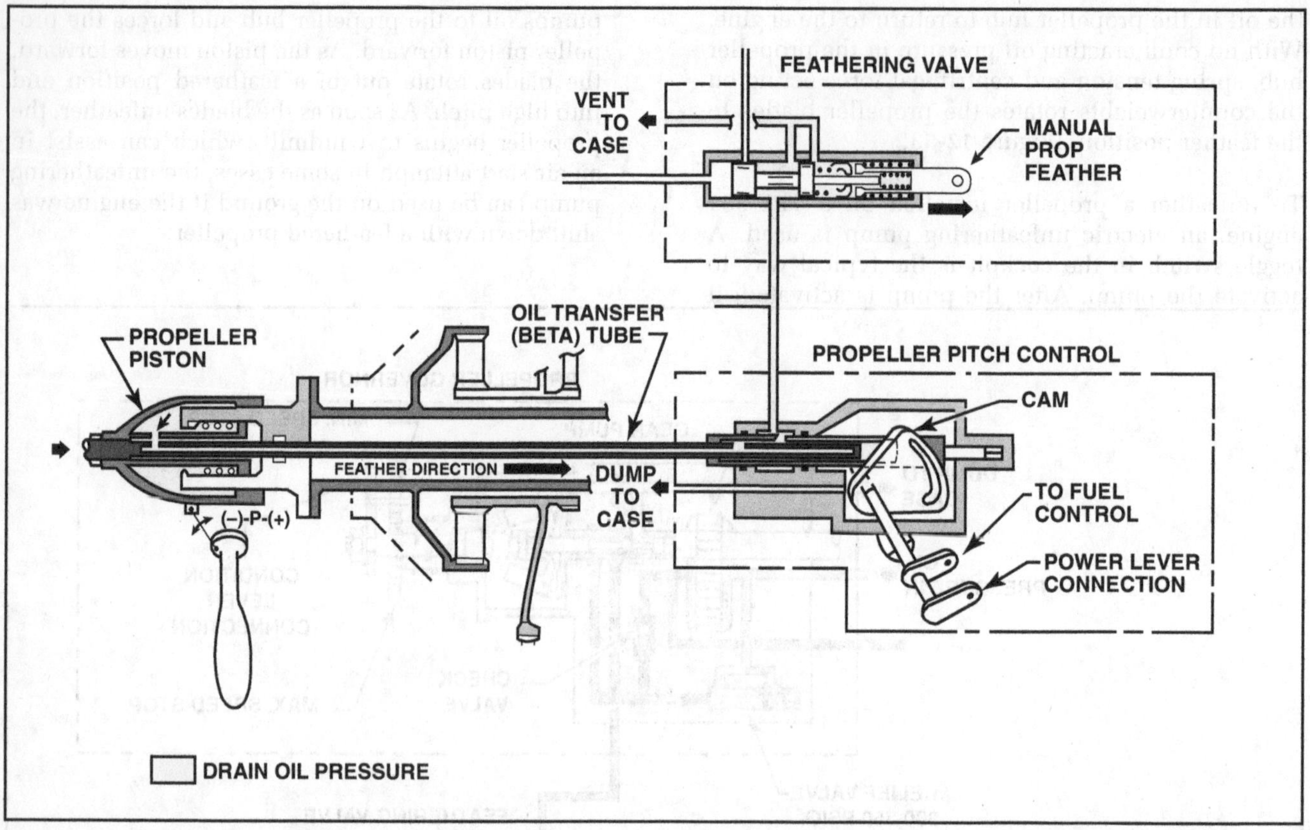


**Figure 12-53. To feather a propeller on a TPE-331 engine, the feathering valve must be shifted so that the oil in the propeller hub can drain back to the engine. After oil pressure is relieved, spring tension and centrifugal force acting on the blade counterweights rotate the blades to the feathered position.**

## PRATT & WHITNEY PT6

The PT6 engine is a free-, or power-turbine, engine capable of producing more than 600 horsepower at a gas generator speed near 38,000 r.p.m. In a free-turbine engine, no mechanical connection exists between the power turbine and the gas generator. Instead, the hot gasses produced by the gas generator section are directed through the power turbine, which causes it to rotate. The rotational force of the power turbine is then transmitted by a shaft to the reduction gear assembly to turn the propeller. In a typical PT6 turboprop engine, the reduction gear assembly produces a propeller speed of 2200 r.p.m. when the gas generator operates at 100 percent.

When a free-turbine engine is shut down, the propeller blades are placed in a feathered position. This is because during a normal engine start, only the compressor and its turbine are rotated by the starter while the power turbine remains motionless. This design reduces the load on the starter motor and eliminates the need for pitch stops.

### PROPELLER

One propeller that is commonly used with the PT6 engine is the Hartzell HC-B3TN-3. This particular type of propeller is flange-mounted, has three blades in a steel hub, and is reversible. With this type of propeller, governor oil pressure rotates the propeller blades to a low or reverse pitch while a feathering spring and counterweights attached to the blades rotate the blades to high pitch and to the feather position. [Figure 12-54]

The Hartzell propeller used on the PT6 engine is similar in construction to the Hartzell steel hub propeller used on the TPE-331 engine. However, to provide blade angle information to the propeller governor and fuel control when operating in the Beta mode, a **feedback ring**, or **Beta slip ring**, is installed on the rear of the propeller assembly.

### GOVERNOR

The PT6 engine uses a primary governor and an overspeed governor. Some engines also use a fuel topping governor. The primary governor is generally mounted in the 12 o'clock position above the gear reduction case and works similar to a conventional propeller governor. The key components of a primary governor include a gear oil pump, rotating flyweights, a speeder spring, and a pilot valve. In addition, depending on engine model, the governor might incorporate either a **Beta valve** or a **Beta lift**

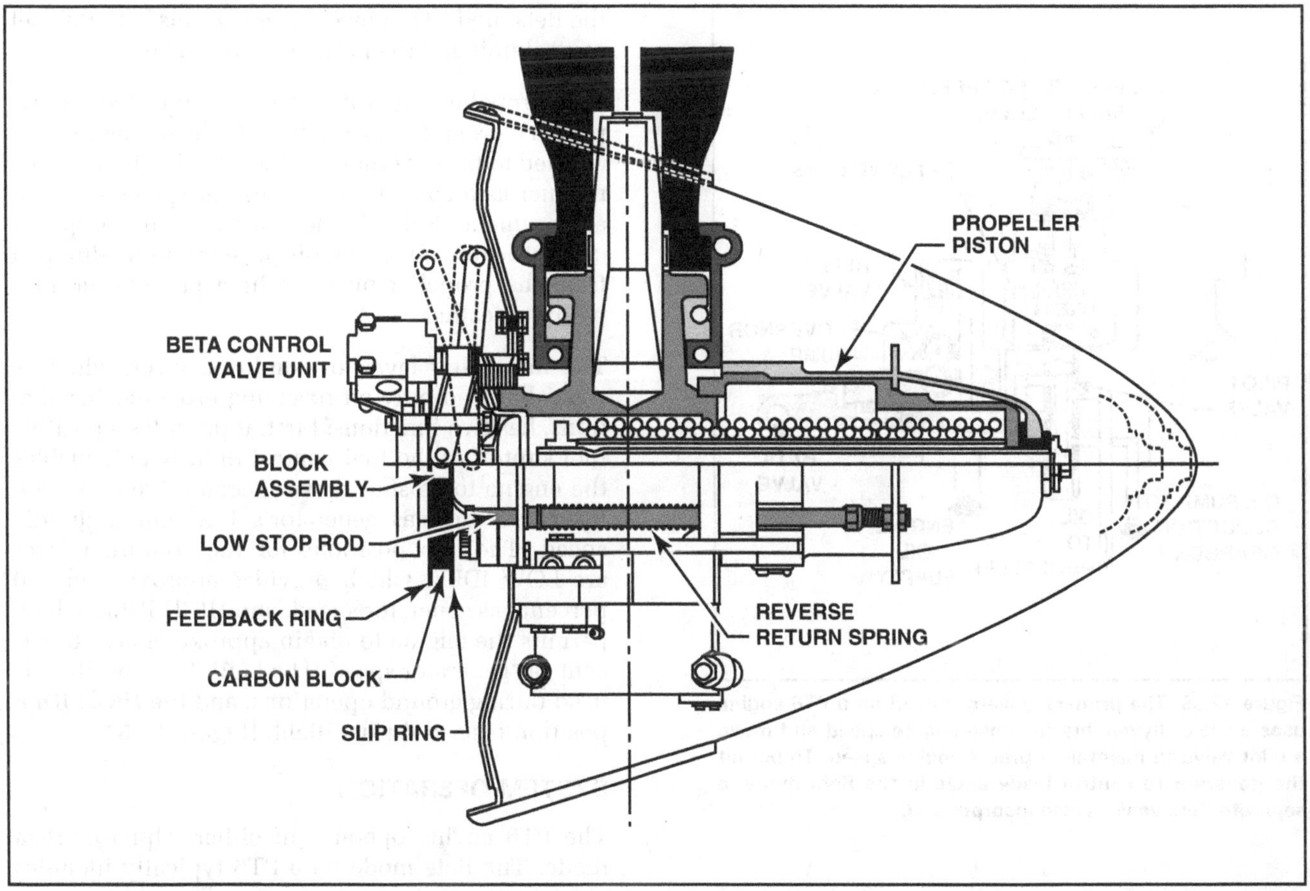


**Figure 12-54. A propeller commonly installed on the PT6 is a Hartzell with three blades, a steel hub, and capability to feather and reverse. Oil pressure rotates the propeller's blades to low pitch, while the combined forces of a feathering spring and blade counterweights rotate the blades to high pitch and feather.**

**rod** to control the blade angle when the propeller is operated in the Beta mode. [Figure 12-55]

As a precaution in the event that the primary propeller governor fails to limit the propeller's speed to its normal maximum speed, PT6 engines include an **overspeed governor**. This governor uses a speeder spring and flyweight arrangement to prevent the propeller from overspeeding. The speeder spring tension cannot be controlled from the cockpit and it is not adjustable in the field. Only the manufacturer or an approved repair facility can make adjustments. [Figure 12-56]

The operation of the overspeed governor is fairly straightforward. A speeder spring applies a predetermined amount of pressure to a set of flyweights. As the engine accelerates, centrifugal force pulls the flyweights outward, which, in turn, raise a pilot valve. If the engine exceeds its maximum rated speed, the centrifugal force acting on the flyweights pulls the flyweights out far enough to raise the pilot valve so that oil can escape from the propeller hub. This reduction in oil pressure enables spring tension and centrifugal force acting on the propeller blade counterweights to increase blade angle and slow the engine.

To check the overspeed governor's operation, an electrical test solenoid is typically incorporated in the governor. This solenoid is activated by momentarily closing a switch in the cockpit. During a ground runup, this switch is depressed while the engine is run at a high speed. If the overspeed governor is functioning properly, the propeller's maximum speed is somewhat less than its normal amount. Care should be taken, however, to make certain that this test switch is not released while the power lever is advanced or an actual overspeed situation can occur.

As another safeguard to prevent propeller overspeed conditions, a fuel topping governor is also installed on some PT6 engines. This governor also senses

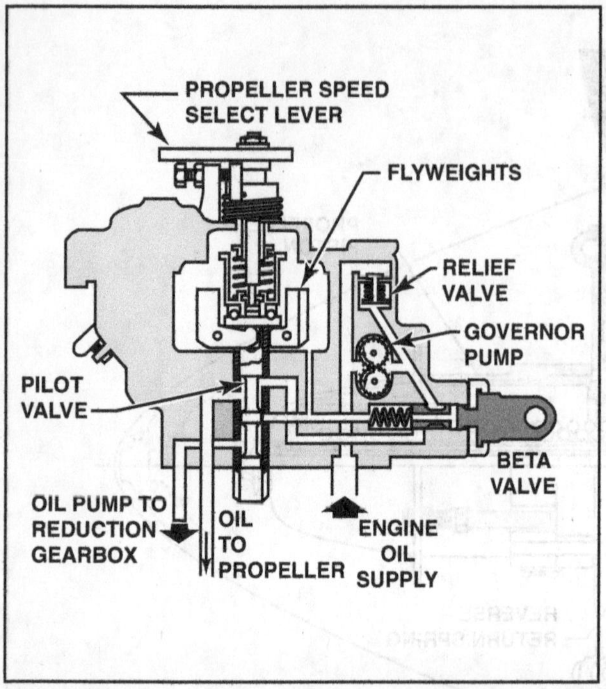


**Figure 12-55. The primary governor used on a PT6 engine uses a set of flyweights to sense engine speed and move a pilot valve to maintain a preset engine speed. To permit the governor to control blade angle in the Beta mode, a separate Beta valve is also incorporated.**

propeller speed. In the event that propeller speed exceeds the maximum limit of the overspeed governor, the fuel topping governor dumps a portion of bleed air from the fuel control unit. This action causes the fuel control to reduce fuel to the engine. The gas generator's speed is reduced, which, in turn, reduces the propeller speed.

## FUEL CONTROL UNIT

The fuel control unit is installed on the rear of the engine and is linked to the Beta valve on the primary propeller governor and to the Beta slip ring on the propeller through a cam assembly. The interconnection of the fuel control unit and the Beta valve and Beta slip ring is designed to provide input to the fuel control unit during operations in the Beta mode.

## COCKPIT CONTROLS

The cockpit controls for the PT6 turboprop consist of a power lever, a propeller control lever, and, in most installations, a fuel cutoff lever, or condition lever. The power lever controls a cam assembly on the engine. From the cam assembly, mechanical linkages connect to the fuel control unit and the Beta valve on the primary governor. In the Alpha mode, the power lever controls engine power output by adjusting the fuel control to schedule proper fuel flow for the desired gas generator performance. However, in the Beta mode, the power lever controls both the fuel control unit and the propeller blade angle.

The propeller control lever is connected to the primary propeller governor and adjusts the tension applied to the governor's speeder spring in the same manner as a conventional constant speed governor arrangement. Full aft movement of the propeller control lever causes the oil pressure to be dumped from the propeller piston, which permits the propeller to feather.

The fuel cutoff lever, or condition lever, which is typically used only on reversing propeller installations, has two functions. First, it provides a positive fuel shutoff at the fuel control unit, which enables the engine to be shut down. Second, the condition lever sets the gas generator's low and high idle speed. The two positions for the condition lever are LOW IDLE, which provides approximately 50 percent gas generator speed, and HIGH IDLE, which permits the engine to obtain approximately 70 percent gas generator speed. The LOW IDLE position is used during ground operations, and the HIGH IDLE position is used during flight. [Figure 12-57]

## SYSTEM OPERATION

The PT6 engine operates in either Alpha or Beta mode. The Beta mode on a PT6 typically includes

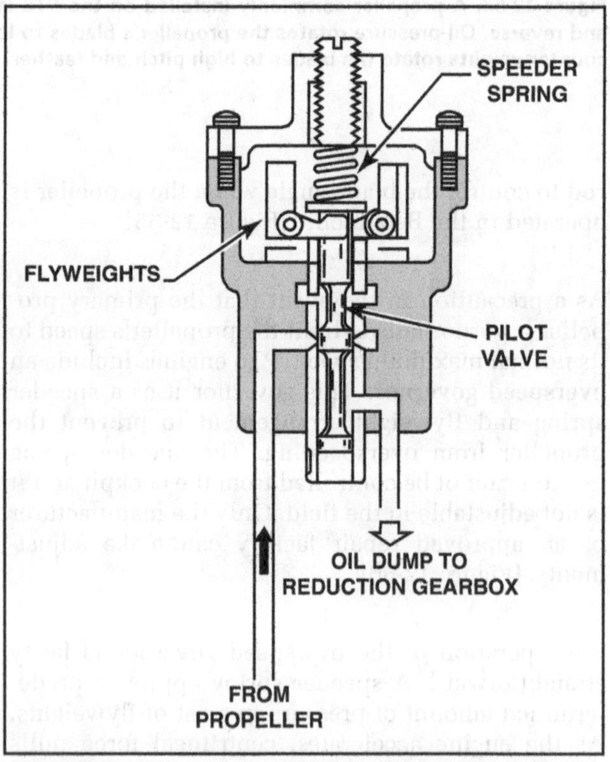


**Figure 12-56. As a backup to the primary governor, many PT6 engines incorporate an overspeed governor to prevent the propeller and engine from exceeding a maximum speed.**

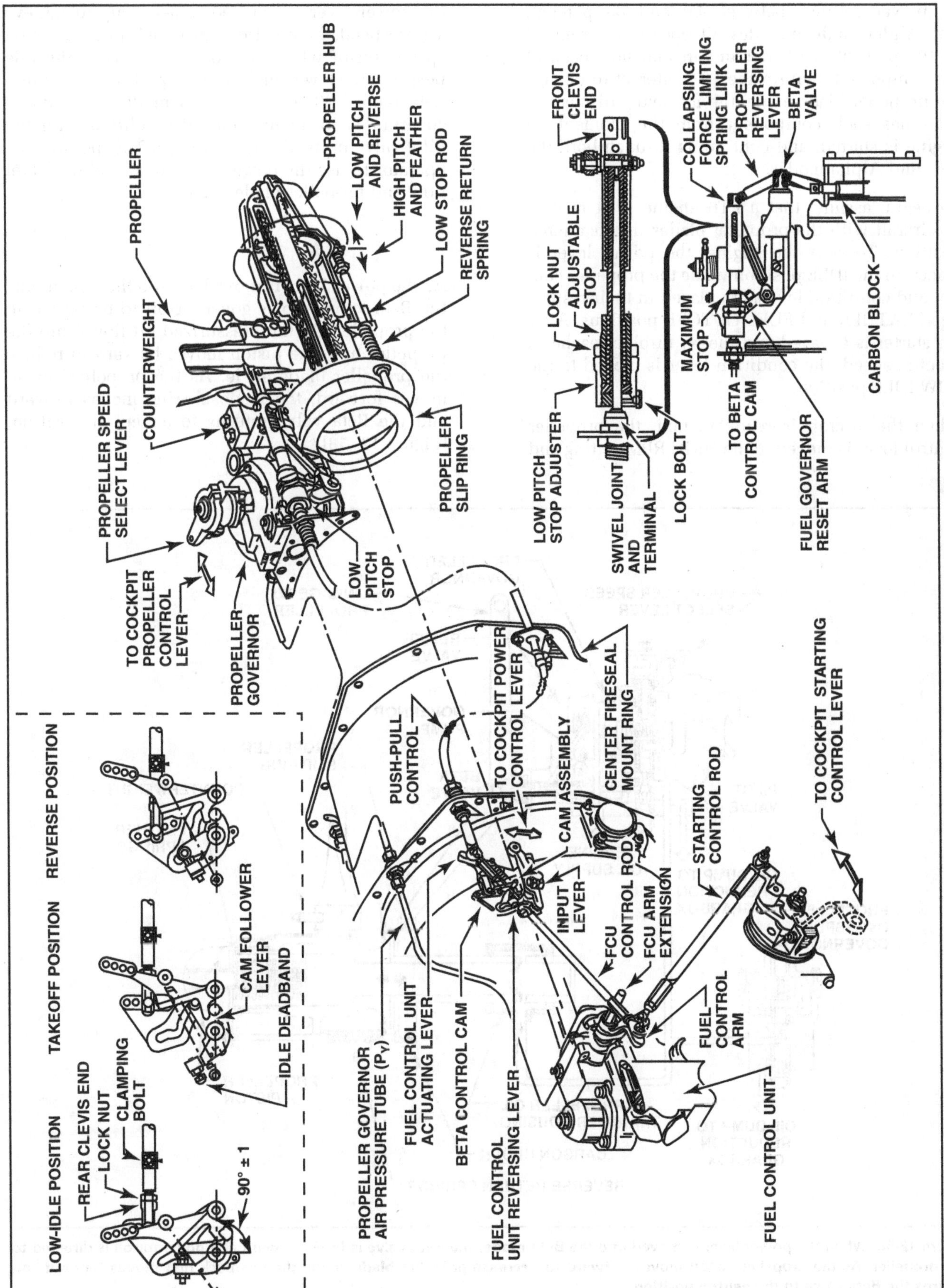


**Figure 12-57. The location of the components on a PT6 engine that are used to control engine speed and propeller pitch.**

all power settings between 50 and 85 percent. The Alpha mode includes all operations from 95 to 100 percent. To better understand how each of the components within the PT6 interact to change the propeller blade angle, the following discussion examines each component from the moment an engine is started, and continuing through both the Beta and Alpha modes.

To begin, assume that a PT6 engine is at rest on an aircraft with the propeller blades in a feathered position. To start the engine, the power lever is placed in the IDLE position while the propeller control and condition levers are placed in their respective FEATHER and FUEL CUTOFF positions. After the starter is engaged and the $N_1$ turbine reaches a specific speed, the condition lever is moved to the LOW IDLE position.

When the aircraft is ready to taxi, the propeller control lever is moved to the HIGH RPM setting and the power lever is adjusted as necessary to achieve a taxi speed. In situations in which excessive taxi speeds result when the power lever is in the idle position, the lever can be moved past the detent into Beta mode. When in the Beta mode, the primary governor is in an underspeed condition with the pilot valve in its lowered position. This permits the operator to use the power lever to control both fuel flow and propeller blade angle.

As the power lever is moved aft into the Beta mode, the Beta valve allows governor oil to be ported to the propeller. As the pressurized oil flows into the propeller hub, the piston moves forward to reduce the propeller blade angle. As the propeller piston moves forward, the feedback ring moves forward and the Beta valve returns to a neutral position. [Figure 12- 58]

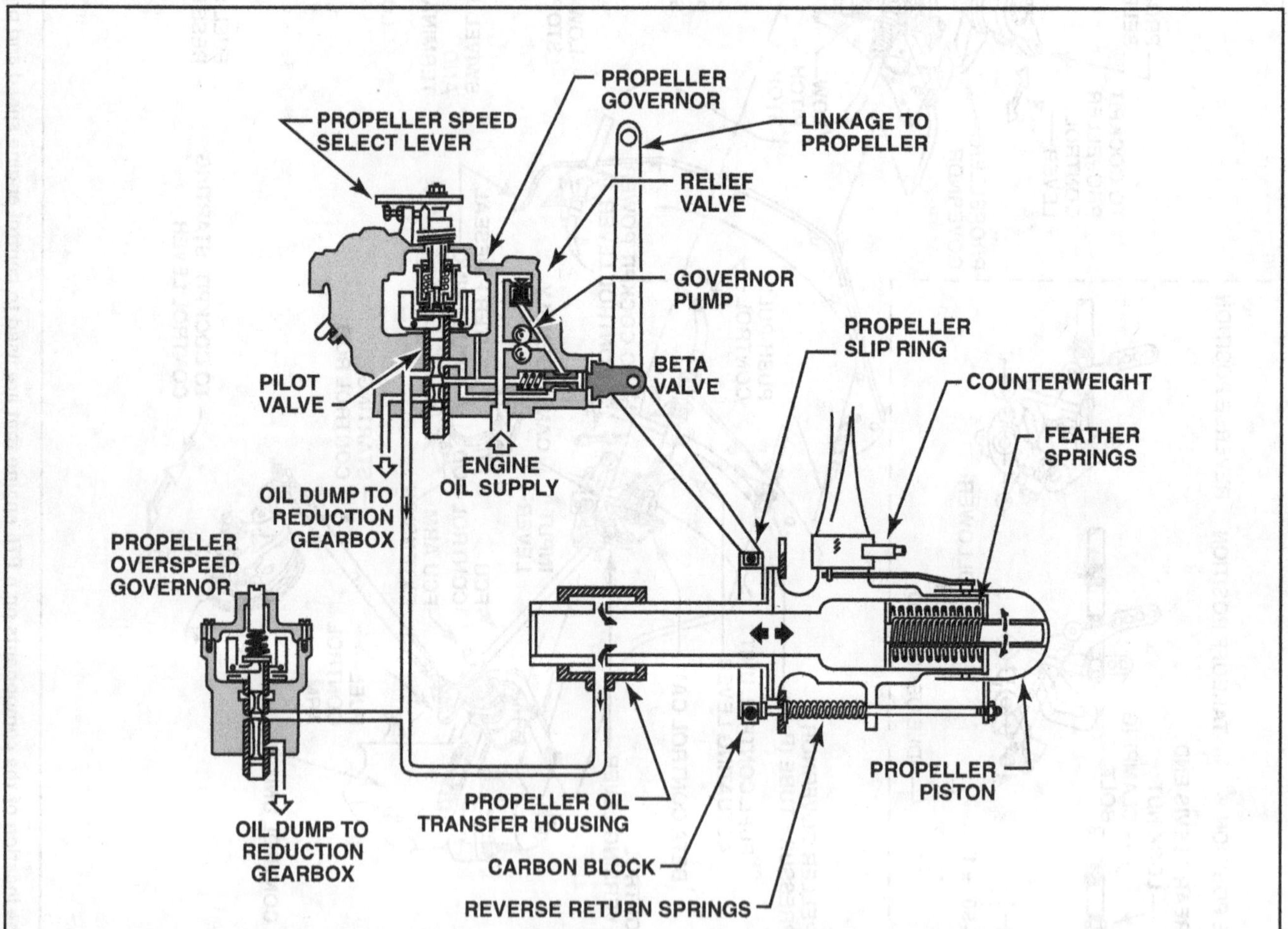


**Figure 12-58. When the power lever is moved into the Beta mode, the Beta valve is forced inward and governor oil is directed to the propeller. As the propeller piston moves outward to decrease propeller blade angle, the feedback ring moves forward and returns the Beta valve to the neutral position.**

To feather the propeller on a PT6 engine, the propeller control lever is moved full aft. This action causes the pilot valve in the primary governor to rise and permit the oil pressure in the propeller hub to return to the engine. With no oil pressure in the propeller hub, spring tension and centrifugal force act on the counterweights attached to the base of each blade to rotate them to the feathered position.

Before the propeller can be unfeathered, the engine must first be operating. After the engine is operating and the propeller is rotating, the propeller control lever is moved out of the feather position; pressurized oil rotates the blades to the selected blade angle or governor setting.

# SUMMARY CHECKLIST

✓ Propeller systems for turboprop engines require reduction gears to turn the propeller at a speed for optimal efficiency.

✓ On turboprop engines, the propeller governor and fuel control unit are interconnected for proper operation.

# KEY TERMS

free turbine
power turbine
Alpha range
Beta range
Beta for taxi range
Beta plus power range
negative-torque-sense system
NTS
thrust sensitive signal
TSS
spacer
Beta tube
underspeed governor
propeller pitch control
power lever
speed lever
condition lever
feedback ring
Beta slip ring
Beta valve
Beta lift rod
overspeed governor

# QUESTIONS

1. The blades of a ______________-type propeller can be rotated to a negative angle to produce reverse thrust.

2. The Beta mode of operation of a reversible propeller system is primarily the ________ (ground or flight) operation.

3. A negative torque signal (NTS) provides a signal which ______________ (increases or decreases) propeller blade angle to limit negative shaft torque.

4. If a power loss occurs during takeoff, the thrust sensitive signal of a turbo-propeller system causes the propeller to ______________ (what action) automatically.

5. During ground operation, the ________ (power or speed) lever used with a TPE-331 engine controls the propeller blade angle.

6. During flight operation, the ________ (power or speed) lever used with a TPE-331 engine sets the engine rpm by varying the propeller blade angle.

7. An electric pump is used to ______________ (feather or unfeather) the propeller on a TPE-331 engine.

8. The propeller shaft ________ (is or is not) connected to the gas generator turbine in a PT-6 engine.

9. The propeller governor on an airplane equipped with a PT-6 engine ________ (does or does not) function as a control unit when operating in the Beta mode.

10. Full aft movement of the ______________ (propeller or power) control lever causes the propeller system on a PT-6 engine to go into the feather position.

# SECTION E

## AUXILIARY PROPELLER SYSTEMS

Several auxiliary systems are installed in aircraft to improve propeller performance and enhance the aircraft's all-weather capabilities. For example, some aircraft incorporate a synchronization system designed to reduce propeller noise and vibration. Other systems remove ice from propeller blades to improve performance during flight in freezing precipitation.

## SYNCHRONIZATION SYSTEMS

Whenever an aircraft has more than one propeller, the potential for excessive vibration and noise exists. A contributing factor to this problem is dissimilar speed settings between the propellers. One way to reduce noise and vibration is to match, or **synchronize**, the speed settings on the engines. Several synchronization systems are in use on multiengine aircraft, including the master motor synchronization system, the one engine master control system, and the synchrophasing system. Synchronizing systems control engine speed and reduce vibration by setting all propellers to the same speed. These systems can be used for all flight operations except takeoff and landing.

### MASTER MOTOR SYNCHRONIZATION

An early type of synchronization system used on WWII four-engine aircraft consisted of a synchronizer master unit, four alternators, a master tachometer, a tachometer generator and contactor unit for each engine, an r.p.m. master control lever, and the associated switches and wiring. When activated, these components automatically control the speed of each engine and synchronize all engines at a selected speed.

The **synchronizer master unit** incorporates a **master motor** which mechanically drives four **contactor units**, each connected to an alternator. The frequency of the voltage produced by the alternator is directly proportional to the speed of the engine. When the system is activated, the desired engine speed is selected by manually adjusting the r.p.m. control lever until the master tachometer on the instrument panel indicates the desired speed. After the master motor speed is set, any difference in speed between an engine and the master motor causes the corresponding contactor unit to operate the pitch-change mechanism of the propeller until its engine speed matches that of the master motor.

### ONE ENGINE MASTER CONTROL SYSTEM

Many twin-engine aircraft are equipped with a one engine master control system. This system consists of a control box that includes a comparative circuit, a special **master governor** on the left engine, a **slave governor** on the right engine, and an activator in the right engine nacelle. Both governors incorporate a frequency generator that produces a frequency proportional to the engine's rotational speed. [Figure 12-59]

With this type of system, the frequency generators built into the propeller governors generate a signal that is sent to the control box. A comparison circuit in the control box compares the signal from the slave engine to the signal from the master engine. If a difference in engine speed exists, the control box sends a correcting signal to the actuator to adjust the slave governor until the engine speeds match. In most installations, the comparator circuit has a limited range of operation. For example, the slave engine must be within approximately 100 r.p.m. of the master engine for synchronization to occur. [Figure 12-60]

### SYNCHROPHASING

Synchrophasing systems are a refinement of propeller synchronization systems in that they permit the pilot to control the angular difference in the plane of rotation between propeller blades. This angular difference is known as **phase angle** and can be adjusted to achieve minimum noise and vibration levels. [Figure 12-61]

A typical synchrophasing system equips each engine with a magnetic pickup device known as a **pulse generator**. The pulse generator is keyed to the same blade of its respective propeller for comparison. As the designated blade of each propeller passes the pulse generator, an electric signal is sent to the phasing control unit. Consider a twin engine

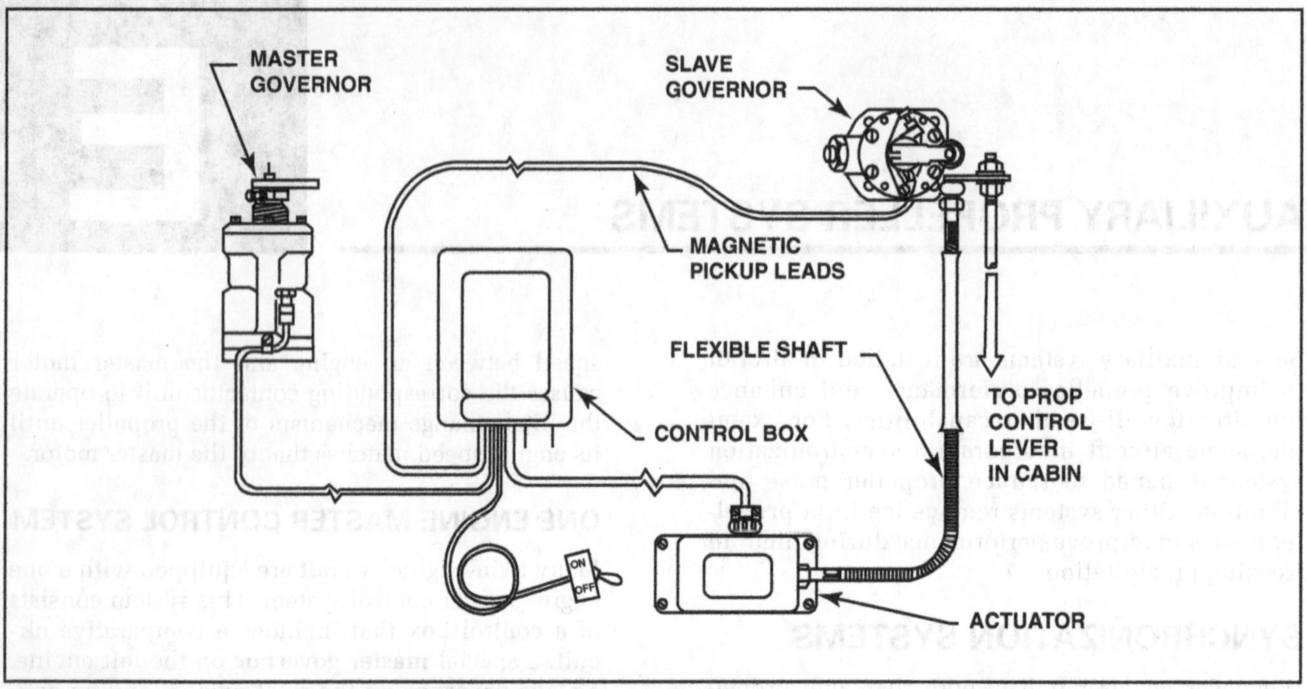


**Figure 12-59. The basic units of a light twin propeller synchronization system are a control box, master governor, slave governor, and actuator.**

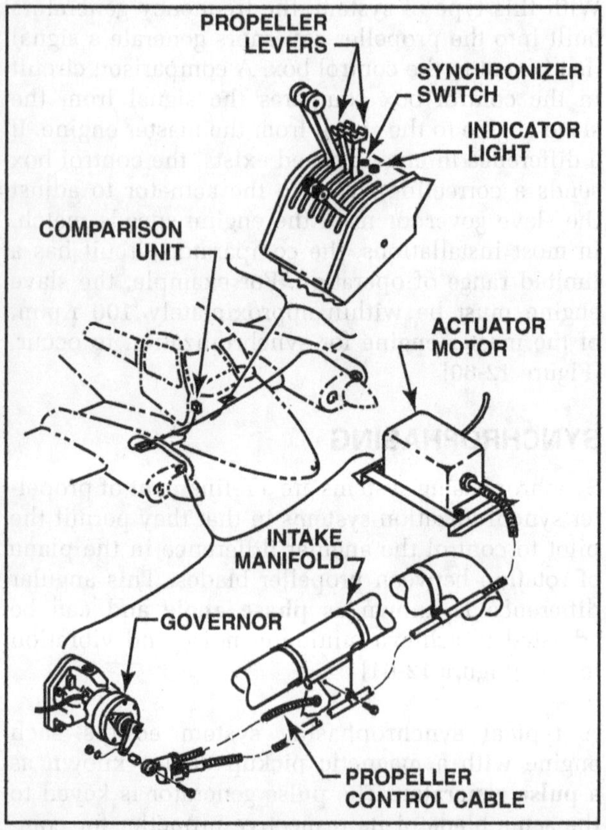


**Figure 12-60. This view of a propeller synchronizer system shows the location of various components installed in a light twin-engine aircraft.**

aircraft with pulse generators keyed to blade number one. Based on the electrical signal, the phasing control unit determines the relative position of each propeller's number one blade. A propeller manual phase control in the cockpit enables the pilot to manually select the phase angle that produces the minimum vibration and noise. The pulses from each engine are then compared, and, if a difference exists, the phasing control unit electrically drives the slave governor to establish the selected phase angle between propellers. [Figure 12-62]

## PROPELLER ICE CONTROL SYSTEMS

As aircraft use became more vital for moving cargo and passengers, the necessity to fly in inclement weather conditions became more important. However, before such operations could be conducted safely, the development of auxiliary systems was necessary to prevent or remove ice formations from an aircraft. If allowed to accumulate, ice can distort the airfoil shape of a propeller blade, causing a loss in propeller efficiency and thrust. Furthermore, because ice often forms unevenly on a propeller blade, it produces an unbalanced condition that can result in destructive vibration.

Currently, aircraft propellers can use either an anti-ice or a deice system. The difference between the two is that **anti-icing systems** prevent the formation of ice whereas **deicing systems** remove ice after it has accumulated.

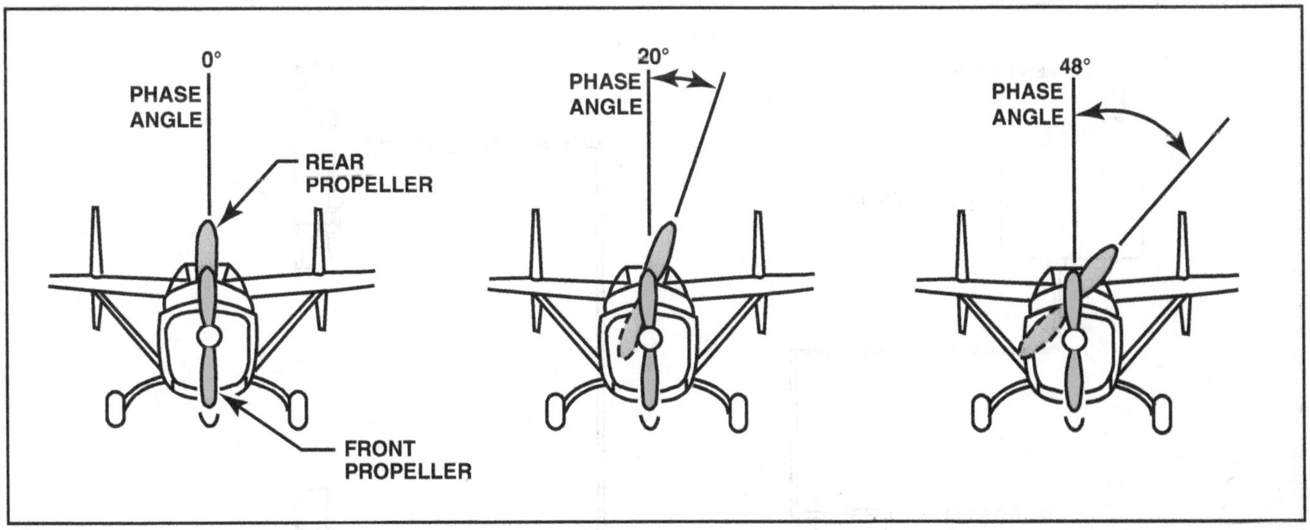


**Figure 12-61. Synchrophasing enables a pilot to adjust the phase angle between propellers for minimum noise and vibration levels.**

## FLUID ANTI-ICING

A typical fluid anti-icing system consists of a control unit, a tank that holds anti-icing fluid, a pump to deliver fluid to the propeller, and nozzles. The control unit determines pump output. Fluid is pumped from the tank to a stationary nozzle installed just behind the propeller on the engine nose case. As fluid passes through the nozzle, it enters a circular U-shaped channel called a **slinger ring**. A typical slinger ring is designed with a delivery tube for each propeller blade and is mounted on the rear of the propeller assembly. After the fluid is in the slinger ring, centrifugal force sends the anti-icing fluid out through the delivery tubes to each blade shank. [Figure 12-63]

In order to disperse the fluid to areas that are more prone to ice buildups, feed shoes are typically installed on the leading edge of each propeller blade. Each **feed shoe** consists of a narrow strip of rubber that extends from the blade shank. Feed shoes are molded with several parallel open channels along which centrifugal force directs fluid from the blade shank toward the blade tip. As anti-icing fluid flows along the channels, the relative wind also carries the fluid laterally from the channels over the leading edge of each blade. The most common anti-icing fluid is glycol-based.

## ELECTRIC DEICING

An electric propeller deicing system consists of a power source, power relay, resistance heating elements, system controls, and a timer or cycling unit. The resistance heating elements can be mounted

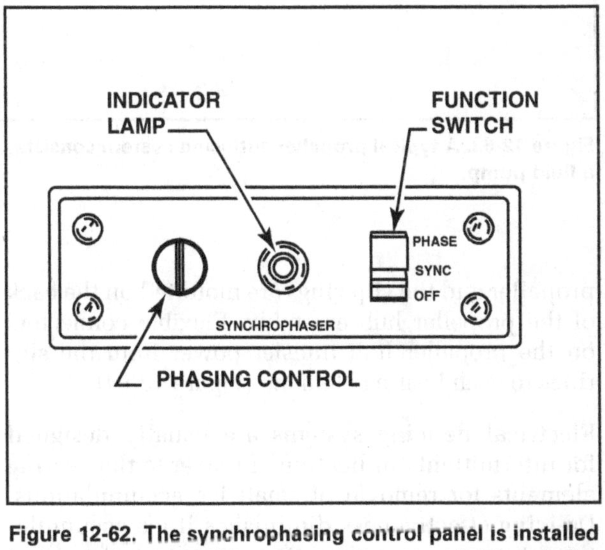


**Figure 12-62. The synchrophasing control panel is installed in the cockpit to enable crew members to adjust propeller blade phase angles in flight.**

either internally or externally on each propeller blade. Externally mounted heating elements are known as de-icing boots and are attached to each blade with an approved bonding agent. System controls include a power switch, loadmeter, and protective devices such as current limiters or circuit breakers. The loadmeter is an ammeter that permits monitoring of individual circuit currents and visual verification of proper timer operation.

A typical electric propeller de-ice system supplies aircraft system power to the propeller hub through a set of brush blocks and slip rings. The **brush blocks** are mounted on the engine case just behind the

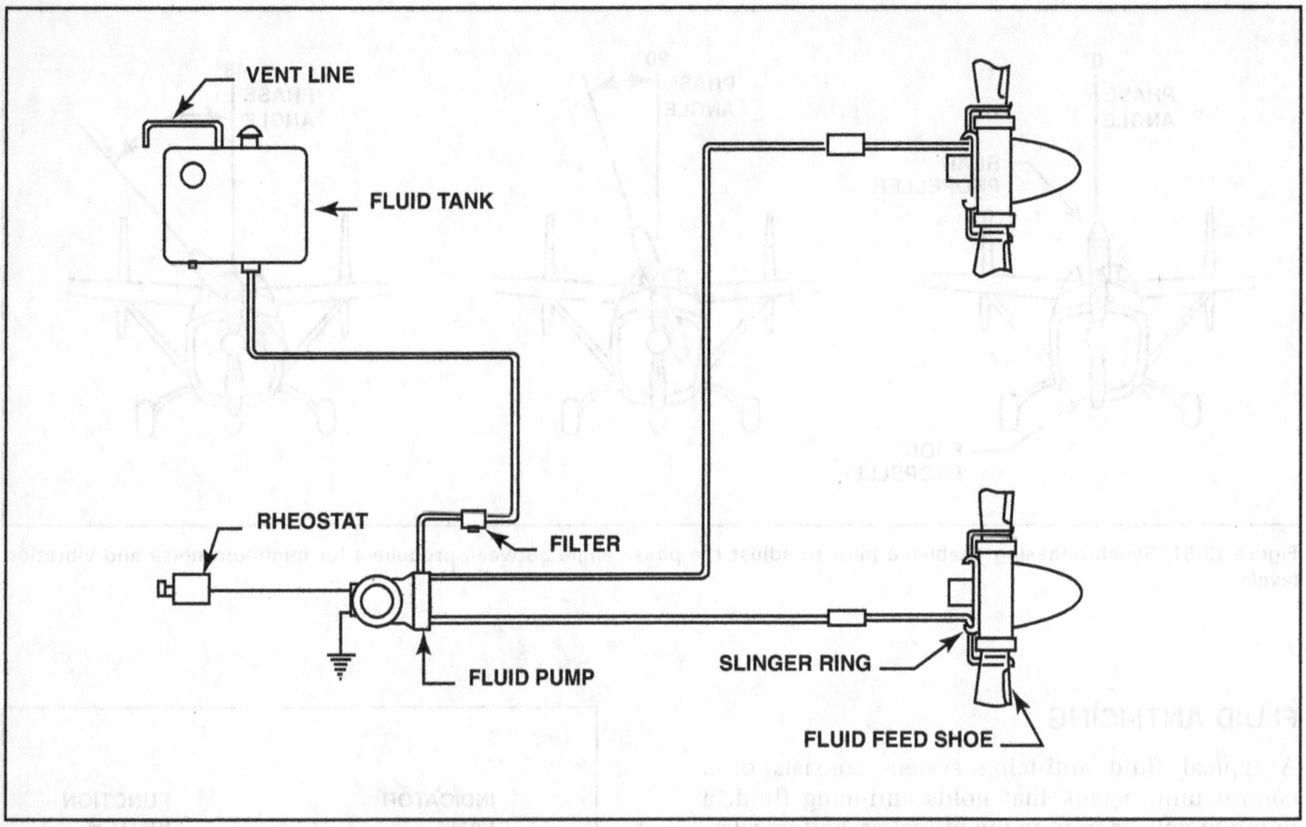


**Figure 12-63. A typical propeller anti-icing system consists of a fluid tank, a rheostat control, a slinger ring for each propeller, and a fluid pump.**

propeller and the **slip rings** are mounted on the back of the propeller hub assembly. Flexible connectors on the propeller hub transfer power from the slip rings to each heating element. [Figure 12-64]

Electrical de-icing systems are usually designed for intermittent application of power to the heating elements for removal of small ice accumulations. De-icing effectiveness diminishes if ice accumulations become excessive. Proper control of heating intervals is critical in the prevention of runback. **Runback** refers to a condition where melted ice reforms behind a blade's leading edge. Heat should be applied just long enough to melt the ice face in contact with the blade. If the applied heat is more than that required to loosen the ice, but insufficient to evaporate all the resulting water, water can run back over the unheated blade surface and freeze again. Runback can result in a dangerous build-up of ice on areas of the blade that lack de-icing protection.

In addition to preventing runback, heating intervals are carefully controlled to avoid excessive propeller vibrations. Ice accumulations must be removed from propeller blades evenly from opposite blades to prevent excessive vibration. This is accomplished through the use of timing circuits that cycle power in a predetermined sequence to blade heating elements. Cycling timers energize the heating elements for periods of 15 to 30 seconds with a complete cycle time of two minutes.

During preflight inspections, de-icing boots should be checked for proper warming sequences by activating the system and verifying that the boots provide heat. However, exercise caution and limit ground testing to prevent element overheating. Electric propeller de-icing systems are designed for use when the propellers are rotating and for short periods of time during ground runup.

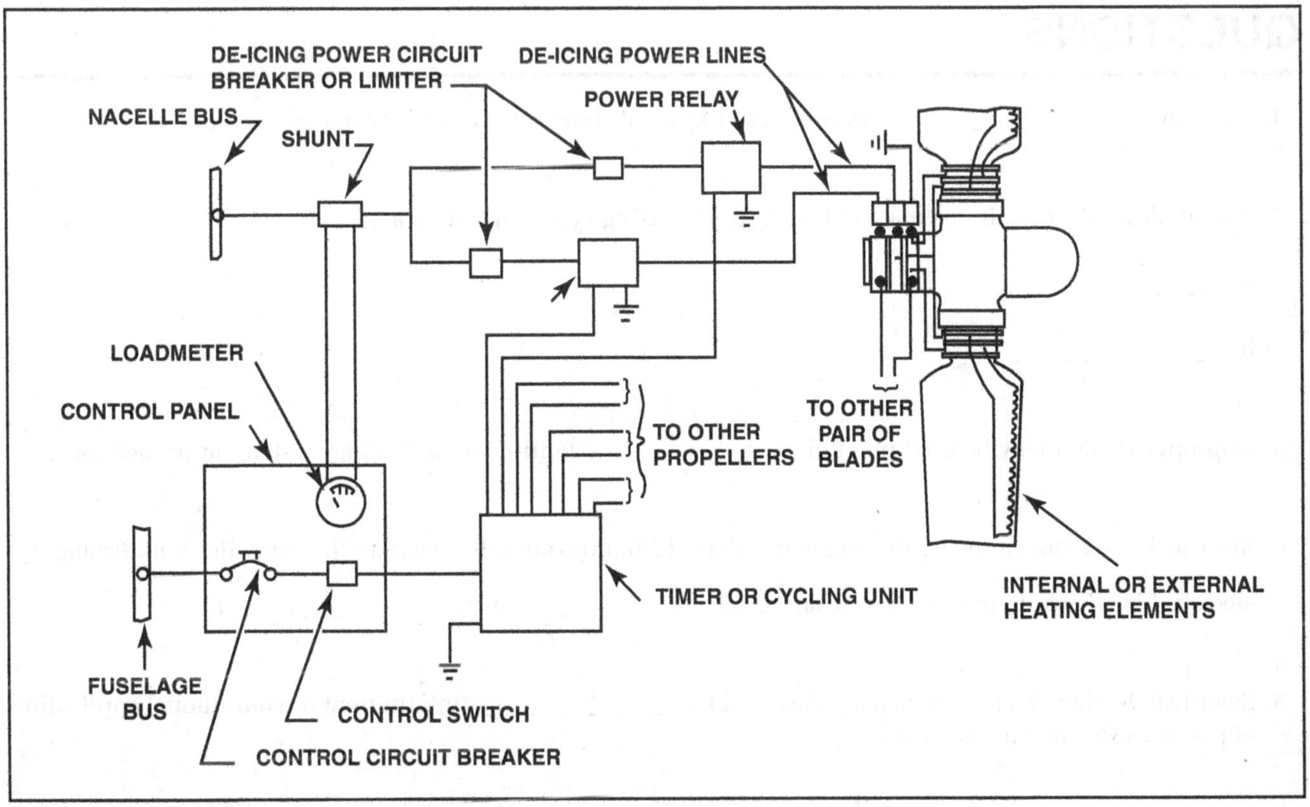


**Figure 12-64. Aircraft electrical power is used to operate this propeller de-icing system. When the timer closes the relay, electrical current flows to the carbon brushes, which pass current to the rotating slip rings on the propeller hub. Flexible connectors carry current from the slip rings to each heating element.**

# SUMMARY CHECKLIST

✓ Synchronizing systems adjust the speed settings of multiengine propellers to match each other, which reduces noise and vibration.

✓ Propeller ice control systems use deicing fluid or electric heaters to remove and prevent the formation of ice on blades.

# KEY TERMS

synchronize
synchronizer master unit
master motor
contactor units
master governor
slave governor
phase angle
pulse generator
anti-icing system
de-icing system
slinger ring
feed shoe
brush blocks
slip rings
runback

# QUESTIONS

1. The propeller ______________ system is used to set all propellers at exactly the same rpm.

2. Two undesirable conditions that are minimized by using synchrophasing are:

   a. ______________

   b. ______________

3. Isopropyl alcohol may be used in a fluid ______________ (anti-icing or deicing) system on propellers.

4 Electrical power for propeller deicing is transferred from the aircraft system to the propeller hub through electrical leads which terminate in what units? _______ _______ and _______ _______

5. Electrical deicing systems are usually designed for ______________ (intermittent or continuous) application of power to the heating elements.

SECTION F

# PROPELLER INSPECTION, MAINTENANCE, AND INSTALLATION

As an aviation maintenance technician, you are likely to inspect and perform routine maintenance on various types of propellers. Therefore, in addition to being familiar with propeller maintenance procedures, you must possess a basic knowledge of the maintenance regulations concerning propellers. A certified aircraft maintenance technician with a powerplant rating is authorized to perform only minor repairs and minor alternations to propellers.

## MAINTENANCE REGULATIONS

14 CFR 43, Maintenance, Preventative Maintenance, Rebuilding, and Alteration, defines the different classes of maintenance for propeller systems. Appendix D contains the minimum requirements for the 100-hour and annual inspections of propellers and their controls. For example, as a minimum during an annual or 100-hour inspection, you must check propeller assemblies for cracks, nicks, and oil leakage. In addition, you must inspect bolts for proper torque and appropriate mechanical safety. If the propeller is equipped with anti-icing devices, you are required to inspect those devices for improper operations and obvious defects. You are also required to inspect propeller control mechanisms for improper operation, insecure mounting, and restricted travel.

Appendix A of 14 CFR 43 lists propeller major alterations and repairs that can be performed only by the manufacturer or an approved certified repair station. Propeller major alterations include changes in blade design, hub design, and governor or control design. Also included in the list are installations of propeller governors, feathering systems, deicing systems, and parts not approved for the propeller. For wood propellers, major repairs include items such as retipping, replacement of fabric covering, and inlay work. Replacing outer laminations and repairing elongated bolt holes in a hub are also major repairs. Any repairs to or straightening of steel propeller blades is a major repair, as are repairs to, or machining of, a steel hub. For aluminum propeller blades, major repairs include shortening or straightening of blades and repairing deep dents, cuts, scars, and nicks.

Other major repairs listed in Appendix A include controllable pitch propeller overhauls, repair of propeller governors, and the repair or replacement of internal blade elements such as internal deice heating elements. Given the number of items that are considered major repairs or alterations to propellers, you might have difficulty knowing whether a specific repair or alteration is major or minor. If you are in doubt about the status of a contemplated alteration or repair, contact your local Flight Standards District Office or equivalent regulatory office.

## AUTHORIZED MAINTENANCE PERSONNEL

Except when working under the authority of a certified repair station or the manufacturer, you are restricted from performing major propeller alterations or repairs. However, you are permitted to perform minor repairs and alterations. In addition, you may install a propeller and its related components as well as perform a 100-hour inspection. An aviation maintenance technician holding an Inspection Authorization may perform an annual inspection on a propeller and related components. Remember that after major repairs and alterations to propellers and related parts and appliances, only an appropriately rated facility, such as a propeller repair station or the propeller manufacturer, may return these parts to service.

## INSPECTION AND MAINTENANCE

Specific inspection items and minor maintenance tasks vary depending on the type of propeller and its accessories. The following discussion provides generic information on typical inspection and maintenance procedures. Always consult the appropriate aircraft or propeller maintenance manuals and service bulletins for specific instructions and service limits.

### WOOD PROPELLERS

A fixed-pitch wood propeller is relatively simple; however, its fine details of construction require close visual inspection. For example, at 100-hour and annual inspections you will check for cracks and nicks, and verify that bolts are properly tightened and secured. While the required visual inspections are mostly conducted with the propeller mounted on the engine, you might occasionally need to remove the propeller. For example, if excessive vibration is detected or reported, you might need to remove the propeller to check for elongated mounting bolt holes or proper balance.

Before you begin a propeller inspection, you should clean it. Use a brush or cloth and clean warm water and soap to clean wood propellers. If the aircraft operates near salt water, the propeller should be flushed with fresh water regularly. If visual inspection after cleaning reveals defects that must be further examined or repaired, you might need to remove the propeller. Removing a wood propeller is usually a simple matter of removing the spinner, safety devices such as cotter pins or wire, and the mounting bolts. In all instances, follow the removal procedures recommended in the maintenance instructions for the aircraft and engine.

Common defects found in wood propellers include separation between laminations and dents or bruises on the surface. Cracks or scars across the blade back or face, broken sections, warping, and worn or oversize center bore and bolt holes are also possible. If you find a dent, bruise, or scar on a blade surface, inspect the damage with a magnifying glass while flexing the blade to expose any cracks.

When inspecting metal tipping, look for looseness or slipping, loose screws or rivets, and cracks in the solder joints. Cracks in a solder joint near the blade tip indicate possible wood deterioration. Therefore, inspect the area near a crack closely while applying pressure to the blade tip. If you find no defects, you can resolder the joint; you should also recommend more frequent inspections of the blade tips to check for a recurrence of cracking. [Figure 12-65]

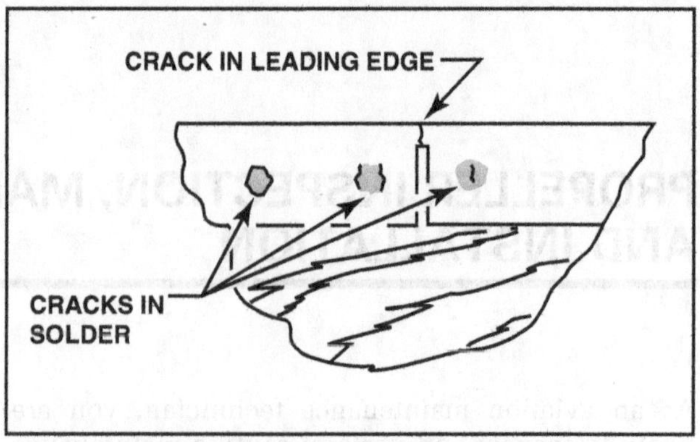


**Figure 12-65. The metal tipping on a wood propeller should be inspected for cracks in the leading edge and in the solder that covers the retaining screws. If you locate a crack, closely inspect the area near the crack.**

When you inspect wooden blades on a ground-adjustable propeller, give special attention to the metal sleeve and shank area. The presence of cracks in these areas might indicate broken or loose lag screws.

## REPAIRS

Typically, small cracks parallel to the grain or small cuts on a wood propeller can be repaired by working resin glue into the crack. After the glue dries, sand the area with fine sandpaper and refinish it with an approved varnish. Repairable tip fabric defects include cracks, bubbles, paint chipping, and wrinkles that appear when the tip is twisted or flexed. If the tip fabric has surface defects of 3/4 inch or less, and you do not suspect a breakdown in the wood structure, you can fill the defect with several coats of lacquer. After the lacquer dries, blend in the defect with the fabric surface. Refer any defects larger than 3/4 inch to a repair station.

Typically, separations in the outer lamination are repairable. However, a certified propeller repair station or the manufacturer must do the repair. Additional repairs that a propeller repair station or the propeller manufacturer can make include large cracks that require an inlay or restoration of elongated bolt holes with metal inserts. In addition, broken sections might be repairable, depending on the location and severity of the break; however, only a repair station or the manufacturer can determine reparability.

The final step of repair work to a wooden propeller blade is to apply a protective coating. Be aware that, restoration of the protective coating could change the propeller blade balance. Therefore, you must check propeller balance after the blade is refinished. If an out-of-balance condition exists, you might need to apply more protective coating on one of the blades to achieve a balance condition. More information on propeller balancing procedures is provided later in this section.

As with all propellers, some defects cannot be repaired. For wooden propellers these include:

- A crack or deep cut across the grain.
- A split blade.
- Separated laminations, except for the outside laminations of a fixed-pitch propeller.
- Empty screw or rivet holes.

- Any appreciable warp.
- An appreciable portion of missing wood..
- An oversized crankshaft bore in a fixed-pitch propeller.
- Cracks between the crankshaft bore hole and bolt holes.
- Cracked internal laminations.
- Oversized or excessively elongated bolt holes.

### STORAGE

Store wood propellers in an area that is cool, dark, dry, and well ventilated. Propellers should be placed in a horizontal position to maintain an even distribution of water throughout the wood. Do not wrap propellers in any material that seals them from airflow; an airtight wrapping promotes decay.

## ALUMINUM PROPELLERS

The properties of aluminum alloy make it a good material for propellers that are durable and relatively inexpensive to maintain. However, some types of damage can lead to blade failure. Therefore, aluminum propellers must be carefully inspected at regular intervals. In addition, if any damage is discovered that jeopardizes the integrity of a propeller, it must be repaired before further flight.

### BLADE INSPECTION

For both annual and 100-hour inspections, you are required to check aluminum propellers for cracks, nicks, and properly tightened and secured bolts. As with inspections of wood propellers you will carry out most inspections of a fixed-pitch aluminum propeller while it is attached to the engine. However, if operational problems such as vibrations occur, you might need to remove the propeller for a detailed inspection of the hub area.

Removal procedures for a fixed-pitch aluminum propeller are the same as for a fixed-pitch wood propeller. Be aware that an aluminum propeller might be heavier than a comparably sized wood propeller. If necessary, obtain help to support the propeller during removal and to prevent damage to the propeller and avoid personal injury.

Prior to the inspection, clean the aluminum propeller a solution of mild soap and water using a soft brush or cloth to remove all dirt and grease. Never use acid or caustic cleaning materials on aluminum propellers because they can corrode the metal. Furthermore, avoid using power buffers, steel wool, steel brushes, or any other abrasive that could scratch or mar the blades. If a propeller has been exposed to salt water, flush it with fresh water until all traces of salt are gone. This should be done as soon as possible after exposure to salt spray.

After the aluminum blades are clean, inspect the propeller for pitting, nicks, dents, cracks, and corrosion. Areas that are especially susceptible to damage include the leading edges and the blade face. To aid in the inspection process, you should inspect the entire propeller with a magnifying glass of at least four-power. If you suspect a crack, perform a dye penetrant inspection to verify. In many cases, a dye penetrant inspection enables you to determine whether visible lines and other marks are cracks or only scratches.

Inspect the hub boss for damage and corrosion inside the center bore and on the surfaces that mount on the crankshaft. Also, inspect the bolt holes for cracks, excessive wear, and proper dimensions. Clean any light corrosion from the hub boss with sandpaper, and then paint or treat the affected area to prevent further corrosion. If the propeller has sustained damage, dimensional wear, or heavy corrosion in the boss area, refer it to a repair station for repair.

### REPAIRS

If your inspection reveals surface damage such as nicks, scratches, or gouges on an aluminum-alloy propeller blade, make repairs as soon as possible. By making prompt repairs, you eliminate stress concentration points that can lead to cracks and fatigue failure. You can dress out defects on a blade's leading and trailing edges with a combination of round and half round files. When you complete a repair, blend it smoothly with the edge to remove sharp edges or angles. In all cases, the repair of surface defects on aluminum propeller blades must be made parallel to the length of the blade. In addition, the approximate maximum allowable size for a typical field repair on a propeller edge is less than or equal to 1/8 inch deep and 1 1/2 inches in length. [Figure 12-66]

When you are repairing the face and back of a blade, use a spoon-like **riffle file** to dish out the damaged area. The maximum allowable repair size of a typical surface defect on a blade face or back is 1/16 inch deep by 3/8 inch wide by 1 inch long. After you remove the damage, finish by polishing with very fine sandpaper in a direction parallel to the length of the blade. After the surface is sanded, treat it with **Alodine®** and then apply paint or another approved protective coating. [Figure 12-67]

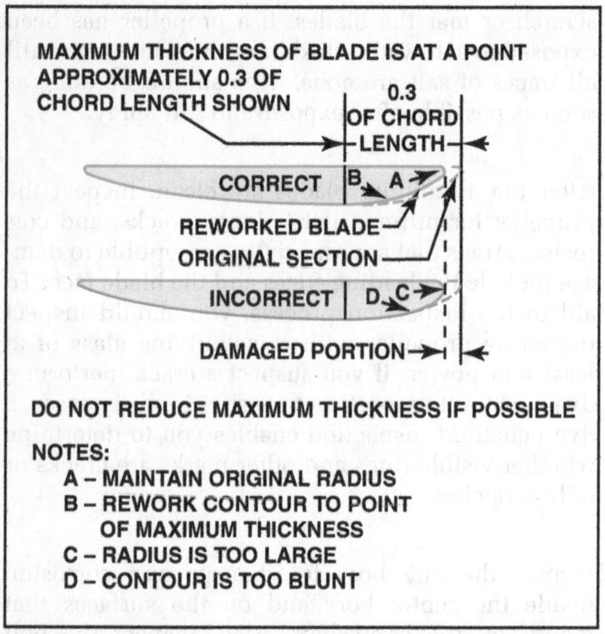


**Figure 12-66. When repairing the leading or trailing edge of a propeller, ensure that the repair does not exceed the propeller blade's minimum dimensions or change the profile of its leading edge.**

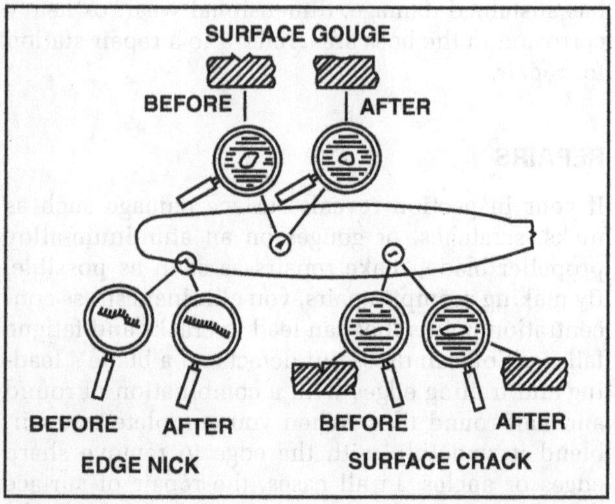


**Figure 12-67. Repairs on the blade face and leading edge should blend into the blade profile to maintain smooth airflow over the propeller.**

Because all forces acting on a propeller blade concentrate at the shank, any damage in this area is critical. Damage in the shank area of a propeller blade cannot be repaired in the field; the propeller must be sent to an approved overhaul facility for corrective action. Furthermore, transverse cracks of any size render an aluminum alloy blade irreparable.

In some cases, bent blades can be repaired. To determine whether a blade is repairable, measure the thickness of the blade where the bend is located. Then determine the blade station of the bend by measuring from the center of the hub to the center of the bend. With the center of the bend located, mark the blade one inch on each side of the bend and measure the bend angle at these tangent points. [Figure 12-68]

Many propeller manufacturers furnish charts to identify whether a bend is repairable. In most cases, the chart consists of a graph with the blade station on one axis and the degree of bend on the opposite axis. Any bend below the graph line is repairable; any bend above the line is not repairable. If a chart is not available, contact a propeller repair station for a decision before shipping a propeller for straightening. [Figure 12-69]

After you repair an aluminum propeller, clean the propeller with an approved solvent to remove all traces of any dye penetrant materials. If the propeller was painted, repaint the face of each blade with one coat of zinc chromate primer and two coats of flat black lacquer from the six inch station to the tip. The back of each blade should have the last four inches of the tip painted with one coat of zinc chromate primer and two coats of a high visibility or contrasting color.

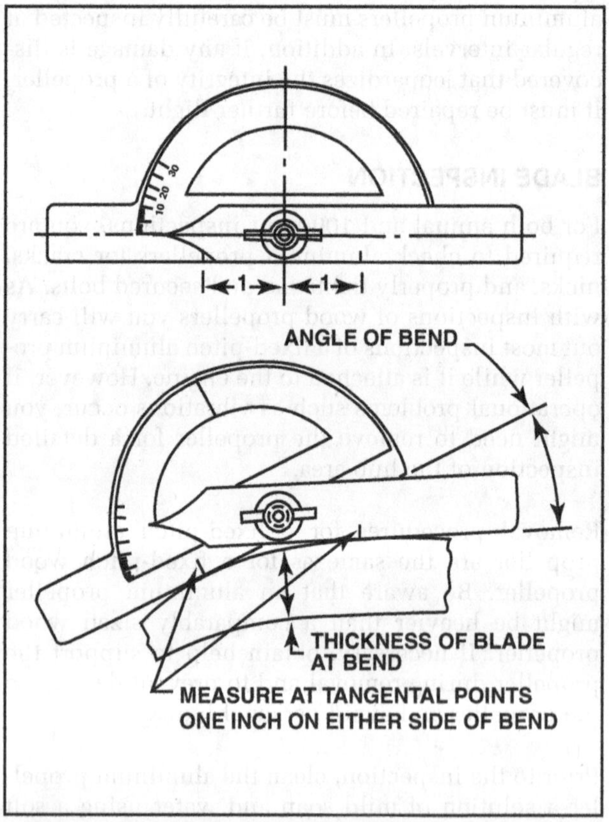


**Figure 12-68. Use a protractor to determine the amount of bend in a propeller blade. Place the hinge over the center of the bend and set the protractor legs to touch the blade one inch on each side of the bend centerline. Read the amount of bend in degrees on the protractor.**

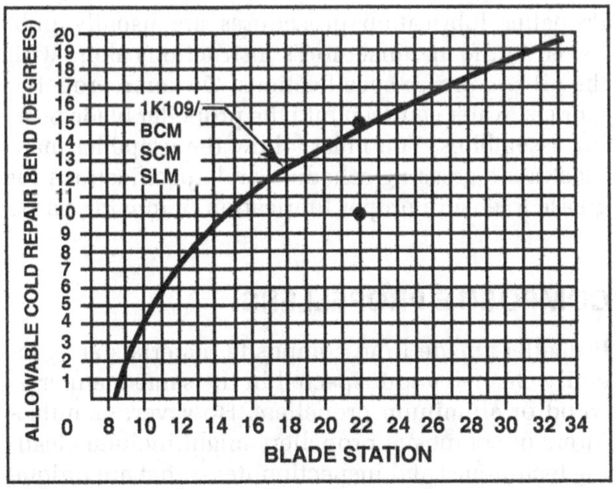


**Figure 12-69. This chart shows the amount of bend damage at a given blade station that can be repaired by cold bending. Values below the curve are repairable. For example, a 10-degree bend at blade station 22 can be repaired by cold bending; however, a 15-degree bend at station 22 cannot.**

If a high polish is desired, several grades of commercial metal polish are available. After you complete the polishing operation, remove all traces of polish.

## GROUND-ADJUSTABLE PROPELLERS

When inspecting a ground-adjustable propeller, inspect the blades in the same manner as discussed earlier, but pay particular attention to the areas around the retention shoulders at the base of the blades. The corresponding blade retention areas of the hubs should also be closely inspected. A dye-penetrant inspection is recommended on the external surfaces in these areas during routine, 100-hour, and annual inspections. Unless complete disassembly of the propeller is necessary for other reasons, disassembly is not recommended at these inspection intervals. [Figure 12-70]

## McCAULEY CONSTANT-SPEED PROPELLERS

Constant-speed propellers require a more detailed inspection and, in general, more maintenance than fixed-pitch propellers. For example, oil leaking from the propeller hub might indicate a defective piston-to-cylinder O-ring. On some models, the O-ring can be replaced in the field by a technician following the procedures outlined in the propeller or aircraft service manual. On other models, the propeller must be returned to a propeller repair facility. Any leaking seals other than the piston-to-cylinder O-ring require replacement by a propeller repair facility.

On certain models of McCauley propellers, the hub breather holes are sealed, and the hub is partially

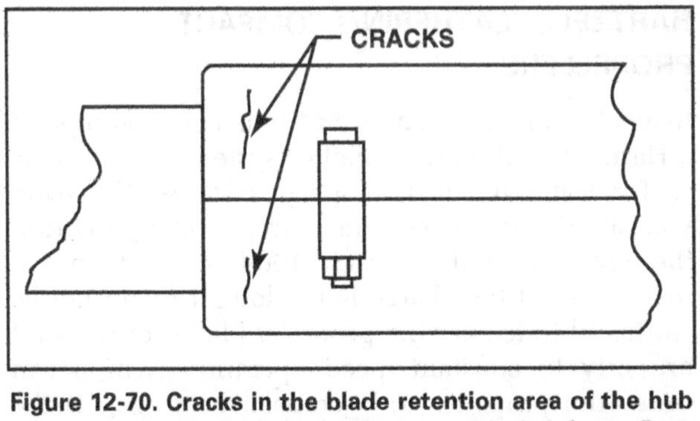


**Figure 12-70. Cracks in the blade retention area of the hub of a ground-adjustable propeller are critical defects. Dye-penetrant inspection methods are used to detect such cracks.**

filled with oil that is dyed red. The red dye makes the location of developing cracks apparent; if you detect red dye, remove the propeller from service.

## HARTZELL CONSTANT-SPEED PROPELLERS

Hartzell constant-speed propeller systems require similar inspections, maintenance, and repair as that required by other constant-speed systems. However, an additional recommended inspection is to check steel hub propellers for cracks. Magnetic particle inspection is the preferred method of inspection when checking steel propeller hubs for cracks.

If you detect grease leakage on a Hartzell propeller, determine the cause and correct it as soon as possible. The most common cause of a grease leak is a loose, missing, or defective grease fitting, or **zerk**. Other causes could be loose blade clamps, defective blade clamp seals, or overlubrication of the blade-to-hub joints.

If a zerk fitting is loose, missing, or defective, tighten or replace it as appropriate. Loose blade clamps should be tightened to the specified value and then secured. Check the blade angle to verify that it did not change during tightening.

When servicing a Hartzell constant-speed propeller, take care when lubricating the blade-to-hub joints to prevent damage to the blade seals. First, remove one of the two hub zerk fittings for each blade. Next, grease the blade-to-hub joint through the remaining zerk. Some propeller models should be serviced until grease comes out of the hole from which the zerk was removed; other models require less grease. The manufacturer's recommended procedures are established to prevent excessive pressure from building up in the blade grease chamber and damaging the blade seals. After lubrication, reinstall the zerk fittings, replace the protective cap, and secure the cap to the zerk fitting with safety wire.

## HARTZELL FEATHERING COMPACT PROPELLERS

Inspection, maintenance, and repair procedures for a Hartzell feathering propeller system are the same as for Hartzell constant-speed systems. However, you should also check the nitrogen charge within the propeller hub at each 100-hour and annual inspection. If the charge is too low, it might not be sufficient to feather the propeller blades or respond properly to constant-speed operation (which can cause the propeller to overspeed or surge). If the charge is too high, the propeller system might not reach full speed and might feather at engine shutdown. Before checking the nitrogen charge, ensure that the blades are latched in their low pitch position. Follow the manufacturer's instructions to service with nitrogen.

## HAMILTON- STANDARD HYDROMATIC PROPELLERS

Hydromatic propellers are inspected, maintained, and repaired similar to other constant-speed systems. Inspections primarily involve a check for proper operation, looking for oil leaks, and inspecting external oil lines for signs of deterioration or abrasion.

Oil leaks in the propeller are normally caused by a defective gasket or loose hardware. If oil covers the entire propeller, the likely cause is a leaking dome plug. If oil appears on the barrel immediately behind the dome, the dome gasket is likely leaking or the dome nut is loose. Oil leakage around the rear cone usually indicates a defective spider-shaft oil seal. The dome plug seal and the dome-to-barrel gasket are field repairable.

Signs of leaking oil around the blade shank area or between the barrel halves might indicate loose hub bolts or defective gaskets. You can retighten loose hub bolts, but leaking gaskets must be replaced at an overhaul facility. Because the Hydromatic propeller is lubricated by engine operating oil, it requires no other lubrication.

## PROPELLER LUBRICATION

All adjustable pitch propeller systems discussed require inspection and service at regular intervals. Lubrication is, in many cases, one of the required servicing procedures. The grease used to lubricate a propeller must have the proper anti-friction and plasticity characteristics. In other words, an approved grease reduces the frictional resistance of moving parts and molds easily into any form under pressure.

Propeller lubrication procedures are usually published in the manufacturer's instructions along with the oil and grease specifications. On some propeller models, water can seep into the propeller blade bearing assemblies. You must follow the propeller manufacturer's greasing schedule and specifications for grease to ensure proper lubrication of moving parts.

## COMPOSITE PROPELLERS

Propellers made from composite materials are generally cleaned and inspected in the same manner as wood or aluminum propellers. However, manufacturers of composite propellers might include cleaning techniques and inspection items that are unique to the materials in use. Manufacturer's instructions take precedence over general cleaning and inspection techniques.

With these propellers, some field repairs might be approved, but most typically require that a maintenance technician has received specific training. Generally, a maintenance technician is restricted to inspections and cleaning. Any major repairs made to correct defects in composite propellers must be accomplished by an appropriately rated repair station or the manufacturer.

## BLADE CUFF INSPECTION

Some propeller blades are fitted with blade cuffs to improve airflow over the blade shank and increase cooling airflow through the engine. When installed, blade cuffs must be inspected and checked for proper clearance. Longitudinal clearance of constant-speed propeller blades or cuffs must be at least 1/2 inch between propeller parts and stationary parts of the aircraft. This clearance must be measured with the propeller blades feathered or in the most critical pitch configuration.

## GOVERNORS

As mentioned earlier, an aviation maintenance technician is somewhat limited with regard to maintaining propeller systems. This is especially true of propeller governors. Inspection of governors is usually limited to checking the security of mounting and looking for oil leaks. Maintenance is limited to rigging the governor controls and verifying freedom of motion. Although you are permitted to remove and install a propeller governor on an engine, inspections and repairs that require governor disassembly must be carried out by a properly equipped and certified repair station.

## BALANCING

Propeller balance is critical to proper engine and propeller performance. Whenever maintenance is conducted or a repair is made that adds or removes weight from a propeller, you must check the propeller's balance. For example, if a wood propeller is refinished, the new varnish can create an imbalance if it is unevenly applied. In another example, a metal blade that is shortened because of tip damage requires shortening of the opposite blade to maintain balance.

Propellers are balanced both statically and dynamically. A propeller is in **static balance** when its center of gravity coincides with its axis of rotation. A propeller is in **dynamic balance** when the center of gravity of each individual propeller blade rotates in the same plane.

### STATIC BALANCE

You determine static balance by supporting the propeller with a knife-edge or by using the suspension method. Of the two methods for static balancing, the knife-edge is simpler and more accurate.

A test stand consisting of two hardened steel edges is used to balance a propeller with the knife-edge method. The test stand should be located in a room or area that is free from any air motion or heavy vibration. Before checking a propeller's balance, verify that the blade angles are all the same. If the blade angles are correct, use the following steps to check the static balance.

Insert a bushing in the propeller hub bore hole. Insert a mandrel or arbor through the bushing to support the propeller on the balance knives. Place the propeller assembly with the arbor on the test stand. The propeller must be free to rotate.

To check a two-bladed propeller assembly for vertical balance, position one blade in the vertical position. If the propeller is balanced vertically, it will remain in a vertical position regardless of which blade is pointing up. If a vertical imbalance exists, the propeller will have a tendency to come to rest in a horizontal position. Next, repeat the check with the blade positions reversed. [Figure 12-71]

To check a two-bladed propeller assembly for horizontal balance, position the propeller in a horizontal position. If the propeller is horizontally balanced, it will remain parallel to the floor. If a horizontal imbalance exists, one blade will tend to move downward causing the propeller to come to rest in a vertical position. [Figure 12-72]

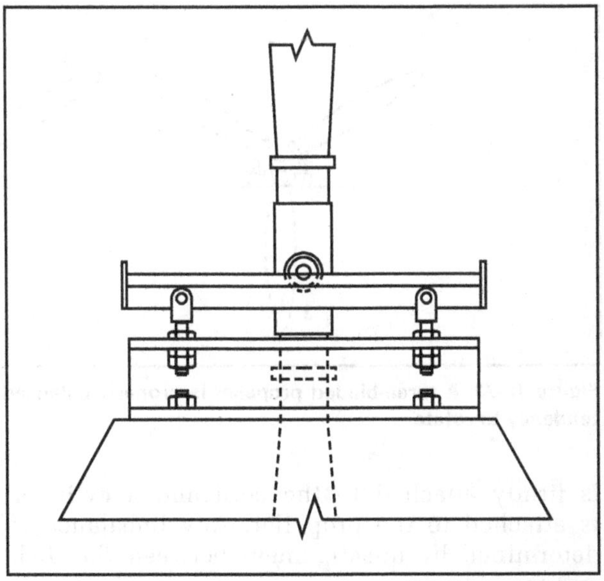

**Figure 12-71. In a vertical balance check, the propeller blades are aligned vertically and an imbalance condition causes them to rotate.**

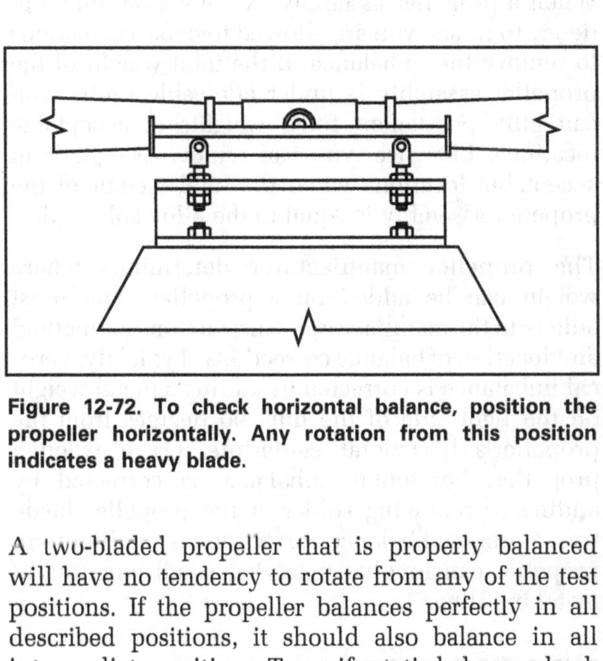

**Figure 12-72. To check horizontal balance, position the propeller horizontally. Any rotation from this position indicates a heavy blade.**

A two-bladed propeller that is properly balanced will have no tendency to rotate from any of the test positions. If the propeller balances perfectly in all described positions, it should also balance in all intermediate positions. To verify static balance, check for balance in four or five intermediate positions.

Static balancing of a three-bladed propeller requires checking the propeller in three test positions. First, rotate the propeller until blade number one is pointing down. Subsequently place blade numbers two and three pointing down. A properly balanced three-bladed propeller has no tendency to rotate from any of the three positions. [Figure 12-73]

In the suspension method for checking static balance, the propeller is hung by a cord with its center of rotation perpendicular to the ground. A disk

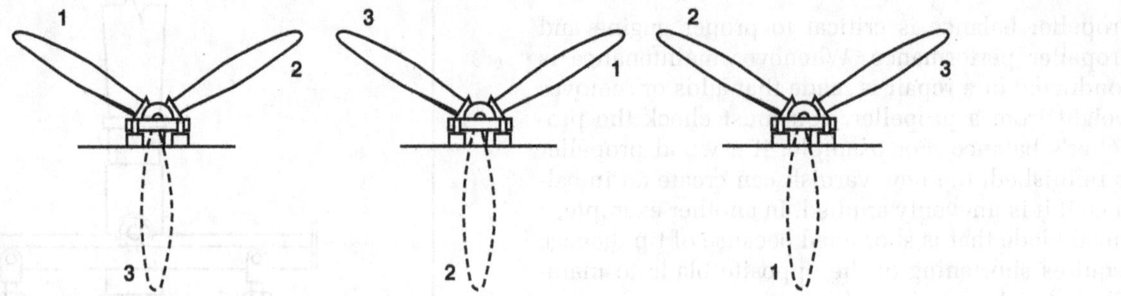


**Figure 12-73. A three-bladed propeller is properly balanced when each blade can be placed in the six o'clock position with no tendency to rotate.**

is firmly attached to the cord and a cylinder is attached to the propeller. Any imbalance is determined by misalignment between the disk and the cylinder.

### Out-of-Balance Repairs

When a propeller assembly exhibits a definite tendency to rotate, you are allowed to make corrections to remove the imbalance. If the total weight of the propeller assembly is under allowable limits, you can affix permanent fixed weights at acceptable locations. Likewise, you can remove weight from acceptable locations when the total weight of the propeller assembly is equal to the allowable limit.

The propeller manufacturer determines where weight can be added on a propeller. You must adhere to the manufacturer's instructions for method and location of balance corrections. Typically, vertical imbalance is corrected by adding a metal weight on the light side of the hub, 90 degrees from the propeller's horizontal centerline. On a wooden propeller, horizontal imbalance is corrected by adding or removing solder at the propeller blade tips. Horizontal balance correction on an aluminum propeller can involve removing small amounts of metal by filing.

## DYNAMIC BALANCE

A propeller exhibits dynamic balance when the centers of gravity of rotating propeller elements, such as the propeller blades, track in the same plane of rotation. A dynamic imbalance resulting from improper mass distribution is usually negligible if the blades on a propeller track within limits.

Checking dynamic balance can be accomplished only with the propeller, spinner, and related equipment installed on the aircraft. With the engine running, electronic equipment senses and pinpoints the location of an imbalance. Additionally, the test equipment typically determines the amount of weight required to balance the propeller.

## CHECKING BLADE ANGLE

If you are required to check the blade angle at a specific blade station, you typically use a **universal propeller protractor**. The frame of a typical protractor is made of aluminum alloy with three flat sides with square angles. A bubble spirit level mounted on the frame swings out to indicate when the protractor is level. A movable ring is located inside the frame and is used to set the zero reference angle. The ring is engraved with vernier index marks to provide readings as small as one tenth of a degree. A center disk is engraved with a degree scale from zero to 180 degrees, both positive and negative. In addition, the center disk contains a spirit level to indicate when the center disk is level. [Figure 12-74]

Before measuring a propeller blade angle, determine the reference blade station from the aircraft manufacturer's maintenance manual. Mark this reference station on each blade with chalk or a grease pencil. Next, establish the reference plane from the engine crankshaft centerline. Do not reference the airframe attitude because some engines are installed at an angle to help counter the effects of torque. To zero the protractor, loosen the ring-to-frame lock, align the zeros on the disk and the ring, and engage the disk-to-ring lock. Place the edge of the protractor on a flat surface of the propeller hub that is either parallel to, or perpendicular to, the crankshaft centerline. Now, turn the ring adjuster until the spirit level in the center of the disk is level. The corner level should also be leveled. Now, tighten the ring-to-frame lock, and release the disk-to-ring lock. The protractor is now aligned with the engine crankshaft. [Figure 12-75]

After you zero the protractor, rotate the propeller until the blade to be measured is horizontal. Place the protractor on the blade face at the reference station mark. You should stand on the same side of the propeller as you did when zeroing the protractor. If you need to measure from the other side, you

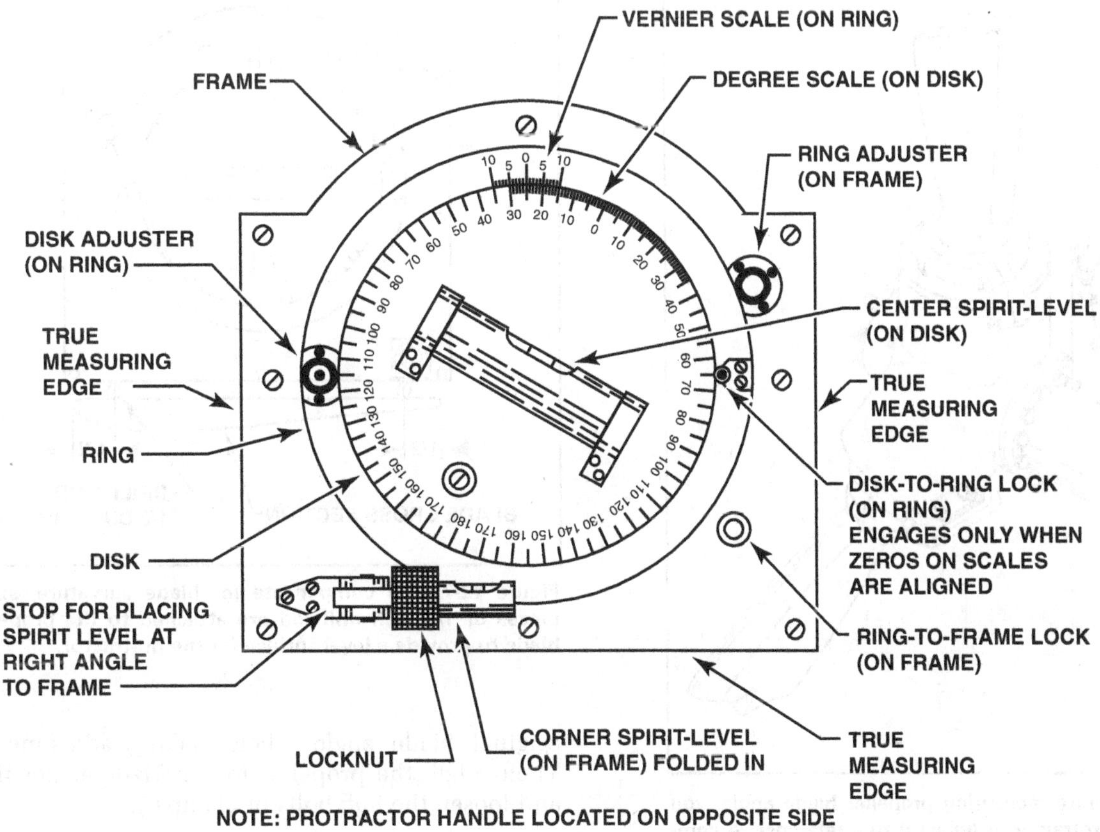


**Figure 12-74. A universal propeller protractor is used to check propeller blade angle.**

must zero the protractor from that side. With the protractor resting on the face of the blade, turn the disk adjuster until the spirit level centers. Read the blade angle using the zero line on the index ring. Accuracy in tenths of degrees can be read from the vernier scale. To measure the angle of another blade, rotate it to the same horizontal position and repeat the process. [Figure 12-76]

If the face of the propeller blade is curved, use masking tape to attach two pieces of the same, small diameter rod 1/2 inch from the leading and trailing edges. After you secure the rods, measure the angle with the protractor resting on the rods. [Figure 12-77]

If dissimilar blade angles exist on an aluminum fixed-pitch propeller, a propeller repair station or the manufacturer can repitch the blades. Consult the propeller repair facility and provide details on the amount of allowable pitch variation between blades.

## BLADE ANGLE ADJUSTMENTS

All propeller systems other than fixed-pitch propellers require occasional blade angle adjustments. For example, ground-adjustable propellers are set to one blade angle while controllable pitch propellers require the setting of low and high blade angle limits. The method used to make blade angle adjustments depends on the propeller type. The following examples represent the more commonly used methods for adjusting blade angle.

### GROUND-ADJUSTABLE PROPELLER

To adjust the propeller blade angle on a ground-adjustable propeller, you must first determine which reference blade station to use. This information is typically contained in the propeller or aircraft maintenance manual. After you determine the reference station, check the specifications for the approved blade angle range for the aircraft. A typical range for a ground-adjustable propeller is from 7 to 15 degrees.

In most cases, you can make a blade angle adjustment to a ground-adjustable propeller with the propeller on the aircraft or on a propeller bench. To make an adjustment, place a grease pencil mark across the hub and blade to mark relative positions. The mark provides a visual means to identify the

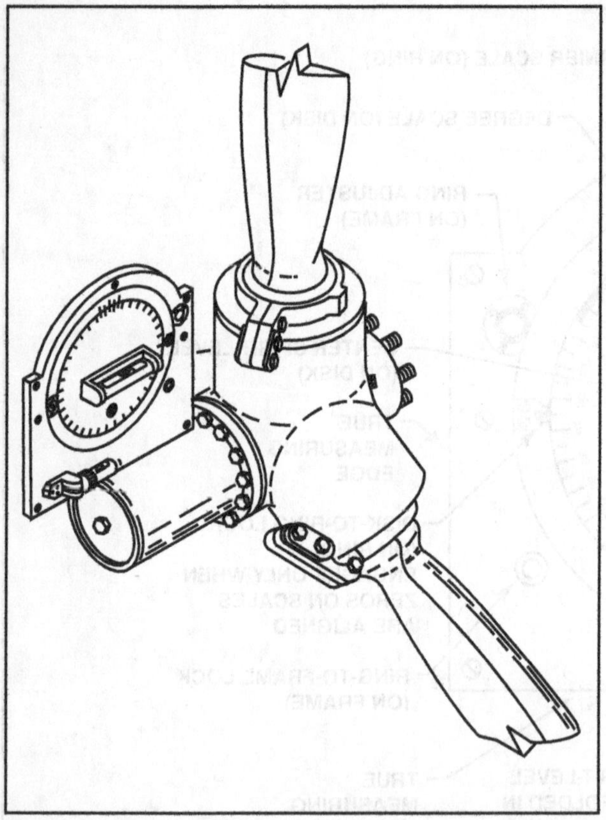

Figure 12-75. Before measuring propeller blade angle, you must zero the protractor or adjust it to a reference. A common reference is the propeller hub.

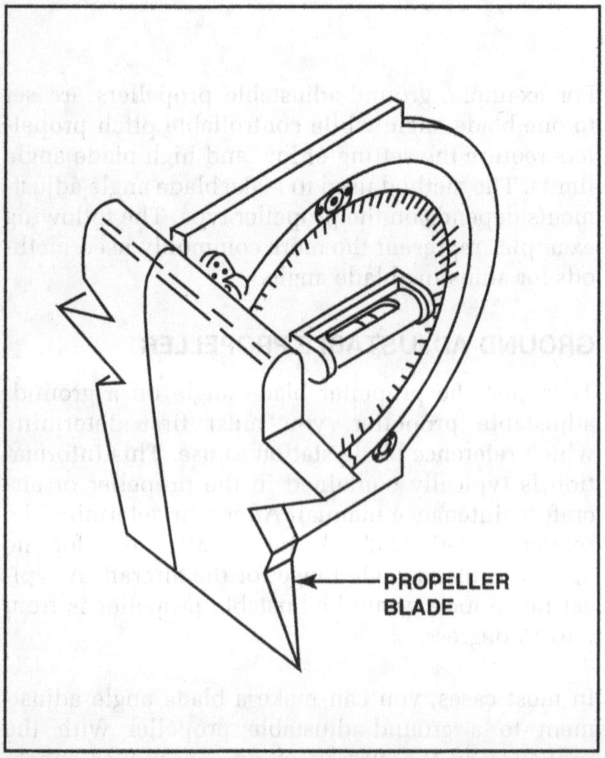


Figure 12-76. To measure the blade angle, hold the protractor against the blade face and rotate the disk adjuster to center the spirit level.

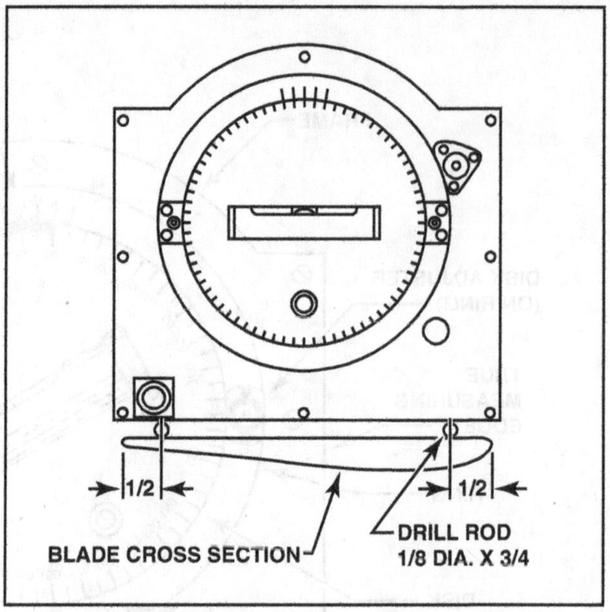


Figure 12-77. To compensate for blade curvature, small pieces of 1/4 inch drill rod are attached to the propeller blade to provide a level surface for the protractor.

original blade angle when making adjustments. Then rotate the propeller to a horizontal position and loosen the hub bolts or clamps.

To change the blade angle, slightly separate the hub halves after the clamps or bolts are loosened. You can then rotate the blades in the hub to the desired blade angle. You typically use a propeller blade paddle to rotate a propeller blade. If a blade binds, wiggle it as you rotate it to the new angle. [Figure 12-78]

Using the universal propeller protractor, recheck the blade angle after tightening the hub clamps or bolts. When loose in the hub, blades droop slightly, and they will move a small amount as the hub is tightened. Because of this, you might need to repeat the procedure a few times until the blades are set properly. Typically, an acceptable blade angle tolerance between the desired angle and the actual angle is 0.1 degrees. After the blade meets the specified tolerance, you can tighten the propeller hardware and secure it with a safety lock mechanism.

## COUNTERWEIGHT PROPELLER

On a counterweighted propeller, an adjustable set of stop nuts on an index pin located under each counterweight cap sets the propeller blade angles. To access the index pin, remove the clevis pin that safeties the counterweight cap and remove the cap. Pull the index pin out of its recess in the counterweight, or push it out from behind the counterweight bracket with a small tool. [Figure 12-79]

**Figure 12-78. A propeller blade paddle is used to adjust blade angles.**

Along the recess which houses the index pin is a scale calibrated with half-degree marks and a scale from zero to ten. This scale is used to adjust and set the stop nuts on the index pin.

The propeller blade index number, also known as the base setting, is normally stamped in a lead plug located near the index pin recess. This number indicates the maximum blade angle for which the propeller was adjusted during its last overhaul. The maximum blade angle is typically 25 degrees and is used to calculate where the stop nuts on the index pin should be positioned. For example, if the blade index is 25 degrees and the aircraft specifications specify a low blade angle of 17 degrees and a high angle of 22 degrees, determine the stop nut positions by subtracting the appropriate blade angle

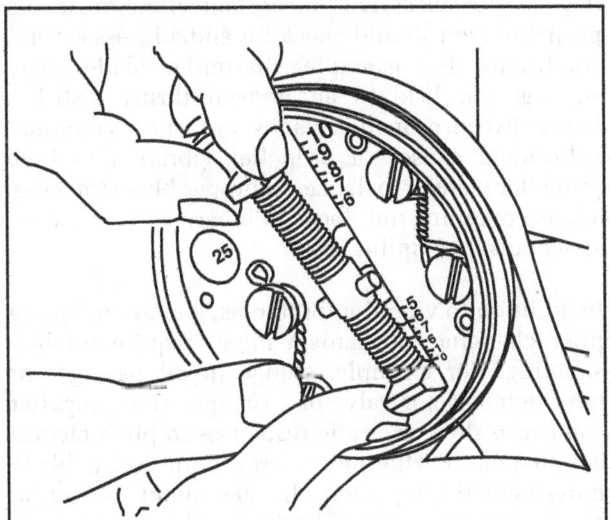


**Figure 12-79. Adjust the blade angle of a counterweight propeller with the stop nuts located on the index pins inside each counterweight.**

from the blade index. Therefore, to set the 17-degree low blade angle, position the stop nut on the index pin so that the edge toward the center of the pin aligns with the 8 degrees (25 – 17 = 8) mark on the scale. To set the 22-degree high blade angle, position the stop nut so its edge aligns with the 3-degree (25 – 22 = 3) mark.

After you set the stop nuts, reinstall the index pins in the counterweights and replace the caps. With everything secure, move the blades through their full range of travel. Reposition the blades at their maximum blade angle and measure at the specified reference station. A common reference station for a counterweighted propeller is the 42-inch station. Then, move the blades to their low blade angle stop and check these angles. Make small adjustments to the stop nut positions as necessary to bring the angles within acceptable limits.

## HARTZELL CONSTANT-SPEED PROPELLERS

Hartzell steel hub propellers can be adjusted for the desired low blade angle by loosening the hub clamps and rotating the blades. Be aware, however, that because the piston within the propeller hub can travel only a fixed amount, whenever the low blade angle is changed the high blade angle will also change. After you set the desired blade angle, retorque and safety the clamps.

The low-pitch setting on a Hartzell compact propeller is adjusted with the adjusting screw on the hub cylinder. To make a blade adjustment, begin by loosening the jam nut on the adjusting screw. Then either rotate the screw clockwise to increase the low blade angle or counterclockwise to decrease the angle. After you set the desired angle, retighten the jam nut. When changing the blade angles, always refer to the aircraft specifications and the propeller manufacturer's manual for instructions about specific propeller models. [Figure 12-80]

## BLADE TRACKING

Propeller blade tracking is the procedure by which you check the track of each propeller blade tip as it turns through its arc of rotation. In this procedure, you are comparing the positions of the propeller blade tips relative to each other. You typically check blade tracking during an inspection, when troubleshooting a vibration problem, or as a final check after balancing and reinstalling a propeller. The blades of metal propellers up to six feet in diameter on light aircraft must track within 1/16 inch of each other. The blades of a wood propeller should track within 1/8 inch.

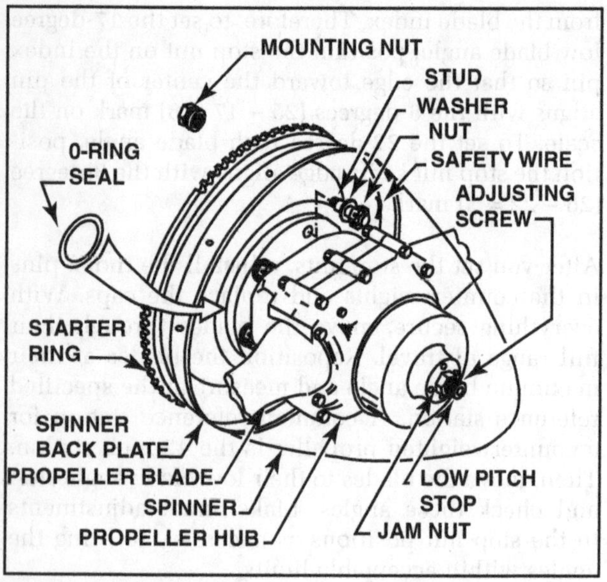


**Figure 12-80. Adjust the low pitch setting for Hartzell compact propellers with an adjusting screw on the hub cylinder.**

Before you can track the blades of a propeller, you must lock the aircraft in a stationary position. You typically do this by chocking the wheels to prevent aircraft movement. After the aircraft is locked in place, set a fixed reference point on the ground within 1/4 inch of the propeller arc. You can do this by placing a board on blocks under the propeller arc and taping a piece of paper to the board. With the reference point in place, rotate the propeller blade and mark the track of each blade. The maximum difference in track for all of the blades should not exceed the limits mentioned earlier. [Figure 12-81]

If the propeller track is more than the allowable limit, determine the reason and correct the condition. The easiest item to check is the torque of the propeller retaining bolts. If all bolts are properly secured, remove the propeller should and inspect it for the presence of debris or damage. In addition, you might need to check the crankshaft alignment. If you find no obvious problems, you can correct an excessive out-of-track condition by placing shims between the inner flange and the propeller.

## TROUBLESHOOTING

The origins of powerplant vibrations can be difficult to pinpoint. To determine whether the vibrations are emanating from the engine or propeller, observe the propeller hub, dome, or spinner. With the engine running between 1,200 to 1,500 r.p.m., the hub or spinner should rotate around the axis of the crankshaft centerline. If the propeller hub appears to swing in a slight orbit, or if the vibration becomes more apparent at higher speeds, the

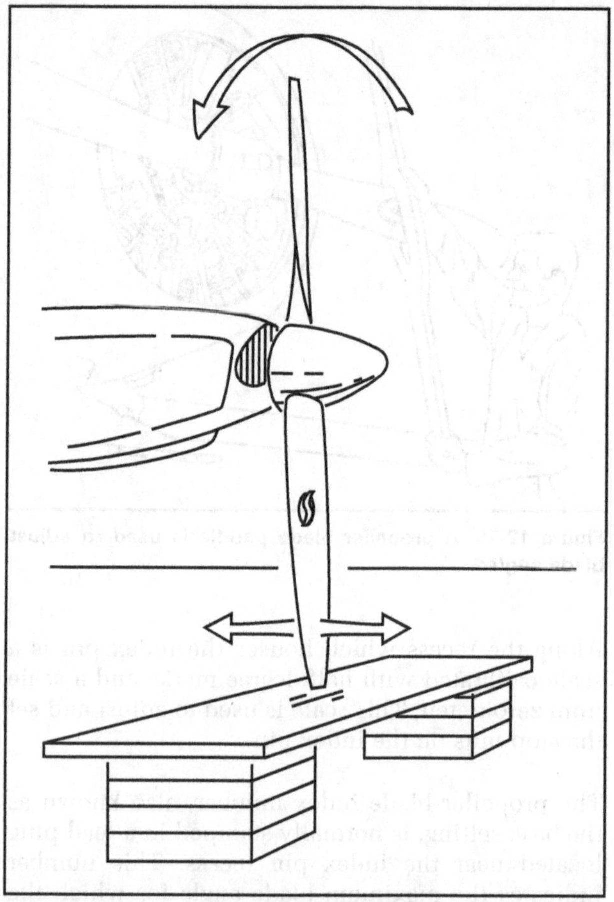

**Figure 12-81. A propeller can be tracked by placing a board within 1/4 inch of the propeller arc. Rotate the propeller and mark the path that each blade tip follows as it passes the board.**

vibration is likely caused by the propeller. If the propeller hub oscillates, the problem is probably caused by engine vibration.

If you trace excessive powerplant vibration to the propeller, you should check for and address several conditions. For example, dissimilar blade angle settings can lead to an uneven thrust distribution between propeller blades and cause vibration. Additional causes of propeller vibration include propeller blade imbalance, improper blade tracking, a loose retaining nut, loose hub hardware, or excessive crankshaft spline wear.

In addition to vibration problems, a malfunctioning pitch-changing mechanism might require troubleshooting. For example, sludge in oil passages or the pitch selector valve of a two-position propeller can cause slow or erratic responses to pitch-change commands. Furthermore, erratic or jerky blade movement during pitch changes might be caused by air trapped in the cylinder. Cycling the propeller through its pitch-change operation several times typically purges air from the system. In addition, the linkage from the cockpit pitch control lever to the selector valve can become loose and fail to activate the selector valve. Operations near an ocean can result in salt-water corrosion around the propeller cylinder and piston, which could also result in sporadic and unreliable pitch changes.

### HAMILTON-STANDARD HYDROMATIC

Troubleshooting procedures and solutions discussed for other systems are generally applicable to the feathering Hydromatic system. If the propeller fails to respond to the cockpit propeller control lever, but can be feathered and unfeathered, the cause is most likely a failure of the governor or governor control system. If the propeller fails to feather, check the system for electrical faults or for open wiring to the electrical components.

If the propeller fails to unfeather after feathering normally, the distributor valve is likely not shifting. However, if the propeller feathers and immediately unfeathers, the problem might be a short circuit in the holding coil wiring or an open circuit in the pressure cutout switch or its associated wiring. The same problem occurs if the feather button is internally shorted.

Sluggish movement of the propeller might be due to a buildup of sludge in the propeller dome or a worn out piston-to-dome seal. Sticking cam rollers can also interfere with smooth pitch-change movement and feathering operations.

Erratic or jerky operation of a Hydromatic propeller can indicate that the wrong preload shim is installed between the dome and barrel assemblies. If this is the case, remove the dome must and install the proper shim.

## PROPELLER INSTALLATION

The method used to attach a propeller to an engine crankshaft varies with the design of the crankshaft. Currently, three types of crankshafts are used on aircraft engines: the flanged crankshaft, the tapered crankshaft, and the splined crankshaft. The following paragraphs discuss general installation procedures for all three types. For specific instructions, always refer to the aircraft and engine maintenance manuals.

### FLANGED SHAFT

Most horizontally opposed reciprocating engines and some turboprop engines use flanged propeller shafts. The front of the crankshaft is formed into a flange four to eight inches across, perpendicular to the crankshaft centerline. Mounting bolt holes and dowel pin holes are machined into the flange. Some flanges have threaded inserts pressed into the bolt holes. [Figure 12-82]

Before installing a propeller on a flanged shaft, inspect the flange for corrosion, nicks, burrs, and other surface defects. In addition, ensure that the bolt holes and threaded inserts are clean and in good condition. Repair any defects in accordance with the engine manufacturer's recommendations. Typically, you can remove light corrosion with very fine sandpaper. If the shaft is free of corrosion, clean the flange after sanding and check for smoothness. Then apply a light coat of engine oil or antiseize compound to the flange to prevent corrosion and to facilitate future propeller removal. If you have any reason to suspect a bent flange, inspect it for runout.

### FIXED-PITCH PROPELLERS

Before installing a fixed-pitch propeller on a flanged shaft, inspect the mounting surface of the propeller to verify that it is clean and smooth. Verify that the attaching bolts are in good condition and inspect them for cracks with either a dye penetrant or a magnetic particle inspection process. You should also inspect washers and nuts, and use new fiber lock nuts when required by an installation.

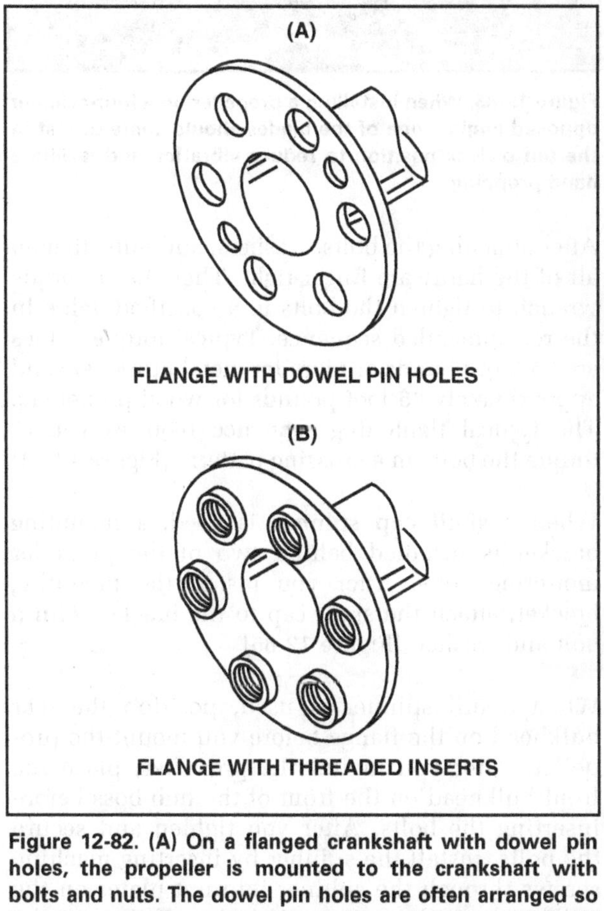


**Figure 12-82. (A) On a flanged crankshaft with dowel pin holes, the propeller is mounted to the crankshaft with bolts and nuts. The dowel pin holes are often arranged so that the propeller can be mounted in only one position. (B) Many installations use threaded inserts pressed into the crankshaft to eliminate the need for nuts.**

Many flanges use dowel pins that limit the propeller-to-shaft mounting to only one position. If the flange does not use dowels, install the propeller in the position specified by the aircraft or engine maintenance manual. This is important because propeller position is critical for maximum engine life in some installations. If no position is specified on a four-cylinder horizontally opposed engine, install the propeller with the blades at the 10 o'clock and 4 o'clock position when the engine is stopped. This position tends to produce the least amount of vibration and puts the propeller in the best position for hand propping. [Figure 12-83]

**Figure 12-83. When installing a propeller on a four-cylinder opposed engine, one of the blades should come to rest at the ten o'clock position to reduce vibration and facilitate hand propping.**

After attaching the bolts, washers, and nuts, tighten all of the hardware finger-tight. Then, use a torque wrench to tighten the bolts to a specified value in the recommended sequence. Typical torque values are 35 foot-pounds or more for metal propellers and approximately 25 foot-pounds for wood propellers. The typical tightening sequence requires you to torque the bolts in a crossing pattern. [Figure 12-84]

When a **skull cap spinner** is used, a mounting bracket is installed behind two of the propeller mounting bolts. After you install the mounting bracket, attach the skull cap to the bracket with a bolt and washer. [Figure 12-85]

When a full spinner is used, position the rear bulkhead on the flange before you mount the propeller. After you mount the propeller, place the front bulkhead on the front of the hub boss before inserting the bolts. After you tighten and secure the bolts, install the spinner by inserting machine screws through the spinner into nut plates on the bulkheads. If the spinner is indexed, line up the index marks during installation to avoid vibration. [Figure 12-86]

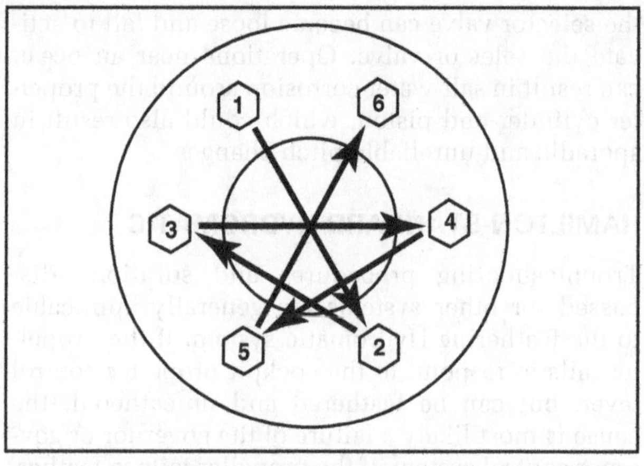


**Figure 12-84. When installing a propeller on a flanged crankshaft, be sure to follow the manufacturer's recommended tightening sequence to avoid inducing stress in the propeller hub.**

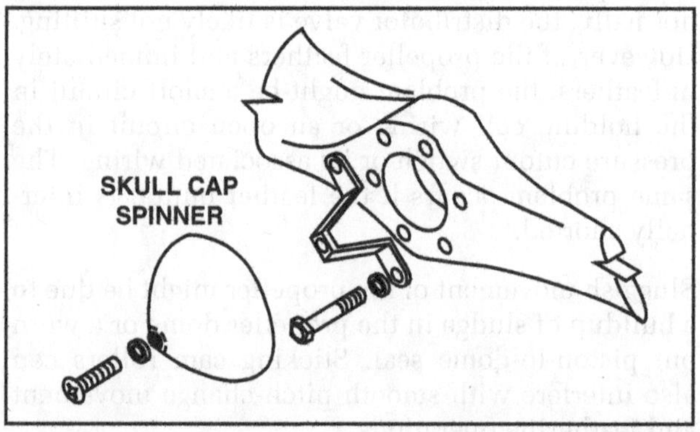


**Figure 12-85. Some small training aircraft with flange-mounted propellers use a skull cap spinner that requires a mounting bracket installed under two of the propeller mounting bolts.**

## CONSTANT-SPEED PROPELLERS

Some Hartzell steel hub propellers and all Hartzell compact propellers are designed to mount on flanged crankshafts. Before mounting a constant-speed propeller on the crankshaft, lubricate the O-ring in the rear of the hub with an approved lubricant or a light coat of engine oil. Then carefully mount the propeller on the flange, being careful to keep the O-ring from becoming damaged.

McCauley constant-speed propellers are also installed on flanged crankshafts. Like Hartzell propellers, an O-ring in the rear of the hub must be lubricated with a light coat of engine oil to allow its movement as the propeller is secured to the crankshaft flange. [Figure 12-87]

When installing a constant-speed propeller that can be feathered, the installation and adjustment procedures are similar to that of other constant-speed models. However, if the blades are in their feathered position, use a blade paddle to reposition each blade to its low pitch angle.

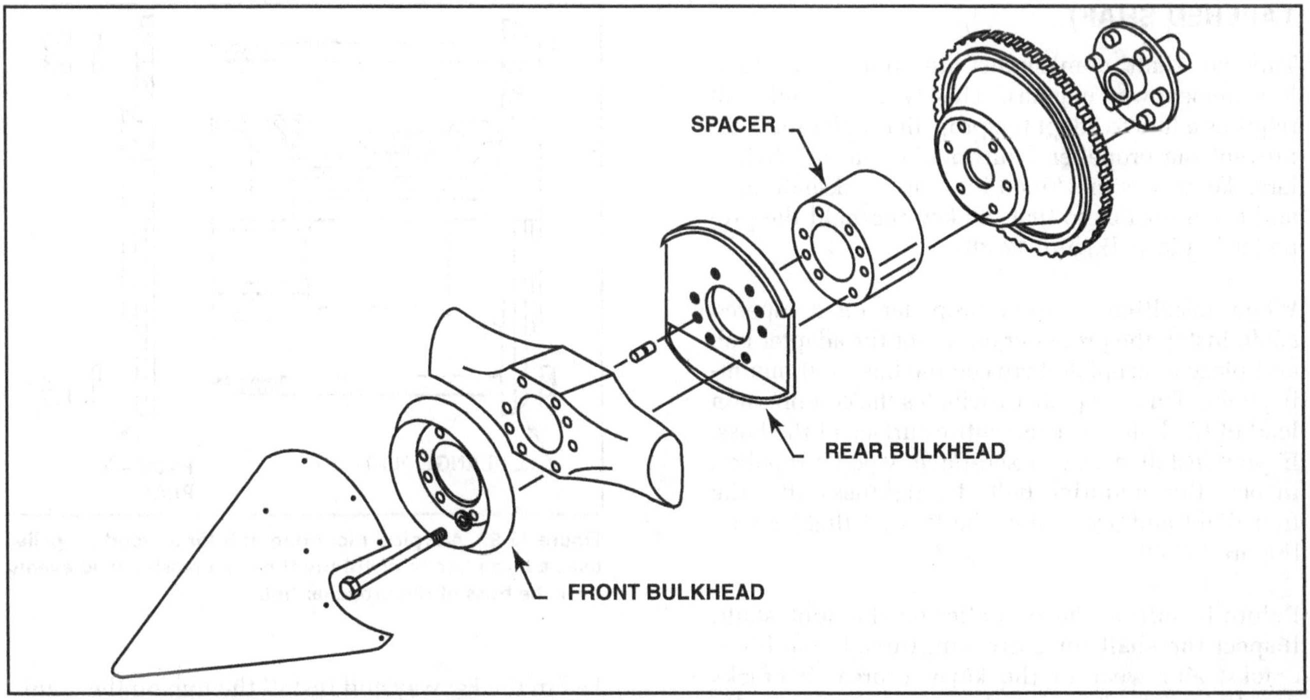


**Figure 12-86. A full spinner mounts to forward and rear bulkheads with machine screws. On some aircraft, a spinner might be mounted to only a rear bulkhead.**

## TURBOPROP PROPELLERS

When installing a constant-speed, reversing propeller, use the same basic procedures that are used for other flanged shaft propellers. One difference, however, is the addition of the Beta tube. The Beta tube is installed through the propeller piston after the propeller is installed and is bolted to the forward part of the piston.

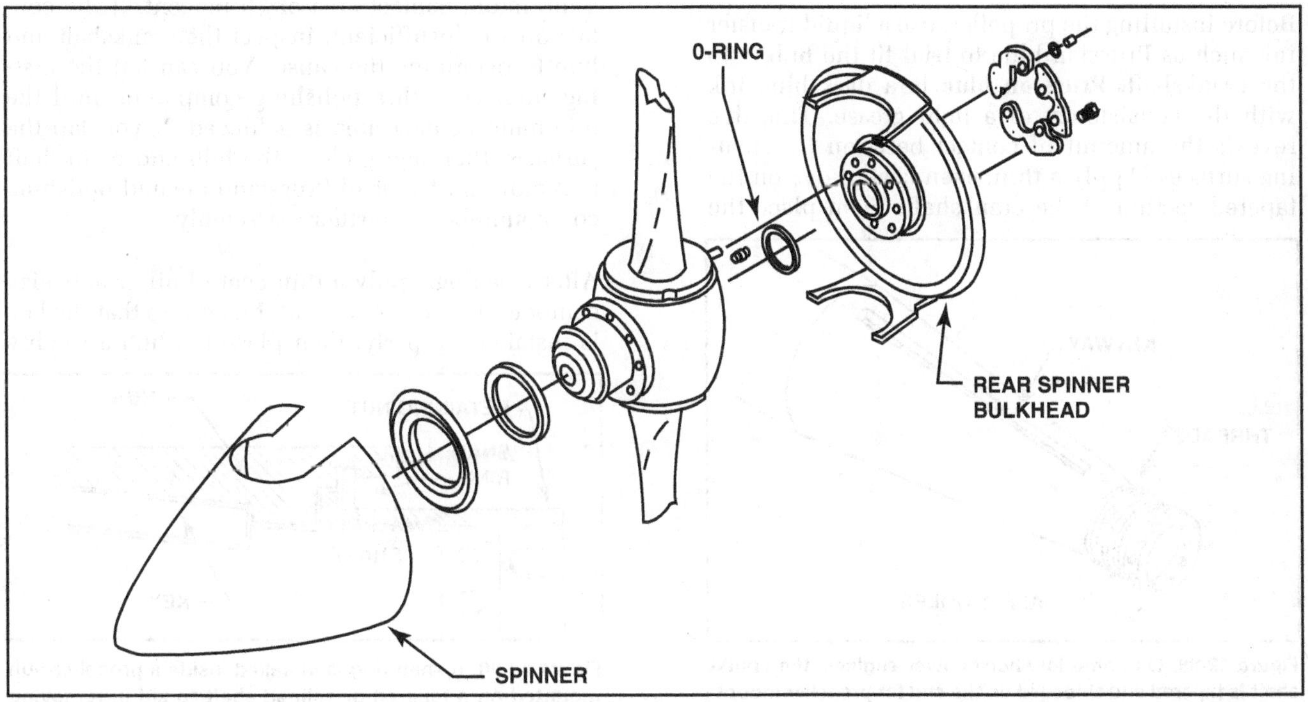


**Figure 12-87. McCauley constant-speed propellers are installed on flanged crankshafts with an O-ring seal to prevent oil leakage.**

## TAPERED SHAFT

Tapered shaft crankshafts are found on older, low horsepower engines. This type of crankshaft requires a hub to adapt the propeller to the shaft. To prevent the propeller from rotating on the shaft, a large keyway is machined into the crankshaft taper and the propeller so that the key can hold the propeller in place. [Figure 12-88]

When installing a wood propeller on a tapered shaft, install the propeller boss over the adapter hub and place a faceplate between the boss and mounting bolts. This faceplate distributes the compression load of the bolts over the entire surface of the boss. If you install a new fixed-pitch wood propeller, inspect the mounting bolts for tightness after the first flight and again after the first 25 flight hours. [Figure 12-89]

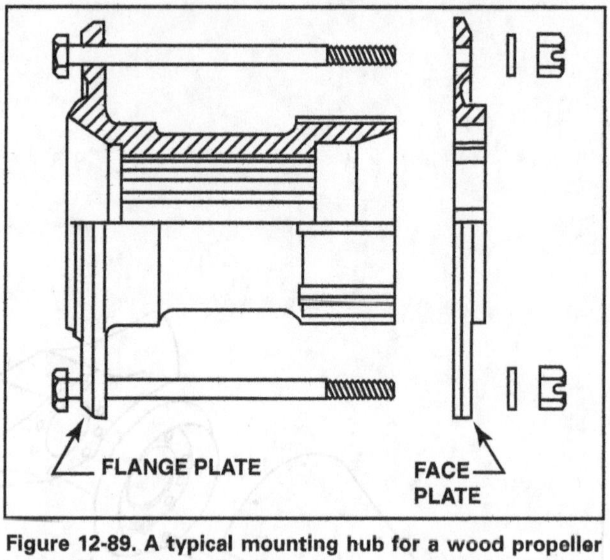

**Figure 12-89. A typical mounting hub for a wood propeller uses a face plate to distribute the compression load evenly over the boss of the propeller hub.**

Before installing the propeller on the crankshaft, inspect the shaft for corrosion, thread condition, cracks, and wear in the keyway area. If cracks develop in the keyway, they can spread rapidly and result in crankshaft failure. It is good practice to inspect the keyway with dye penetrant at every 100-hour or annual inspection. Dress or polish out any minor surface defects found during the preinstallation inspection in accordance with the engine manufacturer's maintenance manual. In addition, inspect the propeller hub components and mounting hardware for wear, cracks, and corrosion, and repair or replace any defective components as necessary.

Before installing the propeller, use a liquid transfer ink such as Prussian blue to trial fit the hub onto the crankshaft. **Prussian blue** is a dark blue ink with the consistency of a light grease. This dye reveals the amount of contact between two mating surfaces. Apply a thin, even coat of dye on the tapered section of the crankshaft. Then place the key in the keyway and install the hub on the crankshaft and torque the retaining nut. In practice, the hub, snap ring, and retaining nut are never disassembled. If, however, they were disassembled for inspection or repair, place the retaining nut against the hub and install the puller snap ring. After assembly, tighten the retaining nut to the specified torque. [Figure 12-90]

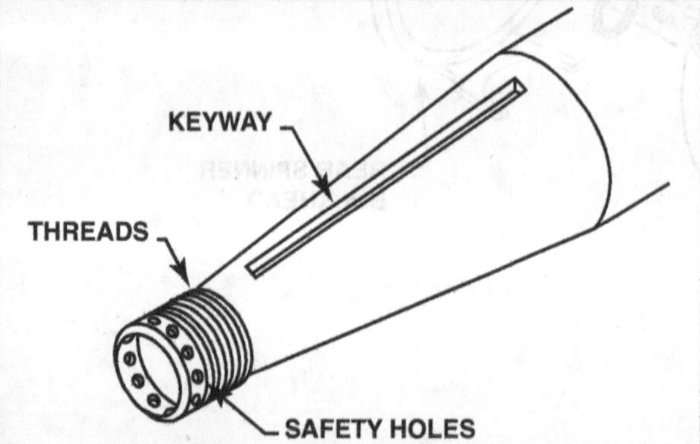

**Figure 12-88. On some low-horsepower engines, the crankshaft is tapered and threaded on the end for propeller mounting.**

Remove the propeller and inspect the crankshaft for the amount of ink transferred from the tapered shaft to the propeller. The ink transfer should indicate a minimum contact area of 70 percent. If the contact area is insufficient, inspect the crankshaft and hub to determine the cause. You can lap the mating surfaces with a polishing compound until the minimum contact area is achieved. If you lap the surfaces, thoroughly clean the hub and crankshaft to remove all traces of Prussian blue and polishing compound before further reassembly.

After cleaning, apply a thin coat of oil or antiseize compound to the crankshaft. Make sure that the key is installed properly; then place the hub assembly

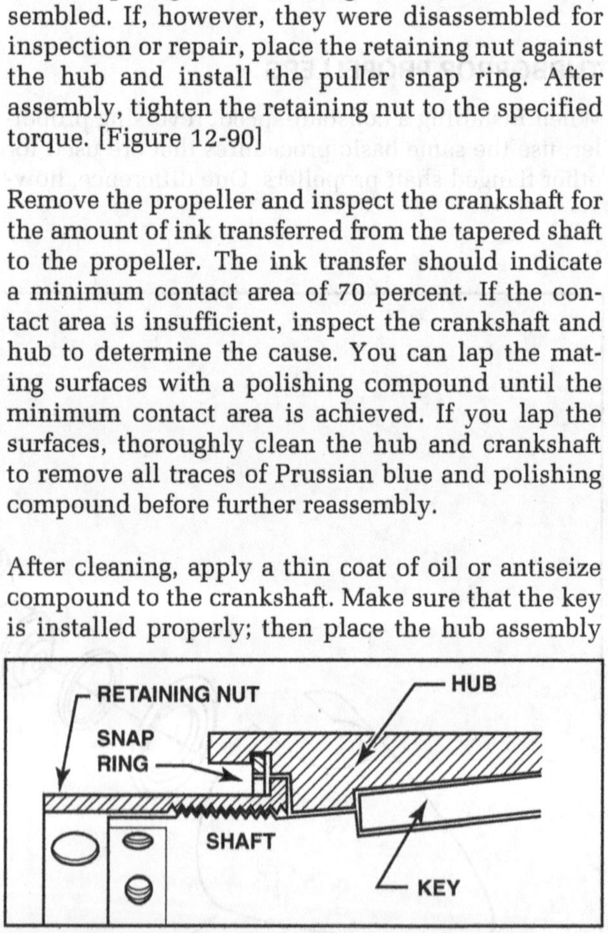

**Figure 12-90. A snap ring is installed inside a propeller hub mounted on a tapered or splined shaft to aid in removing the propeller from the shaft.**

and propeller on the shaft. Be sure that the threads on the shaft and nut are clean and dry. Verify that the puller snap ring is in place before tightening the nut to the proper torque value. Failure to tighten the retaining nut results in play between the propeller and the front and rear cones. Any space between the cones and the propeller produces galling. Complete the installation by securing the retaining nut.

## SPLINED SHAFT

Splined crankshafts are found on most radial engines, some horizontally opposed engines, and some inline engines. The splined shaft has grooves and splines of equal dimensions and a double-width master spline to ensure that a hub can fit on a shaft in only one position. [Figure 12-91]

Before installing a propeller on a splined shaft, inspect the crankshaft for cracks, surface defects, and corrosion. If any defects exist, repair them in accordance with the engine manufacturer's instructions. Inspect the crankshaft and hub splines for wear with a go/no-go gauge that is 0.002 inch larger than the maximum space allowed between the splines. The splines are serviceable if you cannot insert the gauge between the splines for more than 20 percent of the spline length. If the gauge can be inserted more than 20 percent of the way, the hub or the crankshaft is unairworthy and must be replaced.

To help ensure that the propeller hub is centered on the crankshaft, a front and rear cone are installed on each side of the propeller hub. The

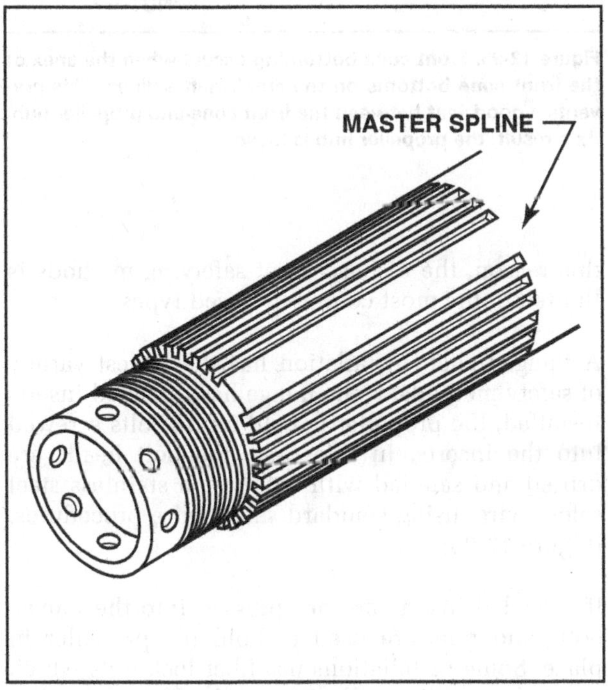


**Figure 12-91. The master spline ensures that a propeller is correctly positioned when installed on the engine.**

rear cone is typically made of bronze and is split to allow flexibility during installation and to ensure a tight fit. The front cone, on the other hand, is made in two pieces as a matched set. The two halves are marked with a serial number to identify them as a set. [Figure 12-92]

In addition to the front and rear cones, a large retaining nut is used to tighten and hold the propeller in place. The retaining nut threads onto the end of the splined shaft and presses against the front cone to sandwich the propeller tightly between the front and rear cones. [Figure 12-93]

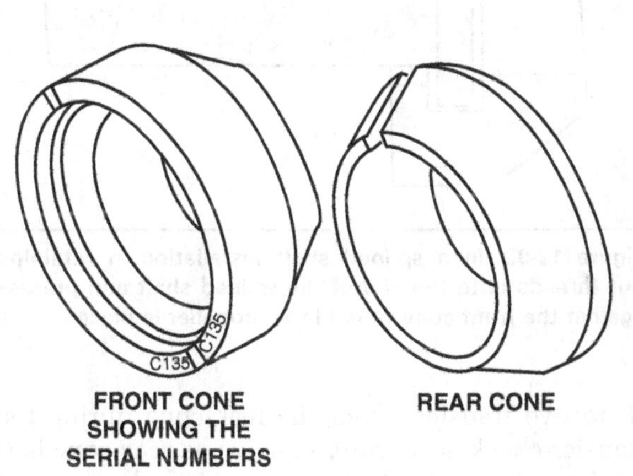


**Figure 12-92. Splined propeller shafts require front and rear mounting cones to ensure that the propeller is properly aligned on the shaft.**

Like the tapered shaft, you should complete a trial installation of the propeller to ensure a proper fit. To do so, begin by applying a thin coat of Prussian blue to the rear cone. Next, slip the rear cone and bronze spacer onto the crankshaft, being sure to push them all the way back on the shaft. With the rear cone in place, align the hub on the master spline and push the hub back against the rear cone. Coat the front cone halves with Prussian blue and place them around the lip of the retaining nut. Install the nut in the hub and tighten it to the proper torque.

After you torque the retaining nut, immediately remove the retaining nut and front cone and note the amount of Prussian blue transferred to the hub. A minimum of 70 percent contact is required. Then, remove the hub from the crankshaft and note the transfer of dye from the rear cone. As with the front cone, a minimum of 70 percent contact is required. If insufficient contact exists, lap the hub to the cones using special lapping tools and fixtures.

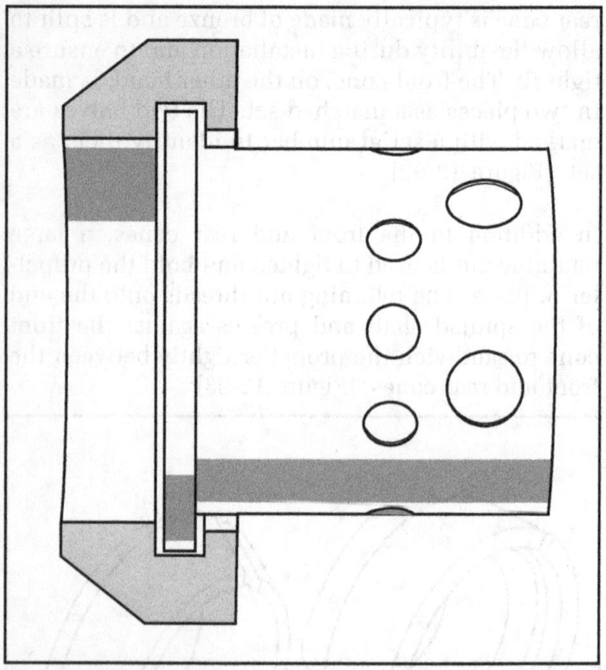

Figure 12-93. In a splined shaft installation, a retaining nut threads onto the end of the splined shaft and presses against the front cone to hold the propeller in place.

If no dye transfers from the rear cone during the transfer check, a condition known as **rear cone bottoming** might exist. This occurs when the apex, or point, of the rear cone contacts the land on the rear seat of the hub before the hub becomes seated on the rear cone. One way to correct rear cone bottoming is to remove up to 1/16 inch from the apex of the cone with sandpaper on a surface plate. [Figure 12-94]

**Front cone bottoming** occurs when the apex of the front cone bottoms on the crankshaft splines before it seats on the hub. Indications of front cone bottoming are the hub being loose on the shaft after you have torqued the retaining nut or no Prussian blue transfer to the front hub seat. You can correct front

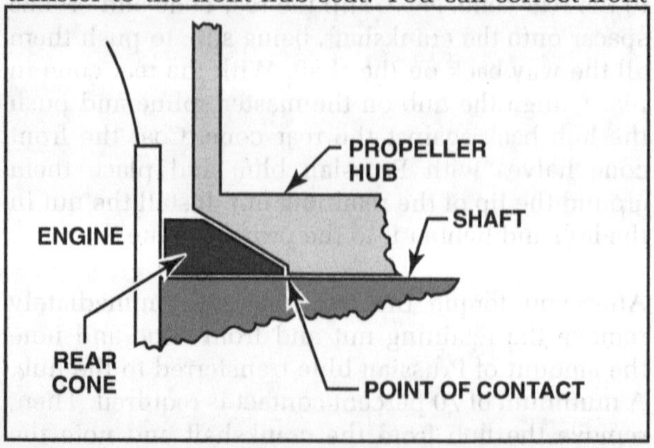


Figure 12-94. Rear cone bottoming occurs when the tip of the rear cone contacts the land on the rear seat of the hub before the hub seats on the cone. Removing a specified amount of material from the cone's apex corrects this problem.

cone bottoming by using a spacer of no more than 1/8 inch thickness behind the rear cone. This moves the hub forward, enabling the hub to properly seat on the front cone. [Figure 12-95]

After you achieve a proper fit between the hub and the splined shaft, reinstall the rear cone and permanently mount the propeller on the shaft. The position of the propeller hub in relation to the master spline is predetermined. Some installations require a certain blade to align with the master spline, while other installations require that the blades be perpendicular to the master spline position. Be sure to consult the engine maintenance manual for the requirements of a particular installation.

## PROPELLER SAFETYING

After a propeller is properly tightened, it must be secured with a mechanical safety mechanism. There is no single way to safety a propeller installation because of the different types of installations. For

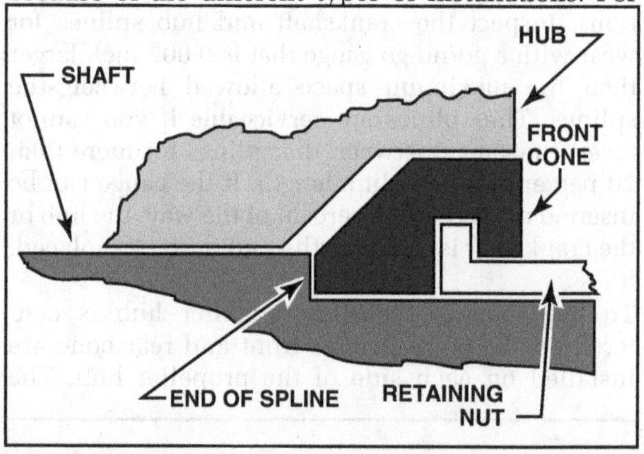


Figure 12-95. Front cone bottoming occurs when the apex of the front cone bottoms on the crankshaft splines. This prevents a good seat between the front cone and propeller hub. As a result, the propeller hub is loose.

this reason, the discussion of safetying methods is limited to the most commonly used types.

A flanged shaft installation has the largest variety of safety methods. If the flange has threaded inserts installed, the propeller is held on by bolts screwed into the inserts. In this case, the bolt heads are drilled and safetied with 0.041 inch stainless steel safety wire, using standard safety wire procedures. [Figure 12-96]

If threaded inserts are not pressed into the flange, bolts and nuts are used to hold the propeller in place. Some installations use fiber lock nuts which require no additional safetying, but the nuts must be replaced each time the propeller is removed.

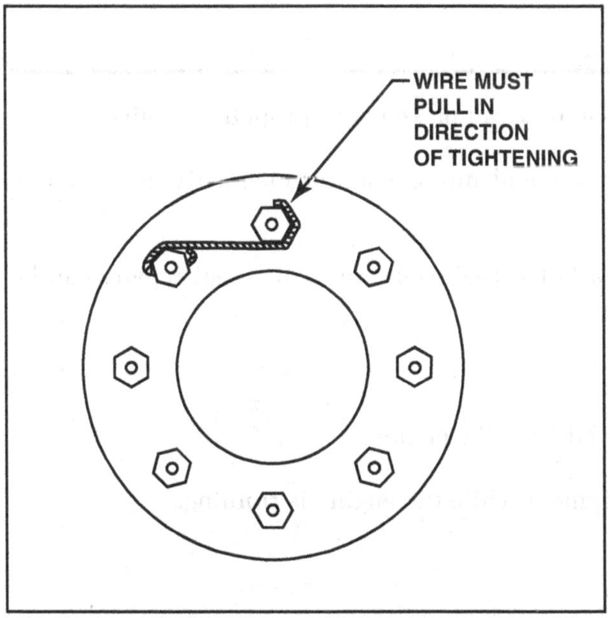


**Figure 12-96. On propellers secured to a flanged hub with bolts, pairs of bolt heads are tied together with safety wire to keep the bolts from loosening.**

For installations using castellated nuts and drilled bolts, the nuts are safetied to the bolts with cotter pins. [Figure 12-97]

The retaining nuts for tapered and splined shaft installations are safetied in a similar way; a clevis pin is installed through the safety holes in the retaining nut and crankshaft. The clevis pin must be positioned with the head toward the center of the crankshaft. A cotter pin holds the clevis pin in place. This allows centrifugal force to hold the clevis pin tightly in the hole against its flanged head. [Figure 12-98]

## OPERATIONAL CHECK

Conduct an operational check after you install and safety a constant-speed propeller. To conduct this check, follow ground runup procedures for the aircraft you are operating and position the aircraft for maximum safety. The first time a newly installed propeller

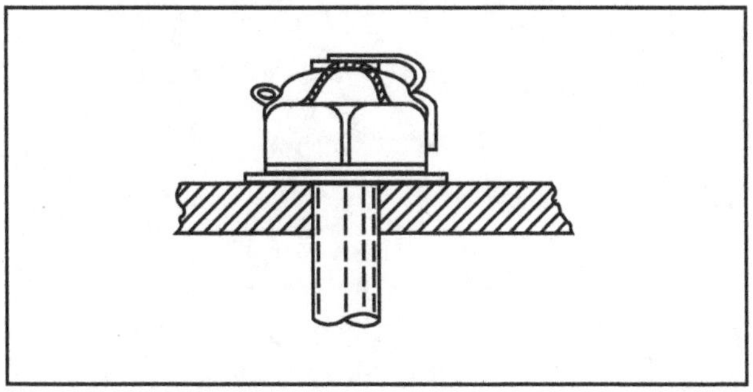

**Figure 12-97. If the propeller installation uses castellated nuts with drilled bolts, safety the nuts with cotter pins.**

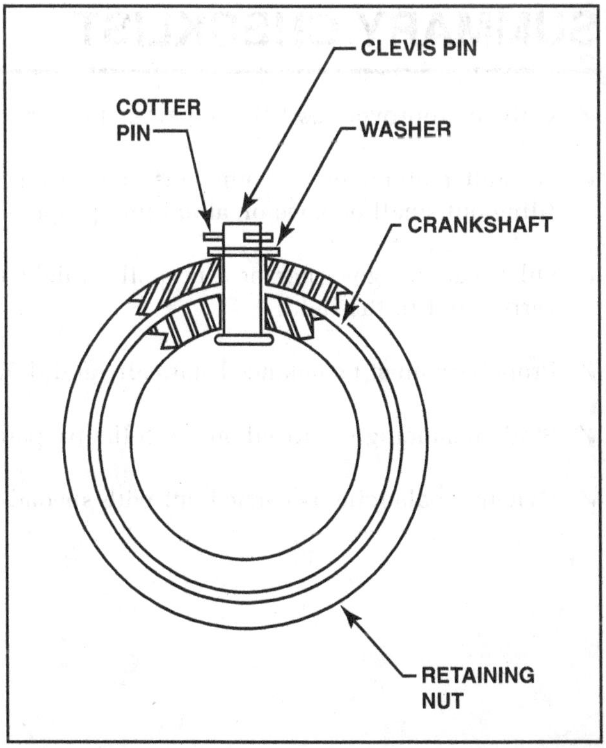


**Figure 12-98. To safety the retaining nut on a tapered shaft propeller installation, a clevis pin is installed through the safety holes in the retaining nut and crankshaft. The clevis pin must be installed with its flanged head toward the center of the crankshaft.**

operates at high speed on an engine, you should be alert to the hazards of possible propeller failure.

All adjustable propeller systems share common features related to their control configuration. Propeller controls must be rigged so that moving the controls forward increases speed and moving the controls aft decreases speed. Furthermore, engine throttles must be arranged so that forward thrust is increased by forward movement of the controls and decreased by aft movement of the control.

When running up an engine and testing a newly installed variable-pitch propeller, you must exercise the propeller several times by moving the governor control through its entire range of travel to remove entrapped air and ensure proper operation.

After you complete all ground checks and adjustments, you should conduct a flight test to verify the propeller system response to dynamic loads and to determine whether any other adjustments are necessary. After the test flight, check for oil leaks and component security.

# SUMMARY CHECKLIST

✓ Only an approved, certified repair station or the manufacturer can make major propeller repairs.

✓ Aircraft maintenance technicians can perform inspections and minor maintenance activities, such as filing out small damage on aluminum propeller blades.

✓ Oil leaks at a governor or a propeller might indicate a failed seal; some propeller seal repairs can be carried out in the field.

✓ Propellers must be balanced statically and dynamically.

✓ Static balancing is carried out with the propeller removed from the engine.

✓ Dynamic balancing is carried out with special test equipment while the engine is running.

# KEY TERMS

riffle file
Alodine
zerk
static balance
dynamic balance
universal propeller protractor
skull cap spinner
Prussian Blue
rear cone bottoming
front cone bottoming

# QUESTIONS

1. Major repairs and alterations to propellers are normally performed by the manufacturer or a ________ ______ ________.

2. When a wood propeller is stored, place it in a ______________ (horizontal or vertical) position.

3. If a propeller has been subjected to salt water, it should be flushed with ________ ________ (what fluid) until all traces of salt have been removed.

4. Two variables enter into the determination of whether a bent aluminum alloy propeller blade can be straightened. They are:

   a. ______________

   b. ______________

5. The Hydromatic propeller is lubricated by ______________ (what source) operating oil and needs no other lubrication.

6. The two types of propeller unbalance that are possible are:

   a. ______________

   b. ______________

7. The ______________ ______________ ______________ (what tool) may be used to check propeller blade angles while the propeller is on the aircraft.

8. The adjusting screw on the hub cylinder of a compact propeller will change the ________ (high or low) blade angle.

9. The ________ (what term) of a propeller is defined as the path which the tips of the blades follow as they rotate, with the aircraft stationary.

10. The maximum amount the tips of a six-foot metal propeller can be out of track is ________ (what fraction) of an inch.

11. The process of determining the positions of the propeller blades tips relative to each other is known as blade ______________.

12. Propellers whose pitch change mechanisms are oil actuated must be checked with the engine ____________ (operating or shut down). ______________________

13. The three types of crankshafts used on aircraft engines are:

a. ____________

b. ____________

c. ____________

14. The ________ (what type) crankshaft requires the use of a hub adapter to install the propeller.

15. McCauley constant speed propellers are found only on ____________ (flanged or splined) crankshafts.

16. The hub to taper contact for a propeller hub must be at least ________% contact area.

17. The snap ring inside a propeller hub used on a tapered crankshaft is there to aid in the

____________ (installation or removal) of the propeller.

18. The ________ (front or rear) cone used on a splined propeller shaft is made in two pieces.

19. Installing a spacer behind the rear cone on a splined propeller shaft is sometimes used to correct

____________ (front or rear) cone bottoming.

20. Propeller controls must be rigged so that moving the control forward will result in a/an ____________

____________ (increase or decrease) in r.p.m.

# POWERPLANT AND PROPELLER AIRWORTHINESS INSPECTIONS

CHAPTER 13

## INTRODUCTION

**An aircraft maintenance technician with a powerplant rating is authorized to conduct 100-hour inspections or phase checks of a progressive inspection program and approve a powerplant or propeller for return to service. The return to service of a powerplant or propeller after an annual inspection requires an inspection by an aircraft maintenance technician holding an Inspection Authorization or company approval under a repair station license. This chapter covers general requirements for conducting airworthiness inspections of powerplants and propellers.**

# SECTION A

## AIRWORTHINESS INSPECTION CRITERIA

All airworthiness inspections determine whether a component or part is safe for flight and conforms to the regulatory requirements of certification. Data for inspections is provided by the Federal Aviation Administration (FAA) and the component manufacturer. The scope and detail of an inspection varies depending on how the aircraft is operated (applicable regulations), the type of aircraft and powerplant, the type of inspection, and the manufacturer's requirements.

### INSPECTION AND MAINTENANCE DOCUMENTS

The FAA publishes a variety of documents; some provide mandatory regulatory information, while others are advisory to assist inspection personnel. Regulatory documentation includes Type Certificate Data Sheets (TCDS), Aircraft Specifications, Supplemental Type Certificates (STC), and Airworthiness Directives (AD). Nonregulatory information includes Advisory Circulars (AC).

Powerplant and propeller manufacturers provide a variety of documents and service publications for inspection, maintenance, and repair. Although the FAA reviews and approves only a limited amount of manufacturer's information, generally speaking, the manufacturers' information is considered to be acceptable data for inspection and maintenance. If manufacturer information is unavailable, use the standard inspection and maintenance criteria specified by the FAA.

The manufacturer is the best source of information for performing engine and propeller airworthiness inspections. In most instances, the FAA directs that manufacturers' information be used for maintenance activities unless an alternate plan has been approved. Where necessary, however, the FAA might require specific actions, which necessitate that the manufacturer's procedures be FAA-approved. For example, if the FAA issues an AD that requires adherence to the specific manufacturer's instructions, the FAA has reviewed and approved the manufacturer's instructions.

You should be familiar with the general content of the current revision of all government and manufacturer documents related to an aircraft component you are inspecting.

### TYPE CERTIFICATE DATA SHEETS

After the FAA approves and verifies the design of a powerplant or propeller, they publish a Type Certificate Data Sheet (TCDS), which lists the drawings and specifications that define the configuration and features of the product. The airworthiness of a component is determined by conformity to the TCDS.

The TCDS is FAA-approved data. Any modification to an aircraft component that deviates from the TCDS is considered a major alteration and must be documented on an FAA Major Repair or Alteration Form 337. These forms must be retained with an aircraft's permanent maintenance records and accounted for during airworthiness inspections.

TCDSs are granted to the manufacturers of airframes, powerplants, and propellers. The airframe TCDS defines the allowable powerplant and propeller combinations that can be installed on an aircraft, but the specific type design requirements of a powerplant or propeller are contained in their respective TCDS. To determine if an engine or propeller can be installed on a particular airframe, you must consult the airframe TCDS. In addition, the airframe TCDS provides other important information about the installation of these components, such as engine and propeller limitations, required placards, and the types and quantities of fuel and engine oil. [Figure 13-1]

### AIRCRAFT SPECIFICATIONS

Prior to 1958, U.S. aircraft were certificated under the Civil Air Regulations (CARs). Certification information pertaining to the airframe, powerplant, and propeller are published in Aircraft Specifications. These documents are similar to TCDSs with the addition of an equipment list.

The equipment list on an Aircraft Specification for a single type of aircraft often requires between 60 or 70 pages of information. Because this information proved difficult to keep current, aircraft and equipment certificated under current regulations (14 CFR 23)

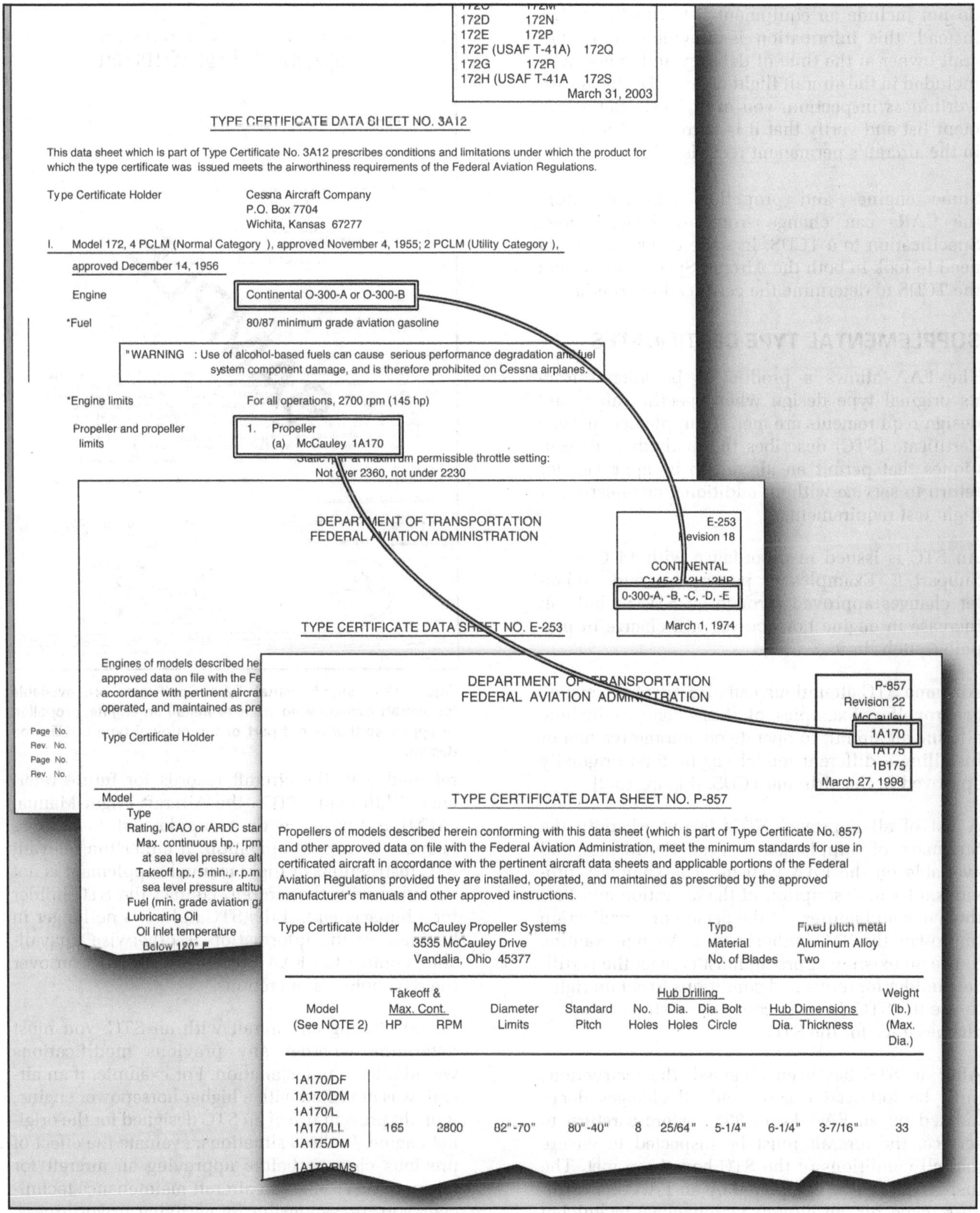


**Figure 13-1. Type certificate data sheets are provided for the airframe, powerplant, and propeller. You may subscribe to receive printed versions of the TCDS, or you can download them from the FAA's Web site at www.faa.gov.**

do not include an equipment list with the TCDS. Instead, this information is provided to the aircraft owner at the time of delivery and is normally included in the aircraft flight manual. During an airworthiness inspection, you must locate the equipment list and verify that it is current and included in the aircraft's permanent records.

Some engines and propellers certified under the CARs can change from an Airworthiness Specification to a TCDS. In some cases, you might need to look in both the Aircraft Specifications and the TCDS to determine the certification criteria.

## SUPPLEMENTAL TYPE CERTIFICATES

The FAA allows a product to be altered from its original type design when specific safety and design requirements are met. A Supplemental Type Certificate (STC) describes the methods and techniques that permit an aircraft to be approved for return to service without additional engineering or flight test requirements.

An STC is issued in accordance with 14 CFR 21, Subpart E. Examples of powerplant and propeller changes approved through an STC include an increase in engine horsepower or a change in propeller pitch limits.

Airframe STC alterations can also affect the engine or propeller. Examples of these changes include altering an aircraft to operate on automotive fuel or installing a different model engine than originally approved in the airframe TCDS. [Figure 13-2]

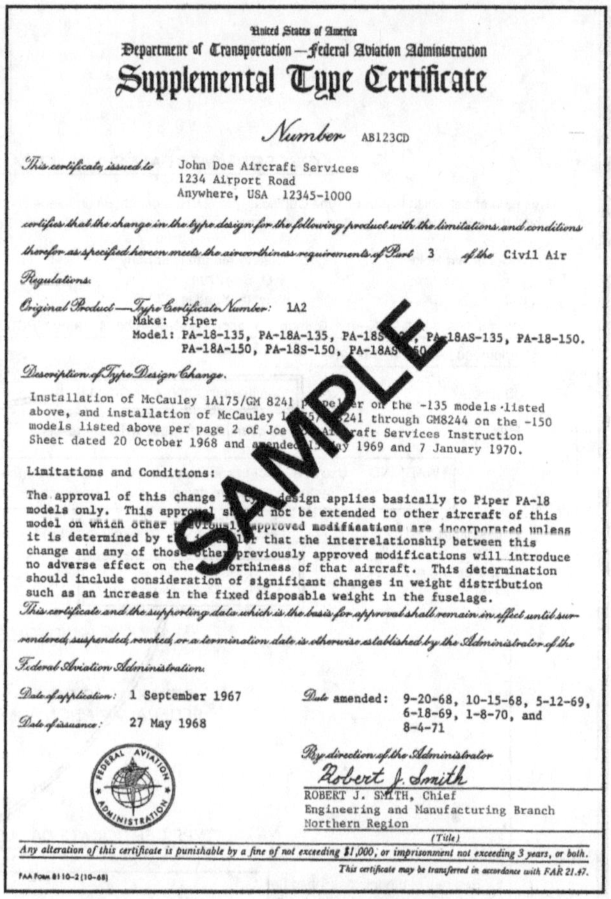

United States of America
Department of Transportation—Federal Aviation Administration
Supplemental Type Certificate

Number AB123CD

This certificate, issued to John Doe Aircraft Services
1234 Airport Road
Anywhere, USA 12345-1000

certifies that the change in the type design for the following product with the limitations and conditions therefor as specified hereon meets the airworthiness requirements of Part 3 of the Civil Air Regulations.

Original Product—Type Certificate Number: 1A2
Make: Piper
Model: PA-18-135, PA-18A-135, PA-18S-[illegible], PA-18AS-135, PA-18-150. PA-18A-150, PA-18S-150, PA-18AS-[illegible]

Description of Type Design Change.

Installation of McCauley 1A175/GM 8241 p[illegible]ller on the -135 models listed above, and installation of McCauley 1[illegible]241 through GM8244 on the -150 models listed above per page 2 of Joe [illegible] Aircraft Services Instruction Sheet dated 20 October 1968 and amended [illegible] 1969 and 7 January 1970.

Limitations and Conditions:

The approval of this change [illegible] design applies basically to Piper PA-18 models only. This approval s[illegible] not be extended to other aircraft of this model on which other [illegible] approved modifications are incorporated unless it is determined by t[illegible] that the interrelationship between this change and any of those other previously approved modifications will introduce no adverse effect on the [illegible]orthiness of that aircraft. This determination should include consideration of significant changes in weight distribution such as an increase in the fixed disposable weight in the fuselage.

This certificate and the supporting data which is the basis for approval shall remain in effect until surrendered, suspended, revoked, or a termination date is otherwise established by the Administrator of the Federal Aviation Administration.

Date of application: 1 September 1967
Date of issuance: 27 May 1968
Date amended: 9-20-68, 10-15-68, 5-12-69, 6-18-69, 1-8-70, and 8-4-71

FEDERAL AVIATION ADMINISTRATION

By direction of the Administrator
Robert J. Smith
ROBERT J. SMITH, Chief
Engineering and Manufacturing Branch
Northern Region
(Title)

Any alteration of this certificate is punishable by a fine of not exceeding $1,000, or imprisonment not exceeding 3 years, or both.

This certificate may be transferred in accordance with FAR 21.47.

FAA Form 8110-2 (10-68)

SAMPLE

**Figure 13-2. Supplemental Type Certificates are available for aircraft owners who want to install an engine, propeller, or appliance that is not part of the original type certificated design.**

A list of all approved STCs is published in the Summary of Supplemental Type Certificates and available on the FAA website. The summary provides a basic description of the alteration and lists the name and address of the person or organization that owns the STC authorization. Anyone wanting to use an existing approval must contact the certificate holder for terms and conditions to obtain rights to use the STC. In most cases, the certificate holder charges a fee for the STC.

After an STC has been obtained, the instructions must be followed exactly and all changes documented on an FAA Form 337. Before a return to service, the aircraft must be inspected to ensure that all conditions of the STC have been met. The inspection can be completed by an FAA airworthiness inspector, an aircraft maintenance technician holding an Inspection Authorization (IA), a properly certificated repair station, or another approved entity.

Because each STC contains unique information, the installation and maintenance instructions must be retained with the aircraft records for future reference. With many STCs, the Aircraft Flight Manual (AFM) is revised with a supplement to address changes in aircraft operation. If either the relevant STC instructions or flight manual supplement is not included with the aircraft, contact the STC holder for a replacement. If the STC holder is no longer in business or the information is otherwise unavailable, contact the FAA office with jurisdiction over the STC holder's operations.

Before altering an aircraft with an STC, you must determine whether any previous modifications would affect the installation. For example, if an aircraft was modified with a higher horsepower engine, it might prevent use of an STC designed for the original engine. In these situations, evaluate the effect of previous changes before approving an aircraft for return to service. As an aircraft maintenance technician, you are responsible for verifying airworthiness. Even when existing documentation states an aircraft is approved for service, you should investigate any installation that seems questionable. If you are uncomfortable with the quality or appropriateness of an alteration, contact an FAA airworthiness inspector to determine if it meets approved guidelines.

## AIRWORTHINESS DIRECTIVES

An Airworthiness Directive (AD) is issued as an amendment to 14 CFR 39 and its instructions must be followed. Registered aircraft owners receive copies of ADs from the FAA whenever a defect is identified that applies to the make and model of their aircraft. The AD is sent to the address indicated on the aircraft registration certificate, or if updated, the address from the FAA database. It is the responsibility of the aircraft owner to determine the necessary action for compliance. During an airworthiness inspection, it is the responsibility of the aircraft maintenance technician to comply with all applicable ADs before returning an aircraft to service. ADs are also available online through the FAA website or commercial providers of aviation data.

Figure 13-3 shows the development of an AD compliance report using the FAA website.

1. Select the first letter of the engine manufacturer's name. Select the name of the engine manufacturer.

2. Select the appropriate engine model and review the pertinent ADs.

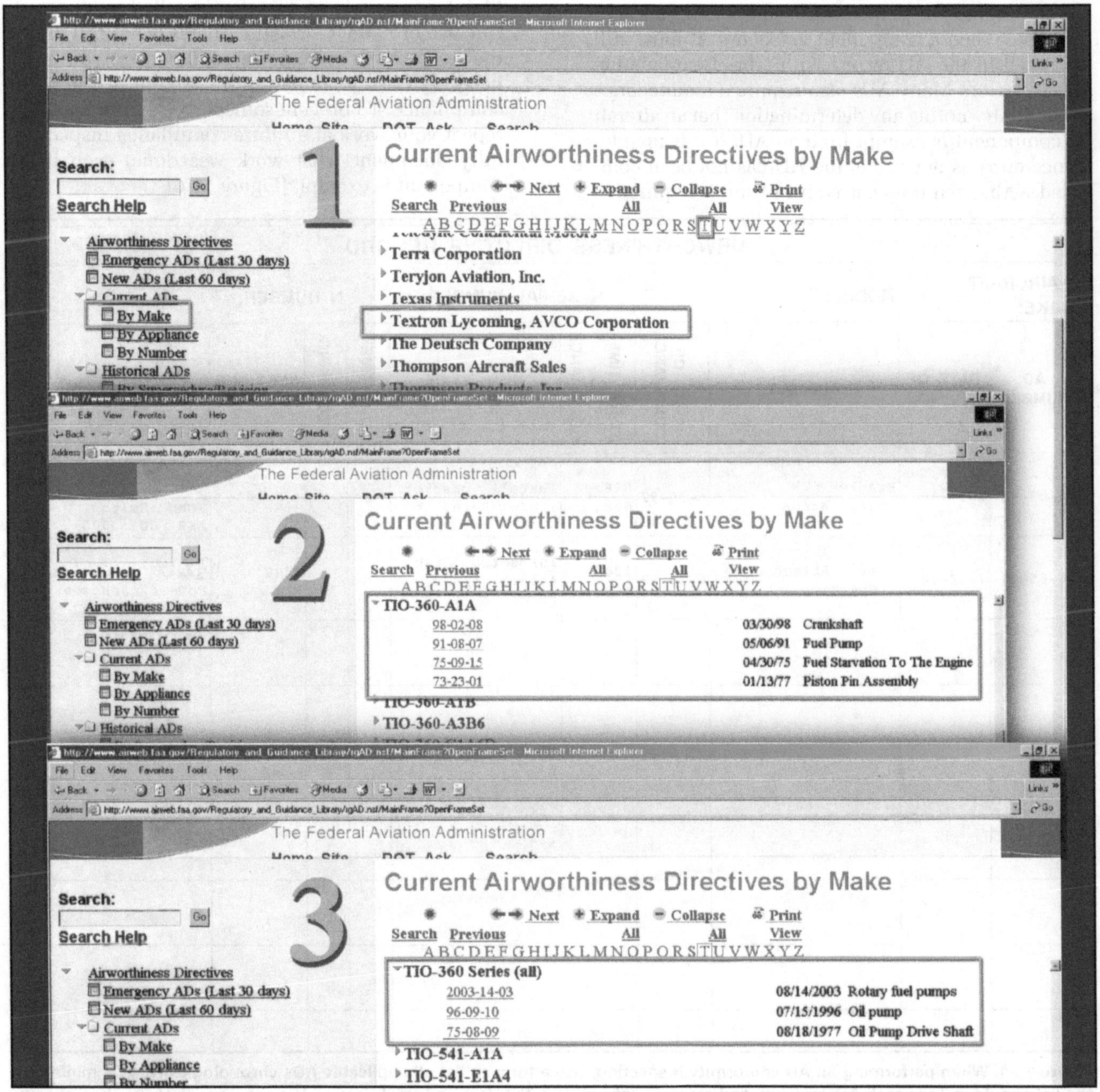


**Figure 13-3. You can conduct an AD conformity inspection online.**

3. In addition to reviewing the specific model, review ADs for the model series. For example, when inspecting a Textron-Lycoming model TIO-360 A1A engine, check the specific ADs for the TIO-360 A1A and also check the TIO-360 series.

During an airworthiness inspection, an aircraft maintenance technician must verify that each AD has been complied with, according to the text of the AD. This task requires a thorough review of each AD record entry in the aircraft's maintenance records and often requires verification by examining the engine or powerplant. [Figure 13-4]

Although an AD might apply to the make and model of an engine or propeller, a component may be exempt. When a component is exempt, it must still be noted in the AD record with a brief explanation of the reason. Many ADs also require a maintenance record entry noting any determination that an aircraft or component is exempt from an AD. If this maintenance entry is not made, the AD has not been complied with, even if no corrective action is required.

AD research on an airframe, powerplant, or propeller is straightforward because the make, model, and serial number of these components are on the data plates and maintenance records. Appliances often require additional attention and research to determine applicable ADs. For example, an AD might have been issued that pertains to a series of magnetos, but a simple search of engine ADs might not reveal this information. To help identify all appliances, use the aircraft's equipment list or create a separate record with the make, model, and serial numbers of all appliances. [Figure 13-5]

Maintenance release tags for installed components can also provide information that is beneficial during the research. In extreme cases, however, you might need to disassemble part of the aircraft to determine compliance. To prevent someone else from having to repeat your work at a future compliance inspection, fully document what work was done, even if the component is exempt. [Figure 13-6]

**AIRWORTHINESS DIRECTIVE RECORD**

AIRCRAFT MAKE: MODEL: SERIAL NUMBER: N NUMBER:

| AD NUMBER | DATE OF REVISION | SUBJECT | DATE OF COMPLIANCE | TOTAL TIME AT COMPLIANCE | METHOD OF COMPLIANCE | ONE TIME | RECURRING | NEXT DUE DATE/TIME | NAME SIGNATURE NUMBER |
|---|---|---|---|---|---|---|---|---|---|
| 76-03-05 | 2-17-90 | Bracket Installation | 6-30-92 | 826 Hrs. | Install bracket i/a/w Para. b | x | | | John M. Smith<br>John Smith<br>A&P 00110000 |
| 76-05-04 | 7-12-90 | Stab. Attach. Inspection | 6-26-92 | 1248 Hrs. | Inspected Stab. Attach i/a/w Para. a & b | | x | 2248 Hrs. | Robert B. Johnson<br>Robert Johnson<br>A&P 110011000 |

**Figure 13-4. When performing an AD conformity inspection, use a form to list all applicable ADs chronologically. At a minimum, the list should include each AD, revision, and amendment number, the date and total time on the component at the time of compliance, the method of compliance, and the next compliance due date, or time, if the AD is recurring in nature.**

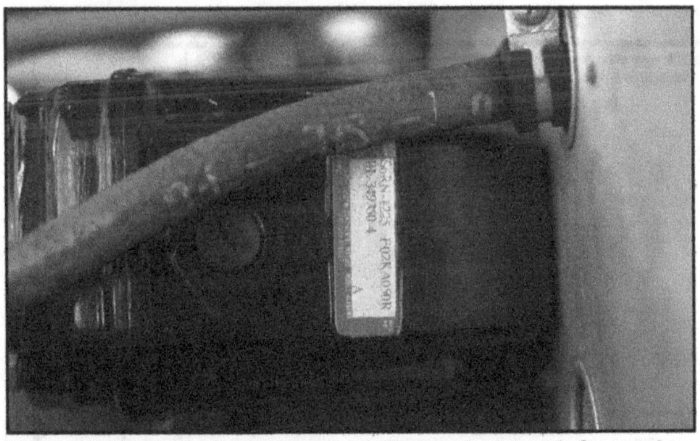

**Figure 13-5. Visually confirm appliance data tag information and record it on a form during appliance AD checks.**

**Airworthiness Directive Conformity Inspection**
**Engine Appliances**

Date_____________

Aircraft:_____________

Make_________ Model_________ Serial Number_________ Reg. Number_________

Engine:_____________

Make_________ Model_________ Serial Number_________ Reg. Number_________

| Component | Make | Model | Serial Number |
|---|---|---|---|
| Carburetor Air Inlet Filter | | | |
| Carburetor/Fuel Injection | | | |
| Compressed Gas Cylinders | | | |
| Vacuum or Air Pump | | | |
| Engine Driven Fuel Pump | | | |
| Engine Gage Units | | | |
| Fire Ext. Discharge Cartridges | | | |
| Fire Detectors | | | |
| Fire Extinguisher | | | |
| Fire Extinguisher Discharge Outlets | | | |
| Fuel Flow Transducer | | | |
| Fuel Regulator | | | |
| Fuel Shutoff Valve | | | |
| Generator | | | |
| Hose Assemblies | | | |
| Magnetos | | | |
| Oil Filter | | | |
| Oil Filter Adapter | | | |
| Oil Cooler | | | |
| Over-speed/Under-speed Governor | | | |
| Propeller Governor | | | |
| Smoke Detector | | | |
| Spark Plugs | | | |
| Starter | | | |
| Starting Vibrator Assembly | | | |
| Turbocharger | | | |

**Figure 13-6. An appliance checklist, similar to the one shown here, helps you identify the components to consider when checking engine or propeller appliance airworthiness directives.**

## ADVISORY CIRCULARS

Many of the technical publications and regulations issued by the FAA are complex. The FAA issues Advisory Circulars (AC) to inform, explain, and provide further guidance for operating and maintaining aircraft. Advisory Circulars are informational only; they cannot be used as approved data unless incorporated in a regulation or airworthiness directive.

Field reports of discrepancies discovered by aviation maintenance technicians during inspections or maintenance are critical pieces of data in a safety management system. When a new or unusual maintenance problem is encountered, a FAA Form 8010-4, Malfunction or Defect Report should be completed and submited. [Figure 13-7]

If the FAA determines a trend emerging with a particular aircraft or component, it liaises with OEMs to investigate and if necessary mitigate or rectify any unsafe conditions in their product. This may be the topic of an Advisory Circular. If the problem is severe, it will work with the OEMs to formulate plans that will be the basis of an airworthiness directive mandating corrective actions. The FAA also provides service difficulty reports (SDR) on their website. By entering an engine or propeller make and model, you can search for all related reports. Although you are not required to check this information, these reports provide useful information for identifying problem areas during an inspection.

## MAINTENANCE AND SERVICE MANUALS

Manufacturers produce technical documents to maintain and service their products. The titles and content of these publications vary between manufacturers. However, the typical maintenance manual provides information on routine servicing, systems descriptions and functions, handling procedures, and removal and installation of components. Additionally, these manuals contain basic repair procedures and troubleshooting guides for common malfunctions. With regard to airworthiness inspections, the manuals contain detailed instructions and checklists for determining the condition of the aircraft and its components.

Engine and propeller airworthiness inspection information is often located in an airframe manufacturer's manuals. However, when inspecting subassemblies such as the engine, the propeller, and accessories, it is extremely beneficial to have access to the component manufacturer's maintenance publications.

## OVERHAUL MANUAL

Manufacturers of engines, propellers, and other components produce overhaul manuals that provide complex disassembly, inspection, and repair instructions. By definition, an overhaul includes disassembly, cleaning, inspection, repair (as required), reassembly, and testing.

Each action is covered in detail and must be followed for an item to be overhauled. The manual is required during overhaul, but the information is also useful when evaluating the condition of a component during an airworthiness inspection.

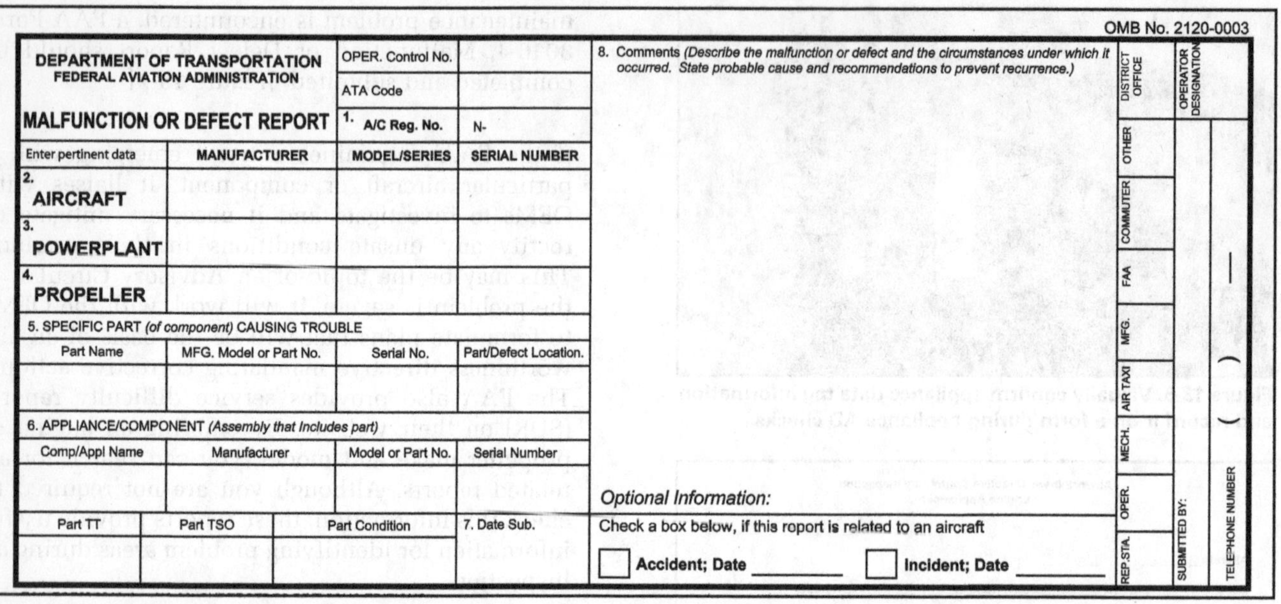
OMB No. 2120-0003

DEPARTMENT OF TRANSPORTATION
FEDERAL AVIATION ADMINISTRATION

OPER. Control No.

ATA Code

MALFUNCTION OR DEFECT REPORT

1. A/C Reg. No. N-

| Enter pertinent data | MANUFACTURER | MODEL/SERIES | SERIAL NUMBER |
|---|---|---|---|
| 2. AIRCRAFT | | | |
| 3. POWERPLANT | | | |
| 4. PROPELLER | | | |

5. SPECIFIC PART *(of component)* CAUSING TROUBLE

| Part Name | MFG. Model or Part No. | Serial No. | Part/Defect Location. |
|---|---|---|---|
| | | | |

6. APPLIANCE/COMPONENT *(Assembly that Includes part)*

| Comp/Appl Name | Manufacturer | Model or Part No. | Serial Number |
|---|---|---|---|
| | | | |

| Part TT | Part TSO | Part Condition | 7. Date Sub. |
|---|---|---|---|
| | | | |

8. Comments *(Describe the malfunction or defect and the circumstances under which it occurred. State probable cause and recommendations to prevent recurrence.)*

Optional Information:

Check a box below, if this report is related to an aircraft

Accident; Date ________ Incident; Date ________

DISTRICT OFFICE
OPERATOR DESIGNATION
OTHER
COMMUTER
FAA
MFG.
AIR TAXI
MECH.
OPER.
REP.STA.
SUBMITTED BY:
TELEPHONE NUMBER ( )

**Figure 13-7. When you discover discrepancies during airworthiness inspections, submit a malfunction and defect report to the FAA, providing thorough details of the discrepancy.**

## ILLUSTRATED PARTS CATALOG

The Illustrated Parts Catalog (IPC) identifies the location and part numbers of items installed on an aircraft, or in a subassembly component. IPCs exist for all components of the airframe, powerplant, propeller, and accessories.

The IPC contains multiple assembly drawings and part number references. They contain detailed exploded views of an aircraft and assist in locating and identifying parts. This information is useful during inspections to help locate components that are called out in the airframe manufacturer's inspection checklists or in an AD.

## SERVICE INFORMATION

Manufacturers also communicate with aircraft owners, operators, and technicians through service information publications, or communiqués. Service information can be contained in Service Bulletins (SB) and Service Advisories. SBs often include instructions for detecting and identifying defective components installed in the aircraft during manufacture or that have been identified as having the potential to become defective while in service. For operations under 14 CFR 91, compliance with this information is not required by regulation; however, manufacturers often consider compliance to be mandatory and compliance is important for equipment reliability. If an aircraft is operated under various regulations such as 14 CFR Part 135, compliance with these publications is required.

Service information can provide additional clarifying instructions regarding a topic that remains difficult as presented in the maintenance manual. For example, service information might be provided to help during inspection of a complex subassembly (or accessory) such as the engine fuel injection system. Service information might also report the availability of modification kits.

## TYPES OF AIRWORTHINESS INSPECTIONS

Aviation maintenance technicians and repair station personnel share the burden of determining whether an aircraft is safe for flight by performing airworthiness inspections at specified intervals and performing, or properly deferring, maintenance discrepancies between inspections. Depending on the type of operation and the operating environment, airworthiness inspections vary in scope, detail, and the interval between inspection phases. For example, an aircraft that is used for transporting passengers for hire must be inspected more frequently than one used for personal transportation. This topic details the different types of inspections required on aircraft used in the conduct of various flight operations.

The types of inspections required on an aircraft are determined by the requirements of federal regulations and several other factors such as the owners' or operators' type of aircraft, choice of inspection programs, or use of the aircraft. In most situations, the owner or operator has a choice of several inspection programs to comply with airworthiness inspection requirements.

## ANNUAL INSPECTION

The most common type of inspection required for light general aviation aircraft is the annual inspection. Every 12 calendar months, the aircraft must have a complete inspection performed to ensure that it meets all requirements for its airworthiness certification. A calendar month is one that ends at midnight on the last day of the month. For example, if the inspection was completed on January 14, it remains valid until midnight, January 31, the following year. An aircraft may not be flown beyond the annual due date unless a special flight permit is obtained authorizing the aircraft to be flown to an inspection facility.

The manufacturer of an aircraft normally provides a checklist in the aircraft service manual that contains at least the minimum items stipulated in 14 CFR 43, Appendix D. Manufacturer checklists are not typically FAA-approved sources, so the inspector must verify that all items addressed in 14 CFR 43 Appendix D are included in the manufacturer's checklist. Aircraft inspectors are permitted to create their own checklist as long as it contains the items required by 14 CFR 43, Appendix D. The general expectation is that all of the items on the manufacturer's checklist are to be inspected.

Annual inspections must be performed by an aircraft maintenance technician who holds an Inspection Authorization (IA) or an inspector authorized by a certified repair station with the appropriate class ratings. When an aircraft passes the inspection, the inspector documents the inspection results in the maintenance records and approves the aircraft for return to service. If an aircraft does not meet airworthiness requirements, the inspector must provide a list that details the discrepancies and unairworthy items to the aircraft owner. Although inspectors may not delegate their inspection responsibility to another person, any certified A&P technician may correct discrepancies and approve the aircraft for return to service (as long as the discrepancy does not require a major repair). The due date of the next annual inspection is based on the date of the inspection, not the date that the discrepancies were corrected. For example, if an aircraft's annual was completed on March 20th, but a discrepancy repair was not completed until April 15th, the next annual is due March 30th, the following year.

## 100-HOUR INSPECTION

If an aircraft is operated for compensation or hire, it must be thoroughly inspected every 100 hours of operation or with an FAA-approved, alternative inspection program such as a progressive inspection. The scope and detail of 100-hour and annual inspections are nearly identical, but an aircraft maintenance technician can perform the inspection and return the aircraft to service. Like the IA performing an annual, an aircraft maintenance technician (AMT) performing a 100-hour inspection may not delegate inspection tasks to anyone else. The maintenance technician performing the inspection is responsible for approving the aircraft for return to service. In other words, the AMT who returns the aircraft to service must be the person who actually performed the inspection. However, the technician may use other individuals to assist with tasks such as removing inspection panels, cowlings, and fairings. Furthermore, any other AMT may correct and sign-off discrepancies found (as long as they are not major repairs or major alterations).

If the AMT who inspects the aircraft has inspection authorization (IA), the 100-hour inspection may be signed off as an annual inspection. A 100-hour inspection may not take the place of an annual inspection; an annual inspection must be performed by an appropriately rated individual and signed-off as an annual inspection in the aircraft maintenance records.

## PROGRESSIVE INSPECTION

When an aircraft is used extensively, an aircraft operator may determine that it is not economical to take the aircraft out of service for a complete annual inspection at one time. As an alternative, an operator may use a progressive inspection program. The scope of a progressive inspection is the same as an annual inspection but the inspection tasks are divided into a series of smaller inspections and spread over time. A progressive inspection schedule must ensure that an aircraft is airworthy at all times and conforms to all applicable FAA aircraft specifications, type certificate data sheets, airworthiness directives, and other required data.

The manufacturer provides guidelines to help operators select an appropriate inspection program for their operation. For example, if an aircraft is flown more than 200 hours per year, a progressive inspection program would likely be recommended to limit aircraft downtime and overall maintenance costs.

Figure 13-8 is an example of a typical inspection table outlining a progressive inspection schedule. For this inspection schedule there are items inspected at 50, 100, or 200 hours. The inspection intervals are separated in such a way that the result is a complete aircraft inspection every 200 flight hours.

| | EACH 50 HOURS | EACH 100 HOURS | EACH 200 HOURS | SPECIAL INSPECTION ITEM |
|---|---|---|---|---|
| **PROPELLER** | | | | |
| 1. Spinner | ● | | | |
| 2. Spinner bulkhead | | | ● | |
| 3. Blades | ● | | | |
| 4. Mounting nuts | | | ● | |
| 5. Hub | | | ● | |
| 6. Governor and control | | | ● | |
| 7. Synchronizing system/Synchrophaser system | | | ● | |
| 8. Unfeathering accumulator | | | ● | |
| 9. Anti-Ice electrical wiring | ● | | | |
| 10. Anti-Ice brushes, slip ring and boots | ● | | | |
| **ENGINE COMPARTMENT** | | | | |
| Check for evidence of oil and fuel leaks, then clean entire engine and compartment, if needed, prior to inspection. | | | | |
| 1. Engine oil screen, filler cap, dipstick, drain plug and external filter element | ● | | | 1 |
| 2. Oil cooler | | ● | | |
| 3. Induction air filter | ● | | | 2 |
| 4. Induction airbox, air valves, doors and controls | | ● | | |
| 5. Cold and hot air hoses | | | ● | |
| 6. Engine baffles | ● | | | |
| 7. Cylinders, rocker box covers and push rod housings | | ● | | |
| 8. Crankcase, oil sump, accessory section and front crankshaft seal | | ● | | |
| 9. Hoses, metal lines and fittings | ● | | | 3 |
| 10. Intake and exhaust systems | ● | | | 4 |
| 11. Ignition harness | | ● | | |
| 12. Spark plugs | | ● | | |
| 13. Compression check | | | ● | |
| 14. Crankcase and vacuum system breather lines | | | ● | |
| 15. Electrical wiring | | ● | | |

**Figure 13-8. The powerplant and propeller inspection items in a progressive inspection schedule are only one phase of a progressive inspection program.**

Before an operator can begin a progressive inspection program, the FAA must approve the inspection plan. The operator must submit a written request to the local Flight Standards District Office (FSDO) outlining the intended progressive inspection. After a progressive inspection program is approved, the aircraft must receive an annual inspection. Thereafter, routine and detailed inspections are conducted as prescribed in the progressive inspection schedule. Routine inspections consist of visual and operational checks of the aircraft, engines, appliances, components, and systems, without disassembly. Detailed inspections consist of thorough checks of the aircraft, engines, appliances, components, and systems including necessary disassembly. The overhaul of a component, engine, or system entails detailed inspections during the overhaul operation.

A progressive inspection program requires that a current, FAA-approved inspection procedure manual is available to both the pilot and the maintenance technician. The manual explains the progressive inspection and outlines the required inspection intervals. All items in the inspection schedule must be completed within the 12 calendar months that are allowed for an annual inspection. The progressive inspection differs from an annual or 100-hour inspection in that a certified mechanic holding an IA, a certified repair station, or the aircraft manufacturer may supervise others performing the inspection.

If a progressive inspection program is discontinued, the owner or operator must immediately notify the local FSDO of the discontinuance. Furthermore, the first complete inspection is due within 12 calendar months or, in the case of commercial operations, 100 hours of operation from the last complete inspection that was performed under the progressive inspection schedule.

## LARGE AND TURBINE-POWERED MULTI-ENGINE AIRCRAFT INSPECTIONS

Aircraft with a gross takeoff weight of 12,500 pounds or multiengine turbine aircraft operating under 14 CFR 91 require inspection programs tailored to a specific aircraft and its unique operating conditions. The program must consider items such as high flight times or extreme operating environments. Due to the size and complexity of most turbine-powered aircraft, the FAA requires a more comprehensive inspection program to meet the needs of these aircraft. Although these aircraft may be operated under Part 91, large and turbine-powered aircraft are often inspected under programs normally used by air carrier or air taxi operations (14 CFR Part 121 and 14 CFR Part 135, respectively).

The registered owner or operator of a large or turbine-powered aircraft operating under Part 91 must select, identify in the aircraft maintenance records, and use one of the following inspection programs: a continuous airworthiness inspection program, an approved aircraft inspection program (AAIP), the manufacturer's current recommended inspection program, or another inspection program developed by the owner/operator and approved by the FAA. The exception to this rule is turbine-powered rotorcraft, in which case, the owner/operator may choose to use the inspection provisions set out for small aircraft—that is, annual, 100-hour, or progressive inspection programs. The operator must submit an inspection schedule, along with instructions and procedures regarding the performance of the inspections, including all tests and checks, to the local FSDO for approval.

A continuous airworthiness inspection program is designed for commercial operators of large aircraft operating under 14 CFR Parts 121 or 135. Continuous airworthiness maintenance programs (CAMP) are used by air carriers that operate a number of a particular make and model aircraft.

An AAIP may be chosen by on-demand charter operators who operate under 14 CFR 135. If the FAA determines that annual, 100-hour, or progressive inspections are inadequate for these operations, it allows (or requires) implementation of an AAIP for any make and model aircraft that the operator uses. The AAIP is similar to the CAMP used most frequently by 14 CFR 121 air carriers. This program integrates maintenance and inspection into an overall continuous maintenance program.

A complete inspection program, as recommended by manufacturers, consists of following the inspection program supplied by the airframe manufacturer, supplemented by the inspection programs provided by the manufacturers of the engines, propellers, appliances, survival equipment, and emergency equipment installed on the aircraft. If an aircraft has been modified, the manufacturer's inspection program must be supplemented. Ultimately, any inspection program must be approved by the FAA.

The purpose of a powerplant inspection is to determine whether an engine and its associated components are properly installed and that their condition meets all regulatory airworthiness requirements. Regardless of whether the inspection is part of an annual, 100-hour, or progressive inspection, the scope and detail is essentially the same.

FAA regulations stipulate the minimum requirements for inspection; however, you should also incorporate items recommended by the manufacturer and industry best practices. As an aircraft maintenance technician, you have the responsibility to determine whether the manufacturer's inspection criteria meet or exceed those set forth in 14 CFR 43 Appendix D. [Figure 13-9]

## INSPECTION

Prior to beginning an inspection, obtain the appropriate items to ensure compliance with regulations and manufacturer recommendations. Gather the aircraft maintenance records and verify the presence of all required documents. Research the Type Certificate Data Sheets, Airworthiness Directives, Service Bulletins, and other applicable reference materials and acquire the necessary checklists.

### CHECKLISTS

14 CFR 43.15 (c) (1) requires the use of a checklist when performing an annual or 100-hour inspection. You can use the manufacturer's checklist or one of your own designs. However, as the AMT performing an airworthiness inspection, you must determine that the checklist covers all items addressed in Part 43, Appendix D and that you have considered manufacturer items. [Figure 13-10]

### PRELIMINARY INSPECTION

Compile a list of the makes, models, and serial numbers of the engine(s), propeller(s), and all engine appliances. This information is primarily obtained by researching the maintenance records, equipment list, maintenance release tags, and by visually inspecting the data tags attached to each component. Verify that each component is approved for installation by referring to the appropriate Type Certificate Data Sheet (TCDS), Supplemental Type Certificate (STC), or other FAA-approved documentation. Record the total time in service and time since the last overhaul for each engine and propeller as well as the status of any life-limited appliances installed on the engine. Keep in mind that although an AD might apply to an airframe component (an ignition switch for example), it can also affect the operation of powerplant systems and components.

Check for applicable Airworthiness Directives and search the service difficulty reports through the FAA website to identify problems that other mechanics have found with similar engines, propellers, and appliances. After you complete the preliminary inspection, review the engine and propeller inspection checklists and procedures that you will use and plan your work. For example, if you discover

Part 43 Appendix D

(d) Each person performing an annual or 100-hour inspection shall inspect (where applicable) components of the engine and nacelle group as follows:

(1) Engine section—for visual evidence of excessive oil, fuel, or hydraulic leaks, and sources of such leaks.

(2) Studs and nuts—for improper torque and obvious defects.

(3) Internal engine—for cylinder compression and for metal particles or foreign matter on screens and sump drain plugs. If there is weak cylinder compression, for improper internal condition and improper internal tolerances.

(4) Engine mount—for cracks, looseness of mounting, and looseness of engine to mount.

(5) Flexible vibration dampeners—for poor condition and deterioration.

(6) Engine controls—for defects, improper travel, and improper safetying.

(7) Lines, hoses, and clamps—for leaks, improper condition and looseness.

(8) Exhaust stacks—for cracks, defects, and improper attachment.

(9) Accessories—for apparent defects in security of mounting.

(10) All systems—for improper installation, poor general condition, defects, and insecure attachment.

(11) Cowling—for cracks, and defects.

**Figure 13-9. Part 43 Appendix D Airworthiness inspection scope and details pertaining to engine airworthiness inspection criteria.**

## INSPECTION REPORT

This form meets requirements of FAR Part 43 Work Order No. ______

| Make | Model | Serial No. | Registration No. |
|---|---|---|---|
| Owner | | Date | |
| Type of Inspection | | Tach Time | |

| A. PROPELLER GROUP | L | R | 100 | 500 | Insp. |
|---|---|---|---|---|---|
| 1. Inspection spinner and back plate | | | | | |
| 2. Inspect blades for nicks and cracks | | | | | |
| 3. Inspect hub for cracks and corrosion | | | | | |
| 4. Check for grease and oil leaks | | | | | |
| 5. Check mounting bolts and safety | | | | | |
| 6. Constant speed — check blades for tightness in hub | | | | | |
| 7. Constant speed — remove prop, remove sludge | | | | | |
| 8. Lubricate as per manual | | | | | |
| 9. Inspect complete assembly | | | | | |
| 10. Replace spinner | | | | | |
| **B. ENGINE GROUP** | | | | | |
| 1. Remove engine cowls | | | | | |
| 2. Clean cowling, check for cracks missing fasteners, etc. | | | | | |
| 3. Compression check: /80<br>L. #1 #2 #3 #4 #5 #6<br>R. #1 #2 #3 #4 #5 #6 | | | | | |
| 4. Drain oil | | | | | |
| 5. Check oil screens and clean | | | | | |
| 6. Replace oil filter element | | | | | |
| 7. Check oil temp sender unit for leaks and security | | | | | |
| 8. Clean and check oil radiator fins | | | | | |
| 9. Remove and flush oil radiator | | | | | |
| 10. Check and clean fuel screens | | | | | |
| 11. Drain carburetor | | | | | |
| 12. Service fuel injector nozzles | | | | | |
| 13. Check fuel system for leaks | | | | | |
| 14. Check oil lines for leaks and security | | | | | |
| 15. Check fuel lines for leaks and security | | | | | |
| 16. Service air cleaner | | | | | |
| 17. Check induction air and heat ducts | | | | | |
| 18. Check condition of carb heat box | | | | | |
| 19. Check mag points for proper clearance. | | | | | |
| 20. Check mags for oil seal leakage | | | | | |
| 21. Check breaker felts for lubrication. | | | | | |
| 22. Check distributor block for cracks, burned areas, corrosion, height of contact springs | | | | | |
| 23. Check ignition harness and insulators. | | | | | |

**Figure 13-10. Part 43.15 (c)(1) requires the use of a checklist during a 100-hour or annual inspection. The checklist must contain, at a minimum, those items listed in Part 43, Appendix D.**

that an AD requires the magnetos to be removed, comply with the AD before checking and adjusting ignition timing.

## PREINSPECTION FUNCTIONAL CHECK

A functional inspection is not required by regulation, but should be completed to identify abnormal

**Figure 13-11. With the engine cowling removed, do a quick visual inspection before starting the engine. Write down any discrepancies that you find during the inspection.**

engine operation. Before starting the engine, conduct a preflight inspection following the checklist in the Airplane Flight Manual. The critical items include verifying that the engine has the proper amount of oil, the aircraft is safely positioned for a run-up, and that the cowling and airframe access panels are secure.

The functional inspection lets you establish engine performance before work is started. This will be compared to the post-inspection functional check. Also, this run-up enables the engine to reach normal operating temperature so that oil drains easily and internal engine condition tests (such as the compression check on a reciprocating engine) are accurate. Record all engine parameters during the run-up for later comparison. Note any discrepancies for troubleshooting during the repair phase of the inspection. [Figure 13-12]

## CLEANING

14 CFR Part 43 requires you to clean the engine to remove oil, grease, and dirt at the start of a 100-hour or annual inspection. Open all necessary inspection plates, access doors, fairings, and cowling.

As you open and remove the cowling, look for accumulations of oil or other fluids that indicate a leak. If fuel stains or accumulations of oil are visible, attempt to locate the source of the leak. Note all suspected leaks for further investigation during the inspection.

Clean the engine and engine compartment using Stoddard solvent or other approved commercial degreaser. To prevent damage to electrical components, tape over all vent holes such as those on magnetos, alternators, and generators. In addition, avoid applying solvent or water directly onto any electrical component, vacuum pump, or starter motor. After cleaning is complete, be sure to remove all items used to protect the components during the cleaning process.

## INSPECTION PHASE

The engine inspection should be thorough to ensure that the engine is in an airworthy condition. In many cases, much of the condition can be determined with a detailed visual inspection of the exterior parts of the engine. Other times you will need to disassemble part of the engine to perform a visual inspection of interior parts. Often you will need to use special inspection tools, such as a borescope, to inspect internal parts.

When necessary, the inspection checklist predicates when disassembly is required. For example,

| RUN-UP CHECKLIST | Pre Inspection | Post Inspection | Variation |
|---|---|---|---|
| 1. Preflight the engine | | | |
| a. Oil level | | | |
| b. Sump fuel | | | |
| c. Check overall condition | | | |
| 2. Start engine in accordance with the pilot's operating handbook. | | | |
| 3. Maneuver to a safe run-up area free of loose debris and FOD. | | | |
| 4. Perform a run-up. | | | |
| a. Determine that all the temperatures are operating in the green. | | | |
| b. Set RPM to that prescribed for run-up in the POH. | | | |
| c. Record oil pressure | | | |
| d. Record suction | | | |
| e. Record voltage or alternator load. | | | |
| f. Record fuel flow | | | |
| g. Perform a magneto check-RPM Drop R/L | | | |
| h. Mixture check | | | |
| i. Propeller control check | | | |
| 5. Accelerate engine to full power | | | |
| a. Record static RPM | | | |

**Figure 13-12. In addition to the aircraft manufacturer's run-up checklist, you should prepare a pre-inspection run-up report to record the results of the engine check before and after the inspection.**

the air filter assembly is typically removed to inspect the interior of the air box or induction plenum. Although the checklist calls for the filter to be removed as a specified step of the inspection checklist, you do not have to follow the order as presented in the checklist. With experience on a particular aircraft, you might want to rearrange the checklist to improve on the organization and convenience of inspection. To verify the completion of all checklist items, you should develop the habit of checking or initialing each completed step.

To determine the internal condition of a reciprocating engine, check the compression of the cylinders and inspect the oil screen and filter for metal particles in the oil.

A cylinder compression test determines whether the valves, piston rings, and pistons are adequately sealing the combustion chamber. Cylinders with good compression provide more power than cylinders with low compression. When you perform a differential compression test, follow the aircraft manufacturer's instructions. The instructions might be contained in the airframe or engine manufacturer's maintenance publications, or the manufacturer might have issued a specific service bulletin or letter that provides extensive details for performing the inspection. For safety, this procedure is best performed by two technicians. [Figure 13-13]

**Figure 13-13. A compression test is used to help determine the internal condition and "health" of an engine.**

The minimum cylinder pressure indications that denote airworthiness vary between manufacturers. Although FAA AC 43.13-1A permits no more than 25% leakage, some manufacturers provide extensive information and calibration tools for standardizing the results of the checks performed on their engines. For example, Teledyne Continental Motors requires you to use the information in Service Bulletin SB 03-3, or a later revision.

To determine the internal condition of a turbine engine, inspect the cold and hot sections. The **cold section** includes the engine inlet and compressor (or diffuser). Compressor blades must be inspected for damage and erosion as well as the accumulation of dirt. You typically use a flashlight, mirror, and borescope to inspect the cold section.

The **hot section**, including the combustion liners, turbine blades, and high pressure nozzle vanes, is also inspected with a borescope. Inspect the hot section for cracks, warping, burned areas, evidence of hot spots, and misalignment of the combustion liner. In addition to the borescope, dye penetrant is used to inspect for cracks in accessible areas. [Figure 13-14]

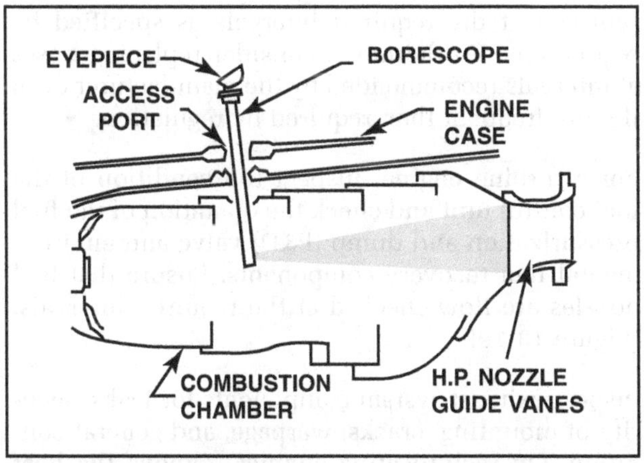


**Figure 13-14. On some engines, the high pressure nozzle guide vanes are inspected with a borescope that is inserted into one of the engine's combustors.**

In addition to inspecting the turbine blades, the turbine disk must also be examined carefully. Since the integrity of a turbine disk is critical to flight safety, any cracking on the disk requires disk replacement. [Figure 13-15]

Removing the oil screen (or oil filter) enables you to discover whether the engine is experiencing excessive and destructive wear of internal components. Look for any metal particles present on the screen and in the screen housing. Oil filters on most modern engines must be cut open for inspection. If you discover metal particles, you must determine the source of the metal and decide whether the engine is airworthy. [Figure 13-16]

Slight accumulations of metal are generally acceptable and indicate normal wear. Large quantities of metal can be checked with a magnet to determine if they originated from ferrous (magnetic) or nonferrous parts. If the metal is ferrous, it may have come from damaged accessory drive gears or worn cylinder walls and piston rings. Conversely, nonferrous materials typically indicate worn crankshaft main or connecting rod bearings, or aluminum shavings that might have been worn from the crankcase or accessory gear housing.

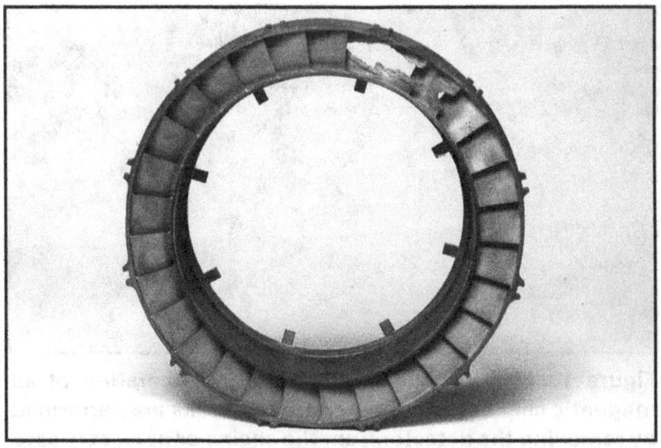

**Figure 13-15. The extreme damage on this turbine inlet guide assembly was caused by a cracked and misaligned fuel nozzle which resulted in fuel nozzle streaking. When damage is this extensive, the compressor turbine (CT) blades must be replaced, and the disk inspected for excessive heat damage.**

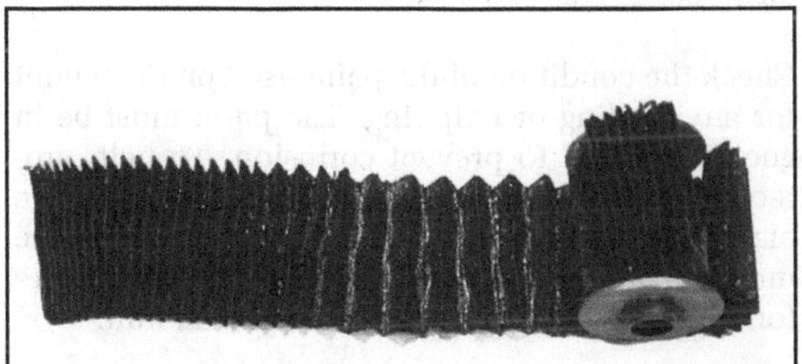

**Figure 13-16. When changing oil during an inspection, the oil filter should be opened so you can check for metal particles or other contamination.**

Some owners and maintenance shops choose to perform a spectrometric oil analysis. While the engine oil is draining, a sample is collected and sent to a lab for analysis. This type of analysis is best used on an ongoing basis to detect wear trends. A single oil sample, however, can help identify the location of damaged internal engine components.

Inspect the oil cooler for leakage, security of attachment, and general condition. Clean out debris from the cooling fins and verify that the fins are not excessively distorted. On turbine powerplants, inspect the condition and operation of the chip detectors and warning circuits. [Figure 13-17]

Because of the extraordinary loads and stresses that it is subject to, the engine mount must also undergo rigorous inspection. Examine the engine mount and

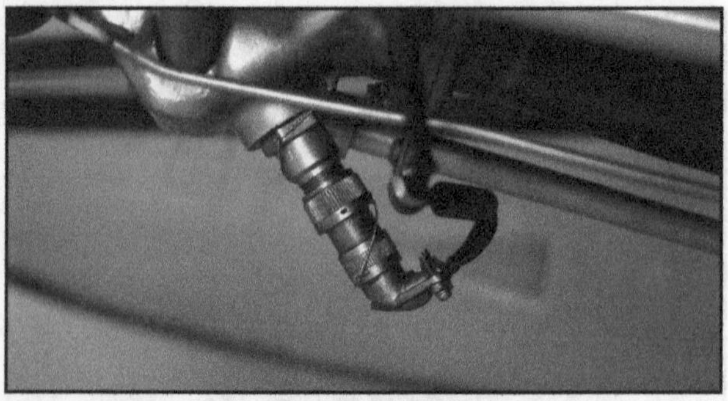

**Figure 13-17. Inspect the condition and operation of all magnetic chip detectors. Operational checks are performed by removing the detector from the engine or accessory case and with the wiring still connected to the detector, bridge across the detector's poles with a metallic tool. When bridged, the chip detection warning light should illuminate.**

attaching structure for cracks, looseness of mounting to the engine, and looseness of the mount to the airframe. [Figure 13-18]

Check the condition of the paint used on the mount for any chafing or chipping. The paint must be in good condition to prevent corrosion. To help protect the paint, do not use nylon ties or other abrasive clamping devices to secure wires or hoses to the mount. Padded clamps are the preferred hardware for attaching components to an engine mount.

Flexible engine mount vibration dampeners absorb engine vibrations and torsional force. Because the dampeners deteriorate over time, inspect them for proper installation, splits, cracks, dry rot, or any other damage.

Inspect engine controls for routing, chafing, security, safety, excessive wear, damage, and general condition. Perform an operational check on each

**Figure 13-18. Examine the engine mount for cracks. If cracks are suspected, use at least a 10-power magnifying glass to perform a more thorough inspection. In some cases, it may be necessary to remove the paint from the mount to perform a dye penetrant inspection.**

control for binding, and proper operation. Inspect all linkages for excessive wear and proper installation of hardware safety locks. Finally, check each control for full travel, bearing in mind that all engine controls should be rigged with a slight amount of cushion away from the limit stops inside the cockpit.

Inspect all lines and hoses for condition, age hardening, chafing, security, routing, kinking, and general condition. For vents and breather tubes, inspect for any blockage or obstructions at the outlet. Determine that the proper clamps are used and installed in such a manner that prevents damage to lines and hoses. Examine flexible air ducts and hoses for condition and security.

Hoses carrying flammable fluids are typically banded or marked to identify the hose manufacturer and fabrication date. Verify that all hoses are replaced at the required intervals as specified by regulations. Furthermore, consider replacing hoses at intervals recommended by the manufacturer even if more frequent than required by regulation.

For a turbine engine, inspect the condition of the fuel control unit and check the operation of the fuel pressurization and dump (P&D) valve and environmental fuel recovery components. Ensure that fuel nozzles are flow-checked at the required intervals. [Figure 13-19]

Inspect exhaust system components for leaks, security of mounting, cracks, warpage, and general condition. On reciprocating engines, remove the heat shroud around each muffler and carefully inspect the muffler for leakage, discoloration, cracks, and general condition. Use a flashlight and a mirror to check the inside of the muffler for loose or missing flame arrestors and baffles. Note that some manufacturers require the system to be pressurized to identify leaks.

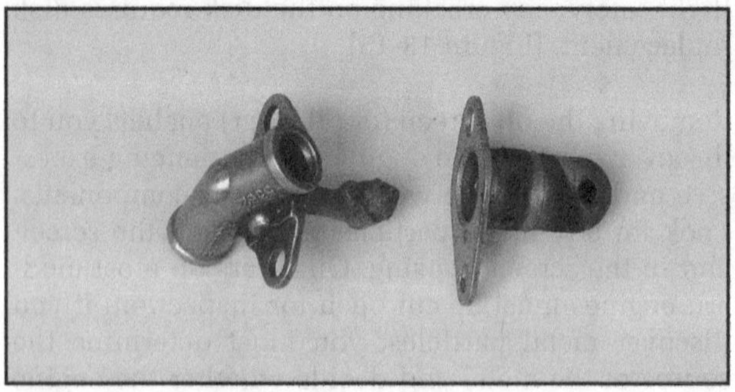

**Figure 13-19. One of the most critical items for promoting proper turbine engine operation and optimum service life is to check that the fuel nozzles are clean and in good condition. This is done by periodically removing the nozzles and performing a flow check. Dirty nozzles can produce fuel streaking, which can cause severe damage to hot section components.**

If a turbocharger is installed, inspect its condition as well as all associated turbocharger control components including the waste gate and waste gate controller. Failed exhaust components on turbocharged engines are particularly hazardous because gases emitted from broken exhaust components can produce extremely hot flames. [Figure 13-20]

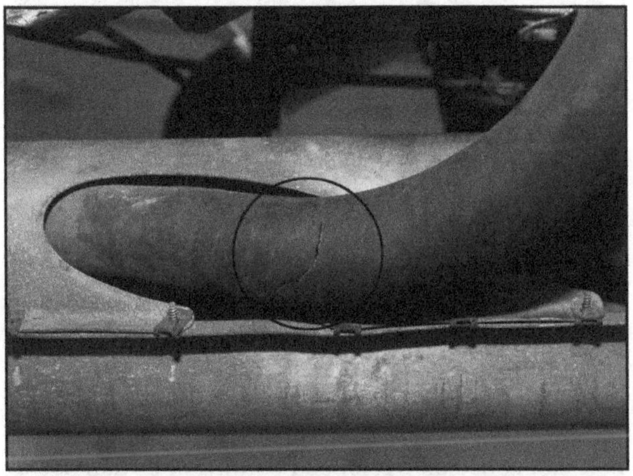

**Figure 13-20. Welds in exhaust manifolds and places where exhaust gases are forced to change direction are particularly susceptible to cracks, distortion and erosion failures. Using a metal probe helps to detect deteriorated wall thickness caused by erosion. Remember to never use dissimilar metal abrasives to clean the exhaust, and do not mark components with a pencil.**

On both reciprocating and turbine engines, check all indicating systems and probes for accuracy. Check the operation and calibration of all engine temperature, pressure, and flow-indicating gauges during pre- and post-inspection run-ups. Special test equipment is used to test the accuracy of gauges and probes [Figure 13-21]

For aircraft with air-driven instruments, check the instrument air system to be sure that all filters are changed according to the manufacturer's recommendations and that the oil separator (for wet air pumps) shows no signs of damage.

**Figure 13-21. Engine indicating systems should be periodically checked during maintenance run-ups using special calibration equipment such as this Jetcal® Analyzer.**

For all lines, and wires that pass through the firewall, check the condition of firewall seals and ensure that no corrosion is present. Verify that the electrical grounding strap between the engine and the airframe is in good condition.

On reciprocating engines, inspect magnetos in accordance with the manufacturer's recommendations for timing, breaker point condition, lubrication, security of mounting, internal oil leakage, lead attachment, and general condition. Rotate the propeller to ensure that impulse couplings (if installed) function properly.

Remove the spark plugs, being sure to track which cylinder and position (top or bottom) each was removed from. Inspect the spark plugs and note the condition of the electrode end, which can reveal discrepancies in the cylinder assembly. [Figure 13-22]

| | |
|---|---|
| 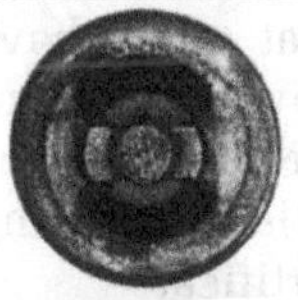 | **NORMAL** Indicates short service time and correct heat range. Clean, regap and test before reinstalling. |
|  | **WORN OUT - NORMAL** Indicates normal service life, electrodes show normal erosion, ground electrodes about half original thickness. Install new plugs. |
|  | **WORN OUT - SEVERE** Excessively eroded center and ground electrodes indicate abnormal engine power operation. Check fuel metering. Install new plugs. |
| 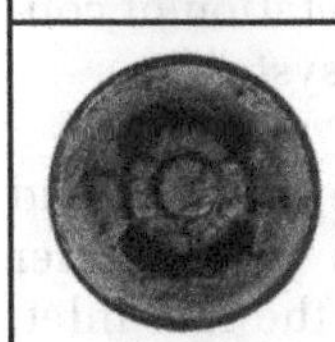 | **LEAD FOULED** Hard, cinder like deposits from poor fuel vaporization, high T.E.L. content in fuel or engine operating too cold. Install new plugs. |
| 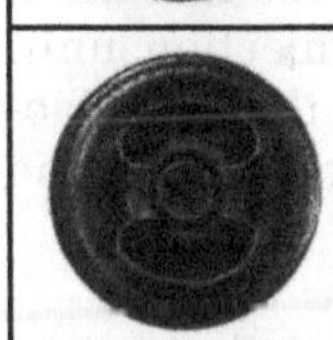 | **CARBON FOULED** Black sooty deposits from excessive ground idling, idle mixture too rich or plug type too cold. If heat range is correct, clean, regap, test and reinstall. |
| 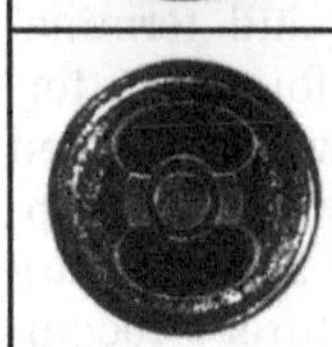 | **OIL FOULED** Wet, oily deposits may be caused by broken or worn piston rings, excessive valve guide clearances, leaking impeller seal or engine still in break-in period. Repair engine as required. Clean, regap, test and reinstall plugs. |
| (Courtesy Champion Aviation Products) | |

**Figure 13-22. The condition of the spark plug indicates a healthy engine, or a potential problem.**

Spark plugs that are not worn beyond limits must be cleaned and gap-adjusted with special equipment. You must test any plug that you recondition. If the plug fires consistently under pressure in a spark plug tester, you can reinstall the plug in the engine. When you reinstall spark plugs, rotate their position according to the engine manufacturer's pattern to equalize electrode wear due to polarity in the ignition system.

On turbine engines, check the condition and operation of igniters and glow plugs. Inspect the condition, routing, and security of ignition leads and the attachment and condition of regulators and igniter boxes. Follow the manufacturer's safety instruction during the operation of ignition components while testing the continuous-duty and auto-ignition modes.

Inspect the intake system for security of attachment and for signs of leakage. Check the air intake and air box for leaks and for any damage to filter attachment hardware. In addition, look for evidence of dust or other solid contaminants that might have leaked past the filter. Be sure to remove, clean, and replace induction air filters as required. Some aircraft use aftermarket air filters installed under the authority of a Supplemental Type Certificate.

Examine engine baffles and seals for cracks, security, mounting, and general condition. Stop drill small cracks to prevent further growth. However, if substantial cracking exists, additional structural repair might be necessary. Inspect the cylinders for cracks or broken fins.

Inspect the condition of pneumatic lines, tubes, ducts, valves, and filters of the bleed air system of a turbine engine. Ensure the proper operation of control valves and the automatic cut-off system.

Check the fuel system for leaks, line security, and proper installation. Clean the main fuel strainer and screen along with the screen in the fuel inlet, gascolator, and carburetor or fuel injection unit. If an engine is fuel-injected, check the manufacturer's schedule and procedures for cleaning the injector nozzles.

Inspect wire bundles, canon plugs, and terminal connections; remove any corrosion found on terminal ends. In addition, check all wires attached to electrical components for security, proper support, and chafing. Because electrical systems vary between aircraft, follow the manufacturer's recommendations in detail. [Figure 13-23]

The cowling directs and routes air for engine cooling. When inspecting the cowling for cracks and

**Figure 13-23. Electrical starter/generator wiring and connections must be secure to prevent abrasion, and free of corrosion or other defects.**

defects, also inspect the cowl flaps for security, condition, and proper operation. Secure all cowling fasteners, replacing any that are defective.

If the engine uses flexible drive belts to transfer motion, inspect the belts and their associated components for cracks, unusual wear, damage, and proper balance. In a helicopter, the failure of a drive belt can cause an overspeed condition or damage to other engine and airframe components.

Turbine engines are equipped with fire detection and extinguishing systems. Inspect all detection system components for security, condition, and operation. Check the condition of the fire zone insulation. Verify that the extinguishing components are secure and that all of the plumbing and nozzles are in good condition. [Figure 13-24]

Inspect the reversing components and indicating systems of thrust reverser and turboprop propeller reverser (beta) systems. Check the installation, rigging, and operation of these systems. [Figure 13-25]

## Propeller Inspection

A propeller inspection is required by 14 CFR Part 43 Appendix D (h). The propeller spinner must be removed to inspect the hub and mounting bolts. Check the hub for cracks, leakage of grease and oil, corrosion, and general condition. Inspect the propeller mounting bolts for proper torque and safety wiring. [Figure 13-26]

Examine blades for nicks, deep scratches, corrosion, cracks, or other obvious damage. If you suspect that the blades are bent, measure propeller track and check blade angles at specified stations as identified in the manufacturer's maintenance manuals.

Carefully blend out all nicks and scratches in the blades by filing, and finish sand the repair area with crocus cloth. If the condition of the blade paint warrants repainting, apply an equal amount of paint to each blade to help maintain propeller balance. If

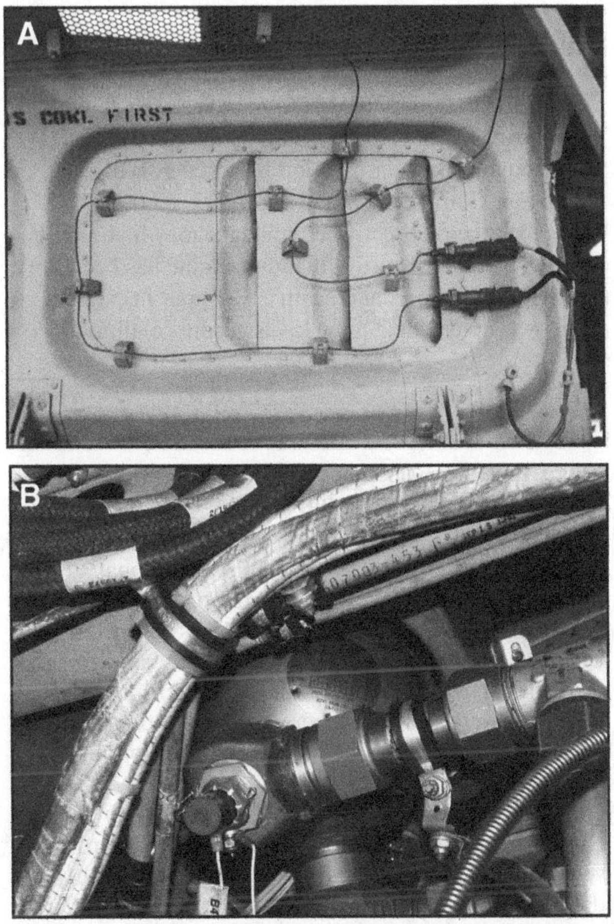


Figure 13-24. (A) Fire detection elements are inspected for condition and security of attachment. (B) Fire suppression systems are checked for weight and state of charge. Also check the expiration date on discharge cartridges or squibs.

Figure 13-25. On turboprop aircraft, check the condition and operation of auto-feather sensors in accordance with the manufacturer's maintenance and run-up instructions.

you notice a pronounced vibration during engine run-ups, the propeller might be out of balance. Special test equipment can be used to dynamically balance a propeller.

## Post Inspection run-up

A functional inspection after the visual inspection is required by 14 CFR Part 43.15 (c) (2). Record engine performance parameters on a checklist and compare with the preinspection values. Investigate any large deviations and determine the cause. [Figure 13-27]

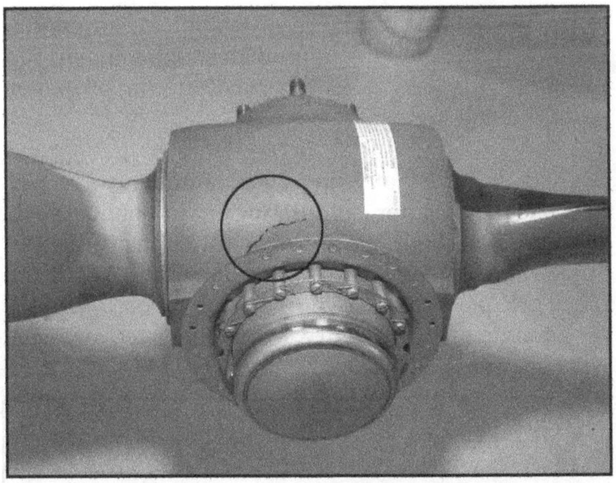

Figure 13-26. For some constant-speed propellers, red-colored oil coming from the propeller hub is indicative of a crack. If red oil is detected, the propeller must be removed for servicing at an authorized propeller repair facility.

> (2) Each person approving a reciprocating-engine-powered aircraft for return to service after an annual or 100-hour inspection shall, before that approval, run the aircraft engine or engines to determine satisfactory performance in accordance with the manufacturer's recommendations of—
>
> (i) Power output (static and idle r.p.m.);
>
> (ii) Magnetos;
>
> (iii) Fuel and oil pressure; and
>
> (iv) Cylinder and oil temperature.

Figure 13-27. Part 43.15(c)(2) requires you to perform a post inspection run-up of each engine before approving an aircraft for return to service after airworthiness inspections.

Whenever you remove or replace a component that requires a seal or gasket, always inspect the component for a leak after completing the functional inspection. New gaskets, crush washers, O-rings, and other sealing materials can fail during installation and permit leaks. Also inspect all fuel and oil system components for leaks.

## MAINTENANCE RECORD ENTRIES

Federal Aviation Regulations require an entry in the aircraft's permanent maintenance record whenever an inspection is completed. For annual and progressive inspections, the return to service record entry must be done in the airframe logbook (although many technicians also document the work in the other equipment logbooks). For 100-hour inspections, the return to service statement for an engine is made in the engine maintenance logbook, and the propeller inspection is recorded in the propeller maintenance logbook.

Bear in mind that when a maintenance record entry is made after completing maintenance such as repairs or servicing, the signature constitutes the approval of the aircraft for return to service *only* for the work performed. Figure 13-28 shows a sample maintenance record entry for compliance with an Airworthiness Directive.

> April 26, 2004 Total Time 1459.3 Hours
>
> Performed pump relief valve attaching screws torque check in accordance with SB No. 529B as per AD 2003-14-03 paragraph (2)(b)(1). Correct torque applied to pump relief valve attaching screws. Next inspection due at 1509.3 hours or October 26, 2004, whichever occurs first.
>
> *Linda P. Brown* A&P No. 1347890
> Linda P. Brown

**Figure 13-28. Airworthiness Directive compliance entries should be clear and concise as to what work was done, how it was done, and if recurring, when it must be redone.**

The maintenance logbook entry for an airworthiness inspection should include:

- The date the inspection is completed.
- The total time in service of the aircraft, engine, or propeller, as appropriate to the equipment inspected.
- The type of inspection performed.
- A certification statement that is worded similarly to that shown in figure 13-29.
- Your signature.
- Your certificate number and type of ratings held.

The maintenance logbook entry for a repair differs from an inspection. This type of entry should include:

- The date the work was completed.
- A description or reference to data acceptable to the FAA for the work performed.
- The name of the person performing the work if you did not do the work.
- Your signature.
- Your certificate number and type of ratings held.

> April 26, 2004 Total Time 1459.3 Hours
>
> Performed 100-Hour inspection in accordance with FAR part 43 appendix D and manufacturer's maintenance manual, section B1 through B10. Cylinder Compressions: #1 72, #2 73, #3 69, #4 77. Airworthiness Directive compliance may be found in engine records. I certify that this engine has been inspected in accordance with a 100-hour inspection and was determined to be in airworthy condition.
>
> *Linda P. Brown* A&P No. 1347890
> Linda P. Brown

**Figure 13-29. A maintenance record entry for conducting and approving a 100-hour inspection on an engine should be made similar to that shown in this figure.**

A log entry should be legible and neat. Some mechanics type their entries and print them out to insert in the maintenance record. It is important that the entry is permanently attached; it is required that the entry does not become dislodged and lost for one year. However, most owners and operators retain all entries for the life of the aircraft or component.

If an aircraft is not approved for return to service because of needed maintenance, noncompliance with applicable specifications, airworthiness directives, or other approved data, the certification statement should be worded similar to that shown in figure 13-30.

> April 26, 2004 Total Time 1459.3 Hours
>
> Performed 100-Hour inspection in accordance with FAR part 43 appendix D and manufacturer's maintenance manual, section B1 through B10. Cylinder Compressions: #1 72, #2 73, #3 69, #4 54. Airworthiness Directive compliance may be found in engine records. I certify that this engine has been inspected in accordance with a 100-hour inspection and a list of discrepancies and unairworthy items dated April 26th, 2004 has been provided for the aircraft owner.
>
> *Linda P. Brown* A&P No. 1347890
> Linda P. Brown

**Figure 13-30. When an aircraft has been determined to be in unairworthy condition, you should make a maintenance record entry similar to the one shown in this figure. You must also remember to provide the aircraft owner with a list of defects that, once repaired, will authorize the aircraft to be approved for return to service.**

In addition to maintenance record entries, compile a cumulative list of all ADs for the engine, propeller, and associated appliances. A separate list should be provided for each component, because in the future, the component could be installed on another aircraft.

If either a major repair or major alteration is performed on an engine or propeller, you must record an appropriate log entry and complete two identical FAA Form 337s. Provide one form to the aircraft owner and submit the other to the local FAA Field Service District Office within 48 hours from the aircraft's approval for return to service.

## HUMAN FACTORS

Over the past four decades, there has been a noticeable shift in the causes of aircraft accidents and incidents. The number of structural and mechanical failures has decreased, but improvements in aircraft design and mechanical reliability have been largely negated by human errors. Further analysis revealed that improved policies and procedures could have prevented many of these accidents and incidents. Accidents and incidents that occur in part because of human error or oversight are commonly referred to as human factor events.

During inspections, the following human factor errors have been observed:

- Failure to properly follow regulatory and manufacturer's inspection instructions, including incomplete work due to missed steps or failure to follow maintenance instructions in the correct sequence
- Failure to perform follow-up maintenance activities with a secondary inspection by a person with equal or better qualifications than the original inspector
- Failure to identify defects due to improper or inadequate inspection procedures or inspector complacency
- Inappropriate or inadequate use of special tools when conducting inspections
- Deviation from established and approved inspection methods and procedures

These are only a few examples of ways that human error affects aircraft maintenance and inspection. Individuals and repair facilities should establish policies and procedures to minimize the opportunity for human factor events to occur. However, any failure to identify discrepancies or to follow policies and procedures properly increases the potential for maintenance-related human factor accidents and incidents.

# SUMMARY CHECKLIST

✓ The Type Certificate Data Sheet (TCDS) provides critical information about the engine or the propeller.

✓ The airworthiness of a part is determined by conformity to its Type Certificate Data Sheet.

✓ A Supplemental Type Certificate (STC) describes a change to an aircraft or part. An STC allows a product to be altered from its original type design when specific safety and design requirements are met.

✓ Airworthiness Directives (AD) are FAA-approved regulations specific to a particular aircraft, component, or installation.

✓ Advisory Circulars (AC) are FAA-acceptable publications that provide explanations of complex regulations and acceptable maintenance data.

✓ Aircraft component manufacturers are required to provide instructions for continued airworthiness. These instructions are often included within the maintenance manual.

✓ Regular airworthiness inspections for light aircraft include the annual, 100-hour, and progressive inspection.

✓ Most large and turbine-powered aircraft are inspected according to some type of continuous airworthiness program.

✓ Aircraft inspections must be conducted with a checklist. The manufacturer's checklists should be followed and the requirements in 14 CFR 43, Appendix D must be met.

✓ Maintenance logbook entries document all maintenance performed and all inspections completed. A signed maintenance entry constitutes an approval for return to service.

# QUESTIONS

1. What rating must an aircraft maintenance technician have to perform a 100-hour inspection on an engine or propeller? ______________

2. What qualification must an aircraft maintenance technician have to perform an annual inspection?

______________ ______________

3. The ______________ is the document that defines the airworthiness of an aircraft.

4. The information in a Type Certificate Data Sheet is considered FAA- ______________

5. Any aircraft modification that deviates from the Type Certificate Data Sheet is considered a ______________ and requires documentation on FAA Form ________.

6. For which three major components are Type Certificate Date Sheets issued?

______________

______________

______________

7. A ______________ contains the methods and techniques that permit an aircraft to be modified and returned to service without additional engineering or flight test requirements.

8. An ______________ is a regulatory instruction that must be followed.

9. ______________ ______________ provide interpretive and clarifying information about aircraft maintenance practices that are considered acceptable by the FAA Administrator.

10. A manufacturer provides ______________ ______________ to communicate potential discrepancies and remedies to aircraft owners, operators, and maintenance technicians

11. Given that an annual inspection is required every 12 calendar months, an inspection completed on June 4 is valid until ______________ ______ of the following year.

12. Where does the FAA list the regulatory inspection items? ______________

______________

13. Before you can inspect an aircraft according to a progressive inspection program, the plan must be submitted to the local ______________ and approved for use.

14. Large and turbine-powered multiengine aircraft are typically inspected in accordance with a ____________ ______________________________ .

15. An entry in the aircraft's ____________________________________________ is required after every inspection.

16. Every maintenance logbook entry for an airworthiness inspection must contain:

__________________________________________

__________________________________________

__________________________________________

__________________________________________

__________________________________________

__________________________________________

17. Every maintenance logbook entry for a repair must contain:

__________________________________________

__________________________________________

__________________________________________

__________________________________________

__________________________________________

18. ________________ __________________ refers to the range of nontechnical causes of accidents and incidents that can be mitigated by thoughtful, efficient policies and procedures.

CHAPTER

14

# POWERPLANT TROUBLESHOOTING

## INTRODUCTION

Troubleshooting is an important skill for a maintenance technician. Successful troubleshooting requires a thorough knowledge of the systems, components, and operational theory of an engine. Without this background, even simple troubleshooting is an exercise in trial and error, which can be time-consuming and expensive. This chapter provides basic troubleshooting principles and techniques for diagnosing and isolating discrepancies (or faults) in reciprocating and turbine engines.

# SECTION A

## TROUBLESHOOTING PRINCIPLES

Aircraft maintenance technicians who are highly skilled at troubleshooting apply their knowledge of a system (or systems) to determine the cause of a discrepancy and correct it. While troubleshooting is referred to as a skill, in reality it is a process. Good troubleshooting is systematic, but also fluid depending on the time and resources available before the intended return to service. In every case, before you begin troubleshooting, carefully consider the symptoms of the discrepancy as you work to isolate a fault. Keep in mind that sometimes multiple faults contribute to a discrepancy.

In some cases it is best to start with the simplest or least expensive solution and then, as necessary, move toward more complex or more expensive solutions. For example, when an alternator is not producing power, replacing the alternator would be the last step after checking items such as the wiring, the circuit breaker, the voltage regulator, and the alternator switch. Of course, you should consider more than the cost of the part; the cost of labor must also be considered.

In other cases, starting with the most likely solution is smart. Of course, it is not possible to have every component and part available to exchange, or swap, when attempting to isolate a problem. However, it might be possible to swap like components within the aircraft from one location to another. For example, if a reciprocating engine cylinder produces a low EGT reading, exchanging the EGT probe or wire harness with one from another cylinder can isolate whether the problem is a faulty wire or probe, or can possibly reveal another problem such as low cylinder compression. Keep in mind that in complex systems, the cost (in both time and money) of merely swapping parts without a conducting a thorough analysis can become burdensome.

### RESOURCES

An abundance of resources is available to learn more about aircraft systems and the process of troubleshooting discrepancies. Information is available in manufacturer publications, online (including the FAA), in industry magazines and books, in training courses (from the manufacturer or a professional training organization), and from experienced maintenance technicians.

### MANUFACTURER PUBLICATIONS

One of the best resources for troubleshooting information is provided in the manufacturer's maintenance publications. Nearly all airframe and engine manufacturers provide extensive information useful for diagnosing faults. Manufacturer maintenance manuals typically include troubleshooting tables or logic flow charts that address common discrepancies; these present the symptoms as well as possible repair actions to perform. [Figure 14-1]

Troubleshooting tables are generally presented in a two- or three-column format. Typically, the leftmost column identifies the discrepancy, while another column lists possible causes for the discrepancy. These are arranged with the most likely cause first. Subsequent items are then listed in an organized format from the simplest to most difficult. When included, the third column provides possible actions to resolve a given fault. In developing these tables, the manufacturer uses a logical process based upon actual experience. However, because it is not possible to provide every cause for every fault and because new discrepancies appear from time to time, these tables cannot address every issue.

Manufacturers can also provide logic flow charts to depict troubleshooting procedures. These charts are based on principles of If/Then logic. The charts are designed to help you isolate a fault. Based on your answers to simple Yes/No questions about the condition of the engine or component, the flow chart directs you to the next item to consider.

When a manufacturer table or chart is inadequate, you can study a schematic diagram to determine the logical place to start troubleshooting. Schematics are typically available for major components such as carburetors, alternators, and thrust reverser actuators; and systems including the fuel, ignition, lubrication, electrical, and hydraulic systems. [Figure 14-2]

| Trouble | Probable Cause | Remedy |
|---|---|---|
| Fluctuating fuel pressure of fuel flow | Defective manifold valve | Replace manifold valve |
| | Restriction in engine-driven fuel pump vapor ejector | Clean vapor ejector on fuel pump. Do not use wires to clean jet. |
| | Defective check valve in vapor vent return line | Clean vapor return vent line and repair or replace check valve. |
| | Air in line manifold valve to gage | Bleed air from line. |
| Low metered fuel pressure | Malfunctioning relief valve in engine-driven fuel pump | Clean or replace relief valve if defective. |
| | Defective gage or restricted gage line | Replace gage. Clean restriction from line. |
| | Plugged main fuel strainer | Clean strainer. |
| | Air leak on suction side of engine-driven fuel pump | Repair leak. Replace defective parts. |
| Fuel drained from manifold valve vent | Ruptured diaphragm | Replace diaphragm or manifold valve. |
| Poor idle cut-off | Dirt in fuel pump or defective pump | Remove pump and flush out thoroughly. Check that mixture arm contacts cut-off stop. |
| | Dirty of defective fuel manifold valve | Remove and clean in accordance with paragraphs 10-58 and 10-59. |

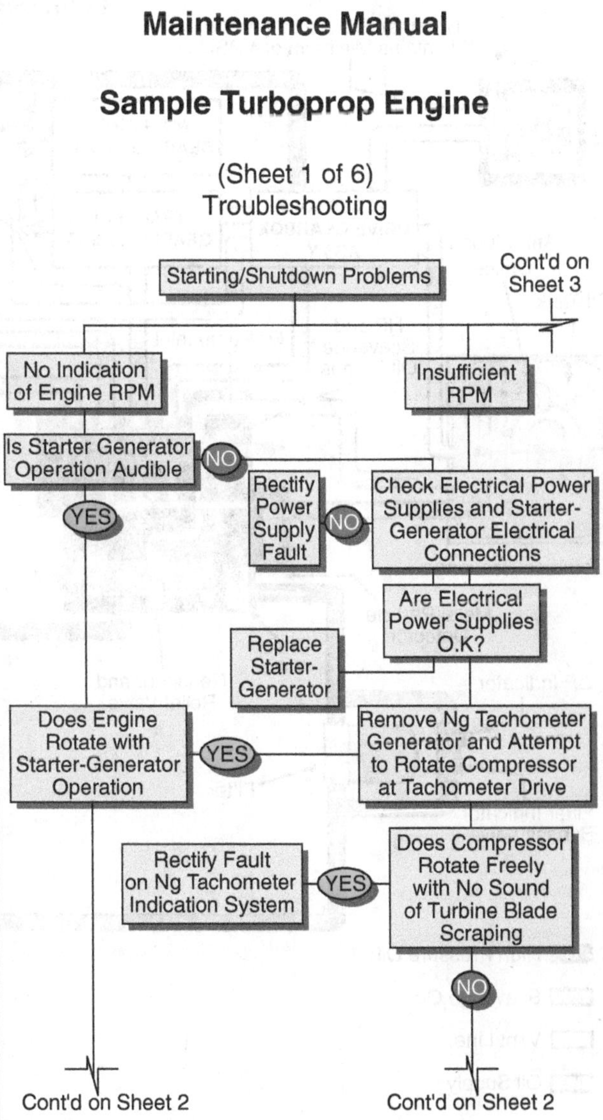


**Figure 14-1. Engine and airframe manufacturers commonly provide troubleshooting information in (A) tables or (B) logic flow charts. Both formats identify steps or actions to logically and systematically diagnose faults.**

Schematic diagrams illustrate what parts are used in a particular component or system. The schematic can be instructive about which components you should consider while troubleshooting. A schematic is like a map—it helps you to determine the paths and connections of lines, cables, wiring, and passages within a system or component. When you understand how each part works in relation to the others, you can establish what steps or actions to take and the order in which to perform them.

With schematic diagrams, each manufacturer develops their own method to portray symbols and codes. Before using a schematic, you should refer to the legend to become familiar with these items. Some legends are presented on the same page as the schematic while others have the legend printed elsewhere such as on a separate page of the manual or on another diagram.

## FAA DATA

Professional mechanics often submit information to the FAA when they discover the cause of a discrepancy that was difficult to isolate or has the potential to significantly affect safety. An FAA Form 8010-4, Malfunction or Defect Report, is submitted by

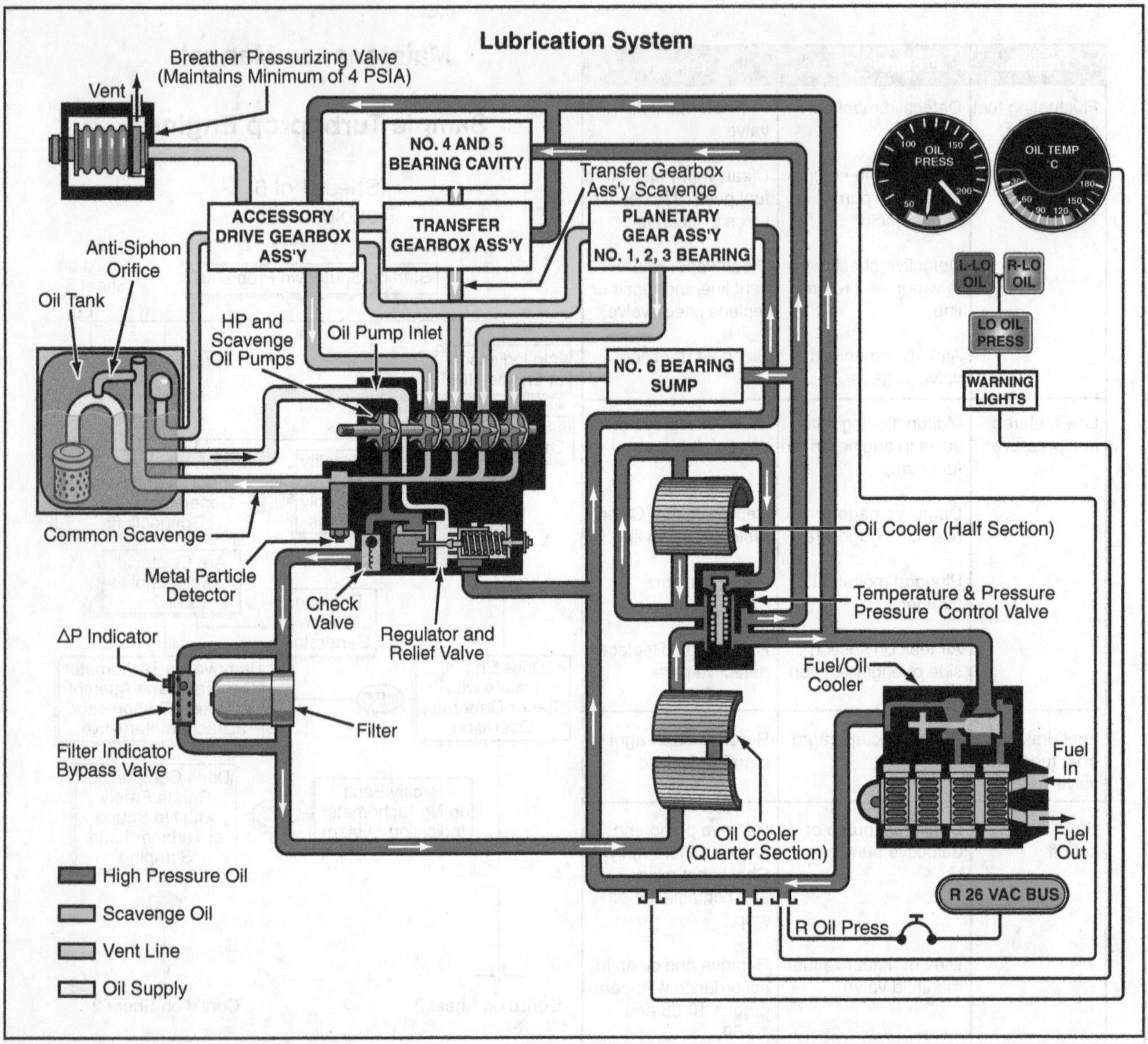


**Figure 14-2. Schematic diagrams depict the arrangement of systems or the operation of individual components.**

mail or through the internet. The FAA distributes the information through monthly updates of AC 43-16A, Aviation Maintenance Alerts, a database through which you can search on the FAA website. This database enables technicians to learn from the experience of their peers, and information about discrepancies and corrective actions is rapidly disseminated.

## OTHER RESOURCES

Whenever available, the manufacturer's troubleshooting information should be followed. However, as you gain experience (with a particular aircraft as well as with similar aircraft), your ability to identify and isolate common faults more rapidly should increase. Experience is not the only teacher available. Manufacturers and professional training organizations make training courses, seminars, and other resources available to help you develop your knowledge and skills. Books and industry trade magazines provide additional opportunities to learn. Many technicians keep a notebook to record what they have learned from experience and from information collected from others.

## INTERVIEWS

Many pilots oversimplify discrepancy reports (or squawks) with simple statements such as "engine runs rough," and neglect to accurately or adequately describe the symptoms and conditions when the fault occurred. When you interview the person who reported the discrepancy, you can ask questions that eliminate unlikely problems and target the most likely areas to begin your troubleshooting. Figure 14-5 provides a sample list of questions to ask a pilot.

During an interview, consider the experience level of the pilot. An experienced pilot is more likely to help you identify the precise source of a fault. On the other hand, a student pilot might only be able to provide basic information about the conditions of flight. When talking with pilots, take time to share your thoughts about what might have happened. If you have experience repairing this type of discrepancy, offer the operator suggestions about how to how to prevent the problem from recurring. Taking time to help pilots understand their aircraft will demonstrate your professionalism and earn their respect.

## TROUBLESHOOTING TOOLS AND EQUIPMENT

Some aircraft are equipped with instruments and trend-monitoring devices that provide a wealth of information for troubleshooting. These systems enable a pilot to observe many parameters of engine performance over time. Some systems store data that you can retrieve and view on a computer.

For reciprocating engine aircraft, multiprobe EGT and CHT systems might be installed; these systems assist in isolating individual cylinder faults. For example, a gradual decrease in a cylinder's EGT over an extended period of time might indicate a loss of cylinder pressure. Multiprobe EGT and CHT systems can indicate faults in the ignition path, or the delivery of fuel to a specific cylinder. For example, while checking magnetos, a sudden drop in the EGT of one cylinder indicates a fault in the ignition system for that particular cylinder. [Figure 14-3]

For most turbine aircraft, performance data is collected in cruise during each flight. The flight crew can record performance data and relay it to base maintenance personnel, or the information can be automatically transmitted by radio through an automatic crew alerting and reporting system (ACARS).

Careful analysis of trend monitoring information helps you determine what items to check during the troubleshooting process. For example, if a pilot reports that a turbine engine is running hot, a trend analysis will reveal if the condition has been progressing slowly, or if it occurred relatively suddenly. If the condition occurred gradually, the interior of the engine should be suspected. On the other hand, if the problem appeared suddenly, you would suspect an external problem, such as an indicator or bleed air system fault.

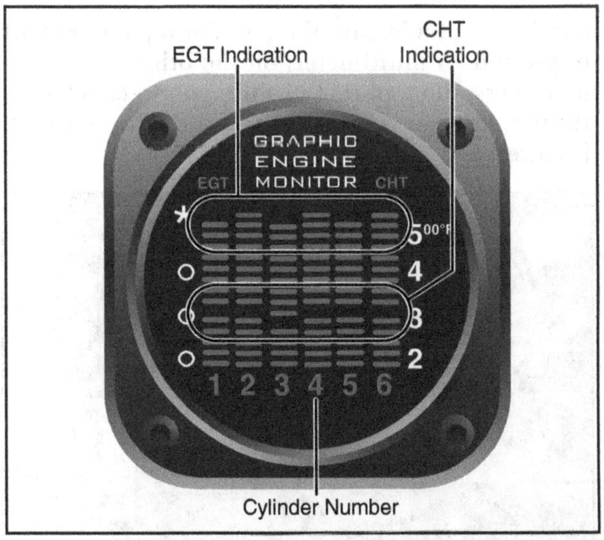


**Figure 14-3. Digital engine monitoring systems use illuminated bars to graphically portray engine operating parameters. In this unit the columns rise to indicate the EGT of each cylinder, and the omitted line in each column indicates CHT. A comparison of the columns can identify any cylinder that is not functioning properly.**

Not all aircraft are equipped with engine monitoring systems or equipment; before these systems were introduced, maintenance technicians developed a variety of tools and techniques to simplify troubleshooting. For example, an ignition fault on a reciprocating engine can be isolated by operating the engine on the magneto causing rough running for a few minutes, and then, after shut-down, using a cold cylinder tester or water spray to identify the hot cylinders. An inoperative cylinder will be cold, which helps you to narrow your inspection to the inoperative cylinder's ignition components, rather than the entire ignition system.

Other tools for troubleshooting include pressure gauges, volt-ohmeters (known as VOMs or multimeters), test lights, and many others. Be sure that any tools that require calibration are in date and within limits. Engine and component manufacturers sometimes develop special tools for troubleshooting their specific equipment. When a manufacturer requires special tools for adjusting or calibrating components, you should use them. However, sometimes during troubleshooting you can often improvise tools, as long as they do not affect the integrity of the aircraft.

The many multimeters and test lights available are versatile tools used electrical troubleshooting tools for diagnosing electrical system faults. Test lights are lightweight, portable, and fairly inexpensive tools used to check for power at a given location in a circuit. Powered test lights can quickly check the continuity of a length of circuit, or a path or short to ground. A multimeter, on the other hand, is a more versatile tool that enables you to check continuity, voltage, and, to a limited degree, current. [Figure 14-4]

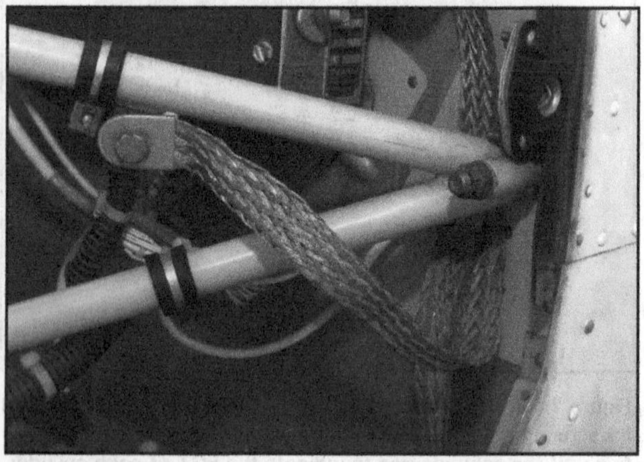

**Figure 14-4. A common fault affecting powerplant electrical systems is a defective ground circuit. Always check that ground wires are properly secured and free of corrosion. Also, verify that any bonding cables or straps are in place and properly attached between the engine and airframe.**

Most handheld multimeters are limited to measuring current loads of 10 amps or less. To identifying faults in a circuit where the amperage exceeds 10 amps, inductive ammeters are often used. Inductive clamps (sometimes called amp clamps) detect current flow in a circuit. These tools can be used in both D.C. and A.C. electrical circuits and some can handle current loads over 1,000 amps.

Amp clamps, which permit you to place the clamp around a conductor to measure the amount of current flowing in the circuit, enable you to troubleshoot electrical circuits without having to disconnect wires. These devices save time, and are safer to use when troubleshooting high-current electrical circuits.

Pressure gauges are often used to diagnose problems with cylinders, actuators, fuel and oil components, and others. When using gauges to diagnose a fault, ensure that they are clean and accurate to prevent false readings.

Pressure gauges function in much the same way that voltmeters are used to diagnose electrical circuit faults. In electrical circuits, a voltmeter isolates the location of a fault by observing the electrical potential at various locations within a circuit. In a similar manner, pressure gauges enable you to analyze how a fluid acts within a system. For example, if a pilot reports low fuel pressure, you can use a pressure gauge to evaluate the condition of individual components such as the fuel pump, filters, valves, and metered or un-metered fuel pressures.

When troubleshooting hydraulic systems, you often need to tap into the system to install a pressure gauge. Some manufacturers provide service ports that enable you to easily connect a gauge to various locations in the system. For systems without service ports, you will need an assortment of tee fittings and hoses in order to fabricate your own connections.

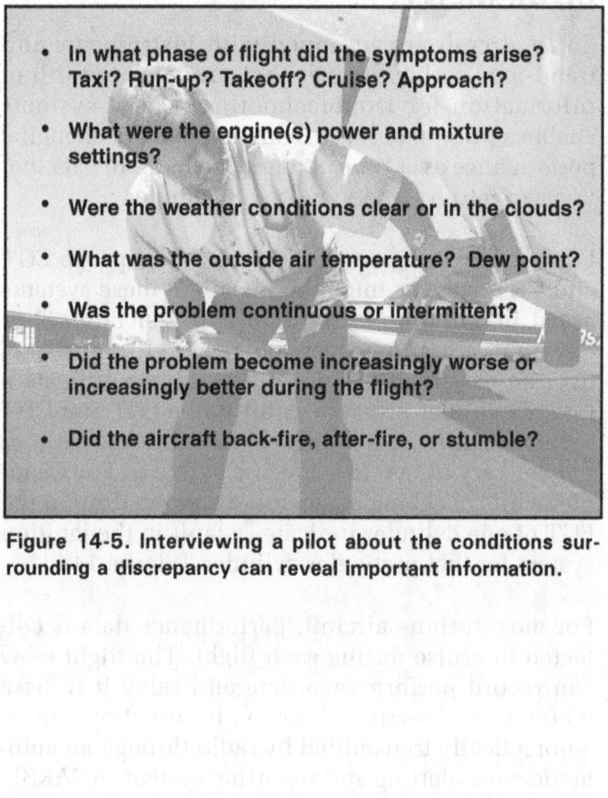


**Figure 14-5. Interviewing a pilot about the conditions surrounding a discrepancy can reveal important information.**

# SUMMARY CHECKLIST

✓ Efficient troubleshooting is based on a thorough knowledge of the systems, components, and operational theory of an engine.

✓ Effective troubleshooting is the application of a systematic process to isolate faults that can cause a discrepancy.

✓ Key troubleshooting resources include manufacturer publications, industry information online and in print, training courses (from the manufacturer or professional training organizations), and the experience of aircraft maintenance technicians.

✓ Manufacturers' technical publications often include troubleshooting tables and logic flow charts to aid in troubleshooting.

✓ Maintenance technicians can send reports of malfunctions and defects to the FAA.

✓ The discrepancies and remedies of issues that could affect flight safety are published in monthly Aviation Maintenance Alerts.

# QUESTIONS

1. Troubleshooting requires that you understand the ______________ and ____________________ of an aircraft.

2. The best process for troubleshooting is ____________________ .

3. The manufacturer's maintenance manual often provides ________________ and ______________.

4. The FAA publishes information submitted by aircraft maintenance technicians about discrepancies that were difficult to resolve or that might affect safety. These reports are stored in a searchable database called

   ______________ ______________ ______________.

5. Maintenance technicians often receive written reports of a discrepancy from a pilot. You can sometimes obtain additional information by ______________________ the pilot.

# SECTION B

# RECIPROCATING ENGINE TROUBLESHOOTING

## RECIPROCATING ENGINE TROUBLESHOOTING

When troubleshooting, it is often necessary to evaluate multiple systems to determine the cause of a fault. For example, if an engine runs rough at idle, the problem may be an induction air leak, poor ignition system performance, or improperly rigged fuel metering devices, among many other possibilities. This section addresses typical reciprocating engine discrepancies that you may encounter. A brief discussion of each of these discrepancies will help you understand how engine operations are affected by various faults and their possible causes. In addition, this section provides information that shows you how to use graphic engine monitoring instruments to troubleshoot reciprocating engine discrepancies.

## FAULT ISOLATION

When determining the cause of an engine fault, you will likely try to duplicate and confirm the problem first, and then progressively perform checks to diagnose the individual component or system that is creating the fault. Finally, you will repair or replace defective components and perform checks to verify that the fault has been corrected.

As previously discussed, engine discrepancies may be reported in a number of ways, and by people with varying experience levels. When you receive a discrepancy report, first determine how best to duplicate the problem to confirm its existence. It is not uncommon to find that some discrepancies are actually normal occurrences under certain circumstances. For example, if a pilot reports that an engine was running rough in flight, carburetor icing may have created the problem. During a subsequent run-up, you may find that the engine actually functions properly.

In all situations, you must determine the best actions to take. In some cases a discrepancy may be so obvious that time spent confirming the problem would be wasted. If, on the other hand, you must diagnose the problem, you may want to perform an engine run-up to confirm or analyze the symptoms further. This depends on whether the engine will start, and if it does, confidence that no further damage will occur to the engine during its operation.

## ENGINE RUN-UP

The run-up may not produce the symptoms that the operator experienced, but it may give indications of the problem in other ways. However, some faults can not be duplicated except in flight. If you find no obvious faults during the run-up, a maintenance check flight may be required to duplicate the symptoms. Before conducting a flight test, you must make a determination that the aircraft is safe for flight, and then only fly with required personnel on board. In any case, when operating an aircraft, adhere to the manufacturer's procedures and limitations published in the Pilot's Operating Handbook (POH) and aircraft maintenance manuals.

The following is an example of the tasks, or steps, that you will likely take during a maintenance run-up. Beneath each step is a list of possible discrepancies that you may encounter. Following each discrepancy is a bulleted list of possible causes for the problem, along with a table reference provided in parenthesis after each bulleted item. Subsequent to the run-up inspection, a series of Roman Numeral headings contain alphabetically organized lists of the discrepancies discussed in the run-up inspection. Refer to these headings for further information regarding each discrepancy, or fault.

1. Pre-start inspect the engine
   a. Check the oil level

      Oil leak at crankcase nose seal
      - Blow-by of combustion gases (Mechanical)
      - Frozen or blocked crankcase breather vent (Lubrication)
      - Turbocharger pressurizing the crankcase (Turbocharger)
      - Crack in the crankshaft (Mechanical)

      High oil consumption
      - Improper oil weight (Lubrication)

- Oil out crankcase breather (Lubrication)
- Rings do not seat (Mechanical)
- Failing bearings (Mechanical)
- Dirty or blocked fuel nozzle (Fuel)
- Polished bore (Mechanical)
- Worn valve guides (Mechanical)
- Oil leaks (Lubrication)

Unexplained oil level rise
- Fuel pump failure (Fuel)

b. Sample fuel from the sump

Water in fuel
- Leaking fuel caps (Fuel)
- Condensation (Fuel)

c. Check overall condition

Carburetor fuel leak
- Leaking primer system (Fuel)
- Carburetor float set too high (Fuel)
- Accelerator pump seal worn (Fuel)
- Carburetor float needle leaking (Fuel)
- Leak in float or deteriorated float (Fuel)

2. Start the engine in accordance with the pilot's operating handbook

Hard to start
- Bad starter (Electrical)
- Slow or fast cranking speed (Ignition)
- Impulse coupling not engaging (Ignition)
- Starter vibrator malfunction (Ignition)
- Improper timing (Ignition)
- E-gap improperly adjusted (Ignition)
- P-lead grounding (Ignition)
- Starter switch malfunction (Ignition)
- Carbon deposits (Ignition)
- Lead deposits (Ignition)
- Low battery voltage (Electrical)
- Flooded (Fuel)
- High resistance in circuit (Electrical)
- Inadequate ground (Electrical)

Hard to start in cold weather
- Insufficient prime (Fuel)
- Low battery voltage (Electrical)
- Spark plugs iced over (Ignition)
- Improper oil weight (Lubrication)

3. Taxi to a safe run-up area free of loose debris and other foreign objects.
4. Perform the run-up.
   a. Determine that all engine temperatures are registering in the green or normal operating range.
   b. Set the r.p.m. to that prescribed for the run-up as called for in the POH.
   c. Record oil pressure
   d. Record instrument vacuum (suction) or air pressure
   e. Record voltage, or alternator/generator load.
   f. Record fuel flow
   g. Perform a magneto check – When performing the magneto check, make note of all engine temperature gauges and the r.p.m, loss on each magneto. An engine equipped with a multi-probe CHT and EGT gauge can provide immediate indications of a fault, as discussed later in this section.

Excessive loss of r.p.m. on one magneto
- Improper timing (Ignition)
- Lead deposits (Ignition)
- Carbon Deposits (Ignition)
- Worn or loose ignition lead (Ignition)
- Damaged spark plug (Ignition)
- Incorrect spark plug gap (Ignition)
- Shorted ignition vibrator (Ignition)

Excessive loss of r.p.m. on both magnetos
- Improper timing (Ignition)
- Rich mixture (Fuel)
- Lean mixture (Fuel)
- Incorrect fuel (Fuel)
- Incorrect spark plug gap (Ignition)

Intermittent loss of r.p.m.

- P-lead intermittently grounding (Ignition)

No loss of RPM on one or both magnetos
- Starter switch malfunction (Ignition)
- Broken P-lead (Ignition)

Large increase in EGT and drop in r.p.m. on one magneto
- Broken impulse coupling spring (Ignition)
- Improper timing (Ignition)

h. Mixture check – Check the mixture check by slowly leaning the mixture while watching the EGT and r.p.m., and listening for changes in engine sound. When leaning, a proper fuel/air mixture from the carburetor or fuel injection unit is indicated when the EGT rises to a peak value, accompanied by a slight increase in r.p.m.. Further leaning beyond peak causes a drop in EGT and r.p.m., accompanied by engine roughness. If the mixture leaving the fuel control is too rich, such as when the carburetor float level is set too high, the r.p.m. rise is more prominent during leaning. If the mixture is too lean, the r.p.m. shows little or no rise to reach peak EGT. Further leaning causes the EGT and r.p.m. to decrease quickly, accompanied by engine roughness.

Rich mixture
- Fuel pump pressure too high (Fuel)
- Carburetor float level set too low (Fuel)
- Leak in float or deteriorated float (Fuel)
- Leaking primer system (Fuel)
- Leaking bowl gasket (Fuel)
- Intake leak (Miscellaneous)

Lean mixture
- Intake leak (Miscellaneous)
- Carburetor float set too high (Fuel)
- Carburetor float touches and drags against bowl (Fuel)
- Fuel pump pressure too low (Fuel)
- Fuel injector air bleed shroud leak (Fuel)

i. Propeller control check – Constant speed propellers should maintain a static r.p.m. very near the engine tachometer red line. The airframe Type Certificate Data Sheet (TCDS) lists the acceptable static r.p.m. range. As you move the propeller control aft, the r.p.m. should smoothly decrease, accompanied by a rise in manifold pressure and a decrease in oil pressure. If the engine is equipped with a full-feathering propeller, perform a feather check by cycling the propeller control into, and back out of, the feathering range. The r.p.m. should drop quickly as the propeller attempts to feather.

Propeller fails to change pitch
- Disconnected control cable (Propeller)

Sluggish pitch change
- High friction in hub parts (Propeller)
- Cold oil (Lubrication)

Failure to increase r.p.m.
- Low oil pressure (Lubrication)
- Nitrogen pressure charge too high (Propeller)

Failure to feather
- Improper propeller control cable rigging (Propeller)
- High pitch pin malfunction (Propeller)
- Air charge lost or low (Propeller)
- High friction in hub parts (Propeller)

5. Accelerate engine to full power

Engine hesitates or stumbles during acceleration
- Lean mixture (Fuel)
- Fuel pump pressure too low at idle (Fuel)
- Loose venturi (Fuel)
- Cold oil (Lubrication)
- Leaking primer system (Fuel)
- Rich mixture (Fuel)
- Accelerator pump seal worn (Fuel)
- Stuck intake or exhaust valve (Mechanical)
- Intake leak (Miscellaneous)
- Leaking carburetor bowl gasket (Fuel)

Engine surges
- Propeller governor malfunction (Propeller)
- Fluctuating waste gate (Turbocharger)
- Frozen or blocked breather vent (Lubrication)
- Dirty or blocked fuel nozzle (Fuel)
- Leak in fuel system (Fuel)
- Fuel injector air bleed shroud leak (Fuel)

Fluctuating oil pressure (Lubrication)
- Intake leak (Miscellaneous)

Engine shudders
- Stuck intake or exhaust valve (Mechanical)
- Fuel contamination (Fuel)
- Intake leak (Miscellaneous)
- Lean mixture (Fuel)
- Air in fuel system (Fuel)

a. Record static r.p.m.

Low static r.p.m. with fixed pitch propeller
- Wrong propeller installed (Propeller)
- High field elevation (Miscellaneous)
- Low power (Miscellaneous)

Low static r.p.m. with constant speed propeller
- Governor improperly adjusted (Propeller)
- Low oil pressure (Lubrication)
- Nitrogen charge pressure too high (Propeller)
- Low power (Miscellaneous)
- High field elevation (Miscellaneous)

- Improper propeller control cable rigging (Propeller)

High static r.p.m. with constant speed propeller
- Governor improperly adjusted (Propeller)
- Improper blade low-pitch stop setting (Propeller)

High EGT at full power
- Lean mixture (Fuel)
- Intake leak (Miscellaneous)
- Fuel pressure set too low (Fuel)
- Improper timing (Ignition)

b. Record manifold pressure

Low manifold pressure
- Waste gate stuck open (Turbocharger)
- Intake leak (Miscellaneous)
- High manifold pressure (Overboost)
- Waste gate stuck closed (Turbocharger)
- Pressure relief fails to open (Turbocharger)
- Rate controller malfunction(Turbocharger)

c. Record oil pressure

Fluctuating oil pressure
- Metal in oil (Mechanical)
- Oil pump sucking air (Lubrication)
- High oil pressure
- Oil pressure relief valve set improperly (Lubrication)
- Improper oil weight (Lubrication)
- Plugged oil passage (Lubrication)
- Cold oil (Lubrication)
- Low oil pressure
- Oil pressure relief valve set improperly (Lubrication)
- Plugged oil passage (Lubrication)
- Improper oil weight (Lubrication)
- Hot oil (Lubrication)

d. Record vacuum

Low vacuum
- Leak in instrument or airfoil de-icing system (Vacuum)
- Vacuum regulator improperly adjusted (Vacuum)
- High vacuum
- Dirty filters (Vacuum)
- Vacuum regulator improperly adjusted (Vacuum)

No vacuum
- Vacuum pump failure (Vacuum)
- Vacuum line collapse (Vacuum)
- Leak in vacuum system (Vacuum)

e. Record voltmeter or load meter readings

Voltmeter reads battery voltage or ammeter shows discharge
- Malfunctioning voltage regulator (Electrical)
- Broken or disconnected alternator field wire (Electrical)
- Failed alternator/generator (Electrical)
- Alternator/generator belt slipping or broken (Electrical)

f. Record fuel flow

High fuel flow indication
- Dirty or blocked fuel nozzle (Fuel)
- Improperly adjusted fuel metering unit (Fuel)
- Incorrect nozzle flow (Fuel)
- Cracked or broken fuel injector line (Fuel)

Low fuel flow indication
- Dirty fuel filter screen (Fuel)
- Incorrect nozzle flow (Fuel)
- Flow divider or distributor valve malfunction (Fuel)

Fuel pump pressure too low (Fuel)

Fluctuating fuel flow
- Fuel pump inlet air leak (Fuel)
- Clogged fuel tank vent (Fuel)
- Fuel line blockage (Fuel)
- Defective fuel pump (Fuel)

6. Retard throttle to idle

a. Record idle r.p.m.

Engine quits at idle
- Rich mixture (Fuel)
- Lean mixture (Fuel)

Rough idle
- Rich mixture (Fuel)
- Lean mixture (Fuel)
- Dirty or blocked fuel injector nozzle (Fuel)
- Lead-fouled spark plugs (Ignition)
- Carbon-fouled spark plugs (Ignition)
- Intake leak (Miscellaneous)
- Engine mounts worn or improperly installed (Mechanical)
- Fuel injector air bleed blocked (Fuel)
- Stuck intake or exhaust valve (Mechanical)
- Low cylinder compression (Miscellaneous)
- Incorrect spark plug gap (Ignition)
- Leaking primer system (Fuel)
- Loose carburetor venturi (Fuel)
- Leak in fuel system (Fuel)

b. Record idle manifold pressure

High idle manifold pressure
- Improperly adjusted fuel metering unit (Fuel)
- Intake leak (Miscellaneous)
- Leaks in manifold pressure line (Miscellaneous)
- Missing primer plug in cylinder (Miscellaneous)

c. Record oil pressure at idle

d. Record suction at idle

e. Record voltage, or alternator load at idle

7. Pull mixture to idle cut-off
   Rough or slow engine shut down
   - Improper mixture control rigging (Fuel)
   - Fuel Injection flow divider diaphragm valve sticking open (Fuel)
   - Leaking primer system (Fuel)
   - Mixture valve not seating (Fuel)

## FAULT ANALYSIS

When a fault is discovered, you must perform a proper analysis to determine its source. Only then can the problem be remedied. The following reciprocating-engine discrepancies are organized into the following headings on the following pages:

I. Electrical System Faults
II. Fuel System Faults
III. Ignition System Faults
IV. Lubrication System Faults
V. Mechanical Faults
VI. Miscellaneous Faults
VII. Propeller Faults
VIII. Turbocharger Faults
IX. Vacuum System Faults

Each group contains the faults that were presented in the previous discussion in alphabetical order. Along with each fault, there is a brief discussion of why the fault is producing the symptom and what may have caused the fault. While some of the faults may seem obvious, others will help you gain insight into how a fault can be elusive to troubleshoot. Remember that when you are trying to isolate the cause or causes of a fault, you should troubleshoot by working from the easiest and cheapest solution toward more difficult or more expensive solutions.

## I. ELECTRICAL SYSTEM FAULTS

**Alternator belt slipping or broken** — An alternator with a loose belt may produce normal voltage under light electrical loads, but the belt may start to slip under high loads, causing the output voltage to drop. Obviously, an alternator with a broken belt produces no voltage. [Figure 14-6]

Causes:

Belt is improperly installed

Belt deteriorated over time

Belt has stretched over time

**Figure 14-6. Inadequate belt tension is a possible cause of low voltage on the electrical system of a small airplane.**

**Bad starter** — A bad or weak starter that does not crank fast enough makes starting difficult. Before concluding that the starter is bad, inspect the wiring and engine ground cable.

Causes:

Worn or damaged starter bearings or brushes

Dirt or oil on brushes

Shorted armature or field windings

**Broken or disconnected alternator field wire** — An alternator produces electricity by cutting a magnetic field produced by a small amount of current passing through the rotor. If the rotor field wire is broken or disconnected, the magnetic field collapses and the alternator will not provide any output.

Causes:

Broken or disconnected field wire

Wire worn through or not secure

Corrosion on alternator terminal posts

**Failed alternator** — While the engine is shut-down and the master switch is on, if the voltage regulator is providing battery voltage to the alternator field (rotor), but the alternator fails to produce power with the engine running, there may be an open circuit in the stator or stator lead. A continuity test between the output post and ground will isolate if the stator is intact. If there is continuity through the stator, the brushes may be defective, preventing current from flowing through the rotor.

Causes:

Broken wire from vibration

Worn brushes

Dirty brushes

Broken or weak brush springs

**Inadequate ground** — With a negative ground system, the engine must be properly bonded to the airframe. Rubber engine mounts prevent an adequate ground back to the airframe, therefore a bonding strap must be installed between the airframe and the engine. If the strap is missing, loose, or corroded, the electrical current seeks ground through other components. In this situation, the current may travel through the engine control cables. Discrepancy reports of hard starting or that the engine controls become warm or hot is indicative of a poor engine-to-airframe ground.

Causes:

Loose connection

Corroded connection

Missing bonding strap

**Low battery voltage** — The aircraft's battery must be serviced regularly with water to insure that it can hold a full charge. If the battery is low on acid, it may still show full voltage and initially provide normal cranking power, but continued cranking will quickly deplete the battery. If a battery seems to be weak, service it with water, apply a trickle charge, and test the battery under a load. Be aware that a battery may show full voltage, but under a load, the voltage may drop significantly.

A battery does not deliver as much current in cold weather as it does in warm weather. This, coupled with thick oil, may prevent an engine from turning over at a speed sufficient for starting.

Causes:

Bad cell

Low electrolyte

Cold battery

**Malfunctioning voltage regulator** — A voltage regulator senses the output of the alternator and adjusts the field current to maintain the desired output voltage. If the voltage regulator fails to send current to the field, the voltmeter will register that the alternator is producing zero volts. If the voltage regulator fails in a manner that causes it to send full current to the field circuit, the alternator will produce an over voltage condition and trip the alternator output circuit breaker. If resetting the circuit breaker causes a spike in aircraft voltage and causes the circuit breaker to trip again, test the voltage regulator.

Causes:

Normal wear over time

Dirt and contaminants

**Resistance in circuit** — Corroded or loose electrical connections create high resistance. When current flows, resistance causes a voltage drop and reduces both the voltage and current being delivered to the starter, causing slow cranking.

Causes:

Improper installation of connectors

Corroded terminals

## II. FUEL SYSTEM FAULTS

**Accelerator pump seal worn** — The accelerator pump sprays a stream of fuel into the carburetor venturi when the throttle is advanced to provide an adequately rich mixture for acceleration. If the pump seal is worn and insufficient fuel is delivered into the carburetor, the mixture will become excessively lean during acceleration and the engine will stumble. A bad seal also allows fuel to leak around it and drain from the carburetor. [Figure 14-7]

Causes:

Lack of use

Deteriorated

Improper or contaminated fuel

**Air in fuel system** — A leak in the fuel system that allows air to enter the delivery hose may cause the mixture to vary in and out of a burnable ratio, making the engine surge.

Causes:

Cracked lines

Loose fittings

**Figure 14-7. Fuel stains may indicate a leak from a worn accelerator pump seal.**

**Carburetor float needle leaking** — If the carburetor float needle does not seat properly, fuel will flood the float chamber. It will then exit through the main fuel nozzle, dripping down into the air box, and eventually out onto the ground.

Causes:

Corrosion

Debris under seat

**Carburetor float set too high** — If the carburetor float is set too high, the fuel level in the bowl will be low, resulting in insufficient fuel entering the airflow and causing a lean mixture.

Causes:

Improper adjustment

**Carburetor float set too low** — If the carburetor float is set too low, the fuel level in the bowl will be high, allowing excess fuel to enter the venturi, which produces a rich mixture.

Causes:

Improper assembly

Leaking float

**Carburetor float touches bowl** — If the float touches the bowl, the resistance may inhibit the float from dropping when the fuel level is low to prevent fuel from filling the bowl. The resulting lower level of fuel results in a lean mixture.

Causes:

Improper assembly

**Clogged fuel tank vent** — The fuel tank is vented to the atmosphere to allow air to fill the void in the tanks created by fuel consumption. Venting may be done by extending tubes out from the tanks, or the fuel caps may be equipped with vents. If the vents are obstructed, a vacuum will form in the tank that ultimately inhibits fuel flow to the engine and may also cause fuel flow gauge fluctuations.

Causes:

Insect nests

Ice and snow

Dust and dirt

**Condensation** — This occurs when a temperature drop causes water in the air to condense. This is normal; however, it can be minimized by keeping fuel tanks full, which minimizes the amount of air and subsequent water that condenses out.

Causes:

High humidity with an associated temperature drop

**Cracked or broken fuel injector line** — A cracked line increases the fuel flow and causes a lean mixture in the cylinder. Fuel stains around the soldered ends indicate a fuel leak. This may also cause a high fuel flow rate. [Figure 14-8]

Causes:

Damage during maintenance

Loose mounting allowing line vibrations

**Defective fuel pump** — A weak or defective fuel pump may cause variations in the fuel flow and an overall low fuel pressure.

Causes:

Improper assembly

Normal wear over time.

**Dirty fuel filter screen** — A dirty fuel filter screen in a fuel control unit or flow divider restricts the flow of fuel to the cylinders and results in a lean mixture. The filters must be removed and cleaned periodically.

Causes:

Fuel contamination

**Dirty or blocked fuel nozzle** — If fuel flow is restricted by a blocked or dirty fuel nozzle, the cylinder will experience a lean mixture that causes a rise in EGT or a complete lack of combustion. At high power settings, lean mixtures can cause high temperatures and detonation.

On engines with a fuel flow meter that measures pressure differential, a restriction in the fuel nozzle will also increase the pressure in the fuel line. The higher fuel pressure causes a higher fuel flow indication, even though the fuel flow has actually decreased.

Cause:

Damaged fuel filter allowing contaminants to pass

**Figure 14-8. Improperly secured fuel injector lines could cause the soldered ends to fracture and leak.**

Dirt or contaminants entering the nozzle during maintenance

Varnish build up over time

**Flooded** — When too much fuel is distributed into the induction air, the mixture may become too rich to burn. While a flooded engine may be caused by poor starting technique, it can also stem from a mechanical problem. A leaking carburetor, primer system, or other fuel system component can allow fuel to enter the intake manifold, making it difficult to start the engine. If the pilot primes the engine when already flooded, the condition is made worse, and starting becomes even more difficult.

Causes:

Poor starting technique

Leaking carburetor

Leaking primer system

Carburetor float level set too low

**Flow divider diaphragm valve sticking open** — The flow divider diaphragm valve closes from a lack of fuel pressure, providing a positive fuel cutoff to the cylinders. If the diaphragm sticks open, fuel may continue to flow to the cylinders, slowing engine shut-down.

Causes:

Corrosion

Contamination

Deterioration

**Flow divider malfunction** — The flow divider contains a spring-assisted diaphragm that halts fuel flow to ensure a positive idle cutoff. If the diaphragm sticks and fails to open all the way, it will inhibit fuel flow.

Causes:

Fuel contamination

Corrosion

Damaged diaphragm

**Fuel contamination** — Fuel contaminated with water, dirt, or the wrong fuel type will cause the engine to run rough and may cause detonation at high power settings. As the contaminants are pulled into the fuel metering system, they drastically change the mixture, causing the engine to shudder and possibly quit.

Causes:

Improper fueling

Leaky fuel caps allowing water to enter tanks

Deteriorating fuel bladders

Items dropped in fuel tanks

**Fuel injector air bleed blocked** — Fuel injectors have air bleed holes that allow air to enter and combine with the fuel to assist in fuel atomization. If the holes are blocked, the fuel will not atomize properly, and the engine will run rough.

Causes:

Fuel contamination

Nozzles not cleaned during installation

**Fuel injector air bleed shroud leak** — On turbocharged engines, the nozzle's air bleed holes are shrouded and upper deck pressure is ducted to them. A leak in the system allows the engine to run normally when manifold pressure is below atmospheric, but when manifold pressure is higher than atmospheric, fuel leaks into the shrouded area, causing a lean mixture and the engine to surge.

Causes:

Loose connection

Broken or cracked line

**Fuel line blockage** — Fuel line blockage inhibits the flow of fuel and may cause the fuel flow gauge to fluctuate. It is also likely to reduce the fuel pressure down line.

Causes:

Deteriorating fuel bladders

Items dropped in fuel tanks

**Fuel pump failure** — A fuel pump failure prevents the engine from running except with the electrical boost or auxiliary pump on. A sudden rise in oil level is an indication of a failing pump. Shaft wear at the drive end of the pump will allow fuel to spill into the crankcase, raising the oil level.

Causes:

Worn shaft seal

Wear over time

Fuel contamination

**Fuel pump inlet air leak** — Air entering the fuel pump inlet causes the pump to cavitate, which subsequently causes the fuel pressure to fluctuate, resulting in low output pressure.

Causes:

Broken O-ring

Crack in line

**Fuel pump pressure too high** — A fuel metering unit requires that the fuel delivered is in the proper pressure range. If the pressure is too high, the valves and seats may cause the fuel to flow at an incorrect rate and allow too much fuel to be delivered, resulting in a rich mixture.

Causes:

Improper installation and rigging

**Fuel pump pressure too low at idle** — An engine-driven fuel pump that is weak may not provide enough fuel pressure at low r.p.m.. However, as r.p.m. increases, the pressure is more than sufficient to supply an adequate amount to the engine. The resulting lean fuel/air mixture at idle causes the engine to stumble when the throttle is opened to accelerate the engine.

Causes:

Worn out fuel pump

**Fuel pump pressure too low** — If the fuel pump pressure is too low, there may be sufficient fuel flow at low power. However, at high power settings, the fuel flow may be inadequate, as indicated by a low fuel flow indication and a lean mixture.

Causes:

Improper installation and rigging

**Improper mixture control rigging** — If the mixture control is not rigged properly, the mixture valve may not achieve its full range of travel. If the control cable does not move the mixture valve to the full rich position, then engine may operate lean or if it will not move to idle cutt-off, it may prevent the engine from shutting down.

Causes:

Improper rigging

**Improperly adjusted fuel metering unit** — An improperly adjusted fuel metering unit can result in excessively rich or lean mixtures at any power setting. A properly adjusted unit will deliver a slightly rich mixture at all power settings, with idle and full power being even richer. The rich mixture at idle is to allow for extra cooling during prolonged idling, and the rich mixture at full power is to increase the octane of the fuel-air mixture and provide increased cooling. The fuel metering unit should also be able to lean the mixture all the way to mixture cut-off. See "rich mixture" and "lean mixture" for more information.

Causes:

Improper adjustment

Worn valves and seats

**Incorrect fuel** — If jet fuel is mixed with avgas, the engine will run rough and excessive r.p.m. drops will occur during the magneto check. The engine will also likely experience detonation and may suffer severe damage at high power settings.

Causes:

Improper fuel

**Incorrect nozzle flow** — Fuel injector nozzles are ported to allow for a precise flow of fuel at a given fuel pressure. If one of the nozzles is the wrong size, the mixture to all cylinders will be affected. If the port is too large, the mixture will be rich and that cylinder will run lean compared to the other cylinders. If the port is too small, the affected cylinder will be lean and the rest will run rich. Examine the nozzle of the cylinder with the varying EGT to determine if it is the correct size.

If there is no varying EGT, then all the nozzles may be the wrong size. Compare the fuel flow settings to those specified in the POH. If the fuel flow settings do not coincide, check the nozzles for proper size.

Causes:

Installation of wrong size nozzle.

**Insufficient prime** — Engines require a rich mixture during start-up because the spark from the spark plug is weak and the fuel is not atomized sufficiently. In cold weather, the fuel does not vaporize easily and a great deal of extra fuel may be required to insure adequate fuel vapor.

Causes:

Starting technique

Cold weather

**Leak in float or deteriorated float** — A leak in the float or a deteriorated float will cause the float to sit lower in the fuel bowl, causing a high fuel level and excess fuel to enter the airflow. This creates an overly rich condition.

Causes:

Damaged during assembly

Deterioration over time

**Leak in fuel system** — A leak in the fuel system may cause large changes in the mixture, leading to the engine surging as the mixture moves into and out of a combustible ratio.

Causes:

Cracked fuel line

Loose fitting

**Leaking bowl gasket** — The float bowl chamber in most carburetors is vented to the carburetor throat, ahead of the venturi. The pressure is slightly lower than atmospheric due to the restriction of the air filter and intake ducting. A leaking float bowl gasket allows the slightly higher pressure atmospheric air to enter increases the push on the fuel to the main nozzle creating a higher flow and a rich mixture.

Causes:

Improper assembly

Deterioration

**Leaking fuel caps** — If the fuel tank caps do not seal properly, water may enter the fuel tanks. This typically happens as the caps age and the seal becomes brittle.

Causes:

Deterioration over time

**Leaking primer system** — The primer connects to the manifold near the cylinder intake port. If the primer pump does not seal properly to prevent fuel flow, the vacuum created in the manifold pulls fuel in through the primer line. Since there is a larger vacuum at idle than at high power settings, the amount of fuel drawn into the engine will be higher at idle and low power settings, and lower at high power settings.

A leaking primer system may also allow fuel to flow while the engine is off. The fuel enters the manifold, drains down to the carburetor, and then drips into the airbox. This may also prevent the engine from shutting down at idle cut-off.

Causes:

Check valve not seating properly

Primer not locked

**Lean Mixture** — When the fuel mixture is lean, an engine will run rough. Lean mixtures can be identified by a very clean exhaust pipe and increased roughness while leaning during run-up or a decrease in roughness when carburetor heat is applied. Also note the EGT gauge. If the mixture is excessively lean, the EGT decreases as the mixture is leaned further.

A lean mixture may only ignite when both spark plugs fire, but fail to ignite when only one plug fires. A lean mixture also burns very slowly, and if excessively lean, much of the combustion process takes place after the exhaust valve opens, resulting in a loss of power and high EGT.

Causes:

Improperly adjusted fuel metering device

Leak in intake manifold allowing more air to enter after metering device

**Loose venturi** — The two piece venturi used in some carburetors is prone to become loose. When this happens, the turbulence that forms in the carburetor causes improper fuel distribution, which ultimately may lead to the engine hesitating during acceleration. [Figure 14-9]

Causes:

Improper assembly

Worn loose over time

**Mixture valve not seating** — If the mixture control valve in either a carbureted or fuel injected engine does not seat properly, fuel may continue to flow after shut-down. Any scoring in the seat or damage to the valve may cause fuel to leak past the mixture control and allow the engine to continue running with the mixture at idle cut-off.

Causes:

Wear over time

Damage during installation

Corrosion

**Rich Mixture** — An engine will run rough with an excessively rich mixture. The best method to determine if an engine is running excessively rich is to examine the exhaust pipe for black soot. Also, the engine will smooth out when the mixture is leaned during run-up.

The inadequate supply of oxygen in a rich mixture may inhibit proper combustion. This causes incomplete combustion and a loss of r.p.m. and power.

During acceleration, a carbureted engine may stumble if the accelerator pump adds a large amount of unmetered, excessively rich fuel to the air, enriching the mixture beyond a burnable ratio. When the accelerator pump stops, the mixture leans out as the air continues into the manifold, at which point the engine begins to run too lean, slowing acceleration.

**Figure 14-9. A loose venturi produces turbulence in the intake which can cause engine hesitation during acceleration.**

An engine that quits at idle may have an excessively rich mixture. An engine can typically handle an excessively rich mixture better at higher power settings, but at idle, the engine may run rough and quit.

Causes:

Improperly adjusted fuel metering device

Carburetor heat reduces density, causing an enriched mixture.

In fuel injected, turbocharged aircraft, a leak in the intake manifold allows air to escape when upper deck pressure is higher than atmospheric pressure, leading to a rich mixture.

## III. IGNITION SYSTEM FAULTS

**Broken impulse coupling spring** — The impulse coupling spring holds the drive gear and the magneto in the advanced position when impulse coupling is not engaged. If the spring breaks, the magneto is no longer held in the advanced position and the timing moves toward the retarded position. This causes an increase in EGT and a drop in RPM. The increase in EGT is a result of the fuel/air mixture igniting late and still burning as it enters the exhaust manifold.

Causes:

Natural fatigue

Engine kickback during starting

**Broken P-lead**—A magneto produces a spark when the p-lead is not grounded. When grounded, the energy from the magneto is sent to ground instead of through the coil. A broken P-lead prevents the magneto from being shut off with the ignition or magneto switches.

Causes:

Failure to reinstall after maintenance

P-lead is cut by a sharp object or broken by vibration.

**Carbon deposits** — Carbon forms from an excessively rich mixture leaving unburned carbon on the spark plugs and valves. Carbon deposits on spark plugs can prevent the plugs from firing. This is very common on training aircraft that fly short trips or frequent patterns without proper leaning. It may be possible to lean the engine during the run-up to burn off the excess carbon.

Causes:

Rich mixture

Short flights

Spark plug with a heat range that is too cold

**Damaged spark plug** — Spark plugs contain ceramic insulators that ensure the high voltage from the ignition lead only arcs at the spark plug electrode. A crack in the insulator allows the spark to jump to ground inside the plug, causing the plug to misfire or not fire at all.

Causes:

Dropped spark plug

Detonation

Thermal shock

Improper cleaning

**E-gap improperly adjusted** — An improperly adjusted E-gap produces a weak spark, which may prevent ignition of the fuel/air mixture.

Causes:

Improperly adjusted

Changes due to wear, over time

**Improper timing** — If the engine runs smoothly on one magneto but has a large RPM drop on the other, check the timing. A magneto firing the spark plugs too early causes the cylinder pressures to increase drastically to the point where detonation may occur. CHT increases while EGT decreases with an advanced timing setting.

Retarding the timing reduces the pressures, resulting in decreased power. Because the air/fuel mixture is burning late, the exhaust valve opens, allowing combustion to continue into the exhaust manifold, which causes a rise in EGT.

Causes:

Loose magneto mounting nuts

Improper installation

Worn magneto

Improper E-gap

**Impulse coupling not engaging** — The magneto impulse coupling produces a distinct snap noise as the engine is cranking. An audible snap when turning the prop by hand, but not when cranking the engine with the starter, indicates that the impulse coupling's springs are worn. This allows the fly weights to move out at the cranking RPM to disengage the impulse coupling. Other signs that the springs are failing are that the engine starts after the start switch is disengaged and the RPM is slowing, or after the battery has been slightly discharged and the cranking speed is much slower.

A broken impulse coupling spring may prevent the engine from starting because the coupling's flyweights never engage. [Figure 14-10]

Causes:

Worn out over time

Broken flyweight springs

**Incorrect spark plug gap** — A spark plug's gap must be within a specified range in order for it to fire properly. If the gap is too small, the spark will be weak and may not ignite the surrounding fuel/air mixture. If the gap is too wide, the spark plug may fire at low power settings when there is less pressure in the cylinders, but not at higher power settings.

Causes:

Dropped spark plug

Improperly gapped

**Lead deposits** — 100LL avgas contains tetraethyl lead for increased anti-detonation properties. An engine that remains cool with a rich mixture may allow the lead to combine and form deposits. These deposits form in the head of the spark plug and may eventually bridge the gap of the electrodes and ground out the plug. Running the engine with a lean mixture during run-up will not clear out a lead fouled plug. The plugs must be removed and cleaned.

Causes:

Rich mixture

Short flights

Spark plug with a heat range that is too cold

Wrong grade of fuel

**P-lead grounding** — The P-lead grounds the magneto, preventing it from firing when the engine is stopped. Should the P-lead become grounded in flight, the magneto will shut-off. If the P-lead becomes grounded during start-up, it can make starting the engine difficult or impossible.

**Figure 14-10. A broken flyweight spring prevents an impulse coupling from retarding ignition for starting.**

Causes:

Wire worn through from vibration

**Shorted shower of sparks vibrator**—When the starter is engaged, the ignition switch grounds both advanced magneto points and provides pulsating current to the left magneto retard points. A shorted vibrator that causes the left magneto to remain in the retarded position causes an excessive RPM loss on the left magneto and a rise in EGT.

Causes:

Wire worn through

Improper installation

**Shower of sparks malfunction** — On engines equipped with a shower of sparks system, you should hear a buzzing sound when you engage the starter, if the vibrator unit is installed inside the cockpit. If the buzzing is not heard, check the start switch and vibrator circuit.

Causes:

Improperly wired

Broken or disconnected wire

Open circuit in vibrator coil

**Slow or fast cranking speed** — Starters and impulse couplings must be matched for the best starting performance. Magneto impulse couplings have a lag angle that varies with the cranking speed of the engine. If the engine is cranked too slow or too fast, the spark plug may fire to early or too late. If you change the starter to one of a different cranking speed, you must also change the impulse coupling lag angle.

Causes:

Improper matching of starter and magneto

**Spark plugs iced over** — Water is a by-product of combustion. This is evident in the water vapor coming from exhaust pipes on cold days. If an engine is very cold and during start-up the engine fires a few times, quits, and then will not start, ice may have bridged the spark plug electrodes or the plugs may have become frosted.

Causes:

Lack of pre-heating

Very cold weather

Balked start

**Starter switch malfunction** — If the starter switch fails to ground the right magneto, then the right magneto could fire, causing the engine to kickback on start-up.

Causes:

Damaged during installation

Worn over time

**Worn or loose ignition lead** — The ignition leads transmit very high voltages to the spark plugs. If the insulation is worn even partially to the core, the high voltage spark can jump to any part of the engine instead of across the spark plug gap. A loose ignition lead increases the resistance of the total circuit. The plug may fire at low manifold pressures because the voltage required to jump the gap is lower than that required at high power settings. When power is advanced, the voltage may not be high enough to fire the plug.

Causes:

Wires not secure

Lead nut not tightened

## IV. LUBRICATION SYSTEM FAULTS

**Cold oil** — The higher viscosity of oil in cold temperatures causes an increased resistance to flow which, in turn, causes an increase in oil pressure and reduced oil flow. This condition may result in premature wear of insufficiently lubricated parts. Propeller pitch changes may be sluggish, and the oil pressure may indicate high when the oil is cold and viscous.

In cold weather, the engine oil should be heated prior to start. Electric oil pan heaters work well when electrical power is available. In remote locations, the oil can be drained and kept inside, and then returned to the engine prior to start.

Causes:

Improper preheating in cold weather

Insufficient warm up

Oil cooler winterization kit not installed

**Fluctuating oil pressure** — Fluctuating oil pressure causes the propeller pitch to vary, which will appear as if the engine is surging. Fluctuating oil pressure may be from air in the lubrication system or metal in the oil. Never allow an aircraft with fluctuating oil pressure to fly. An in-flight engine failure may occur. [Figure 14-11]

Causes:

Air in lubrication system

Metal in oil

**Figure 14-11. A fluctuating oil pressure gauge may indicate an impending failure in the engine.**

**Frozen or blocked breather vent** — The crankcase is subject to varying pressures as the piston moves up and down. A blocked crankcase breather vent can cause excessive pressure to build up in the crankcase, leading to an oil leak at the nose seal.

Cause:

Cold temperatures

Sludge in breather vent

**Hot oil** — Hot oil is less viscous than cold oil. When the temperature of oil rises, it flows more freely and provides less resistance. Lower resistance in a lubrication system causes reduced oil pressure, and lower oil pressure may cause some parts to be inadequately lubricated.

Causes:

Winterization kit not removed in summer

High ambient temperatures

High CHT

Lean mixtures

High power settings

Improper grade oil

**Improper oil weight** — The weight of the oil is very important in maintaining the health of an engine. A lightweight oil in summer may become too thin when hot and not provide adequate lubrication, cushioning, and sealing properties, resulting in high wear and high oil consumption. Heavyweight oil may be too thick in the winter, making it difficult to start the engine, and after start-up the oil may fail to reach engine parts before damage occurs.

Causes:

Improper servicing

**Low oil pressure** — Low oil pressure can lead to inadequate lubrication, causing excessive wear and metal-to-metal contact. Any engine that is operated with low oil pressure must be inspected for damage. On feathering propellers, oil pressure moves the propeller blades to the low pitch, high RPM setting, and air and spring pressures move the propeller blades to the high pitch, low RPM, and feather positions. If the oil pressure is too low, the force the oil exerts on the propeller piston may be insufficient to counter the air and spring pressure to move the propeller toward low pitch, high RPM.

Causes:

Oil pressure relief valve set too low

Wrong oil grade/viscosity too low

High oil temperature

Failing oil pump

Insufficient oil quantity

Malfunctioning oil pump

Weak or broken oil pressure relief valve spring

Clogged filter or strainer

Debris under oil pressure relief valve

Leaking oil pressure relief

Oil cooler plugged

Collapsed oil filter

**Oil leaks** — An oil leak along the crankcase parting surfaces is quite common and difficult to repair. A small leak may appear to be a large amount of oil. Be sure the oil leak is excessive before spending a great deal of resources tracking it down. Fluorescent dye and a black light can help locate an oil leak in minutes.

Causes:

Deteriorated seal

Bad gasket

Improper assembly

**Oil out breather** — The breather tube vents the crankcase to the atmosphere to prevent excess pressure from building in the crankcase. Should the crankcase become pressurized, oil will be forced out the breather.

Causes:

Blow-by of combustion gases

Excessive valve guide clearance in turbocharged engines

Ram air entering crankcase through leaking nose seal gasket

**Oil pump sucking air** — If the oil level is too low and air enters the sump, the oil pump will cavitate and show a fluctuating oil pressure.

Causes:

Low oil level

**Oil relief valve set improperly** — The oil relief valve regulates oil pressure. If the valve is improperly set, the oil pressure may be excessively high or low. The engine manufacturer's maintenance manual explains how to adjust the valve.

Causes:

Improper adjustment

**Plugged oil passage** — A plugged oil passage causes high oil pressure before the blockage and low pressure after the blockage. Depending on where the oil pressure gauge reads pressure, the gauge may show low or high.

Causes:

Sludge build up over time

Synthetic Mobile One oil used with 100LL fuel

## V. MECHANICAL FAULTS

**Blow-by of combustion gases** — Blow-by of combustion gases can lead to excessive carbon in the oil and high crankcase pressure. The high crankcase pressure can cause the nose seal to leak oil.

Causes:

Worn or broken piston rings

**Crack in crankshaft** — An oil leak at the nose seal within 100 hours of a prop strike may be evidence of a crack in the crankshaft. After cleaning, rotate the crankshaft and look for a thin line of oil. The oil will flow out of the seal where the crankshaft crack is located.

Causes:

Prop strike

**Engine mounts worn or improperly installed** — Engine mounts absorb engine vibrations. Worn or improperly installed engine mounts transmit these vibrations, causing the engine to appear to be running rough, when it is not.

Causes:

Wear over time

Improper installation

**Failing bearings** — A failing bearing produces heat and metal. The metal shows up in the oil filter and screen, as well as in an oil analysis. The heat causes increased oil consumption.

Causes:

Inadequate lubrication

Lack of engine preheat in cold weather

Excess carbon and silicon in oil

**Metal in oil** — Metal in oil from a failing bearing will restrict oil flow at the sump pickup and oil screen or filter. A fluctuating oil pressure or drop in oil pressure over a few hours may be the result of metal in the oil. Do not allow an aircraft to fly with a fluctuating oil pressure gauge until the filters, screens, and oil can be inspected and analyzed. [Figure 14-12]

Causes:

Failing bearings, piston rings, or other parts

**Polished bore** — A cylinder wall has many peaks and valleys to control oil. If the engine sits for long periods of time without running, the peaks begin to rust. When the engine starts, the rust is removed by the piston rings. Over time, the peaks are worn away until the cylinder wall is smooth and polished. Oil cannot be controlled and oil consumption increases, while power decreases due to a loss of cylinder compression.

Causes:

Long periods of inactivity

**Rings do not seat** — Piston rings not only prevent the combustion gases from escaping the combustion chamber, they also control oil distribution on the walls of the cylinder. Improperly seated rings do not scrape oil off the cylinder wall properly, and excess oil burns in the combustion process. The oil lowers the octane of the fuel/air mixture, which can lead to detonation.

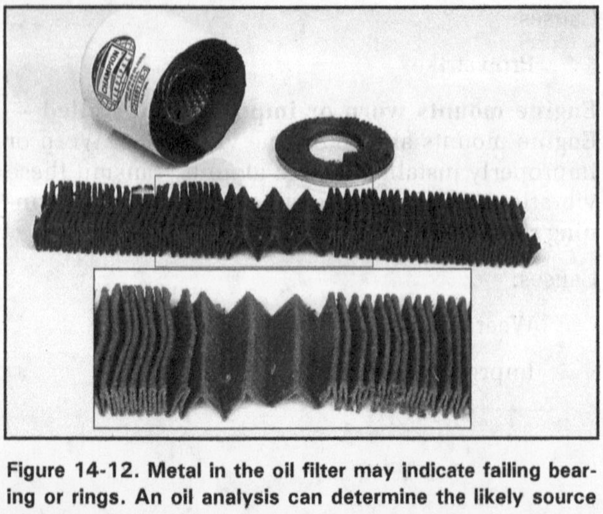

**Figure 14-12. Metal in the oil filter may indicate failing bearing or rings. An oil analysis can determine the likely source of the metal.**

Causes:

Improper cylinder overhaul

Inadequate engine operations over time, causing the cylinder to become polished

**Stuck valve** — Exhaust valves typically stick because high temperatures have caused oil to oxidize and form carbon build up in the valve guide. The symptoms of hesitation, missing, or occasional backfires often appear on the first start of the day when the engine is cold. As the engine warms up, the symptoms disappear. If left untreated, the symptoms may occur in flight and result in a substantial loss of engine power and possible engine damage. A valve can stick open, which can lead to the piston striking the valve, damaging both valve and piston. A valve that sticks closed causes the pushrod to bend, and, if the push rod shroud is damaged, a loss of engine oil.

Causes:

Improper engine cool down

Overheating engine

Over-leaning the engine

**Worn valve guides** — When valve guides become worn, oil that is used to lubricate the rockers can flow down the valve and into the intake or exhaust ports, causing an excessive oil consumption rate.

Causes:

Wear over time

Dirty oil

Carbon coking on hot exhaust valve

## VI. MISCELLANEOUS FAULTS

**Intake leak** — In a turbocharged, fuel injected engine, the fuel is metered at the fuel control unit, but is delivered into the air at the cylinder intake port. Any change in the volume of air between the fuel control unit and the intake port results in a mixture change. In normally aspirated engines and in turbocharged engines with manifold pressures maintained below atmospheric, a leak allows air to be sucked into the manifold, causing a lean mixture. However, when the manifold pressure in a turbocharged engine is maintained above atmospheric, air will escape through the leak, causing a low manifold pressure and rich mixture at high power settings.

Causes:

Improper installation

Deteriorating gasket

Crack in intake manifold

**Leaks in manifold pressure line** — A leak in the manifold pressure line allows ambient air pressure to enter the line and are indicated by a higher than normal reading.

Causes:

Cracked line

Loose fitting

**Low cylinder compression** — An engine with low compression on one or more cylinders may run normally at high power settings and appear to deliver full power. However, as power is reduced and RPM decreases, the amount of time for combustion gases to blow past the rings or valves increases, and power loss increases. This will show up as a rough running engine at idle that smoothes out as power is increased.

Causes:

Wear over time

Contaminants in oil

**Low power** — An engine that is not producing full power may not achieve the minimum static RPM. An engine producing low power may have any number of problems. It is important to look at other indications such as high or low EGT, high or low manifold pressure, and high or low fuel flow.

Causes:

Carburetor ice

Carburetor heat on

Dirty air filter

Intake restriction

Ignition problem

Mixture problem

Bearing failure

Poor combustion

Leak in intake

Leak in exhaust

Improper fuel flow

Exhaust restriction

Throttle not opening fully

Propeller governor malfunction

Turbocharger controllers improperly adjusted

Improper valve rocker arm clearance

Carburetor heat stuck open

Leaking primer

Stuck carburetor float

Fuel pump malfunction

Water ingestion

**Missing primer plug in cylinder** — Most engines have a primer plug in every cylinder that allows for primer installation in any cylinder. However, most engines do not have primer lines running to all cylinder primer ports. For cylinders that do not have a primer installed, the hole for the primer line is sealed with a plug. If this plug falls out, there will be a large hole for ambient air to enter the intake port, thereby causing a rise in the manifold pressure and an excessively lean mixture. [Figure 14-13]

Causes:

Plug falls out from vibration

Failure to reinstall after maintenance

**High field elevation** — Normally aspirated engines produce less power as altitude increases. The minimum static RPM listed in a TCDS or STC is for sea level run-ups. At higher altitudes, a naturally aspirated engine with a fixed-pitch propeller installed may not achieve the minimum static RPM.

Causes:

High field elevation

## VII. PROPELLER FAULTS

**Nitrogen charge lost or low** – On propellers that use an air charge to assist in moving the propeller to high pitch/low RPM and feather, a low or lost air charge may prevent the propeller from feathering altogether.

Causes:

Air leak

Improper servicing

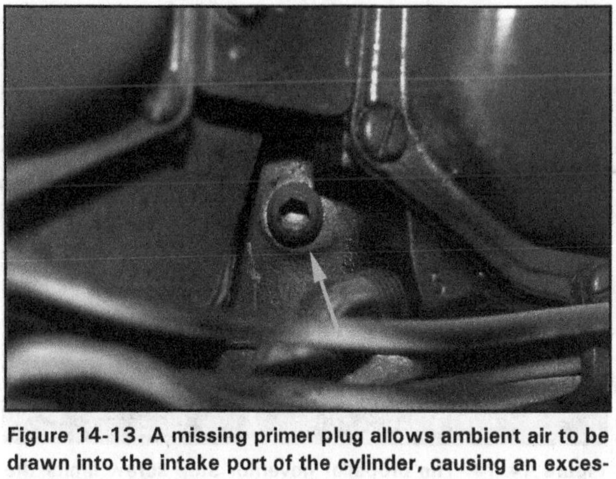

**Figure 14-13. A missing primer plug allows ambient air to be drawn into the intake port of the cylinder, causing an excessively lean mixture.**

**Nitrogen charge pressure too high** — If the air charge pressure in the propeller is too high, it may prevent the oil pressure from moving the propeller into the low pitch high RPM setting.

Causes:

Improper servicing

**Disconnected control cable** — The propeller governor control arm is spring-loaded to the low pitch/high RPM position. A disconnected cable would prevent the pilot from moving the governor into a low RPM setting.

Causes:

Improper installation

Bird strike

Loose nut on wire end

**Governor improperly adjusted** — Propeller governors have an adjustable maximum RPM stop screw. The maximum propeller RPM is set to coincide with the maximum engine RPM. [Figure 14-14]

Causes:

Improper adjustment

**High friction in hub parts** — High friction in the pitch change mechanisms in the hub cause the pitch to change slowly and may prevent the propeller from feathering. This condition must be resolved by a certified propeller shop.

Causes:

Corrosion

Improper assembly

**High pitch pin malfunction** — Feathering propellers that use air and spring pressure to feather the blades have spring-loaded, high pitch stop pins that prevent the blades from feathering every time the engine is shut down. In flight, the high propeller RPM causes centrifugal force to move the pins out, allowing the propeller to feather in flight. If these pins become stuck in place, they will prevent the propeller from feathering.

**Figure 14-14. The propeller governor stop screw limits the propeller's high RPM setting.**

Causes:

Corrosion

**Improper propeller control cable rigging** — The propeller control cable must be installed and rigged to allow the full governor range to be selected from the propeller control. If the cable is too short, the low pitch, high RPM setting may not be achieved. If it is too long, the feather stop may not be reached, preventing feathering.

Causes:

Improper installation or rigging

**Propeller governor malfunction** — The propeller governor augments oil flow to the propeller to adjust its pitch in order to maintain a set RPM. A malfunctioning governor may prevent the propeller from changing pitch, limiting the engine to a low RPM or causing over-speeding of the engine. The governor may also fail in such a way as to cause the engine to surge and the RPM to vary.

Causes:

Broken spring

Stuck flyweights

Worn over time

**Wrong propeller installed** — An aircraft's TCDS lists the engine and propeller combinations approved for installation. The TCDS also lists the minimum static RPM for the various combinations. An STC may have previously been approved to install a different engine or propeller on the aircraft, in which case the STC will list the minimum static RPM for a given engine and propeller combination.

Causes:

STC issued

Wrong installation

## VIII. TURBOCHARGER FAULTS

**Fluctuating wastegate** — A fluctuating wastegate causes the manifold pressure to change as the turbocharger speeds up and slows down. This causes the engine to surge.

Causes:

Air in oil line

Sticking wastegate valve

Fluctuating oil pressure

**Pressure relief fails to open** — On the upper deck side of some turbocharged engines, a pressure relief valve opens to prevent an engine overboost condition. If this valve fails to open, the manifold pressure may exceed maximum limits.

Causes:

Corroded valve

Improper setting

**Rate controller malfunction** — A rate controller prevents the upper deck pressure of a turbocharged engine from increasing too rapidly by relieving oil pressure to the wastegate and allowing it to open. If it malfunctions, the upper deck pressure could exceed limits during a rapid throttle increase.

Causes:

Malfunctioning bellows

Oil control malfunction

**Turbocharger pressurizing the crankcase** — An engine with worn intake valve guides may allow upper deck pressure to pass around the valve into the valve cover, down the push rod shroud, and into the crankcase. This will pressurize the crankcase and may cause the nose seal to leak.

Causes:

Worn intake valve guide

**Wastegate stuck closed** — The wastegate regulates the amount of exhaust gases that flow through the turbine, which, in-turn, spins the compressor and maintains a certain intake pressure. If the wastegate sticks closed, all exhaust gases are directed through the turbine, thereby turning the compressor at full speed. This results in a high manifold pressure or overboost condition

Causes:

Carbon build up on wastegate shaft

Wastegate controller malfunction

Hydraulic restriction

**Wastegate stuck open** — The wastegate regulates the amount of exhaust gases that flow through the turbine, which, in-turn, spins the compressor and maintains a certain intake pressure. If the wastegate sticks open, the turbine and compressor will not spool up, and the manifold pressure will remain low.

Causes:

Carbon build up on wastegate shaft

Wastegate controller malfunction

## IX. VACUUM SYSTEM FAULTS

**Dirty vacuum filters** — Dirty vacuum filters restrict the air entering the system, which causes a rise in vacuum. The regulator opens to allow more air into the system to maintain a set value of suction. If the regulator opens fully and the filters are still very dirty, the vacuum will start to increase. However, because more air is entering at the regulator and less at the filters, the gyros may fail to achieve the proper RPM.

Causes:

Dirty over time (Normal)

Operation in dusty environment

**Leak in vacuum system** — If air is allowed to enter the vacuum system at any place other than the filters, the suction will fall and the gyro instruments may fail to achieve the proper RPM to remain erect.

Causes:

Broken, cut, or deteriorated vacuum line

**Vacuum line collapse** — Vacuum lines become weak and fragile over time and will collapse from the vacuum.

Causes:

Deterioration over time

**Vacuum pump failure** — Vacuum pumps are engine driven, and like all mechanical devices, are prone to failure. When a vacuum pump fails, check the oil filter and screen, and analyze the oil to insure there is no other contributing factor to the pump failure.

Causes:

Metal in oil

Wear over time

**Vacuum regulator improperly adjusted** — The vacuum regulator allows air to enter the system to regulate the vacuum in the lines. If too much air is allowed to enter, the vacuum will be too low. If too little air is allowed to enter, the vacuum will be high. Ideally, the vacuum should be set so that it is as low as possible to prevent pump overheating, but still within the green arc.

Causes:

Improper adjustment

# IN-FLIGHT SQUAWKS

Many times a squawk cannot be verified on the ground, but if the reporting pilot documents it well the fault may be easily discovered with a thorough knowledge and understanding of the affected systems. Some squawks that pilots may report are:

## CABIN LOSES PRESSURIZATION AT PARTIAL POWER

Pressurized piston-engine aircraft pressurize the cabin from air that is supplied by the turbocharger. The flow into the cabin is constant at a given power setting, and the pressure is adjusted by a relief valve in the pressure vessel. If the cabin loses pressurization at a partial power setting, there may be a cabin air leak. At high power settings, the flow is adequate to maintain the pressurization, but as the flow rate is reduced when power is reduced, the cabin may leak faster than the inflow, even with the pressure relief valve fully closed. Another possibility is that the pressure relief valve has become stuck open to relieve pressure at a certain power setting, and when that power is reduced, the valve releases too much air for the inflow.

## FAILURE TO REACH CRITICAL ALTITUDE

A turbocharged engine maintains rated horsepower up to a specific altitude, known as the engine's critical altitude. If the engine begins losing power before that altitude is reached, then the turbocharger is malfunctioning. The cause may be a damaged compressor, a leak in the induction system, or a seizing bearing.

The lack of exhaust gases being directed through the turbine may be caused by a leak in the exhaust, or a stuck or misadjusted wastegate controller that is allowing too much exhaust gas to bypass the turbine. Because the wastegate is closed by oil pressure, low oil pressure can prevent its proper operation.

## EGT DECREASE ON ALL CYLINDERS

A decrease in EGT on all cylinders is normal when enriching the mixture on the rich side of peak, and leaning the mixture on the lean side of peak. However, if the EGT decreases in flight without a change in the mixture or throttle setting, the probable cause is carburetor ice, induction icing, or a blockage of the induction air filter. An interview with the pilot will help determine if the problem was likely icing, or if there may be an intake obstruction.

If the EGT decreases after maintenance, the mixture may have been set too rich, or the timing may have been set too advanced. With the mixture too rich, the CHT will also be lower. If the timing is set too far advanced, the CHT will show an increase.

## EGT DECREASE ON ONE CYLINDER

A decrease in EGT on one cylinder may be an indication that the rings or valves are not holding cylinder compression, causing a lowering of the combustion pressures and temperatures.

Fuel injector nozzles have air ports to allow atomization of fuel as it is injected into the intake manifold. In naturally aspirated engines, these air ports are vented to the atmosphere because the atmospheric pressure will always be higher than manifold pressure. Turbocharged aircraft engines have a shroud around the injectors that vent the ports to the upper deck pressure. If these ports become blocked, the fuel will not be mixed with air and more fuel will be injected into the cylinder, resulting in a rich mixture.

A plugged nozzle may show a low EGT on one cylinder, when the remaining cylinders are operating at or near peak EGT. This occurs because the restriction is inhibiting fuel flow through the plugged injector and the pressure to the remaining cylinders is increased slightly.

If one spark plug in a cylinder fails to fire, the EGT will drop slightly. A magneto check will determine which plug is not firing.

A blown exhaust gasket will allow exhaust gases to escape, causing a pressure and temperature drop across the EGT probe.

## ENGINE FIRE DURING START-UP

An engine fire during start-up is caused by fuel pooling in the carburetor airbox and being ignited by a backfire. The pooling fuel can be caused by a leaking primer system, a leaking float needle, or a float level that is set too high. However, the most likely cause is improper priming. A common technique to prime an engine is to pump the throttle. If the carburetor is equipped with an acceleration pump, the fuel sprays directly into the carburetor throat where it immediately falls into the airbox. The engine's primer system should be used if installed. If pumping the throttle is the only means of priming, then the throttle should only be pumped while the engine is cranking.

## EGT INCREASE ON ALL CYLINDERS

A lean mixture to all cylinders will show an EGT increase. This may be the result of a fuel metering problem, or an intake leak. On a fuel-injected engine, if the EGT increases more than normal as power is increased, the problem may be caused by the fuel pressure being too low to deliver enough fuel at high power settings.

If one magneto fails to fire, all cylinders will show a 50°F – 100°F EGT rise. On the ground, a magneto check will determine if this is the problem.

An EGT rise after maintenance has been performed may be the result of the magnetos being set to a retarded timing position.

## EGT INCREASE ON ONE CYLINDER

An increase in EGT on one cylinder may be the result of a lean mixture in that cylinder. A lean mixture burns slower than a rich mixture, so the fuel/air mixture may still be burning when the exhaust valve opens. As the mixture continues to burn out the exhaust pipe, the higher resultant temperature is indicated on the EGT gauge. The lean mixture may be the result of an intake leak in the portion of the intake manifold leading to that cylinder, or a damaged or blocked fuel nozzle limiting the amount of fuel entering the cylinder. Flow check the nozzles to obtain equal fuel distribution.

An exhaust valve leaking exhaust gases will also show a high EGT on that cylinder. A compression test will determine if this is the problem.

A spark plug that is not firing will show a 50°F – 100°F EGT rise in that cylinder.

## HIGH CYLINDER HEAD TEMPERATURE

High cylinder head temperatures may indicate inadequate cooling. The engine baffles must be in good condition with no breaks or excessive leaks. In the cowling, air is forced to take a specific path, and broken or missing baffles will cause the air to take the path of least resistance. It may neglect to travel around the cylinder to provide the required cooling air.

Cylinder cooling fins are also vital to dissipate heat. Cracked cylinder fins will not transfer heat properly and must be repaired. Obstructions on the fins such as paint, grease, or metal bridges formed during casting, inhibit airflow and lead to high CHT readings.

Apart from inadequate cooling, advanced timing, lean mixtures, broken exhaust gaskets, pre-ignition, and detonation can all lead to high CHT. Conversely, high CHT can lead to detonation and pre-ignition.

If a rise in CHT is associated with a low or complete loss of oil pressure, engine failure is imminent. The engine must be torn down and inspected.

## HIGH OIL TEMPERATURE

If the oil temperature is high in addition to high CHT, there is inadequate cooling, or the engine is producing too much heat. If CHTs are normal, but oil temperature is high, then the oil is not cooling properly. This may be caused by the failure to remove a winterization kit in warm weather. If the oil is hot, but the oil cooler is not, then there is a lack of flow through the oil cooler caused by blockage, failed Vernatherm® valve, failed bypass valve, or air in the oil cooler. If the belly of the aircraft is covered in oil and the oil in the crankcase is black, the piston rings are letting combustion gases blow by. Perform a compression test to confirm the analysis.

## LOSS OF POWER WHILE CLIMBING TO ALTITUDE

It is normal for naturally aspirated and supercharged engines to lose power as the aircraft climbs. A turbocharged engine should not lose power during a climb until the aircraft reaches the engine's critical altitude. If manifold pressure does drop off as the aircraft climbs, then it is likely that there is a problem with the wastegate actuating system.

A leak in the exhaust system prevents the turbine from achieving the proper RPM and manifold pressure limits. An exhaust leak shows up as powdery white or yellow stains on and in the vicinity of the exhaust manifold.

An intake leak when the manifold pressure is higher than atmospheric will cause a rich mixture. If the engine runs rough with very low EGTs and leaning improves the condition, then inspect for an intake leak.

If the density controller fails, the turbocharger wastegate will not close as altitude increases, resulting in a loss of power during the climb.

The turbocharger should spin freely without any binding. If the turbo does not spin freely by hand, it must be overhauled.

Air acts as an electrical insulator. As an aircraft climbs to high altitude, the lower atmospheric pressure allows the electrical energy of the magneto to jump to the wrong spark plug. To counter this, magnetos are built with large diameters, or they are pressurized. If the aircraft has pressurized magnetos and the loss of power at altitude is associated with backfires, a magneto may have a pressure leak.

On carbureted engines, another possible cause for a loss of power is carburetor ice.

## LOW OIL TEMPERATURE

Low oil temperature is often due to cold weather and excessive airflow through the oil cooler. Installing a winterization kit will bring the oil temperature into the proper range.

## BACKFIRING

When an excessively lean fuel/air mixture passes into a cylinder, the mixture may not burn at all or will burn so slowly that combustion continues through the power and exhaust strokes. If this occurs, the flame can linger in the cylinder and ignite the contents of the intake manifold and the induction system when the intake valve opens. This causes an explosion known as backfiring, which can damage the carburetor and other parts of the induction system.

Backfiring is seldom the fault of the carburetor and, in most cases, is limited to one or two cylinders. Usually, backfiring is the caused by incorrect valve clearance, defective fuel injector nozzles, or other conditions that result in a leaner mixture entering the cylinder. In some instances, an engine backfires in the idle range, but operates satisfactorily at medium and high power settings. The most likely cause, in this case, is an extremely lean idle fuel/air mixture. Enriching the mixture usually corrects this difficulty. Because backfiring cylinders fire intermittently, they typically run cooler than cylinders that are operating normally. Therefore, a backfiring cylinder can sometimes be detected by a cold cylinder check.

## AFTERFIRING

Afterfiring, sometimes called afterburning, often results when the fuel/air mixture is too rich. Overly rich mixtures, like excessively lean mixtures, also burn slowly. However, the slow burn rate of a rich mixture is due to the lack of sufficient oxygen. If an overly rich mixture burns past the power stroke and into the exhaust stroke, unburned fuel can be forced out of a cylinder into the exhaust gases. If this occurs, air from outside the exhaust stacks will mix with the unburned fuel, causing it to ignite and explode in the exhaust system. Afterfiring is perhaps more common with engines that have long exhaust ducting that can retain greater amounts of unburned fuel. Typical causes of afterfiring include an improperly adjusted carburetor or an unseated exhaust valve.

Afterfiring can also be caused by cylinders that are not firing because of faulty spark plugs, defective fuel injection nozzles, or incorrect valve clearances. The unburned mixture from these dead cylinders passes into the exhaust system, where it ignites and burns. Unfortunately, the resulting afterburn can easily be mistaken for evidence of a rich carburetor. Cylinders which are afterfiring intermittently can cause a similar effect.

## DIAGNOSING FAULTS WITH GRAPHIC ENGINE DISPLAYS

A Graphic Engine Display (GED) can provide a technician with an overview of the engine operating parameters. A sudden change or large deviation in a displayed parameter may indicate an engine fault. Several graphic engine displays will provide an annunciation or alarm to the pilot if certain parameters are exceeded, or a large change occurs in a short period of time. Because the pilot may be too busy flying the aircraft to study the problem in detail, the memory feature of these instruments can recreate the instrument indications to provide you with the information necessary to diagnose a fault. The following examples provide easily recognizable faults, causes, and solutions. Remember, if no conditions exist to explain an out of range parameter, test for a faulty probe.

### GED SHOWS AN EGT RISE IN ONE CYLINDER

An EGT rise in one cylinder is likely the result of a lean mixture, a spark plug failing to fire due to fouling, a cracked insulator, or a worn ignition lead allowing the spark to jump to ground. [Figure 14-15]

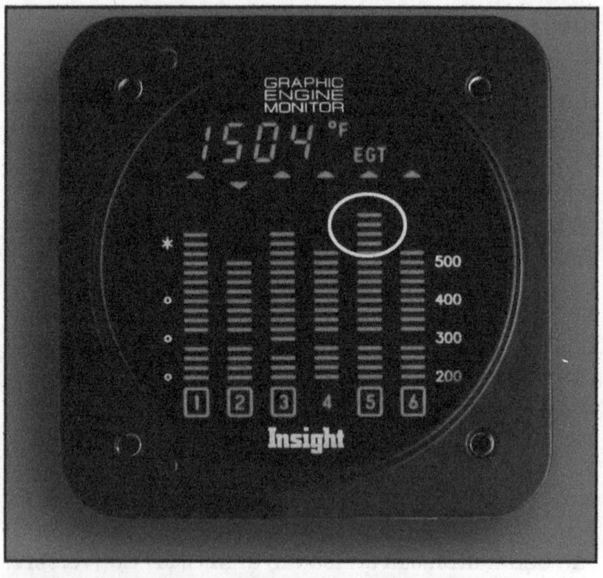


**Figure 14-15. A rise in EGT in one cylinder may be the result of a lean mixture in that cylinder.**

Run the engine on each magneto individually. If the fault is in the ignition system, when you select the magneto with the affected plug, the EGT will drop on the affected cylinder and all others will rise. If no change occurs, it is likely a fuel problem. If the pilot reports this fault only at high altitude, it may possibly be a cracked spark plug insulator.

With an ignition problem, locate the failed component by swapping the ignition leads and perform a second operational check to determine if the fault is still on the same magneto. If it is, then the problem lies in the ignition lead. If the fault switches magnetos, the fault lies with the spark plug.

With a fuel problem, examine the fuel lines for leaks, and if none exist, remove and clean the injector.

## GED SHOWS A CHT RISE IN ONE CYLINDER

A high CHT on one cylinder may be the result of broken rings, or damaged or missing cylinder fins or baffling. Visually inspect the cylinder fins for damage or cracks. Insure the baffling is secure and in place and that no large leaks will prevent air from being forced through the cylinder fins. Finally, perform a compression check to determine if the rings are sealing properly. If the rings do not seal, it is likely that a ring has broken and the cylinder will require removal for repairs. [Figure 14-16]

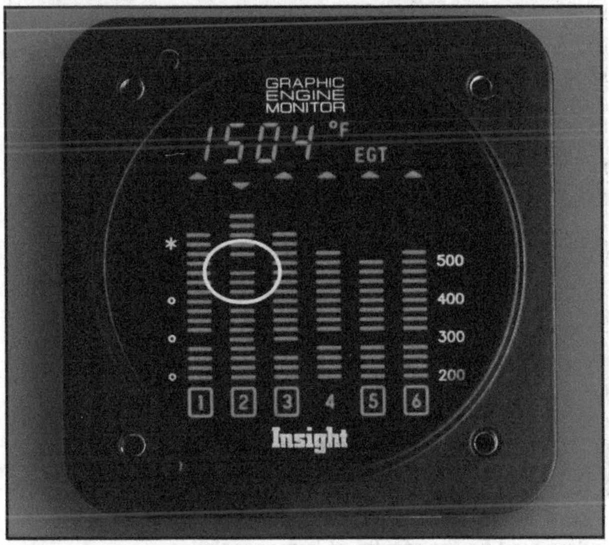


**Figure 14-16. A high CHT in one cylinder may be the result of cracked cylinder fins.**

## GED DISPLAYS AN EGT RISE IN ALL CYLINDERS

When a sudden uniform rise in all cylinders is displayed, the likely cause is a failed magneto. If both magnetos appear to be operating normally during run-up, then inspect the P-lead for intermittent grounding. Another possible cause is a weak magneto not providing enough current at high power settings. The magneto check may show normal at run-up RPM, but at full power, the magneto may fail to fire. [Figure 14-17]

**Figure 14-17. An EGT rise in all cylinders may be the result of a failed magneto.**

## GED DISPLAYS LOW EGT IN ONE CYLINDER

A low EGT in one cylinder may be the result of exhaust gases leaking from the exhaust manifold to cylinder gasket. A visual inspection will reveal carbon deposits or yellow exhaust stains where the gasket is leaking.

If an intake valve fails to open completely, thereby preventing a full charge of air from entering the cylinder, the EGT will be lower than normal. A bent push rod or a failing lifter may cause this.

If the intake or exhaust valves or piston rings fail to seal properly, the compression will be low, resulting in lower combustion temperatures. [Figure 14-18]

If an intake leak exists in the induction of a turbocharged, fuel-injected engine, the mixture will be excessively rich when the manifold pressure is greater than atmospheric. When manifold pressure is reduced to near atmospheric, the EGT will appear normal compared to the other cylinders. However, as manifold pressure is further reduced, the mixture will become lean and the EGT may show higher than the other cylinders.

**Figure 14-18. A low EGT may be the result of inadequate airflow into the cylinder.**

## GED DISPLAYS EXTREMELY HIGH CHT ON ONE CYLINDER

A blown exhaust gasket or a loose or cracked exhaust manifold will allow exhaust gases to leak. If these gases strike the CHT probe, the CHT temperature will climb rapidly. This symptom may also be associated with many backfires at high power settings if the exhaust gases heat the intake manifold to the point that it ignites the fuel/air mixture. [Figure 14-19]

## GED DISPLAYS HIGHER OR LOW ON ALL CYLINDERS

Improper ignition timing can lead to an increase or decrease of EGT on all cylinders. Advanced timing, or early ignition, typically leads to a low EGT. Retarded timing, or late ignition, causes high EGT on all cylinders. [Figure 14-20]

**Figure 14-19. A broken or cracked exhaust manifold may direct hot exhaust gases on a CHT probe, causing an extremely high CHT in one cylinder.**

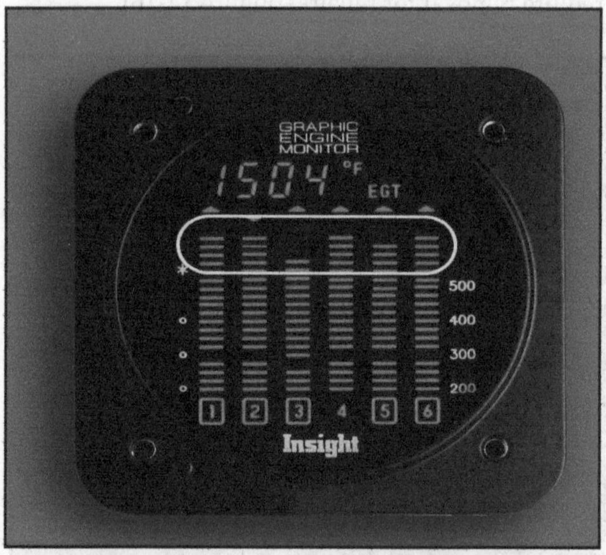


**Figure 14-20. A temperature increase or decrease in all cylinders may be the results of improper timing.**

# SUMMARY CHECKLIST

✓ Isolating the cause of a fault is key to correcting a discrepancy.

✓ Operating an engine is an important activity when attempting to reproduce a reported discrepancy.

SECTION C

# TURBINE ENGINE TROUBLESHOOTING

Turbine engine discrepancies can be either obvious or hidden. Hidden problems, when not detected and corrected, often cause major problems with continued engine operations. Hidden troubles are detected by continuously monitoring engine operating parameters, comparing them over time to detect subtle changes that indicate wear and transient problems. By analyzing engine trends and consulting the airframe and engine manufacturer's troubleshooting information, you can systematically isolate and correct defects before they cause major problems.

## TREND MONITORING

One of the most useful procedures used to detect hidden and subtle problems with turbine engines is to perform continuous evaluations of engine performance parameters over time. A properly operating turbine engine produces fairly predictable and consistent compressor rpm, exhaust gas temperature, fuel flow, and power output for a given ambient pressure altitude and temperature. By recording parameter data during each flight, and analyzing changes when they occur, problems can often be detected and corrected early in their development.

Performance monitoring of engines, commonly referred to as trend monitoring, is a technique used by aviation maintenance organizations and engine manufacturers to improve engine service life and reduce operating costs. The monitoring of an engine's performance and condition over a period of time provides a database for trend analysis. Trend analysis alerts an operator to deteriorating performance, providing an opportunity to take corrective action before substantial engine damage or failure occurs.

Proper trend monitoring begins when an engine is new or recently overhauled. Data collected during the initial operations establishes a baseline to compare to all subsequent operations data. After establishing an initial relationship between performance parameters, operating data is reviewed at regular intervals. Significant changes in the relationships between performance parameters may signal impending failures.

Data collection methods range from onboard computers to manual entries on paper forms. Regardless of the method used, conditions under which a certain parameter is measured should be consistent to be useful in a trend analysis. For example, EGT measurements and fuel flow indications should always be taken at the same power setting, and under the same ambient conditions. However, since ambient conditions often vary between flights, correction factors must be taken into account with data. If this is not done, it is possible to obtain data which skews the trend analysis and gives false indications of a problem. [Figure 14-21]

Since it takes a great deal of experience to identify subtle trend variations, aircraft and engine manufacturers often provide trend monitoring services for their customers. In some cases, second party companies may also provide these services. By using an FAA-approved trend monitoring program, engine operating times between overhaul, or times and cycles between required inspections, may be extended. While trend monitoring improves safety, it also provides tremendous economic benefits.

| ENG PERFORMANCE | Left | Right |
|---|---|---|
| ITT / EGT | 660 | 670 |
| N1 | 94.6 | 98.8 |
| Torque / N 2 | 1940 | 1940 |
| Prop / EGT | 1700 | 1690 |
| F / F | 340 | 360 |
| Gen. Load | 44A | 38A |
| Pressure Altitude 29.92 | FL 190 | |
| IAS / OAT | 198 | -14°C |
| Oil Pressure | 120 | 120 |
| Oil Temp | 55 | 43 |
| Anti-Ice | | OFF |
| De Ice Vane | retracted | |

**Figure 14-21. On most turbine aircraft, engine operating parameters are recorded by the flight crew during cruise flight. The record includes ambient temperature and pressure altitude at the time of the reading.**

Trend analysis information can be broken down into two broad categories; performance and mechanical. Typical performance parameters include information on EPR or torquemeter (Np) readings, compressor $N_1$ and $N_2$ speeds, gas generator speed (Ng), fuel flow (Wf), and EGT or ITT. On the other hand, mechanical parameters typically include instrument readings for oil pressure, oil temperature, oil quantity, vibration, oil pressure warning lights, and bypass lights. Accurately interpreting a trend analysis requires the ability to discern small shifts in operating parameters on one or more gauges and to accurately compare the information to base line data. [Figure 14-22]

## SPECTROMETRIC OIL ANALYSIS

Another technique used to detect hidden problems in turbine engines is done by performing a spectrometric oil analysis. A spectrometric oil analysis program, or SOAP, is available to aircraft operators to help detect developing problems in an engine. Spectrometric analysis for metal particles suspended in oil is possible because metallic ions emit characteristic light spectra when vaporized by an electric arc. Each metal produces a unique spectrum, allowing easy identification of the metals present in an oil sample. The wavelength of spectral lines identifies each metal and the intensity of the line is used to measure the quantity of that metal in a sample.

When participating in a spectrometric oil analysis program, periodic samples of oil are taken from the engine after shutdown or prior to servicing. Samples are taken from a sediment free location in the main oil tank and sent to an oil analysis laboratory. In the lab, a film of the used oil sample is picked up on the rim of a rotating, high purity, graphite disk electrode. A precisely controlled, high voltage, AC spark is discharged from a vertical electrode to the

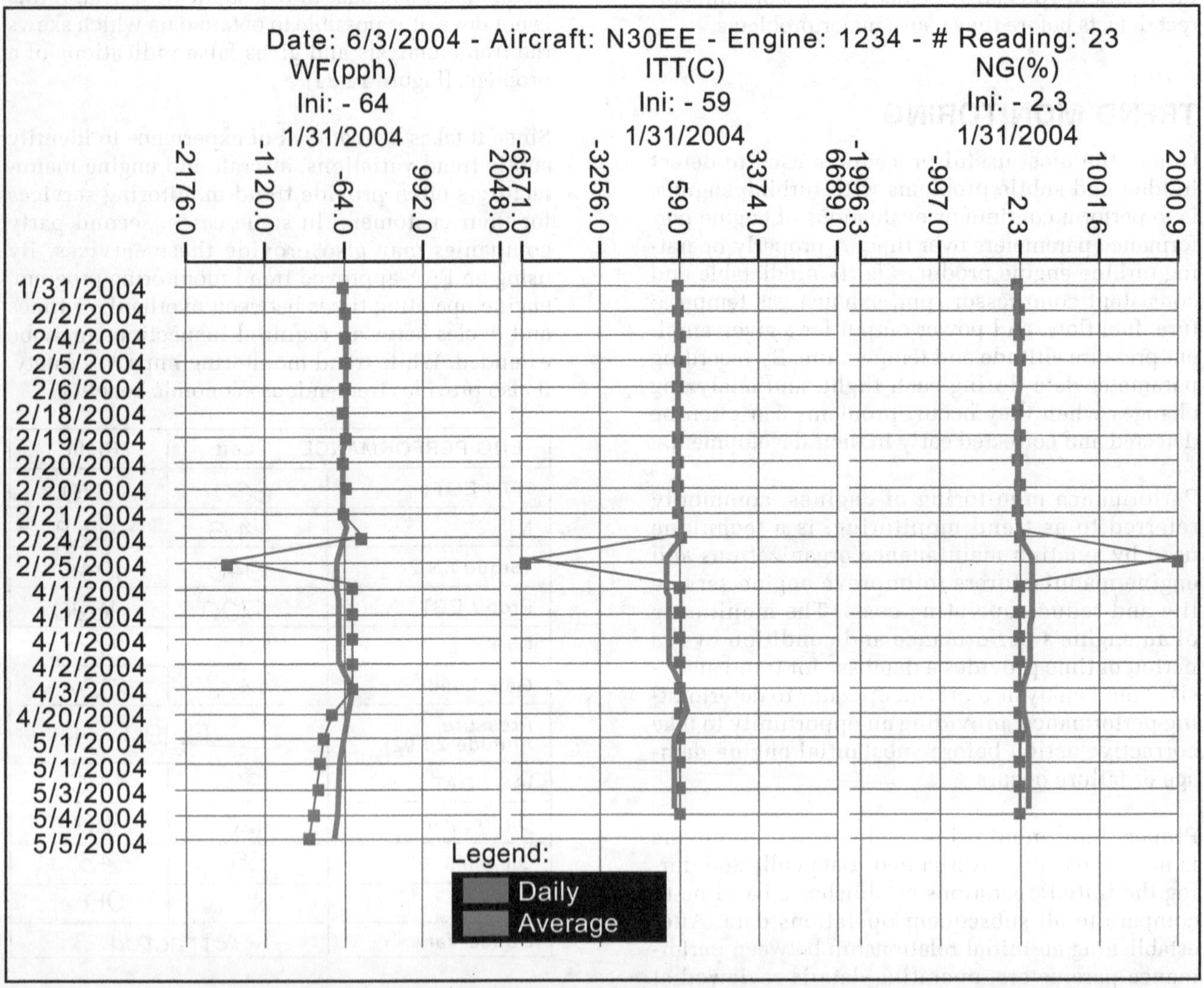


**Figure 14-22. Engine data collected over a period of time is plotted on a graph. By observing deviations from established parameters, hidden problems may be detected. In this example, engine temperatures are gradually decreasing while fuel flow and power remains about the same. This indicates that the temperature sensing system may be in error and should be checked or recalibrated at the next maintenance event.**

rotating disk. When this occurs, the film of oil on the disk begins to burn. Light emitted by the burning oil passes through a series of slits, precisely positioned to detect the wavelengths of various metals. As light passes through the slit, photo multiplier tubes electronically convert the light waves into energy, which automatically prints the analytical results on the laboratory record sheets. The wear metals present are so small that they flow freely through an engine's system filters. The spectrometric therefore measures the particles that move in suspension in the oil and are too small to appear on either the oil screen or chip detector. [Figure 14-23]

Alloyed metals in turbine engines may contain amounts of aluminum, iron, chromium, silver, copper, tin, magnesium, lead, nickel, or titanium. Silver is accurately measured in concentrations down to one-half part silver in one million parts of oil. Most other metals are measured accurately in concentrations down to two or three parts per million. The maximum amount of normal wear has been determined for each metal of the particular system in the program. This amount is called its threshold limit of contamination and is measured by weight in parts per million (PPM). If after interpreting the results, the lab identifies a sharp increase of abnormal concentrations of metal, the lab will immediately notify you.

The types of metals identified during a spectrometric oil analysis provide invaluable information to help you determine the source of the contamination. Engine manufacturers provide a list of engine components and the materials used in their construction. Consult this information to identify areas where to begin troubleshooting and for corrective actions to take when the source of contamination has been identified.

## TROUBLESHOOTING RESOURCES

Instructions for troubleshooting gas turbine powerplants are contained in the aircraft and engine manufacturer's maintenance manuals. The information contained in the airframe manual provides operational considerations in relation to the airframe systems and general powerplant troubleshooting guidance. For additional, and often more specific engine troubleshooting information, consult the powerplant manufacturer's manuals.

Standard engine instrument readings are used with troubleshooting guides to provide clues as to the cause of a given engine malfunction. In addition, some aircraft are equipped with built-in test equipment, or BITE test systems. BITE systems consist of sensors, transducers, and computer monitoring devices, which detect and record engine data such as vibration levels, temperatures, and pressures. A typical BITE test requires you to make entries on a keypad in the cockpit or at a remote terminal in order to receive engine data. However, even this sophisticated equipment can only provide you with the symptoms of a problem, leaving you to determine the actual problem.

A typical turbine engine maintenance manual provides one or more troubleshooting tables or flow diagram charts to aid in pinpointing the cause of common malfunctions. However, it is not possible for these to identify all malfunctions. Instead, troubleshooting tables and flow charts provide you

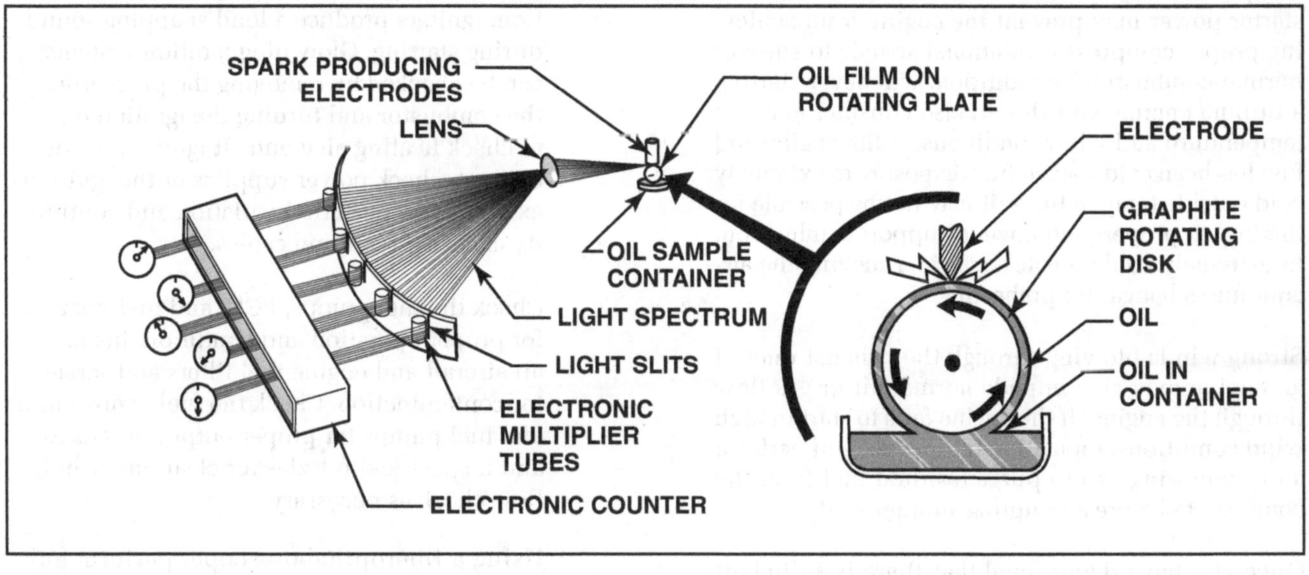


**Figure 14-23. In spectrometric oil testing, the used oil sample is applied to a rotating, graphite disk and ignited by a high voltage, AC spark. The light emitted by combustion passes a series of slits designed to detect the wavelengths of different metals. The light energy passing through the slits is measured by an electronic counter.**

with a starting point in the troubleshooting process. This, combined with a thorough knowledge of the engine systems, logical reasoning, and experience provides you with the information necessary to diagnose and correct complicated or intermittent malfunctions. See figure 14-24.

Most powerplant manufacturers group engine troubles into categories similar to the following:

- Starting and shutdown faults
- Operational faults
- Performance faults and engine trend monitoring (ETM) shifts
- Lubrication faults and oil contamination

To isolate a fault, it is necessary to have reports of previous problems and any actions that may have been taken to correct them. You should check the probable source of the trouble, by use of diagnostic tests, until the defect has been isolated. As always, use a systematic sequence to isolate the fault to prevent making wrong and costly assumptions as to the cause of a problem.

## STARTING AND SHUTDOWN FAULTS

Aside from internal engine problems, inappropriate starting techniques and other problems that are external from the engine may cause starting malfunctions. When attempting to start a turbine engine for maintenance checks, it is advisable to always use auxiliary pneumatic or electric power sources. Insufficient starter power may prevent the engine from achieving proper compressor rotational speeds to support normal combustion. In addition, whenever starting a turbine engine, you should also consider ambient temperature and wind conditions. If the engine and fuel has been cold soaked from exposure to extremely cold outside temperatures, it may not be possible for the fuel to properly atomize to support combustion. In extremely cold climates, consider moving the aircraft into a hangar for preheating.

Strong winds blowing through the exhaust duct of an engine may also impede normal air or gas flow through the engine. If the engine fails to start in high wind conditions, reposition the aircraft and perform a dry motoring run to purge residual fuel from the combustors before attempting another start.

Once you have determined that there is sufficient power for starting and after eliminating all other external factors, begin systematically isolating possible engine problems that may be affecting the start. Typical starting problems caused by engine and engine accessory faults consist of the following:

Does the starter motor operate? Audibly confirm that you can hear the starter during the start cycle. If there is no indication of starter operation, check the following:

> Check electrical or pneumatic sources to determine that they are adequate and being delivered to the starter. When cross-bleeding pneumatic air from a secondary source such as an APU or another engine, check the operation and position of all bleed-air and start control valves. For electric starters, check the operation of all starter relays and contactors, and the condition of electrical wires and terminal ends.

If the starter operates, does the engine rotate? This may be confirmed with the compressor tachometer (Low pressure compressor or $N_1$, high pressure compressor or $N_2$, or gas generator compressor or Ng, as appropriate to the type of engine) or by visually checking for engine rotation.

> If there is no rotation, or if rotation is sluggish, check the starter driveshaft for condition and engagement. Manually attempt to rotate the engine by hand and listen for abnormal scrapping or rubbing sounds. Determine the source of any irregularities.

If the engine rotates to an appropriate rpm, but still fails to start, check the following items:

> Inspect the ignition system for proper operation. Igniters produce a loud snapping sound during starting. Glow plug ignition systems can be checked by removing the plugs from the combustor and turning the ignition on to check heating elements. If ignition is not evident, check power supplies or the ignition exciter. Also perform insulation and continuity checks on ignition cables.

> Check the fuel pumps, FCU, and fuel nozzles for proper operation and condition. Inspect all aircraft and engine fuel filters and screens for contamination. Check the fuel control unit and fuel pumps for proper output pressures, and inspect fuel nozzles for cleanliness and flow check as necessary.

> Using a fiberoptic borescope, perform an engine inspection to check for severely damaged internal hot section and compressor components.

| INDICATED MALFUNCTION | POSSIBLE CAUSE | SUGGESTED ACTION |
|---|---|---|
| Engine has low RPM, exhaust gas temperature, and fuel flow when set to expected engine pressure ratio. | Engine pressure ratio indication has high reading error. | Check inlet pressure line from probe to transmitter for leaks.<br>Check engine pressure ratio transmitter and indicator for accuracy. |
| Engine has high RPM, exhaust gas temperature, and fuel flow when set to expected engine pressure ratio. | Engine pressure ratio indication has low reading error due to:<br>Misaligned or cracked turbine discharge probe.<br>Leak in turbine discharge pressure line from probe to transmitter.<br>Inaccurate engine pressure ratio transmitter or indicator. | Check probe condition.<br>Pressure test turbine discharge pressure line for leaks.<br>Check engine pressure ratio transmitter and indicator for accuracy. |
| NOTE: Engines with damage in turbine section may have tendency to hang up during starting. | If only exhaust gas temperature is high, other parameters normal, the problem may be thermocouple leads or instrument. | Recalibrate exhaust gas temperature instrumentation. |
| Engine vibrates throughout RPM range, but indicated amplitude reduces as RPM reduced. | Turbine damage. | Check turbine as outlined in preceeding item. |
| Engine vibrates at high RPM and fuel flow when compared to constant engine pressure ratio. | Damage to compressor section. | Check compressor section for damage. |
| Engine vibrates throughout RPM range, but is more pronounced in cruise or idle RPM range. | Engine-mounted accessory such as constant-speed drive, generator, hydraulic pump, etc. | Check each component in turn. |
| No change in power setting parameters, but oil temperature high. | Engine main bearings. | Check scavenge oil filters and magnetic plugs. |
| Engine has higher than normal exhaust gas temperature during take-off, climb, and cruise. RPM and fuel flow higher than normal. | Engine bleed air valve malfunction.<br>Turbine discharge pressure probe or line to transmitter leaking. | Check operation of bleed valve.<br>Check condition of probe and pressure line to transmitter. |
| Engine has high exhaust gas temperature at target engine pressure ratio for takeoff. | Engine out of trim. | Check engine with Jetcal Analyzer. Retrim as desired. |
| Engine rumbles during starting and at low power cruise conditions. | Pressurizing and drain valve malfunction.<br>Cracked air duct.<br>Fuel control malfunction. | Replace pressurizing and drain valves.<br>Repair or replace duct.<br>Replace fuel control. |
| Engine RPM hangs up during starting. | Subzero ambient temperatures.<br>Compressor section damage.<br>Turbine section damage. | If hang up is due to low ambient temperature, engine usually can be started by turning on fuel booster pump or by positioning start lever to run earlier in the starting cycle.<br>Check compressor for damage.<br>Inspect turbine for damage. |
| High oil temperature. | Scavenge pump failure.<br>Fuel heater malfunction. | Check lubricating system and scavenge pumps.<br>Replace fuel heater. |
| High oil consumption. | Scavenge pump failure.<br>High sump pressure.<br>Gearbox seal leakage. | Check scavenge pumps.<br>Check sump pressure as outlined in manufacturer's maintenance manual.<br>Check gearbox seal by pressurizing overboard vent |
| Overboard oil loss. | Can be caused by high airflow through the tank, foaming oil, or unusual amounts of oil returned to the tank through the vent system. | Check oil for foaming; vacuum-check sumps; check scavenge pumps. |

**Figure 14-24. Troubleshooting guides provide suggestions to help determine the cause of a malfunction and possible remedies.**

If the engine starts, but tends to hang up, or is sluggish to accelerate, check the following items:

Check all pneumatic bleed air reference lines to the fuel control unit (FCU) and other parts of the engine for leakage, or blockage.

Check starting bleed air valves for proper operation. Often, bleed air valves remain open during the initial part of the start sequence to reduce the load on the compressor, but close at higher rpm before light off. Also ensure that all auxiliary airframe system bleed air valves are properly positioned during the start.

Check the pressurization and dump valve (P&D or purge valve) for proper operation. After shutdown, the valve should open to allow excess fuel to drain, but should close during the start sequence.

Perform additional checks as required for the specific engine as called for in the manufacturer's troubleshooting procedures.

## OPERATIONAL FAULTS

Operational faults include items that become apparent during normal operations. Faults may include failure of the engine to accelerate or decelerate properly, compressor surges or stalls, transient over temperature conditions, abnormal vibrations, and others.

Engine indicating systems sometimes erroneously show values that are outside normal operating parameters. You should always verify that the engine indicating systems are calibrated and working properly before beginning to diagnose internal engine faults. A Jetcal Analyzer, as described in Chapter 4 of this textbook, or similar equipment, should be used to check the integrity of the indicating gauges, transmitters, sensing elements, and wiring harnesses.

Some typical operational faults and actions to take to diagnose them are as follows:

During mid to low power operations, if a hooting or huffing sound is emitted:

Check for excess compressor air leakage through bleed air valves. In some instances, manufacturers may recommend blanking off bleed air outlets to diagnose whether the problem is caused by an engine bleed air problem, or possibly that the problem is leakage in an airframe bleed air (pneumatic) system.

Check the condition of the compressor inlet, blades, and guide vanes for foreign object damage (FOD) and cleanliness. If the compressor section is found dirty, perform an engine performance recovery wash, in accordance with the manufacturer's instructions, also described in Chapter 4 of this textbook. If other damage is discovered, consult the manufacturer's maintenance instructions to determine the extent of field repairs that are allowed or if the engine must be disassembled and repaired in an overhaul facility.

Engine rpm is excessively high or too low:

Check the operation of all engine controls. Check power and fuel cutoff controls for full travel to the stops at the FCU (Also condition lever and propeller controls for turboprop engines).

Check for hang-up or distortion in any cam linkages.

Check the adjustment of the FCU especially if changes have been recently made during engine trimming operations.

If the engine experiences an uncontrolled overspeed, check the FCU driveshaft for engagement and FCU bleed air reference lines for obstructions and leakage.

Check the FCU for contamination, and if detected, isolate the source and replace the FCU with a new or overhauled unit.

The engine is slow to accelerate or surges during power application:

Check bleed air reference delivery tubes for leakage and obstructions.

Inspect the compressor for cleanliness and FOD damage. Perform a power recovery wash, as required.

Check bleed air valves for proper operation and the airframe auxiliary bleed air system for leakage.

Check the FCU fuel filters and screens for contamination. Check the airframe fuel source for contamination and fuel quality.

When acceleration controls are installed on the FCU, attempt to make adjustments. If maximum adjustments do not obtain desired results, replace the FCU with a new or overhauled unit.

If the engine experiences a transient over temperature during operation (exhaust gas temperature or EGT, turbine inlet temperature or TIT, or interstage turbine temperature or ITT):

Perform a check of the engine temperature indicating instruments to determine the actual extent of the over temperature condition. Determine the maximum temperature value and the length of time of operation above maximum limits. (Consult the engine manufacturer's maintenance instructions to determine required actions. If the engine is allowed to remain in service, isolate the cause of the fault).

Check for excessive airframe accessory power loading. For example, excess generator loads or excessive bleed air requirements may cause transient engine over temperatures.

Perform a fiberoptic borescope inspection of the compressor inlet, blades, and guide vanes. Perform a power recovery wash if the compressor is found dirty or corroded. If corrosion is present, follow the manufacturer's instructions for continued operations.

Inspect the combustors and turbine sections for damage and distortion. Flow check the fuel nozzles and verify their alignment in the fuel manifold upon reinstallation.

If excessive vibrations are indicated during normal operation:

Inspect the engine for loose mounting and the condition of all isolation dampeners.

For turboprop engines, check the propeller balance and the condition of the power section and gearbox.

Perform a visual inspection (with fiberoptic borescope, as required) of the compressor and turbine sections for FOD damage.

Check the bleed air valves for proper operation.

Inspect the oil filter element or screen for signs of contamination and perform a spectrometric oil analysis.

Flame out during normal operation:

Inspect the airframe fuel system for contamination and delivery pressures.

Check the engine driven fuel pump and FCU for proper fuel delivery.

Check the acceleration time of the engine and if outside of specifications inspect the FCU and fuel nozzles for contamination.

Inspect the compressor and turbine sections for FOD damage.

Low power or if all engine indicating parameters are showing low.

Verify proper operation of the indicating systems.

Check engine control linkages for proper operation and travel limits.

Check bleed air reference lines to the FCU and other engine accessories.

Attempt to perform engine trimming as specified by the engine manufacturer. If unable to achieve desired results, inspect the FCU and fuel nozzles for contamination and proper operation.

Unusual noises such as squealing or rubbing heard during operation:

Rotate the engine by hand to detect unusual rubbing at low rotational speeds. If squealing is only heard at high rpm, inspect the compressor and turbine sections for evidence of blade tip to shroud rubbing.

Check all engine mounted accessories for proper operation.

Inspect the engine oil filter element or screen for evidence of contamination and perform a spectrometric oil analysis to check for wear of internal engine parts.

## PERFORMANCE FAULTS AND ENGINE TREND MONITORING (ETM) SHIFTS

As previously discussed, most turbine-powered aircraft engine performance is continuously evaluated through a trend monitoring program. By performing a trend analysis, corrective actions can be taken to correct an unsafe condition as soon as the engine's operating parameters deviate from their established baseline.

It is not uncommon for turbine engines to display slight parameter variations and degradation in performance as a factor of normal wear. Significant changes indicate abnormal conditions that must be isolated to assure maximum engine efficiency and safety. Variations in fuel flow ($W_f$), temperatures, and power ($N_1$, EPR or torquemeter $N_p$) are the primary parameters used to evaluate the engine's performance, but other parameters such as oil pressure and chip detector warning systems are also used to indicate mechanical irregularities.

Common performance faults include the following symptoms along with their possible causes:

Rapid shift in engine temperature monitoring parameter that is not accompanied by shifts in fuel flow, compressor speed, or power output:

> An indicator or sensing system fault almost always causes rapid temperature shifts without other parameters being affected. Check the condition and operation of temperature probes and bus bars. Perform an operational check of the temperature sensing system using a Jetcal Analyzer, or similar calibration equipment.
>
> For multi-engine aircraft, when both engines have a similar rapid temperature shift, check the airframe outside air temperature (OAT) system, and altitude or airspeed indicating systems since malfunctions may cause erroneous data reports from the flight crew.
>
> A slight shift of engine temperature parameters without other accompanying parameter shifts may indicate fuel nozzle contamination. Remove the fuel nozzles for flow checks and verify nozzle alignment in the fuel manifold upon reinstallation.

Changes in a single operating parameter without corresponding changes to other operating parameters, or changes to all operating parameters in a proportionate amount.

> Again, if fuel flow shows a rapid change without an engine temperature or compressor speed change, this is usually indicative of an instrument system fault. Perform a Jetcal analysis to check each instrument indicating system.
>
> If all parameters indicate a decrease in a proportionate amount, it often indicates that the engine power sensing, or airframe OAT, airspeed, or pressure altitude instruments are at fault. For example, if the EPR or torquemeter is in error, the flight crew will set power in accordance with the erroneous indication. This will always be reflected in changes to all other operating parameters in proportionate amounts.

Exhaust temperature, compressor speed, and fuel flow all show an increase beyond baseline when desired power settings are established:

> Perform a calibration check of all engine instruments and indicating systems.
>
> Check for engine inlet obstructions, distortion, and FOD damage to the compressor.
>
> Perform a power recovery wash if the compressor is found dirty or corroded. However, this is generally not considered to be the fault when sudden parameter shifts occur, but may be useful to partially regain performance losses.
>
> Check the operation and condition of all bleed air valves and airframe auxiliary bleed air systems. Airframe systems can be isolated from the engine by the installation of blanking plates, as previously discussed.
>
> Check for any seal damage or other sources of hot air being ingested back into the engine intake. For ground operations, this may be caused by the use of reverse thrust or by high winds blowing into the tailpipe or carrying hot exhaust gases toward the engine intake.
>
> Determine if any hot starts may have been recently encountered, which may explain the rapid parameter shift. If evidence suggests that a hot start may have been encountered, perform a hot section inspection to determine the engine's internal component integrity. Consult the engine manufacturer's hot start inspection procedures and over temperature limitations.

Engine temperature and fuel flow increase while compressor speeds decrease or remain unchanged:

> Inspect the turbine section for damage to exhaust nozzles, turbine blades and turbine disk.
>
> Check the pressurization and dump valve (purge valve) for proper operation.
>
> Check for bleed air leakage and for proper bleed air valve operation.

Inspect the compressor section for damage and cleanliness. Perform a power recovery wash if the compressor is found dirty or corroded.

## LUBRICATION FAULTS AND OIL CONTAMINATION

Mechanical faults are sometimes detected by performance monitoring systems including oil pressure gauges, oil temperature gauges, metallic chip detectors, and other components. In addition, internal engine faults are detected during oil filter inspections and spectrometric oil analysis of oil samples. Typical lubrication system faults and oil contamination considerations include the following:

Low oil pressure indications

Insufficient oil quantity. Follow the engine manufacturer's instructions for checking the oil level. In most cases, the oil level must be checked within a specified time after the engine has been operated.

Check the indicating system to verify proper pressure gauge indications.

Check the oil filter and screens for obvious signs of contamination or debris.

Inspect external components of the lubrication system such as oil to fuel heat exchangers for signs of leakage.

Inspect the oil pressure relief valve for proper functioning and attempt to adjust the oil pressure to specified levels.

High oil pressure indications

Check the oil pressure indicating system for proper operation.

Check the oil pressure relief valve for proper operation and attempt to adjust the valve to achieve specified limits.

Fluctuating oil pressure.

Check the oil level. Insufficient or excessive oil quantity may cause fluctuating oil pressures.

Check the oil pressure indicating system for proper operation.

Check the airframe oil cooler system for leaks or blockage.

Inspect and clean the oil filter and screens, as required.

High or low oil temperature indications

Check the oil level. Low quantities cause elevated lubrication system operating temperatures.

Check the oil temperature indicating system for proper operation.

Inspect the oil cooler for signs of leakage and proper thermostatically controlled bypass valve operations.

Check the operation of the oil pressure relief valve.

Evidence of oil in the tailpipe or exhaust duct.

Consult the engine manufacturer's troubleshooting instructions to isolate possible internal engine carbon or labyrinth seal failure.

Excessive oil consumption.

Check for leakage or blockage in the pressure and scavenge oil tubes and ports. Leaking scavenge and pressure ports and tubes may also cause fluctuating oil pressures or total loss of oil pressure due to the lubrication pump(s) losing their prime.

Check for oil leaks in the oil filter element housing, the fuel heater, and the airframe oil cooler assembly.

Inspect the tailpipe and around case seals for signs of oil. If leakage is evident, refer to the engine manufacturer's instructions for further guidance to isolate the source of the leak.

Metallic chip detector warnings

Perform an operational check of the chip detector by removing the sensing element. Once removed, inspect for metallic particles between the sensing elements. If the detector is found clean, repair or replace the detector.

If metallic particles are found, refer to the engine manufacturer's troubleshooting procedures and maintenance manual for information on how to detect the type of metal and probable sources.

Evidence of metallic particles in the engine oil and/or filter.

Perform a spectrometric oil analysis to determine the exact type of metal and quantity. Compare the results of the analysis to the engine manufacturer's guidance material to determine if the engine can continue in service, and the conditions that must be met for continued service, or if the engine must be removed for disassembly and repair.

# SUMMARY CHECKLIST

✓ Trend monitoring describes activities that document engine condition over time. Subtle changes in performance data can indicate a discrepancy developing before a failure occurs. These discrepancies are monitored and corrected appropriately.

✓ Troubleshooting can be aided by information from built-in test equipment (BITE) systems.

# GLOSSARY

## A

**abrasion** — **1.** An area of roughened scratches or marks usually caused by foreign matter between moving parts or surfaces. **2.** The wearing or rubbing away of a surface by a substance used for grinding, grating, polishing, and so on.

**abrasive grit blast cleaning** — The removal of carbon and other deposits from a turbine engine using a blast of air containing ground walnut shells or apricot pits.

**absolute pressure controller (APC)** — An instrument that regulates the maximum turbocharger compressor discharge pressure in a reciprocating engine turbocharger system.

**AC generator** — A device that converts mechanical energy into electrical energy by electromagnetic induction. This type of generator produces alternating current.

**ACC** — *See* active tip clearance control.

**accessory drive gearbox** — A component that provides mounting space for engine accessories. Also referred to as the main gearbox.

**accessory section** — The part of an engine that provides the necessary mounting pads for accessory units such as magnetos, fuel pumps, oil pumps, and generators.

**accumulator** — A hydraulic component consisting of two chambers separated by a piston, diaphragm, or bladder. Compressed air in one chamber holds pressure on hydraulic fluid in the other chamber, which enables the fluid to be stored under pressure. An accumulator can be used to assist in bringing the propeller out of the feathered position by providing a burst of oil pressure to the hub when the control lever is moved out of the feather position.

**active thermocouple** — The active component of an Edison fire detection system that uses thermocouples to detect the presence of an overheat condition or a fire. Reference and test thermocouples are also used in this system to determine system functionality and integrity.

**active tip clearance control (ACC)** — A system in some high-bypass turbofan engines that controls thermal expansion of the turbine case by adjusting the amount of airflow around the turbine case.

**AD** — *See* airworthiness directive; ashless-dispersant oil.

**Adel clamps** — A rubber-cushioned, loop-type clamp used to support or separate cables, wire bundles, fuel lines, and similar components.

**ADI** — *See* anti-detonation injection.

**aeolipile** — A simple, steam-powered jet engine invented in the first century A.D.

**aerodynamic twisting force** — A force that tends to twist the blade angle toward the feather position.

**aero-thermodynamic duct** — An open tube that produces thrust when fuel is ignited inside. Fuel is added to incoming air as the athodyd moves through the air at a high speed. The burning fuel/air mixture causes air expansion that speeds up the air and produces thrust. Also known as athodyd.

**afterfiring** — A condition that often results from either too rich a fuel/air mixture or unburned fuel being pumped into the exhaust system of a reciprocating engine and ignited when it comes in contact with a hot component. Sometimes referred to as afterburning or torching.

**aft-fan engine** — A turbofan engine that has a fan constructed as an extension of the turbine blades.

**air bleed** — **1.** A small hole in the fuel passage between the float bowl and the discharge nozzle of a float carburetor. The hole introduces air into the liquid fuel to aid atomization. **2.** A small hole used in gas turbine engines to draw pressurized bleed air from the engine's compressor section for a variety of purposes.

**air metering force** — The force used in Bendix pressure carburetors and fuel injection systems in which venturi and ram air pressures control the amount of fuel metered.

**air throttle assembly** — The component in a fuel injection system that regulates air to the cylinders for combustion.

**air-oil separator** — A device that separates and collects oil from the breather line of a reciprocating engine or the oil reservoir of a gas turbine engine. Also known as deaerator.

**airworthiness directive (AD)** — A regulatory notice issued by the FAA to the registered owner of an aircraft informing the owner of a condition that prevents the aircraft from continuing to meet its conditions for airworthiness. The owner must comply with an airworthiness directive within the required time limit, and the fact, date, and method of compliance must be recorded in the aircraft's maintenance records.

**Airworthiness Limitations** — A section in the maintenance manual of an aircraft component which establishes mandatory replacement times, inspection intervals, and cycle limits.

**alnico** — An alloy of iron, aluminum, nickel, and cobalt. Alnico has an extremely high permeability and excellent retentivity for use in magnets.

**Alodine®** — A conversion coating chemical that forms a hard, unbroken aluminum oxide film, chemically deposited on a piece of aluminum alloy. Alodining is the functional equivalent of anodizing, but without the electrolytic bath. It conforms to specification MIL-C-5541 B.

**Alpha range** — The pitch of a turbopropeller system that maintains a constant engine speed in flight idle conditions.

**alternate air door** — A spring-loaded (automatic) or cable-activated (manual) door that permits unfiltered air to enter the induction system when the induction filter is blocked.

**alternate air supply** — Unfiltered air from within an engine nacelle used to support combustion when the induction filter is blocked.

**AMC** — *See* automatic mixture control.

**American Petroleum Institute (API)** — A U.S.-based trade association that conducts research, develops standards, issues certifications, and provides educational resources for the oil and natural gas industry.

**American Society of Testing and Materials (ASTM)** — An organization that provides a global forum for the development and publication of voluntary consensus standards for materials, products, systems, and services. Many standards in the aircraft industry are ASTM standards.

**American Wire Gage (AWG)** — A standardized system for nonferrous wire that establishes the proper size of wire to be used based on the length of wire and its current-carrying capability. The larger the wire size number, the smaller its diameter.

**angle of attack** — **1.** The acute angle formed between the relative wind striking an airfoil and the zero lift line of the airfoil. The chord line of the airfoil is often substituted for the zero-lift line. **2.** (Absolute) The angle of attack of an airfoil, measured from the attitude of zero lift. **3.** (Critical) The angle of attack at which the flow about an airfoil changes abruptly as shown by corresponding abrupt changes in the lift and drag. **4.** (For infinite aspect ratio) The angle of attack at which an airfoil produces a given lift coefficient in a two-dimensional flow. Also referred to as "effective angle of attack." **5.** (Turbine compressor) The acute angle formed between the chord line of the compressor blades and the direction of the air that strikes the blades.

**annular combustor** — A ring-shaped combustor lining in a gas turbine engine. This lining can be either basket- or can-type.

**anti-detonation injection (ADI)** — A system that adds a mixture of water and alcohol to the airstream of a carbureted engine to prevent detonation by cooling the air.

**anti-icing system** — **1.** Any system or method that provides heat or supplies anti-icing fluid to critical external surfaces to prevent ice formation. **2.** A system in a gas turbine engine in which some of the hot compressor bleed air is routed through the engine air inlet system to warm it and prevent ice from forming.

**APC** — *See* absolute pressure controller.

**API** — *See* American Petroleum Institute.

**APU** — *See* auxiliary power unit.

**armature reaction** — The distortion of the generator field flux by the current flowing in the windings of the armature. Armature reaction causes the brushes to pick up current from the armature at a point on the commutator where there is a potential difference, which causes the brushes to spark.

**armor coat** — A plastic covering over a wood propeller that increases resistance to chipping.

**articulated rod** — A link rod that connects the pistons in a radial engine to the master rod. There is one fewer articulated rod than the number of cylinders in each row in a radial engine because one piston is attached to the master rod.

**ashless-dispersant oil** — A lubricant with two cleaning additives. The additives ensure that the oil does not leave behind ash or burning embers as it cleans. Furthermore, the particles created and removed by cleaning are suspended (dispersed) within the oil for collection by the oil filter.

**aspect ratio** — The ratio of the span of an airfoil to its chord.

**ASTM** — *See* American Society of Testing and Materials.

**ASTM union colorimeter** — A device to determine the color of oil.

**athodyd** — *See* aero-thermodynamic duct.

**automatic high pitch stop** — A spring-loaded latch mechanism in a Hartzell compact feathering propeller that prevents feathering below 800 r.p.m.

**automatic mixture control (AMC)** — A device in a fuel metering system (carburetor or a fuel injection system) that keeps the fuel-air mixture ratio constant as the density of the air changes with altitude.

**automatic propeller** — *See* constant-speed propeller.

**autosyn** — The synchronous-motor principle, in which the angular position of the rotor of one motor at the measuring source is duplicated by the rotor of the indicator motor. Used in fuel-quantity or fuel-flow measuring systems, position-indicating systems, and so on.

**auxiliary air-intake doors** — *See* blow-in doors.

**auxiliary power unit (APU)** — A gas turbine, usually located in the aircraft fuselage, that provides either electrical power, air pressure for starting main engines, or both. Similar in design to ground power units.

**averaging function** — A function of a pneumatic, continuous loop fire-detection system that provides a warning if the average temperature of the area where the loop is placed increases. As the area temperature rises, gas pressure in the loop increases until it is sufficient to close the diaphragm switch in the responder unit and activate the warning system alarm.

**AWG** — *See* American Wire Gage.

# B

**backfire** — A burning or explosion within the induction system of a reciprocating engine when the fuel-air mixture is ignited by gases that are still burning in the cylinder when the intake valve opens.

**ball check valve** — A check valve in a fluid power system that uses a spring-loaded steel ball and a seat to permit flow in one direction only. The ball is forced tightly against its seat by fluid flowing into the valve from the end that contains the spring, thereby stopping the fluid flow through the valve. Fluid flowing into the valve from the ball end forces the ball off its seat, permitting flow through the valve.

**bayonet gauge** — A dipstick gauge used to measure the quantity of a liquid such as oil or hydraulic fluid.

**BDC** — *See* bottom dead center.

**bearing race** — A grooved, hardened, and polished steel surface that supports a bearing.

**bearing retainer** — The device that supports the balls or rollers in a bearing assembly.

**bell gear** — The large stationary gear in a spur gear planetary reduction gearing system. Also known as ring gear.

**bellows** — A circular, pleated, or corrugated capsule or compartment used to measure pressure. A bellows can be either evacuated or filled with a specific pressure of inert gas and exposed to the pressure to be measured.

**Bendix drive** — A type of assembly with a pinion gear used with electric starters to engage and disengage with an engine.

**Bernoulli's principle** — In physics, the interrelation between pressure, velocity, and gravitational effects in moving fluids. It states that for the steady flow of a frictionless and incompressible fluid, the total energy (consisting of the sum of the kinetic energy due to the velocity, the potential energy due to elevation in a gravitational field, and the pressure energy given by the pressure divided by the density) is a constant along the flow path. An increase in velocity at constant elevation must therefore be matched by a decrease in pressure. This principle explains the lift of an airfoil, the theory of carburetors, and so on.

**best economy mixture** — The fuel-air mixture in reciprocating engines that achieves the greatest range of flight. This mixture setting can be used only with reduced power, as it does not have the additional fuel needed for cooling.

**best power mixture** — The fuel-air mixture that enables the engine to produce its maximum power. The best power fuel-air mixture is richer than the best economy mixture. The excess fuel provides additional cooling.

**Beta for taxi range** — A range of power settings on a turboprop engine between the bottom of the alpha range and zero thrust.

**Beta lift rod** — A mechanism on some turboprop governors that controls propeller blade angle in the beta range.

**Beta plus power range** — A range of power settings on a turboprop engine from zero thrust to negative thrust. These settings permit an aircraft to quickly decelerate during landing and move backwards while taxiing.

**Beta range** — The range of propeller settings which includes Beta for taxi and Beta plus power.

**Beta slip ring** — A mechanical device that transmits propeller blade position to the fuel control unit and propeller governor. Also known as a feedback ring.

**Beta tube** — An oil transfer tube between the propeller pitch control unit and the propeller dome. The Beta tube functions as a reverse pitch stop. Also known as spacer.

**Beta valve** — A valve on some turboprop governors that controls propeller blade angle in the Beta range.

**bimetallic thermal switch** — A heat-activated switch comprised of two different metals with different coefficients of expansion.

**blade angle** — The angle formed by the plane of propeller rotation and the face of the propeller blade.

**blade back** — The cambered side of a propeller blade that corresponds to the curved upper surface of an airfoil, similar to that of an aircraft wing. The opposite side of the blade face.

**blade connecting rod** — Half of a fork-and-blade connecting rod assembly. The blade connecting rod fits between the prongs of the fork connecting rod.

**blade cuff** — A metal, wood, or plastic fairing installed around the shank of a propeller blade to carry the airfoil shape of the blade all of the way to the propeller hub. The airfoil shape of the cuff pulls cooling air into the engine nacelle.

**blade face** — The flat portion of a propeller blade, the bottom (or back) portion of an airfoil.

**blade root** — The portion of a propeller blade that fits into the propeller hub. The blade root is also called the blade butt.

**blade shank** — The thick, rounded portion of a propeller blade near the hub.

**blade station** — Any of several reference points on the blade measured in inches from the center of the propeller hub. Blade station measurements are used to identify locations along the blade of a propeller.

**blade tip** — The part of a blade furthest from the hub.

**blade vibration** — A force exerted on a spinning propeller that tends to bend the propeller blade tips forward. The forward-bending action produces buffeting and vibration.

**bleed air** — Compressed air tapped from the compressor stages of a turbine engine by ducts and tubing. Bleed air can be used for deicing, anti-icing, cabin pressurization, heating, and cooling systems. Also known as compressor bleed air.

**bleed port** — In a turbine engine, an opening adjacent to a compressor stage used to collect bleed air.

**blending** — A procedure of metal filing used to recontour damaged compressor and turbine blades to an aerodynamic shape. A fine stone is used to blend (smooth) the reworked area into the original surface of the blade.

**blister** — **1.** An enclosed raised spot on the surface of a finish on a metal. It might be filled with vapor or with products of corrosion. **2.** In composites, an undesirable rounded elevation of the surface of a plastic, and somewhat resembling the shape of a blister on the human skin.

**bloom** — The color of an oil that, when subjected to indirect light, can indicate its chemical properties of origin.

**blow-away jet** — *See* vortex dissipater.

**blow-by** — The expanding gases from combustion in a cylinder that pass the piston ring seal and enter the engine crankcase.

**blower** — **1.** A mechanical device such as a fan that moves a column of air. **2.** An internal, gear-driven supercharger in an aircraft reciprocating engine. Blowers are used to increase the pressure of the fuel/air mixture after it has passed through the carburetor and to improve the distribution of the fuel-air mixture to all of the cylinders.

**blow-in doors** — Spring-loaded doors located ahead of the first stage of the compressor in gas turbine engines. Springs hold them closed, but under conditions of low airspeed and high engine power, they open automatically to permit more air to enter the compressor. Blow-in doors help prevent compressor stall. Also known as auxiliary air-intake doors.

**blue arc** — An instrument marking that indicates an operating range. For example, a blue arc might indicate the manifold pressure gauge range in which an engine can be operated with the carburetor control set at automatic lean.

**bonnet assembly** — The operating head of a fire extinguisher, which contains an electrically ignited powder charge used to rupture a disk and release the extinguishing agent.

**boost venturi** — A small venturi whose discharge end is at the throat of the main venturi and which surrounds the main discharge nozzle of a float-type carburetor. The boost venturi increases the pressure drop for a given airflow.

**bootstrapping** — **1.** Technique by which something achieves a desired state through its own action. Derived from the term "picking oneself up by the bootstraps." **2.** A condition in a turbocharged engine when a turbocharger system senses small changes in temperature or speed and continually changes its output in an attempt to establish equilibrium. Boot strapping typically occurs during part-throttle operation and is characterized by a continual drift or transient increase in manifold pressure.

**bottom dead center (BDC)** — The crankshaft position when the piston is at the bottom extreme of its stroke, and the crank pin is below and directly in line with the wrist pin and the center of the crankshaft.

**Bourdon tube** — The mechanism in a pressure gauge consisting of a flat or elliptical cross-sectioned tube bent into a curve or spiral. When pressure is applied, the tube attempts to straighten. The amount that the tube straightens is proportional to the amount of pressure inside the tube, and as it straightens, it moves a pointer across an instrument dial.

**bow** — The amount that the side of a surface deviates from being straight.

**brake thermal efficiency (BTE)** — The ratio of the amount of heat energy converted into useful work to the amount of heat energy in the fuel used. Brake thermal efficiency is determined by using brake horsepower.

**Brayton cycle** — The name given to the thermodynamic cycle of a gas turbine engine to produce thrust. This varying volume, constant pressure cycle is sometimes called the continuous combustion cycle because of the four continuous and constant events: intake, compression, expansion (including power), and exhaust. Also known as the constant pressure cycle.

**breaker points** — Interrupter contacts in the primary circuit of a magneto or battery ignition system that are opened by a cam at the instant that the highest current flows in the primary circuit, thus producing the maximum rate of collapse of the primary field.

**brinelling** — Indentations in bearing races usually caused by high static loads or application of force during installation or removal. The indentations are usually rounded or spherical due to the impressions left by contacting balls or the rollers of the bearing.

**British Thermal Unit (BTU)** — A unit of heat. One BTU equals the heat energy required to raise one pound of water one degree Fahrenheit. For example, one pound of jet fuel contains approximately 18,600 BTUs.

**brush block** — A housing for electrical contact brushes.

**brushless alternator** — An electrical generator used in large jet-powered aircraft in which the power generation is induced through an exciter rather than by a direct connection with conductive brushes.

**BTE** — *See* brake thermal efficiency.

**BTU** — *See* British Thermal Unit.

**bulb** — A shape used at the root of a turbine rotor blade to fit loosely but securely in a compressor wheel.

**bulge** — An outward bending or swelling caused by excessive pressure or weakening due to excessive heat.

**burning** — The combustion process that occurs when fuel is mixed with air and ignited.

**burnishing** — The process of polishing a surface by sliding contact with a smooth, harder surface. Displacement or removal of metal does not usually occur during burnishing.

**burr** — A sharp or roughened projection of metal usually resulting from machine processing.

**bushing** — A removable cylindrical lining used to minimize resistance and serve as a guide.

**butterfly valve** — A damper or valve consisting of a disk turning about one of its diameters to control the flow of fluid in a round tube.

**bypass jacket** — An annular bypass around an oil cooler through which oil flows when it does not require cooling.

**bypass ratio** — The ratio of the mass airflow in pounds per second through the fan section of a turbofan engine to the mass airflow that passes through the gas generator portion of the engine.

**bypass system** — An oil system where the filter is installed in parallel with the engine bearings. Only a small percentage of the oil passes through the filter each time it cycles through the engine. Also known as a partial flow system.

**bypass valve** — A valve whose function is to maintain a constant system pressure. When the system pressure is exceeded by a predetermined amount, the valve permits excess pressures to bypass the system, which prevents system damage.

# C

**cam** — An eccentric plate or shaft used to impart motion to a follower riding on its surface or edge.

**cam follower face** — The smooth, hardened surface of a hydraulic lifter that rides on a cam lobe.

**cam ramp** — The gradual increase in material before a cam lobe on the cam ring of a radial engine.

**cam ring** — A driven gear in a radial engine with a series of lobes on its circumference to activate the valve operating mechanism.

**cam roller** — A wheel that runs along the cam track and lobes of a radial engine to control the valve operating mechanism.

**cam track** — The smooth surface of the outer circumference of a cam ring on which a cam roller runs.

**cam-ground piston** — A slightly oval shaped piston that compensates for the uneven expansion of a piston at operating temperatures.

**camshaft** — A long shaft running parallel to the crankshaft of an inline or horizontally opposed reciprocating engine. Lobes are ground at intervals along its length to operate the valves through push rods and rocker arms.

**capacitance afterfiring** — The undesired effect of electrical energy being induced into the shielding when current flows through an ignition lead. To prevent this energy from being discharged across the spark plug air gap, most spark plugs have internal resistors.

**capacitor** — A device used to store electrical energy in the form of electrostatic fields. A capacitor is essentially two conductors separated by an insulator. Also known as condenser.

**capacitor-discharge ignition** — An ignition system consisting of two identical independent ignition units operating from a common low-voltage DC electrical power source: the aircraft battery. A high voltage, supplied by the ignition exciter unit, charges a storage capacitor with a charge, up to four joules, that generates an arc across a wide igniter spark gap to ignite the fuel.

**capillary attraction** — An action causing a liquid to be drawn up into extremely tiny tubes or between close fitting parts.

**capillary tube restrictor** — A restriction in a capillary tube designed to prevent fluid from draining out of a component when pressure is removed from the system.

**carbon seal** — An oil seal used in gas turbine engines. Carbon seals are usually spring-loaded and are similar in material and application to the carbon brushes used in electrical motors. Carbon seals rest against a surface to prevent oil from leaking out along the shaft into the compressor airflow or the turbine sections.

**carbon tracking** — A fine track of carbon deposited inside the magneto, distributor, or terminal cavity of a spark plug as a result of a flashover. Carbon tracking residue acts as an electrical conductor to ground or to another electrical lead.

**carbon-pile** — A resistor created by stacking or piling carbon disks.

**carburetor air box** — A formed shroud with a valve that directs filtered air to the carburetor inlet in normal conditions. If the filter becomes blocked by dirt or ice, the valve can be opened to direct heated, unfiltered air to the carburetor from within the engine nacelle.

**carburetor air temperature gauge (CAT)** — An instrument that reports the temperature of induction air before it enters a carburetor. Knowledge of this temperature is important to prevent carburetor icing.

**carburetor heat** — Warm air drawn from a jacket around the exhaust manifold into the carburetor to prevent carburetor ice formation.

**carburetor ice** — Ice that forms inside the carburetor due to the temperature drop caused by the vaporization of the fuel. Induction system icing is an operational hazard because it can cut off the flow of the fuel/air charge or vary the fuel/air ratio.

**cascade vane** — An air-turning vane. Cascade vanes are commonly used in thrust reversers.

**CAT gauge** — *See* carburetor air temperature gauge.

**centistokes (cSt)** — A unit of measure for expressing the viscosity of a fluid.

**centrifugal force** — The outward pull on a body as it rotates or spins.

**centrifugal twisting force** — An aerodynamic force that tends to adjust the blades of a propeller toward a lower pitch position.

**CermiChrome®** — A cylinder wall coating of silicon carbide embedded in chrome.

**CermiNil™** — A cylinder wall coating of silicon carbide embedded in nickel plating.

**chafing** — A rubbing action between adjacent or contacting parts under light pressure that results in wear.

**chip detector** — *See* electric pulsed chip detector.

**chipping** — The breaking away of pieces of material by excessive stress or by careless handling.

**choke bore cylinder** — The cylinder of a reciprocating engine whose bore is slightly smaller in the part of the cylinder that is screwed into the cast aluminum head than it is in the center of the cylinder barrel. The cylinder head expands at normal operating temperature enough so that the bore straightens out and has the same diameter throughout.

**chord line** — An imaginary line drawn through an airfoil from its leading edge to its trailing edge. The chord, or chord line, is used as a reference (a datum line) for laying out the curve of the airfoil.

**chrome channeling** — A process in which reverse current is applied to the inside of a cylinder during the application of chrome plating to create microcracks for retaining lubricating oil.

**chrome-plating** — A method of hardening a cylinder by applying chromium to the inside of a cylinder barrel.

**circlet** — A safety ring that retains a valve in some models of radial engines if the valve tip were to break off. Also known as a spring ring.

**circular mil** — A measurement of area equal to that of a circle having a diameter of 1/1,000 inch, 1 mil., or 0.001 inch.

**clamping ring** — A ring used to hold the two pieces of a propeller hub together.

**Class A fire zone** — An area in a nacelle in which a large quantity of air flows past regular arrangements of similarly shaped obstructions. The power section of a reciprocating engine is an example of a Class A fire zone.

**Class A fire** — A fire that involves solid combustible materials such as paper, wood, and cloth.

**Class B fire zone** — An area in a nacelle in which a large quantity of air flows past aerodynamically clean obstructions. Heat exchangor ducts and exhaust manifold shrouds are examples of Class B fire zones.

**Class B fire** — A fire that involves combustible liquids such as gasoline, oil, solvents, etc.

**Class C fire zone** — An area in a nacelle in which relatively little air flows. On a twin-engine aircraft, the area aft of the engine firewall is an example of a Class C fire zone.

**Class C fire** — A fire that involves energized electrical equipment.

**Class D fire zone** — An area in a nacelle with little or no airflow. A landing gear wheel well is an example of a Class D fire zone.

**Class D fire** — A fire that involved flammable metals such as magnesium.

**Class X fire zone** — An area in a nacelle in which the quantity of airflow is large but irregular. Class X fire zones are common in nacelles and make up the most difficult areas from which to extinguish fires.

**climb propeller** — A fixed-pitch propeller that provides the aircraft with the best performance during takeoff and climb.

**cobalt chloride** — An additive to silica gel dehydrator plugs that serves as an indicator of the amount of moisture absorbed by the plug. A dry dehydrator with this additive is bright blue, but one that has been exposed to excessive moisture turns pink.

**coke** — A solid, carbon-like residue left by mineral oil after the removal of the volatile material by heat.

**cold clearance** — The space between the components in a valve operating system when the engine is at ambient temperature but not running.

**cold flow** — The distortion, deformation, or dimensional change which takes place in materials under continuous load at temperatures within the working range (cold flow is not due to heat softening).

**cold junction** — In electricity, the reference junction in a thermocouple. A thermocouple produces current in relation to the temperature differential between a reference junction (cold junction) and the junction at which temperature measurement is taken (hot junction).

**cold section** — The air inlet and compressor sections of a gas turbine engine.

**cold tank system** — A lubrication system in which the oil cooler is located in the scavenge oil subsystem. The oil passes through the cooler and returns to the tank.

**combustion air** — *See* primary airflow.

**combustion chamber** — The section of the engine into which fuel is injected and burned. Also known as combustor.

**combustion chamber inlet duct** — A duct that redirects primary airflow from a radial to an axial direction. Also known as outlet duct or outlet elbow.

**combustor** — *See* combustion chamber.

**coming-in speed** — The speed at which a generator produces its normal voltage.

**commutator** — The copper bars on the end of a generator armature to which the rotating coils are attached. AC is generated in the armature, and the brushes riding on the commutator act as a mechanical rectifier to convert it into DC.

**compensated cam** — The magneto cam used on high performance radial engines. One lobe is provided for each cylinder, and the lobes are ground in such a way that the magneto points will open when the piston is a given linear distance from the top of the cylinder rather than a given angular distance. This compensates for the relationship of the master rod pistons and those connected to the crankshaft through the link rods.

**compensated oil pressure relief valve** — An oil pressure relief valve with a thermostatic valve that decreases the regulated oil pressure when the oil warms up. High pressure is permitted to force the cold oil through the engine, but the pressure is automatically decreased when the oil temperature increases.

**compression** — The second stroke and event in an Otto cycle engine where the fuel-air mixture is compressed before ignition.

**compression rings** — In reciprocating engines, the top piston rings. Compression rings provide a seal for the gases in the cylinder and transfer heat from the piston into the cylinder walls.

**compressor impeller** — A rotating airfoil in a turbine engine that compresses and accelerates the air before arrival at the combustion chamber.

**compressor manifold** — The ducting that smoothly delivers compressed air from the compressor to the combustion section.

**compressor pressure ratio** — The ratio of compressor discharge pressure to compressor inlet pressure.

**compressor stall** — In gas turbine engines, a condition in an axial-flow compressor in which one or more stages of rotor blades fail to pass air smoothly to the succeeding stages. A stall occurs when the pressure ratio is incompatible with the engine speed.

Compressor stall is indicated by a rise in exhaust temperature or speed fluctuation, and if allowed to continue, can result in flameout and physical damage to the engine.

**condenser** — *See* capacitor.

**condenser tester** — A device that evaluates the condition of a capacitor.

**condition lever** — A lever in the cockpit of a turboprop aircraft. On some aircraft, it serves as propeller control lever for flight (Alpha range). On other aircraft it serves only as a fuel shutoff lever. Also known as a speed lever.

**connecting-rod bearing journal** — The machined crankshaft throw surface to which the connecting rod is attached. Also known as crankpin.

**constant head idle spring** — A spring in the fuel regulator of an RSA fuel injection system that permits fuel to flow when airflow is insufficient to open the valve.

**constant pressure cycle** — *See* Brayton cycle.

**constant-speed drive (CSD)** — A hydraulic transmission that can be controlled either electrically or mechanically. Constant speed drives are used with alternators and enable the alternator to produce the same frequency regardless of the engine's speed, from idle to maximum speed.

**constant-speed propeller** — A controllable-pitch propeller whose pitch is automatically varied in flight by a governor to maintain a constant speed regardless of varying air loads. Also known as automatic propeller.

**constant-speed range** — The range of travel in which a feathering propeller is controlled by a governor that automatically adjusts pitch to maintain a constant speed in spite of varying air loads.

**constrained-gap igniter** — A turbine igniter plug that has the center electrode recessed in the insulator in order to cause the spark to arc well past the tip of the igniter. This configuration enables it to operate at cooler temperatures than other igniter plugs.

**contactor unit** — A component in early propeller synchronization systems that transmitted signals to the propeller pitch change mechanism until the propellers turned at the same speed.

**continuous-flow fuel injection system** — A fuel injection system that constantly delivers fuel under pressure to the intake port of each cylinder of a reciprocating engine.

**continuous-loop system** — A type of fire detection system consisting of a small-diameter, Inconel® tube with a center wire insulated by a eutectic salt material that acts as a long single switch. A continuous-loop system replaces several individual switches and surrounds the engine in turbine and turbojet-powered aircraft.

**controllable-pitch propeller** — A propeller with a pitch that can be changed in flight.

**convection cooling** — The internal cooling air that escapes through small holes and slots, as opposed to transpiration cooling through porous walls.

**conventional system** — A generic term for legacy fire suppression systems. The conventional system consists of a steel cylinder containing pressurized carbon dioxide and a remotely controlled valve assembly that distributes the extinguishing agent through a main distribution line. Although conventional systems are still used in older aircraft, nearly all of these systems have been replaced with halogenated agents and high rate discharge (HRD) systems.

**convergent-divergent inlet** — A supersonic engine inlet duct. The forward section is convergent to increase air pressure and reduce air velocity to subsonic speed. The aft section is divergent to increase air pressure still further and slow airflow to approximately Mach 0.5 before entering the engine.

**cooling fin** — A rib projecting from the surface of a component to increase its area so that heat can be more easily transferred into the airstream flowing over it.

**copper loss** — Energy loss in a motor due to power dissipation in the form of heat as electrons are forced through the copper armature and field windings.

**corrosion** — An electrochemical process in which a metal transforms into powdery chemical compounds that have little mechanical strength.

**counterweight** — A weight attached to the crankshaft of a reciprocating engine to balance the piston/connecting rod/crankshaft assembly.

**crack** — A partial separation of material usually caused by vibration, overloading, internal stresses, defective assemblies, fatigue, or rapid and excessive changes in temperature.

**crank throw** — The distance from the crankshaft centerline to the centerline of the rod journal. Crankshaft throw is equal to half the stroke.

**crankpin** — The part of a crankshaft to which the connecting rod is attached.

**crankshaft** — In a reciprocating engine, the forged and machined component that converts linear motion to rotary motion.

**creep** — A condition of permanent elongation in a material, often due to stretching and high heat. Also known as growth.

**crimping** — Forming a series of small bends into a piece of sheet metal to shorten its length. Crimping is also used to create a bend in angle stock by crimping the sock on one leg of the angle.

**critical altitude** — The maximum altitude at which a turbocharged reciprocating engine can deliver its rated horsepower.

**critical range** — A range of speeds for some engine/propeller combinations in which operation is restricted to prevent severe vibration and aircraft damage.

**crossfeed** — A fuel system in which a series of valves permits any engine to receive fuel from any fuel tank, or to move fuel from one tank to another for fuel balance.

**cruise power** — A power setting, approximately sixty to seventy percent of maximum continuous power, used for fuel economy and engine life during cruising.

**cruise propeller** — A fixed-pitch propeller that provides the aircraft with the best performance during cruise flight.

**CSD** — *See* constant speed drive.

**cSt** — *See* centistokes.

**cumulative-compounded** — A compound-wound generator in which the series field aids the shunt field.

**CUNO® filter** — The proprietary name of a fluid filter made up of a stack of disks separated by scraper blades. Contaminants collect on the edge of the disks and are periodically scraped out and collected in the bottom of the filter case.

**current limiter** — A device that limits the generator output to a level within that rated by the generator manufacturer.

**cushion** — In engine-control rigging, the stop at the engine component that should be contacted before the stop at the cockpit control lever. The extra travel of the control lever provides assurance that the engine component has achieved the full position.

**compressor bleed air** — *See* bleed air.

**cut** — An appreciable loss of metal caused by a sharp object, such as a saw blade, chisel, or screwdriver.

**cycle** — A period of time during which a sequence of recurring events is completed.

**cylinder bore** — The diameter of the cylinder barrel.

**cylinder pad** — The machined surface on the crankcase of an aircraft engine on which a cylinder is mounted.

# D

**DC generator** — A device that converts mechanical energy into electrical energy by electromagnetic induction. This type of generator produces direct current.

**deaerator** — *See* air-oil separator.

**degauss** — To remove magnetic properties from an object.

**deglaze** — To remove the glazed surface of a cylinder wall with a deglazing hone.

**degree of compounding** — The amount of influence of the series field coils of a compound-wound generator that affects the output voltage.

**dehydrator plug** — A threaded plastic plug screwed into a spark plug opening of an aircraft engine cylinder. Dehydrator plugs are filled with silica-gel to remove moisture from the air inside the cylinder and changes color to indicate the condition of preservation of the cylinder.

**deicing system** — A system that removes ice from the structure of an aircraft. A deicing system can use deicing fluid, pneumatic boots, electric boots or panels, or bleed air to remove ice.

**density altitude** — Pressure altitude corrected for nonstandard temperature variations.

**density controller** — A device in a turbonormalized, or sea level boosted, reciprocating engine that regulates the bleed oil flow during full throttle operation by comparing upper deck pressure to the pressure within a nitrogen-filled bellows.

**dent** — A depression in a surface usually caused by a strike from another object.

**desalinization wash** — A type of fluid wash that uses water to remove salt deposits from a gas turbine engine.

**desiccant** — Any form of absorbent material.

**detonation** — The sudden release of heat energy from fuel in an aircraft engine caused by the fuel-air mixture reaching its critical pressure and temperature. Detonation occurs as a violent explosion rather than a smooth burning process.

**diaphragm** — A flexible material that separates chambers. Diaphragms react to differential pressures between the chambers.

**diester** — Asynthesized extract of mineral, vegetable, or animal oil that is used to make synthetic oils.

**differential pressure controller** — A device that regulates turbocharger output of a turbonormalized, or sea level boosted, reciprocating engine at all power settings below full throttle.

**differential pressure test** — A test that determines the condition of the seal in the cylinders of reciprocating engines. The test pressurizes the cylinder, and then measures the loss of pressure, which can indicate leaking rings or valves.

**differentially-compounded generator** — A compound-wound generator in which the series field opposes the shunt field.

**diffuser** — **1.** A duct used on a centrifugal flow turbine engine to reduce the velocity of the air and increase its pressure. **2.** The divergent section of a gas turbine engine that converts velocity energy of compressor discharge air into pressure energy.

**direct compression test** — A seldom-used test for reciprocating engines that measures the compression developed in a cylinder while the engine is turned over for a few revolutions, powered by the starter.

**direct fuel injection system** — A system that delivers fuel directly to each cylinder of a reciprocating engine.

**discharge cartridge** — *See* squib.

**discharge nozzle** — The portion of a carburetor that atomizes and sprays the fuel into the intake airstream.

**discrete function** — The fire detection function of a pneumatic, continuous-loop fire detection system. When the loop is exposed to a localized high temperature such as a fire or bleed air leak, the titanium wire inside the tube releases hydrogen gas. The released gas increases the total gas pressure, which closes the diaphragm switch and activates the alarm.

**dispersant** — A substance that keeps particles suspended in solution. An example is ashless dispersant (AD) oil, which contains a dispersant that causes ash and other contaminants suspended in the oil to be filtered out.

**distribution impeller** — A crankshaft-driven component in some large, radial engines that evenly distributes induction air to the cylinders.

**distribution valve** — *See* fuel manifold valve.

**distributor** — The part of a high-tension magneto that distributes the high voltage to each spark plug at the proper time. Distributors for low-tension ignition systems distribute the low voltage to the transformers at each spark plug at the proper time for air-fuel ignition.

**divergent duct** — A cone-shaped passage or channel in which gas at supersonic speed is forced to flow from its smallest area to its largest area, which results in decreased velocity and increased pressure.

**diverter** — A variable shunt across the series field in a compound-wound generator.

**double-loop system** — An aircraft fire detection system in which two continuous loops are installed side by side on the same support tube for system redundancy. Commonly referred to as Loop A and Loop B, each loop has it own control box and testing capabilities.

**double-entry impeller** — *See* double-sided impeller.

**double-row radial engine** — A radial engine having two rows of cylinders and using two master rods attached to a single crankshaft having two throws.

**double-sided impeller** — A compressor wheel for a gas turbine engine with back-to-back impellers. Also known as a double-sided impeller.

**double-stage compressor** — A two-stage impeller arrangement that creates a higher compressor pressure ratio than possible with a single-stage impeller.

**dovetail** — A method of joining two pieces in which one piece has a base shaped like a widened, inverted, triangle that fits into a similarly shaped cutout in the adjoining piece. Dovetail joints are often used for attaching turbine and compressor blades to rotor disks.

**downdraft** — A type of carburetor or fuel control unit in which induction air is routed through the device from top to bottom.

**drag cup** — The component of a magnetic tachometer that moves the instrument pointer in response to the speed of a permanent magnet.

**drum-type armature** — A type of armature in DC generators that has coils placed in slots on the core of the armature and held in place with wooden or fiber wedges.

**dry-lifter clearance check** — A procedure to measure lash (or space) in the valve train of a system with hydraulic lifters. Oil must be removed from the hydraulic lifter to permit it to compress.

**dry-sump** — An engine lubrication system in which most of the lubricating oil is carried in a separate reservoir.

**dual-spool compressor** — A turbine engine with two separate compressors, each with its own stage of turbine. The low-pressure compressor is $N_1$ and the high-pressure compressor is $N_2$.

**ducted fan** — A turbofan in which bypass air is ducted along the length of the engine.

**ducted ultra-high bypass engine** — A turbine engine that can reach Mach 0.9.with a propfan ducted in a conventional cowl.

**dwell time** — The time required for a liquid penetrant to cure based on the size and shape of the discontinuity.

**Dynafocal® engine mount** — A mount that attaches an aircraft engine to an airframe in which a projected, extended center line of all of the mounting bolts would intersect at the powerplant center of gravity.

**dynamic balance** — The condition that exists in a rotating body in which all of the rotating forces are balanced within themselves and no vibration is produced by the body in motion.

**dynamic balancing** — A procedure that balances the main rotating assembly of a propeller or turbine engine both in its rotational plane and along its axis.

**dynamic damper** — A counterweight on the crankshaft of an aircraft engine. It is attached in such a way that it can rock back and forth while the shaft is spinning and absorb dynamic vibrations, changing the resonant frequency of the engine/propeller combination.

# E

**economizer system** — A power compensator or a power enrichment system in a carburetor or fuel injection system that enriches the fuel mixture at high power engine operations. The economizer is closed during cruising speeds.

**eddy current losses** — The electrical losses in the core of a transformer or other electrical machine. The induction of eddy currents into the core robs the machine of some of its power.

**Edison system** — A fire detection system used in early air carrier aircraft. Edison fire detection systems are now obsolete, having been replaced by more conventional pneumatic responder systems.

**effective pitch** — The actual distance that a propeller moves forward through the air in one revolution. It is the difference between the geometric pitch of the propeller and the propeller slip.

**efficiency gap (E-gap)** — The number of degrees of magnet rotation beyond its neutral position at which the primary magneto breaker points open. It is at this point that the primary current flow is the greatest and, therefore, the rate of collapse of the primary field will induce the greatest voltage into the secondary winding.

**EICAS** — *See* engine indicating and crew alerting system.

**electric dynamometer** — An instrument that measures torque force or power.

**electric pulsed chip detector** — A metal detection warning system in the lubrication system of a gas turbine engine. When metal particles bridge an electrode in the drain plug, they close an electric circuit to alert the operator of excessive contamination. Also known as chip detector or indicating chip detector.

**electrical losses** — One of two main types of energy losses in motors. Electrical losses can be further classified as copper losses and iron losses.

**electrolytic action** — The action of conducting electrical current through a nonmetallic conductor by the movement of ions.

**electronic control unit** — **1.** A device that monitors the status of test and sensor loops of an aircraft fire detection system. **2.** The unit in a Teledyne Continental Motors FADEC system that calculates the timing and generates the impulse energy for each spark plug.

**electroplating** — An electrochemical method of depositing a thin layer of metal on an object. The object to be plated is the cathode, the metal to be deposited is the anode, and the electrolyte is a nonmetallic conductor that forms ions of the plating metal.

**elevated induction air temperature** — A factor that decreases engine performance by decreasing air density.

**end bend** — The increased camber on the extremities of some compressor blades which limits stagnation of the airflow near the tips.

**end gap** — The space between the two ends of a piston ring when installed in a cylinder.

**engine condition monitoring** — A system for tracking engine performance over time to determine the component service life.

**engine indicating and crew alerting system (EICAS)** — A computer-controlled system that uses digital displays to show relevant engine indications and system alerts to the aircraft crew.

**engine pressure ratio (EPR)** — In gas turbine engines, the ratio of turbine discharge pressure to compressor inlet pressure. EPR is displayed in the cockpit as an indication of engine thrust.

**EPR** — *See* engine pressure ratio.

**erosion** — The removal of material by any combination of abrasion, dissolution, and corrosion.

**eutectic salt** — A chemical salt used in continuous-loop fire detection systems. The salt insulates the positively charged center wire from the sides of the negatively charged tube. When heated, the eutectic salt liquefies, which lowers the resistance and permits the center wire to electrically contact the side of the tube—completing the circuit to ground and powering the alarm circuit.

**exhaust** — **1.** The gasses that are a byproduct of combustion. **2.** The fourth stroke and fifth event of the Otto cycle.

**exhaust bypass valve assembly** — A valve on a turbonormalized, or sea level boosted, engine that regulates turbocharger output by adjusting how much exhaust is directed to the turbocharger.

**exhaust valve** — The valve in an aircraft engine cylinder through which the gases leave the combustion chamber.

**external combustion** — The process where the

chemical energy in a fuel is converted into heat energy outside of the engine. Heating water to produce steam that is put to mechanical use is a form of an external combustion engine.

# F

**FADEC** — *See* full authority digital engine control.

**fan pressure ratio** — The comparison of the air pressure leaving the fan to the air pressure entering the fan of a turbofan engine.

**FCU** — *See* fuel control unit.

**feather** — To change the angle of propeller blades so that the chords become approximately parallel to the line of flight.

**feathering** — The action that changes the pitch angle of propeller blades to be parallel to the line of flight by rotating them around their feathering (spanwise) axis.

**feed shoe** — A narrow strip of grooved rubber attached to the leading edge of a propeller blade to direct deicing fluid toward the tip.

**feedback ring** — *See* Beta slip ring.

**field coil** — A coil or winding used to produce a magnetic field.

**field pole** — The field assembly part of an electric generator or motor. Also known as a pole shoe.

**field saturation** — An undesirable condition in a shunt-wound generator caused by rapidly fluctuating loads.

**film cooling** — *See* convection cooling.

**fin area** — The total area of both sides of a cylinder cooling fin that is exposed to air.

**fir tree** — A shape used for the root of a turbine rotor blade to fit loosely, but securely in a compressor wheel.

**fir tree slots** — The negative shape in a compressor wheel that receives the fir tree root of a turbine rotor blade.

**fire detection system** — A system in an aircraft that informs the pilot of a fire on board the aircraft.

**fire sleeve** — A hollow, fire resistant, silicone-coated fiberglass tube that is positioned over a hose during fabrication.

**fixed shaft engine** — A turboprop engine in which the main turbine contains a shaft that directs energy to the propeller reduction gearbox.

**fixed-pitch propeller** — A rotating airfoil with fixed blade angles. Fixed-pitch propellers are designed as climb propellers, cruise propellers, or standard propellers.

**flaking** — The breaking loose of small pieces of metal or coated surfaces caused by defective plating or excessive loading.

**flame holder** — A tubular grid or spoke-shaped obstruction aft of the fuel bars to ensure the proper fuel and air mixture of a gas turbine engine equipped with afterburners.

**flame propagation tubes** — Tubes that interconnect the individual combustors of a multiple-can combustion chamber in a gas turbine engine.

**flameout** — A condition in the operation of a gas turbine engine in which the fire in the engine goes out due to either too much or too little fuel sprayed into the combustors.

**flanged propeller shaft** — A propeller shaft that accommodates the attachment of a propeller with bolts (or studs) and nuts.

**flashing the field** — A procedure in which a battery is momentarily connected to the field coil of an aircraft DC generator. Current flows through the coil for a few seconds to magnetize the field frame. This process restores the residual magnetism.

**flashover** — A condition inside the distributor of a high-tension magneto in which the spark jumps the air gap to the wrong electrode. This condition can be caused by moisture inside the distributor or by a dirty distributor block.

**flat machine tips** — A compressor or turbine blade with tips that have a constant cross section.

**flat-compounded generator** — A generator that has both a series and a parallel winding. The series field is adjusted by a regulator to keep the output voltage of the generator constant from a no-load condition to the maximum load that the generator can produce.

**flat-headed valve** — A classification of reciprocating engine valve that describes its head shape.

**flat-rated engine** — An engine configured to produce takeoff thrust.

**flight idle** — Engine speed, usually in the 70 to 80 percent range, for minimum flight thrust.

**float chamber** — The area in a float carburetor in which fuel is stored.

**floating cam ring** — A special type of cam ring used on large radial engines that requires special procedures when adjusting valve clearance.

**floating control thermostat** — An thermostat that operates an electric actuator to control the air exit of an oil cooler.

**flock** — Pulverized wool or cotton fibers attached to screen wire for use as an air filter. The flock-covered screen is lightly oiled to prevent dirt and dust from entering the engine.

**flow control valve** — A valve that controls the direction or amount of fluid flow.

**flowing** — The spreading out of a plated or painted surface caused by poor adhesion to the base or excessive loading on the part's surface.

**fluid wash** — A method of removing dirt and salt deposits from a turbine engine by spraying fluid into an engine that is motored by the starter. Also known as motoring wash.

**flyweight assembly** — An assembly used for various applications, such as propeller governors and mechanical tachometers, to measure or control speed.

**flyweight** — An L-shaped speed sensing unit pivoted (in pairs) on the outer edges of a rotating disc. When rotational speed is high enough, centrifugal force moves the weights to an angular position. This force can be used for various applications.

**foot-pound** — **1.** A unit of work; one pound of force moved through a distance of one foot. **2.** A unit of torque; the amount of torque produced when a force of one pound is applied one foot from the pivot point.

**fork connecting rod** — Half of a fork-and-blade connecting rod assembly. The prongs of the fork connecting rod fit around the blade connecting rod.

**forward-fan engine** — A turbofan engine with the fan located forward of the compressor. The fan can be part of the compressor or a separate rotor.

**four-stroke engine** — An engine that operates on the four-stroke, five event cycle, or Otto cycle. The cycle consists of five discrete mechanical processes occurring in the following order: intake stroke, compression stroke, ignition, power stroke, and exhaust stroke.

**frangible disk** — A component of a high rate discharge (HRD) fire suppression container system that seals the pressurized extinguishing agent in the container. When a fire is detected, the discharge cartridge is electrically ignited by a crew member, and a bullet-like projectile is fired into the disc. As the disk ruptures, the pressurized agent is sent into the distribution lines and out to the fire. A strainer installed in the bonnet assembly catches the fragments of the broken disc.

**free turbine** — A turboshaft engine with no physical connection between the compressor and the power output shaft.

**Freon®** — A fluorinated hydrocarbon compound used as a fire extinguishing agent or a refrigerant for vapor-cycle air conditioning systems. A registered trademark of E.I. DuPont de Nemours & Company.

**fretting** — Surface erosion caused by a slight movement between two overlapping parts.

**friction horsepower** — The amount of horsepower required to turn the engine against the friction of the moving parts and to compress the charges in the cylinders.

**front cone bottoming** — A condition in the installation of a propeller on a splined crankshaft in which the apex of the front cone contacts the end of the spline. When this condition occurs, the cone and propeller hub are not properly seated and the hub remains loose.

**fuel control assembly** — The component of a Teledyne Continental Motors fuel control unit that meters fuel based on the position of the throttle and mixture levers.

**fuel control unit (FCU)** — **1.** (gas turbine engine) The main fuel scheduling device, which receives a mechanical input signal from the power lever and various other signals, such as Pt2, Tt2, and so on. These signals provide for automatic scheduling of fuel at all ambient conditions of ground and flight operation. **2.** (reciprocating engine) The component of a pressure carburetor or a device in a fuel injection system that meters fuel for engine operations. Also known as a fuel regulator.

**fuel evaporation ice** — Ice formed by fuel evaporation in the induction system of reciprocating engines. This evaporative process causes carburetor and induction system parts to become very cold and enables moisture in the air to condense, collect, and freeze on them. This type of ice is most troublesome in float carburetors.

**fuel manifold** — A pipe-like fitting that distributes fuel flow to the individual fuel injection nozzles. The manifold contains one single fuel line when used with single-line duplex nozzles and two lines for dual-line duplex nozzles.

**fuel manifold valve** — The component in a fuel-injected system that divides pressurized fuel for distribution to the fuel injection nozzles. The valve provides a metering force for low fuel-flow conditions and a positive fuel shutoff when the engine is shut down. Also known as a distribution valve.

**fuel metering force** — The force that results from inlet and metered fuel in an RSA system. Fuel metering force balances with the air metering force.

**fuel metering head** — The distance between the fuel surface and the outlet for the main discharge nozzle in the float chamber. This gap prevents fuel from leaking out of the nozzle when the engine is shut down.

**fuel regulator** — *See* fuel control unit.

**fuel totalizer** — An instrument that measures fuel delivered to an engine and calculates and displays fuel remaining.

**full authority digital engine control (FADEC)** — A computerized system that manages ignition timing and fuel delivery to an engine.

**full register position** — The position of the rotating magnet in a magneto when the poles are fully aligned with the pole shoes of the magneto frame. At this point, the maximum number of lines of flux flow in the frame.

**full rich** — That position of the mixture control that permits the maximum amount of fuel to flow to the engine relative to air flow.

**full-floating knuckle pin** — A pin in radial engines that attaches an articulating rod to the master rod. Full-floating pins are not anchored to either rod.

**full-floating piston pin** — A piston pin that is not secured to either the piston or the connecting rod.

**full-flow filter system** — A lubricating system in which all of the oil passes through the filter assembly each time it cycles through the engine.

**fusible safety plug** — A thermal fuse in the container of extinguishing agent for a high rate discharge system that relieves pressure if the system is exposed to extreme temperatures.

## G

**galling** — Fretting or chafing of a mating surface by sliding contact with another surface or body. The heat friction causes the material from one surface to be welded or deposited onto the other surface, ultimately damaging the surface area.

**gauss meter** — A device used to check residual magnetism in a part.

**generator** — A mechanical device consisting of a conductor being turned within a magnetic field. Generators produce electricity by electromagnetic induction.

**geometric pitch** — The distance that a propeller should advance forward in one revolution without any slip.

**glazing** — The development of a hard, glossy surface on bearing surfaces in the presence of oil, heat, and pressure.

**gouging** — A furrowing condition in which surface material is displaced or damaged. Gouging is typically caused by foreign material between tight-fitting, moving parts.

**governor** — A device that controls the maximum rotational speed of a device.

**gravity-feed system** — A fuel system on high-wing, single-engine aircraft in which gravity delivers fuel to the engine-driven fuel pump.

**green arc** — An instrument marking that indicates a normal operating range.

**grooving** — A recess or channel with rounded and smooth edges that usually results from improperly aligned parts.

**gross thrust** — The thrust developed by an engine, not taking into consideration any pressure of initial air mass momentum. Also referred to as static thrust and symbolized as $F_g$.

**ground boost blower** — A blower, consisting of a single, gear-driven impeller, used to increase the pressure of induction air. Ground boost blower systems are used on some radial engines.

**ground idle** — A gas turbine engine speed usually in the range of 60% to 70% of the maximum speed, used as a minimum thrust setting for ground operations.

**ground-adjustable propeller** — A propeller whose pitch can be adjusted and locked on the ground when the engine is not operating but cannot be adjusted in flight.

**growler** — Test equipment used to check generator and starter armatures for shorts. The growler forms the primary circuit of a transformer and the armature forms the secondary. Shorts can be easily detected because they cause vibration in a thin piece of metal, such as a hacksaw blade, held over the armature.

**growth** — *See* creep.

**guttering** — Deep, concentrated erosion resulting from enlargement of cracks or repeated exposure to a concentrated flame.

## H

**halogens** — Any of five chemical elements (fluorine, chlorine, bromine, iodine, and astatine) in Group VIIb of the periodic table of elements. Halogens are used in some fire extinguishing systems.

**Halon 1301** — A halogenated fire suppressant used in high rate discharge (HRD) systems.

**heat engine** — Any mechanical device that converts heat energy into mechanical energy. For example, reciprocating and turbine engines are heat engines.

**heat range** — The classified operating temperature of a spark plug.

**heater muff** — A shroud around a muffler that forms a chamber in which fresh air is heated to provide cabin heat in a reciprocating, single-engine aircraft.

**helical seal** — A seal with rotating fins that uses reverse threading to prevent oil leaking.

**Heli-Coil® insert** — A special helical steel insert

screwed into specially cut threads to restore threads that have been stripped out or to provide durable threads in soft castings.

**high blower** — The high-speed operation of a single-stage, two-speed, internal supercharger system.

**high-energy capacitor discharge system** — An ignition source for many gas turbine engines that consists of an exciter unit, two high-tension cables, and two spark igniters.

**high-pressure compressor** — The $N_2$ or $N_3$ compressor in a dual or triple spool compressor section.

**high rate discharge systems (HRD)** — A fire suppression system that incorporates pressurized containers of halon gas that is expelled by an explosive charge and distributed through tubes to specific locations in the aircraft.

**hopper** — A funnel-shaped container used for storing the abrasive in a sand-blasting machine. The container has an opening in the top for loading and a smaller opening in the bottom for dumping.

**hot clearance** — *See* running clearance.

**hot junction** — One end of a thermocouple. When combined with a cold junction, a small current is generated. The same principle is used in many fire detection systems. The cold junction is sometimes referred to as the reference junction.

**hot section** — The portion of a turbine engine aft of the diffuser, in which combustion takes place.

**hot start** — In gas turbine engines, a start that occurs with normal engine rotation, but with exhaust temperatures that exceed prescribed limits. This condition is usually caused by an excessively rich mixture in the combustor. The fuel to the engine must be terminated immediately to prevent engine damage.

**hot tank system** — A turbine engine lubrication system in which the oil cooler is installed in the pressure subsystem.

**HRD** — *See* high rate discharge system.

**hub** — The originating or attaching point for propeller blades.

**hung stall** — A severe stall of a compressor wheel in a gas turbine engine.

**hung start** — In gas turbine engines, a condition in which the fuel ignites normally, but engine speed remains at a low value rather than increasing to the normal idle speed. A hung start often occurs when the starter cannot provide sufficient power.

**hydraulic dynamometer** — An instrument that measures torque force or power.

**hydraulic lifter** — The hydraulic unit in the valve train of a reciprocating engine that automatically adjusts for heat expansion, keeps the operating clearance in the valve mechanism at zero, and cushions the impact of operation with oil pressure. Also known as a tappet.

**hydraulic plunger** — The spring-loaded component within a hydraulic lifter that bears against the push rod.

**hypoid lubricant** — An extreme-pressure lubricant formulated to provide protection under high loads.

**hysteresis losses** — A type of energy loss in a motor resulting from the armature revolving in an alternating magnetic field and becoming magnetized in two directions.

## I

**ICA** — *See* instructions for continued airworthiness.

**IDG** — *See* integrated drive generator.

**idle discharge port** — A passage in a carburetor that regulates and emulsifies fuel at engine idle speeds. Also known as idle jet.

**idle jet** — *See* idle discharge port.

**idle-cutoff** — That position of the mixture control in which fuel is prevented from flowing from the metering system into the engine.

**ignition** — **1.** The process whereby the fuel-air mixture in either a turbine or reciprocating aircraft engine begins to burn. **2.** The third event of the Otto cycle.

**ignition coil** — A step-up transformer that increases voltage by induction in a magneto.

**ignition harness** — The complete set of wires that carry high-voltage current from the magneto to the spark plugs.

**IMEP** — *See* indicated mean effective pressure.

**impact pressure annulus** — A passageway that collects air in a pressure carburetor that does not enter the venturi. The pressure of this air is compared with pressure at the venturi to establish the air metering force.

**impeller** — A disk with vanes that picks up and accelerates the air outwardly to increase the pressure in a supercharger for a reciprocating engine, or to provide the pressurized air for a centrifugal turbine engine.

**improper valve timing** — In a reciprocating engine, the condition in which the valves do not open and close at the proper time. Improper valve timing adversely affects the efficiency and operation of the engine.

**impulse blades** — A stator vane and rotor blade arrangement in which the vanes form convergent ducts and the blades form straight ducts. The rotor is then turned by impulse as gases impinge on the blades. This design is common in accessory turbines such as those that power air starters.

**impulse-reaction turbine blades** — A stator vane and rotor blade arrangement in which the base area is an impulse design and the tip is a reaction design. This design is common in aviation turbine engines meant to provide thrust.

**inclusion** — The presence of a foreign material within a metal or metal alloy.

**incomplete scavenging** — A condition in which exhaust gases remain in a cylinder after combustion and displace some of the intake air required for efficient combustion.

**index mark** — A machined or otherwise marked reference indicator.

**indicated mean effective pressure (IMEP)** — The average measured pressure inside an engine cylinder during the power stroke, expressed in pounds per square inch.

**indicated thermal efficiency (ITE)** — The ratio of the amount of heat energy converted into useful work to the amount of heat energy in the fuel used. Indicated thermal efficiency is determined by using indicated horsepower.

**indicating chip detector** — *See* electric pulsed chip detector.

**induction bends** — A design consideration for the induction system of a reciprocating engine. Friction in the bends of an induction system slows and reduces the air delivered to the cylinders for combustion.

**induction vibrator** — A coil and set of contact points that produce pulsating DC from straight DC. Pulsating DC can be used in the primary winding of a magneto to produce a high voltage in the secondary winding.

**inlet guide vanes** — In gas turbine engines, stationary airfoils that precede the first stage compressor rotor blades. These guide vanes form straight through passages that direct air onto the blades at the optimum angle.

**inner cone** — The conical-shaped portion of a turbine engine exhaust system that is used to produce the proper area increase for the gases as they leave the engine.

**Instructions for Continued Airworthiness (ICA)** — The section of a manufacturer's maintenance manual that provides information to inspect an engine, a propeller, or a component in an airworthy condition.

**intake** — The first stroke and event of an Otto cycle engine where air is drawn into a cylinder for combustion.

**intake valve** — A reciprocating engine valve, located in the head of a cylinder, which provides the passage of the fuel-air mixture into the combustion chamber.

**integrated drive generator (IDG)** — A type of generator assembly that combines the generator and constant speed drive in one unit.

**integrity switch** — A switch in the responder unit of a Systron-Donner fire detection system that provides a way to verify the integrity of the system.

**intercooler** — A device that reduces the temperatures of the compressed air before it enters the fuel metering device. The resulting cooler air has a higher density, which permits the engine to be operated at a higher power setting.

**inter-cylinder baffles** — Sheet metal air deflectors installed between and around air-cooled cylinders to aid in uniform cooling.

**interference fit** — A fit between two parts in which the part being put into a hole is larger than the hole itself. To fit the pieces together, the hole is expanded by heating and the part is shrunk by chilling. After assembly, when the two parts reach the same temperature, they will not separate. The area around the hole is subject to tensile stress and thus vulnerable to stress corrosion.

**intermediate compressor** — On a triple-spool turbine engine, the middle or $N_2$ compressor.

**intermediate gearbox** — A reduction gearbox, from the accessory gearbox, for slower-turning accessories.

**internal combustion** — The process in which power is produced from the combustion of a fuel air mixture within the cylinder of an engine.

**interpole** — A field pole in a compound-wound electrical generator used to correct for armature reaction. Armature reaction is the distortion of the generator field flux by the current flowing in the windings of the armature.

**interstage turbine temperature (ITT)** — The temperature between two turbine stages. Interstage turbine temperature is directly proportional to turbine inlet temperature.

**ITE** — *See* indicated thermal efficiency.

**ITT** — *See* interstage turbine temperature.

## J

**jet calibration test unit** — An electronic test apparatus for checking the calibration of the EGT system, the r.p.m. system, and the accuracy of their associated instruments.

**Jetcal® Analyzer** — A trade name for a jet calibration test unit.

**joule** — The international system unit of energy equal to the work done when a current of 1 ampere is passed through a resistance of 1 ohm for 1 second.

# K

**keeper key** — A lock ring used to retain the valve and spring assemblies in a cylinder.

**kinematic viscosity rating** — Tho ratio of absolute viscosity and density, expressed in units of centistokes.

**knuckle pin** — The hardened steel pin that holds an articulating rod in the master rod of a radial engine.

# L

**labyrinth seal** — A main bearing oil seal. It is threaded with grooves that permit gas path air to leak inward to the bearing sump and keep oil mist from escaping. Unlike a carbon seal, which rides on a surface, the labyrinth oil seal has a small clearance between its sealing lands and the rotating shaft.

**lapping** — The act of rubbing two surfaces together with a fine abrasive between them to produce an extremely close fit.

**last chance filter** — The final filter located just before the spray nozzle of a turbine lubrication system and used to prevent foreign matter from clogging the spray nozzle.

**leading edge** — The foremost edge of an airfoil section.

**lead** — An individual wire in an ignition harness.

**lean** — A fuel/air mixture characterized by an excess amount of air for a given amount of fuel.

**lean best power** — The low end of a range of mixture settings for a reciprocating engine in which the maximum speed or manifold pressure is developed for a given throttle position.

**lean die-out** — A condition of turbine engine operation in which combustion instability causes the fire extinguish in the normal airstream.

**line maintenance** — Any maintenance to an aircraft engine or component that does not require removal of the component from the aircraft.

**liquid-fuel rocket** — A rocket in which the fuel and oxygen necessary for combustion are stored in their liquid state and then combined for combustion.

**lobe** — The eccentric portion of a cam or camshaft.

**long-shunt connection** — A compound-wound generator in which the shunt field is connected across the armature and series field.

**low blower** — The lower speed setting of a two-speed internal supercharger.

**low pressure compressor** — The front section of a dual compressor gas turbine engine Also referred to as the $N_1$ compressor or low-speed compressor.

**low speed compressor** — *See* low pressure compressor.

**Lubbock nozzle** — A variable-port, atomizing fuel nozzle with an internal, spring-loaded piston used to vary the size of the inlet ports.

# M

**magnetic tachometer** — An instrument that senses engine (or component) speed by detecting the presence and frequency of a pulsing or intermittent magnetic field.

**magneto** — A self-contained, permanent-magnet AC generator with a set of current interrupter contacts and a step-up transformer. The magneto supplies the high voltage required for ignition in a reciprocating aircraft engine.

**magneto safety check** — An operational check on an aircraft reciprocating engine in which the magneto switch is placed in the OFF position with the engine idling to ascertain that the switch grounds both magnetos.

**magnetometer** — An instrument that measures the intensity of a magnetic field. Magnetometers can also be used to detect the presence of a ferrous metallic object.

**magnetomotive force** — The magnetizing force in a magnetic field. Measured in gilberts or ampere-turns.

**main bearing journals** — The machined surface of a crankshaft that rotates in the main bearings.

**main metering jet** — The calibrated orifice in a fluid flow system that controls the amount of primary fuel flow for a given pressure drop across the jet.

**manual primer** — A small, hand-operated pump used to spray gasoline directly into an engine cylinder to provide an excessively rich fuel/air mixture for starting.

**master governor** — The governor that the comparison circuit in a one engine master control synchronization system uses to adjust the slave governor through an activator.

**master motor** — A component of an early, multiengine propeller synchronization system. The master motor drives contactor units that are electrically connected to an alternator. The contactor units adjust propeller blade angle to synchronize engine speed with the master motor.

**master rod** — The connecting rod in a radial engine that attaches directly to the crankshaft. All of the other rods connect to the master rod rather than to the crankshaft.

**master rod bearing** — The plain bearing in a master rod that rides on the crank throw.

**maximum climb power rating** — The setting of a turbine engine for normal climb to cruise altitude.

**maximum continuous power** — The setting of a turbine engine for unusual and emergency situations, used at the pilot's discretion. In some aircraft, this setting is the same as maximum cruise power.

**maximum cruise power** — The maximum power setting of a turbine engine for cruise flight without limitations.

**mechanical loss** — A type of energy loss in a motor due to the friction of various moving parts.

**mechanical tachometer** — A device that indicates engine speed through a mechanical cable that is turned by the engine.

**metallic sodium** — A material that changes from solid to liquid at 208 degrees Fahrenheit. Metallic sodium is used inside some exhaust valves to transfer heat from the head to the stem.

**modular construction** — A manner of assembling an engine with a series of subassemblies. Major assemblies, or modules, can be removed and replaced with minimal time and expense and returned to a repair facility for testing and repairs.

**motor slip** — The difference in speed between the rotor and the stator's rotating field expressed as a percentage of the synchronous speed.

**motoring** — Rotating a turbine engine with the starter for a purpose other than starting—for example, for cleaning.

**motoring wash** — *See* fluid wash.

**mounting flange** — A ridge that extends outward from a machine, motor, or other mechanism to accommodate attachments.

**multiple-piece master rod** — A master rod for a radial engine that is formed in two pieces for attachment to a solid crankshaft.

**multiple-row radial engines** — A radial engine in which more than one row of cylinders are arranged around a single crankshaft.

**mushroom head** — A class of reciprocating engine valves that are shaped like mushrooms.

## N

**$N_1$ compressor** — The low pressure, low speed stage (first stage) of a gas turbine engine compressor.

**$N_2$ compressor** — The high pressure, high speed stage (second stage) of a gas turbine engine compressor. In triple-spool compressors, the $N_2$ compressor is identified as the intermediate compressor.

**$N_3$ compressor** — In a triple-spool compressor, the high pressure, high speed stage, or third stage of a gas turbine engine compressor.

**NACA cowling** — A cowling enclosing an air-cooled radial engine, consisting of a hood, O-ring, and a portion of the body behind the engine, arranged so that the cooling air smoothly enters the hood at the front and leaves through a smooth annular slot between the body and the rear of the hood; the whole forming a relatively low-drag body with a passage through a portion of it for the cooling air.

**needle valve** — A tapered-end, fluid control needle valve that fits into a seat or recess to control or restrict the flow of fluid through an orifice.

**negative torque system (NTS)** — A system in a turboprop engine that prevents the engine from being driven by the propeller. The NTS increases the blade angle when the propellers try to drive the engine.

**neutral position** — The position of the rotating magnet of a magneto between the pole shoes. In the neutral position, no lines of flux flow in the magneto frame.

**newton** — The unit of force in the meter-kilogram-second system equal to the force required to impart an acceleration of one meter per second squared to a mass of one kilogram.

**nick** — A sharp-sided gouge or depression with a V-shaped bottom that is generally the result of careless handling.

**Nickel+Carbide™** — A proprietary cylinder coating of nickel and silicon carbide composite applied by Engine Components, Inc.

**Nikasil®** — A trademarked name for an electro-chemically-deposited nickel matrix silicon carbide coating on engine components.

**nitriding** — A case-hardening process in which a steel part is heated in an atmosphere of ammonia (NH3.) The ammonia breaks down, freeing the nitrogen to combine with aluminum in the steel to form an extremely hard abrasive-resistant aluminum nitride surface. Cylinder walls and crankshaft journals can be nitrided.

**nose section** — The forward section of a radial engine.

**nozzle diaphragm** — A ring of stationary blades in a turbine engine ahead of the turbine wheel. Used to direct the flow of hot gases into the turbine for maximum efficiency.

**NTS** — *See* negative torque system.

**Nu-Chrome®** — A cylinder wall coating of silicon carbide embedded in the chrome.

## O

**octane** — The rating system of aviation gasoline with regard to its antidetonating qualities. Fuel with an octane rating of 87 is made up of a mixture of 87% isooctane and 13% heptane.

**oil bypass valve** — A valve whose function is to maintain a constant pressure in the lubrication system. When the system pressure is exceeded by a predetermined amount, the oil bypass valve permits oil under excess pressure to bypass the system to prevent the system from rupturing. Also known as a thermostatic control valve.

**oil control ring** — The piston ring below the compression rings that controls the amount of oil between the piston and the cylinder wall of an aircraft reciprocating engine. It is usually a multipiece ring that fits into a groove with holes to drain part of the oil back to the inside of the piston. Also known as an oil ring.

**oil cooler** — A heat exchanger used to cool oil. Some coolers use air as a cooling agent; others use fuel.

**oil pressure chamber** — The area in a hydraulic lifter where oil under pressure is stored to cushion the impact of the cam lobe.

**oil ring** — *See* oil control ring or oil scraper ring.

**oil scraper ring** — A piston ring located at the bottom or skirt end of a piston that wipes the oil either toward or away from the oil control ring, depending on the design of the engine. Also known as an oil ring.

**oil screen** — A fine mesh screen in the engine lubrication system used to stop and hold impurities to prevent their passage through the engine and causing damage.

**oil supply chamber** — The area in a hydraulic lifter where a supply of high pressure is available to the oil pressure chamber.

**oil temperature regulator** — A control device that maintains the oil temperature within the desired operating range by either passing the oil through the core of the cooler or around the jacket of the cooler.

**oil wiper ring** — The bottom ring on a piston that directs oil up between the piston and the cylinder wall for lubrication and sealing.

**one-piece master rod** — A master rod for a radial engine forged as a single piece. A one-piece master rod is used in conjunction with a multipiece crankshaft.

**operating head** — A component attached to the high rate discharge (HRD) container of an aircraft fire suppression system. The operating head holds the discharge cartridge and provides the attach point for the halon distribution lines. After the cartridge is discharged, the agent flows from the container, through the operating head, into the distribution lines, and out to the fire.

**Otto cycle** — A constant-volume cycle of events used to explain the energy transformation that takes place in a reciprocating engine. In this type of engine, four strokes are required to complete the required series of events or operating cycle of each cylinder. Two complete revolutions of the crankshaft (720°) are required to complete the four strokes and the ignition event.

**outlet duct** — *See* combustion chamber inlet duct.

**outlet elbow** — *See* combustion chamber inlet duct.

**outlet vane assembly** — The stator vanes at the aft end of the compressor section that straighten airflow before it enters the combustion section.

**overboost** — A condition in which the manifold pressure of a reciprocating engine has exceeded the maximum pressure specified by the manufacturer. Overboost can damage internal engine components.

**over-compound generator** — A generator with a full-load voltage that is higher than its no-load voltage.

**overheat function** — A function in a fire warning system that causes the warning circuit to close so that the alarm will sound when abnormally high temperatures occur in an area of the aircraft.

**overheat sensing element** — The sensing wire portion of a continuous-loop fire detection system.

**overservicing** — The condition of overfilling an engine or a component with a necessary lubricant.

**overshoot** — A condition caused by rapid increase in throttle, which causes the controller to exceed the requirement for the engine boost, resulting in overboost.

**overspeed governor** — A speed-limiting device. Governors regulate speed through the fuel control unit.

# P

**P-lead** — The primary lead for an aircraft magneto, which is connected to the ignition switch.

**parallelism gauge** — A tool used to determine whether the bosses of a connecting rod are parallel (or convergent).

**partial flow system** — *See* bypass system.

**particle separator** — A device used to separate sediment from air drawn into the inlet of a helicopter engine.

**peening** — A series of blunt surface depressions.

**performance recovery wash** — A type of fluid wash using water and an emulsifying cleaner to remove baked-on dirt and soot deposits from a gas turbine engine.

**Permalloy** — An alloy of iron and nickel used in the manufacture of permanent magnets.

**phase angle** — **1.** The number of degrees of generator rotation between the time the voltage passes through zero and the time the current passes through zero in the same direction. **2.** In AC electricity, the amount of phase shift between the current and voltage.

**pick up** — *See* scuffing.

**piston end** — The end of a connecting rod that is attached to a piston with a piston pin.

**piston head** — The top surface of a piston.

**piston pin bearing** — The bearing in the piston end of a connecting rod through which the piston pin extends.

**piston pin boss** — The enlarged area on the interior of a piston that provides additional bearing area for the wrist pin.

**piston skirt** — The lower portion of a piston.

**piston-pin plug** — A plug of soft material (often aluminum) that is installed on both sides of a full-floating piston pin to maintain the position of the pin and prevent it from scratching the cylinder walls.

**pitch distribution** — The gradual decrease in the blade angle of a propeller from hub to tip.

**pitting** — The formation of small pockets on the surface of a metal.

**plane of commutation** — The plane at right angles to the magnetic field created by two opposed coils of a generator. Also referred to as the neutral plane.

**planetary gears** — The intermediate gears in a planetary gear reduction system which orbit a sun gear.

**planetary reduction gear system** — A reduction gearing arrangement in which the propeller shaft is attached to an adapter holding several small planetary gears. These gears run between a sun gear and a ring gear, either of which can be driven by the crankshaft, while the other is fixed into the nose section. Planetary gears reduce the propeller speed without reversing the direction of rotation.

**PLANK** — The variables used to calculate horsepower in the formula: PLANK ÷ 33,000. P represents the indicated mean effective pressure in a cylinder during its power stroke. L represents the length of the piston stroke in feet. The letter A represents the area of a piston head in square inches. N represents the number of power strokes per minute for a single cylinder. K represents the number of cylinders on an engine.

**plenum chamber** — An enclosed volume of air in which the air is held at a slightly higher pressure than that of the surrounding air.

**plunger spring** — The spring in a hydraulic lifter that pushes the plunger against the push rod.

**pneumatic continuous-loop detector** — An electrical switch that is activated by a change in gas pressure to detect a fire in a fire detection system.

**pneumatic system** — A system that uses a gas-filled continuous tube to detect fire in a nacelle. The gas expands when heated and acts on a diaphragm to close an electrical circuit and illuminate a warning light in the cockpit.

**polarity** — The property of an electrical device having two different types of electrical charges: positive (deficiency of electrons) or negative (excess of electrons).

**pole shoe** — The field assembly of an electric generator or motor. Also known as a field pole.

**polyphase alternator** — *See* three-phase alternator.

**poppet valve** — A circular-headed, T-shaped valve used to seal the combustion chamber of a reciprocating engine, and at the proper time, either admit the fuel/air mixture into the cylinder or conduct the burned exhaust gases out of the cylinder.

**positive displacement pump** — A fluid pump that moves a specific amount of fluid each time it rotates. Examples of positive displacement pumps include gear pumps, gerotor pumps, and vane pumps.

**post-emulsifying penetrant** — A penetrant used to inspect for cracks that can be removed from the surface of a part only with an emulsifying agent.

**power** — **1.** The time-rate of doing work and expressed by the formula Power = (Force X Distance) ÷ Time. Power can be expressed in terms of foot-pounds of work per minute, or in horsepower (HP). One HP is 33,000 ft.-lbs. of work per minute. The basic unit of electrical power is the watt, and 746 watts of electrical power is equal to one mechanical horsepower. In electrical problems, power is the product of voltage (E) times current (I) (P = E X I). Power in watts delivered to a circuit varies directly with the square of the applied voltage and inversely with the circuit resistance. **2.** The third stroke and fourth event of the Otto cycle in a reciprocating engine.

**power lever** — The cockpit lever that connects to the fuel control unit for scheduling fuel flow to the combustor. Also referred to as power control lever or throttle.

**power recovery turbine (PRT)** — A device used on the Wright R-3350 engine to recover power from the exhaust gases. The exhaust gases spin a series of small turbines that are coupled to the crankshaft by fluid-coupling devices.

**power section** — The portion of a radial engine on which the cylinders are mounted.

**power turbine** — A turbine rotor connected to an output shaft but not connected to the compressor. Also known as free power turbine.

**preignition** — Ignition occurring in the cylinder before the time of normal ignition. Preignition is often caused by a local hot spot in the combustion chamber that ignites the fuel-air mixture.

**pressure baffle** — A sheet metal shield that directs the flow of air between and around the cylinders of an air-cooled reciprocating engine.

**pressure capsule** — The portion of a structure subjected to pressurization. The pressure capsule usually consists of the cabin and cockpit.

**pressure cooling** — The cooling of cylinders by ram air ducted through a hood or nacelle.

**pressure recovery** — *See* ram recovery.

**pressure relief valve** — A valve that limits the pressure in a system by releasing excess pressure at a preset value.

**pressure stage** — A compressor rotor and its associated stator row.

**pressure-feed system** — A system in which fuel, delivered under pressure by a pump, is supplied to the engine-driven pump.

**primary airflow** — The portion of compressor output air used for combustion. Also known as combustion air.

**primary creep** — The first stage of turbine vane creep, which occurs during the first operational run of an engine.

**primary venturi** — The air restrictor in the throttle body of many fuel metering devices that meters fuel for normal operations above idle speed.

**profile** — The contour or aerodynamic shape of a blade or surface.

**profile tip** — A type of turbine blade with an area of reduced thickness at the tips.

**prony brake dynamometer** — A device used to measure the usable power output of an engine on a test stand. A prony brake dynamometer consists of a hinged collar, or brake, that can be clamped to a drum that is splined to the propeller shaft. The collar and drum form a friction brake that can be adjusted by a wheel. A lever arm of known length is attached to the collar and terminates at a point that bears on a scale. As the propeller shaft rotates, the lever arm indicates the torque produced by the rotating shaft.

**propeller blank** — An assembly of laminated layers of wood for manufacturing a propeller before machining or shaping occurs.

**propeller pitch** — The acute angle between the chord of a propeller and a plane perpendicular to the axis of its rotation.

**propeller pitch control** — A device to meter oil in and out of a propeller hub to control blade angle.

**PRT** — *See* power recovery turbine.

**Prussian blue** — A compound used in checking the contact of a valve with its seat. A thin coating of Prussian blue is applied to the valve and the valve is pressed against the seat. The amount and pattern of Prussian blue transferred to the seat determines whether the contact is uniform.

**pulse generator** — An electronic circuit designed to produce sharp pulses of voltage.

**push rod** — The component in the valve operating system of a reciprocating engine that transmits the movement of the cam to the rocker arm.

**pusher propeller** — A propeller that fits onto an engine whose shaft points to the rear of the aircraft. The thrust pushes the aircraft through the air rather than pulling it.

## Q

**QECA** — *See* quick engine change assembly.

**quick engine change assembly (QECA)** — An assembly made up of an engine, a propeller, all accessories, and all necessary cowling and engine mounts. A QECA minimizes downtime during an engine change. Also referred to as a QEC unit or QEC kit.

**quill shaft** — A hardened steel shaft with a hollow cross section and splines on each end. Torsional flexing of the shaft is used to absorb torsional vibrations.

## R

**radial outflow compressor** — An impeller-shaped device that receives air at its center and directs it outward at high velocity into a diffuser for increased pressure.

**ram effect** — An increase in ram air pressure before delivery to the compressor inlet.

**ram recovery** — The function of the air inlet duct, which is to deliver available ram air pressure to the compressor inlet of a gas turbine engine. *See* pressure recovery.

**ratiometer** — A direct current, remote-indicating system whose pointer movement is determined by the ratio of current between two resistors or between portions of a variable resistor.

**reaction turbine** — A stator vane and rotor blade arrangement in which the vanes form straight ducts and the blades form convergent ducts. Gases leaving the trailing edge of the blades turn the rotor.

**rear cone bottoming** — A condition in the installation of a propeller on a splined crankshaft in which the apex of the rear cone contacts the land of the propeller hub. When this condition occurs, the cone and propeller hub are not properly seated and the hub remains loose.

**rebuilt engine** — An engine that has been disassembled, cleaned, inspected, repaired as necessary, reassembled, and tested to the same tolerances and limits as a new engine.

**red arc** — A marking on an instrument that indicates a range in which operation should not be conducted.

**red line** — A marking on an instrument that indicates a maximum allowable operating condition.

**reference junction** — One of the two junctions in a thermocouple system. The reference junction is held at a constant or stable temperature and serves as a reference for the measuring junction.

**reference thermocouple** — In a thermocouple fire warning system, the thermocouple that is isolated from the active fire zones but still exposed to the same air temperature as the active thermocouples. When a fire occurs, the temperature differential between the reference thermocouple and the active thermocouples causes the current to flow and activate the warning light and horn.

**Reid vapor pressure** — The amount of pressure acting on a liquid to hold the vapors in the liquid at a given temperature.

**relative wind** — The airflow caused by the motion of the aircraft through the air. Relative wind (also called relative airflow) is opposite and parallel to the direction of flight.

**relay box** — In a thermocouple fire warning system, the component that houses the sensitive relay, the slave relay, and the thermal test unit. The thermocouples control the relays and the relays control the fire warning lights. Together, these components comprise one circuit. Each potential fire zone typically has between one and eight circuits.

**remanufactured engine** — An engine assembled by the manufacturer or an authorized agent using used parts that are held to the dimensional limits of new parts. A remanufactured engine is assigned zero time records and usually the same warranty and guarantee as a new engine.

**responder** — A type of pneumatic pressure switch used in a pneumatic, continuous-loop fire detection system. The responder is permanently connected to one end of the loop and is an integral part of the system; it cannot be removed in the event of a failure. It provides the connection to the control unit, which generates the alarm.

**retard breaker points** — An auxiliary set of breaker points in a magneto equipped with the Shower of Sparks starting system. These points are operative only during the starting cycle and open later than the run, or normal, points. This provides a late or retarded spark. Also referred to as retard points.

**reverse flow annular combustor** — A combustor design that forms an S-shaped path in which the gases flow from the diffuser to the exhaust. This design shortens the entire length of the engine because the liner is coaxial to the turbines rather than in front of them as with a conventional annular combustor.

**reverse-current cutout** — One of the units in a three-unit voltage regulator, this unit disconnects the battery from the generator when the generator output is lower than the battery output.

**reversible-pitch propeller** — A propeller system with a pitch change mechanism that includes full reversing capability. When the pilot moves the throttle controls to reverse, the blade angle changes to a pitch angle and produces reverse thrust, which slows the airplane during landing.

**revolving-armature alternator** — A type of alternator in which the armature rotates within a stationary magnetic field.

**revolving-field alternator** — An alternator with a stationary armature winding and a rotating field winding.

**rich** — A fuel/air mixture characterized by an excess amount of fuel for a given amount of air.

**rich best power** — The high end of a range of mixture settings for a reciprocating engine in which the maximum speed or manifold pressure is developed for a given throttle position.

**rich blowout** — A condition of turbine engine operation in which the fire goes out in the engine because the fuel/air mixture is too rich to support combustion.

**riffle file** — A file with a surface similar to the back side of a spoon, used to remove damage from the face or back of a propeller blade.

**right-hand motor rule** — A memory aid used to determine the direction that a current-carrying wire moves in a magnetic field.

**ring gear** — The outer gear of a planetary gear reduction system.

**ring grooves** — The grooves in the circumference of a piston into which the piston rings fit.

**ring land** — The area around the circumference of a piston between adjacent ring grooves.

**ripple** — A small periodic variation in the voltage level of a direct current power supply.

**rocker arm** — A pivoting arm in a reciprocating engine that transfers pushrod motion to the valve stem.

**rocker arm boss** — That portion of the cylinder head of an engine that provides support for the rocker arm shaft.

**root** — The supporting base or structure of a wing, propeller blade, or turbine blade.

**rotary-type radial engines** — An early style of radial engine in which the propeller is bolted to the crankcase. The propeller and crankcase rotate around a fixed crankshaft.

**rotator cap** — A cap installed on a valve stem tip to increase service life.

**rotor** — **1.** The rotating element in an alternator. The rotor is excited by direct current, and the interlacing fingers on the faces of the rotor form the alternating north and south poles. **2.** The rotating blades of a helicopter. **3.** The portion of a turbine compressor that spins. **4.** Any rotating disk or drum to which a series of blades is attached.

**RS** or **RSA** — A designation for a fuel injection system manufactured by Precision Airmotive.

**runback** — A condition in which ice melted for removal from a propeller blade refreezes behind the leading edge in an area without icing protection.

**running clearance** — The space between the components in a valve operating system when the engine is at operating temperature, not running. Also known as hot clearance.

**runout** — A term frequently used interchangeably with eccentricity but that normally refers to the amount that the outside surface of one component moves with respect to the outside surface of another component. As such, it includes eccentricity, angularity and bow. The amount of runout is usually expressed in terms of total indicator reading (TIR).

## S

**SAE** — *See* Society of Automotive Engineers.

**safety gap** — A specifically designed space in a high-tension magneto that permits a spark to jump without damaging the magneto's internal parts. This can occur in the event that the spark plug lead is disconnected from the spark plug.

**salient pole** — The field pole of a motor or generator that extends outward from the field frame toward the armature.

**Saybolt Universal Seconds (SUS or SSU)** — A unit used to identify the viscosity of a fluid by timing how long it takes for 60 cu. cm to flow through its calibrated orifice.

**Saybolt Universal Viscosimeter** — A device that measures the viscosity of lubricating oils by measuring the time in seconds necessary for 60 cu. cm of oil to flow through its calibrating orifice. Aviation 80 engine oil has an SUS viscosity of 79.2, and Aviation 100 oil has an SUS viscosity of 103.0.

**scavenge pump** — A constant displacement pump in an engine that picks up oil after the oil has passed through the engine and returns it to the oil reservoir.

**scoring** — Deep scratches on the surface of a material caused by foreign particles between moving parts.

**scratch** — A shallow thin line or mark caused by improper handling of a component or by the presence of a fine foreign particle on the component during operation.

**scuffing** — A dulling or moderate wear of a surface resulting from a slight amount of rubbing. Usually caused by improper clearance and insufficient lubrication. Typical parts affected are rollers, rings, and steel parts that are bolted together. Also known as pick up.

**scupper** — A recess around the filler neck of a fuel, or fluid, tank. The scupper collects any fuel or fluid spilled during the fueling operation and drains it overboard rather than letting it enter the aircraft structure. Also known as scupper drain.

**scupper drain** — *See* scupper.

**seated** — A condition in which moving parts have worn together until a minimum of leakage exists between them.

**secondary airflow** — The portion of compressor output air that cools engine parts and combustion gases.

**secondary creep** — The second stage of turbine vane creep, which occurs slowly over many hours of operation.

**self-ionizing igniter** — A gas turbine igniter in a low-tension system that uses a semiconductor that bridges the gap between electrodes. When current is applied, it heats the semiconductor, which increases its resistance. Also known as a shunted-gap igniter.

**semifloating piston pin** — A piston pin that is secured to the connecting rod, but not to the piston.

**semi-tulip head** — A class of reciprocating engine valves with heads shaped like tulips.

**shaft horsepower** — Exhaust thrust converted to a rotating shaft. Turboshaft engines are rated in shaft horsepower, which is measured with a dynamometer.

**shear** — A stress exerted on a material that tends to tear it apart.

**shell** — The external shroud, or duct, for exhaust gas.

**shifting the brushes** — A design consideration in a generator that moves the position of the brushes forward in the direction of normal rotation to short the magnetic field perpendicularly and reduce arcing between the brushes and the commutator.

**shock mount** — A shock absorbing attachment used to mount an engine to an airframe to minimize vibration.

**shop maintenance** — Any maintenance to an aircraft engine or component that requires removal of the component from the aircraft.

**short-shunt connection** — A compound-wound generator with the shunt field connected across the armature.

**shroud** — A cover or housing that helps confine an air or gas flow to a desired path.

**shunted-gap igniter** — *See* self-ionizing igniter.

**side clearance** — The space between a piston ring and its ring land.

**silica gel** — A desiccant used as a drying or moisture-absorbing agent. Silica gel is often used to package products that can be damaged by excess moisture.

**since major overhaul (SMOH)** — The time in service of a component, engine, or propeller since it was removed for disassembly and inspection according to manufacturer standards.

**single loop system** — A type of fire detection system made by Fenwal that employs a number of thermoswitches that are wired in parallel with each other and in series with the indicator lights. Also referred to as a single loop or a continuous-loop fire detection system.

**single-phase alternator** — A type of AC alternator comprising a stator with multiple windings connected in series to form a single circuit and connected to ensure that the voltage induced into each winding is in phase.

**single-row radial engine** — A reciprocating engine with only one row of cylinders arranged around a crankshaft.

**single-spool compressor** — An axial flow compressor with a single rotating mass. Also known as a single-stage compressor.

**single-stage compressor** — *See* single-spool compressor.

**single-throw crankshaft** — The crankshaft used in a single-row radial engine, which incorporates only one crankshaft throw.

**siphon tube** — A tube installed in a $CO_2$ fire extinguisher cylinder to ensure that $CO_2$ directed to the discharge nozzle remains in its liquid state.

**six-throw crankshaft** — The crankshaft used on a six-cylinder inline or opposed reciprocating engine.

**skirt** — The extended base of a piston, which helps maintain alignment within the cylinder.

**skull cap spinner** — A round-nosed cover for the hub of a fixed-pitch propeller. Normally the same diameter as the hub, such a spinner is usually attached to a bracket secured by propeller mounting bolts.

**slave governor** — The governor that is adjusted by an actuator in response to the comparison circuit in a one-engine master control system synchronization system to match the master governor.

**slinger ring** — A tubular ring mounted around the hub of a propeller onto which deicing fluid is directed and slung out onto the blades.

**slip** — The difference between geometric and effective pitch of a propeller. Slip can be expressed as a percentage of the mean geometric pitch or as a linear dimension.

**slip ring** — A smooth circular ring used to transfer field current into the armature of a DC alternator.

**sludge** — A heavy, slimy deposit in aircraft lubricating oil resulting from oxidation of the oil and contamination by water.

**SMOH** — *See* since major overhaul.

**SOAP** — *See* spectrometric oil analysis program.

**Society of Automotive Engineers (SAE)** — A professional organization for engineers that develops standards and classifications of materials used in manufacturing. These standards are used by a variety of industries including the aerospace and automotive industries.

**soft iron keeper** — A device placed across the poles of the rotating magnet when a magneto is disassembled. Keepers retain the magnetism by linking the magnetic poles and providing a path for the magnetic lines of flux to flow.

**solid lifter** — *See* tappet.

**solid-propellant rocket** — A rocket that carries solid fuel and an oxidizer that burns when ignited.

**sonic venturi** — A device that accelerates turbocharged air, creating a shockwave, the purpose of which is to slow remaining airflow in the venturi for use as a source of cabin pressurization air.

**spacer** — *See* Beta tube.

**spalling** — A bearing defect in which chips of the hardened bearing surface are broken out.

**spectrometric oil analysis program (SOAP)** — A system of oil analysis in which an oil sample is burned and the wavelengths of the resulting light are examined. This test can determine the amount of metals in the oil and can warn of an impending engine failure.

**speed lever** — *See* condition lever.

**speed ring** — *See* Townsend ring.

**speeder spring** — The control spring used in a centrifugal governor to establish a reference force opposed by the centrifugal force of the spinning flyweights.

**spill passage** — A passage within a turbine-engine fuel metering system that returns fuel from the spin chamber to the nozzle inlet during low power operations.

**spiral-wound element** — A type of edge filter in which a strip of wedge-shaped metal is wound in a spiral.

**splined propeller shafts** — A shaft with a series of grooves that meshes with a similarly-configured propeller hub so that the two units rotate as one, but are able to move laterally without interrupting the rotation.

**split key** — *See* split valve key.

**split valve key** — A tapered, cylindrical wedge used in pairs to lock a valve spring retainer to the stem of a valve. Also known as a split key.

**split-field motor** — A type of DC motor that has two windings wound in opposite directions on the same pole, and a single-pole, double-throw switch to reverse the motor direction.

**split-type master rod** — A master rod for a radial engine formed from two pieces to provide a means for installation on a solid crankshaft.

**spot-detection system** — A type of fire detection system that uses individual fire detectors, each dedicated to one location or one section of an assembly. The detectors must be placed in locations where a fire is likely to occur because they can respond only when a fire is present in their immediate proximity. Spot detectors are also known as thermal switches.

**spray-bar** — An afterburner fuel nozzle that protrudes into the exhaust stream.

**spring ring** — *See* circlet.

**springback** — *See* cushion.

**spur gear** — An external toothed gear.

**square mil** — An area equivalent to a square having sides 1 mil (0.001 in.) in length.

**squib** — A small, electrically-activated explosive device that discharges a projectile into the frangible disk of a fire extinguishing bottle in a high rate discharge system. Also known as a discharge cartridge.

**SSU** — *See* Saybolt Universal Seconds.

**staggered ignition timing** — A reciprocating engine ignition timing method using a dual ignition system to provide spark plug firing at different points in the combustion cycle.

**stagnation density** — A combination of three variables (atmospheric changes in temperature, altitude, and airspeed) that affect the production of thrust in a gas turbine engine.

**standard propeller** — A fixed-pitch propeller on which the blade angle is set between the ideal settings for cruise and climb.

**starting flow control unit** — A component within a hydropneumatic fuel control unit for a turboprop engine that ensures the correct fuel pressure to the nozzles. In addition, the unit drains residual fuel from the manifold when the engine is shutdown.

**static balance** — A condition of balance that does not involve any dynamic forces.

**static balancing** — The act of balancing a propeller or turbine rotor on a bench or test fixture.

**static-type radial engine** — An engine with cylinders radiating from a small central crankcase. The crankshaft has one throw for each row of cylinders. Most single-row radial engines have an odd number of cylinders. Two or more rows of cylinders can be used depending on power requirements.

**stationary piston pin** — A piston pin that rotates in the connecting rod but is secured to the piston with a set screw.

**stator** — **1.** The stationary part of an electrical machine such as a motor or alternator. **2.** The stationary portion of an axial flow turbojet compressor.

**STC** — *See* Supplemental Type Certificate.

**Stellite®** — An extremely hard, wear-resistant metal used for valve faces and stem tips. Stellite contains cobalt, tungsten, chromium, and molybdenum.

**stoichiometric mixture** — A mixture of fuel and air in which all of the oxygen and fuel are consumed in an engine and the maximum amount of heat energy is extracted from the fuel.

**straight roller bearing** — An anti-friction bearing used to support radial loads.

**strainer** — A fine mesh screen located in the fuel system and used to remove impurities.

**stroke** — In a reciprocating engine, the distance that a piston travels from bottom dead center (BDC) to top dead center (TDC). Stroke is two times the crankshaft throw.

**strut** — An aerodynamic support in the exhaust system between the exhaust cone and outer duct.

**sudden speed reduction** — A condition in which engine speed abruptly drops, usually due to the propeller striking a fixed object, but then quickly returns.

**sudden stoppage** — A condition in which the aircraft engine has come to a complete stop in less than one revolution, usually caused by the propeller hitting an immovable object. Sudden stoppage requires a special inspection to determine internal engine damage.

**sun gear** — The center gear in a planetary gear system around which the planetary gears rotate.

**supercharger** — An engine- or exhaust-driven air compressor that provides additional pressure to the induction air so the engine can produce additional power.

**supercharger section** — The section on a radial engine that compresses air and distributes it to the cylinders.

**Supplemental Type Certificate (STC)** — A type certificate issued by the FAA that allows a modification to an aircraft from its original type-certificated design.

**surface tension** — A cohesive condition that exists on the surface of a liquid because of molecular attraction.

**SUS** — *See* Saybolt Universal Seconds.

**swirl chamber** — A compartment in the induction system of a turboshaft engine in which inlet air is accelerated and redirected to remove sediment from the induction air delivered to the engine.

**swirl vanes** — Air circulation vanes that surround fuel nozzles, creating a small vapor-retaining vortex. Fuel vapor trapped in this way is recirculated and used more efficiently.

**switch method** — A method of DC motor direction reversal that uses a double-pole, double- throw switch to change the direction of current flow in the armature or the field.

**synchronize** — To cause two events to occur at the same time.

**synchronized ignition timing** — Ignition timing in which both magnetos fire simultaneously for every cycle.

**synchronizer master unit** — The assembly that controls the speed of multiple propellers on some early synchronization systems.

**system discharge indicator disk** — A small yellow plastic disk installed in a fitting at the termination point of a pressure line connected to a fire suppression system. The fitting is installed in the aircraft fuselage so that the disk can be viewed from the outside of the aircraft. When a system discharge occurs through normal operation, the disk is blown out of the fitting. During preflight inspection, evidence of the missing disk should prompt an inspection of the fire suppression system.

# T

**tachometer generator** — A small electrical generator that supplies current at frequencies proportional to the speed of the unit on which it is mounted.

**tail cone** — The conical-shaped portion of a turbine engine exhaust system that produces the proper area increase for gases as they leave the engine.

**takeoff power rating** — **1.** (reciprocating engines) The brake horsepower developed under standard sea level conditions and under the maximum conditions of crankshaft rotational speed and engine manifold pressure approved for the normal takeoff, and limited in continuous use to the time shown in the approved engine specification. **2.** (turbine engines) The brake horsepower developed under static conditions at a specified altitude and atmospheric temperature, and under the maximum conditions of rotor shaft rotational speed and gas temperature approved for the normal takeoff, and limited in continuous use to the time shown in the approved engine specification.

**tapered propeller shaft** — The tapered-end crankshaft to which a propeller is mounted.

**tapered roller bearing** — An anti-friction bearing made of hardened steel cylinders rolling between two cone-shaped, hardened steel races. A tapered roller bearing is designed to support both thrust and radial loads.

**tappet** — The component in an aircraft reciprocating engine that rides on the face of the cam and transmits a reciprocating motion to the push rods to open the poppet valves in the engine cylinders. Also known as a solid or hydraulic lifter.

**tappet guide** — The machined hole in a crankcase assembly in which a tappet is installed.

**TBO** — *See* time between overhaul.

**TDC** — *See* top dead center.

**TEL** — *See* tetraethyl lead.

**temperature accelerating well** — A secondary tank built into the main oil tank. The well, or hopper, retains only the portion of fluid being circulated through the engine, which hastens oil warm-up during engine warm-up. The well also makes oil dilution practical.

**tension** — The stress produced in a body by forces acting along the same line but in opposite directions.

**tertiary creep** — The third stage of turbine vane creep, which occurs at an accelerated rate after many hours of operation.

**test thermocouple** — A special thermocouple in an Edison fire detection system that is part of the detector circuit. The thermocouple includes a heater and is used to test system function.

**tetraethyl lead (TEL)** — A heavy, oily, poisonous liquid ($Pb(CH_2CH_3)_4$) mixed into aviation gasoline to increase its octane rating.

**thermal resistor material** — A type of material used by Kidde in their continuous-loop fire detection system. A small Inconel tube sensing element is filled with a thermal resistor material in which two conductors are embedded. As the ambient temperature increases, the resistance of the material decreases, which creates an electrical connection between the two conductors. Also known as thermistor material.

**thermistor material** — *See* thermal resistor material.

**thermo discharge indicator disk** — A small plastic red or green disk installed at the termination point of a pressure line connected to the fire suppression system or oxygen system. A fitting installed at the termination point in the aircraft fuselage holds the disks so that they can be viewed from the outside of the aircraft. When a thermal discharge of either system occurs through thermal overpressurization, the disks are blown out of the fitting. During the preflight inspection, evidence of the missing disks should prompt an inspection of the associated system.

**thermocouple** — A temperature measuring device consisting of two dissimilar metal wires joined together. Current flowing through the wires is proportional to the difference in temperature between the two junctions.

**thermostatic control valve** — *See* oil bypass valve.

**three-phase alternator** — An alternator with three single-phase windings spaced so that the voltage induced in each winding is 120 degrees out of phase with the voltage in the other two windings. *See* polyphase alternator.

**throttle ice** — Carburetor ice that forms on the rear side of a throttle valve when the throttle is partially closed. Throttle ice occurs because the lower pressure causes a drop in temperature.

**throttle valve** — The valve in the carburetor of a fuel control unit that determines the amount of fuel/air mixture to be fed to the engine.

**throw** — The part of a crankshaft to which a connecting rod is attached.

**thrust augmentor** — A specially shaped tube mounted around the exhaust tail pipe of an aircraft reciprocating engine. When exhaust gases flow through the tube, they produce a low pressure in the engine compartment that draws cooling air into the compartment.

**thrust bending force** — The aerodynamic force that attempts to bend propeller tips forward.

**thrust ratio** — The comparison of thrust produced by the fan to the thrust produced by the engine exhaust on a turbofan engine.

**thrust sensitive signal (TSS)** — A feature that activates the feather mechanism of the propeller on some gas turbine engines.

**tie rod** — *See* strut.

**tight fit** — The resulting fit when a hole is undersized and the part is oversized; fastening of the parts is achieved by friction.

**time between overhaul (TBO)** — The manufacturer's recommended amount of time that the engine can operate under average conditions before it should be overhauled.

**tinning** — The process of treating a stripped section of electrical wire with a thin coating of soft solder.

**TIT** — *See* turbine inlet temperature.

**top dead center (TDC)** — The uppermost position of the piston in a cylinder.

**top overhaul** — The overhaul of the cylinders of an aircraft engine. It consists of grinding the valves, replacing the piston rings, and doing anything else necessary to restore the cylinders to their proper condition. The crankcase of the engine is not opened.

**torque** — **1.** A resistance to turning or twisting. **2.** Forces that produces a twisting or rotating motion. **3.** In helicopters with a single, main rotor system, the tendency of the helicopter to turn in the opposite direction of the main rotor rotation.

**torque bending force** — An aerodynamic force on a propeller that exerts a pressure opposite the direction of rotation.

**TOT** — *See* turbine outlet temperature.

**total time (TT)** — The elapsed time that a component, engine, or propeller has been in service since it was new.

**Townend ring** — A cowling used on radial-engine aircraft to improve airflow and engine cooling. Also known as a speed ring.

**tractor propeller** — A propeller mounted to the front of an engine that pulls the airplane through the air.

**trailing edge** — The rearmost edge of an airfoil.

**transducer** — An electrical device that either changes electrical energy into mechanical movement or mechanical movement into electrical energy.

**transfer gearbox** — *See* intermediate gearbox.

**transient compressor stall** — A mild or minor stall of a compressor wheel in a gas turbine engine.

**transpiration cooling** — Internal cooling air that exits through porous walls of turbine blades and vanes.

**triple-spool compressor** — A section with three separate compressor wheels that compress air.

**TSS** — *See* thrust sensitive signal.

**TT** — *See* total time.

**tulip head** — A class of reciprocating engine valves that are shaped like tulips.

**turbine** — A rotary wheel device fitted with vane-like airfoils and actuated by impulse or reaction of a fluid flowing through the vanes or blades.

**turbine disk** — The metal disk to which turbine blades are attached.

**turbine guide vanes** — Stationary airfoil sections positioned radially around the inside of the engine. The airfoils direct the flow of air or gases from one major engine part to another.

**turbine inlet temperature (TIT)** — Temperature taken in front of the first-stage turbine nozzle vanes. TIT is the most critical temperature taken within the engine and essential to the operation of the fuel control.

**turbine nozzle** — The orifice assembly through which exhaust gases are directed prior to passing into the turbine blades.

**turbine outlet temperature (TOT)** — Temperature taken at the discharge of the turbine. Turbine outlet temperature is essentially the same as exhaust gas temperature.

**turbine wheel** — A rotating device actuated by reaction, impulse, or a combination of both. Used to transform some of the kinetic energy of the exhaust gases into shaft horsepower to drive the compressors and accessories.

**turning vane** — The component within a compressor manifold that provides a smooth turning surface to change airflow from a radial motion to an axial motion.

**twin-spool compressor** — A section with two separate compressor wheels that compress air.

**twist** — The change in chord line from the blade root to the blade tip of a propeller blade.

**two-phase alternator** — An alternator with two or more single-phase windings spaced symmetrically around the stator so that voltage induced in one winding is 90 degrees out of phase with the voltage induced in the second winding.

**two-stroke cycle** — A reciprocating engine in which a power impulse occurs on every other stroke of a piston. As the piston moves outward, fuel-air mixture is drawn into the crankcase below the piston; while above the piston, the mixture is compressed. Near the top of the stroke, ignition occurs and power is produced and transferred to the crankshaft. Near the bottom of the stroke, exhaust action takes place on one side of the cylinder and intake action occurs on the opposite side.

**two-throw crankshaft** — The crankshaft used in a twin-row radial engine, in which each row of cylinders requires a throw for its master rod.

# U

**UDF engine** — *See* unducted fan engines.

**UHB propfan** — *See* ultra-high bypass propfan.

**ultra-high bypass propfan (UHB)** — *See* unducted fan engine.

**ultrasonic cleaner** — A cleaning apparatus that uses cleaning fluid agitated by sound waves transmitted through the fluid. Ultrasonic cleaners are widely used for filter and bearing cleaning. Also known as vibrator cleaner.

**uncompensated cam** — A cam lobe used in magnetos for reciprocating engines in which an equal distance exists between lobes because the firing of each spark plug is uniform.

**under-compound generator** — A compound generator (both series and shunt-wound) that is more influenced by the shunt winding than the series winding. Voltage output drops as load increases.

**undercut** — To remove a portion of the mica between bars on a commutator.

**underspeed governor** — A component on some turboprop engines that controls propeller blade angle during ground operations.

**unducted fan engine (UDF)** — A modified propfan design in which the fan is external from the nacelle. Also known as an ultra-high bypass propfan.

**universal propeller protractor** — A precision measuring device used to determine the amount of propeller blade angle.

**untwist** — A straightening and loss of turbine blade curvature resulting from gas loads, thermal stress, and centrifugal loading.

**unusable fuel** — The small amount of fuel in the tanks that cannot be safely used in flight or drained on the ground. Unusable fuel is considered part of the empty weight of the aircraft.

**updraft** — A type of carburetor or fuel control unit in which induction air is routed through the device from bottom to top.

**upper deck pressure** — The pressure of the air between the compressor and the throttle plate on a supercharged, reciprocating engine. This air is also used for pressurization of the cabin and the fuel injection system.

**upsetting** — A displacement of material beyond the normal surface contour commonly referred to as a bulge or a bump.

# V

**valve clearance** — The clearance between a valve head and rocker arm when the valve is seated.

**valve float** — In reciprocating engines, a condition in which, at high speed, the valve lifters lose contact with the cam lobes because the valve springs are not strong enough to overcome the momentum of the various valve train components. This condition permits the valve to open further and stay open longer than design specifications call for. Extended periods of valve float will damage the valve train. Also known as valve surge.

**valve guide** — The component in an aircraft reciprocating engine cylinder head that guides the valve and holds the valve head concentric with the valve seat.

**valve lag** — The number of degrees of crankshaft rotation after top or bottom center at which the intake or exhaust valves open or close. For example, if the intake valve closes at 60° of crankshaft rotation after the piston passes over top center and starts down on its intake stroke, the intake valve lag is 60°.

**valve lead** — The number of degrees of crankshaft rotation before top or bottom center at which the intake or exhaust valves open or close. For example, if an intake valve opens 15° before the piston reaches top center on the exhaust stroke, it is said to have a 15° valve lead.

**valve lifter** — *See* tappet.

**valve overlap** — The degrees of crankshaft rotation when both the intake and exhaust valves are open. In a four-stroke-cycle reciprocating engine, valve overlap improves the efficiency of engine operation by letting the low pressure caused by the exhaust gases leaving the cylinder help the fresh charge of fuel-air in the induction system to start moving into the cylinder.

**valve seat** — A hardened ring of steel or bronze, embedded in the cast aluminum cylinder head to provide proper seating for the poppet valve.

**valve spring retainer** — A pair of devices, similar to large area washers, that transfer the force of valve springs between the cylinder and the valve.

**valve springs** — Helical-wound steel wire springs used to close the poppet valves in an aircraft engine cylinder.

**valve stem** — The portion of a poppet valve that rides in the valve guide and maintains concentricity between the head of the valve and its seat.

**valve stretch** — Elongation of the valve stem caused by overheating.

**valve surge** — *See* valve float.

**valve tip** — The surface at the top of an intake or exhaust valve stem that is depressed by a rocker arm to open the valve.

**VAPC** — *See* variable absolute pressure controller.

**vapor ejector** — A restriction in the vapor return line of a fuel injector pump that draws fuel vapor from a swirl chamber for return to the fuel tank.

**vapor lock** — A condition in a fuel system in which liquid fuel has turned into a vapor in the fuel lines. The vapor prevents the flow of liquid fuel to the carburetor or fuel injectors.

**vapor pressure** — The pressure, at a specific temperature, exerted by the vapor above a liquid. Vapor pressure can prevent the release of additional vapor.

**variable absolute pressure controller (VAPC)** — A device that monitors compressor discharge pressure and limits the maximum pressure. The VAPC also maintains the discharge pressure slightly higher than manifold pressure. The VAPC controls the discharge pressure by regulating the oil flow through the waste gate actuator. The variable portion of the pressure controller is mechanically connected to the throttle. Opening the throttle to maintain a higher manifold pressure also adjusts the VAPC to maintain a higher compressor discharge pressure. The system's design prevents the turbocharger from working at maximum output when the excess pressure is unnecessary.

**variable inlet guides** — Compressor guide vanes, working in conjunction with stator vanes that change angle to accommodate the oncoming airstream. The position of the inlet guides is controlled automatically by the fuel control unit.

**variable restrictor valve** — A unit that can be adjusted to control the amount of fluid flow and thereby control operating speed.

**variable speed motor** — A shunt- or series-type DC motor whose speed is controlled by varying the current in the field windings.

**ventilated oil control ring** — A type of oil control ring with slots that permit excess oil to drain into the ring groove and back to the crankcase.

**vibrating voltage regulator** — A voltage regulator for direct current generators or alternators. This type of regulator uses vibrating points to sense the voltage and provide a varying resistance for the generator field current.

**vibrator cleaner** — *See* ultrasonic cleaner.

**viscosity index** — The measure of a fluid's change in viscosity due to a change in temperature.

**volatility** — The ease with which a fluid changes from a liquid to a vapor.

**vortex destroyer** — *See* vortex dissipater.

**vortex dissipater** — A system that directs a stream of high pressure turbine bleed air forward of an engine to prevent the formation of a low pressure vortex that could pull in debris. Also known as blow-away jet or vortex dissipater.

**V-type engines** — A type of reciprocating engine in which two banks of cylinders are operated by a single crankshaft.

## W

**wastegate** — A valve mechanism in the exhaust pipe of a turbocharged reciprocating engine that opens and closes to control how much exhaust is routed through or around the turbocharger.

**water injection** — A system in which water is injected with the fuel to avoid damage to the engine. As compression ratios are raised, or supercharging and turbocharging is added to engines, temperatures rise and an increased chance of detonation arises. Injecting water provides a water/air/fuel mixture that not only burns more efficiently and avoids spontaneous detonation but also provides additional inlet air cooling and denser air.

**water jacket** — Passageways for coolant that surround the combustion sections of a liquid-cooled reciprocating engine.

**water-soluble penetrant** — A penetrant used to inspect for cracks, which can be removed from the surface of a part with water.

**weather checking** — Cracks in the outer surface of rubber hoses that can extend into the hose's reinforcement webbing.

**wet-sump** — An engine in which all of the oil supply is carried within the engine itself rather than in a separate oil reservoir.

**Wheatstone bridge** — An electrical measuring circuit in which the current through the indicator is determined by the ratio of the resistances of the four resistors that form the legs of the bridge.

**windmilling** — The rotation of an aircraft propeller created by air flowing around it with the engine not operating.

**wrist pin** — The hardened steel pin that attaches the small end of a connecting rod to a piston.

## Y

**yellow arc** — A yellow marking on an instrument that indicates a region of caution. For example, on an airspeed indicator, the yellow arc indicates a range of speeds that are tolerable to fly in calm air, but not in turbulence.

## Z

**zerk** — A grease fitting with a check valve that permits grease to be pumped through the fitting into a bearing surface. Removal of the grease gun enables the check valve to reseat, which prevents grease from leaking out and dirt from entering the fitting.

**zero clearance** — A condition in a valve train in a reciprocating engine in which hydraulic valve lifters eliminate all of the clearance is from the valve train.

**zero lash lifter** — A hydraulic device in a reciprocating engine that eliminates the clearance between a valve and the valve lifter due to changes in the engine operating temperature.

**zero time** — An engine overhauled by the factory. Only a new or factory overhauled engine can be called a zero-time engine.

# ANSWERS A

# ANSWERS

## CHAPTER 1

## RECIPROCATING ENGINES

### SECTION A

1. rotary, static
2. horizontally opposed
3. aluminum
4. silk thread
5. a. journal
   b. crank pin
   c. crank cheek
6. nitriding
7. static
8. dynamic dampeners
9. a. Plain
   b. Ball
   c. Roller
10. plain
11. connecting rod
12. crank pin
13. a. Plain
    b. Fork and blado
    c. Master and articulated
14. plain
15. master and articulated
16. knuckle
17. aluminum
18. cast iron
19. compression
20. oil control
21. oil scraper
22. full floating
23. wrist
24. thickness
25. a. cylinder head
    b. cylinder barrel
26. choke
27. a. chrome plating
    b. nitriding
28. orange
29. blue
30. Nitrided
31. aluminum
32. coolingfins
33. exhaust
34. front
35. rear
36. a. mushroom
    b. tulip
    c. semi-tulip
    d. flat
37. sodium
38. lift
39. duration
40. shaft
41. 1/2
42. a. solid
    b. hydraulic
43. push rods
44. rocker arm
45. rings
46. 1/8
47. zero lash
48. zero
49. the same
50. 1.775, 9
51. a. tapered
    b. splined
    c. flange
52. Flange
53. a. 1. = radial engine
       2. = 985 cubic inch displacement
    b. 1. = horizontally opposed engine
       2. = 300 cubic inch displacement
       3. = D series
    c. 1. = left-hand rotation
       2. = turbocharged
       3. = fuel injected
       4. = horizontally opposed engine
       5. = 540 cubic inch displacement

### SECTION B

1. heat, mechanical
2. a. internal combustion
   b. external combustion
3. a. intake
   b. compression
   c. ignition
   d. power
   e. exhaust
4. volume
5. a. exhaust
   b. compression
   c. power
   d. intake
   e. compression
6. exhaust, intake
7. a. c, a, b, d
   b. b, d, c, a
8. a. 1-3-2-4
   b. 1-3-2-4
   c. 1-4-5-2-3-6
   d. 1-6-3-2-5-4
   e. 1-3-5-7-9-2-4-6-8
   f. 1-12-5-16-9-2-13-6-17-10-3-14-7-18-11-4-15-8
9. work
10. power
11. 33,000, 550
12. brake
13. friction
14. indicated
15. 118.69
16. 462.25
17. 233.02
18. 6
19. 20,000
20. 778
21. 29.10
22. cannot
23. decreases
24. mechanical
25. Detonation
26. 7.21

27. 6.70
28. Preignition
29. late
30. the speed of sound
31. rpm manifold pressure
32. 14.1
33. 30

# CHAPTER 2

## RECIPROCATING ENGINE OPERATION, MAINTENENCE, INSPECTION, AND OVERHAUL

### SECTION A

1. a. position
   b. shape
   c. color
2. Red
3. green
4. precautionary
5. white
6. Pounds per square inch.
7. absolute
8. low oil quantity
9. 30
10. pull the propeller through, in the direction of rotation, a min imum of two complete turns.
11. spark plugs
12. cold
13. into
14. low
15. lean
16. idle cutoff
17. lean
18. a. Magnetos
    b. Ignition Harness
    c. Spark Plugs
19. systematic
20. Backfiring
21. afterfiring
22. a. direct
    b. differential
23. differential
24. 80
25. compression
26. lubricated
27. solid
28. intake
29. rings
30. lengthened
31. 1.15
32. early, late
33. ignition

### SECTION B

1. sudden stoppage
2. spectrometric oil analysis
3. magnetic particle
4. Dynafocal
5. top
6. major
7. Overhauled
8. Rebuilt
9. decarbonizing
10. a. 4
    b. 6
    c. 1
    d. 10
    e. 7
    f. 5
    g. 8
    h. 2
    i. 9
    j. 3
11. magnetic particle
12. are not
13. longitudinal, circular
14. at the same time
15. demagnetized
16. should not
17. dye-penetrant
18. a. brushing
    b. dipping
    c. spraying
19. dwell
20. a. serviceable
    b. new
21. bend
22. a. End gap
    b. Side clearance
23. a. cylinder taper
    b. out-of-roundness
    c. bore diameter
    d. flange warpage
    e. piston skirt to cylinder clearance
24. 90
25. dial
26. red
27. interference
28. feather
29. a. grinding oversize
    b. chrome plateing
    c. replacement
30. a. rough
    b. finishing
    c. polishing
31. gun
32. Prussion Blue
33. 1/3, 2/3
34. 15, 45
35. steel
36. cast iron
37. staggered
38. block
39. Cushion
40. pre-oiling
41. should not
42. silica
43. blue

# CHAPTER 3

## TURBINE ENGINES

### SECTION A

1. 1939
2. third
3. turbojet, turboshaft, turbopro peller, turbofan
4 reduction gearbox
5. turboshaft
6 4
7. free turbine
8. a. Low bypass
   b. Medium bypass
   c. High bypass
9 fan, jet thrust
10. Ultra
11. airframe
12. decrease
13. diverging
14. converging-diverging
15. To supply enough air to support combustion and produce thrust
16. a. centrifugal
    b. axial
17. a. impeller
    b. diffuser
    c. manifold
18. 2
19. 15
20. a. rotor
    b. stator
21. 1.25
22. blades
23. vanes

24. a. better performance at high altitudes
    b. ability to obtain higher com pression ratios
    c. small frontal area
    d. high fan efficiency
25. profile
26. Shrouded
27. speed up
28. a. Inlet air velocity
    b. Compressor rpm
29. slow down
30. a. variable inlet guide vanes
    b. bleed valves
    c. variable stator vanes
31. swirling
32. hybrid
33. bleed
34. a. cabin pressurization
    b. heating
    c. cooling
    d. de-iceing and anti-icing
    e. pneumatic engine starting
35. diffuser
36. diffuser
37. swirl vanes
38. a. multiple-can
    b. can-annular
    c. annular or basket type
39. reverse-flow
40. a. lean die-out
    b. rich blow-out
41. 60-80%
42. a. Convert some of the exhaust gases pressure energy into velocity energy
    b. Direct the flow of exhaust gasses to strike the turbine rotor at the correct
43. wheel
44. fir tree
45. a. impulse
    b. reaction
    c. impulse-reaction
46. shrouded
47. 25
48. increase
49. 3, 5
50. seldom
51. ball, roller
52. 85

## SECTION B

1. Brayton
2. pressure
3. 50
4. less
5. decrease
6. water injection
7. decrease
8. will
9. ram recovery
10. EPR

# CHAPTER 4

# TURBINE ENGINE OPERATION, INSPECTION, MAINTENANCE, AND OVERHAUL

## SECTION A

1 last
2. a. 4
   b. 5
   c. 1
   d. 2
   e. 3
3. exhaust gas temperature
4. hot start
5. does not
6. hung start
7. continue cranking
8. a. 2
   b. 4
   c. 1
   d. 3
9. flight cycle
10. hot cold
11. erosion
12. cracking
13. borescope
14. fuel control unit
15. desalination
16. operating
17. a. fluid wash
    b. abrasive grit blast
18. Jetcal Analyzer
19. trend analysis
20. spectrometric

## SECTION B

1. does not
2. fod
3. Quick Engine Change Assembly
4. major
5. air
6. are
7. hot streaking
8. at right angles to
9. during the first run
10. red
11. two, three
12. perpendicular
13. temperature
14. untwist
15. creep
16. is not
17. original
18. thickness gauge
19. heat treated
20. erosion
21. moment weight
22. transmission
23. spring back
24. trimming
25. a. Engine change
    b. Fuel control change
    c. When the engine is not developing full thrust
26. max, idle
27. desiccants
28. maximum rated thrust

# CHAPTER 5

# INDUCTION SYSTEMS

## SECTION A

1. a. Air scoop
   b. Air filter
   c. Fuel metering device
   d. Intake manifold
2. a. Flocked screen
   b. Paper
   c. Polyurethane foam
3. a. Naturally aspirated
   b. Supercharged
4. oil sump
5. a. Cools the oil
   b. Warms the induction air
6. is not
7. cold
8. less

9. alternate
10. manuallyautomatically
11. downstream
12. engine
13. ground boosted
14. low
15. altitude
16. turbochargers
17. upstream
18. a. Compressor housing
    b. Bearing housing
    c. Turbine housing
19. false
20. a. Lubricate the bearings
    b. Remove heat
21. overboosting
22. waste gate
23. all
24. oil
25. upper deck
26. closed
27. inlet
28. parallel
29. throttle
30. a. Ambient
    b. Manifold air pressure
31. high
32. pressure relief valve
33. sea level boosted
34. a. Exhaust bypass valve
    b. Density controller
    c. Differential pressure controller
35. full throttle
36. sonic venturi
37. overshoot
38. bootstrapping
39. is not
40. turbocompound

## SECTION B

1. divergent, increases
2. Mach 1
3. Ram Effect
4. fan
5. a. Subsonic
   b. Transsonic
   c. Supersonic
6. converging diverging
7. diverging
8. bellmouth
9. particle separator

# CHAPTER 6

# EXHAUST SYSTEMS

## SECTION A

1. a. Short stack
   b. Collector
2. Bellows
3 shroud
4. ball joints
5. augmentors
6. lead
7. flat, sooty
8. a. Fire
   b. Carbon monoxide
9. coke
10. higher

## SECTION B

1. higher
2. converging
3. covergent
4. converging diverging
5. very little
6. a. Aid in braking and direc tional control during normal landing and reduce brake maintenance.
   b. Provide braking and direc tional control during emer gency landings and balked takeoffs.
   c. Back an aircraft out of a parking spot.
7. 20
8. mechanical, aerodynamic
9. cold
10. hot, cold
11. cold
12. hush kits
13. less

# CHAPTER 7

# ENGINE FUEL AND FUEL METERING

## SECTION A

1. vapor lock
2. vapor lock
3. cavitation, vapor lock
4. a. Jet A
   b. Jet A1
   c. Jet B
5. spur gear
6. centrifugal
7. a. Steel mesh
   b. Cellulose fiber
8. a. Oil
   b. Bleed air
9. 2
10. alcohol
11. thrust
12. a. Compressor inlet
    b. Combustion chamber

## SECTION B

1. decrease
2. 15
3. 12
4. altitude
5. updraft
6. venturi
7. upstream
8. a. Venturi
   b. Main metering jet
   c. Main discharge nozzle
   d. Throttle valve
9. Decrease the pressure
10. decreases
11. 1/8
12. mixture control
13. idle cutoff
14. discharge nozzle
15. acceleration
16. economizer
17. spring-back
18. downstream
19. a. Impact air
    b. Venturi suction
20. air
21. anti-detonation
22. a. Idle speed
    b. Idle mixture
23. Continuous flow

24. a. Create downstream pressure for the fuel control
    b. Cuts off the fuel and leaves the lines full of fuel
25. are
26. richens
27. high
28. low
29. fuelpump
30. bellows
31. turbocharger discharge
32. selector
33. metering orifice
34. a. Distribute fuel evenly to all cylinders
    b. Provide a positive shutoff of fuel
35. more
36. Acetone, lacquer thinner

## SECTION C

1. a. Lean die-out
   b. Rich blow-out
2. weight
3. a. Hydromechanical
   b. Electronic
   c. Hydro-pneumatic
4. shutoff valve
5. hydromechanical
6. hydromechanical, pneumatic
7. a. Atomizing
   b. Vaporizing
8. simplex
9. a. Single line
   b. Dual line
10. vaporizing
11. pressurizing and dump
12. boiling
13. trimming
14. increase
15. springback

# CHAPTER 8

# ELECTRICAL, STARTING, AND IGNITION SYSTEMS

## SECTION A

1. DC
2. a. Series
   b. Shunt
   c. Compound
3. series
4. compound
5. cumulative
6. voltage regulation
7. field
8. 1 1/8, 1 1/2
9. increase
10. a. Voltage Regulator
    b. Current limiter
    c. Reverse current cutout
11. motoring
12. carbon pile
13. flashing the field sandpaper

## SECTION B

1. diodes
2. 120
3. master switch
4. will not
5. a. Short or open diode
   b. Open in field circuit
6. diodes
7. never
8. low
9. high
10. up, down
11. transformer
12. arcing, altitude
13. exciter field
14. hydraulic motor
15. frequency

## SECTION C

1. armature, field windings
2. shunt, series
3. field windings
4. universal, induction, synchronous
5. flywheel
6. series
7. helical
8. Teledyne Continental
9. a. Motor assembly
   b. Gear section
10. high
11. a. direct cranking
    b. starter-generator
12. starter-generator
13. weight
14. low
15. a. Aircraft mounted auxiliary power unit
    b. Ground power unit
    c. Bleed air from operating engine
16. fuel/air combustion

## SECTION D

1. stranded
2. 22759
3. 7072
4. 600
5. 6
6. 2
7. current, voltage drop
8.

| NOMINAL SYSTEM VOLTAGE | ALLOWABLE VOLTAGE DROP VOLTS | |
|---|---|---|
| | CONTINUOUS OPERATION | INTERMITTANT OPERATION |
| 14 | 0.5 | 1.0 |
| 28 | 1.0 | 2.0 |
| 115 | 4.0 | 8.0 |
| 200 | 7.0 | 14.0 |

9. a. 6
   b. 10
   c. 10
   d. 1/0
10. a. Open wiring
    b. In conduit
11. above
12. 3
13. cushion
14. a. Bonding
    b. Shielding
15. 25
16. Shielding
17. a. blue
    b. red
    c. yellow
    d. red
18. 100%
19. 10
20. 4
21. vertically
22. Bonding
23. 3
24. emits smoke
25. trip-free
26. are not
27. a. 4.37
    b. 8.75
    c. 11.7
    d. 17.5

28. upward
29. fixed, moveable

## SECTION E

1. true
2. alternating
3. high-
4. low-tension
5. a. Housing
   b. Rotating magnet
   c. Cam
6. a. Mechanical
   b. Magnetic
   c. Primary electrical
   d. Secondary electrical
7. 36
8. a. Base mount
   b. Flange mount
9. laminated steel
10. maximum
11. neutral
12. opposes
13. after
14. full-register
15. E-gap
16. a. point arcing
    b. electromagnetic radiation
17. built-in
18. Secondary
19. secondary
20. impulse coupling
21. slow
22. a. Booster magneto
    b. Induction vibrator
    c. shower of sparks system
    d. Impulse coupling
23. shower of sparks
24. retard
25. right
26. left
27. C
28. E-gap
29. maximum opening
30. 1
31. should not
32. timing light
33. vernier coupling
34. early
35. oscilloscope
36. stranded copper, stainless steel
37. 5/8-24, 3/4-20
38. capacitance
39. resistor
40. reach
41. 1/2, 13/16
42. hot
43. cold
44. rich
45. lead fouling
46. cold
47. a. Broken piston ring
    b. Worn valve guides
48. 1/2
49. fuel metering
50. vibrator
51. is not
52. 6, top
53. second
54. acetone, M.E.K.

## SECTION F

1. false
2. joules
3. 2000
4. 2
5. a. Low tension (voltage)
   b. High tension (voltage)
6. 28 volt DC
7. low
8. vibrator
9. wider
10. glow
11. liquid
12. should not
13. are not
14. snapping noise

# CHAPTER 9 LUBRICATION SYSTEMS

## SECTION A

1. a. Reduce friction
   b. Provide cooling
   c. Seal and cushion
   d. Protect against corrosion
   e. Clean
2. viscosity
3. low
4. high
5. viscosity index
6. high
7. flash
8. 40
9. a. New/overhauled engines
   b. Older engines
10. are not
11. multi-
12. flush, refill
13. do not
14. are not

## SECTION B

1. a. dry-sump
   b. wet-sump
2. a. pressure
   b. splash
   c. Combination pressure/splash
3. a. The oil supply is limited by the oil sump capacity.
   b. Cooling is more difficult.
   c. Oil temperatures are likely to be higher.
4. a. "OIL"
   b. Tank capacity
5. propeller feathering
6. constant
7. do
8. a. full flow
   b. bypass
9. bypass
10. semi-depth
11. edge
12. flow control
13. around
14. Oil dilution
15. outlet
16. a. Gasoline
    b. Moisture
    c. Acids
    d. Dirt
    e. Carbon
    f. Metallic particles
17. engine overhaul
18. clockwise

## SECTION C

1. lower
2. synthetic
3. dry-
4. 10
5. a. Sight gauge
   b. Dipstick
6. a. Vane
   b. Gear
   c. Gerotor
7. positive
8. .000039
9. a. Disposable paper or fiber
   b. Cleanable screen
   c. Screen and disc type
10. last chance
11. accessory gearbox
12. downstream
13. does not
14. hot
15. a. fuel/oil
    b. air/oil
16. heat

# CHAPTER 10

## COOLING SYSTEMS

### SECTION A

1. 30
2. NACA
3. Intercylinder baffles
4. low
5. open
6. low
7. blast
8. fan
9. a. Bayonet
   b. Gasket
10. coil and tie
11. stop drilled
12. left alone

### SECTION B

1. through
2. primary
3. secondary
4. compressor inlet
5. air
6. air
7. turbine
8. convection, film
9. transpirational
10. Insulation blanket

# CHAPTER 11

## ENGINE FIRE PROTECTION

### SECTION A

1. spot detector
2. thermocouple
3. reference
4. a. Sensitive
   b. Slave
5. spot detector
6. overheat
7. a. Fenwall
   b. Kidde
8. Kidde
9. a. Lindberg
   b. Systron-Donner
10. cargo
11. Jetcal Analyzer
12. short

### SECTION B

1. a. Fuel
   b. Heat
   c. Air
2. a. D
   b. C
   c. A
   d. B
   e. A
3. Halon
4. a. Conventional
   b. High rate of discharge
5. carbon dioxide
6. halogenated hydrocarbon
7. red
8. yellow
9. may not
10. state, charge
11. a. Arms the fire extinguisher bottle switch
    b. Disconnects the generator field relay
    c. Shuts off the fuel to the engine, hydraulic fluid to the pump, and bleed air
    d. Deactivates the engine driven hydraulic pump low pressure lights
12. shrinkage

# CHAPTER 12

## PROPELLERS

### SECTION A

1. thrust
2. plane, rotation
3. face
4. centerhub
5. blade cuff
6. pitch distribution
7. highest
8. a. Centrifugal force
   b. Thrust bending force
   c. Torque bending force
   d. Aerodynamic twisting moment
   e. Centrifugal twisting moment
   f. Vibration
9. forward
10. opposite
11. high
12. low
13. false
14. red arc
15. geometric
16. effective
17. slip
18. Tractor
19. constant speed

### SECTION B

1. climb, cruise
2. Fixed
3. birch, ash
4. forged
5. 74, 48

### SECTION C

1. r.p.m.
2. manifold pressure, tachometer
3. pilot
4. flyweights
5. raise
6. speeder
7. overspeed
8. increases
9. a. Threaded
   b. Threadless
10. increase
11. a. Steel hub
    b. Compact
12. a. Head
    b. Body
    c. Base
13. steel hub
14. Woodward
15. feathering
16. does not
17. feathering
18. high
19. air pressure
20. can
21. unfeathering
22. Hamilton Standard
23. a. Hub, or barrel
    b. Dome
    c. Distributor valve
24. engine, governor
25. electrically
26. feathering

## SECTION D

1. reversing
2. ground
3. increases
4. feather
5. power
6. speed
7. unfeather
8. is not
9. does not
10. propeller

## SECTION E

1. synchronization
2. a. Noise
   b. Vibration
3. anti-icing
4 Carbon brushes, slip rings
5. intermittent

## SECTION F

1. Certified Repair Station
2. horizontal
3. fresh water
4. a. Bend angle
   b. Blade station
5. engine
6. a. Static
   b. Dynamic
7. universal propeller protractor
8. low
9. track
10. 1/16
11. tracking
12. operating
13. a. Tapered
    b. Flange
    c. Spline
14. taper
15. flanged
16. 70
17. removal
18. front
19. front
20. increase

# CHAPTER 13

# Powerplant and Propeller Airworthiness Inspections

## SECTION A

1. Powerplant
2. Inspection Authorization
3. Type Certificate Data Sheet
4. approved
5. major alteration, 337
6. Airframes
   Powerplants
   Propellers
7. A Supplemental Type Certificate (STC)
8. Airworthiness Directive
9. Advisory Circulars
10. Service Bulletins (SBs)
11. June 30
12. 14 CFR 43, Appendix D (or FAR 43, Appendix D)
13. local Flight Standards District Office
14. continuous airworthiness inspection program
15. permanent maintenance record (maintenance logbook)
16. Date that the inspection was completed;
    Total time in service of the aircraft, engine, or propeller (as appropriate);

    Type of inspection;
    Certification statement;
    Signature of the inspector;
    Inspector's certificate number and type of ratings or Repair Station number
17. Date that the work was completed;
    Total time in service of the aircraft, engine, or propeller (as appropriate);
    Description of (and reference of data for) the work performed;
    Signature of maintenance technician;
    Maintenance technician's certificate number and type of ratings (or Repair Station number)
18. Human Factors

# CHAPTER 14

1. systems, operation
2. systematic
3. troubleshooting tables, logic flow charts
4. Aviation Maintenance Alerts
5. interviewing

INDEX

# INDEX

# B



# C

# F

# G

# H



# I

# J



# K



# L

# M



# N

# O



# P

# Q



# R

# S

# T

# U



# V



# W



# X



# Y



# Z